P9-DMW-676

GEOSYSTEMS

Combination of satellite *Terra* MODIS sensor image and *GOES* satellite image produces a true-colour view of North and South America from 35,000 km (22,000 mi) in space. [Courtesy of MODIS Science Team, Goddard Space Flight Center, NASA and NOAA.]

The top predator in the Arctic region is a marine mammal, the polar bear (*Ursus maritimus*). This female bear is raising and training her cubs to hunt, feed, and get about on Arctic Ocean pack ice. The cubs are 8 months old and will stay with their mother for more than 2 years. Changes in climate and pack ice conditions are affecting the survivability of these bears. The International Polar Year 2007–2008 of science and research will focus on Earth's polar regions and the impact of these changes. [Photo by Bobbé Christopherson.]

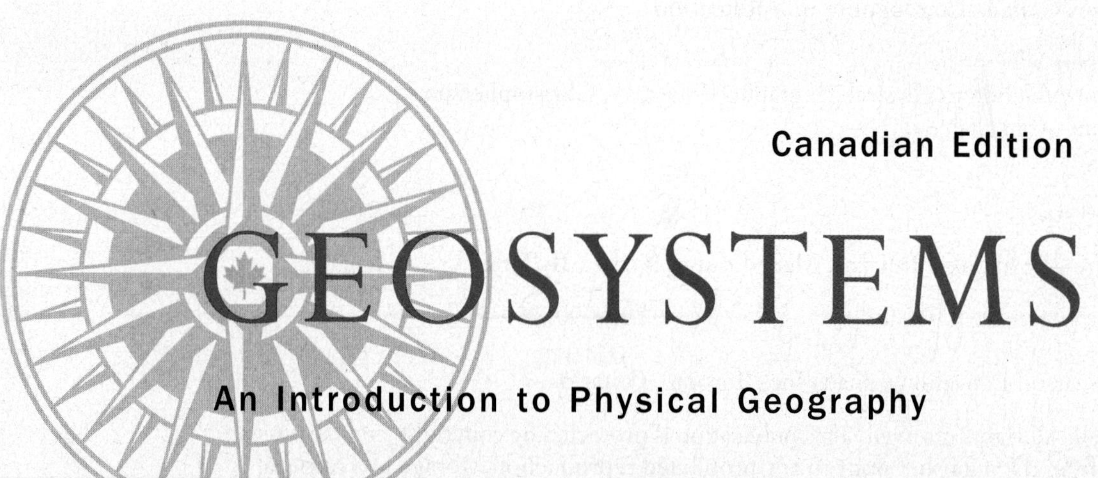

Canadian Edition

GEOSYSTEMS

An Introduction to Physical Geography

Robert W. Christopherson
American River College, Emeritus

Mary-Louise Byrne
Wilfrid Laurier University

In collaboration with
Alec Aitken
University of Saskatchewan

Toronto

Library and Archives Canada Cataloguing in Publication

Christopherson, Robert W.
Geosystems: An introduction to physical geography/Robert W. Christopherson, Mary-Louise Byrne—Canadian ed.

Includes index.
ISBN 0-13-124863-4

1. Physical geography—Textbooks. I. Byrne, Mary-Louise, 1961– . II. Title.

GB54.5.C47 2006 910'.02 C2004-907259-5

0-13-124863-4

Vice President, Editorial Director: Michael J. Young
Acquisitions Editor: Kelly Torrance
Executive Marketing Manager: Marlene Olsavsky
Developmental Editor: Madhu Ranadive
Production Editor: Marisa D'Andrea
Copy Editor: Jennifer Therriault
Proofreader: Lu Cormier
Production Coordinator: Patricia Ciardullo
Literary Permissions and Photo Researcher: Lisa Brant
Page Layout: Hermia Chung
Art Director: Julia Hall
Interior Design: ArtPlus Ltd.
Cover Design: Julia Hall
Cover Photo: Melting iceberg near the Yalour Islands (65 °S) along the Antarctic Peninsula in February 2004 by Bobbé Christopherson
Back Cover Photos: Arctic and Antarctic scenes by Bobbé Christopherson

Dedication section quote by B. Kingsolver, *Small Wonder* (New York: HarperCollins Publishers, 2002), p. 39.

Statistics Canada information is used with the permission of the Minister of Industry, as Minister responsible for Statistics Canada. Information on the availability of the wide range of data from Statistics Canada can be obtained from Statistics Canada's Regional Offices, its World Wide Web site at http://www.statcan.ca, and its toll-free access number 1-800-263-1136.

4 5 10 09 08 07

Printed and bound in the United States.

Contents

9 Water Resources 251

10 Global Climate Systems 283

PART THREE
The Earth–Atmosphere Interface 328

11 The Dynamic Planet 331

Preface

During the life of this first Canadian edition of *Geosystems*, important scientific research and global trends in Earth systems science will unfold. As pointed out on the back cover of the text, climate change and its many impacts are hitting the high latitudes at a faster pace than elsewhere on Earth. To reflect global system linkages with these regions, this Canadian edition of *Geosystems* weaves high-latitude themes through the chapters.

The scientific community is responding with the comprehensive Arctic Climate Impact Assessment (ACIA) Report, published in late 2004, in which Canadian scientists were active contributors. This historic scientific effort is detailed in Chapter 21. The International Polar Year (IPY) for science and research in the polar regions is set for March 2007 to March 2009, to cover two polar seasons. Robert Christopherson and his photographer wife Bobbé completed four polar expeditions in 2003 and 2004, gathering materials and photos for this edition. As you study physical geography, you will find your textbook responsive to the latest science, such as the IPY process. Armed with the spatial analysis tools of geographic science, physical geographers are well equipped to participate in a planetary understanding of environmental conditions.

Geosystems presents introductory physical geography as a contemporary spatial science, integrating the latest science across the broad sweep of this discipline. Students and instructors alike continue to express their appreciation of the up-to-date content, systems organization, scientific accuracy, clarity of the summary and review sections, and overall relevancy.

Your selection of *Geosystems* and its companion text *Elemental Geosystems* made them the leaders in Canadian physical geography through all their editions. To honour this position and to better serve Canadian geographic education, we embarked on this project. *Geosystems*, Canadian Edition, represents the first authentic text with a detailed Canadian perspective throughout; there are not just spelling changes, but hundreds of new Canadian examples, illustrations, photos, maps, and Career Links. Therefore, we say "Welcome to physical geography in Canada!"

New to the Canadian Edition of *Geosystems*

This Canadian edition includes geographic images that are familiar to all Canadians. Captivating Canadian photographs, maps, illustrations, and satellite images, as well as many compound figures and new content, enhance the sense and coverage of Canada in this text.

Space limitations do not permit a listing of all the additions and changes, but a focus on Canadian examples and concepts is emphasized throughout. Among many, here are a few highlights. Begin by examining all 21 chapter-opening and four part-opening photos and read their captions. Three of the four part-opening photos are new and all but four of the chapter-opening photos are new. These are content-specific and begin the learning process from the start of the chapter.

This edition contains the "High Latitude Connection" feature, linking chapter material to the polar regions, which includes a portion of Canada. The world is turning its attention to the high latitudes to better understand present global climate change. These High Latitude Connection items include:

- 3.1: Arctic Haze,
- 5.1: Overview of Trends in the Polar Regions,
- 10.1: Climate Change in the Polar Regions,
- 11.1: Isostatic Rebound in Alaska,
- 16.1: A Rebounding Shoreline and Coastal Features,
- 17.1: Climate Change Impacts an Arctic Ice Shelf,
- 21.1: Report from Reykjavik—Arctic Climate Impact Assessment.

New polar region temperature maps are shown in Figures 5.13 and 5.15. The Chapter 21 opening photo was made at the ACIA Symposium in Iceland in November 2004. The report that emerged from this scientific process is summarized in this book. Wherever possible, maps portray the entirety of Canada including the Arctic Archipelago. Soils maps that illustrate the distribution of the soil orders in Canada were drawn specifically for this edition. For beauty as you learn, check out the photo galleries on the *Student Animations CD*.

A strong Canadian focus emphasizes our national organizations and societies. For example, in Chapter 1, News Reports focus on measuring "North" and the text outlines the unique aspects of measuring time across this vast country.

Other examples include expanded coverage of jet-contrail impacts on Earth–atmosphere energy budgets; analysis of "earthshine" as a diagnostic tool; four new polar-region temperature maps; new treatment of North Atlantic, Arctic, and Pacific Decadal Oscillations; a rewritten section on humidity for clarity of concepts; a revised midlatitude weather teaching map; mention of the 2004 Atlantic hurricane season with summaries, along with satellite-loop coverage on the text CD; summary of severe weather in Canada with a focus on Hurricane Juan and the 1998 ice storm; new sections on water use in Canada and the Walkerton, Ontario, tragedy; a new genetic climate classification map and discussion, with causitive forces portrayed on the climate map; an updated section on global climate change including the latest science; climate change and increased aridity in Canada; a new Focus Study on the Frank Slide; a new section on the Mackenzie River basin and the Mackenzie GEWEX; a revised and expanded glacial and periglacial chapter; new maps of soils distribution in Canada; a new section on evolution and the tremendous biodiversity that results from the process; new treatment of polar climates and biomes; and an updated capstone Chapter 21, among many new or updated items.

Geosystems Communicates the Science of Physical Geography

The goal of physical geography is to explain the spatial dimension of Earth's dynamic systems—its energy, air, water, weather, climate, tectonics, landforms, rocks, soils, plants, ecosystems, and biomes. Understanding human–Earth relations is part of the challenge of physical geography—to create a holistic (or complete) view of the planet and its inhabitants. Exclusive to this Canadian edition are "Applied Physical Geography" boxes containing applied examples of chapter materials. These highlight and clarify the science of physical geography.

Geosystems analyzes the worldwide impact of environmental events, synthesizing many physical factors into a complete picture of Earth-system operations. A good example is the eruption of Mount Pinatubo in the Philippines. The global implications of this major event (one of the largest eruptions in the 20th century) are woven through seven chapters of the book (see Figure 1.7 for a summary). Our update on global climate change and its related potential effects is part of the fabric of these seven chapters. These content threads weave together the variety of interesting and diverse topics crucial to a thorough understanding of physical geography.

Systems Organization Makes *Geosystems* Flow

Each section of this book is organized around the flow of energy, materials, and information. *Geosystems* presents subjects in the same sequence in which they occur in nature. In this way, you and your instructor logically progress through topics that unfold according to the flow of individual systems, or in accord with time and the flow of events. See Figure 1.8 in the text for an illustration of this systems organization.

For flexibility, *Geosystems* is divided into four parts, each containing chapters that link content in logical groupings. The diagram in Figure 1.9 illustrates our part structure. A quick check of the Table of Contents and this illustration shows you the order of chapters within these four parts.

The text culminates with Chapter 21, "Earth and the Human Denominator," a unique capstone chapter that summarizes physical geography as an important discipline in understanding Earth's present status and possible future. Think of the world's population and the totality of our impact as the *human denominator*. Just as the denominator in a fraction tells how many parts a whole is divided into, so the growing human population and the increasing demand for resources and rising planetary impact suggest how much the whole Earth system must adjust. This chapter is sure to stimulate further thought and discussion, dealing as it does with the most profound issue of our time—Earth's stewardship.

Geosystems Is a Text That Teaches

Teaching and learning begin with the front and back cover photographs. The melting iceberg on the front cover indicates rising temperatures along the Antarctic Peninsula. On the back cover, photos from the Arctic Ocean region and an Adélie penguin standing on an iceberg in Antarctica frame an introduction to this edition. *Geosystems* is written to assist you in the learning process.

Three heading levels are used throughout the text and precise topic sentences begin each paragraph to help you outline and review material. **Boldface** words are defined where they first appear in the text. These terms and concepts are collected alphabetically in the Glossary with chapter-number references. Our complete Glossary appears on the *Student Animations CD* that accompanies this text. *Italics* are used in the text to emphasize other words and phrases of importance. Every figure has a title that summarizes the caption. Also, in the introduction to each chapter, a feature called "In this chapter" gives you an overview.

An important continuing feature is a list of *Key Learning Concepts* that opens each chapter, stating what you should be able to do upon completing the chapter. These objectives are keyed to the main headings in the chapter. At the end of each chapter is a unique *Summary and Review* section that corresponds to the key learning concepts. Grouped under each learning concept is a narrative review that defines the boldfaced terms, along with a key terms list with page numbers and specific review questions for that concept. You can conveniently review each concept, test your understanding with review questions, and check key terms in the Glossary, then return to the chapter and the next learning concept. In this way, the chapter content is woven together using specific concepts.

A *Critical Thinking* section ends each chapter, challenging you to take the next step with information from the chapter. The key learning concepts help you determine what you want to learn, the text guides you in developing information and more questions, the summary and review assesses what you have learned and what more you might want to know about the subject, and the critical thinking section provokes action and application.

Career Link essays feature geographers and other scientists in a variety of professional fields practising their spatial analysis craft. Seven of these are young Canadian scientists or practitioners of physical geography. You read about an astronaut with over 1200 hours in orbit; an environmental scientist; a meteorologist at The Weather Network; a geographer who specializes in risk analysis; an Earth scientist who studies Canadian drylands; a coordinator for climate change impact studies on the coasts; a soils geographer who coordinates programs for a northern study centre; and a professor who studies climate-change impacts on coastal salt marshes, among others.

Focus Study essays, some completely revised and several new to this edition, provide additional explanation of key topics. A few examples from this diverse collection include the timely search for longitude; the stratospheric ozone predicament; the continuing blight of acid deposition; solar energy collection and wind power; the newly (2001) calibrated wind-chill chart; status of the High Plains Aquifer; groundwater quality and the impact of pollution in Walkerton, Ontario; the 1997–1998 El Niño phenomenon; the tectonic setting of the Pacific Coast of Canada; geothermal energy and power; exotic terranes in Western Canada; the Mount St. Helens eruption; the effects of the Frank Slide; floodplain strategies; the status of the Colorado River and the Western drought; an environmental approach to shoreline planning; selenium concentration in Western U.S. soils; the continuing global loss of biodiversity; the current state of the Great Lakes; and the dramatic ice cores in Greenland and in Antarctica at Dome C that look back almost a million years into past climates.

News Reports relate topics of special interest—GPS; careers in GIS; a 34-kilometre sky dive to study the atmosphere; new studies of "earthshine"; jet streams and airline flight times; how one culture harvests fog; the UV Index; coordination of global climate-change research (accompanied by many URLs); the disappearing Nile Delta; water issues in the Middle East; artificial scouring experiments in the Grand Canyon to restore beaches and habitats; survival issues in the sinking Mississippi River Delta; how sea turtles read Earth's magnetic field; alien and exotic plant and animal invasions; and threats to the Arctic National Wildlife Refuge.

We now live on a planet served by the Internet and its World Wide Web, a resource that weaves threads of information from around the globe into a vast fabric. The fact that we have Internet access in almost all the compartments aboard Spaceship Earth is clearly evident in *Geosystems*. Many entry points link directly from the words in a chapter to an Internet source, allowing you to be up to the minute. You will find more than 200 URLs (Internet addresses) in the body of the text (printed in blue and boldface), many for Canadian sources of information. Given the fluid nature of the Internet, URLs were rechecked at press time for accuracy. If some URLs changed since publication, you can most likely find the new location using elements of the old address. This Internet link begins with Table 1.1 presenting the URLs for major geography organizations.

The *Geosystems* Learning/Teaching Package

The Canadian edition provides a complete physical geography program for you and your instructor.

For You, the Student:

- *Student Animations CD*, by Robert Christopherson, is included in each copy of the book. This exciting learning tool contains 65 animations, satellite loops (including the 2004 Florida hurricanes), three exclusive photo galleries, a map reference library, and a searchable version of the text Glossary. Each animation features a self-test with pop-up reinforcement for correct answers. Text references provided throughout help you relate the CD to your use of the book.
- *Geosystems Companion Website* (**http://www.pearsoned.ca/christopherson**): This site, adapted by William Gough, gives you the opportunity to further explore topics presented in the book using the Internet. The site contains numerous review exercises (from which you get immediate feedback), exercises to expand students' understanding of physical geography, and resources for further exploration. This site provides an excellent opportunity from which to start using the Internet for the study of geography.

U.S. Sixth Edition Student Supplements:

- *Student Study Guide*, Sixth Edition (ISBN 0-13-133092-6), by Robert Christopherson and Charlie Thomsen. The Study Guide includes additional learning objectives, a complete chapter outline, critical thinking exercises, problems, short essay work using actual figures from the text, and a self-test with answer key in the back.
- *Student Lecture Notebook* (ISBN 0-13-186353-3). All of the line art from the transparency set is reproduced in this full-colour notebook. Students can now fully focus on the lecture and not be distracted by replicating drawings. Each page is three-hole punched for easy integration with other course materials.

For You, the Instructor:

Geosystems is designed to give you flexibility in presenting your course. The text is comprehensive in that it is true to each scientific discipline from which it draws subject matter. Although this diversity is a strength of physical geography, it makes it difficult to cover the entire book in a school term. *Geosystems* is organized to help you customize your presentation. You should feel free to use the text based on your specialty or emphasis, rearranging parts and chapters as desired. The four-part structure of chapters, systems organization within each chapter, and Focus Study and News Report features will all assist you in sampling some chapters while covering others in greater depth. The following materials are available to assist you—have a great class!

- *Instructor Resource CD-ROM (IRCD), Canadian Edition* (ISBN: 0-13-171565-8), contains everything you need for efficient course preparation. All the supplements on the IRCD have been revised to reflect changes made to the Canadian edition. Find all your digital resources in one well-organized, easy-to-access place. Included on this CD-ROM are:

  Figures—JPEGs of most illustrations and photos from the book.

  Animations—All the animations ready to use in your classroom presentations as PowerPoint® slides or Flash files.

  PowerPoint—Pre-authored slides by Robert Christopherson, Charlie Thomsen, and Myrka Hall-Beyer outline the concepts of each chapter with embedded art for use in the classroom or to customize with other items for your own presentation needs.

TestGen—A complete TestGen-EQ software by Robert Christopherson, Charlie Thomsen, and Mungandi Nasitwitwi, featuring a thorough and revised test bank with questions and answers. This collaboration has produced the most extensive and fully revised test bank available in physical geography. This test bank employs TestGen-EQ software. TestGen-EQ is a computerized test generator that lets you view and edit test bank questions, transfer questions to tests, and print customized formats. Included is the QuizMaster-EQ program that lets you administer tests on a computer network, record student scores, and print diagnostic reports. Mac and IBM/DOS computer formats are served.

Instructor's Resource Manual by Robert Christopherson, Charlie Thomsen, and Mary-Louise Byrne. The Instructor's Resource Manual, intended as a resource for both new and experienced instructors, includes lecture outlines, key terms, additional source materials, teaching tips, complete annotation of chapter review questions, and a list of overhead transparencies. The manual is available in both Word and PDF formats.

U.S. Sixth Edition Instructor Supplements:

- *Overhead Transparencies* (ISBN: 0-13-133095-0) includes more than 350 illustrations from the text on 300 transparencies, all enlarged for excellent classroom visibility.
- *Applied Physical Geography—Geosystems in the Laboratory*, Sixth Edition (ISBN: 0-13-133093-4), by Robert Christopherson and Charlie Thomsen of American River College. The new sixth edition is the result of a careful revision. Twenty-one lab exercises, divided into logical sections, allow flexibility in presentation. Each exercise comes with a list of learning concepts. Our manual is the only one that comes with its own complete glossary and stereolenses and stereomaps for viewing photo stereopairs in the manual. A complete *Solutions and Answers Manual* is available to instructors (ISBN: 0-13-133094-2).

Acknowledgments

Robert and Mary-Louise offer thanks to the many authors and scientists who published research articles and books that enrich this work; to all the colleagues who served as specific reviewers to this edition, or those who offered helpful suggestions at our national and regional geography meetings; and, although unnamed here, to all the correspondence received from students and instructors from across the globe who shared with Robert over the Internet, e-mail, fax, and phone—a continuing appreciated dialogue. We are grateful to all of them for their generosity of ideas and sacrifice of time.

The authors and publishers thank all of the reviewers who participated in reading material at various stages during the development of this Canadian edition and previous *Geosystems* editions:

Peter Ashmore, *University of Western Ontario*
Chris Ayles, *Camosun College*
Bill Buhay, *University of Winnipeg*
Ian Campbell, *University of Alberta–Edmonton*
Norm Catto, *Memorial University*
Ben Cecil, *University of Regina*
Gail Chmura, *McGill University*
Robin Davidson-Arnott, *University of Guelph*
Dirk H. de Boer, *University of Saskatchewan*
Joseph R. Desloges, *University of Toronto*
John Fairfield, *Malaspina University College*
William Gough, *University of Toronto*
Mryka Hall-Beyer, *University of Calgary*
Peter Herren, *University of Calgary*
J. Peter Johnson, Jr., *Carleton University*
David Jordan, *Trinity Western University*
Colin Laroque, *Mount Allison University*
Joyce Lundberg, *Carleton University*
Robert McClure, *North Island College*
Ben Moffatt, *Medicine Hat College*
Catherine Moore, *Concordia University*
Mungandi Nasitwitwi, *Douglas College*
Lawrence C. Nkemdirim, *University of Calgary*
Ann-Marie Ryan, *Dalhousie University*
Dave Sauchyn, *University of Regina*
Geraldine Sweet, *University of Winnipeg*
Alan Trenhaile, *University of Windsor*
Michael Tripp, *Malaspina University College*
Susan Vajoczki, *McMaster University*
James Voogt, *University of Western Ontario*
Gordon Weary, *Northwest Community College*

We extend gratitude to the editorial, production, and sales staff of Pearson Education/Prentice Hall. Thanks to Michael Young, Vice President, Editorial Director, at Pearson for his oversight and guidance, and to ESM President Paul Corey for his leadership strength in the publishing industry and for his friendship. Thanks to Dan Kaveney, Robert's Geosciences Executive Editor, for his role in both *Geosystems* and *Elemental Geosystems* and in geographic education in general; every author should have such an editor—tireless, energetic, willing to risk new ideas and technologies, and a lifetime friend. Many thanks to Madhu Ranadive, Senior Developmental Editor, and Marisa D'Andrea, Editorial Coordinator, for dealing with all our promises of getting things in on time and for coordinating all the work. Thanks to Executive Marketing Manager Marlene Olsavsky for her feel of physical geography's needs, Jennifer Therriault for her expert copy edit of the manuscript, Kelly Torrance for helping us launch the project, and the many sales representatives who spend months in the field communicating the *Geosystems* approach. They are all a tremendous asset to the book—thanks and safe travels to them.

Thanks to the art and design team at Pearson Education/Prentice Hall for this powerful cover using Bobbé's photo and the beautiful text design, and for letting us in on many decisions. Many thanks to Pam Schaus, a miracle worker with maps, who contributed many hours to create a visual feast. And to colleagues Jessica Mueller and James Hamilton at Wilfrid Laurier who gave freely of their time and photo collections to help shape this work.

From Robert: I give special gratitude to all the students and colleagues over 29 years at American River College for defining the importance of Earth's future, for their questions, and their enthusiasm. To all students and instructors, and to our expedition leader Rinie van Meurs on three polar voyages, we dedicate this book.

My continuing partnership with a special collaborator, photographer, and production assistant, Bobbé Christopherson, is at the heart of the success of *Geosystems* and of my life's work. My wife has worked tirelessly on all the *Geosystems'* projects. You see many of her photographs in this edition, all carefully made to illustrate physical geography principles. Please visit the three photo galleries on the *Student Animations CD* and learn more from her artistry with a camera. Bobbé's love for the smallest of living things is evident in the beautiful and insightful photographs she has in this edition. And, she continues as my best friend and colleague and expedition companion.

Robert W. Christopherson
Geography Professor Emeritus,
American River College
P. O. Box 128
Lincoln, California 95648
E-mail: bobobbe@aol.com
Web sites:
http://www.pearsoned.ca/christopherson (Cdn)
http://www.prenhall.com/christopherson (U.S.)

From Mary-Louise: I began this incredible journey and owe thanks to so many. First of all, I thank my immediate and extended family for their support while I worked on this project—my husband, Alain Pinard, and our children, Madeleine and Julianne, who coined the new verb "textbooking" to describe my frequent absences from family activities.

Robert and Bobbé Christopherson created an incredible textbook, and I thank them for allowing me to take part in its evolution. Thanks to Paul McInnis and Kelly Torrance for suggesting that I was the one to become involved in this project. This project would never have finished this year if not for Alec Aitken and his contribution to Chapters 11 and 12, as well as for Keith Bigelow, who worked with Alec to create new maps for those chapters. Thanks also to Doug Linzey for his work on the Canadian Career Links. I thank all my colleagues in the geographic community in Canada who, by comment, communication, or review, helped shape the contents of this text. I am forever indebted to Brian McCann for teaching me to look at physical processes from many perspectives and to integrate in order to explain. He is sadly missed.

Finally, to all the students with whom I had contact in 14 years of teaching at Wilfrid Laurier, your enthusiasm and curiosity kept me focused on the goal of explaining planet Earth. To future students, our planet is in your hands: Care for it.

Mary-Louise Byrne
Associate Professor,
Geography and Environmental Studies
Wilfrid Laurier University
Waterloo, Ontario
N2L 3C5
Email: mlbyrne@wlu.ca

And from both Robert and Mary-Louise: Physical geography teaches us a holistic view of the intricate supporting web that is Earth's environment and our place in it. Dramatic changes that demand our understanding are occurring in many human–Earth relations as we alter physical, chemical, and biological systems. Our attention to the polar regions is in recognition of the linkages between all planetary systems and the high latitudes. All things considered, this is a critical time for you to be enrolled in a physical geography course! The best to you in your studies—and *carpe diem*!

To all the students and teachers of Earth, our home planet, and a sustainable future.

And to Rinie van Meurs, and the other expedition leaders who teach us the polar regions.

The land still provides our genesis,
however we might like to forget that
our food comes from dank, muddy Earth,
that the oxygen in our lungs was recently inside
a leaf, and that every newspaper or book
we may pick up is made from the hearts
of trees that died for the sake of our imagined lives.
What you hold in your hands right now, beneath these words,
is consecrated air and time and sunlight.

–Barbara Kingsolver

Terra satellite image of northern Canada made October 4, 2003, at 19:05 Coordinated Universal Time (UTC). Northern British Columbia through Alberta's Peace River Country, to the Peace Athabasca Delta region in northwestern Saskatchewan, is across the lower portion of the image. To the north the Mackenzie River flows from Great Slave Lake (in the centre) northwestward through the Northwest Territories. Great Bear Lake is clearly shown in the upper left corner. A portion of Nunavut is in the upper right. [Image courtesy of NASA/GSFC.]

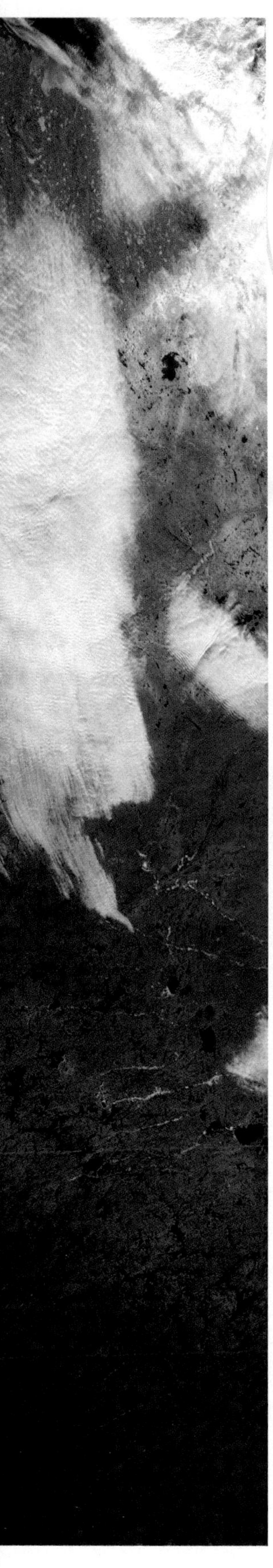

1 Essentials of Geography

Key Learning Concepts

After reading the chapter, you should be able to:

- *Define* geography and physical geography in particular.
- *Describe* systems analysis, open and closed systems, feedback information, and system operations and *relate* those concepts to Earth systems.
- *Explain* Earth's reference grid: latitude, longitude, latitudinal geographic zones, and time.
- *Define* cartography and mapping basics: map scale and map projections.
- *Describe* remote sensing and *explain* geographic information system (GIS) methodology as a tool used in geographic analysis.

During this first Canadian edition of *Geosystems*, we celebrate the International Polar Year (IPY) beginning in 2007. This interdisciplinary research effort combines many scientific fields that are at the core of physical geography. Bringing together various disciplines is essential to understanding the ongoing dynamics of Earth's systems. The polar regions, which link to all systems across the globe, are experiencing profound change and much preparation is underway toward IPY research, exploration, and discovery (see: **http://dels.nas.edu/us-ipy/index.html**).

Therefore, this is a scientifically exciting time to be enrolled in a physical geography course, and perhaps to be considering it for a major—we'll see. Physical geography deals with our environment and the powerful Earth systems that influence our lives and the many ways humans are altering Earth's systems. Most natural ecosystems now bear the imprint of civilization. This book is an assessment of the operation of Earth's physical systems, in both their natural state and as they are changed by human actions.

Physical geography provides essential information needed to understand and sustain our planetary journey in this new century. United Nations Secretary General and recipient of the 2001 Nobel Peace Prize, Kofi Annan, speaking to the Association of American Geographers annual meeting on March 1, 2001, offered this assessment:

> As you know only too well the signs of severe environmental distress are all around us. Unsustainable practices are woven deeply into the fabric of modern life. Land degradation threatens food security. Forest destruction threatens biodiversity. Water pollution threatens public health, and fierce competition for freshwater may well become a source of conflict and wars in the future. . . . the overwhelming majority of scientific experts have concluded that climate change is occurring, that humans are contributing, and that we cannot wait any longer to take action. . . environmental problems build up over time, and take an equally long time to remedy.

Scientists and governments scramble to understand the worldwide impact of global changes in weather, climate, water resources, and the landscape. We are experiencing unprecedented environmental conditions: increasing air and ocean temperatures, stratospheric ozone losses, increased rates of sea-level rise, heightened thunderstorm intensity, large losses of glacial ice worldwide, increasing plant and animal species extinctions, weather-related damage with massive floods in one region contrasted with severe droughts elsewhere, and related wildfires. In Canada, high-latitude warming is a significant impact of climate change. Former Minister of the Environment, David Anderson, stated,

> Current preoccupation is with terrorism, but in the long term climate change will outweigh terrorism as an issue for the international community. Terrorism will come and go; it has in the past . . . and it's very important. But climate change is going to make some very fundamental changes to human existence on the planet.*

Why do all of these conditions occur? How are these events different from past experience? Why does the environment and rates of global change vary from equator to midlatitudes, between deserts and polar regions? How does solar energy influence the distribution of trees, soils, climates, and lifestyles? How does energy produce the patterns of wind, weather, and ocean currents? How do natural systems affect human populations, and, in turn, what impact are humans having on natural systems? In this book, we explore those questions, and more, through geography's unique perspective. Welcome to an exploration of physical geography!

We live in an extraordinary era of **Earth systems science**. This science contributes to our emerging view of Earth as a complete entity—an interacting set of physical, chemical, and biological systems that produce a whole Earth. Physical geography is at the heart of Earth systems science as we answer the *spatial* questions concerning Earth's physical systems and their interaction with living things.

Physical geographers analyze interactions and changes that are occurring in natural systems to better quantify Earth systems over diverse *temporal* (time) and *spatial* (space or area) scales, and to address the question of how these changes might affect life on Earth. In an editorial in the journal *Science*, John Lawton stated,

> One of the great scientific challenges of the twenty-first century is to forecast the future of planet Earth . . . we find ourselves, literally, in uncharted territory, performing an uncontrolled experiment with planet Earth . . . . Wrestling to understand these challenges is the young, and still emerging, discipline of Earth systems science.†

In this chapter: Our study of *Geosystems*—Earth systems—begins in this chapter with a look at the science of physical geography and the geographic tools we use. Physical geography is key to studying entire Earth systems because of its integrative approach.

Physical geographers analyze systems to study the environment. Therefore, we discuss systems and the feedback mechanisms that influence system operations. We then consider location, a key theme of geographic inquiry—the latitude, longitude, and time coordinates that inscribe Earth's surface, and the new technologies in use to measure them. The study of longitude and a universal time system provide us with interesting insights into geography.

*Environmental News Network, February 6, 2004, **http://www.enn.com**.
†John Lawton, "Earth systems science" *Science* 292 (June 15, 2001): 1965.

Next, we examine maps as critical tools that geographers use to portray physical and cultural information. This chapter concludes with an overview of the technology that is adding exciting new dimensions to geography: remote sensing from space and computer-based geographic information systems (GIS).

The Science of Geography

Geography (from *geo*, "Earth," and *graphein*, "to write") is the science that studies the relationships among natural systems, geographic areas, society, cultural activities, and the interdependence of all of these *over space*. The term **spatial** refers to the nature and character of physical space, its measurement, and the distribution of things within it. For example, think of your own route to the classroom or library today and how you used your knowledge of street patterns, traffic trouble spots, parking spaces, or bike rack locations to minimize walking distance. All of these are spatial considerations.

Humans are spatial actors, both affecting and being affected by Earth. We profoundly influence vast areas because of our mobility and access to energy and technology. In turn, Earth's systems influence our activities in a most obvious way—these systems give us life.

The Canadian Council for Geographic Education (CCGE) was established in 1993 to guide geographic education. CCGE is mandated to increase emphasis on geography at all levels of education by supporting geography teachers in the classroom and by facilitating national-level action to strengthen the position of geography in the school curricula. The organization also exists to improve geography teaching methods, to promote the flow of geographic knowledge, and to foster development of geographic skills. Finally, the CCGE works to promote public awareness of geography, the importance of geographic literacy, and geographic education. For a listing of some important geography organizations and their URLs, see Table 1.1.

We simplify the standards of geographic science using five important spatial themes: **location**, **region**, **human-Earth relationships**, **movement**, and **place**, which are illustrated and defined in Figure 1.1. *Geosystems* draws on each theme.

Geographic Analysis

Within these five geographic themes, geography is governed by a *method* rather than a specific body of knowledge, and the method is **spatial analysis**. Using this method, geography synthesizes (brings together) knowledge from many fields, integrating information to form a whole Earth concept. Geographers view phenomena as occurring in spaces and areas having distinctive characteristics. The language of geography reflects this spatial view: *space*, *territory*, *zone*, *pattern*, *distribution*, *place*, *location*, *region*, *sphere*, *province*, and *distance*. Geographers analyze the differences and similarities among places and locations.

Process, a set of actions or mechanisms that operate in some special order, governed by physical, chemical, and biological laws, is central to geographic analysis. As examples will show in *Geosystems*, numerous processes are involved in Earth's vast water–atmosphere–weather system, or in continental crust movements and earthquake occurrences, or in ecosystem functions. Geographers use spatial analysis to examine how Earth's processes interact over space or area.

Therefore, **physical geography** is the *spatial analysis of all the physical elements and processes that make up the environment: energy, air, water, weather, climate, landforms, soils,*

Table 1.1

A Few Geography Organizations	URL Addresses
Canadian Council for Geographic Education	http://www.ccge.org/ccge/english/home.htm
Canadian Association of Geographers	http://www.cag-acg.ca/en/index.html
Canadian Geophysical Union	http://www.cgu-ugc.ca
Canadian Geoscience Council	http://www.geoscience.ca
Canadian Geomorphology Research Group	http://cgrg.geog.uvic.ca/index.html
Canadian Society of Soil Science	http://www.csss.ca/index.html
Royal Canadian Geographical Society	http://www.rcgs.org/rcgs/
American Geographical Society	http://www.amergeog.org/
Association of American Geographers	http://www.aag.org/
National Council for Geographic Education	http://www.ncge.org/
National Geographic Society	http://www.nationalgeographic.com/
Institute of Australian Geographers	http://www.iag.org.au
Australian Geography Teachers Association	http://www.agta.asn.au/
European Geography Association	http://egea.geog.uu.nl/
Royal Geographical Society, Institute of British Geographers	http://www.rgs.org/
Complete global listing of geography organizations	http://www.geoggeol.fau.edu/Links/GeographicalSites.htm

Location

Absolute and relative location on Earth. Location answers the question *Where?*—the specific planetary address of a location. This road sign, posted along Bruce County Road 9 in Ontario, is located on the 45th parallel of latitude, halfway between the equator and the North Pole.

Region

Portions of Earth's surface have uniform characteristics; how they form and change; how they are related to other regions. The northwest region of the United States and southern British Columbia in Canada feature dramatic coasts and the Gulf Islands.

Human–Earth Relationships

Humans and the environment: resource exploitation, hazard perception, and environmental modification—the oldest theme of geographic inquiry. French River, Prince Edward Island, is typical of the small fishing villages on the east coast of Canada. The water in the foreground is part of New London Bay.

Place

Tangible and intangible living and nonliving characteristics that make each place unique. No two places on Earth are exactly alike. Haughton Crater on Devon Island, Nunavut, is unique in that the slow pace of erosion in the Canadian High Arctic has not been able to mask an impact crater that is 23 million years old. The site was selected as a Mars analog by NASA's Haughton-Mars project.

Movement

Communication, movement, circulation, and diffusion across Earth's surface. Global interdependence links all regions and places—both physical and human systems. Winds and ocean currents form circulations of energy and water. Trees in Point Pleasant Park, Halifax, Nova Scotia, were blown down by Hurricane Juan in September 2003.

FIGURE 1.1 Five themes of geographic science.
Definitions of five fundamental themes in geographic science with examples of each—location, region, human–Earth relationships, movement, and place. Drawing from your own experience, can you think of several more examples of each theme? [Location photo by Mary-Louise Byrne; Human–Earth Relationships photo by Philip Giles; Region photo by Bobbé Christopherson; Place photo by Bob Weber/CP Photo Archive; Movement photo by Len Wagg.]

animals, plants, microorganisms, and Earth itself. We add to this the oldest theme in the geographic tradition, that of human activity. As a science, geographers employ the **scientific method**, a methodology important to physical geography. Focus Study 1.1 explains this essential process of science.

The Geographic Continuum

Geography is eclectic, integrating a wide range of subject matter from diverse fields; virtually any subject can be examined geographically. Figure 1.2 shows a continuous distribution—a continuum—along which the content of geography is arranged. Disciplines in the physical and life sciences are at one end, and those in the human and cultural sciences are at the other. As the figure shows, various specialties within geography draw from these subject areas.

The continuum in Figure 1.2 reflects a basic duality, or split, within geography—*physical geography* versus *human and cultural geography*. Society parallels this duality. Humans sometimes think of themselves as exempt from physical Earth processes—like actors not paying attention to their stage, props, and lighting. We all depend on Earth's systems to provide oxygen, water, nutrients, energy, and materials to support life. The growing complexity of the human–Earth relation requires that we shift our study of geographic processes, and perhaps our link to Earth systems, toward the centre of the continuum in Figure 1.2 to attain a more *holistic*, or balanced, perspective—such is the thrust of Earth systems science.

In the twenty-first century we face unique patterns of spatial change, for we are taxing Earth's systems in new ways. More people are alive today than ever before in Earth's history and their lifestyles are increasing in complexity and resource demands. We surpassed the population milestone of 6 billion in 1999 with virtually all population growth occurring in less-developed countries—present forecasts are for 7.8 billion people by 2025 and 9 billion by 2050 (a 47% increase over 2001). Again quoting from UN Secretary General Kofi Annan, "Environmental concerns are the national security issues of the future."

Some past civilizations adapted to crises, whereas others failed. Perhaps this ability to adapt is the key. If so, understanding our relationship to Earth's physical geography is important to human survival.

> . . . during the last few decades, humans have emerged as a new force of nature. We are modifying physical,

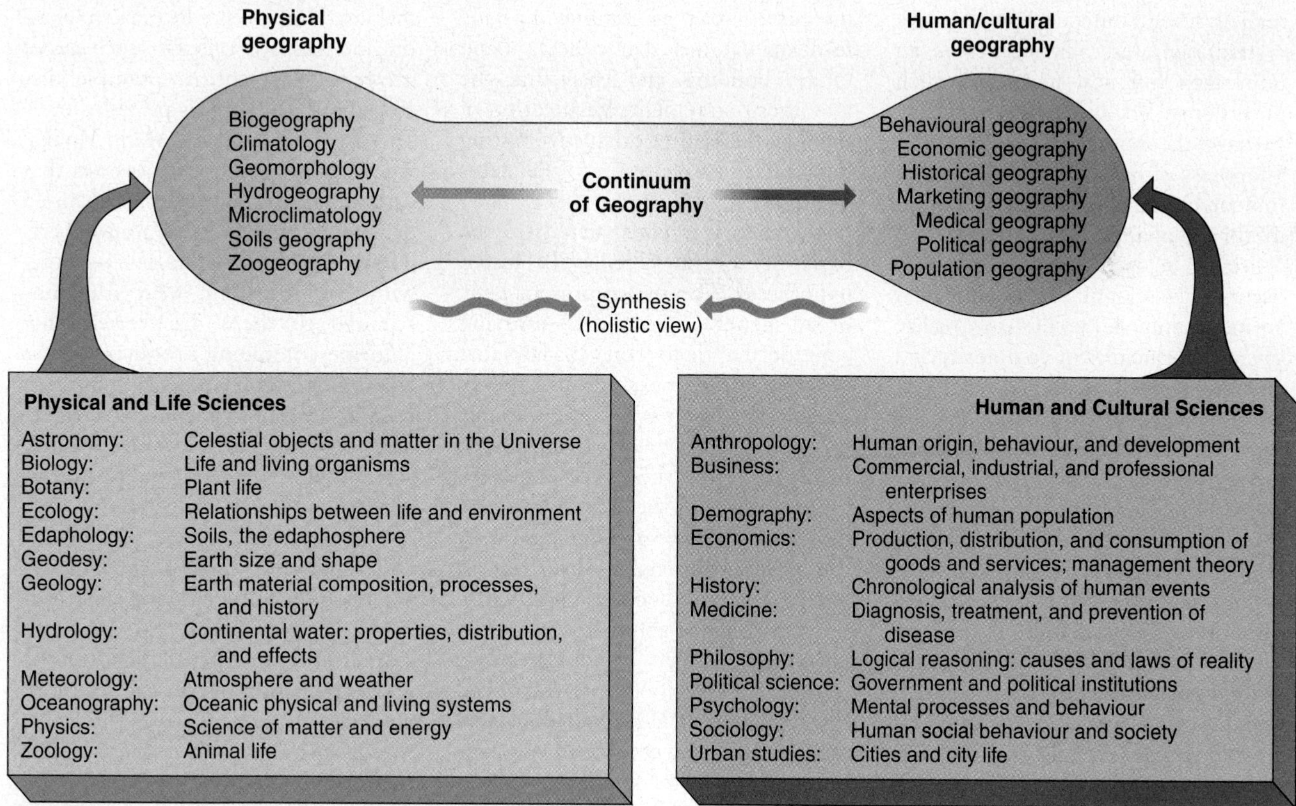

FIGURE 1.2 The content of geography.
Distribution of geographic content along a continuum (a continuous distribution). Geography derives subject matter from many different sciences. The focus of this book is physical geography, but we also integrate some human and cultural components. Synthesis of Earth topics and human topics is suggested by movement toward the middle of the continuum—a *holistic*, or balanced, view. Examine the subjects listed in the two boxes for any course you completed. Do you find any subjects you have taken? Think for a moment and recall any spatial aspects you remember studying in that course.

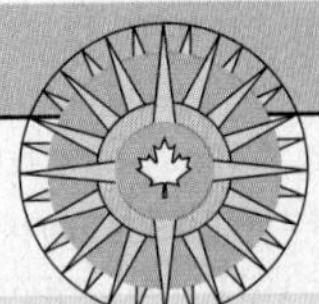

Focus Study 1.1

The Scientific Method

The term *scientific method* may have an aura of complexity that it should not. The scientific method is simply the application of common sense in an organized and objective manner. A scientist observes, makes a general statement to summarize the observations, formulates a hypothesis, conducts experiments to test the hypothesis, and develops a theory and governing scientific laws. Sir Isaac Newton (1642–1727) developed this method of discovering the patterns of nature, although the term *scientific method* was applied later.

Scientists are curious about nature and appreciate the challenge of problem solving. Society depends on the discoveries of science to decipher mysteries, find solutions, and foster progress. *Complexity* dominates nature, making several outcomes possible as a system operates. Science serves an important function to reduce such uncertainty. Yet, the more knowledge we have, the more the uncertainty and awareness of other possible scenarios (outcomes and events) increases. This in turn demands more precise and aggressive science. A danger in society occurs when scientific uncertainty fuels an anti-science viewpoint. As we realize scientific principles of complexity and chaos in natural and human-made systems, the need for critical thinking and the scientific method deepens in all aspects of life.

Follow the scientific method illustration in Figure 1 as you read. The scientific method begins with our perception of the real world and a determination of what we know, what we want to know, and the many unanswered questions that exist. Scientists who study the physical environment turn to nature for clues that they can observe and measure. They discern what data are needed and begin to collect those data. Then, these observations and data are analyzed to identify coherent patterns that may be present. This search for patterns requires *inductive reasoning*, or the process of drawing generalizations from specific facts. This step is important in modern Earth systems sciences, in which the goal is to understand *a whole functioning Earth*, rather than isolated, small compartments of information. Such understanding allows the scientist to construct models that simulate general operations of Earth systems.

If patterns are discovered, the researcher may formulate a *hypothesis*—a formal generalization of a principle. Examples include the planetesimal hypothesis, nuclear-winter hypothesis, and moisture-benefits-from-hurricanes hypothesis. Further observations are related to the general principles established by the hypothesis. Further data gathered may support or refute the hypothesis, or predictions made according to it may prove accurate or inaccurate. All these findings provide feedback to adjust data collection and model building and to refine the hypothesis statement. Verification of the hypothesis after exhaustive testing may lead to its elevation to the status of a *theory*.

A theory is constructed on the basis of several extensively tested hypotheses. Theories represent truly broad general principles—unifying concepts that tie together the laws that govern nature (for example, the theory of relativity, theory of evolution, atomic theory, Big Bang theory, stratospheric ozone depletion theory, or plate tectonics theory). A theory is a powerful device with which to understand both the order and chaos (disorder) in nature. Using a theory allows predictions to be made about things not yet known, the effects of which can be tested and verified or disproved through tangible evidence. The value of a theory is the continued observation, testing, understanding, and pursuit of knowledge that the theory stimulates. A general theory reinforces our perception of the real world, acting as positive feedback.

Pure science does not make value judgments. Instead, pure science provides people and their institutions with objective information on which to base their own value judgments. Social and political judgments about the applications of science are increasingly critical as Earth's natural systems respond to the impact of modern civilization. From Jane Lubchenco's 1997 AAAS Presidential Address:

> Science alone does not hold the power to achieve the goal of greater sustainability, but scientific knowledge and wisdom are needed to help inform decisions that will enable society to move toward that end.

The growing awareness that human activity is producing global change places increasing pressure on scientists to participate in decision making. Numerous editorials in scientific journals have called for such *applied science* involvement. An example, discussed in Chapter 3, is provided by F. Sherwood Rowland and Mario Molina, who first proposed a hypothesis that certain human-made chemicals caused damaging reactions in the stratosphere. They hypothesized in 1974—along with Paul Crutzen, who also contributed to these discoveries—that chlorine-containing products such as chlorofluorocarbons (CFCs), commonly used as aerosol propellants, refrigerants, foaming agents, and cleaning solvents, were depleting our protective stratospheric ozone (O_3) layer.

Subsequently, surface, atmosphere, and satellite measurements confirmed the photochemical reactions and provided data to map the real losses that were occurring. International treaties and agreements to ban the chemical culprits followed. In 1995 the Royal Swedish Academy of Sciences awarded these three scientists the Nobel Prize for chemistry for their pioneering work. Such successful applied science is strengthening society's resolve and provoking treaties to ban problem chemicals and practices and introduce sustainable substitutes.

Focus Study 1.1 ***(continued)***

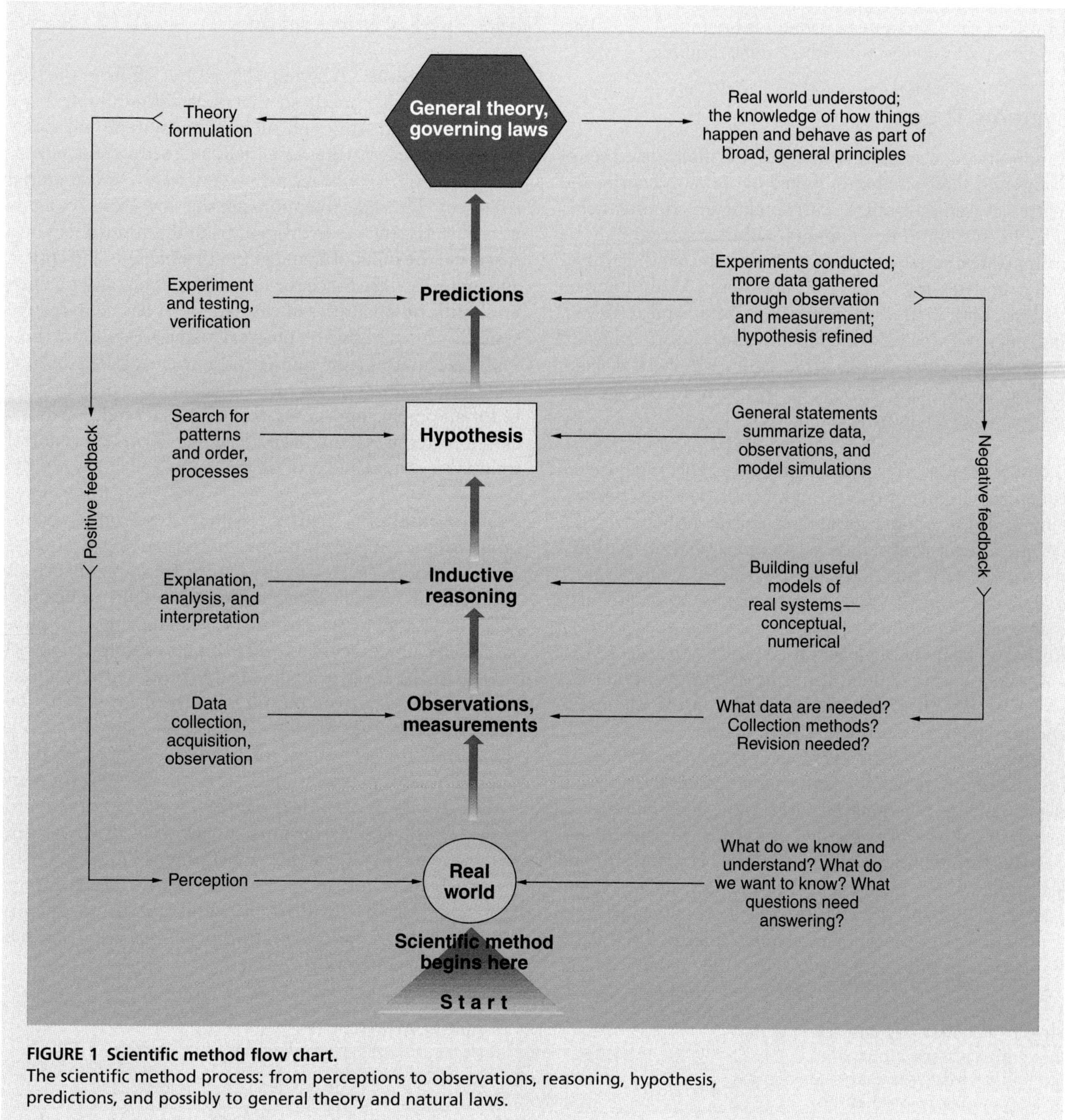

FIGURE 1 Scientific method flow chart.
The scientific method process: from perceptions to observations, reasoning, hypothesis, predictions, and possibly to general theory and natural laws.

chemical, and biological systems in new ways, at faster rates, and over larger *spatial* scales than ever recorded on Earth. Humans have unwittingly embarked upon a grand experiment with our planet. The outcome of this experiment is unknown, but has profound implications for all of life on Earth.*

*Jane Lubchenco, Presidential Address, American Association for the Advancement of Science, February 15, 1997.

Earth Systems Concepts

The word *system* pervades our lives daily: "Check the car's cooling system"; "How does the grading system work?"; "There is a weather system approaching." Systems of many kinds surround us. Not surprisingly, *systems analysis* has moved to the forefront as a method for understanding operational behaviour in many disciplines. The technique began with studies of energy and temperature (thermodynamics) systems in the nineteenth century and was further developed in engineering during World War II. Today, geographers use systems methodology as an analytical tool. In this book's four parts and 21 chapters, content is organized along logical flow paths consistent with systems thinking.

Systems Theory

Simply stated, a **system** is any ordered, interrelated set of things and their attributes, linked by flows of energy and matter, as distinct from the surrounding environment outside the system. The elements within a system may be arranged in a series or interwoven with one another. A system comprises any number of subsystems. Within Earth's systems, both matter and energy are stored and retrieved, and energy is transformed from one type to another. (Remember: *Matter* is mass that assumes a physical shape and occupies space; *energy* is a capacity to change the motion of, or to do work on, matter.)

Open Systems Systems in nature are generally not self-contained: Inputs of energy and matter flow into the system, and outputs of energy and matter flow out of the system. Such a system is called an **open system**. Within a system, the parts function in an interrelated manner, acting together in a way that gives each system its character. Earth is an open system *in terms of energy*, for solar energy enters freely and heat energy leaves freely back into space. Most natural systems are open in terms of energy. Figure 1.3 schematically illustrates an open system using the inputs and outputs of an automobile as an example.

Most Earth systems are dynamic (energetic, in motion) because of the tremendous infusion of radiant energy from thermonuclear reactions deep within the Sun. This energy penetrates the outermost edge of Earth's atmosphere and cascades through the terrestrial systems, being transformed along the way into various forms of energy, such as *kinetic energy* (of motion), *potential energy* (of position), or other expressions as chemical or mechanical energy. Eventually, Earth radiates this energy back to the cold vacuum of space as heat energy. Researchers are examining Earth's energy system to distinguish natural operations from those changes being forced by human activities.

Closed Systems A system that is shut off from the surrounding environment so that it is self-contained is a **closed system**. Although such closed systems are rarely found in nature, Earth is essentially a closed system *in terms of physical matter and resources*—air, water, and material resources. The only exceptions are the slow escape of lightweight gases (such as hydrogen) from the atmosphere into space and the input of frequent but tiny meteors and cosmic and meteoric dust. Since the initial formation of our planet, no significant quantities of new resources have entered the system. This is it! Earth's physical materials are finite (limited). No matter how numerous and daring the technological reorganizations of matter become, our physical base is, for all practical purposes, fixed. The fact that Earth is a closed material system makes recycling efforts inevitable if we want a sustainable economy.

System Example Figure 1.4 illustrates a simple open-flow system, using plant photosynthesis and respiration as an example. In *photosynthesis* (Figure 1.4a), plants use an energy input (certain wavelengths of sunlight) and material inputs of water, nutrients, and carbon dioxide. The photosynthetic process converts these inputs to stored chemical energy in the form of plant sugars (carbohydrates). The process also releases an output from the plant system: the oxygen we breathe.

Reversing the process, plants derive energy for their operations from respiration. In *respiration*, the plant consumes inputs of chemical energy (carbohydrates) and oxygen and releases outputs of carbon dioxide, water, and heat energy into the environment (Figure 1.4b). Thus, a plant acts as an open system, in which both energy and materials freely flow into and out of the plant. (Photosynthesis and respiration processes are discussed further in Chapter 19.)

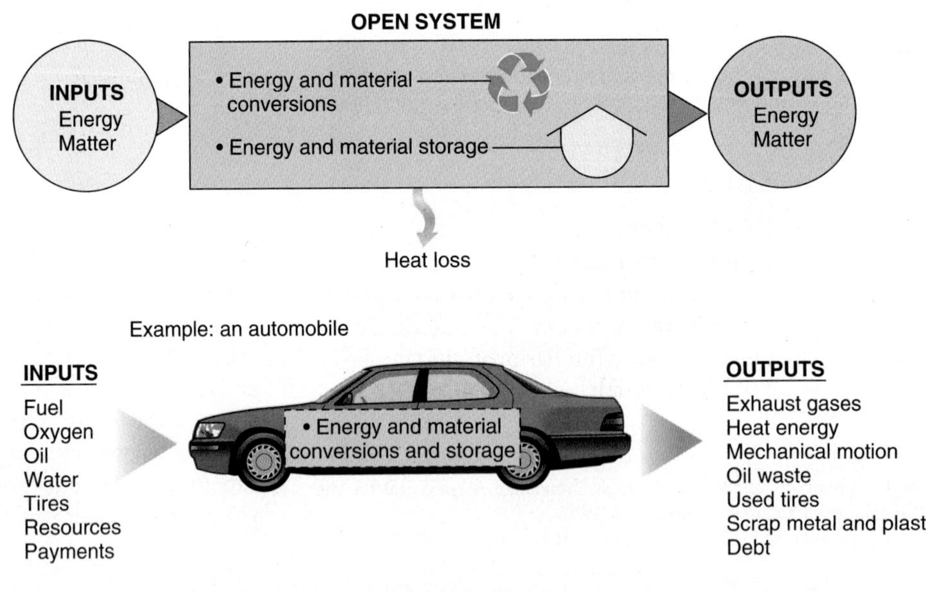

FIGURE 1.3 An open system. In an open system, inputs of energy and matter undergo conversions and are stored as the system operates. Outputs include energy and matter and heat energy (waste) that flow from the system. See how the various inputs and outputs are related to the operation of a car: Matter and energy are converted, stored, and produced in an automobile—an open system. Expand your viewpoint to the entire system of auto production, from raw materials, to assembly, to sales, to car accidents, to junkyards. Can you identify other open systems that you encounter in your daily life?

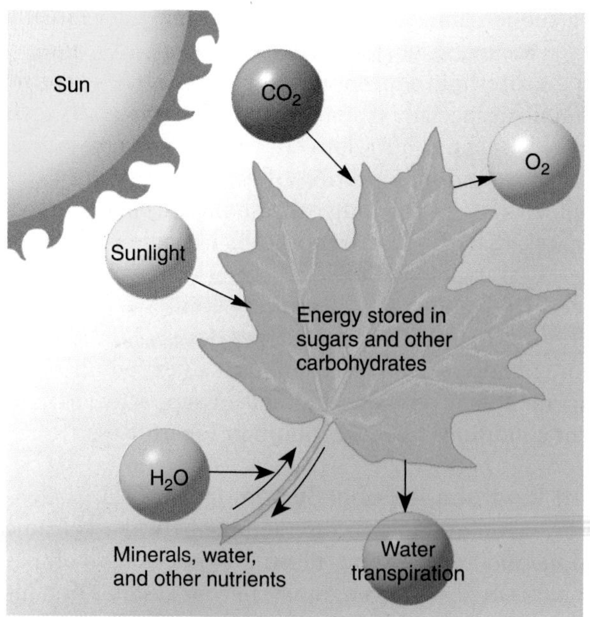

(a) Plant photosynthesis

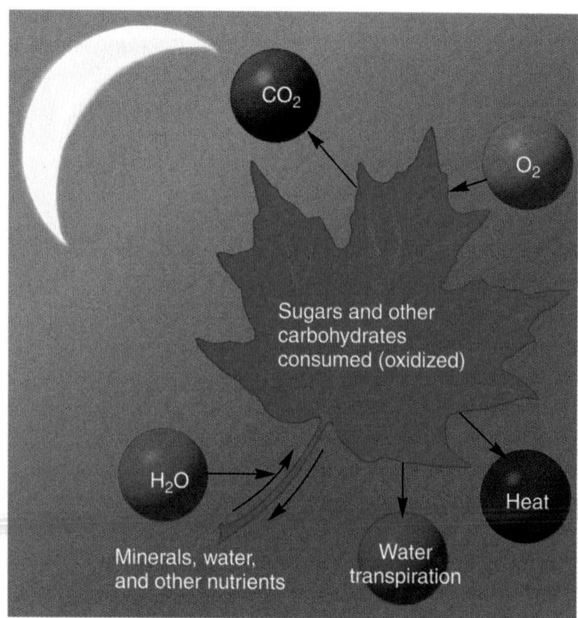

(b) Plant respiration

FIGURE 1.4 A leaf is a natural open system.
A plant leaf provides an example of a natural open system. (a) In the process of photosynthesis, plants consume light, carbon dioxide (CO_2), nutrients, and water (H_2O), and produce outputs of oxygen (O_2) and carbohydrates (sugars) as stored chemical energy. (b) Plant respiration, illustrated here at night, approximately reverses this process and produces outputs of carbon dioxide (CO_2) and water (H_2O), using oxygen and consuming (oxidizing) carbohydrates to produce energy for cell operations.

System Feedback As a system operates, it generates outputs that influence its own operations. These outputs function as "information" that is returned to various points in the system via pathways called **feedback loops**. Feedback information can control (or at least guide) further system operations. In the plant's photosynthetic system (see Figure 1.4), any increase or decrease in daylength (sunlight availability), carbon dioxide, or water will produce feedback that elicits (causes) specific responses in the plant. For example, decreasing the water input will slow the growth process; increasing daylength will increase the growth process within limits.

If the feedback *information* discourages response in the system, it is called **negative feedback**—like bad reviews affecting ticket sales for a film or play. *Further production in the system decreases the growth of the system.* Such negative feedback causes self-regulation in a natural system, stabilizing and maintaining the system. Think of a weight-loss diet—the human body is an open system. When you stand on the scales, the good or bad news reported about your weight both act as negative feedback to you. This, in turn, provides you with guidance (negative feedback) as to how inputs (food Calories) need to be adjusted (such as not buying and eating that burrito grande in the school cafeteria), or how exercise and increased metabolism is needed to burn excess Calories.

If feedback *information* encourages increased response in the system, it is called **positive feedback**—like good reviews affecting ticket sales for a film. *Further production in the system stimulates the growth of the system.* In finance, a compound interest-bearing account provides an example: The larger the account becomes, the more interest it earns, thus the larger the account becomes, and so on. Unchecked positive feedback in a system can create a runaway ("snowballing") condition. In natural systems, such unchecked growth will reach a critical limit, leading to instability, disruption, or death of organisms.

Think of the numerous devastating wildfires that occurred in Indonesia, Mexico, and Florida in 1998, and the western United States and Canada between 1999 and 2003, as examples of positive feedback. As the fires burned, they dried wet shrubs and green wood around the fire, thus providing more fuel for combustion. The greater the fire, the greater becomes the availability of fuel, and thus more fire is possible—a positive feedback for the fire. Control of the input of flammable fuel and oxygen is the key to extinguishing such fires. Knowing this process allows us to design strategies for controlling fuel availability, regulating excessive landscaping in vulnerable urban areas, and practicing "control burns."

Another example of positive feedback is the significant increase in meltponds on icebergs, ice shelves, and the Greenland ice sheet. As explained in High Latitude Connection 17.1 in Chapter 17, meltponds are darker and reflect less sunlight (have a lower albedo) and therefore absorb more solar energy, which in turn melts more ice, which forms more meltponds. Thus, a positive feedback system is in operation, further enhancing the effects of higher temperatures and warming trends. One estimate placed the spatial increase in meltpond distribution at 400% between 2001 and 2003 across the Arctic (Figure 1.5).

Take a moment to assess negative and positive feedback in the automobile illustration in Figure 1.3. For instance, how would the inputs and outputs be affected if tailpipe exhaust emission standards are weakened or strengthened? What if the automobile is operated at high elevation? Or if the car is a sports utility vehicle (SUV) that weighs 2300 kg (5070 lb)? Or if the price of gasoline increases or decreases? Assess the effect of such changes on automobile system operations.

System Equilibrium Most systems maintain structure and character over time. An energy and material system that remains balanced over time, in which conditions are constant or recur, is in a *steady-state condition.* When the rates of inputs and outputs in the system are equal and the amounts of energy and matter in storage within the system are constant (or more realistically, as they fluctuate around a stable average, such as a person's body weight), the system is in **steady-state equilibrium.**

However, a steady-state system fluctuating around an average value may demonstrate a changing trend over time, a condition described as **dynamic equilibrium.** These changing trends of either increasing or decreasing system operations may appear gradual. Examples of dynamic equilibrium include long-term climatic changes and the present pattern of increasing temperatures in the atmosphere and ocean, or the erosion and loss of many beaches along the U.S. West Coast in the late 1990s, or the ongoing loss of barrier islands along the East and Gulf coastlines. The present rate of species extinction exhibits a downward trend in numbers of living species. Figure 1.6 illustrates these two states.

Note that, given that it is the nature of systems to maintain their operations, they tend to resist abrupt change. However, a system may reach a *threshold* at which it can no longer maintain its character, so it lurches to a new operational level. This abrupt change places the system in a *metastable equilibrium.* An example of such a condition is a landscape, such as a hillside or coastal bluff, which adjusts after a sudden landslide. A new equilibrium is eventually achieved among slope, materials, and energy over time.

This threshold concept raises concern in the scientific community, especially if some natural systems reach such threshold limits. The relatively sudden collapse of ice shelves surrounding a portion of Antarctica serves as an example of systems reaching a threshold and changing to a new status, that of disintegration. The bleaching (death) of living coral reefs worldwide accelerated dramatically between 1997 and 2001. Warming conditions and some pollution in the ocean led to such a threshold and coral system collapse. A sudden change to a new equilibrium arrangement may not be as desirable or supportive to us as present conditions (see inset photo in Figure 1.6).

Mount Pinatubo—Global System Impact A particularly dramatic example of interactions between volcanic eruptions and Earth systems illustrates the strength of spatial analysis in physical geography and the systems organization of this textbook. Mount Pinatubo in the Philippines erupted violently in 1991, injecting 13–18 million metric tons (15–20 million tons) of ash and sulphuric acid mist into the upper atmosphere (Figure 1.7). This was the second greatest eruption during the twentieth century; Mount Katmai in Alaska (1912) is the only one greater. The eruption materials from Mount Pinatubo affected Earth systems in several ways noted on the map.

As you progress through this book, you will see the story of Mount Pinatubo and its implications woven through seven chapters: Chapter 1 (systems theory), Chapter 4 (effects on energy budgets in the atmosphere), Chapter 6 (satellite images of the spread of debris by atmospheric winds), Chapter 10 (temporary effect on global atmospheric temperatures), Chapters 11 and 12 (volcanic processes), and Chapter 17 (past climatic effects of volcanoes).

Systems in *Geosystems* To further illustrate the conceptual systems organization used in this textbook, you will notice that chapters and portions of chapters are presented in simple sequences organized around the flow of energy, materials, and information (Figure 1.8). This book presents subjects in the same sequence in which they occur in nature.

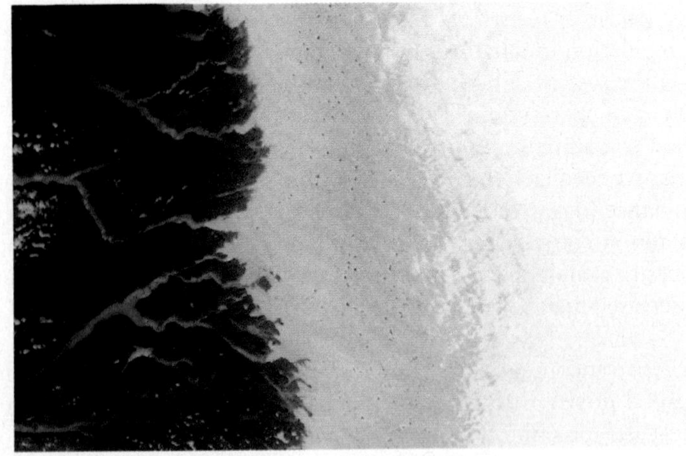

FIGURE 1.5 High-latitude meltpond increase results from positive feedback.
Meltponds on the western region of the Greenland ice sheet in 2003. The darker water-saturated surface layer from melt and blue-coloured meltponds indicate significant change in surface energy budgets on the ice. [Image by MODIS sensor, *Terra* satellite, courtesy of MODIS Rapid Response Team, NASA/GSFC.]

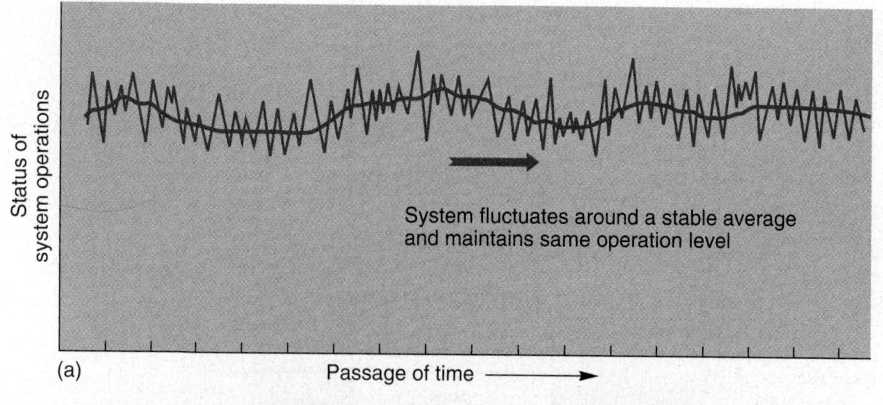

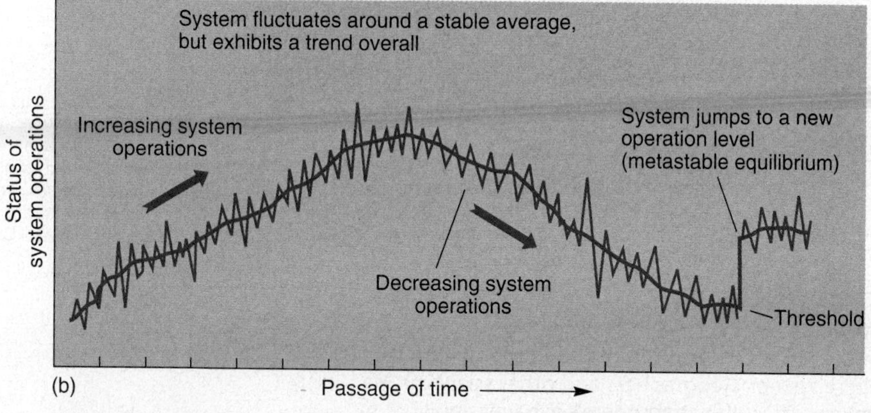

FIGURE 1.6 System equilibria: steady-state and dynamic. Some systems exhibit a steady-state equilibrium over time; system operations fluctuate around a stable average (a). Other systems are in a condition of dynamic equilibrium, with an increasing or decreasing operational trend (b). Rather than changing gradually, some systems may reach a threshold at which system operations lurch (change abruptly) to a new set of relations. The Saguenay, Québec, flood of 1996 that killed 10 people and caused more than $700 million in damage is one example of a river system crossing a threshold. [Inset photo by Jacques Boissinot/CP Photo Archive.]

In this way a logical progression is followed through topics that unfold according to the flow within individual systems, or in accord with time and the flow of events.

The sequence (Figure 1.8a)—*input* (components and driving force), *actions* (movements, processes, and storage changes), *outputs* (results and consequences), and *human impacts/impact on humans* (measure of relevance)—is seen in Part 1, for example. The Sun begins Chapter 2, the energy flows across space to the top of the atmosphere, through the atmosphere to the surface and surface energy budgets (Chapters 3 and 4). Then we look at the outputs of temperature (Chapter 5) and winds and ocean currents (Chapter 6). Note the same logical systems flow in the other three parts and in each chapter of this text—Part 2 and Chapter 16 also are shown as examples.

Models of Systems A **model** is a simplified, idealized representation of part of the real world. Models are designed with varying degrees of generalization. You may have built or drawn a model of something in your life that was a simplification of the real thing. Physical geographers construct simple system models to demonstrate complex associations in the environment. The simplicity of a model makes a system easier to comprehend and to simulate in experiments (for example, the leaf model in Figure 1.4). A good example is a model of the *hydrologic system*, which models Earth's entire water system, its related energy flows, and the atmosphere, surface, and subsurface environments through which water moves.

Adjusting the variables in a model produces differing conditions and allows predictions of possible system

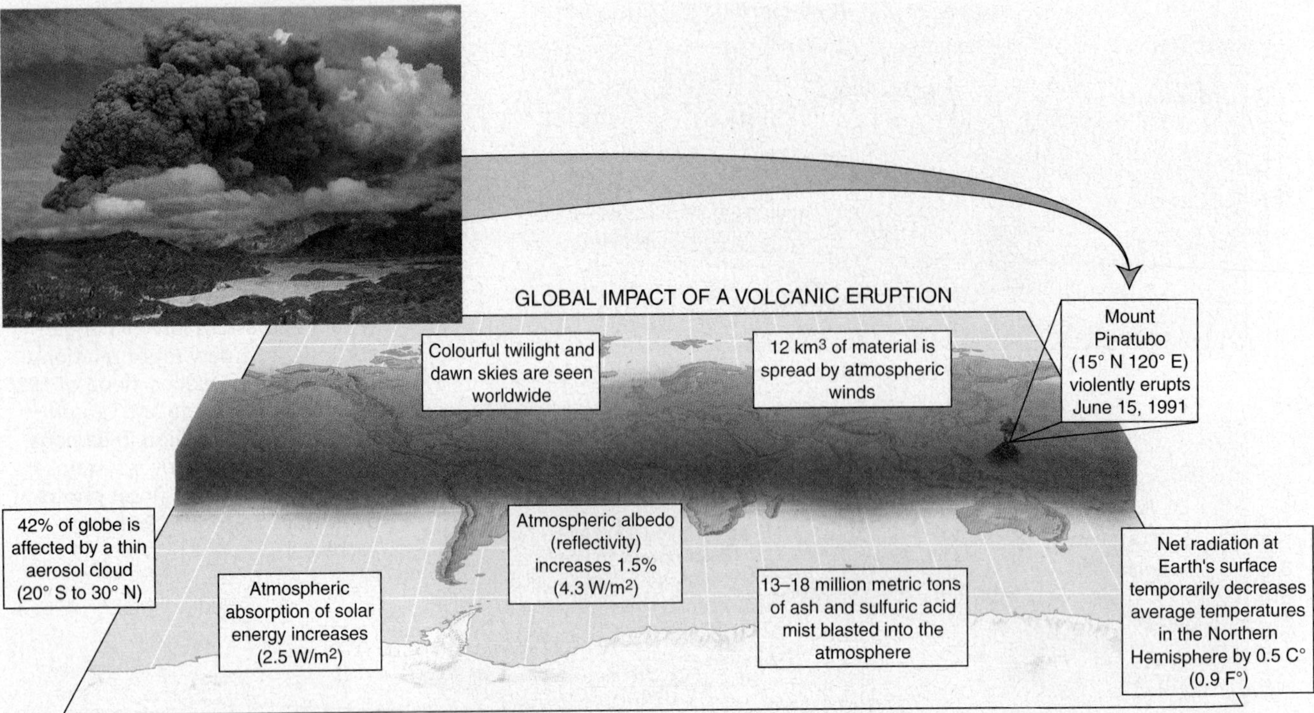

FIGURE 1.7 The eruption of Mount Pinatubo.
The 1991 Mount Pinatubo eruption, one of the largest volcanic eruptions in the twentieth century, widely affected the Earth–atmosphere system. Geographers and other scientists use the latest technology to study how such eruptions affect the atmosphere's dynamic equilibrium. For a summary of the impacts from this eruption you can refer to Chapter 12. [Inset photo by Van Cappellen/REA/SABA.]

operations to be made. A general circulation model (GCM) of the atmosphere (see Figure 10.31), operated by the Goddard Institute, accurately predicted the effect of Mount Pinatubo's ash on the atmosphere, the lowering and subsequent recovery of global air temperatures. However, predictions are only as good as the assumptions and accuracy built into the model. It is best to view a model for what it is—a simplification to help us understand a complex process.

We discuss many *system models* in this text, including the hydrologic system, water balance, surface energy budgets, earthquakes and faulting as outputs of Earth systems, river drainage basins, glacier mass budgets, soil profiles, and various ecosystems. Computer-based models are in use to study most natural systems—from the upper atmosphere, to climate change, to Earth's interior. Each of Earth's four "spheres" represents such a model.

Earth's Four "Spheres"

Earth's surface is a vast area of 500 million square kilometres (193 million square miles) where four immense open systems interact. Figure 1.9 shows a simple model of three **abiotic** (nonliving) systems overlapping to form the realm of the **biotic** (living) system. The abiotic spheres are the *atmosphere*, *hydrosphere*, and *lithosphere*. The biotic sphere is called the *biosphere*. Because these four systems are not independent units in nature, their boundaries must be understood as transition zones rather than sharp barriers. As noted in the figure, these four spheres form the part structure in which chapters are grouped in this text. The content in each part and among chapters overlaps and interrelates as we build our discussion of Earth's abiotic and biotic systems.

Atmosphere (Part 1, Chapters 2–6) The **atmosphere** is a thin, gaseous veil surrounding Earth, held to the planet by the force of gravity. Formed by gases arising from within Earth's crust and interior, and the exhalations of all life over time, the lower atmosphere is unique in the Solar System. It is a combination of nitrogen, oxygen, argon, carbon dioxide, water vapour, and trace gases.

Hydrosphere (Part 2, Chapters 7–10) Earth's waters exist in the atmosphere, on the surface, and in the crust near the surface. Collectively, these quantities form the **hydrosphere**. The portion of the hydrosphere that is frozen is the **cryosphere**—ice sheets, ice caps and fields, glaciers, ice shelves, sea ice, and subsurface ground ice and frozen ground (permafrost)—with related topics covered in chapters in all four parts of the book. Water of the hydrosphere exists in all three states: liquid, solid (the frozen cryosphere), and gaseous (water vapour). Water occurs in two general chemical conditions—fresh and saline (salty). It exhibits important heat-storage properties. And water is an extraordinary solvent. Water is the medium of

Systems in *Geosystems*

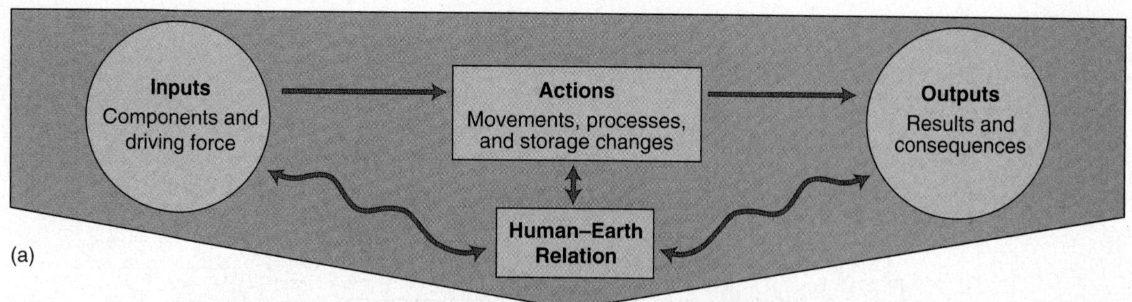

Examples of systems organization in text:

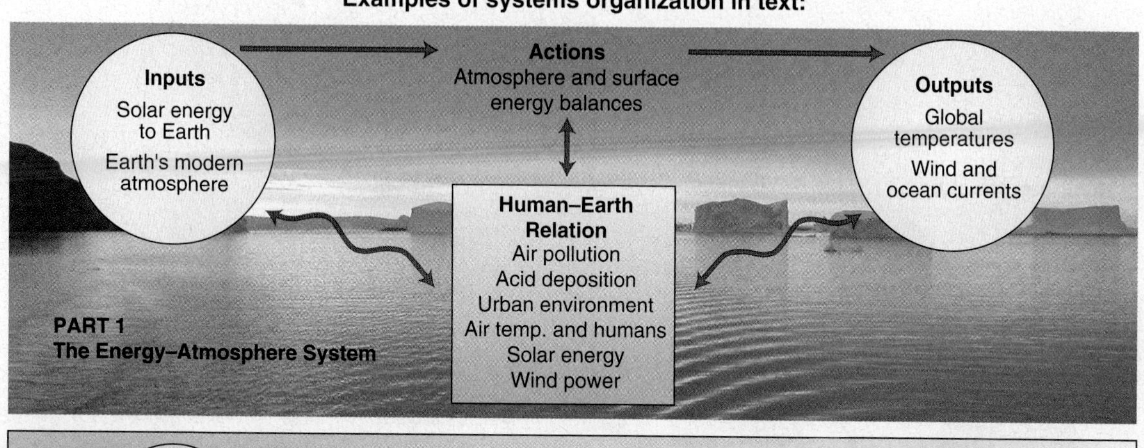

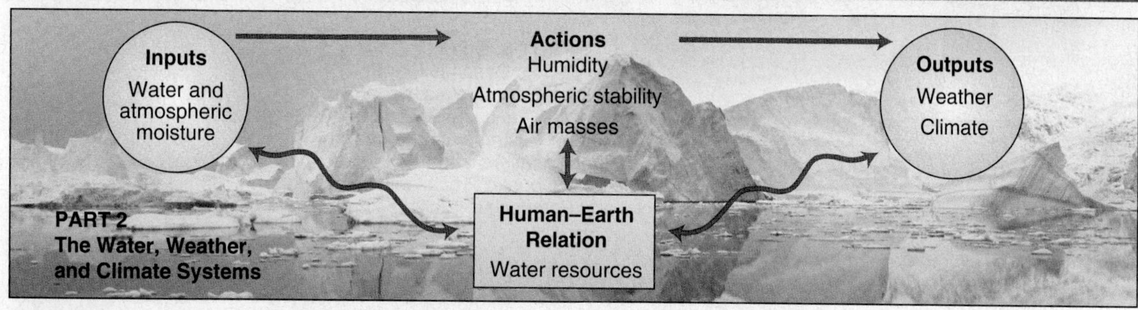

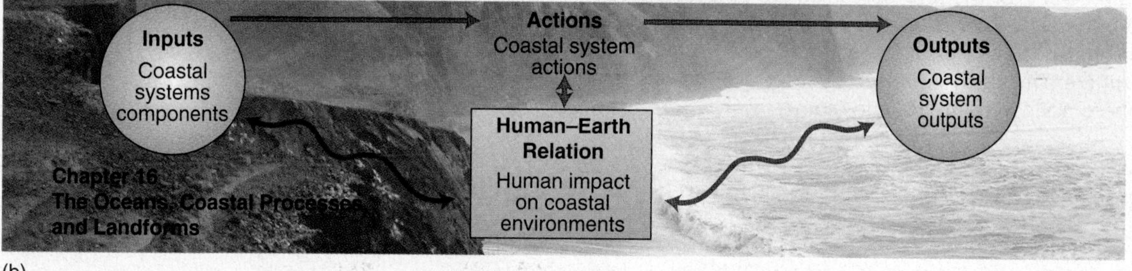

FIGURE 1.8 The systems in *Geosystems*.
(a) Chapters, sections, and topics are organized around simple flow systems, or around time and the flow of events, at various scales. (b) This systems structure as it is applied to Parts 1 and 2. As a chapter example, turn to Chapter 16, which examines coastal processes. Note the outline headings used: Coastal System Components, Coastal System Actions, Coastal System Outputs, and Human Impact on Coastal Environments. Thus, Chapter 16 is organized along the systems flow in (a).

life. Among the planets in the Solar System, only Earth possesses surface water in such quantity, adding to Earth's uniqueness among the planets.

Lithosphere (Part 3, Chapters 11–17) Earth's crust and a portion of the upper mantle directly below the crust form the **lithosphere**. The crust is quite brittle compared to the layers deep beneath the surface, which move slowly in response to an uneven distribution of heat energy and pressure. An important component of the lithosphere is *soil*, which generally covers Earth's land surfaces; the soil layer is sometimes referred to as the *edaphosphere*. (In a broad

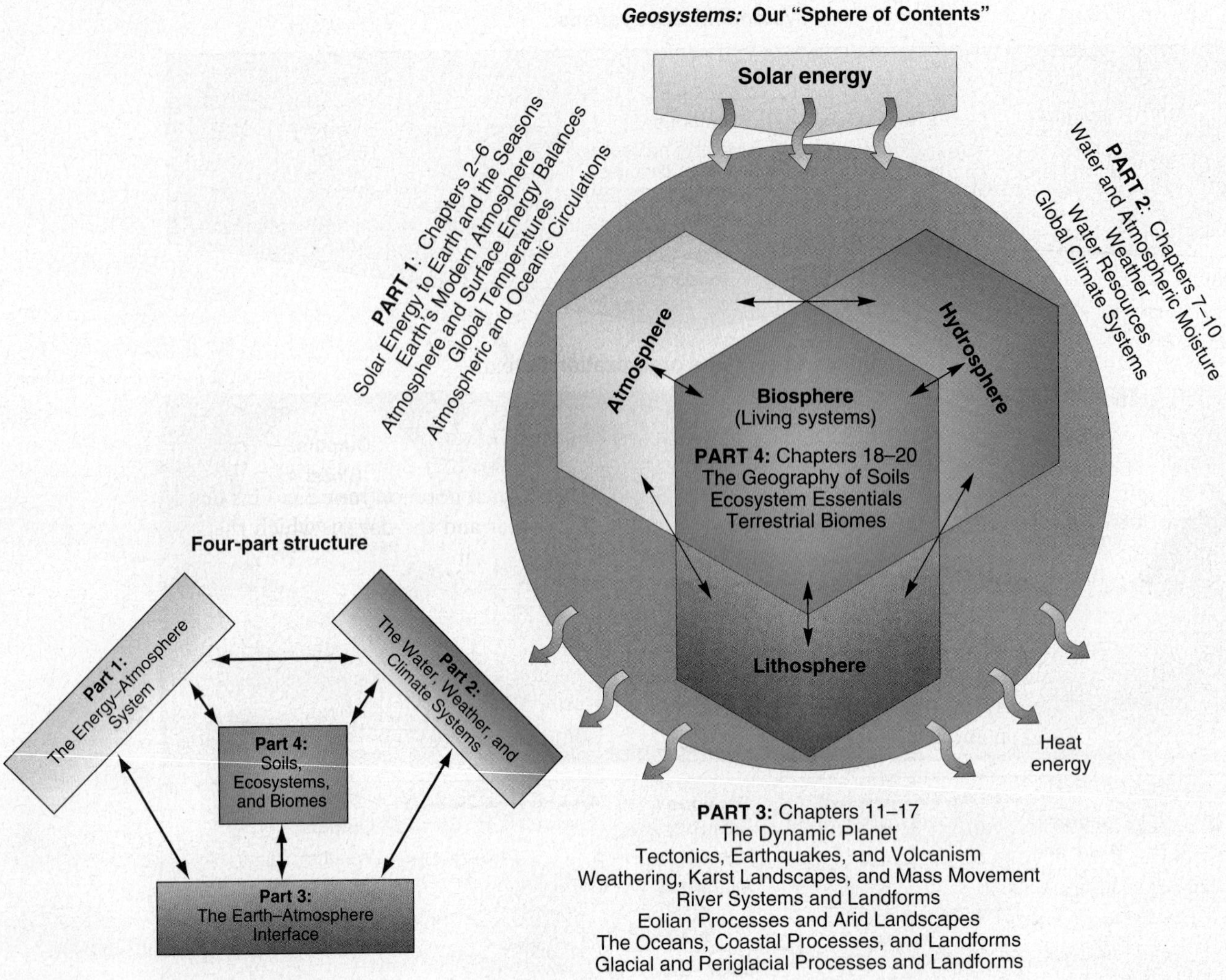

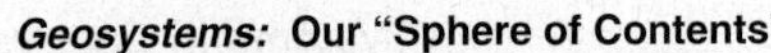

FIGURE 1.9 Earth's four spheres.
Each sphere is a model of vast Earth systems. This general model further provides the organizational framework for the four-part structure of *Geosystems.*

Part 1—Atmosphere: The Energy–Atmosphere System
Part 2—Hydrosphere: The Water, Weather, and Climate Systems
Part 3—Lithosphere: The Earth–Atmosphere Interface
Part 4—Biosphere: Soils, Ecosystems, and Biomes

sense, the term *lithosphere* sometimes refers to the entire solid planet.)

Biosphere (Part 4, Chapters 18–20) The intricate, interconnected web that links all organisms with their physical environment is the **biosphere**. Sometimes called the **ecosphere**, the biosphere is the area in which physical and chemical factors form the context of life. The biosphere exists in the overlap among the abiotic spheres, extending from the seafloor and even the upper layers of the crustal rock to about 8 km (5 mi) into the atmosphere. Life is sustainable within these natural limits. In turn, life processes have powerfully shaped the other three spheres through various interactive processes. The biosphere evolves, reorganizes itself at times, faces some extinctions, and manages to flourish. Earth's biosphere is the only one known in the Solar System; thus, life as we know it is unique to Earth.

A Spherical Planet

We have all heard that some people believed Earth to be flat. Yet Earth's sphericity is not as modern a concept as many think. For instance, more than two millennia ago, the Greek mathematician and philosopher Pythagoras (ca. 580–500 B.C.) determined through observation that Earth is spherical. We do not know what observations led Pythagoras to this conclusion. Can you guess at what he saw to deduce Earth's roundness?

He might have noticed ships sailing beyond the horizon and apparently sinking below the water's surface, only to arrive back at port with dry decks. Perhaps he noticed Earth's curved shadow cast on the lunar surface during an eclipse of the Moon. He might have deduced that the Sun and Moon are not just the flat disks they appear to be in the sky but are spherical and that Earth must be a sphere as well.

Earth's sphericity was generally accepted by the educated populace as early as the first century A.D. Christopher Columbus, for example, knew he was sailing around a sphere in 1492; that is one reason why he thought he had reached the East Indies.

Earth as a Geoid Until 1687, the spherical-perfection model was a basic assumption of **geodesy**, the science that determines Earth's shape and size by surveys and mathematical calculations. But in that year, Sir Isaac Newton postulated that the round Earth, along with the other planets, could not be perfectly spherical. Newton reasoned that the more-rapid rotational speed at the equator—the equator being farthest from the central axis of the planet and therefore moving faster—would produce an equatorial bulge in response to a greater centrifugal force, which, in effect, pulls Earth's surface outward. He was convinced that Earth is slightly misshapen into what he termed an *oblate spheroid*, or more correctly an *oblate ellipsoid* (*oblate* means "flattened"), with the oblateness occurring at the poles.

Today, Earth's equatorial bulge and its polar oblateness are universally accepted and confirmed by satellite observations. Our modern era of Earth measurement is one of tremendous precision and is called the "geoidal epoch" because Earth is a **geoid**, meaning literally "the shape of Earth is Earth-shaped." Imagine Earth's geoid as a sea-level surface that is extended uniformly worldwide, beneath the continents. Both heights on land and depths in the oceans are measured from this hypothetical surface. Think of the geoid surface as a balance between the gravitational attraction of Earth's mass and the centrifugal pull caused by Earth's rotation.

Figure 1.10 gives Earth's polar and equatorial circumferences and diameters. Earth's polar circumference was first measured more than 2200 years ago by the Greek geographer, astronomer, and librarian Eratosthenes (ca. 276–195 B.C.). The ingenious reasoning by which he arrived at his calculation follows.

Measuring Earth in 247 B.C.

Foremost among early geographers, Eratosthenes served as the librarian of Alexandria in Egypt during the third century B.C. He was in a position of scientific leadership, for Alexandria's library was the finest in the ancient world. Among his achievements was calculation of Earth's polar circumference to a high level of accuracy, quite a feat for 247 B.C. Here's how he did it. As you read, follow along on Figure 1.11.

Travellers told Eratosthenes that on June 21 they had seen the Sun's rays shine directly to the bottom of a well at Syene, the location of present-day Aswan, Egypt. This meant that the Sun had to be directly overhead. North of Syene in Alexandria, Eratosthenes knew from his own observations that the Sun's rays were never directly overhead, even at noon on June 21. This day is the longest day of the year and the day on which the Sun is at its northernmost position in the sky. Unlike objects in Syene, he knew objects in Alexandria always cast a noontime shadow. Using the considerable geometric knowledge of the era, Eratosthenes conducted an experiment.

In Alexandria at noon on June 21, he measured the angle of a shadow cast by an obelisk (a perpendicular column). Knowing the height of the obelisk and measuring the length of the Sun's shadow from its base, he solved the triangle for the angle of the Sun's rays, which he determined to be 7.2° off from directly overhead. However, at Syene on the same day, the angle of the Sun's rays was 0° from a perpendicular—that is, the Sun was directly overhead.

Geometric principles told Eratosthenes that the distance on the ground between Alexandria and Syene formed an arc of Earth's circumference equal to the angle of the Sun's rays at Alexandria. Since 7.2° is roughly 1/50 of the 360° (360° ÷ 7.2° = 50) in Earth's total circumference, the distance between Alexandria and Syene must represent approximately 1/50 of Earth's total circumference.

Next, Eratosthenes determined the surface distance between the two cities as 5000 stadia. A *stadium*, a Greek

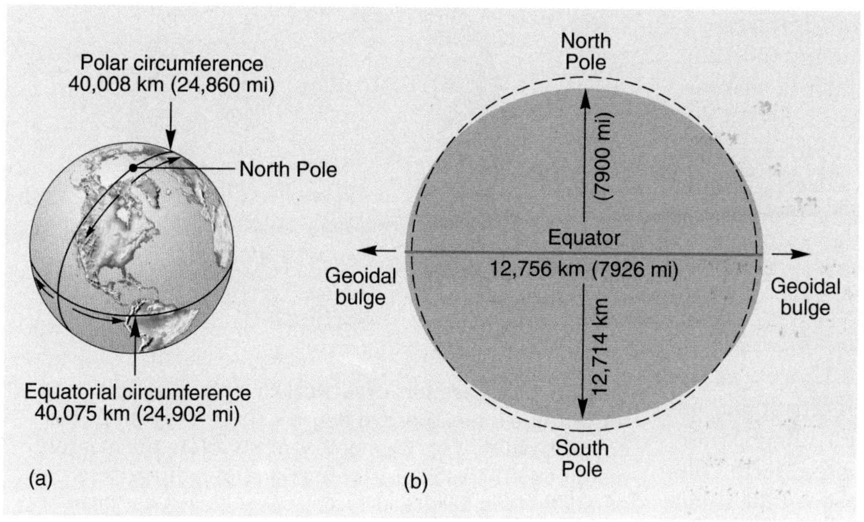

FIGURE 1.10 Earth's dimensions. Earth's circumference (a) and diameter (b)—equatorial and polar—are shown. The dashed line is a perfect circle for reference to Earth's geoid.

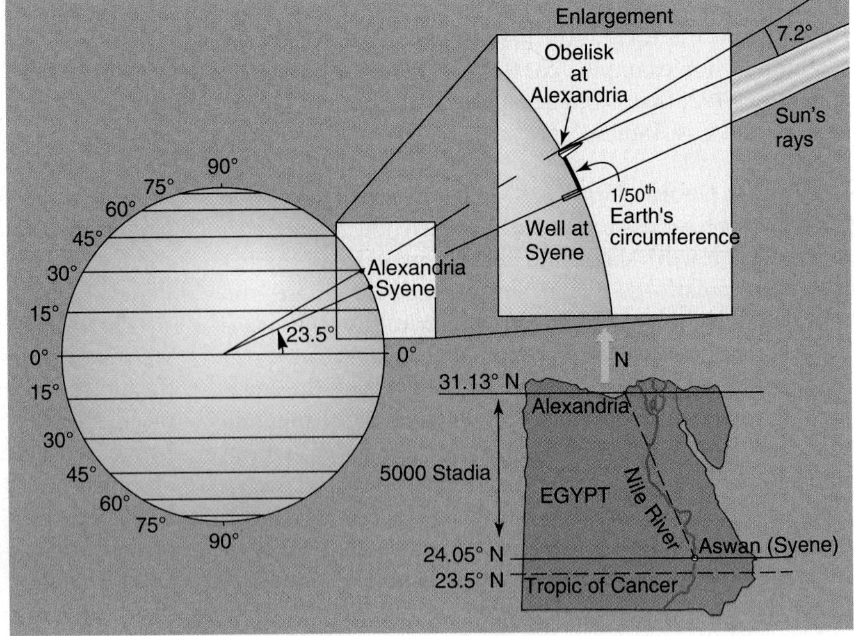

FIGURE 1.11 Eratosthenes' calculation. Eratosthenes' work teaches the value of observing carefully and integrating all observations with previous learning. Calculating Earth's circumference required application of his knowledge of Earth–Sun relationships, geometry, and geography to his keen observations. His estimate was remarkably close to modern measurements. (Several values can be used for the distance of a Greek stadium—the 185 m used here represents an average value.)

unit of measure, equals approximately 185 m (607 ft). He then multiplied 5000 stadia by 50 to determine that Earth's polar circumference is about 250,000 stadia. Eratosthenes' calculations convert to roughly 46,250 km (28,738 mi), which is remarkably close to the correct value of 40,008 km (24,860 mi) for Earth's polar circumference. Not bad for 247 B.C.!

Location and Time on Earth

An essential for geographic science is a coordinated grid system to determine location on Earth, a system of coordinates agreed to by all peoples. The terms *latitude* and *longitude* were in use on maps as early as the first century A.D., with the concepts themselves dating back to Eratosthenes and others.

The geographer, astronomer, and mathematician Ptolemy (ca. A.D. 90–168) contributed greatly to modern maps, and many of his terms and configurations are still used today. Ptolemy divided the circle into 360 degrees (360°), with each degree comprising 60 minutes (60′) and each minute including 60 seconds (60″), in a manner adapted from the ancient Babylonians. He located places using these degrees, minutes, and seconds. However, the precise length of a degree of latitude and a degree of longitude remained unresolved for the next 17 centuries.

Latitude

Latitude *is an angular distance north or south of the equator*, measured from the centre of Earth (Figure 1.12a). On a map or globe, the lines designating these angles of latitude run east and west, parallel to the equator (Figure 1.12b). Because Earth's equator divides the distance between the North Pole and the South Pole exactly in half, it is assigned the value of 0° latitude. Thus, latitude increases in value from the

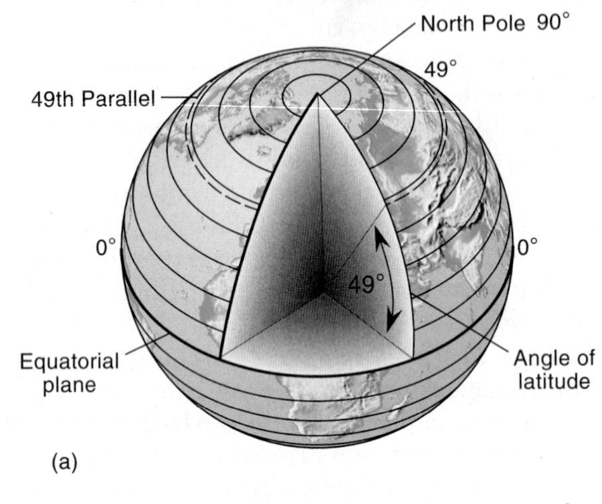

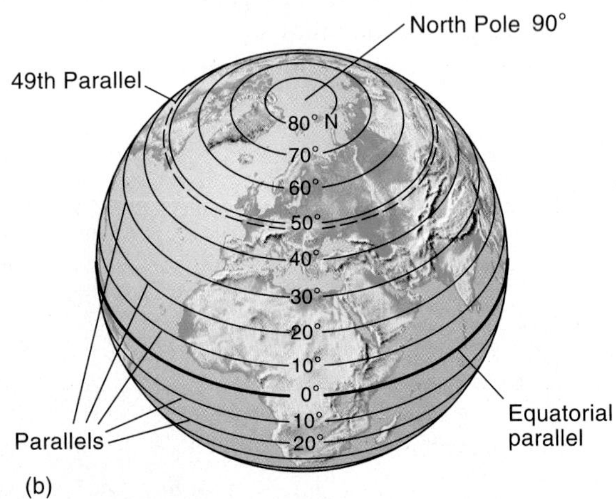

FIGURE 1.12 Parallels of latitude.
(a) Latitude is measured in degrees north or south of the equator, which is 0°. Each pole is at 90°. Note the measurement of 49° latitude. (b) These angles of latitude determine parallels along Earth's surface. Do you know your present latitude?

equator northward to the North Pole, at 90° north latitude, and southward to the South Pole, at 90° south latitude.

A line connecting all points along the same latitudinal angle is called a **parallel**. In the figure, an angle of 49° north latitude is measured, and, by connecting all points at this latitude, we have the 49th parallel. Thus, *latitude* is the name of the angle (49° north latitude), *parallel* names the line (49th parallel), and both indicate distance north of the equator. The 49th parallel is a significant one in the Western Hemisphere, for it forms the boundary between Canada and the United States from Lake of the Woods on the Ontario–Manitoba border to the Pacific Ocean.

Latitude is readily determined by reference to *fixed celestial objects* such as the Sun or the stars, a method dating to ancient times. During daylight hours, the angle of the Sun above the horizon indicates the observer's latitude, after adjustment is made for the seasonal tilt of Earth and for the time of day. Because Polaris (the North Star) is almost directly overhead at the North Pole, persons anywhere in the Northern Hemisphere can determine their latitude at night simply by sighting Polaris and measuring its angle above the local horizon (Figure 1.13). The angle of elevation of Polaris above the horizon equals the latitude of the observation point.

In the Southern Hemisphere, Polaris cannot be seen because it is below the horizon. Instead, latitude measurement south of the equator is accomplished by sighting on a constellation that points to a celestial location above the South Pole. This indicator constellation is the Southern Cross (Crux Australis). Tracking the location of the North Pole is the focus of News Report 1.1.

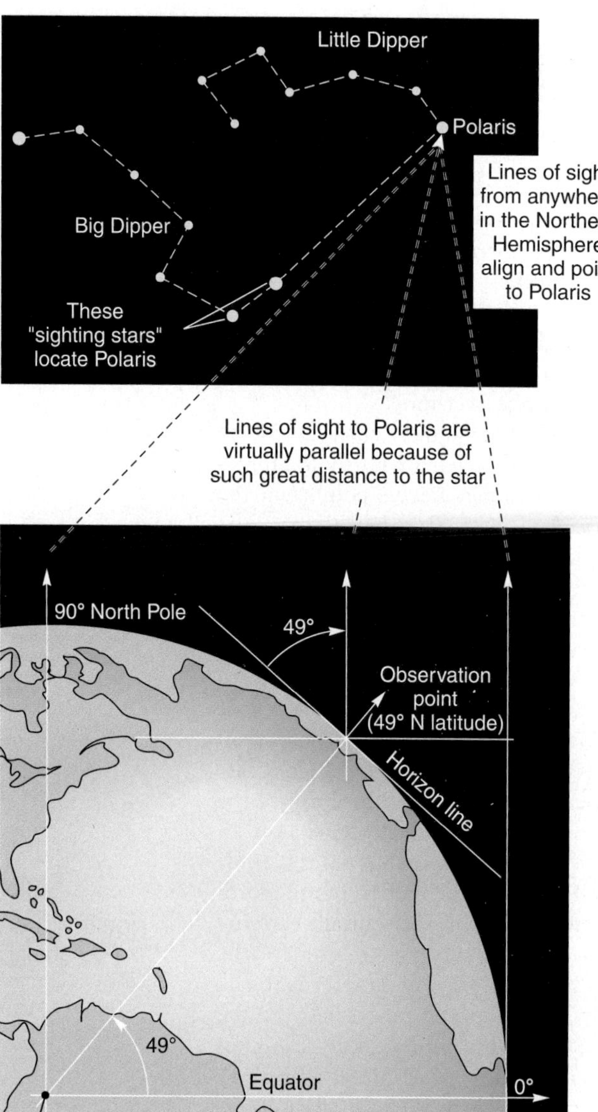

FIGURE 1.13 Determining latitude by using Polaris (the North Star).
To locate Polaris from anywhere in the Northern Hemisphere, you can use the "sighting stars" in the Big Dipper constellation. Next, measure the angular distance between Polaris and the local horizon. This angular distance of Polaris above the horizon is the same as your latitude. In this case Polaris appears 49° above the horizon, so you are standing at 49° north latitude. (Note that Polaris is at such a great distance from Earth that lines of sight from anywhere in the Northern Hemisphere can be considered parallel.) On the next clear night, take a protractor and stick or ruler and sight on Polaris to determine your latitude manually.

Latitudinal Geographic Zones Natural environments differ dramatically from the equator to the poles, in both their processes and their appearance. These differences result from the amount of solar energy received, which varies by latitude and season of the year. As a convenience, geographers identify *latitudinal geographic zones* as regions with fairly consistent qualities. Figure 1.14 portrays these zones, their locations, and their names: *equatorial* and *tropical*, *subtropical*, *midlatitude*, *subarctic* or *subantarctic*, and *arctic* or *antarctic*. "Lower latitudes" are those nearer the equator, whereas "higher latitudes" are those nearer the poles. These generalized latitudinal zones are useful for reference and comparison, but don't think of them as having rigid boundaries.

The *Tropic of Cancer* (23.5° north parallel) and the *Tropic of Capricorn* (23.5° south parallel) are the most extreme northern and southern parallels that experience perpendicular (directly overhead) rays of the Sun at local noon. When the Sun arrives overhead at these tropics, it marks the first day of summer in each hemisphere. (The tropics are discussed further in Chapter 2.) The *Arctic Circle* (66.5° north parallel) and the *Antarctic Circle* (66.5° south parallel) are the parallels farthest from the poles that still experience 24 uninterrupted hours of night during local winter or of day during local summer. There are many ways to define latitudinal geographic zones. News Report 1.2 outlines how Statistics Canada attempts to quantify the concept of north.

Longitude

Longitude *is an angular distance east or west of a point on Earth's surface*, measured from the centre of Earth (Figure 1.15a). On a map or globe, the lines designating these angles of

News Report 1.1

The Coordinates of North

What is North and where is it located? There are several ways to measure the most northern point of the planet. The first method is to coordinate the north geographic pole—the axial pole centred where the meridians of longitude converge. This is *true north* and does not change over time.

The second way to measure North is by use of magnetic north (the direction a compass needle points). At the *North Magnetic Pole*, Earth's magnetic field is directed vertically downward (the magnetic dip) relative to Earth's surface. This is the observed magnetic pole, located and mapped by magnetic surveys. As the magnetic field of Earth changes, the North Magnetic Pole slowly drifts across the Canadian Arctic. Scientists have traced a long history of change in the location of the North Magnetic Pole (Figure 1).

The Geological Survey of Canada (GSC) tracks the motion of the North Magnetic Pole by periodically carrying out magnetic surveys to re-establish the Pole's location. The most recent survey, a collaborative effort between the GSC and the Bureau de Recherches Géologiques et Minières (BRGM), France, began in 1999 with four observations, and again in 2001, with an additional four observations. Through this effort the GSC and BRGM calculated an updated position for the pole and established that it is moving northwest at approximately 40 km per year. The observed position for 2001–2004 and the estimated position for 2005 are given in Table 1.

The third method to coordinate North is through the use of the *North Geomagnetic Pole*. This is a mathematical model of Earth's magnetic field. The Canadian Geomagnetic Reference Field (CGRF) is a mathematical model of the geomagnetic field over Canada. It is produced by synthesizing numerous observations—made between 1960 and 1999—of the magnetic field on the ground, at sea, in the air, and at satellite altitudes. This model is run periodically to refine locations for the time interval 1960 to 2005. Values of magnetic declination, or any other magnetic field measurement over Canada and adjacent areas, are obtained using the Magnetic Information Retrieval Program (MIRP) and the CGRF. Outside Canada, MIRP automatically uses the International Geomagnetic Reference Field (IGRF) to calculate magnetic field values. At present, the north geomagnetic pole position is 79.3° N 71.5° W and the south geomagnetic pole position is 79.3° S 108.5° E. These positions are used frequently to generate the geomagnetic coordinate system.

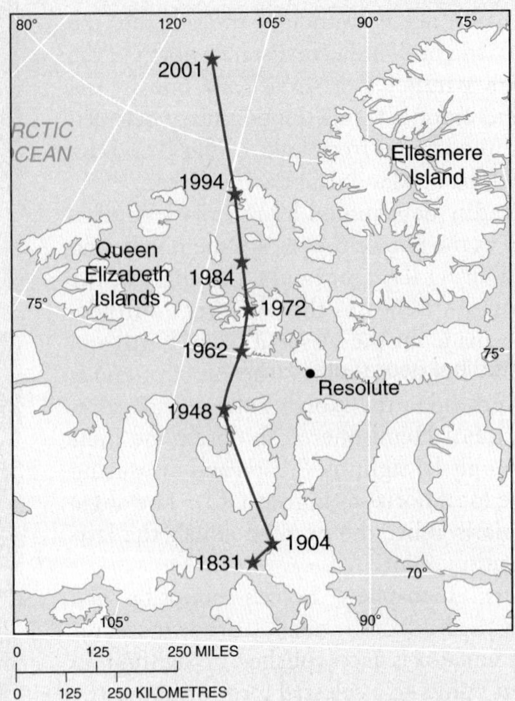

FIGURE 1 The location of the North Magnetic Pole from 1831 to 2001. The geographic location of the North Magnetic Pole changes with variations in Earth's magnetic field. [Used by permission of the Minister of Public Works and Government Services Canada and Natural Resources Canada, Geological Survey of Canada.]

Table 1 Coordinates of the North Magnetic Pole 2001 to 2005

Year	Latitude (°N)	Longitude (°W)
2001	81.3	110.8
2002	81.6	111.6
2003	82.0	112.4
2004	82.3	113.4
2005	82.7	114.4

Source: **http://www.geolab.nrcan.gc.ca/geomag/northpole_e.shtml**. Reproduced with the permission of the Minister of Public Works and Government Services Canada; Natural Resources Canada, Geological Survey of Canada.

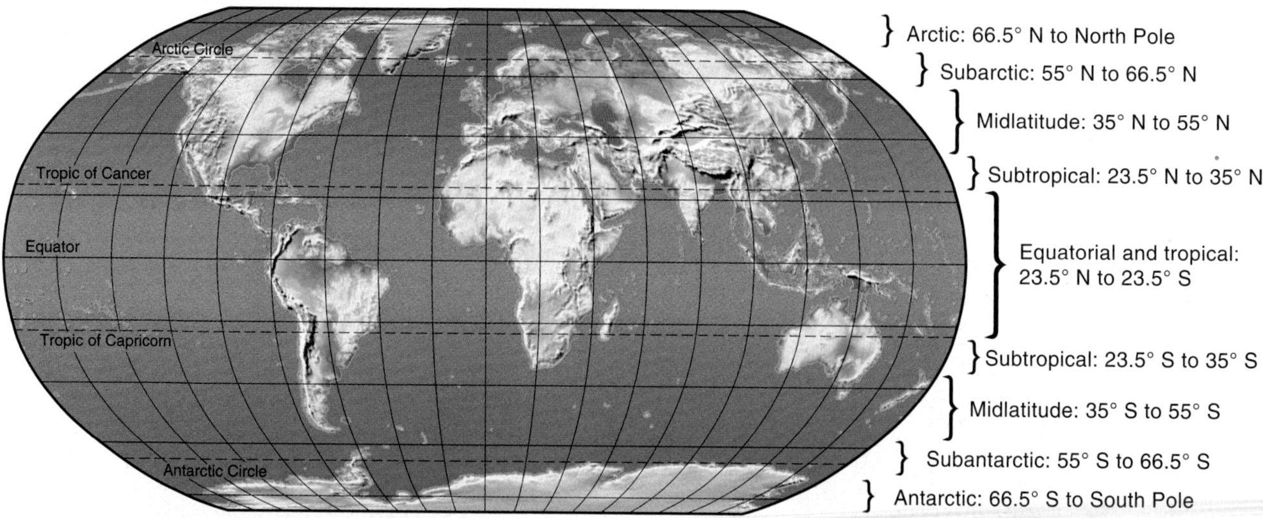

FIGURE 1.14 Latitudinal geographic zones.
Geographic zones are generalizations that characterize various regions by latitude. Think of these as transitional into one another over broad areas.

News Report 1.2

The Great White *North*?

In Canada, the concept of *north* is something that pervades our national identity. But, how far north is north? When are you south? Traditionally, north was defined as latitude greater than 60° N. A team of geographers at Statistics Canada collaborated to define north in a more detailed manner. They began with the concept of *nordicity*—the degree of "northerliness," a quantitative measure of place that was first calculated in the 1970s. The team proposed a new, inclusive definition of the concept of north by examining a wide range of variables, including physical characteristics of climate and biota as well as social and cultural measures.

The results of the study are summarized in a map that illustrates four zones: the north, the north transition, the south transition, and the south (Figure 1). The majority of Canadians live in the south and south transition zones—there are no large urban centres in the north or the north transition zones. Divisions between zones do not simply follow lines of latitude, but deviate to the north or south in various parts of the country.

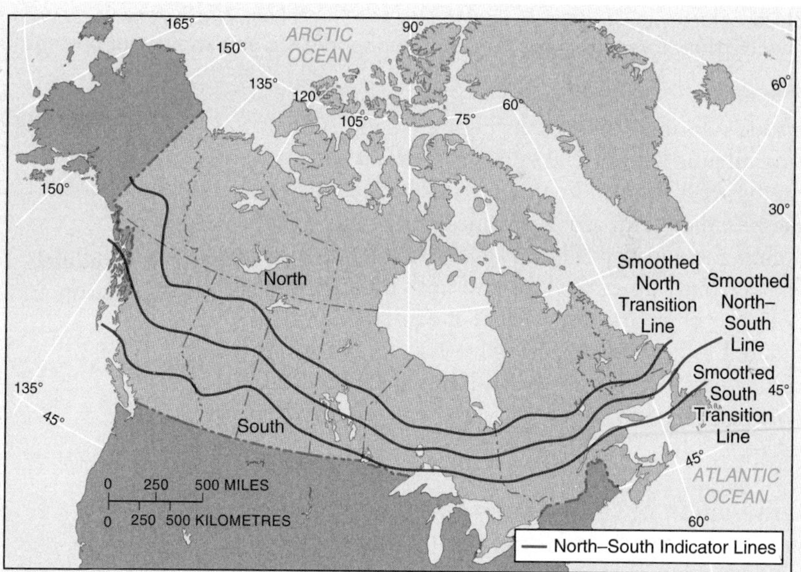

FIGURE 1 A new definition of north.
The Statistics Canada definition of north and south indicators with boundary lines drawn to reflect average values of northerliness based on physical, biological, social, economic, and cultural measures. In which region do you live? Do your perceptions agree with Statistics Canada? [Adapted from *Delineation of Canada's North: An Examination of the North–South Relationship in Canada*, catalogue 92F0138, February 3, 2000, map 4.]

Using this index of *northerliness*, Labrador, the northern parts of Québec, Ontario, Manitoba, Saskatchewan, Alberta, and a portion of northern British Columbia qualify as "*the north*" even though they lie south of 60° N, a traditional boundary line. The study is important because it emphasizes the idea of "the north" as a concept rather than a geographic area. There is no clearly demarcated line that separates north from south, but a transition from Canada south to Canada north that extends in a broad band across the country. The idea of the transition

(continued)

News Report 1.2 (continued)

zones was intended to deal with comparisons of "north" and "south" that may interfere with recognition of the interesting physical, social, economic, and cultural differences within northern regions.

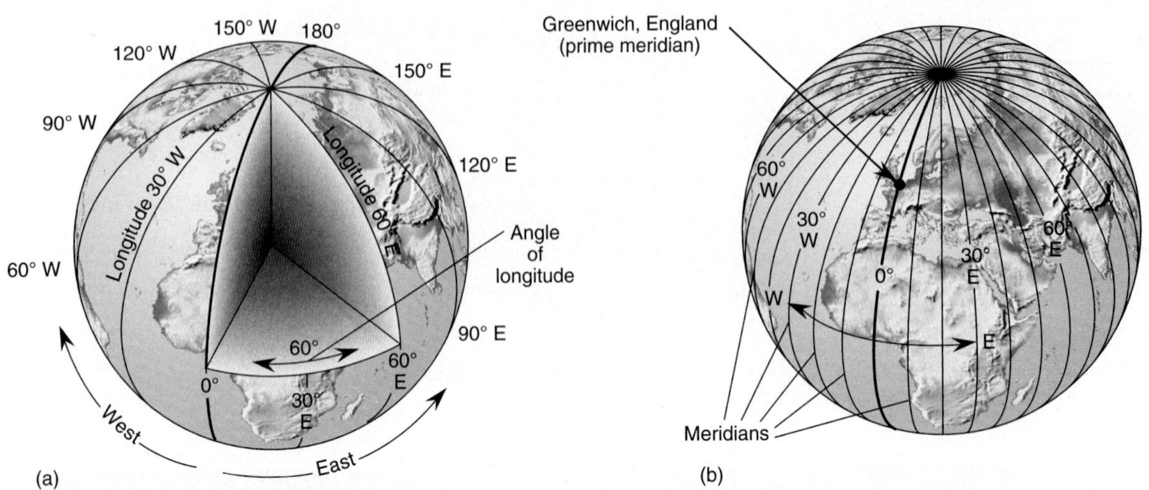

FIGURE 1.15 Meridians of longitude.
(a) Longitude is measured in degrees east or west of a 0° starting line, the prime meridian. Note the measurement of 60° E longitude. (b) Angles of longitude measured from this prime meridian determine other meridians. The prime meridian is drawn from the North Pole through the Royal Observatory in Greenwich, England, to the South Pole. North America is west of Greenwich; therefore, it is in the Western Hemisphere. Do you know your present longitude?

longitude run north and south (Figure 1.15b). A line connecting all points along the same longitude is a **meridian**. In the figure a longitudinal angle of 60° E is measured. These meridians run at right angles (90°) to all parallels, including the equator. Thus, *longitude* is the name of the angle, *meridian* names the line, and both indicate distance east or west of an arbitrary **prime meridian**—a meridian designated as zero degrees (Figure 1.15b). Earth's prime meridian passes through the old Royal Observatory at Greenwich, England, as set by treaty—the *Greenwich prime meridian*.

Determination of Latitude and Longitude Table 1.2 compares the length of latitude and longitude degrees. Because meridians of longitude converge toward the poles, the actual distance on the ground spanned by a degree of longitude is greatest at the equator (where meridians separate to their widest distance apart) and diminishes to zero at the poles (where meridians converge). Note the consistent distance represented by a degree of latitude from equator to poles, yet the decreasing value a degree of longitude covers as meridians converge toward each pole.

We have noted that latitude is easily determined by sighting the Sun or the North Star or by using the Southern Cross as a pointer. In contrast, a method of accurately determining longitude, especially at sea, remained a major difficulty in navigation until the late 1700s. The key to measuring the longitude of a place lies in accurately knowing time. The relation between time and longitude and an exciting chapter in human discovery is the topic of Focus Study 1.2.

Table 1.2 Physical Distances Represented by Degrees of Latitude and Longitude

Latitudinal Location	Latitude Degree Length km	(mi)	Longitude Degree Length km	(mi)
90° (poles)	111.70	(69.41)	0	(0)
60°	111.42	(69.23)	55.80	(34.67)
50°	111.23	(69.12)	71.70	(44.55)
40°	111.04	(69.00)	85.40	(53.07)
30°	110.86	(68.89)	96.49	(59.96)
0° (equator)	110.58	(68.71)	111.32	(69.17)

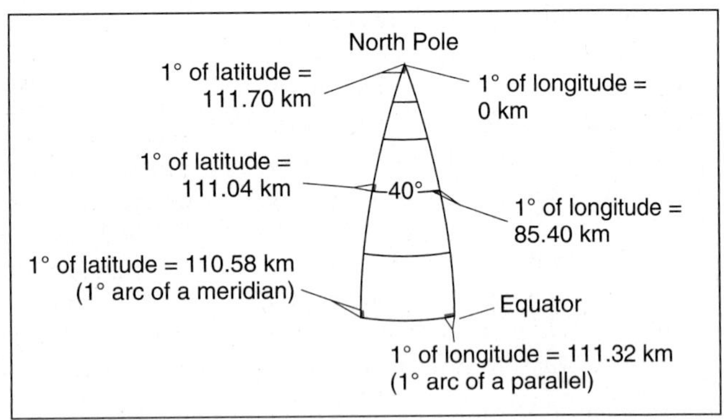

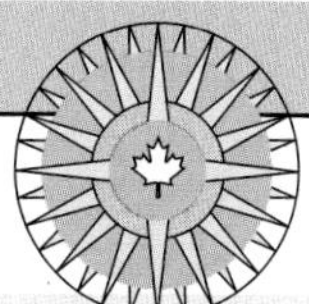

Focus Study 1.2

The Timely Search for Longitude

Unlike latitude, longitude cannot be determined readily from fixed celestial bodies. The problem is Earth's rotation, which constantly changes the apparent position of the Sun and stars. Determining longitude is particularly critical at sea, where no landmarks are visible.

In his historical novel *Shogun*, author James Clavell expressed the frustration of the longitude problem through his pilot, Blackthorn: "Find how to fix longitude and you're the richest man in the world. . . . The Queen, God bless her, 'll give you ten thousand pound and dukedom for answer to the riddle. . . . Out of sight of land you're always lost, lad."*

In the early 1600s, Galileo explained that longitude could be measured by using two clocks. Any point on Earth takes 24 hours to travel around the full 360° of one rotation (one day). If you divide 360° by 24 hours, you find that any point on Earth travels through 15° of longitude every hour. Thus, if there were a way to measure time accurately at sea, a comparison of two clocks could give a value for longitude. One clock would indicate the time back at home port (Figure 1). The other clock would be reset at local noon each day, as determined by the highest Sun position in the sky (solar zenith). The time difference then would indicate the longitudinal difference travelled: 1 hour for each 15° of longitude. The principle was sound; all that was needed were accurate clocks. Unfortunately, the pendulum clock invented by Christian Huygens in 1656 did not work on the rolling deck of a ship at sea!

In 1707 the British lost four ships and 2000 men in a sea tragedy that was blamed specifically on the longitude problem. In response, Parliament passed an act in 1714—"Publik Reward . . . to Discover the Longitude at Sea"—and authorized a prize worth more than $2 million in today's dollars to the first successful inventor of an accurate seafaring clock. The Board of Longitude was established to judge any devices submitted.

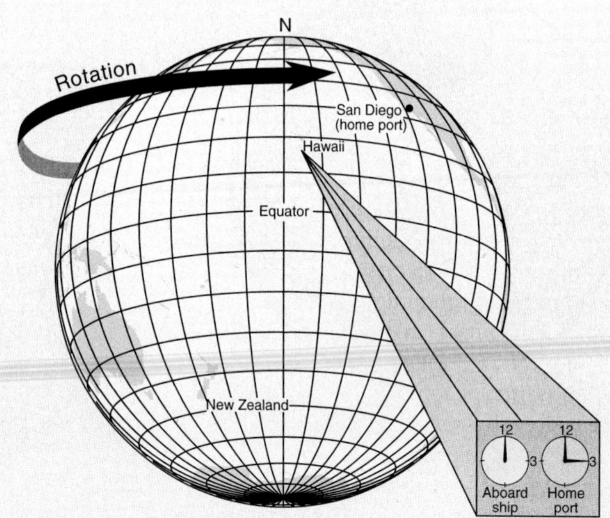

FIGURE 1 Clock time determines longitude.
Using two clocks on a ship to determine longitude. For example, if the shipboard clock reads local noon and the clock set for home port reads 3:00 P.M., ship time is 3 hours earlier than home time. Therefore, calculating 3 hours at 15° per hour puts the ship at 45° west longitude from home port.

John Harrison, a self-taught country clockmaker, began to work on the problem in 1728 and finally produced his brilliant marine chronometer, known as Number 4, in 1760. The clock was tested on a voyage to Jamaica in 1761. When taken ashore and compared to land-based longitude, Harrison's ingenious Number 4 was only 5 seconds slow, an error that translates to only 1.25′ or 2.3 km (1.4 mi), well within Parliament's standard. After many delays, Harrison finally received most of the prize money in his last years of life.

> With his marine clocks, John Harrison tested the waters of space-time. He succeeded, against all odds, in using the fourth-temporal-dimension to link points on the three-dimensional globe. He wrested the world's whereabouts from the stars, and locked the secret in a pocket watch.†

From that time on, it was possible to determine longitude accurately on land and sea, as long as everyone agreed upon a meridian to use as a reference for time comparisons—the Royal Observatory in Greenwich, England. In this modern era of atomic clocks and satellites in mathematically precise orbits, we have far greater accuracy available for the determination of longitude on Earth's surface and a basis for precise navigation.

*From J. Clavell, *Shogun*, Copyright ©1975 by James Clavell (New York: Delacorte Press, a division of Dell Publishing Group, Inc.), p. 10.
†From Dava Sobel, *Longitude, The Story of a Lone Genius Who Solved the Greatest Scientific Problem of His Time* (New York: Walker and Co., 1995), p. 175.

Today, using a hand-held instrument that reads radio signals from satellites, you can accurately calibrate latitude, longitude, and elevation. This is the **Global Positioning System (GPS)** technology. News Report 1.3 discusses the dramatic applications of the GPS.

Great Circles and Small Circles

Great circles and small circles are important concepts that help summarize latitude and longitude (Figure 1.16). A **great circle** is any circle of Earth's circumference whose

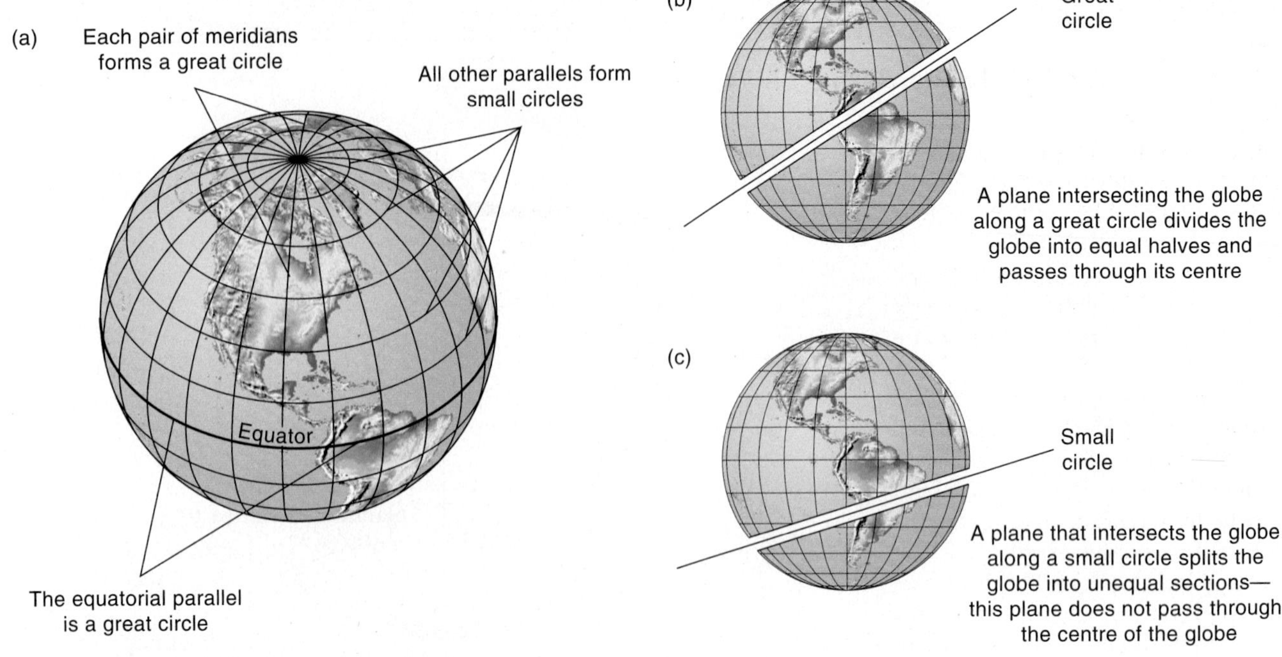

FIGURE 1.16 Great circles and small circles.
(a) Examples of great circles and small circles on Earth. (b) Any plane that divides Earth into equal halves will intersect the globe along a great circle; this great circle is a full circumference of the globe and is the shortest distance between any two surface points. (c) Any plane that splits the globe into unequal portions will intersect the globe along a small circle.

centre coincides with the centre of Earth. An infinite number of great circles can be drawn on Earth. Every meridian is one-half of a great circle that passes through the poles. On flat maps, airline and shipping routes appear to arch their way across oceans and landmasses. These are *great circle routes*, the shortest distance between two points on Earth (discussion with Figure 1.23 is just ahead).

Only one parallel is a great circle—the equatorial parallel. All other parallels diminish in length toward the poles and, along with any other non-great circles that one might draw, constitute **small circles.** These circles have centres that do not coincide with Earth's centre.

Figure 1.17 combines latitude and parallels with longitude and meridians to illustrate Earth's complete coordinate grid system. Note the dot that marks our measurement of 49° N by 60° E, a location in western Kazakstan. Next time you see a world globe, follow the parallel and meridian that converge on your location.

Prime Meridian and Standard Time

Coordination of international trade, airline schedules, business and agricultural activities, and daily living depends on a worldwide time system. Today we take for granted standard time zones and an agreed-upon prime meridian, but such a standard is a relatively recent development.

Setting time was not a great problem in small European countries, most of which are less than 15° wide. But in North America, which spans more than 90° of longitude (the equivalent of six 15° time zones), the problem was serious. In 1870 railway travellers going from Maine to San Francisco made 22 adjustments to their watches to stay consistent with local time!

In 1870, a traveller going from Halifax to Toronto had to change time at Saint John, Québec City, Montreal, Ottawa, and Toronto. When it was noon in Washington, D.C. in the United States, it was 12:54 P.M. in Halifax, 12:14 P.M. in Montreal, and 11:51 A.M. in Toronto! In 1878, Sandford Fleming, a railway surveyor and engineer who immigrated to Canada from Scotland, suggested a method

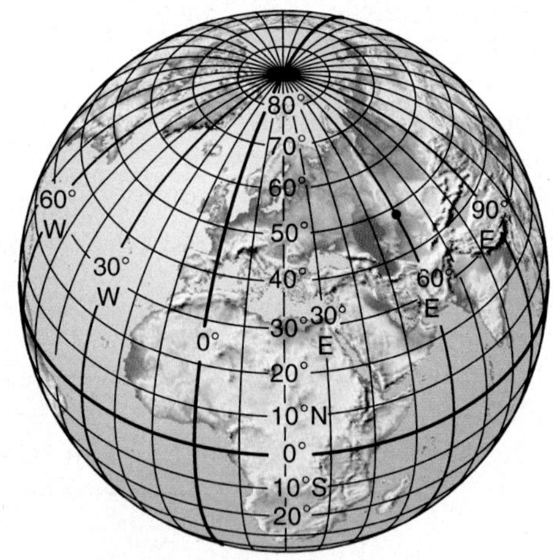

FIGURE 1.17 Earth's coordinate grid system.
Latitude and parallels, longitude and meridians, allow all places on Earth to be precisely located. The dot is at 49° N latitude by 60° E longitude.

News Report 1.3

GPS: A Personal Locator

The Global Positioning System (GPS) comprises 24 orbiting satellites, in six orbital planes, that transmit navigational signals for Earth-bound use (backup GPS satellites are in orbital storage as replacements). Originally devised in the 1970s by the U.S. Department of Defense for military purposes, the present system is commercially available worldwide.

Small receivers, some about the size of a pocket radio, receive signals from four or more satellites at the same time, calculate latitude and longitude within 10-m (33-ft) accuracy and elevation within 15 m (49 ft), and display the results. With the shutdown in 2000 of the Pentagon Selective Availability, commercial resolution is the same as that for military applications and its Precise Positioning Service (PPS). *Differential GPS (DGPS)* increases accuracy by comparing readings with another base station (reference receiver) for differential correction (Figure 1).

FIGURE 1 Surveying topography with a GPS.
A DGPS unit in operation, surveying the elevation changes in the dunes at Sauble Beach on Lake Huron, Ontario. [Photo by Mary-Louise Byrne.]

FIGURE 2 GPS used to measure Everest's summit height.
Installation of a Trimble 4800 GPS unit at Earth's highest bench mark, only 18 m (60 ft) below the 8850 m (29,035 ft) summit of Mount Everest. This GPS-based revised height measurement was announced in 1999. Scientists are using the data collected from a regional GPS network to accurately analyze the height of the world's tallest mountain and the rate that the mountain range is moving due to tectonic forces. [Photo and GPS installation by Wally Berg, May 20, 1998.]

GPS is useful for diverse applications, such as ocean navigation, land surveying, tracking small changes in Earth's crust, managing the movement of fleets of trucks, mining and resource mapping, tracking wildlife migration and behaviour, and environmental planning. Relative to earthquakes in southern California, Jet Propulsion Laboratory (JPL) operates the GPS Observation Office that monitors a network of 250 seismic stations. GPS also is useful to the backpacker and sportsperson. Commercial airlines use GPS to improve accuracy of routes flown and thus increase fuel efficiency. Scientists used GPS to accurately determine the height of Mount Everest in the Himalayan Mountains—now 8850 m as compared to the former 8848 m (29,035 ft, 29,028 ft) (Figure 2). In contrast, GPS measurements of Mount Kilimanjaro lowered its summit from 5895 m to 5892 m (19,340 ft, 19,330 ft).

Farmers use GPS to determine crop yields on specific parts of their farms. A detailed plot map is made to guide the farmer to where more fertilizer, proper seed distribution, irrigation applications, or other work is needed. A computer and GPS unit on board the farm equipment guides the work. This is the science of *variable-rate technology*, made possible by GPS. Assiniboine Community College, Brandon, Manitoba (**http://www.assiniboine.net/public/old/ag/program.htm**) and Ridgetown College University of Guelph, Ridgetown, Ontario (**http://www.ridgetownc.on.ca**) both offer certificate programs in Precision Agriculture.

The importance of GPS to geography is obvious because this precise technology reduces the need to maintain ground control points for location, mapping, and spatial analysis. Instead, geographers working in the field can

(continued)

News Report 1.3 *(continued)*

determine their position accurately as they work. Boundaries and data points in a study area are easily determined and entered into a data base, reducing the need for traditional surveys. For this and myriad other applications, GPS sales are exceeding $10 billion a year. As additional frequencies were added since 2003, accuracy was increased significantly. Also, the European Union plans to launch its own GPS system of 20 satellites beginning in 2005. (For a GPS overview, see **http://www.colorado.edu/geography/gcraft/notes/gps/gps.html**.)

for standardizing time. Despite early objections, Canada and the United States adopted his system for railway scheduling in 1883. Standard time was widely accepted after the International Prime Meridian Conference in 1884 (see **http://wwp.greenwichmeantime.com/info/time-zones-history.htm**). Today, only four adjustments are needed to cross Canada—standard time zones include Atlantic, Eastern, Central, Mountain, and Pacific—and three changes to cross the United States. Newfoundland Standard Time is one-half hour earlier than Atlantic Standard Time because the island of Newfoundland lies entirely in the eastern half of the Atlantic Time zone.

Twenty-seven countries attended the 1884 International Meridian Conference in Washington, D.C. Before that year, most nations used their own national capital as a prime meridian for their land maps, whereas more than 70% of the world's merchant ships were using Greenwich as a prime meridian on marine charts. After lengthy debate at the conference, most participating nations chose the highly respected Royal Observatory at Greenwich, London, England, as the place for the prime meridian of 0° longitude for all maps. Thus, a world standard was set—**Greenwich Mean Time (GMT)**—and a consistent Universal Time was established. (See **http://www.gmt2000.co.uk/meridian/place/plco0a1.htm**.)

The basis of time is that Earth revolves 360° every 24 hours, or 15° per hour (360° ÷ 24 = 15°). Thus, a time zone of 1 hour is established for each 15° increment of longitude, or 7.5° on either side of a *central meridian*. Assuming it is 9:00 P.M. in Greenwich, then it is 5:30 P.M. in St. John's (+3.5 hrs), 5:00 P.M. in Halifax (+4 hrs), 4:00 P.M. in Toronto (+5 hrs), 3:00 P.M. in Winnipeg (+6 hrs), 2:00 P.M. in Edmonton (+7 hrs), and 1:00 P.M. in Vancouver (+8 hrs). To the east, it is midnight in Ar Riyāḑ, Saudi Arabia (–3 hrs). (The designation A.M. is for *ante meridiem*, "before noon," whereas P.M. is for *post meridiem*, "after noon." A 24-hour clock avoids the use of these designations.)

As you can see from the modern international time zones in Figure 1.18, national boundaries and political considerations distort time zone boundaries. For example, China spans four time zones, but its government decided to keep the entire country operating at the same time. Thus, in some parts of China clocks are several hours off from what the Sun is doing. In the United States, parts of Florida and west Texas are in the same time zone.

International Date Line An important corollary of the prime meridian is the 180° meridian on the opposite side of the planet. This meridian is called the **International Date Line** and marks the place where each day officially begins (at 12:01 A.M.). From this "line" the new day sweeps westward. This *westward* movement of time is created by Earth's turning *eastward* on its axis.

At the International Date Line, the west side of the line is always one day ahead of the east side. No matter what time of day it is when the line is crossed, the calendar changes a day (Figure 1.19). Note in the illustration how the IDL deviates from the 180° meridian; this deviation is due to local administrative and political preferences.

Locating the date line in the sparsely populated Pacific Ocean minimizes most local confusion. However, early explorers before the date-line concept were "lost." For example, Magellan's crew returned from the first circumnavigation of Earth in 1522, confident from their ship's log that the day of their arrival home was Wednesday, September 7. They were shocked when informed by insistent local residents that it was actually Thursday, September 8! Of course, without an International Date Line, they had no idea that they must advance a day somewhere when sailing around the world in a westward direction. Imagine the confusion as the crew accounted for each day in their log!

Coordinated Universal Time For decades, Greenwich Mean Time from the Royal Observatory's astronomical clocks was the world's Universal Time (UT) standard for accuracy. GMT was broadcast using radio time signals as early as 1910. The French government took the initiative in 1912 and called a gathering of nations to better coordinate the various radio time signals from many countries. At this conference, GMT was made standard, and a new organization established to be the custodian of the most "exact" time—the International Bureau of Weights and Measures (BIPM) outside Paris (see **http://www.bipm.fr/**). Progress in accurately measuring time progressed rapidly with the invention of a quartz clock in 1939 and atomic clocks in the early 1950s.

The time signal system of **Coordinated Universal Time (UTC[*])** replaced GMT universal time in 1972 and became the legal reference for official time in all countries. Although the prime meridian still runs through Greenwich, UTC is based on average time calculations collected by the BIPM near Paris and broadcast worldwide.

[*]UTC is in use because agreement was not reached on whether to use the English word order, CUT, or the French order, TUC. UTC was the compromise and is recommended for all timekeeping applications; use of the term GMT is discouraged.

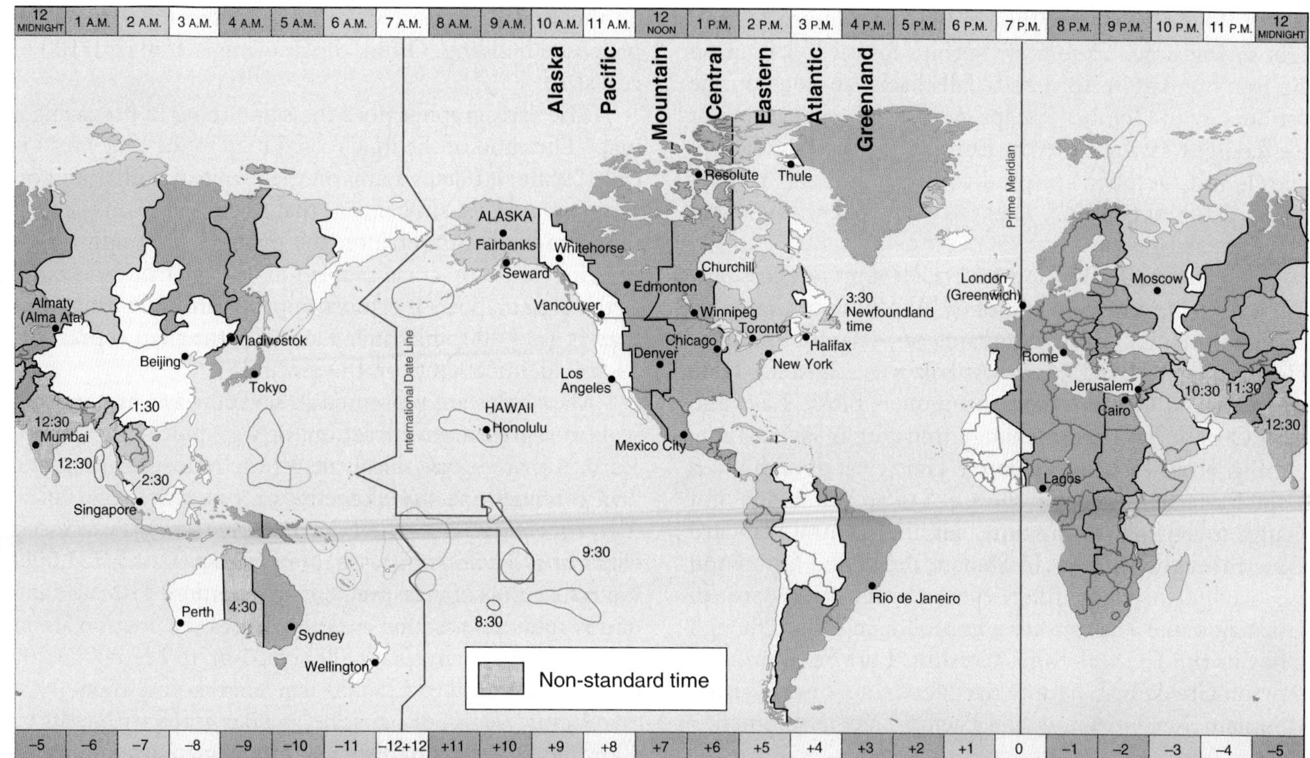

FIGURE 1.18 Modern international standard time zones.
Numbers along the bottom of the map indicate how many hours each zone is earlier (plus sign) or later (minus sign) than Coordinated Universal Time (UTC) at the prime meridian. Canada has six time zones; the United States is divided into five. If it is 7 P.M. in Greenwich, determine the present time in Moscow, London, Halifax, Chicago, Winnipeg, Denver, Los Angeles, Fairbanks, Honolulu, Tokyo, and Singapore. The island country of Kiribati moved the International Date Line to its eastern margin (150° west longitude) to be the first to experience each new day. These distortions of the International Date Line only apply to the countries and their territorial waters and not to international waters between them and the 180th meridian. [Adapted from Standard Time Zone Chart of the World, Defense Mapping Agency, Bethesda, Maryland.]

Regular vibrations (natural frequency) of cesium atoms in primary standard clocks measure the length of a second and UTC—accuracies now range down to 15 decimal places, or nanoseconds of time. Time and Frequency Services of the National Institute for Standards and Technology (NIST), U.S. Department of Commerce, operates several of the most advanced clocks. (For more on time, call 303-499-7111 or 808-335-4363, or see **http://nist.time.gov/** for UTC.) In Canada, the Institute for Measurement Standards, National Research Council Canada, participates in determining UTC (English, 613-745-1578; French, 613-745-9426; for more see **http://www.nrc-cnrc.gc.ca/**).

Daylight Saving Time In many countries, time is set ahead 1 hour in the spring and set back 1 hour in the fall—a practice known as **daylight saving time**. The idea to extend daylight for early evening activities (at the expense of daylight in the morning) was first proposed by Benjamin Franklin. It was not adopted until World War I and again in World War II, when Great Britain, Australia, Germany, Canada, and the United States used the practice to save energy (one less hour of artificial lighting needed).

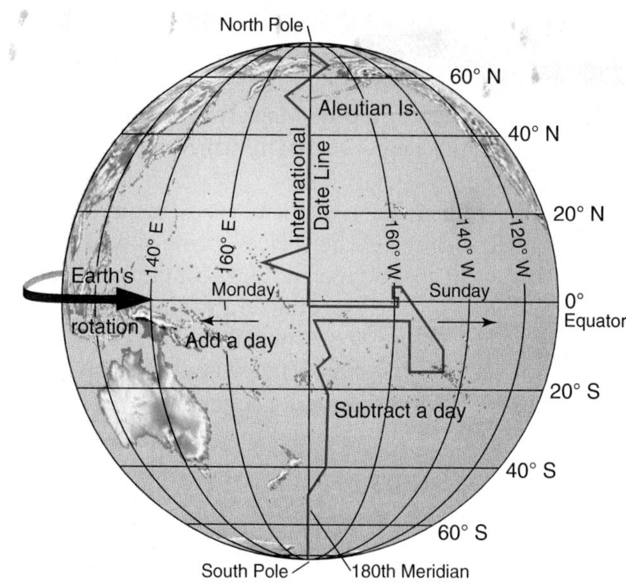

FIGURE 1.19 International Date Line.
International Date Line location, approximately along the 180th meridian (see the IDL location on Figure 1.18). Note that it is officially one day later west of the IDL.

In 1986, Canada and the United States increased daylight saving time. Time now "springs forward" 1 hour on the first Sunday in April and "falls back" an hour on the last Sunday in October, except in a few places that do not use daylight saving time. In Europe, the last Sundays in March and October are used to begin and end what is called "summer time." (See **http://webexhibits.org/daylightsavings/**.)

Despite standardization efforts, local preferences persist. In Québec, the area east of 63° W does not change to daylight saving time and remains on Atlantic Standard Time year round. In Ontario, Atikokan uses Eastern Time in winter and Central Time in summer; Pickle Lake and New Osnaburgh do not change to daylight saving time, and Big Trout Lake uses Central Time even though it lies in the Eastern Time zone. Most of Saskatchewan does not change to daylight saving time, but uses Central Standard Time throughout the year. Denare Beach and Creighton use daylight saving time even though they are in Saskatchewan. Lloydminster uses Mountain Time although it lies in the Central zone. Creston, Fort St. John, and Dawson Creek, B.C., ignore daylight saving time by using Mountain Time in winter and Pacific Time in summer.

Maps, Scales, and Projections

The earliest known graphic map representations date to 2300 B.C., when the Babylonians used clay tablets to record information about the region of the Tigris and Euphrates Rivers (the area of modern-day Iraq). Today, the making of maps and charts is a specialized science as well as an art, blending aspects of geography, engineering, mathematics, graphics, computer science, and artistic specialties. It is similar in ways to architecture, in which aesthetics and utility combine to produce a useful product.

A **map** is a generalized view of an area, usually some portion of Earth's surface, as seen from above and greatly reduced in size. The part of geography that embodies mapmaking is called **cartography**. Maps are critical tools with which geographers depict spatial information and analyze spatial relationships.

We all use maps at some time to visualize our location and our relationship to other places, or maybe to plan a trip, or to coordinate commercial and economic activities. Have you found yourself looking at a map, planning real and imagined adventures to faraway places? Maps are wonderful tools! Understanding a few basics about maps is essential to our study of physical geography.

The Scale of Maps

Architects, toy designers, and mapmakers have something in common: they all create scale models. They reduce real things and places to the more convenient scale of a drawing, model car, train, plane, diagram, or map. An architect renders a blueprint of a structure to guide the building contractors, selecting a scale so that one centimetre (or inch) on the drawing represents so many metres (or feet) on the proposed building. Often, the drawing is 1/50 to 1/100 of real size.

The cartographer does the same thing in preparing a map. The ratio of the image on a map to the real world is called **scale**; it relates a unit on the map to a similar unit on the ground. A 1:1 scale means that a centimetre on the map represents a centimetre on the ground (although this is certainly an impractical map scale, for the map is as large as the area mapped!). A more appropriate scale for a local map is 1:24,000, in which 1 unit on the map represents 24,000 identical units on the ground.

Map scales are presented in several ways: as a written scale, a representative fraction, or a graphic scale (Figure 1.20). A *written scale* simply states the ratio—for example, "one centimetre to one kilometre" or "one inch to one mile." A *representative fraction* (*RF*, or *fractional scale*) is expressed with either a colon or a slash, as in 1:125,000 or 1/125,000. No actual units of measurement are mentioned because any unit is applicable as long as both parts of the fraction are in the same unit: 1 cm to 125,000 cm, 1 in. to 125,000 in., or even 1 arm length to 125,000 arm lengths, and so on.

A *graphic scale*, or bar scale, is a bar graph with units to allow measurement of distances on the map. An important advantage of a graphic scale is that, if the map is enlarged or reduced, the graphic scale enlarges or reduces along with the map. In contrast, written and fractional scales become incorrect with enlargement or reduction. As an example, you can shrink a map from 1:20,000 to 1:1,000,000, but the scale will still say "1 cm to 200 m," instead of the new correct scale of 1 cm to 10 km.

Scales are *small*, *medium*, and *large*, depending on the ratio described. In relative terms, a scale of 1:24,000 is a large scale, whereas a scale of 1:50,000,000 is a small scale. The greater the denominator in a fractional scale (or the number on the right in a ratio expression), the smaller the scale and the more abstract the map is in relation to what is being mapped. Examples of selected representative fractions and written scales are listed in Table 1.3 for small-, medium-, and large-scale maps.

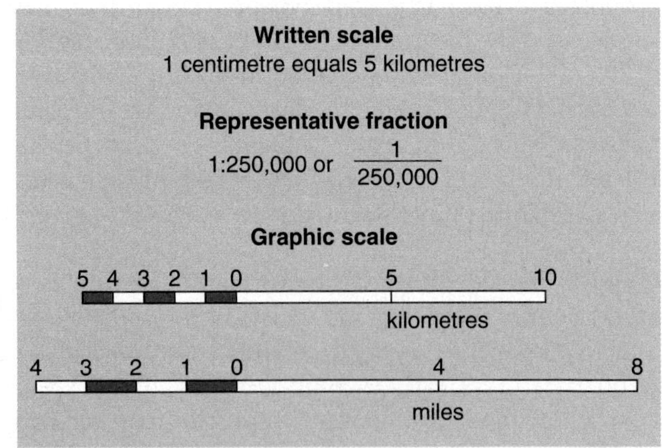

FIGURE 1.20 Map scale.
Three common expressions of map scale—written scale, representative fraction, and graphic scale.

Table 1.3 Sample Representative Fractions and Written Scales for Small-, Medium-, and Large-Scale Maps

System	Scale Size	Representative Fraction	Written Scale
Metric	Small	1:1,000,000	1 cm = 10.0 km
	Medium	1:250,000	1 cm = 2.5 km
	Large	1:10,000	1 cm = 0.10 km
English Units (in the U.S.)			
	Small	1:1,000,000	1 in. = 16 mi
	Medium	1:63,360	1 in. = 1 mi
	Large	1:24,000	1 in. = 2000 ft

If there is a globe or map available in your library or classroom, check to see the scale at which it was drawn. See if you can find examples of written, representative, and graphic scales on wall maps, highway maps, and in atlases. In general, do you think a world globe is a small- or a large-scale map of Earth's surface?

Map Projections

A globe is not always a helpful map representation of Earth. When you go on a trip, you need more detailed information than a globe can provide. Consequently, to provide local detail, cartographers prepare large-scale flat maps, which are two-dimensional representations (scale models) of our three-dimensional Earth. Unfortunately, the conversion from three dimensions to two causes distortion.

A globe is the only true representation of *distance*, *direction*, *area*, *shape*, and *proximity*. A flat map distorts those properties. Therefore, in preparing a flat map, the cartographer must decide which characteristic to preserve, which to distort, and how much distortion is acceptable.

To understand this problem, consider these important properties of a *globe*:

- Parallels always are parallel to each other, always are evenly spaced along meridians, and always decrease in length toward the poles.
- Meridians converge at both poles and are evenly spaced along any individual parallel.
- The distance between meridians decreases toward poles, with the spacing between meridians at the 60th parallel equal to one-half the equatorial spacing.
- Parallels and meridians always cross each other at right angles.

The problem is that all these qualities cannot be reproduced on a flat surface. Simply taking a globe apart and laying it flat on a table illustrates the challenge faced by cartographers (Figure 1.21). You can see the empty spaces that open up between the sections, or gores, of the globe. This reduction of the spherical Earth to a flat surface is called a **map projection**. Thus, no flat map projection of Earth can ever have all the features of a globe. Flat maps always possess some degree of distortion—much less for large-scale maps representing a few kilometres; much more for small-scale maps covering individual countries, continents, or the entire world.

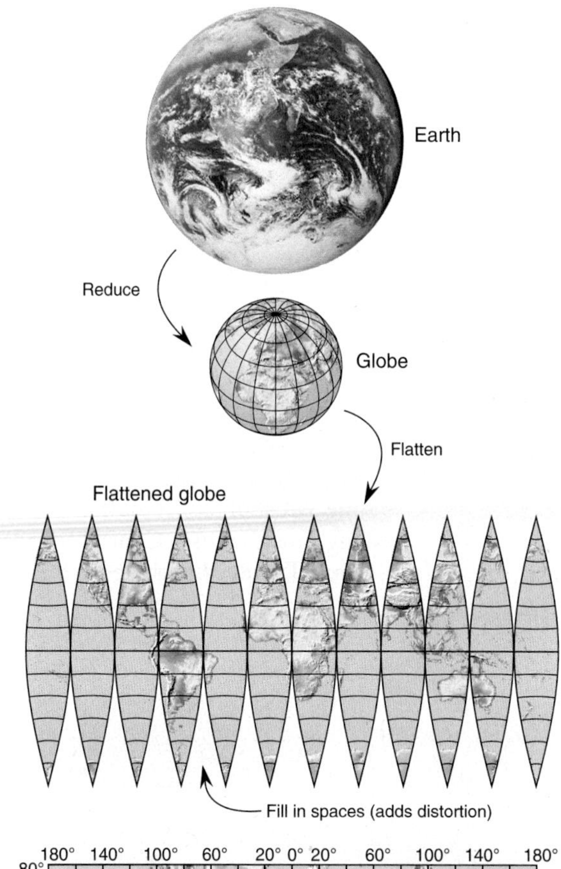

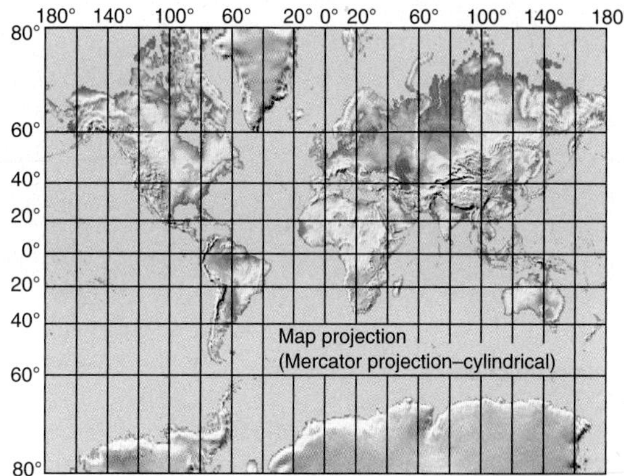

FIGURE 1.21 From globe to flat map.
Conversion of the globe to a flat map projection requires decisions about which properties to preserve and the amount of distortion that is acceptable. [NASA astronaut photo.]

Properties of Projections There are many projections, four of which are shown in Figure 1.22. *The best projection is always determined by its intended use.* The major decisions in selecting a map projection involve the properties of **equal area** (equivalence) and **true shape** (conformality).

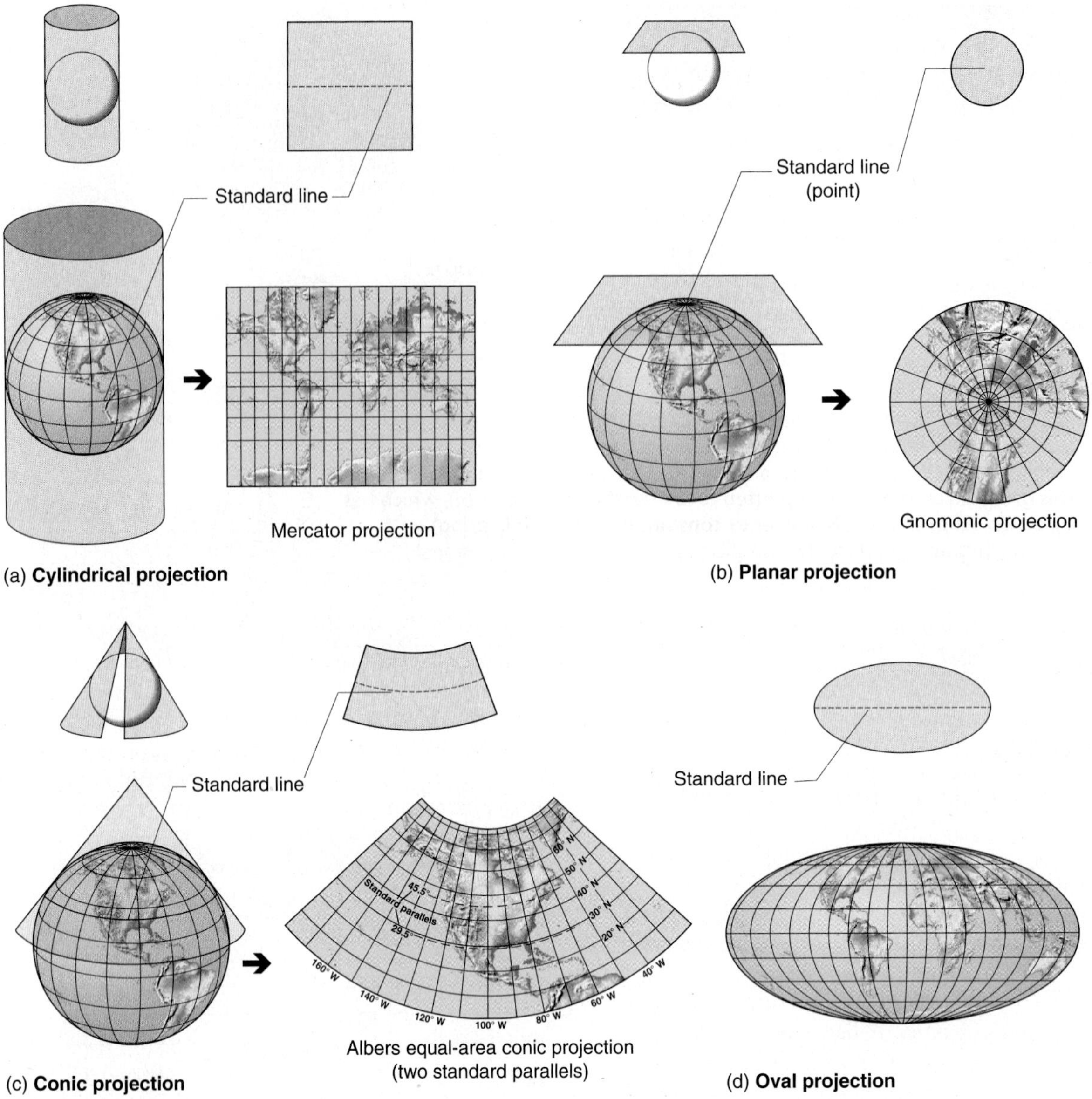

Standard line

Mercator projection

(a) **Cylindrical projection**

Standard line (point)

Gnomonic projection

(b) **Planar projection**

Standard line

Albers equal-area conic projection (two standard parallels)

(c) **Conic projection**

Standard line

(d) **Oval projection**

FIGURE 1.22 Classes of map projections.
Four general classes and perspectives of map projections—cylindrical, planar, conic, and oval projections.

If a cartographer selects equal area as the desired trait—for example, for a map showing the distribution of world climates—then true shape must be sacrificed by *stretching* and *shearing*, which allows parallels and meridians to cross at other than right angles. On an equal-area map, a coin covers the same amount of surface area no matter where you place it on the map. If, on the other hand, a cartographer selects the property of true shape, as for a map used for navigational purposes, then equal area must be sacrificed and the scale will actually change from one region of the map to another.

The Nature and Classes of Projections Despite the fact that modern cartographic technology uses mathematical constructions and computer-assisted graphics, the word *projection* is still used. The term comes from times past, when geographers actually projected the shadow of a wire-skeleton globe onto a geometric surface. The wires represented parallels, meridians, and outlines of the continents. A light source then cast a shadow pattern of latitude and longitude lines from the globe onto various geometric surfaces, such as a *cylinder*, *plane*, or *cone*.

Figure 1.22 illustrates the derivation of the general classes of map projections and the perspectives from which they are generated. The classes shown include cylindrical, planar (or azimuthal), and conic. Another class of projections, which cannot be derived from this physical-perspective approach, is the nonperspective oval shape. Still other projections are derived from purely mathematical calculations.

With projections, the contact line or contact point between the wire globe and the projection surface—called

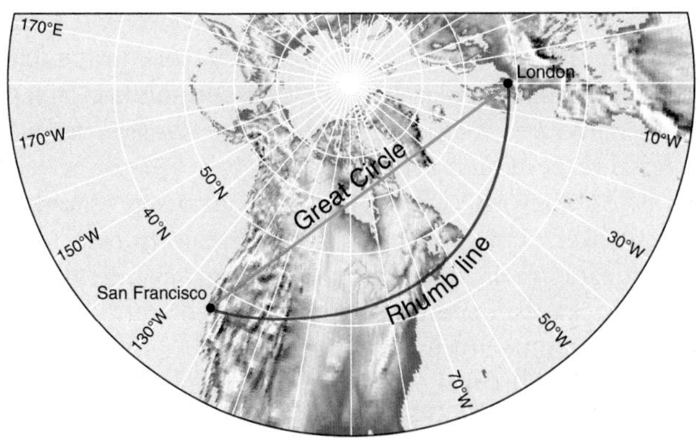

(a) **Gnomonic Projection**

(b) **Mercator Projection (conformal, true shape)**

FIGURE 1.23 Determining great circle routes.
A gnomonic projection (a) is used to determine the shortest distance—great circle route—between San Francisco and London, because on this projection the arc of a great circle is a straight line. This great circle route is then plotted on a Mercator projection (b), which has true compass direction. Note that straight lines of constant direction (or bearing) on a Mercator projection—rhumb lines—are not the shortest routes in terms of distance.

a *standard line* or *standard point—is the only place where all globe properties are preserved.* Thus, a *standard parallel* or *standard meridian* is a standard line true to scale along its entire length without any distortion. Areas away from this critical tangent line or point become increasingly distorted. Consequently, this area of optimum spatial properties should be centred on the region of interest so that the greatest accuracy is preserved there.

The commonly used **Mercator projection** (from Gerardus Mercator, A.D. 1569) is a cylindrical projection (Figure 1.22a). The Mercator is a true-shape projection, with meridians appearing as equally spaced straight lines and parallels appearing as straight lines that are spaced closer together near the equator. The poles are infinitely stretched, with the 84th north parallel and 84th south parallel fixed at the same length as that of the equator. Note in Figures 1.21 and 1.22a that the Mercator projection is cut around the 80th parallel in each hemisphere because of the severe distortion at higher latitudes.

Unfortunately, Mercator classroom maps present false notions of the size (area) of midlatitude and poleward landmasses. A dramatic example on the Mercator projection is Greenland, which looks bigger than all of South America. In reality, Greenland is only one-eighth the size of South America and is actually 20% smaller than Argentina alone!

The advantage of the Mercator projection is that lines of constant direction, called **rhumb lines**, are straight and thus facilitate plotting directions between two points (see Figure 1.23). Thus, the Mercator projection is useful in navigation and is the standard for nautical charts prepared by the National Ocean Service since 1910 (formerly U.S. Coast and Geodetic Survey).

The *gnomonic*, or *planar projection* in Figure 1.22b is generated by projecting a light source at the centre of a globe onto a plane that is tangent to (touching) the globe's surface. The resulting severe distortion prevents showing a full hemisphere on one projection. However, a valuable feature is derived: All great circle routes, which are the shortest distance between two points on Earth's surface, are projected as straight lines (Figure 1.23a). The great circle routes plotted on a gnomonic projection then can be transferred to a true-direction projection, such as the Mercator, for determination of precise compass headings (Figure 1.23b).

For more information on maps used in this text and standard map symbols, turn to Appendix A, "Maps in This Text and Topographic Maps." Topographic maps are essential tools of landscape analysis. Geographers, other scientists, travellers, and anyone visiting the outdoors may use topographic maps. The National Topographic System (NTS) provides topographic maps in Canada. There is good coverage of the entire country at 1:50,000 and 1:250,000 scales (**http://maps.nrcan.gc.ca/index_e.php**).

Additionally, the *Atlas of Canada* (**http://atlas.gc.ca/site/english/index.html**) allows you to select and view maps on-line. U.S. Geological Survey (USGS) topographic maps appear in several chapters of this text because they are useful in depicting the tremendously varied features of the physical landscape. Perhaps you have used a "topo" map in planning a hike.

Remote Sensing and GIS

Geographers probe, analyze, and map our home planet through remote sensing and geographic information systems (GIS). These technologies enhance our understanding of Earth. Geographers use remote-sensing data to study humid and arid lands, natural and economic vegetation, snow and ice, Earth energy budgets, seasonal variation of atmospheric and oceanic circulation, sea-level measurements, atmospheric chemistry, geologic features and events, changes in the timing of seasons, and the human activities that produce global change.

Remote Sensing

In this era of observations from orbit outside the atmosphere and from aircraft within it, scientists obtain a wide array of remotely sensed data (Figure 1.24). Remote sensing is nothing new to humans; we do it with our eyes all the time. When we scan the environment with our eyes, we are sensing the shape, size, and colour of objects from a distance, registering energy from the visible-wavelength portion of the electromagnetic spectrum. Similarly, when a camera views the wavelengths for which its film or sensor is designed (visible light or infrared), it remotely senses energy that is reflected or emitted from a scene.

Our eyes and cameras are familiar means of obtaining **remote-sensing** information about a distant subject without having physical contact. Aerial photographs have been used for years to improve the accuracy of surface maps faster and more cheaply than can be done by on-site surveys. Deriving accurate measurements from photographs is the realm of **photogrammetry**, an important application of remote sensing.

Remote sensors on satellites, the International Space Station, and other craft sense a broader range of wavelengths than can our eyes. They can be designed to "see" wavelengths shorter than visible light (ultraviolet) and wavelengths longer than visible light (infrared and microwave radar).

Satellites do not take conventional-film photographs. Rather, they record *images* that are transmitted to Earth-based receivers in a manner similar to television satellite transmissions, or a digital camera. A scene is scanned and broken down into *pixels* (*pic*ture *el*ements) each identified by coordinates named *lines* (horizontal rows) and *samples* (vertical columns). For example, a grid of 6000 lines and 7000 samples forms 42,000,000 pixels, providing great detail. The large amount of data needed to produce a single image requires computer processing and data storage at ground stations.

Digital data are processed in many ways to enhance their utility: simulated natural colour, "false" colour to highlight a particular feature, enhanced contrast, signal filtering, and different levels of sampling and resolution. Active and passive are two types of remote-sensing systems.

Active Remote Sensing Active systems direct a beam of energy at a surface and analyze the energy reflected back. An example is *radar* (*ra*dio *d*etection *a*nd *r*anging). A radar transmitter emits short bursts of energy that have relatively long wavelengths (0.3 to 10 m) toward the subject terrain, penetrating clouds and darkness. Energy reflected back, known as *backscatter*, is received by a radar receiver and analyzed. An example is the computer image of wind and sea-surface patterns over the Pacific in Figure 6.6a, developed from 150,000 radar-derived measurements made on a single day by the *Seasat* satellite.

Several radar-imaging satellites are operating. Canada operates *RADARSAT–1* and *–2* and the Japanese have *JERS-1* that image in radar wavelengths (Figure 1.25). The European Space Agency (ESA) now operates two Earth resource satellites (*ERS 1* and *2*). They work in tandem, producing a spectacular 10-cm (3.9-in.) resolution, imaging the same area at different times. Pairs of images produce a digital three-dimensional data set.

ESA's newest environment-monitoring satellite, *Envisat*, went into service in 2002. In addition to more sophisticated radar than *ERS*, *Envisat* carries nine passive sensor packages, making it a multitalented craft. It monitors ocean temperatures, sea level, and wave patterns, polar ice, forests, biological activity in the oceans and on land, cloud heights, atmospheric ozone and pollution, and carbon dioxide concentrations (see **http://envisat.esa.int/**).

In addition, NASA sent imaging radar systems into orbit on several Space Shuttles. The subjects of study included oceanography, landforms and geology, and biogeography. Shuttle missions in 1994 by *Endeavour* and *Atlantis* marked dramatic contributions to Earth observations using radar and other sensors to study stratospheric ozone, weather, volcanic activity, earthquakes, and water resources, among many subjects.

One Space Shuttle mission in September 1994 was appropriately loaded with radar sensors to study volcanoes. Only 8 hours after launch, the Kliuchevskoi Volcano on the Kamchatka Peninsula of Russia erupted unexpectedly. Previously this volcano had erupted in 1737 and 1945. The Shuttle radar was able to see through ash and smoke and expose lava flows and the volcanic eruption in dramatic images (Figure 1.26). Astronaut Mission Specialist Dr. Thomas Jones operated the radar and camera to make the image and photo in the figure. He is profiled in a Career Link at the end of this chapter. Chapter 12 discusses volcanic processes.

Passive Remote Sensing Passive remote-sensing systems record energy radiated from a surface, particularly visible light and infrared. Our own eyes are passive remote sensors, as was the *Apollo 17* astronaut camera that made the picture of Earth on the back cover of this book from a distance of 37,000 km (23,000 mi).

Passive remote sensors on five *Landsat* satellites, launched by the United States, provide a variety of data, as shown in images of the Appalachian Mountains in Chapter 12, river deltas in Chapter 14, and the Malaspina and Kuskulana glaciers in Alaska in Chapter 17. Three *Landsats* remain operational (4, 5, and the latest, 7), although *Landsat 4* no longer gathers images and is used for orbital tests. See **http://geo.arc.nasa.gov/sge/landsat/landsat.html** for the *Landsat* home page and other links.

The National Oceanic and Atmospheric Administration's (NOAA, see **http://noaa.gov/**) polar-orbiting satellites carrying the *advanced very high resolution radiometer* (*AVHRR*) sensors on *NOAA-14*, *NOAA-15*, and *NOAA-16* are now operational. These sensors are sensitive to visible and infrared wavelengths. The incredible images of Hurricane Andrew (Chapter 8), among others in this text, were produced by an AVHRR system. In Chapter 19, an AVHRR image portrays clear-cutting of trees and

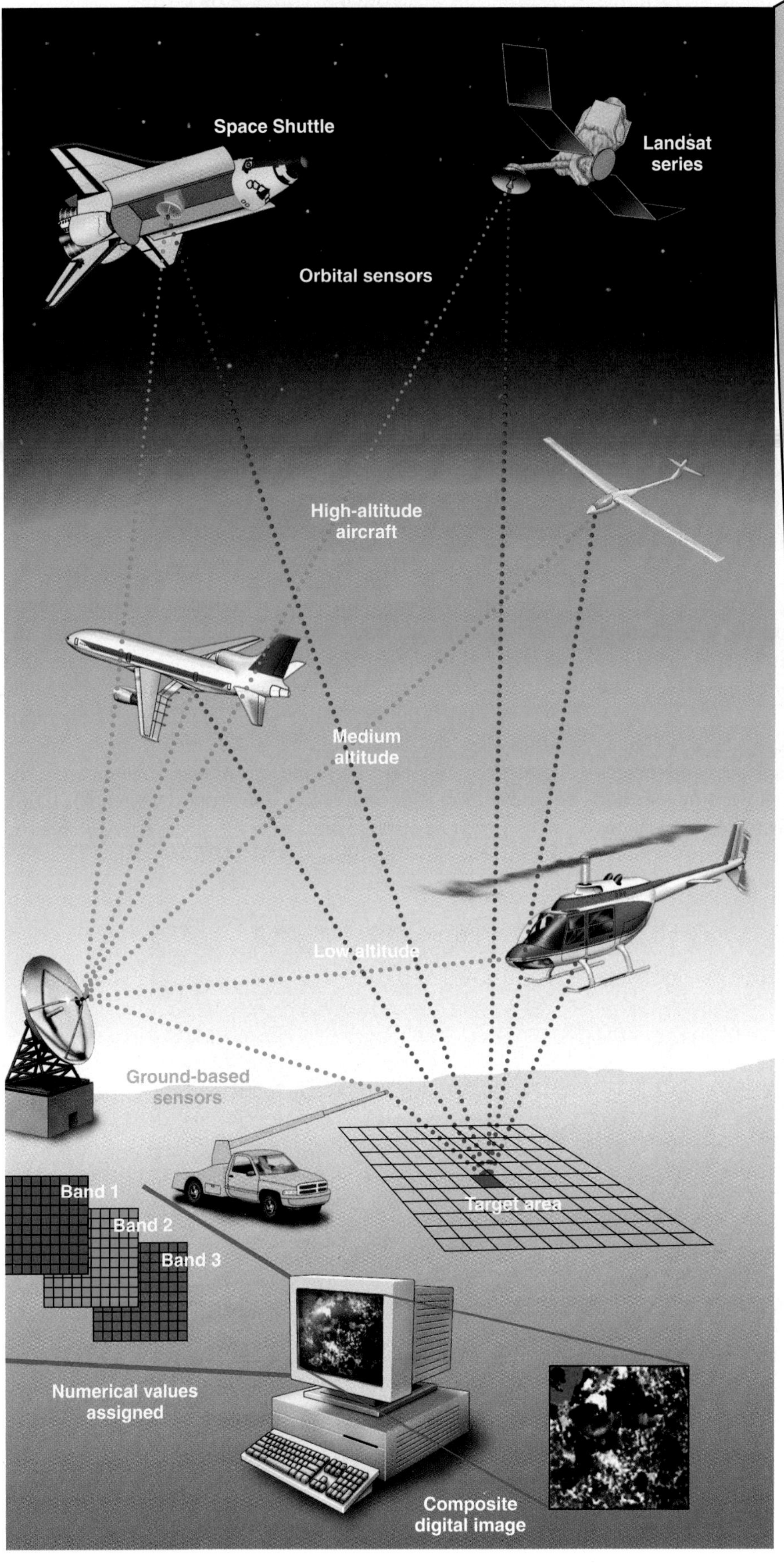

A sample of orbital platforms

Envisat: ESA environment-monitoring satellite; 10 sensors

ERBS: Earth Radiation Budget Satellite

GOES: weather monitoring and forecasting

Landsat: First in 1972 to *Landsat-7* in 1999, millions of images for Earth systems science and global change

NOAA: First in 1978 through *NOAA-15* and *NOAA-16*, global data, short- and long-term weather forecasts

RADARSAT-1, -2: Canadian radar satellites; focus on Earth observations for environmental monitoring

SCISAT-1: Canadian satellite with Fourier Transform Spectometer that simultaneously measures temperature, trace gases, thin clouds, and aerosols in the atmosphere, especially over Canada and the Arctic

Terra* and *Aqua: environmental change, error-free surface images, cloud properties, through five instrument packages

SeaStar: carries the SeaWiFS (Sea-viewing Wide Field-of-View instrument) to observe Earth's oceans and microscopic marine plants

TOMS-EP*:* Total Ozone Mapping Spectrometer, monitoring stratospheric ozone, similar instruments on *NIMBUS-7* and *Meteor-3*

TRMM*:* Tropical Rainfall Measuring Mission, includes lightning detection and global energy budget measurements

UARS: since 1991 measuring atmospheric chemistry and ozone layer changes

For more info see:

Canadian Space Agency
http://www.space.gc.ca/asc/eng/default.asp

NASA
http://www.gsfc.nasa.gov/indepth/earth_esm.html

FIGURE 1.24 Remote-sensing technologies.
Remote-sensing technology is used to measure and monitor Earth's systems from orbiting spacecraft, aircraft in the atmosphere, and ground-based sensors. Various wavelengths (bands) are collected from sensors. Computers process the data to produce digital images for analysis. Many of the physical systems discussed in this text are studied using this technology. A sample of remote sensing platforms is in the margin. The Space Shuttle is shown in its inverted orbital flight mode. (Illustration is not to scale.)

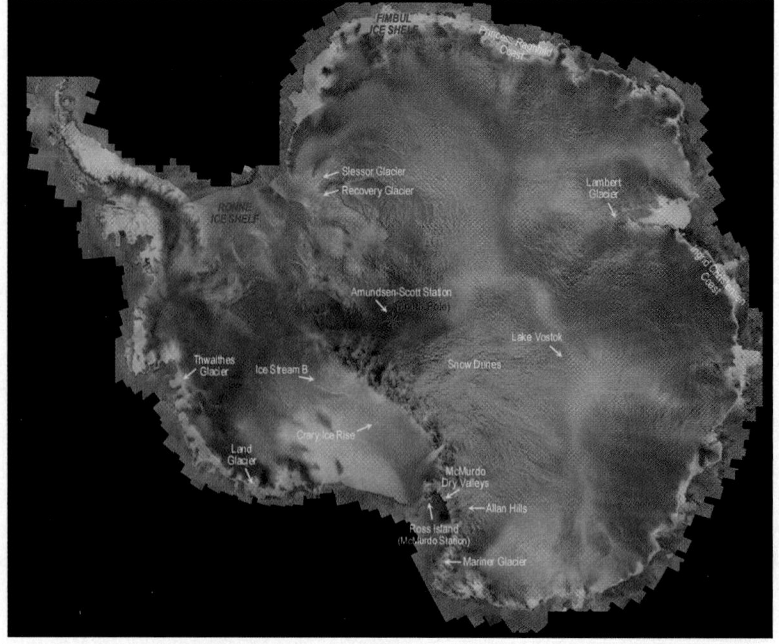

FIGURE 1.25 *RADARSAT* composite image of Antarctica. Mosaic of Antarctica produced by analysis of 18 days of *RADARSAT-1* data collected in September and October 1997 gives us a new view of the entire Antarctic continent. [Photo courtesy of RSI/Canadian Space Agency, 2004.]

production of biomass in the Pacific Northwest. These examples of resource analysis were impossible to perform at such a scale just a few years ago. In addition, these satellites measure ozone concentrations and temperatures in the stratosphere.

Key to NASA's Earth Observing System (EOS) is satellite *Terra*, which began beaming back data and images in 2000 (see **http://terra.nasa.gov**), followed by another satellite in the series called *Aqua*. Five instrument packages observe Earth systems in detail, exploring the atmosphere, landscapes, oceans, environmental change, and climate, among other abilities. For example, the Clouds and the Earth's Radiant Energy System (CERES) instruments aboard *Terra* monitor Earth's energy balance, giving new insights into climate change (see Chapter 4). These monitors offer the most accurate global radiation and energy measurements ever available. Another instrument set, the Moderate-resolution Imaging Spectroradiometer (MODIS), sees Earth's entire surface every 1–2 days in 36 spectral bands, thereby expanding on AVHRR capabilities.

FIGURE 1.26 A volcanic eruption seen from orbit. Photograph (passive, visible light) and image (active, radar) of the eruption of the Kliuchevskoi Volcano on the Kamchatka Peninsula of Siberia, Russia, as captured by the Space Shuttle *Endeavour*, September 1994. [Image and photo by JPL/NASA.]

One of two commercial systems includes the three French satellites (numbered 1, 2, and 4) called *SPOT* (Sysème Probatoire d'Observation de la Terre; see http://spot4.cnes.fr/waiting.htm) that resolve objects on Earth down to 10 to 20 m (33 to 66 ft), depending on which sensors are used. The other commercial system is Space Imaging, Inc., that offers 1–4 metre resolution from its *Ikonos–2* satellite in a Sun-synchronous orbit at 680 km (420 mi) altitude (http://www.spaceimaging.com/).

In addition, previously unavailable intelligence ("spy") satellite images are now becoming available. These images from a CIA program code-named *Corona* were actually photographs taken by satellite cameras with film returned from orbit. Comparative analysis of Earth's surface over time is a potentially valuable use of these photographs that go back to 1960. These images are released through the National Reconnaissance Office, U.S. Department of Defense. This declassified satellite imagery is available through the USGS Eros Data Center, Sioux Falls, South Dakota.

The *Geostationary Operational Environmental Satellites*, known as *GOES*, became operational in late 1994, providing frequent infrared and visible images—the ones you see on television weather reports. Geostationary satellites stay in semipermanent positions because they keep pace with Earth's rotational speed at their altitude of 35,400 km (22,000 mi).

GOES-10, on-line in 1998, operates above 135° W longitude to monitor the West Coast and the eastern Pacific Ocean. *GOES-12* sits above 75° W longitude to monitor central and eastern North America and the western Atlantic and replaces the aging (low manoeuvring fuel) *GOES-8* (Figure 1.27). *GOES-11* is in orbital storage for future weather-satellite replacement as needed. See the Geostationary Satellite Server at http://www.goes.noaa.gov/. The *GOES* Project Science appears at http://rsd.gsfc.nasa.gov/goes/, or see http://www.ghcc.msfc.nasa.gov/GOES/. The image of Earth on the half-title page of this book includes a cloud snapshot from *GOES* added on *Terra* MODIS images over a 16-day period in 2000.

SCISAT, a Canadian satellite launched by NASA in August 2003, contains an Ace Fourier Transform Spectrometer and an instrument known as MAESTRO (Measurements of Aerosol Extinction in the Stratosphere and Troposphere Retrieved by Occultation). These instruments record the concentration and distribution of chemicals in the ozone layer as sunlight passes through Earth's upper atmosphere. The satellite orbits Earth 15 times daily to capture information for 15 sunrises and sunsets. These data provide scientists with improved understanding of global ozone processes (http://www.space.gc.ca/scisat1).

Other satellites used for weather include Japan's *GMS-5* weather satellite (*GOES-9* serving as backup) and China's *Feng Yun-2* covering the Far East, and *METEOSAT-7* for Europe and Africa, operated by the European Space Agency. (See the Remote Sensing Virtual Library at http://www.vtt.fi/tte/research/tte1/tte14/virtual for remote sensing links; click on "Satellite Data" for specific coverage.)

Geographic Information Systems (GIS)

Remote sensing is an important tool for acquiring large volumes of spatial data. The next step is storing, processing,

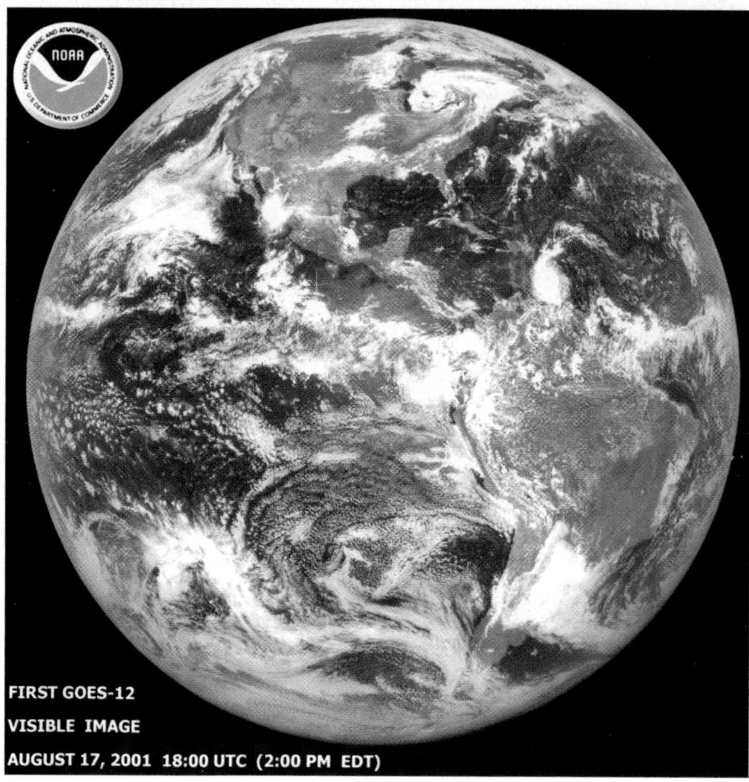

FIGURE 1.27 *GOES-12* first image. New environmental satellite in 2001, the first image of *GOES-12* demonstrates excellent image quality from its 37,500 km (23,300 mi) orbital post. This satellite, along with *GOES-11*, is stored in orbit to replace either of the existing *GOES* satellites as needed. [Image courtesy of NOAA.]

and retrieving those data in useful ways. The value of remote sensing rests on the ability to provide data to powerful information-handling systems. Computers allow the integration of geographic information from direct surveys (on-the-ground mapping) and remote sensing in complex ways never before possible.

A **geographic information system (GIS)** is a computer-based, data-processing tool for gathering, manipulating, and analyzing geographic information. Through a GIS, Earth and human phenomena are analyzed over time. An example is shown in Figure 1.28. GIS is a rapidly expanding career field in many sectors of the economy. Regardless of your academic major, the ability to analyze data spatially is important. Be sure to check some of the URLs listed in News Report 1.4 for information on professional career directions in this exciting field.

The beginning component for any GIS is a coordinate system such as latitude–longitude, which establishes reference points against which to position data. The coordinate system is digitized, along with all areas, points, and lines. Remotely sensed imagery and data are then added on to the coordinate system.

A GIS is capable of analyzing patterns and relationships within a single data plane, such as the floodplain or soil layer in Figure 1.28. The GIS also can generate an overlay analysis where two or more data planes interact. When the layers are combined, the resulting synthesis—a *composite overlay*—is a valuable product, ready for use in analyzing complex problems. A research study may follow specific points or areas through the complex of overlay planes. The utility of a GIS compared with that of a fixed map is the ability to manipulate the variables for analysis—to constantly change the map!

Before the advent of computers, an environmental-impact analysis required someone to gather data and painstakingly hand-produce overlays of information to determine positive and negative impacts of a project or event. Today, this layered information is handled by a computer-driven GIS, which assesses the complex interconnections among different components. In this way, subtle changes in one element of a landscape may be identified as having a powerful impact elsewhere.

GIS is particularly helpful in analyzing natural hazards and society. An example is the European earthquake catalogue that records more than 20,000 earthquakes, dating back to 500 B.C. Having this data base installed in a GIS permits detailed spatial analysis of these events, along with country boundaries, human settlements, rivers, lakes, seas,

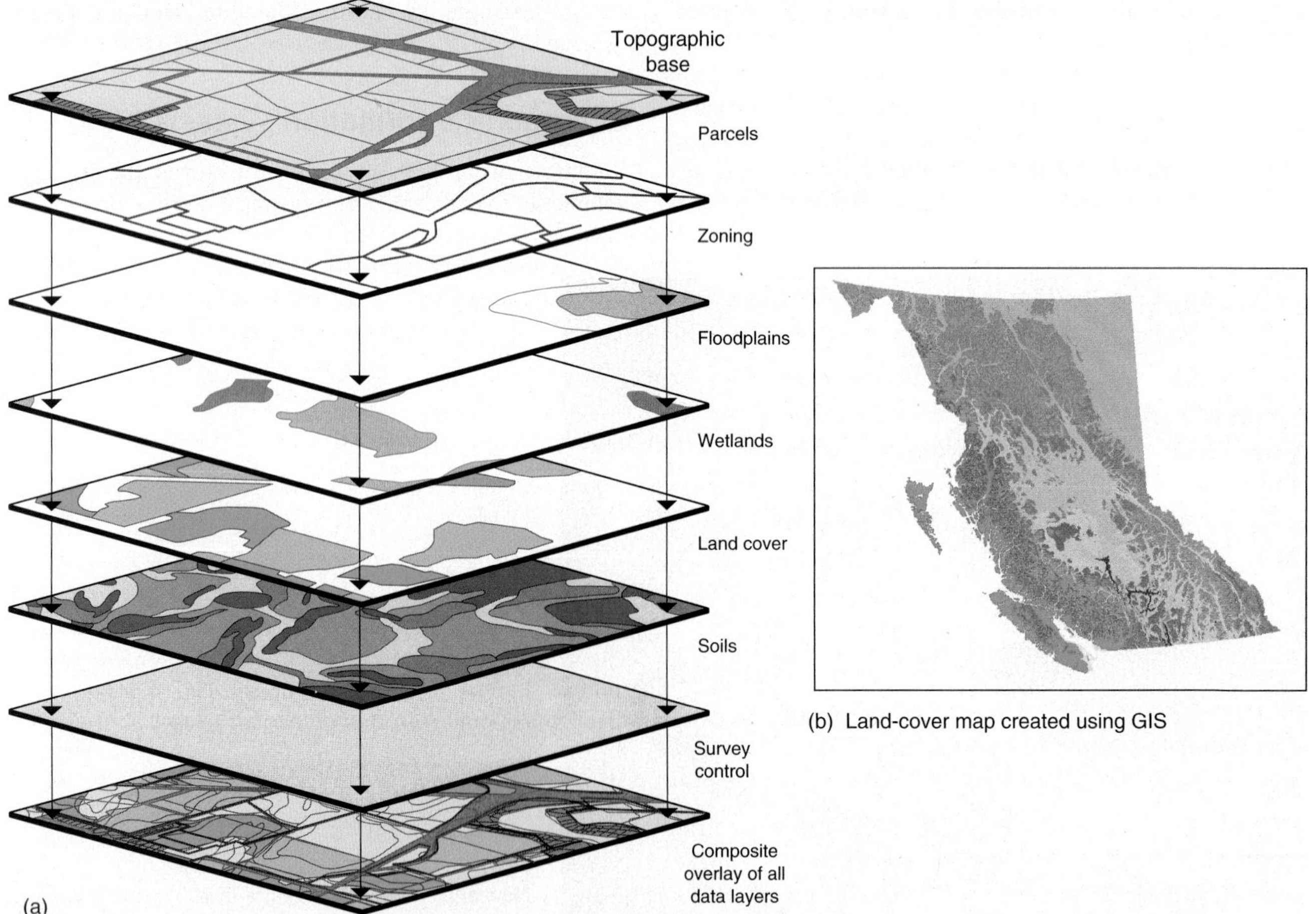

FIGURE 1.28 A geographic information system (GIS) model.
(a) Layered spatial data in a geographic information system (GIS) format. (b) This biogeoclimatic map of British Columbia is a valuable tool for forestry management in the province. [(a) After USGS; (b) copyright © 2004 Province of British Columbia. All rights reserved. Reprinted with the permission of the Province of British Columbia, www.ipp.gov.bc.ca.]

News Report 1.4

Careers in GIS

Geographic information system (GIS) methodology offers great career opportunities in industry, government, business, marketing, teaching, sales, military, and other fields. Right now, geographers trained in GIS analyze ozone depletion, deforestation, soil erosion, and acid deposition. They map ecosystems and monitor the declining diversity of plant and animal species. Geographers plan, design, and survey urban developments, follow the trends of global warming, study the impact of human population, and analyze air and water pollution.

We are in the midst of a growing GIS revolution. Potent new careers are emerging in almost every academic area as GIS programs are implemented at many universities and community colleges. GIS applications are used in environmental analysis, weather forecasting, natural hazard assessment, business and marketing, industry location analysis, criminal justice, and natural resources exploration, among many examples. (For a list of current trends in GIS, simply enter this topic in your search engine; for an alphabetized GIS resources list, check out http://www.geo.ed.ac.uk/home/giswww.html.)

GIS degree programs are available at many colleges and universities. GIS curriculum and certificate programs are now available at several community colleges. Many universities have listings of careers and jobs in GIS. Check out the University of Toronto site (http://www.geog.utoronto.ca/info/facweb/Boyes/GIS/Weblinks_General.htm) for a great summary of GIS information. Additionally, the University of British Columbia (http://www.geog.ubc.ca/gislinks/index.php?mode=search&otherk=kjobs) has a summary of jobs, careers, Web sites, and tools.

nuclear power plant locations, hazardous materials storage sites, and other economic considerations.

One of the most extensive and longest operating systems is the Canada Geographic Information system (CGIS). Roger Tomlinson, a Canadian geographer recognized as the father of GIS (see Royal Canadian Geographic Society award at http://www.rcgs.org/rcgs/awards/awards_gold03.asp) was key in the development of the Canadian GIS. To create the system, environmental data about natural features, resources, and land use were taken from maps, aerial photographs, and orbital sources, reduced to map segments, and entered into the CGIS. The development of this system has progressed with the ongoing Canada land inventory project (visit the Canada Land Inventory Web page at http://geogratis.cgdi.gc.ca/CLI/frames.html). A summary timeline for development of GIS is found at http://www.casa.ucl.ac.uk/gistimeline/welcome.htm.

Scientists at NASA's Goddard Space Flight Center completed a comprehensive GIS of Brazil in an effort to better understand land-use patterns—specifically, loss of the rain forest. The flood-prone country of Bangladesh is undergoing analysis using a GIS. GIS models are also used to analyze regions for their vulnerability to wildfire. The GIS discloses high-risk areas that can guide officials in the placement of fire-fighting equipment and crews. (For GIS resources and information see http://www.geo.ed.ac.uk/home/giswww.html and http://erg.usgs.gov/isb/pubs/gis_poster/#what.

Summary and Review—Essentials of Geography

To assist you, here is a review of the Key Learning Concepts listed on this chapter's title page, in handy summary form. Each concept review concludes with a list of the key terms from the chapter, their page numbers, and review questions. Such summary and review sections follow each chapter in the book.

Define geography and physical geography in particular.

Geography brings together disciplines from the physical and life sciences with the cultural and human sciences to attain a holistic view of Earth—physical geography is an essential aspect of the emerging **Earth systems sciences**. **Geography** is a science of method, a special way of analyzing phenomena over space; **spatial** refers to the nature and character of physical space. Geography integrates a wide range of subject matter. Geographic education recognizes five major themes: **location**, **region**, **human–Earth relationships**, **movement**, and **place** (including environmental concerns). Geography's method is **spatial analysis**, used to study the interdependence among geographic areas, natural systems, society, and cultural activities over space. **Process**—that is, analyzing a set of actions or mechanisms that operate in some special order—is central to geographic synthesis.

Physical geography applies spatial analysis to all the physical elements and processes that make up the environment: energy, air, water, weather, climate, landforms, soils, animals, plants, microorganisms, and Earth itself. Understanding the complex relations among these elements is important to human survival because Earth's physical systems and human society are so intertwined. The development of hypotheses and theories about the Universe, Earth, and life involves the **scientific method**.

Earth systems science (p. 2)
geography (p. 3)

spatial (p. 3)
location (p. 3)
region (p. 3)
human–Earth relationships (p. 3)
movement (p. 3)
place (p. 3)
spatial analysis (p. 3)
process (p. 3)
physical geography (p. 3)
scientific method (p. 5)

1. What is unique about the science of geography? On the basis of information in this chapter, define physical geography and review the geographic approach.
2. In general terms, how might a physical geographer analyze water pollution in the Great Lakes?
3. Assess your geographic literacy by examining atlases and maps. What types of maps have you used—political? physical? topographic? Do you know what projections they employed? Do you know the names and locations of the four oceans, seven continents, and most individual countries? Can you identify the new countries that have emerged since 1990?
4. Suggest a representative example for each of the five geographic themes and use that theme in a sentence.
5. Have you made decisions today that involve geographic concepts discussed within the five themes presented? Explain briefly.

Describe systems analysis, open and closed systems, feedback information, and system operations and *relate* those concepts to Earth systems.

A **system** is any ordered, related set of things and their attributes, as distinct from their surrounding environment. Systems analysis is an important organizational and analytical tool used by geographers. Earth is an **open system** in terms of energy, receiving energy from the Sun, but it is essentially a **closed system** in terms of matter and physical resources.

As a system operates, "information" is returned to various points in the system via pathways called **feedback loops**. If the feedback information discourages response in the system, it is called **negative feedback**. (Further production in the system decreases the growth of the system.) If feedback information encourages response in the system, it is called **positive feedback**. (Further production in the system stimulates the growth of the system.) When the rates of inputs and outputs in the system are equal and the amounts of energy and matter in storage within the system are constant (or fluctuate around a stable average), the system is in **steady-state equilibrium**. A system that demonstrates a steady increase or decrease in system operations—a trend over time—is in **dynamic equilibrium**. Geographers often construct simplified **models** of natural systems to better understand them.

Four immense open systems powerfully interact at Earth's surface: three nonliving **abiotic** systems (**atmosphere**, **hydrosphere** [inclucing the **cryosphere**], and **lithosphere**) and a living **biotic** system (**biosphere**, or **ecosphere**).

system (p. 8)
open system (p. 8)
closed system (p. 8)
feedback loops (p. 9)
negative feedback (p. 9)
positive feedback (p. 9)
steady-state equilibrium (p. 10)
dynamic equilibrium (p. 10)
model (p. 11)
abiotic (p. 12)
biotic (p. 12)
atmosphere (p. 12)
hydrosphere (p. 12)
cryosphere (p. 12)
lithosphere (p. 13)
biosphere (p. 14)
ecosphere (p. 14)

6. Define systems theory as an organizational strategy. What are open systems, closed systems, and negative feedback? When is a system in a steady-state equilibrium condition? What type of system (open or closed) is a human body? A lake? A wheat plant? Meltponds in the Arctic?
7. Describe Earth as a system in terms of both energy and matter—use simple diagrams to illustrate your description.
8. What are the three abiotic spheres (nonliving) that make up Earth's environment? Relate these to the biotic (living) sphere: the biosphere.

Explain Earth's reference grid: latitude, longitude, latitudinal geographic zones, and time.

The science that studies Earth's shape and size is **geodesy**. Earth bulges slightly through the equator and is oblate (flattened) at the poles, producing a misshapen spheroid called a **geoid**. Absolute location on Earth is described with a specific reference grid of **parallels** of **latitude** (measuring distances north and south of the equator) and **meridians** of **longitude** (measuring distances east and west of a prime meridian). A historic breakthrough in navigation and timekeeping occurred with the establishment of an international **prime meridian** (0° through Greenwich, England) and the invention of precise chronometers that enabled accurate measurement of longitude. Latitude, longitude, and elevation are accurately calibrated using a hand-held **Global Positioning System (GPS)** instrument that reads radio signals from satellites. A **great circle** is any circle of Earth's circumference whose centre coincides with the centre of Earth. Great circle routes are the shortest distance between two points on Earth. **Small circles** have centres that do not coincide with Earth's centre.

The prime meridian provided the basis for **Greenwich Mean Time (GMT)**, the world's first universal time system. A corollary of the prime meridian is the 180° meridian, the **International Date Line**, which marks the place where each day officially begins. Today, **Coordinated Universal Time (UTC)** is the worldwide standard and the basis for international time zones. **Daylight saving time** is a seasonal change of clocks by one hour in summer months.

geodesy (p. 15)
geoid (p. 15)
latitude (p. 16)
parallel (p. 17)

longitude (p. 17)
meridian (p. 18)
prime meridian (p. 20)
Global Positioning System (GPS) (p. 21)
great circle (p. 21)
small circles (p. 22)
Greenwich Mean Time (GMT) (p. 24)
International Date Line (p. 24)
Coordinated Universal Time (UTC) (p. 24)
daylight saving time (p. 25)

9. Draw a simple sketch describing Earth's shape and size.
10. How did Eratosthenes use Sun angles to figure out that the 5000-stadia distance between Alexandria and Syene was 1/50 of Earth's circumference? Once he knew this fraction of Earth's circumference, how did he calculate the distance of Earth's circumference?
11. What are the latitude and longitude coordinates (in degrees, minutes, and seconds) of your present location? Where can you find this information?
12. Define latitude and parallel and define longitude and meridian using a simple sketch with labels.
13. Define a great circle, great circle routes, and a small circle. In terms of these concepts, describe the equator, other parallels, and meridians.
14. Identify the various latitudinal geographic zones that roughly subdivide Earth's surface. In which zone do you live? How do the concepts of north and northerliness describe your location?
15. What does timekeeping have to do with longitude? Explain this relationship. How is Coordinated Universal Time (UTC) determined on Earth?
16. What and where is the prime meridian? How was the location originally selected? Describe the meridian that is opposite the prime meridian on Earth's surface.
17. What was Sandford Fleming's greatest contribution to science and engineering?
18. What is GPS and how does it assist you in finding location and elevation on Earth? Give a couple of examples where it was utilized to correct heights for some famous mountains.

Define cartography and mapping basics: map scale and map projections.

A **map** is a generalized view of an area, usually some portion of Earth's surface, as seen from above, and greatly reduced in size. The science and art of mapmaking is called **cartography**. Geographers use maps for the spatial portrayal of Earth's physical systems. **Scale** is the ratio of the image on a map to the real world; it relates a unit on the map to an identical unit on the ground. Cartographers create **map projections** for specific purposes, selecting the best compromise of projection for each application. Compromise is always necessary because Earth's round, three-dimensional surface cannot be exactly duplicated on a flat, two-dimensional map. **Equal area** (equivalence), **true shape** (conformality), true direction, and true distance are all considerations in selecting a projection. **Rhumb lines** are lines of constant direction and appear as straight lines on the **Mercator projection**.

map (p. 26)
cartography (p. 26)
scale (p. 26)
map projections (p. 27)
equal area (p. 27)
true shape (p. 27)
Mercator projection (p. 29)
rhumb lines (p. 29)

19. Define cartography. Explain why it is an integrative discipline.
20. What is map scale? In what three ways may it be expressed on a map?
21. State whether each of the following ratios is a large scale, medium scale, or small scale: 1:1,000,000, 1:50,000, 1:250,000.
22. Describe the differences between the characteristics of a globe and those that result when a flat map is prepared.
23. What type of map projection is used in Figure 1.14? In Figure 1.18? (See Appendix A.)

Describe remote sensing and *explain* geographic information system (GIS) methodology as a tool used in geographic analysis.

The operation of Earth's systems is disclosed through orbital and aerial **remote sensing**. Satellites do not take photographs but record images that are transmitted to Earth-based receivers. Satellite images are recorded in digital form for later processing, enhancement, and generation. Aerial photographs have been used for years to improve the accuracy of surface maps. This is the realm of **photogrammetry**, an important application of remote sensing.

The mountain of data already collected has led to the development of **geographic information system (GIS)** technology. Computers process geographic information from direct surveys and remote sensing in complex ways never before possible. GIS methodology is an important step in better understanding Earth's systems and is a vital career opportunity for geographers.

The science of physical geography is in a unique position to synthesize the spatial, environmental, and human aspects of our increasingly complex relationship with our home planet—Earth.

remote sensing (p. 30)
photogrammetry (p. 30)
geographic information system (GIS) (p. 34)

24. What is remote sensing? What are you viewing when you observe a weather satellite image on TV or in the newspaper? Explain.
25. Describe *Terra*, *Landsat*, *GOES*, *RADARSAT*, and *NOAA* satellites, and explain them using several examples.
26. If you were in charge of planning for development of a large tract of land, how would GIS methodologies assist you? How might planning and zoning be affected if a portion of the tract in the GIS is a floodplain or prime agricultural land?

Critical Thinking

A. Select a location (for example, your campus, home, workplace, a public place, or a city) and determine the following: latitude, longitude, and elevation. Describe the resources you used to gather this geographic information. Have you ever used a GPS unit to determine these aspects of your location?

B. Let's say there is a world globe in the library or geography department that is 61 cm (24 in.) in diameter. We know that Earth has an equatorial diameter of 12,756 km (7926 mi), so the scale of the globe is the ratio of 61 cm to 12,756 km. We divide Earth's actual diameter by the globe's diameter (12,756 km ÷ 61 cm) and determine that 1 cm of the globe's diameter equals about ____ cm of Earth's actual diameter. Thus, the representative fraction for the globe is expressed in centimetres as 1/____. (Hint: 1 km = 1000 m, 1 m = 100 cm; therefore Earth's diameter 12,756 km represents 1,275,600,000 cm.)

C. The various geographic information technologies discussed in your text (GIS, GPS, remote sensing) promise to revolutionize many aspects of modern life. How are they used now, and what sorts of changes might we expect in the near future? Use the Net Search and Destinations sections on the Companion Website to find examples, and write a brief description of what you find. Be sure to include URLs for the sites you visit.

Career Link 1.1

Thomas D. Jones, Ph.D., Astronaut, Earth Observer, and Geographer

I first met Dr. Thomas Jones at an annual meeting of the National Council for Geographic Education (NCGE) in Indianapolis. Earth was the feature as the audience orbited the planet through NASA photos and imagery piloted by his enthusiastic geographic analysis. At one point the photo and radar image of the Kliuchevskoi volcanic eruption, on the Kamchatka Peninsula, appeared on the screen. The same photo and image are in Figure 1.26 in *Geosystems*. Afterward, I asked astronaut Tom Jones to sign the figure in a copy of the book—a real thrill.

His enthusiasm for Earth observation and his spatial analysis of natural and human phenomena—from cities, to rock formations, to hydrology, and weather—makes him a real friend of geographic education. I interviewed Tom in June 2001, at the Johnson Space Center (JSC), in Building 9, where the simulators for both the Shuttle and components of the International Space Station (ISS) are housed for training (Figure 1).

Tom was born and raised in Maryland, living there through high school graduation, becoming a National Merit Scholar. I asked him if he had an early interest in geography. Tom said, "Yes, elementary school geography was fascinating. Even as early as first grade, I can remember looking at maps with my older second-grade friend. In Boy Scouts, I loved compass work and map reading, and all the outdoor activities." Tom said, "These early interests feed right into piloting where you have a map right on your knee and must observe geography."

He received his B.S. degree as a Distinguished Graduate from the U.S. Air Force Academy and served for 6 years on active duty as pilot and commander on B-52D strategic bombers. Tom completed more than 2000 hours of flying time, achieving the rank of Captain. He stated, "Spending thousands of hours in aircraft is a good way to learn how to look carefully at landscapes from above. I have always thought it valuable in my life to have so many hours viewing Earth from above, first in planes, then from orbit."

Tom Jones continued his education at the University of Arizona, earning a Ph.D. in planetary science. He said, "I used remote sensing to study the water and mineral content of asteroids—those chunks of rock between Mars and Jupiter that are the source of many meteors that Earth encounters."

Tom joined NASA in 1990 and became an astronaut in 1991. He flew on Space Shuttle *Endeavour* as a Mission Specialist on STS-59 (April 1994) and STS-68 (October 1994). This later flight is when he captured the volcanic eruption image and photo. Tom next went into space aboard *Columbia* in STS-80 (1996), where he operated the Canadarm to launch a satellite and, incidentally, made the photo of Mount Everest at dawn shown in News Report 12.1. On his fourth flight, aboard *Atlantis* in STS-98 (February 2001), he worked installing the Destiny Laboratory Module for the International Space Station (ISS).

FIGURE 1 Astronaut Thomas Jones. Astronaut Mission Specialist Thomas Jones stands in front of a Space Shuttle simulator at the Johnson Space Center, Houston, Texas. Dr. Jones logged 1272 hours in orbit aboard four Shuttle flights. [Photo by Bobbé Christopherson.]

I inquired about the *Endeavour* flight in October 1994. Tom said, "We were going to study volcanoes with the SIR-C/X-SAR, including the volcanic complex on Kamchatka. So it was on our charts and flight plan. We never expected that the biggest volcano in Asia would erupt right after launch and present us with such a wonderful opportunity. We saw it on our first orbit! This huge smudge on the horizon looked like the strangest thunderstorm. Then we realized that Kliuchevskoi had blown." Tom added, "Earth gave us a gift. We were supposed to fly 6 weeks earlier and would have missed this chance to see an active eruption."

When working outside the Shuttle above the protective layers of the atmosphere, an astronaut must wear protection. The spacesuit must regulate the temperature differences experienced, from nearly 120°C (156°F) where the Sun strikes the spacesuit, to –250°C (–156°F) when in shadows. Oxygen and water must be provided and carbon dioxide buildup managed. Here on Earth's surface the atmosphere does all this for us. Imagine designing a spacesuit that does everything portrayed in Figure 3.2 in this book.

Tom Jones completed three extravehicular activities (EVAs) on his last flight, totalling 19 hours (Figure 2a). He and his partner Bob Curbeam installed the U.S. Destiny Laboratory Module on the ISS. Relative to his spacesuit (extravehicular mobility unit, or EMU), I asked him about any feeling of vulnerability during his EVA while he was an Earth satellite drifting in orbit at more than 28,100 kmph (17,500 mph). Tom answered, "Intellectually you are aware of that, and you can stop and think about your independence from things as you look over the brilliant Earth, but most of the time you are focused on the work and the spacesuit is almost invisible to you. It works so well that you get quite comfortable, you forget that you are next to a vacuum travelling ten times faster than a bullet, or in such a harsh environment."

He continued, "Despite the thermal protection of the EMU spacesuit, when the Sun rises, which it does every 90 minutes in orbit, I could feel the warmth when the light hit me. The thermal tubing in the suit that regulates temperature goes throughout the suit—ankles, to wrists, to neckline. If it does get warm in the suit, you can adjust your thermostat. With sunset, I felt that warmth drop away and when my feet were on a work platform, I felt the coldness of the metal plate and the heat energy conduct out through the feet of the suit, despite the bulky socks I wore. If you feel your feet chilling, you adjust the suit temperature up."

I asked about Earth observation time. "Everyone gets training for Earth observing, including classroom work in physical and human geography and geology. For my last mission we attended lectures and got experience doing actual camera practice. We have NASA's *Space Shuttle Physiographic Atlas* (1:10,000,000 scale), from the Earth Observation Project, organized along flight paths (west to east). Clear, bold labels used in the atlas help us orient the camera to specific photographic targets. Decal black circles are placed on charts so you know what needs to be photographed.

"The Earth Sciences Team chooses three dozen or more candidates for intense observation, depending on research needs. We have electronic maps on our laptops, so we can click on a site and it will tell us the time when the target is within range, and it will suggest camera and film to use. Houston sends a daily Earth Observation Bulletin that lists the times for certain scenes, mission elapsed time to the target, correlating with map notations."

I asked, "After 1272 hours in Earth orbit, more than 52 days total, what are some of your thoughts about Earth?" Tom answered, "Earth never fails to amaze me and captivate me with the beauty it presents, the ever-changing aspects of light, the changing vision, for you are always seeing Earth in a new way. Every time I looked out the window I saw a different angle or lighting that changes something I might have seen many times before. I always found something new to be amazed at! Looking at Earth is relaxing and enjoyable; it refreshes you instantly."

Tom added, "My days in orbit are a privilege, to see Earth from that distance is a life-long memory and one that will never leave me. Yet, it comes with a sense of regret because on this last mission I know there was so much I could have seen, but we had an important mission to complete and there wasn't time to linger by the windows. This is the mixed blessing of working in space."

As to the future, Tom wants to focus on further research related to his dissertation topic and nonfiction writing for the general public on space travel and possible missions to asteroids. Tom is the author of *The Complete Idiot's Guide to NASA* (Indianapolis: Alpha Books, 2002). He said, "The Moon is a close-by testing place for equipment, so we will no doubt be returning. We need to build support for future space exploration."

In closing, I asked Tom about the Insignia patch for STS-98 (Figure 2b). He answered, "The crew thought it was important to show the Earth observing window in the Destiny Laboratory Module, with Earth reflected in it. Uncovering the protective coating to begin operations of this crystal-clear viewing portal was a real thrill for Bob and me on our EVA." This says it all about Tom and the enrichment he gives to geographic education—he has opened a portal for us to better see Earth, our Home Planet.

(a)

(b)

FIGURE 2 Space walk February 2001.
(a) Astronaut Thomas Jones completed three space walks, totalling 19 hours, working on the International Space Station *Destiny* module installation. He is waving to crew members inside *Atlantis*. His partner in the space walks was Robert L. Curbeam. (b) Insignia for the *Atlantis* mission, note the reflection of Earth in the large window in the Destiny module. See http://www.spaceflight.nasa.gov/gallery/images/shuttle/. [Space Shuttle photograph STS98-E-5195 and mission Insignia courtesy of NASA.]

PART ONE

The Energy–Atmosphere System

Sunrise captured in the Scoresby Sund fjord system, East Greenland, September 2003, at approximately 71°N latitude. The extended length of dawn at high latitudes produces wonderful colours and long shadows from transient icebergs. These icebergs probably calved and set sail from glaciers in northern Greenland, were ocean going driven by winds, and floated into this fjord system—all involving physical principles discussed in Part 1, The Energy–Atmosphere System.
[Photo by Bobbé Christopherson.]

Our planet and our lives are powered by radiant energy from the star that is closest to Earth—the Sun. For more than 4.6 billion years, solar energy has travelled across interplanetary space to Earth, where a small portion of the solar output is intercepted. Because of Earth's curvature, the energy at the top of the atmosphere is unevenly distributed, creating imbalances from the equator to each pole—the equatorial region experiences energy surpluses; the polar regions experience energy deficits. Also, the annual pulse of seasonal change varies the distribution of energy during the year.

Earth's atmosphere acts as an efficient filter, absorbing most harmful radiation, charged particles, and space debris so that they do not reach Earth's surface. In the lower atmosphere, the unevenness of daily energy receipt empowers atmospheric and surface energy balances, giving rise to global patterns of temperature and circulation of wind and ocean currents. Each of us depends on many systems that are set into motion by energy from the Sun. These systems are the subject of Part 1, Chapters 2 through 6.

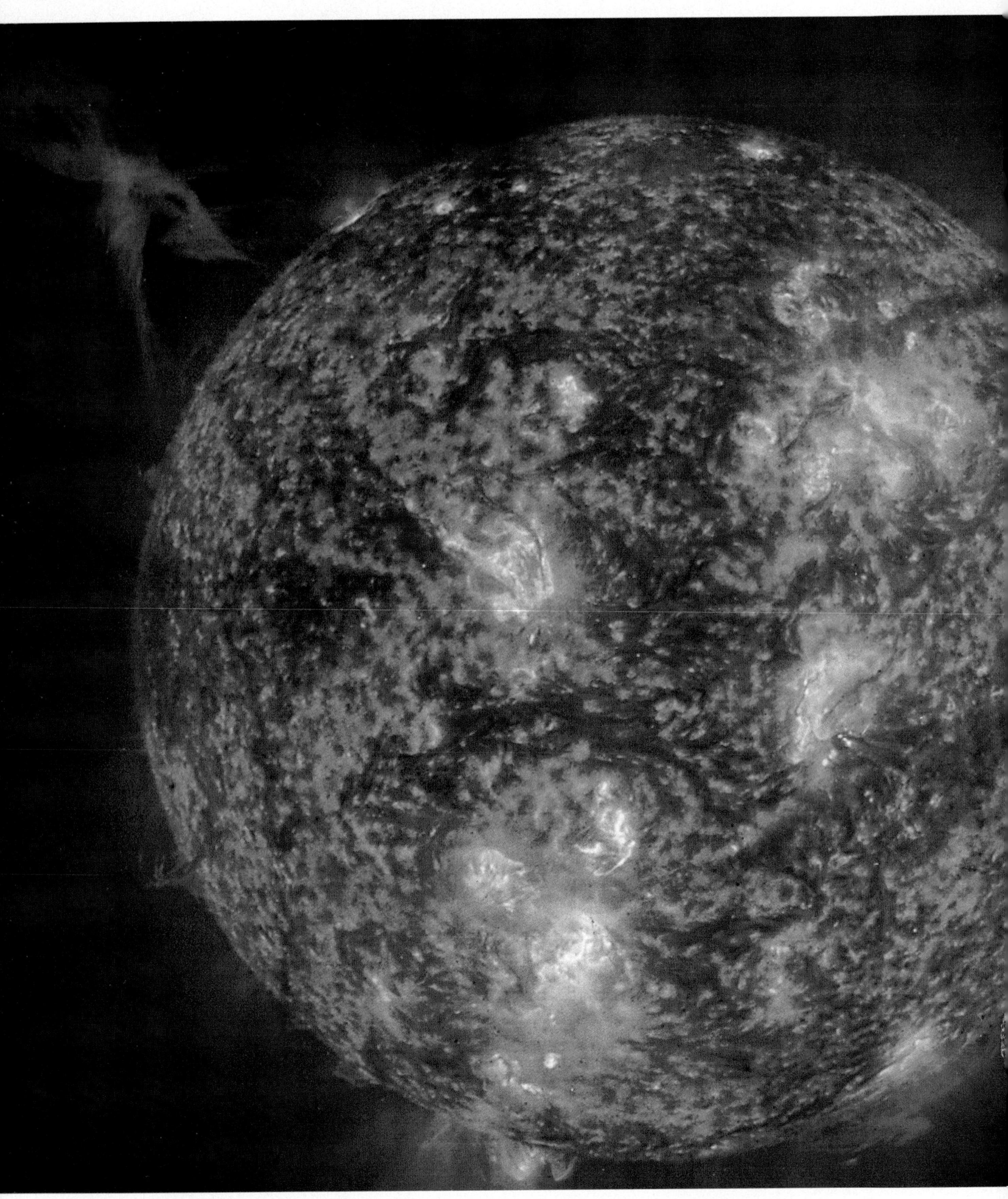

A dramatic Sun captured by instruments aboard the *SOHO* satellite, February 12, 2001. A twirling prominence rises into the Sun's corona, and other prominences are also visible. [Image courtesy of *SOHO/EIT* (Solar and Heliospheric Observatory/Extreme Ultraviolet Imaging Telescope) Consortium. *SOHO* is an international project of cooperation between the European Space Agency and NASA. See **http://sohowww.nascom.nasa.gov/**.]

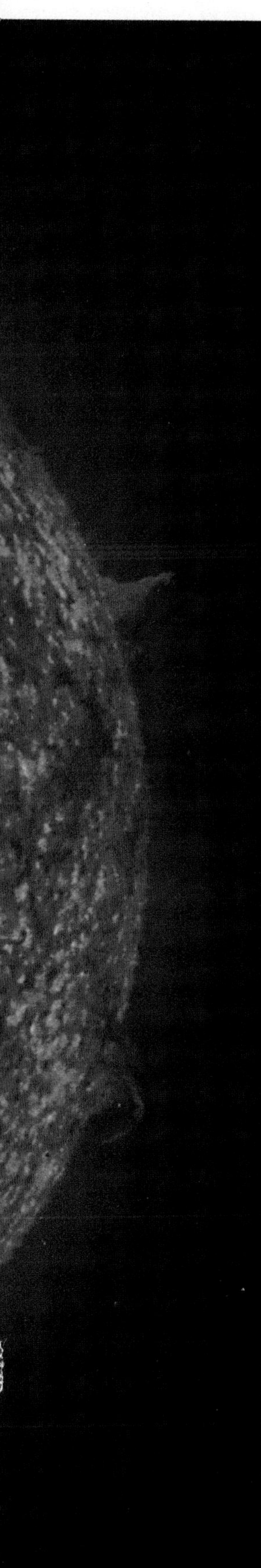

2 Solar Energy to Earth and the Seasons

Key Learning Concepts

After reading the chapter, you should be able to:

- *Distinguish* among galaxies, stars, and planets and *locate* Earth.
- *Overview* the origin, formation, and development of Earth and *construct* Earth's annual orbit about the Sun.
- *Describe* the Sun's operation and *explain* the characteristics of the solar wind and the electromagnetic spectrum of radiant energy.
- *Portray* the intercepted solar energy and its uneven distribution at the top of the atmosphere.
- *Define* solar altitude, solar declination, and daylength and *describe* the annual variability of each—Earth's seasonality.

The Universe is populated with billions of galaxies. One of these is our own **Milky Way Galaxy**, consisting of billions of stars. Among these stars is an average yellow star we call the Sun, although the dramatic *SOHO* satellite image that opens this chapter seems anything but average! Our Sun radiates energy in all directions and upon its family of orbiting planets. Of special interest to us is the solar energy that falls on the third planet from the Sun.

In this chapter: Incoming solar energy that arrives at the top of Earth's atmosphere establishes the pattern of energy input that drives Earth's physical systems and daily influences our lives. This solar energy input to the atmosphere, plus Earth's tilt and rotation, produce daily, seasonal, and annual patterns of changing daylength and Sun angle. The Sun is the ultimate energy source for most life processes in our biosphere.

The Solar System, Sun, and Earth

Our Solar System is located on a remote, trailing edge of the Milky Way Galaxy, a flattened, disk-shaped mass estimated to contain nearly 400 billion stars (Figure 2.1a, b). Our Solar System is embedded more than halfway out from the galactic centre, in one of the Milky Way's spiral arms, called the Orion Arm. A supermassive black hole some two million solar masses in size, named Sagittarius A*, sits in the centre (pronounced *Sagittarius A Star*). From our Earth-bound perspective in the Milky Way, the Galaxy appears to stretch across the night sky like a narrow band of hazy light. On a clear night, the unaided eye can see only a few thousand of these billions of stars.

Solar System Formation and Structure

According to prevailing theory, our Solar System condensed from a large, slowly rotating and collapsing cloud of dust and gas called a *nebula*. **Gravity**, the mutual attracting force exerted by the mass of an object upon all other objects, was the key force in this condensing solar nebula. As the nebular cloud organized and flattened into a disk shape, the early *protosun* grew in mass at the centre, drawing more matter to it. Small accretion (accumulation) eddies swirled at varying distances from the centre of the solar nebula; these were the *protoplanets*.

The early protoplanets, called *planetesimals*, orbited at approximately the same distances from the Sun as the planets are today. The beginnings of the Sun and its Solar System are estimated to have occurred more than 4.6 billion years ago. The explanation of how suns condense from nebular clouds with planetesimals forming in orbits around their central masses is called the **planetesimal hypothesis**, or *dust-cloud hypothesis*. Astronomers study this formation process in other parts of the Galaxy, where planets are observed orbiting distant stars. By the end of 2003, astronomers discovered more than 110 planets orbiting around other stars. Closer to home in our Solar System, 65 new moons (planetary satellites) were discovered since 1999. As of 2004, the new satellite count for the four outer planets is: Jupiter, 61 moons; Saturn, 31 moons; Uranus, 22 moons; and Neptune, 11 moons.

Dimensions and Distances The **speed of light** is 300,000 kmps (kilometres per second), or 186,000 mps (miles per second)—in other words about 9.5 trillion kilometres, or nearly 6 trillion miles, per year. (In more precise numbers, light speed is 299,792 kmps, or 186,282 mps.) This tremendous distance that light travels in a year is known as a *light-year*, and it is used as a unit of measurement for the vast Universe.

The known Universe that is observable from Earth stretches approximately 12 billion light-years in all directions. The Milky Way Galaxy is about 100,000 light-years from edge to edge (Figure 2.1b). For spatial comparison, our entire Solar System of nine planets is approximately 11 hours in diameter, as measured by light speed (Figure 2.1c). The Moon is an average distance of 384,400 km (238,866 mi) from Earth, or about 1.28 seconds from Earth in terms of light speed—for the *Apollo* astronauts this was a three-day journey. (See a Solar System simulator at **http://space.jpl.nasa.gov/**.)

Earth's Orbit Earth's orbit around the Sun is presently *elliptical*—a closed, oval path (Figure 2.1d). Earth's average distance from the Sun is approximately 150 million kilometres (93 million miles), which means that light reaches Earth from the Sun in an average of 8 minutes and 20 seconds. Earth is at **perihelion** (its closest position to the Sun) during the Northern Hemisphere winter (January 3 at 147,255,000 km, or 91,500,000 mi). It is at **aphelion** (its farthest position from the Sun) during the Northern Hemisphere summer (July 4 at 152,083,000 km, or 94,500,000 mi). This seasonal difference in distance from the Sun causes a slight variation in the solar energy intercepted by Earth, but is not an immediate reason for seasonal change.

A plane touching all points of Earth's orbit is termed the **plane of the ecliptic**. Earth's tilted axis remains fixed relative to this plane as Earth revolves around the Sun. The plane of the ecliptic is important to our discussion of Earth's seasons. The structure of Earth's orbit is not a constant but instead exhibits change over long periods. As shown in Chapter 17 in Figure 17.31, Earth's distance from the Sun varies more than 17.7 million kilometres (11 million miles) during a 100,000-year cycle, placing it closer or farther at different periods in the cycle. This variation is thought to be one of several factors that create Earth's cyclical pattern of glaciations (colder) and interglacial (warmer) periods.

Solar Energy: From Sun to Earth

Our Sun is unique to us but is a commonplace star in the Galaxy. It is only average in temperature, size, and colour when compared with other stars, yet it is the ultimate energy source for most life processes in our biosphere.

The Sun captured about 99.9% of the matter from the original nebula. The remaining 0.1% of the matter formed all the planets, their satellites, asteroids, comets, and debris. Consequently, the dominant object in our region of space is the Sun. In the entire Solar System, it is the only object having the enormous mass needed to create the internal temperature and pressure to sustain a nuclear reaction and produce radiant energy.

The solar mass produces tremendous pressure and high temperatures deep in its dense interior. Under these conditions, the Sun's abundant hydrogen atoms, the lightest of all the natural elements, are forced together, and pairs of hydrogen nuclei are joined in a process called **fusion**. In the fusion reaction, hydrogen nuclei form helium, the second-lightest element in nature, and enormous quantities

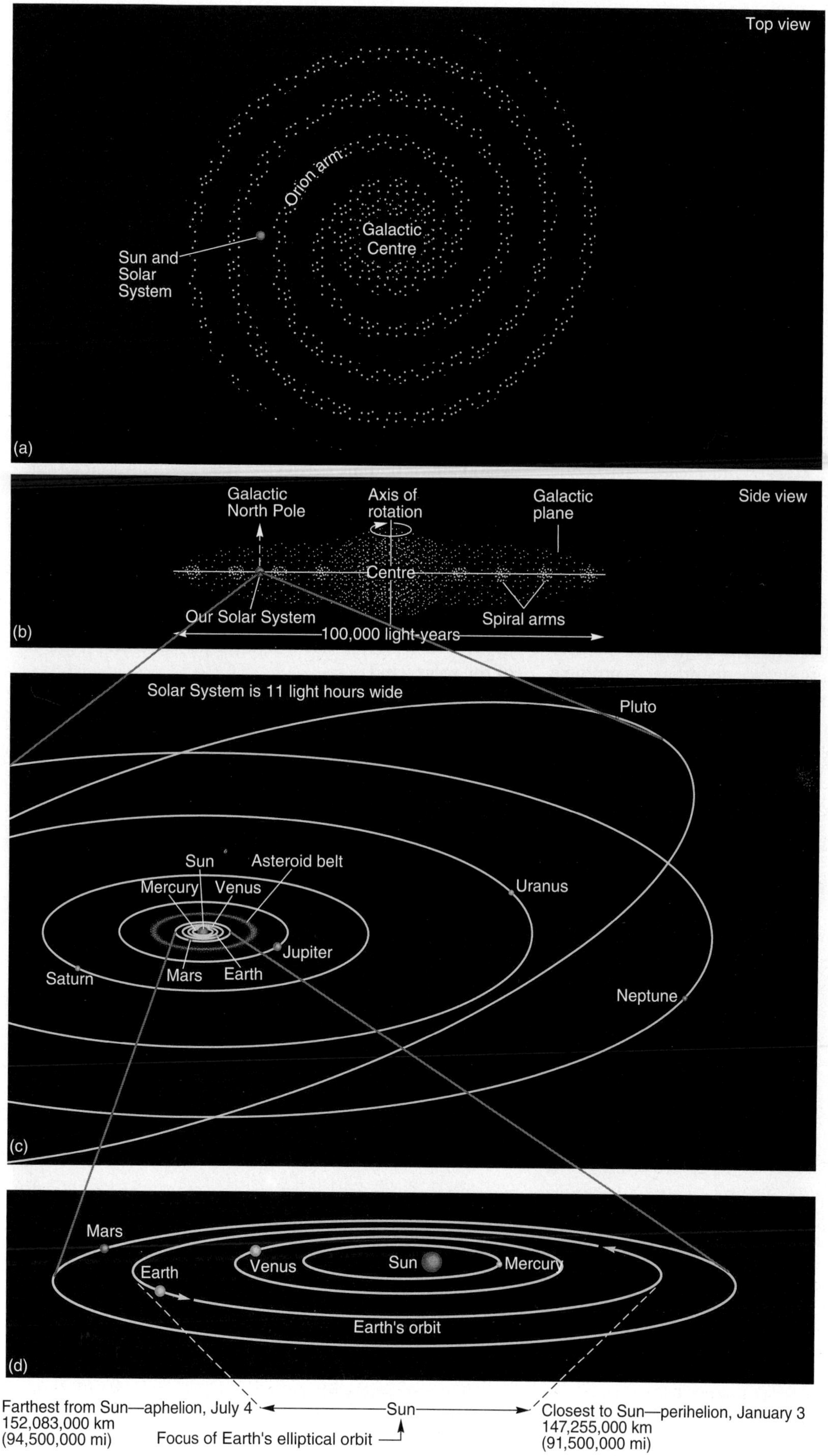

FIGURE 2.1 Milky Way Galaxy, Solar System, and Earth's orbit.
The Milky Way Galaxy viewed from above (a) and cross-section side view (b). Our Solar System of nine planets and asteroids is some 30,000 light-years from the centre of the Galaxy. All of the planets except Pluto have orbits closely aligned to the plane of the ecliptic (c). The four inner terrestrial planets and the structure of Earth's elliptical orbit, illustrating perihelion (closest) and aphelion (farthest) positions during the year, are given in (d). Have you ever observed the Milky Way Galaxy in the night sky?

of energy are liberated—literally, disappearing solar mass becomes energy.

A sunny day can seem so peaceful, certainly belying the violence taking place on the Sun. The Sun's principal outputs consist of the solar wind and radiant energy in portions of the electromagnetic spectrum. Let us trace each of these emissions across space to Earth.

Solar Activity and Solar Wind

The Sun constantly emits clouds of electrically charged particles (principally hydrogen nuclei and free electrons) that surge outward in all directions from the Sun's surface. This stream of energetic material travels much more slowly than light—only about 50 million kilometres (31 million miles) a day—taking approximately 3 days to reach Earth. The term **solar wind** was first applied to this phenomenon in 1958. Solar wind extends from the Sun to a distance beyond Pluto's orbit. The *Voyager* and *Pioneer* spacecraft launched in the 1970s are now far beyond our Solar System and have yet to escape the solar wind.

The Sun's most conspicuous features are large **sunspots**, caused by magnetic storms on the Sun. Individual sunspots may range in diameter from 10,000 to 50,000 km (6200 to 31,000 mi), with some growing as large as 160,000 km (100,000 mi), more than 12 times Earth's diameter (Figure 2.2). These surface disturbances produce flares and prominences. In addition, outbursts of charged material referred to as *coronal mass ejections* contribute to the flow of material to space in the solar wind.

A regular cycle exists for sunspot occurrences, averaging 11 years from maximum to maximum; however, the cycle may vary from 7 to 17 years. In recent cycles, a solar minimum occurred in 1976 and a solar maximum took place during 1979, with more than 100 sunspots visible at maximum. Another minimum was reached in 1986, and an extremely active solar maximum followed in 1990, with more than 200 sunspots visible at some time during the year. In fact, the 1990–1991 maximum was the most intense ever observed—11 years after the previous maximum. A sunspot minimum in 1997 and an intense maximum in 2001, and moving to a minimum in 2006–2007 maintain the average. (For more on the sunspot cycle, see **http://www.ssl.msfc.nasa.gov/ssL/pad/solar/sunspots.htm**.) The order and patterns we see in nature are the result of chaotic interactions of many systems, which are discussed in News Report 2.1.

Solar Wind Effects The charged particles of the solar wind first interact with Earth's magnetic field as they approach Earth. The **magnetosphere** is a magnetic field surrounding Earth, generated by dynamo-like motions within our planet. The magnetosphere deflects the solar wind toward both of Earth's poles so that only a small portion of it enters the atmosphere.

Because the solar wind does not reach Earth's surface, research on this phenomenon must be conducted in space. In 1969 the *Apollo XI* astronauts exposed a piece of foil on the lunar surface as a solar wind experiment (Figure 2.3). When examined back on Earth, the exposed foil exhibited particle impacts that confirmed the presence and character of the solar wind.

Interaction of the solar wind and the upper layers of Earth's atmosphere produces the remarkable **auroras** that occur toward both poles. These lighting effects are the *aurora borealis* (northern lights) and *aurora australis* (southern lights) in the upper atmosphere, 80–500 km (50–300 mi) above Earth's surface (Figure 2.4). During the 2001 solar maximum, auroras were visible as far south as Jamaica, Texas, and California. Also, the solar wind disrupts

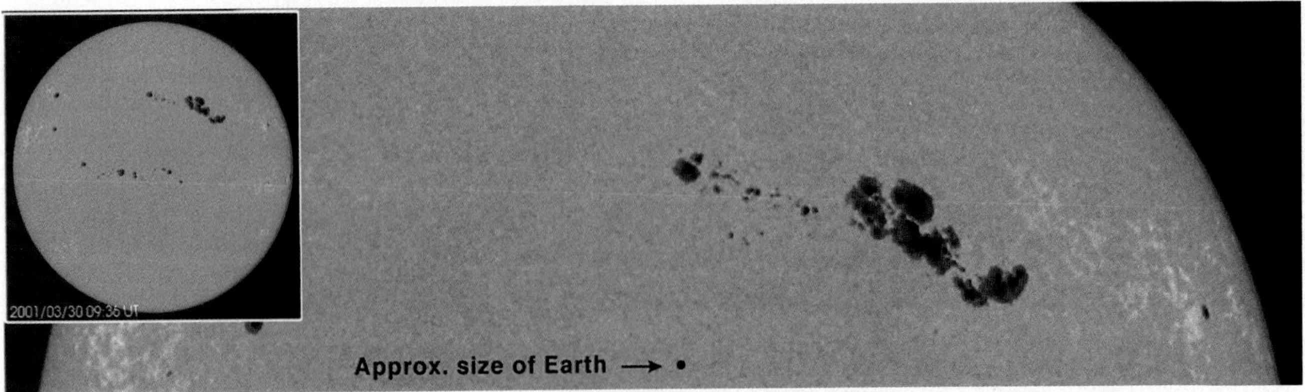

FIGURE 2.2 Image of the Sun and sunspots.
The Sun and large sunspot group in a recent active cycle, imaged March 30, 2001, by the MDI (Michelson Doppler Imager) instrument aboard satellite *SOHO*. This group was the source of numerous flares and coronal mass ejections, including the largest flare in 25 years on April 2. The area within the sunspot group is more than 13 times the entire surface area of Earth (13 times 500 million km^2)—Earth is shown for scale. Sunspots appear as visible dark patches because of their lower temperature relative to the rest of the surface. [Image courtesy of *SOHO/MDI* Consortium. *SOHO* (Solar and Heliospheric Observatory) is a cooperative effort between the European Space Agency and NASA. MDI is from Stanford-Lockheed/Martin Institute for Space Research.]

News Report 2.1

The Nature of Order Is Chaos

In 1960, Edward Lorenz, an MIT scientist, rocked the scientific world with the statement that a butterfly flapping its wings in Brazil might produce a tornado in Texas. He used this strange example to suggest that the interaction of orderly and deterministic systems may produce chaotic and unpredictable results.

For example, ice has a rigid internal structure, forced by bonding between water molecules. This structure dictates that all ice crystals are six-sided, yet no two ice crystals, despite this similarity, are identical. Beneath this chaos of design exists an order dictated by physical principles (see Figure 7.5).

A major shift in our real-world view occurred with the advent of *chaos theory*, a revolution in science that considers the nonlinear and unpredictable behaviour of operational systems. This theory suggests that the scientific method must consider the coexistence of disorder and order, randomness and pattern, and symmetry and chaos in natural systems—the science of complexity and complex systems.

Consider the weather: Mathematical models and numerical equations describe the behaviour of water vapour, temperature, and pressure patterns. Yet weather systems are sensitive to very small fluctuations in any of those ingredients. Therefore, it is difficult to exactly predict how a weather system will develop, what track it will follow, or how severe it might be (see Chapter 8). Two similar chaotic weather systems might produce a similar result, although it is not possible to say exactly what the output will be. This understanding of the role of chaos is helping scientists to improve forecasting of weather phenomena. In a dynamic weather system, chaos is the rule, just as it is in chemical and biological systems.

Chaos theory is useful in studying all of Earth's physical environments. For example, a river flows in branched channels over a floodplain in a pattern to conserve energy. The channels constantly shift in a randomness that is irregular and difficult to predict. See the *Terra* satellite photograph of the many mouths of the Ganges River in Figure 14.25 for an example of such *fractal branching*—irregular, curving channels that may or may not repeat their pattern.

This may seem strange, but the nature of order we observe is the result of chaos and the almost infinite interaction among physical elements! Chaos theory is a new dimension of the scientific method and physical geography.

certain radio broadcasts and some satellite transmissions, causes overloads on Earth-based electrical systems, and may affect weather patterns.

Our understanding of the solar wind is increasing dramatically as data are collected by a variety of satellites: the *SOHO* (*Solar and Heliospheric Observatory*), *FAST* (*Fast Auroral Snapshot*), *WIND*, *Ulysses*, the *Dynamics Explorer*, and the earlier *Voyager-2* and *Pioneers-10* and *11* launched in the 1970s. All satellite data are available on the Internet. (For auroral activity, see **http://www.sec.noaa.gov/pmap/** and for forecasts, see **http://www.gi.alaska.edu**.)

Weather Effects Another effect of the solar wind in the atmosphere is its possible influence on weather and climate cycles. Why do wetter periods in some midlatitude areas tend to coincide with every other solar maximum? Why do droughts often occur near the time of every other solar minimum? For example, sunspot cycles during nearly 260 years from 1740 to 1998 coincided with periods of wetness

FIGURE 2.3 Astronaut and solar wind experiment. Without a protective atmosphere, the lunar surface receives charged particles of the solar wind and all of the Sun's electromagnetic radiation. An Apollo XI astronaut deploys a sheet of foil in 1969 in the solar wind experiment. Earth-bound scientists analyzed the foil that revealed the composition of the solar wind. Why wouldn't this experiment work if deployed on Earth's surface? [Photo by NASA.]

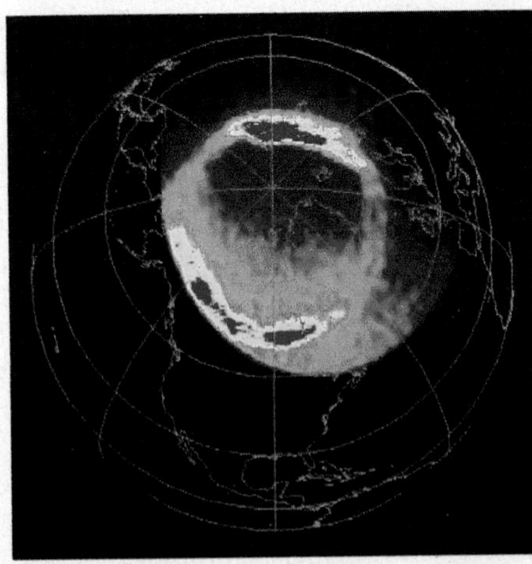

(a)

(b)

FIGURE 2.4 Auroras from an orbital perspective and from the ground in Manitoba.
(a) *Polar* satellite false-colour image of auroral halo over Earth's North Pole region from April 1996—the UVI sensor is able to capture the aurora on the day and night sides of Earth. (b) View from the ground of an aurora borealis in the night sky over Churchill, Manitoba. [(a) Image from the Ultraviolet Imager (UVI) aboard *Polar* satellite courtesy of NASA. (b) Photo by Richard Petrone.]

and drought, as estimated by an analysis of tree growth rings for that period throughout the western United States and elsewhere, as well as instrumental weather records. These variations in weather tend to lag 2 or 3 years behind the solar maximum or minimum.

Regardless of the *cause* for the cyclical patterns of drought and wetness that do occur, a remarkable failure in current planning worldwide is the lack of *attention* given to them. Preparing for such patterns could reduce property loss and casualties. Cyclical drought could be offset through widespread water conservation and more efficient water use. Wet spells might require strengthening of levees along river channels, floodplain zoning to restrict development, and better reservoir management to reduce flooding. As knowledge of the solar wind-weather relation improves, it will demand the attention of policy makers and the public.

Electromagnetic Spectrum of Radiant Energy

The key essential solar input to life is electromagnetic energy of various wavelengths. Solar radiation occupies a portion of the **electromagnetic spectrum** of radiant energy. This radiant energy travels at the speed of light to Earth. The total spectrum of this radiant energy is made up of different wavelengths. Figure 2.5 shows that a **wavelength** is the distance between corresponding points on any two successive waves. The number of waves passing a fixed point in one second is the *frequency*.

The Sun emits radiant energy composed of 8% ultraviolet, X-ray, and gamma-ray wavelengths; 47% visible light wavelengths; and 45% infrared wavelengths. A portion of the electromagnetic spectrum is illustrated in Figure 2.6, with wavelengths increasing from the top of the illustration to the bottom. Note the wavelengths at which various phenomena and human applications of energy occur.

An important physical law states that all objects radiate energy in wavelengths related to their individual surface temperatures: the hotter the object, the shorter the wavelengths emitted. This law holds true for the Sun and Earth. Figure 2.7 shows that the hot Sun radiates shorter wavelength energy, concentrated around 0.4–0.5 μm (micrometre).

The Sun's surface temperature is about 6000°C (11,000°F), and its emission curve shown in the figure is similar to that predicted for an idealized 6000°C surface, or *blackbody radiator*. An ideal blackbody emits as much radiant energy as it absorbs—the hotter the blackbody, the more radiation it emits at all wavelengths, with shorter wavelengths dominant at higher temperatures. The Sun emits a much greater amount of energy per unit area of its surface than does a similar area of Earth's environment.

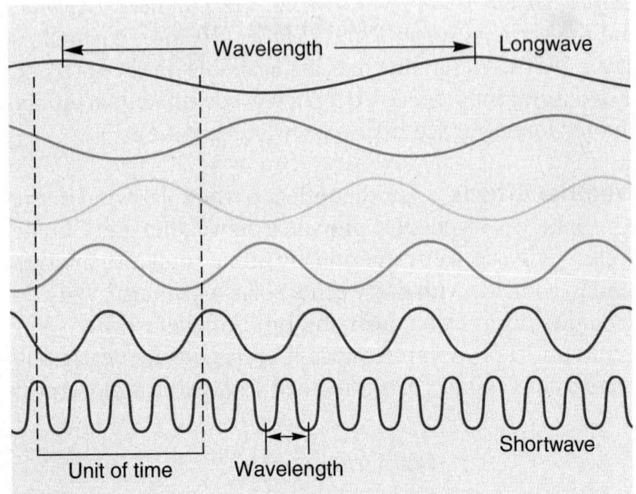

FIGURE 2.5 Wavelength and frequency.
Wavelength and frequency are two ways of describing the same phenomenon—electromagnetic wave motion. More short wavelengths pass a given point during a unit of time, so they are higher in frequency, whereas fewer long wavelengths pass a point in a unit of time, so they are lower in frequency.

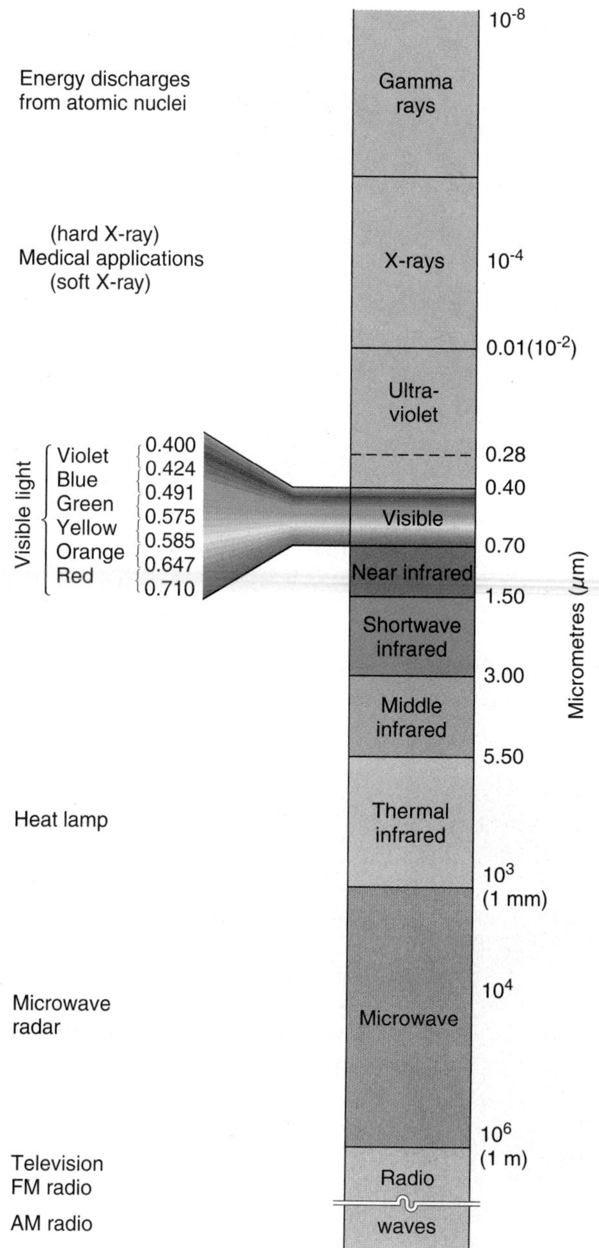

FIGURE 2.6 A portion of the electromagnetic spectrum of radiant energy.
The spectrum is oriented with,shorter wavelengths toward the top and longer wavelengths toward the bottom.

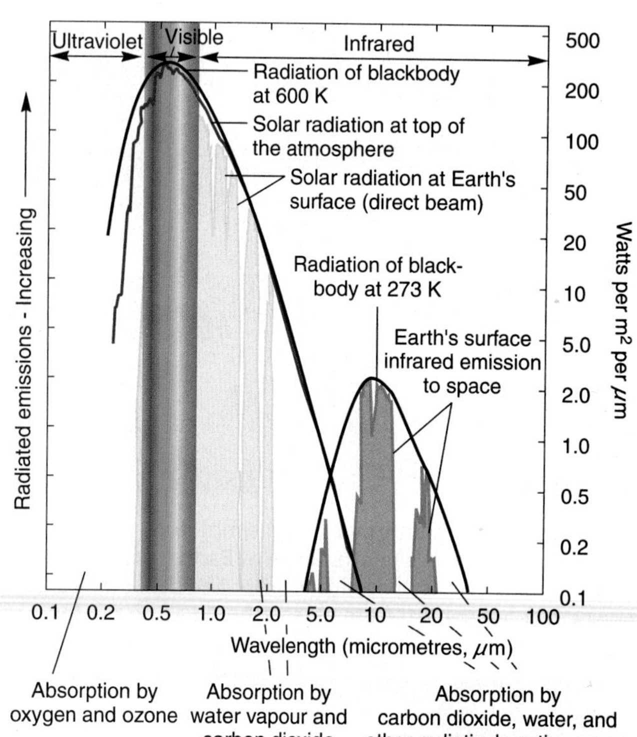

FIGURE 2.7 Solar and terrestrial energy distribution by wavelength.
The solar output peaks in shorter wavelengths of visible light in relation to its higher surface temperature, whereas Earth's emissions are concentrated in the infrared portion of the spectrum in relation to its lower surface temperature. Ideal blackbody curves for a radiating body like the Sun (hotter) and Earth (cooler) illustrate the concept. The dropouts in the plot lines of solar and terrestrial radiation represent absorption bands of water vapour, water, carbon dioxide, oxygen, ozone (O_3), and other gases. [Adapted from W.D. Sellers, *Physical Climatology* (Chicago: University of Chicago Press, 1965), p. 20. Used by permission.]

ANIMATION Electromagnetic Spectrum and Plants

Earth is a cooler radiating body, so longer wavelengths are emitted. In comparison to a shorter-wavelength emitting hot body, the lower temperatures at Earth's surface produce radiation mostly in the infrared portion of the spectrum. Figure 2.7 shows that the radiation emitted by Earth occurs in longer wavelengths, centred around 10 μm and entirely within the infrared portion of the spectrum. Figure 2.8 illustrates the flows of energy into and out of Earth systems.

To summarize, the solar spectrum is *shortwave radiation* that peaks in the short visible wavelengths, whereas Earth's radiated energy is *longwave radiation* concentrated in infrared wavelengths. In Chapter 4, we see that Earth, clouds, sky, ground, and things that are terrestrial are cool-body radiators in contrast to the Sun.

Incoming Energy at the Top of the Atmosphere

The region at the top of the atmosphere, approximately 480 km (300 mi) above Earth's surface, is termed the **thermopause**. It is the outer boundary of Earth's energy system and provides a useful point at which to assess the arriving solar radiation before it is diminished by scattering and absorption in passage through the atmosphere.

Earth's distance from the Sun results in its interception of only one two-billionth of the Sun's total energy output. Nevertheless, this tiny fraction of the Sun's overall output is an enormous amount of energy input to Earth's systems. Solar radiation that reaches a horizontal plane at Earth is called **insolation** (*in*coming *sol*ar radi*ation*), a term

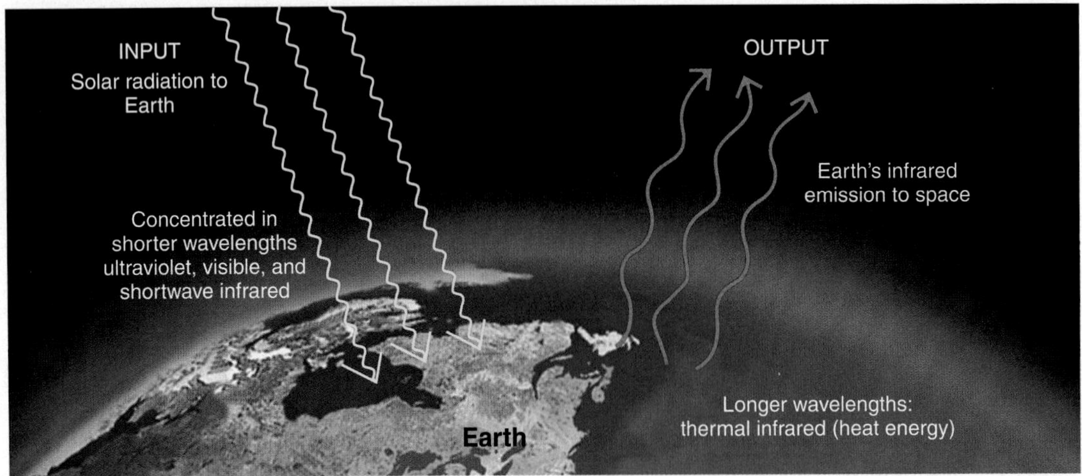

FIGURE 2.8 Earth's energy budget simplified.
Inputs of shorter wavelengths arrive at Earth from the Sun. Outputs of longer wavelengths of infrared radiate to space from Earth. The data plotted in Figure 2.10 and the map in Figure 2.11 are derived from data gathered along the top of the atmosphere.

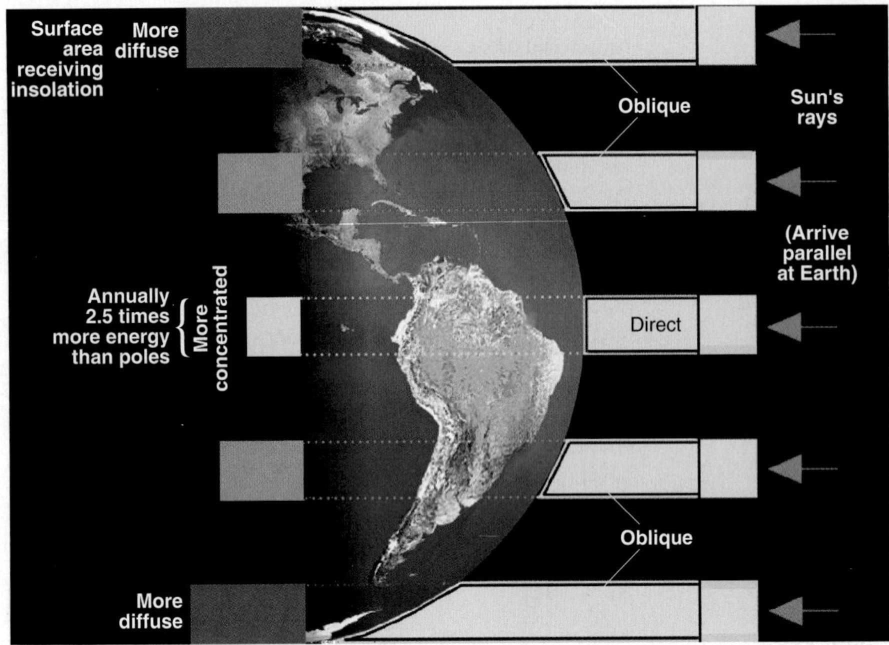

FIGURE 2.9 Insolation receipts and Earth's curved surface.
Solar insolation angles determine the concentration of energy receipts by latitude. Lower latitudes receive more concentrated energy from a more direct solar beam. Higher latitudes receive slanting (oblique) rays and more diffuse energy. Note the area covered by identical columns of solar energy arriving at Earth's surface at higher latitudes (more diffuse, larger area covered) and at lower latitudes (more concentrated, smaller area covered).

specifically applied to radiation arriving at Earth's atmosphere and surface. Insolation at the top of the atmosphere is expressed as the *solar constant*.

Solar Constant Knowing the amount of insolation intercepted by Earth is important to climatologists and other scientists. The **solar constant** is the average insolation received at the thermopause when Earth is at its average distance from the Sun. That value is 1372 W/m^2 (watts per square metre).* The constancy of the solar constant over time is important, for small variations of even 0.5% or 1.0% could prove dramatic for Earth's energy system.

As we follow insolation through the atmosphere to Earth's surface (Chapters 3 and 4), we see that the value of the solar constant is reduced by half or more through reflection, scattering, and absorption of shortwave radiation.

Uneven Distribution of Insolation Earth's curved surface presents a continually varying angle to the incoming parallel rays of insolation (Figure 2.9). Differences in the angle of solar rays at each latitude result in an uneven distribution of insolation and heating. The place receiving maximum insolation is the point where insolation rays are perpendicular to the surface (radiating from directly overhead), called the **subsolar point**. All other places receive insolation at less than a 90° angle and thus experience more

*A watt is equal to 1 joule (a unit of energy) per second and is the standard unit of power in the SI-metric system. (See Appendix C of this text for more information on measurement conversions.) In nonmetric calorie heat units, the solar constant is expressed as approximately 2 calories per square centimetre per minute, or 2 langleys per minute (a langley is 1 cal/cm^2). A calorie is the amount of energy required to raise the temperature of 1 g of water (at 15°C) 1 Celsius degree and is equal to 4.184 joules.

diffuse energy receipts. Solar beam angles become more pronounced at higher latitudes. As a result, during a year's time, the thermopause above the equatorial region receives 2.5 times more insolation than the thermopause above the poles. Lower-angle solar rays toward the poles must pass through a greater thickness of atmosphere, resulting in further losses of energy due to scattering, absorption, and reflection.

Figure 2.10 illustrates the daily variations throughout the year of energy at the top of the atmosphere for various latitudes in watts per square metre (W/m^2). The chart shows a decrease in insolation from the equatorial regions northward and southward toward the poles. However, in June, the North Pole receives more than 500 W/m^2 per day, which is more than is ever received at 50° N latitude or at the equator. Such high values result from the duration of exposure at the poles in summer: 24 hours a day, compared with only 15 hours of daylight at 50° N latitude and 12 hours at the equator. However, at the poles the summertime Sun at noon is low in the sky, so a daylength twice that of the equator yields only about 100 W/m^2 difference.

In December, the pattern reverses. Note that the top of the atmosphere at the South Pole receives even more insolation than the North Pole does in June (more than 550 W/m^2). This is a function of Earth's closer location to the Sun at perihelion (January 3 on Figure 2.1d).

Along the equator, two maximum periods of approximately 430 W/m^2 occur at the spring and fall equinoxes, when the subsolar point is at the equator. Find your latitude on the graph and follow across the months to determine the seasonal variation of insolation where you live. The four graphs to the right show plots of the energy received at the North Pole, along 50° N, along the equator, and at the South Pole during the year to give you energy profiles to compare.

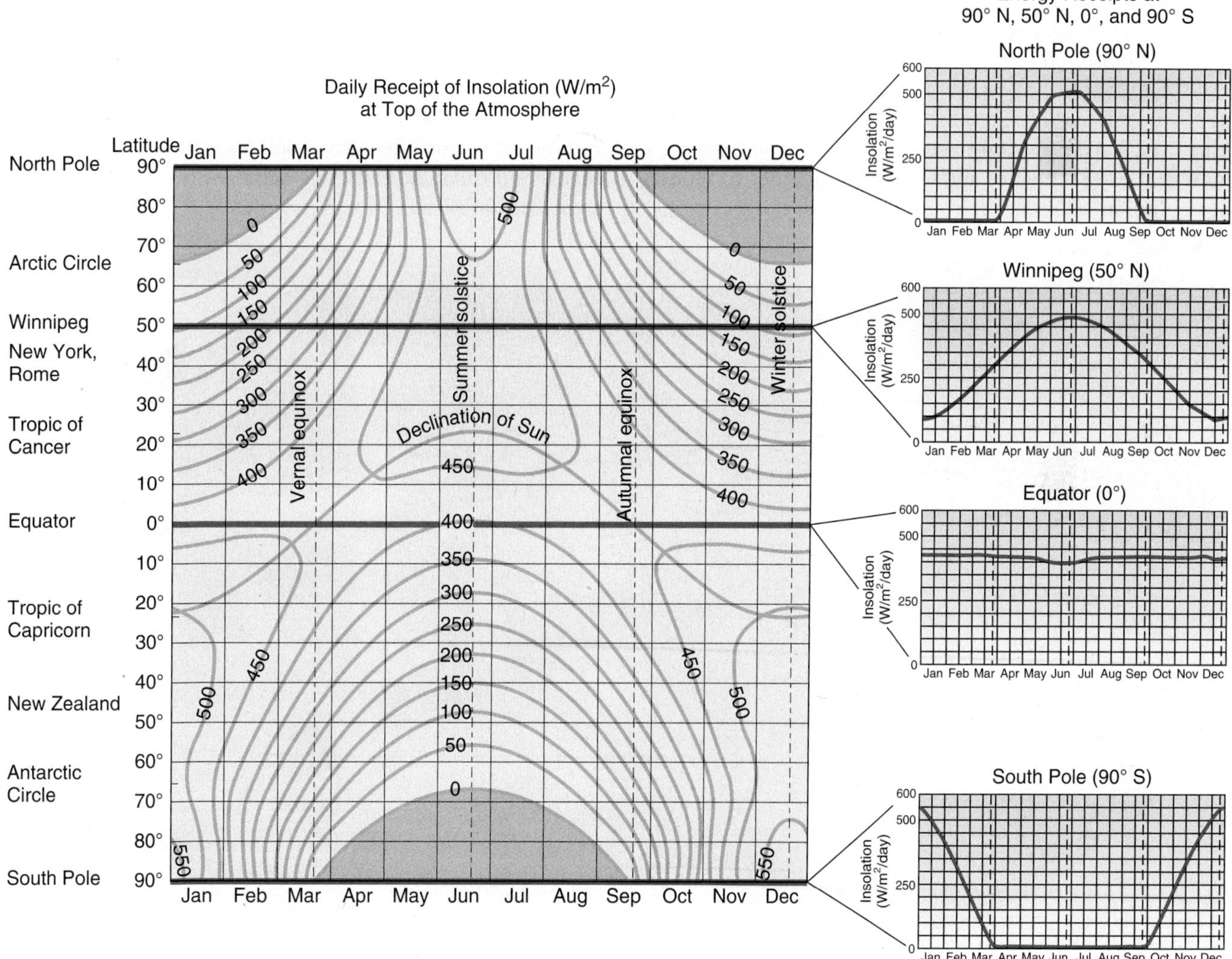

FIGURE 2.10 Daily insolation received at the top of the atmosphere.
The total daily insolation received at the top of the atmosphere is charted in watts per square metre per day by latitude and month (1 $W/m^2/day$ = 2.064 $cal/cm^2/day$). A profile of annual energy receipts is graphed to the right for the North Pole, along 50° north latitude, along the equator, and for the South Pole. [Reproduced by permission of the Smithsonian Institution Press from *Smithsonian Miscellaneous Collections: Smithsonian Meteorological Tables*, vol. 114, 6th edition. Robert List, ed. (Washington, DC: Smithsonian Institution, 1984), p. 419, Table 134.]

Global Net Radiation *Earth Radiation Budget Experiment (ERBE)* instruments aboard several satellites measured shortwave and longwave flows of energy at the top of the atmosphere. ERBE sensors collected the data used to develop the map in Figure 2.11. This map shows *net radiation*, or the balance between incoming shortwave and outgoing longwave radiation—energy inputs minus energy outputs. See News Report 2.2 for more on this experiment.

First, note the latitudinal energy imbalance in net radiation on the map—positive values in lower latitudes (energy sources for Earth systems) and negative values toward the poles (energy sinks). In middle and high latitudes, approximately poleward of 36° north and south latitudes, net radiation is negative. The reason for this in these higher latitudes is that Earth's climate system loses more energy to space than it gains from the Sun, as measured at the top of the atmosphere. In the lower atmosphere, these polar energy deficits are offset by flows of energy from tropical energy surpluses (as we will see in Chapters 4 and 6). The largest net radiation values, averaging 80 W/m^2, are above the tropical oceans along a narrow equatorial zone. Net radiation minimums are lowest over Antarctica.

Of interest is the –20 W/m^2 area over the Sahara region of North Africa. Here, typically clear skies—which permit great longwave radiation losses from Earth's surface—and light-coloured reflective surfaces work together to reduce net radiation values at the thermopause. In other regions, clouds and atmospheric pollution in the lower atmosphere also affect net radiation patterns at the top of the atmosphere by reflecting more shortwave energy to space.

The atmosphere and ocean form a giant heat engine, driven by differences in energy from place to place and causing major circulations within the lower atmosphere and in the ocean. These circulations include global winds, ocean currents, and weather systems—subjects to follow in Chapters 6 and 8. As you go about your daily activities, let these dynamic natural systems remind you of the constant flow of solar energy through the environment.

Having examined the flow of solar energy to Earth and the top of the atmosphere, let us now look at how seasonal changes affect the distribution of insolation as Earth orbits the Sun during the year.

The Seasons

Earth's periodic rhythms of warmth and cold, dawn and daylight, twilight and night, have fascinated humans for centuries. In fact, many ancient societies demonstrated an intense awareness of seasonal change and formally commemorated these natural energy rhythms with festivals, monuments, and calendars. Such ancient seasonal monuments and calendar markings occur worldwide, including thousands of sites in North America.

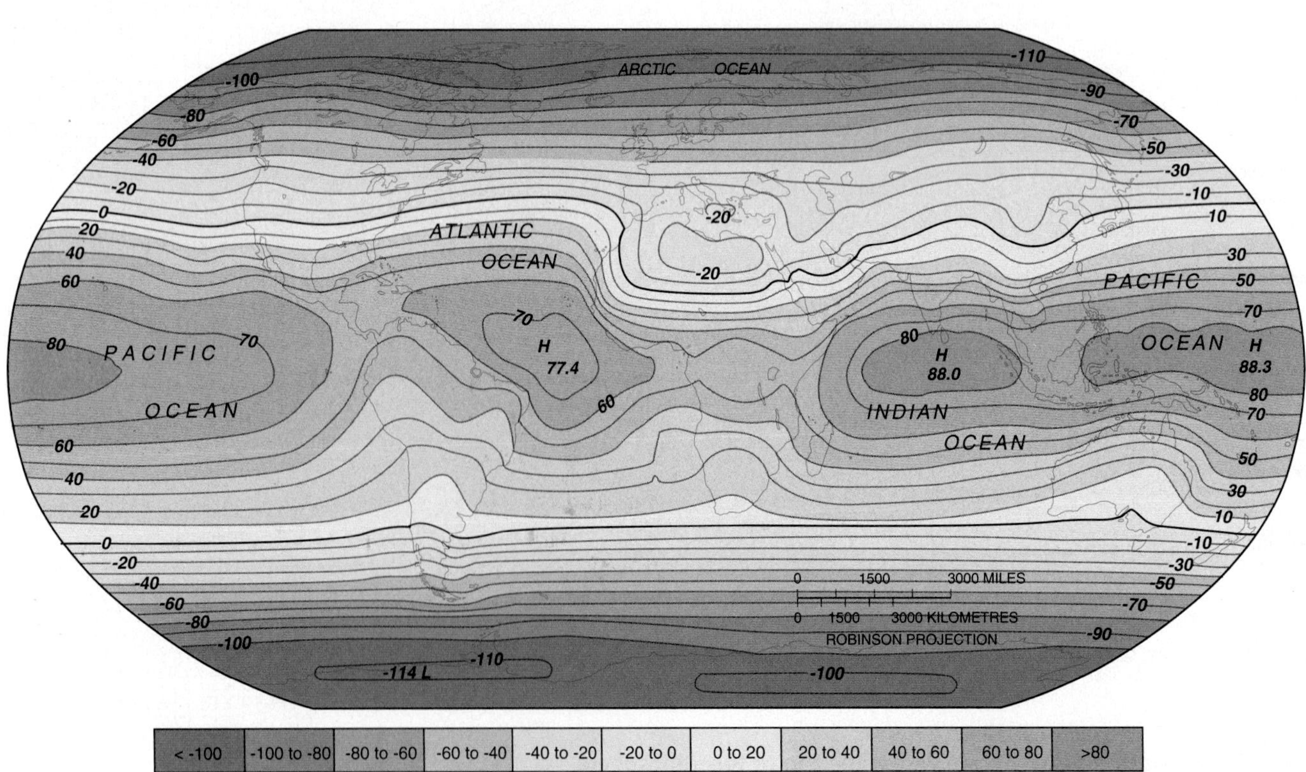

FIGURE 2.11 Daily net radiation patterns at the top of the atmosphere. Averaged daily net radiation flows for a 9-year period (1979–1987), measured at the top of the atmosphere by the Earth Radiation Budget Experiment (ERBE) aboard the *Nimbus-7* satellite. Units are W/m^2. [Data for map courtesy of Dr. H. Lee Kyle, Goddard Space Flight Center, NASA.]

News Report 2.2

Monitoring Earth's Radiation Budget

Earth's weather and climate are a direct result of the balance between sunlight received from space and energy reflected and radiated to space. Patterns of insolation absorption and energy reradiation by Earth systems produce an energy budget. Since 1978, the Earth–atmosphere energy budget was monitored by the Earth Radiation Budget (ERB) package on board the *Nimbus*-7 satellite, and later by the *ERB*, *NOAA-9*, and *NOAA-10* satellites. These satellites collected data for more than a decade. ERB sensors mapped the complex exchanges of energy among atmosphere, ocean, and land.

Measurements included monthly energy budget and variations, seasonal shifts in energy between equator and poles, and daily energy budgets at the regional scale. The map in Figure 2.11 is a direct result of ERBE, showing regions that absorb more energy than radiated (a heat-energy source, rose colour on map in Figure 2.11) and that radiate more energy than received (a heat-energy sink, purple colour).

A new tool in understanding Earth's radiation budget is the CERES (Clouds and Earth Radiant Energy System) sensor aboard satellite *Terra*. CERES monitors shortwave (light) and longwave (heat energy), and thus, Earth's energy balance of incoming and outgoing radiation. A pair of CERES images from March 2000 are shown in Chapter 4.

In addition, ERB measurements determined that solar irradiance, or the luminous brightness of solar radiation, is directly correlated to the sunspot cycle discussed earlier. During the solar maximums of 1979 and 1991, the solar constant exceeded 1374 W/m^2; the 1986 minimum produced a constant of 1371 W/m^2 (remember the solar constant averages 1372 W/m^2). The ERBE findings help scientists better understand the systems described in Part One in this textbook (see **http://asd-www.larc.nasa.gov/erbe/ASDerbe.html**).

Seasonality

Seasonality refers to both the seasonal variation of the Sun's position above the horizon and changing daylengths during the year. Seasonal variations are a response to changes in the Sun's **altitude**, or the angle between the horizon and the Sun. At sunrise or sunset, the Sun is at the horizon, so its altitude is 0°. During the day, if the Sun reaches halfway between the horizon and directly overhead, it is at 45° altitude. If the Sun reaches the point directly overhead, it is at 90° altitude. The Sun is directly overhead (90° altitude, or *zenith*) only at the *subsolar point*, where insolation is at a maximum. At all other surface points, the Sun is at a lower angle, producing more diffuse insolation.

The Sun's **declination** is the latitude of the subsolar point. Declination annually migrates through 47° of latitude, moving between the *Tropic of Cancer* at 23.5° N and the *Tropic of Capricorn* at 23.5° S latitude. Except Hawai'i, which is between 19° N and 22° N, the subsolar point does not reach the United States or Canada; all other states and provinces are too far north.

In addition to changing Sun altitude and declination, seasonality means changing **daylength**, or duration of exposure. Daylength varies during the year, depending on latitude. The equator always receives equal hours of day and night: If you live in Ecuador, Kenya, or Singapore, every day and night is 12 hours long, year-round. People living along 40° N latitude (Philadelphia, Denver, Madrid, Beijing), or 40° S latitude (Buenos Aires, Capetown, Melbourne), experience about 6 hours' difference in daylight between winter and summer. Those at 50° N or S latitude (Winnipeg, Paris, Falkland Islands) experience almost 8 hours of annual daylength variation.

At the North and South Poles, the range of daylength is extreme and extends from a 6-month period of no insolation (ranging from twilight to darkness to dawn) to a 6-month period of continuous 24-hour insolation (daylight)—literally the poles experience one long day and one long night each year! This is evident in Figure 2.14 (p. 56), if you note the illumination of the North Pole in June (to the left) and South Pole in December (to the right). Given this observation, turn to the back cover of this textbook and see whether you can determine the month during which the Apollo astronaut made the Earth photo. (The answer is on the copyright page.)

Reasons for Seasons

Seasons result from variations in the Sun's *altitude* above the horizon, the Sun's *declination* (latitude of the subsolar point), and *daylength* during the year. These in turn are created by several physical factors that operate in concert: Earth's *revolution* in orbit around the Sun, its daily *rotation* on its axis, its *tilted axis*, the unchanging *orientation of its axis*, and its *sphericity* (Table 2.1). Of course, the essential ingredient is having a single source of radiant energy—the Sun. We now look at each of these factors individually. As we do, please note the distinction between revolution—Earth's travel around the Sun—and rotation—Earth's spinning on its axis (Figure 2.12).

Revolution Earth's orbital **revolution** about the Sun is shown in Figure 2.1d. Earth's speed in orbit averages 107,280 kmph (66,660 mph). This speed, together with Earth's distance from the Sun, determines the time required for one revolution around the Sun and, therefore, the

Table 2.1 Five Reasons for Seasons

Factor	Description
Revolution	Orbit around the Sun; requires 365.24 days to complete at 107,280 kmph (66,660 mph)
Rotation	Earth turning on its axis; takes approximately 24 hours to complete at 1675 kmph (1041 mph) at the equator
Tilt	Axis is aligned at a 23.5° angle from a perpendicular to the plane of the ecliptic (the plane of Earth's orbit)
Axial parallelism	Remains in a fixed alignment, with Polaris directly overhead at the North Pole throughout the year
Sphericity	Appears as an oblate spheroid to the Sun's parallel rays; the geoid

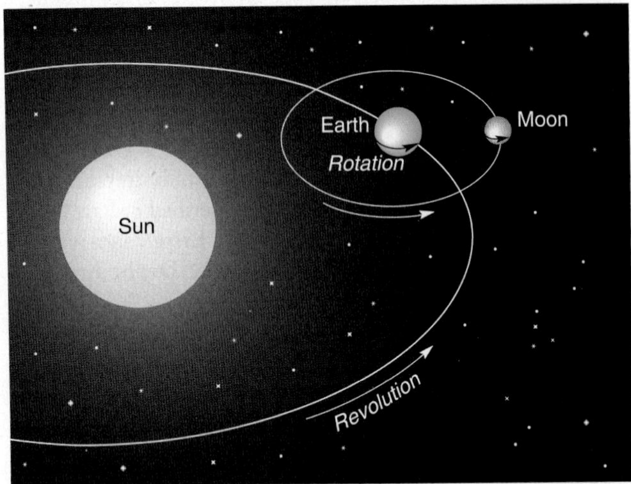

FIGURE 2.12 Earth's revolution and rotation. Earth's *revolution* about the Sun and *rotation* on its axis, as viewed from above Earth's orbit. Note the Moon's rotation on its axis and revolution about Earth are counterclockwise as well.

length of the year and duration of the seasons. Earth completes its annual revolution in 365.2422 days. This number is based on a *tropical year*, measured from equinox to equinox, or the elapsed time between two crossings of the equator by the Sun.

The Earth-to-Sun distance (aphelion to perihelion) might seem a seasonal factor, but it is not significant, even though it varies about 3% (4.8 million kilometres or 3 million miles) during the year, amounting to a 50 W/m^2 difference between local polar summers. Remember that the distance averages 150 million kilometres (93 million miles).

Rotation Earth's **rotation**, or turning on its axis, is a complex motion that averages 24 hours in duration. Rotation determines daylength, creates the apparent deflection of winds and ocean currents, and produces the twice-daily rise and fall of the ocean tides in relation to the gravitational pull of the Sun and the Moon.

Earth rotates about its **axis**, an imaginary line extending through the planet from the geographic North Pole to the South Pole. When viewed from above the North Pole, Earth rotates counterclockwise around this axis. Viewed from above the equator, Earth rotates west to east, or eastward. This eastward rotation creates the Sun's apparent westward daily journey from sunrise in the east to sunset in the west. Of course, the Sun actually remains in a fixed position in the centre of the Solar System. (Note in Figure 2.12 that the Moon both revolves around Earth and rotates on its axis in a counterclockwise direction.)

Although every point on Earth takes the same 24 hours to complete one rotation, the linear velocity of rotation at any point on Earth's surface varies dramatically with latitude. The equator is 40,075 km (24,902 mi) long; therefore, the rotational velocity at the equator must be approximately 1675 kmph (1041 mph) to cover that distance in one day. At 60° latitude, a parallel is only half the length of the equator, or 20,038 km (12,451 mi) long, so the rotational velocity there is 838 kmph (521 mph). At the poles, the velocity is 0. (This variation in rotational velocity establishes the effect of the Coriolis force, discussed in Chapter 6.) Table 2.2 lists the speed of rotation for several selected latitudes.

Earth's rotation produces the continually changing daily pattern of day and night. Half of Earth is in sunlight and half is in darkness at any moment. The travelling boundary that divides daylight and darkness is called the **circle of illumination** (as illustrated in Figure 2.14). Because this day-night dividing circle of illumination is a great circle that intersects the equator, which is another great circle, daylength at the equator is always evenly divided—12 hours of day and 12 hours of night. (Any two great circles on a sphere bisect one another.)

A true day varies slightly from 24 hours, but by international agreement a day is defined as exactly 24 hours, or 86,400 seconds. This average, called *mean solar time*, eliminates predictable variations in rotation and revolution that cause the solar day to change slightly in length throughout the year. The complexity of Earth's rotation is now exactly measured by satellites that are in precise mathematical orbits: GPS (global positioning system, see News Report 1.1, Chapter 1), SLR (satellite-laser ranging), and VLBI (very-long baseline interferometry). All contribute to our knowledge of Earth's rotation. (Monthly and annual reports are issued by the International Earth Rotation Service at http://www.iers.org/.) Earth's rotation is gradually slowing, partially owing to the drag of lunar tidal forces. A "day" on Earth today is many hours longer than a "day" 4 billion years ago.

Tilt of Earth's Axis To understand Earth's **axial tilt**, imagine a plane (a flat surface) that intersects Earth's ellip-

Table 2.2 Speed of Rotation at Selected Latitudes

Latitude	Speed kmph	(mph)	Cities at Approximate Latitudes
90°	0	(0)	North Pole
60°	838	(521)	Seward, Alaska; Oslo, Norway; Saint Petersburg, Russia
50°	1078	(670)	Chibougamau, Québec; Kyyîv (Kiev), Ukraine
40°	1284	(798)	Valdivia, Chile; Columbus, Ohio; Beijing, China
30°	1452	(902)	Pôrto Alegre, Brazil; New Orleans, Louisiana
0°	1675	(1041)	Quito, Ecuador; Pontianak, Indonesia

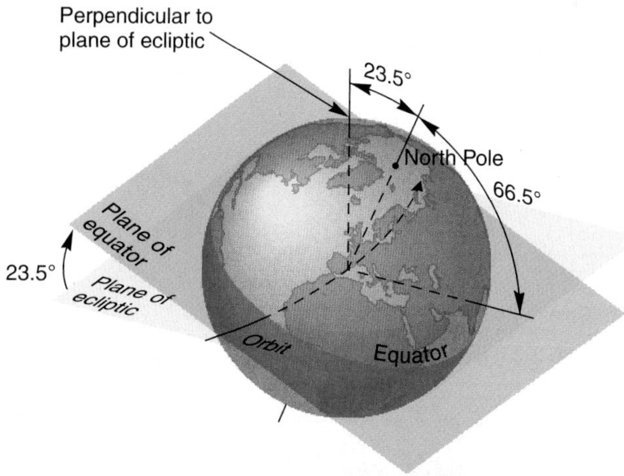

FIGURE 2.13 The plane of Earth's orbit—the ecliptic—and Earth's axial tilt.
Note that the plane of the equator is inclined at 23.5° to the plane of the ecliptic.

tical orbit about the Sun, with half of the Sun and Earth above the plane and half below. This flat surface is termed the *plane of the ecliptic*. Now, imagine a perpendicular (at a 90° angle) line passing through the plane. Earth's axis and equatorial plane are tilted 23.5° from this perpendicular to the plane of the ecliptic. Another way of looking at it is that Earth's axis forms a 66.5° angle from the plane itself (Figure 2.13).

This text uses "about" with the tilt angle just described because Earth's axial tilt changes over a complex 40,000-year cycle (see Figure 17.31). The axial tilt ranges roughly between 22° and 24.5° from a perpendicular to the plane of the ecliptic. The present tilt is 23° 27′ (or 66° 33′ from the plane). In decimal numbers, 23° 27′ is approximately 23.45°. For convenience this is rounded off to a 23.5° tilt (or 66.5° from the plane) in our discussion. Scientific evidence shows that the angle of tilt is lessening in the 40,000-year cycle.

Hypothetically, if Earth were tilted on its side, with its axis parallel to the plane of the ecliptic, we would experience a maximum variation in seasons worldwide. On the other hand, if Earth's axis were perpendicular to the plane of its orbit—that is, with no tilt—we would experience no seasonal changes, just a perpetual spring or fall season, and all latitudes would experience 12-hour days and nights.

Axial Parallelism Throughout our annual journey around the Sun, Earth's axis *maintains the same alignment* relative to the plane of the ecliptic and to Polaris and other stars. You can see this consistent alignment in Figure 2.14. If we compared the axis in different months, it would always appear parallel to itself, a condition known as **axial parallelism**.

Sphericity Earth's *sphericity*, discussed in Chapter 1, is also part of seasonality, for it produces the uneven receipt of insolation from pole to pole shown in Figures 2.9 and 2.10. All five reasons for seasons are summarized in Table 2.1: revolution, rotation, tilt, axial parallelism, and sphericity.

Now, considering all these factors operating together, let us examine the annual march of the seasons.

Annual March of the Seasons

During the annual march of the seasons on Earth, daylength is the most obvious way of sensing changes in season at latitudes away from the equator. Daylength is the interval between **sunrise**, the moment when the disk of the Sun first appears above the horizon in the east, and **sunset**, that moment when it totally disappears below the horizon in the west. Table 2.3 lists the average times of sunrise and sunset and the daylength for various latitudes and seasons in the Northern Hemisphere. (For the Southern Hemisphere, merely switch the solstice column headings and switch the equinox column headings.)

The extremes of daylength occur in December and June. The times around December 21 and June 21 are termed *solstices*. Strictly speaking, however, the solstices are specific points in time at which the Sun's declination is at its position farthest north (Tropic of Cancer at 23.5° N) or south (Tropic of Capricorn at 23.5° S). "Tropic" is from *tropicus*, meaning a turn or change, so a tropic latitude is where the Sun's declination appears to stand still briefly (Sun stance, or *sol stice*); then it "turns" and heads toward the other tropic.

Table 2.4 presents the key seasonal anniversary dates with the specific times the equinoxes or solstices occur, their names, and the subsolar point locations (declinations). During the year, places on Earth outside of the equatorial region experience a continuous but gradual shift in daylength, a few minutes each day, and the Sun's altitude increases or decreases a small amount. You may have noticed that these daily variations become more pronounced in spring and autumn, when the Sun's declination changes at a faster rate.

Figure 2.14 demonstrates the annual march of the seasons and illustrates Earth's relationship to the Sun during

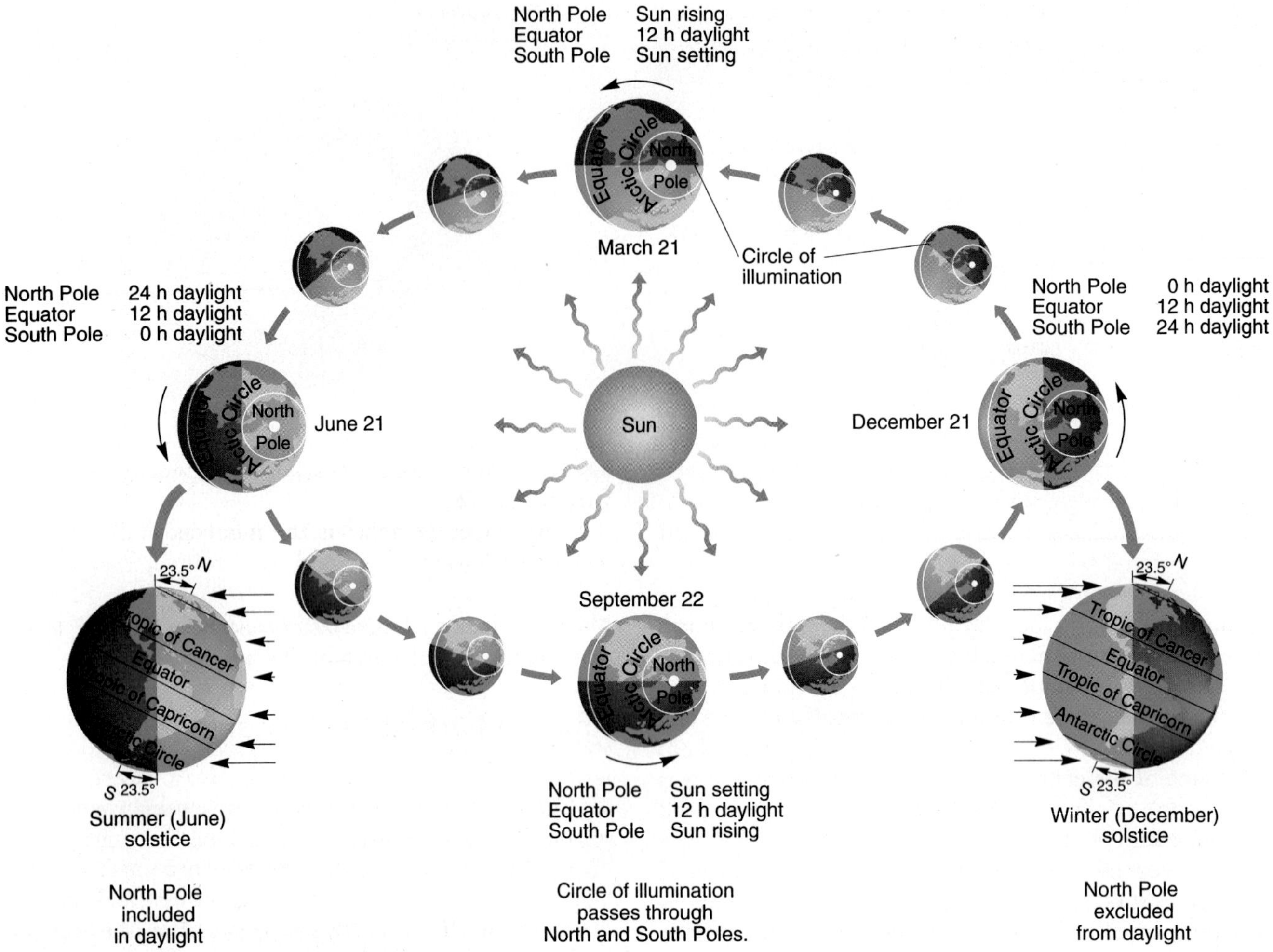

North Pole Sun rising
Equator 12 h daylight
South Pole Sun setting

March 21

Circle of illumination

North Pole 24 h daylight
Equator 12 h daylight
South Pole 0 h daylight

June 21

Sun

December 21

North Pole 0 h daylight
Equator 12 h daylight
South Pole 24 h daylight

September 22

Summer (June) solstice

North Pole Sun setting
Equator 12 h daylight
South Pole Sun rising

Winter (December) solstice

North Pole included in daylight

Circle of illumination passes through North and South Poles.

North Pole excluded from daylight

FIGURE 2.14 Annual march of the seasons.
Annual march of the seasons as Earth revolves about the Sun. Shading indicates the changing position of the circle of illumination. Note the hours of daylight for the equator and the poles. To follow the text, begin on the right side at December 21 and move counterclockwise.

Earth–Sun Relations, Seasons

the year. Let us begin with December. On December 21 or 22, at the moment of the **winter solstice** ("winter Sun stance"), or **December solstice**, the circle of illumination excludes the North Pole region from sunlight but includes the South Pole region. The subsolar point is at 23.5° S latitude, the parallel called the Tropic of Capricorn. The Northern Hemisphere is tilted away from these more direct rays of sunlight—our northern winter—thereby creating a lower angle for the incoming solar rays and thus a more diffuse pattern of insolation.

Table 2.3 Daylength Times (Sunrise and Sunset) at Selected Latitudes (Northern Hemisphere)

Latitude	Winter Solstice (December Solstice) December 21–22			Vernal Equinox (March Equinox) March 20–21			Summer Solstice (June Solstice) June 20–21			Autumnal Equinox (September Equinox) September 22–23		
	A.M.	P.M.	Daylength	A.M.	P.M.	Daylength	A.M.	P.M.	Daylength	A.M.	P.M.	Daylength
0°	6:00	6:00	12:00	6:00	6:00	12:00	6:00	6:00	12:00	6:00	6:00	12:00
30°	6:58	5:02	10:04	6:00	6:00	12:00	5:02	6:58	13:56	6:00	6:00	12:00
40°	7:30	4:30	9:00	6:00	6:00	12:00	4:30	7:30	15:00	6:00	6:00	12:00
50°	8:05	3:55	7:50	6:00	6:00	12:00	3:55	8:05	16:10	6:00	6:00	12:00
60°	9:15	2:45	5:30	6:00	6:00	12:00	2:45	9:15	18:30	6:00	6:00	12:00
90°	No sunlight			Rising Sun			Continuous sunlight			Setting Sun		

Note: All times are standard and do not consider the local option of daylight saving time.

Table 2.4 Annual March of the Seasons

Approximate Date	Northern Hemisphere Name	Location of the Subsolar Point
December 21–22	Winter solstice (December solstice)	23.5° S latitude (Tropic of Capricorn)
March 20–21	Vernal equinox (March equinox)	0° (equator)
June 20–21	Summer solstice (June solstice)	23.5° N latitude (Tropic of Cancer)
September 22–23	Autumnal equinox (September equinox)	0° (equator)

From 66.5° N latitude to 90° N (the North Pole), the Sun remains below the horizon the entire day. This latitude (66.5° N) marks the *Arctic Circle*, the southernmost parallel (in the Northern Hemisphere) that experiences a 24-hour period of darkness or near darkness in twilight conditions in the region. During the following 3 months, daylength and solar angles gradually increase in the Northern Hemisphere as Earth completes one-quarter of its orbit.

The moment of the **vernal equinox**, or **March equinox**, occurs on March 20 or 21. At that time, the circle of illumination passes through both poles so that all locations on Earth experience a 12-hour day and a 12-hour night. People living around 40° N latitude (New York, Denver) have gained 3 hours of daylight since the December solstice. At the North Pole, the Sun peeks above the horizon for the first time since the previous September; at the South Pole the Sun is setting—a dramatic moment for the people working there.

From March, the seasons move on to June 20 or 21 and the moment of the **summer solstice**, or **June solstice**. The subsolar point now has shifted from the equator to 23.5° N latitude, the Tropic of Cancer. Because the circle of illumination now includes the North Polar region, everything north of the Arctic Circle receives 24 hours of daylight—the "midnight Sun." Figure 2.15 is a multiple-image photo of the midnight Sun as seen north of the Arctic Circle. In contrast, the region from the Antarctic Circle to the South Pole (66.5°–90° S latitude) is in darkness the entire 24 hours. Those working in Antarctica call this *Midwinter's Day*.

September 22 or 23 is the moment in time of the **autumnal equinox**, or **September equinox**, when Earth's orientation is such that the circle of illumination again passes through both poles so that all parts of the globe experience a 12-hour day and a 12-hour night. The subsolar point has returned to the equator, with days growing shorter to the north and longer to the south. Researchers stationed at the South Pole see the disk of the Sun just rising, ending their 6 months of darkness. In the Northern Hemisphere, autumn arrives, a time of many colourful changes in the landscape, whereas in the Southern Hemisphere it is spring.

Dawn and Twilight *Dawn* is the period of diffused light that occurs before sunrise. The corresponding evening period after sunset is *twilight*. During both periods, light is scattered by molecules of atmospheric gases and reflected by dust and moisture illuminating the atmosphere. The

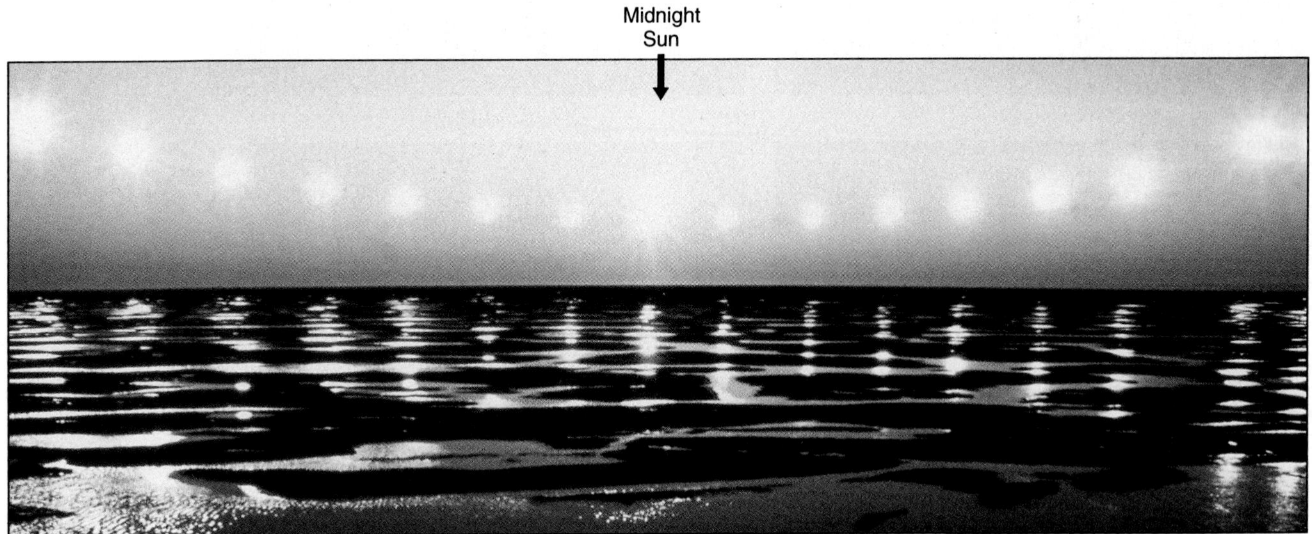

FIGURE 2.15 The midnight Sun.
The midnight Sun north of the Arctic Circle captured in a series of 18 exposures on the same piece of film. The camera is facing due north. Midnight is the exposure showing the Sun closest to the horizon. The photographer removed the lens cap at regular intervals to make the multiple exposures. [Photo by Gary Braasch/Tony Stone Images.]

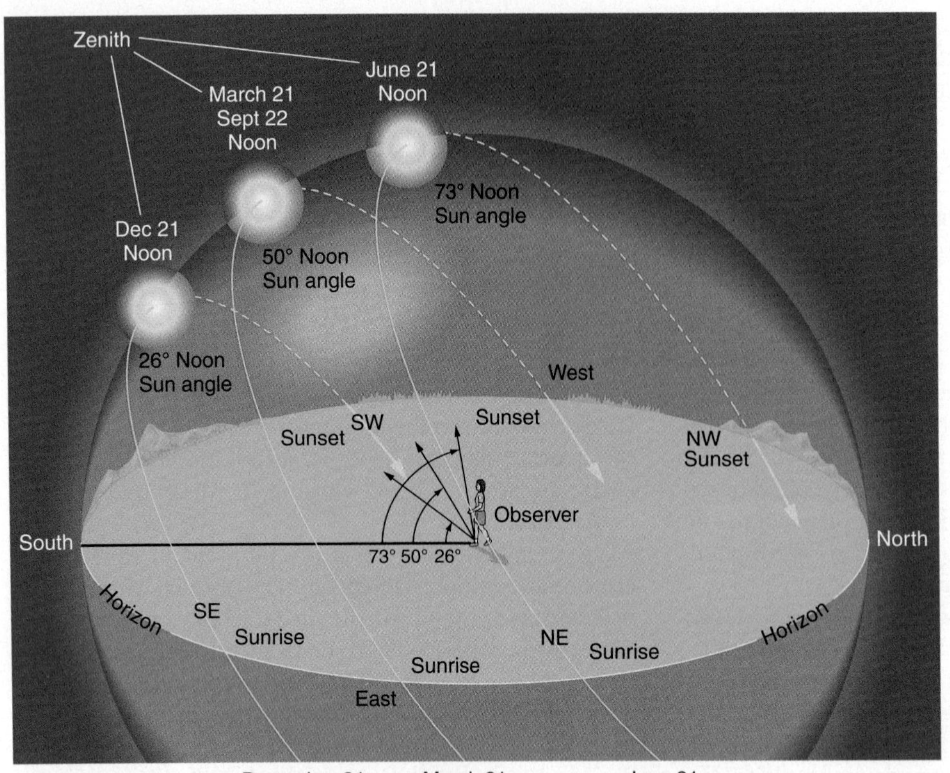

FIGURE 2.16 Seasonal observations—sunrise, noon, and sunset through the year. Seasonal observations are at 40° N latitude for the December solstice, March equinox, June solstice, and September equinox. The Sun's altitude increases from 26° in December to 73° above the horizon in June—a difference of 47°. Note the changing position of sunrise and sunset along the horizon during the year. For a useful sunrise and sunset calculator for any location, go to http://www.srrb.noaa.gov/highlights/sunrise/sunrise.html.

FIGURE 2.17 The four seasons.
Seasonality produces dramatic change in the leaves of an ornamental pear tree (*Pyrus calleryana*) in January, April, July, and November. [Photos by Robert W. Christopherson.]

duration of both is a function of latitude, because the angle of the Sun's path above the horizon determines the thickness of the atmosphere through which the Sun's rays must pass. This effect may be enhanced by the presence of pollution aerosols and suspended particles from volcanic eruptions or forest and grassland fires.

At the equator, where the Sun's rays are almost directly above the horizon throughout the year, dawn and twilight are limited to 30–45 minutes each. These times increase to 1–2 hours each at 40° latitude, and at 60° latitude they each range upward from 2.5 hours, with little true night in summer. The poles experience about 7 weeks of dawn and 7 weeks of twilight, leaving only 2.5 months of darkness during the 6 months when the Sun is completely below the horizon. In the high latitudes this extended period of diffused light produces beautiful colours.

Seasonal Observations In the midlatitudes of the Northern Hemisphere, the position of sunrise on the horizon migrates from day to day, from the southeast in December to the northeast in June. Over the same period, the point of sunset migrates from the southwest to the northwest. The Sun's altitude at local noon at 40° N latitude increases from a 26° angle above the horizon at the winter (December) solstice to a 73° angle above the horizon at the summer (June) solstice—a range of 47° (Figure 2.16).

Seasonal change is quite noticeable across the landscape away from the equator, as shown by the four photos in Figure 2.17. Figure 2.18 presents two composite images of vegetation cover in winter and late summer as recorded by the AVHRR sensors aboard polar-orbiting satellites. Recently, the timing of the seasons is changing as global climates shift in middle and high latitudes. Spring and leafing out is occurring as much as two weeks earlier than expected from average conditions. Think back over the past year. What seasonal changes have you observed in vegetation, temperatures, and weather?

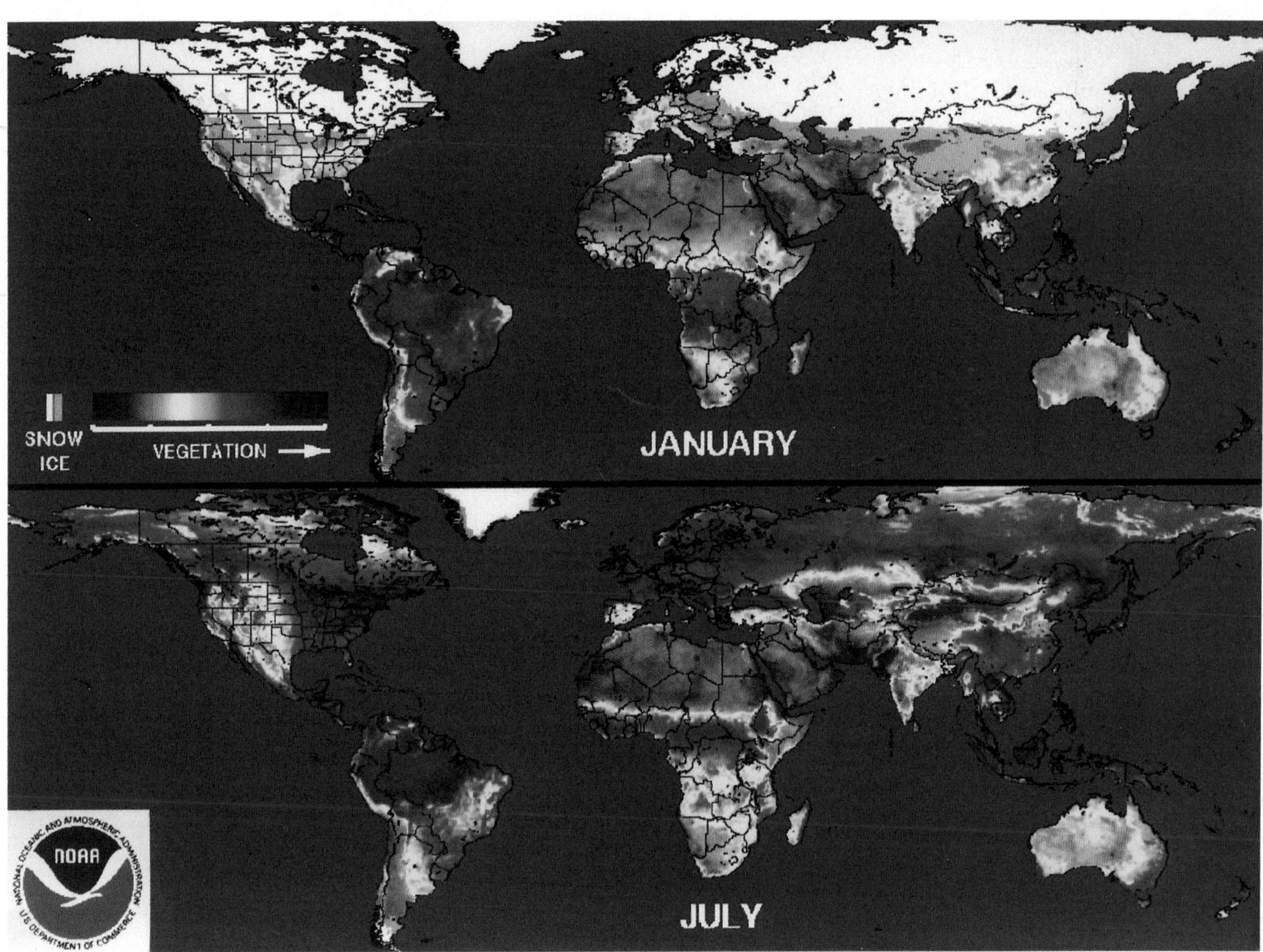

FIGURE 2.18 Seasonal change from orbit.
Seasonal change is monitored and measured by sensors aboard polar-orbiting satellites. Compare and contrast similar regions for January and July: central Canada, China, Argentina, and Europe. Orbital remote sensing is tracking an earlier spring season worldwide. [Images courtesy of Garik Gutman, NOAA, National Environmental Satellite, Data, and Information Service.]

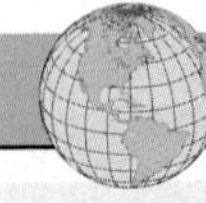

Applied Physical Geography

Calculating the Energy from Sunlight over a 12-Hour Period*

How much energy does any spot on Earth receive over the span of a 12-hour day? How does this vary by season?

Recall that the solar constant, 1372 W/m^2 (expressed in milliwatts as 137.2 mW/cm^2), is a measure of power per unit area at high noon with the Sun directly overhead (as would occur at the equator or in the tropics). The energy from the sunlight can be extracted from this number.

First, remembering that 1 watt is equal to 1 joule per second, if we take energy in mJ (millijoules), from the units alone we obtain

$$mJ = (mW/cm^2) \times (\text{Area in } cm^2) \times (\text{Time in seconds})$$

(since mW = mJ/second). If the Sun were always directly overhead, the amount of energy incident upon a 1-cm^2 solar collector oriented perpendicular to the sun's rays in 12 hours would be

$$(137.2\ mW/cm^2) \times (1\ cm^2) \times (12\ hours)$$
$$= (137.2\ mW/cm^2) \times (1\ cm^2) \times (4.3 \times 10^4\ seconds)$$
$$= 5.93 \times 10^6\ mJ\ .$$

Because of Earth's rotation and orbit around the sun, however, the Sun appears to move East–West throughout the course of a day and North–South throughout the course of a year. This yearly variation can be accounted for. We know that the Sun moves ± 23.5° above and below the equator between the two tropics over the course of a year. Typically, it is on the equator every March 21 and September 21. We may estimate θ, the Sun's position north of the π equator, by calculating

$$\theta = 23.5° \sin (2\{\delta T/365.25\})$$

where δT is the number of days counted from the vernal equinox (April 21). (Notice that for northern winter months, θ is negative). We may then estimate the solar constant for any particular day by calculating

$$\sigma_D = (137.2\ mW/cm^2) \cos (L - \theta)$$

where L is latitude in degrees.

The daily variation is a little more involved. Let the Sun be at altitude A (angle above the eastern horizon) at a given time t during the day. Then at time $t + \delta T$, the altitude will have increased to A + δA. The differential time is related to the differential altitude by

$$\delta T = (12/\pi)\ \delta A\ h$$

because the Sun travels through π radians (180°) in 12 hours.

If we again try to calculate the amount of energy incident upon a 1 cm^2 solar collector oriented perpendicular to the Sun's noon-time rays in 12 hours, we have to use

$$\text{Area} = (\sin A)\ cm^2$$

for the equivalent collecting area as we want only the amount of area projected perpendicular to the Sun's rays at time t. The differential energy (δE) incident upon our solar collector in time δT is

$$\delta E = \sigma_D (\sin A)\ \delta T$$
$$= \sigma_D (\sin A)\ (12/\pi)\ (3600\ seconds/hour)\ \delta A$$
$$= \sigma_D (4.3 \times 10^4\ seconds/\pi)\ [(\sin A)\ \delta A]\ .$$

The expression in square brackets may be integrated from A = 0 to A = π to yield

$$E = \sigma_D (4.3 \times 10^4\ seconds/\pi)\ .$$

If, for comparison, we set σ_D = 137 mW/cm^2 (i.e., if we were to take our collector to the tropics), we find

$$E = 3.7 \times 10^6\ mJ\ .$$

The ratio between this value and the one derived above is 2/π. At latitude 42° N, for example, the midsummer value is

$$E = 1.8 \times 10^6\ mJ$$

and the midwinter value is

$$E = 7.2 \times 10^5\ mJ\ .$$

The ratio of the midwinter to the midsummer values is

$$(7.2 \times 10^5\ mJ)/(1.8 \times 10^6\ mJ) = 0.4,$$

which means that over a 12-hour period at this latitude, the solar collector receives a mere 40% of the energy in midwinter that it would in midsummer.

*Modified from http://www.lerc.nasa.gov/WWW/K-12/Numbers/Math/Mathematical_Thinking/sun12.htm, by Joe Kolecki, Glenn Learning Technologies Project/NASA.

Summary and Review—Solar Energy to Earth and the Seasons

● ***Distinguish*** **among galaxies, stars, and planets and** ***locate*** **Earth.**

Our Solar System—Sun and nine planets—is located on a remote, trailing edge of the **Milky Way Galaxy**, a flattened, disk-shaped mass estimated to contain up to 400 billion stars. **Gravity**, the mutual attracting force exerted by the mass of an object upon all other objects, is an organizing force in the Universe. The process of suns (stars) condensing from nebular clouds with planetesimals (protoplanets) forming in orbits around their central masses is the **planetesimal hypothesis**.

Milky Way Galaxy (p. 43)
gravity (p. 44)
planetesimal hypothesis (p. 44)

1. Describe the Sun's status among the stars in the Milky Way Galaxy. Describe the Sun's location, size, and relationship to its planets.

2. If you have seen the Milky Way at night, briefly describe it. Use specifics from the text in your description.
3. Briefly describe Earth's origin as part of the Solar System.
4. Compare the locations of the nine planets of the Solar System.

Overview the origin, formation, and development of Earth and *construct* Earth's annual orbit about the Sun.

The Solar System, planets, and Earth began to condense from a nebular cloud of dust, gas, debris, and icy comets approximately 4.6 billion years ago. Distances in space are so vast that the **speed of light** (300,000 kmps, or 186,000 mps, which is about 9.5 trillion kilometres, or nearly 6 trillion miles, per year) is used to express distance.

In its orbit, Earth is at **perihelion** (its closest position to the Sun) during our Northern Hemisphere winter (January 3 at 147,255,000 km, or 91,500,000 mi). It is at **aphelion** (its farthest position from the Sun) during our Northern Hemisphere summer (July 4 at 152,083,000 km, or 94,500,000 mi). Earth's average distance from the Sun is approximately 8 minutes and 20 seconds in terms of light speed. In the Solar System, an imaginary plane touching all points of Earth's orbit is termed the **plane of the ecliptic**.

speed of light (p. 44)
perihelion (p. 44)
aphelion (p. 44)
plane of the ecliptic (p. 44)

5. How far is Earth from the Sun in terms of light speed? In terms of kilometres and miles?
6. Briefly describe the relationship among these concepts: Universe, Milky Way Galaxy, Solar System, Sun, and Planet Earth.
7. Diagram in a simple sketch Earth's orbit about the Sun. How much does it vary during the course of a year?

Describe the Sun's operation and *explain* the characteristics of the solar wind and the electromagnetic spectrum of radiant energy.

The **fusion** process—hydrogen atoms forced together under tremendous temperature and pressure in the Sun's interior—generates incredible quantities of energy. The Sun's most conspicuous features are large **sunspots**, caused by magnetic disturbances. Solar energy in the form of charged particles of **solar wind** travels out in all directions from disturbances on the Sun. Solar wind is deflected by Earth's **magnetosphere**, producing various effects in the upper atmosphere, including spectacular **auroras**, the northern and southern lights, which surge across the skies at higher latitudes. Another effect of the solar wind in the atmosphere is its possible influence on weather.

The **electromagnetic spectrum** of radiant energy travels outward in all directions from the Sun. The total spectrum of this radiant energy is made up of different **wavelengths**—the distance between corresponding points on any two successive waves of radiant energy. Eventually some of this radiant energy reaches Earth's surface.

fusion (p. 44)
solar wind (p. 46)
sunspots (p. 46)
magnetosphere (p. 46)
auroras (p. 46)
electromagnetic spectrum (p. 48)
wavelength (p. 48)

8. How does the Sun produce such tremendous quantities of energy?
9. What is the sunspot cycle? At what stage was the cycle in the year 2001?
10. Describe Earth's magnetosphere and its effects on the solar wind and the electromagnetic spectrum.
11. Summarize the presently known effects of the solar wind relative to Earth's environment.
12. Describe the various segments of the electromagnetic spectrum, from shortest to longest wavelength. What are the main wavelengths produced by the Sun? Which are principally radiated by Earth to space?

Portray the intercepted solar energy and its uneven distribution at the top of the atmosphere.

Electromagnetic radiation from the Sun passes through Earth's magnetic field to the top of the atmosphere—the **thermopause**—at approximately 480 km (300 mi) altitude. Solar radiation that reaches a horizontal plane at Earth is called **insolation**, a term specifically applied to radiation arriving at Earth's surface and atmosphere. Insolation at the top of the atmosphere is expressed as the **solar constant**: the average insolation received at the thermopause when Earth is at its average distance from the Sun. The solar constant is measured as 1372 W/m^2 (2.0 cal/cm^2/min; 2 langleys/min). The place receiving maximum insolation is the **subsolar point**, where solar rays are perpendicular to the surface (radiating from directly overhead). All other locations away from the subsolar point receive slanting rays and more diffuse energy.

thermopause (p. 49)
insolation (*in*coming *sol*ar radi*ation*) (p. 49)
solar constant (p. 50)
subsolar point (p. 50)

13. What is the solar constant? Why is it important to know?
14. Select 40° or 60° north latitude on Figure 2.10 and plot the amount of energy in watts per square metre (W/m^2) per day on a graph for each month throughout the year. Compare this with the amount at the North Pole and at the equator.
15. If Earth were flat and oriented perpendicularly to incoming solar radiation (insolation), what would be the latitudinal distribution of solar energy at the top of the atmosphere?

Define solar altitude, solar declination, and daylength and *describe* the annual variability of each—Earth's seasonality.

The angle between the Sun and the horizon is the Sun's **altitude**. The Sun's **declination** is the latitude of the subsolar point. Declination annually migrates through 47° of latitude, moving between the *Tropic of Cancer* at 23.5° N (June) and the *Tropic of Capricorn* at 23.5° S latitude (December). Seasonality means an annual change in the Sun's altitude and changing **daylength**, or duration of exposure.

Earth's distinct seasons are produced by interactions of **revolution** (annual orbit about the Sun), **rotation** (turning on the axis), **axial tilt** (23.5° from a perpendicular to the plane of the ecliptic), **axial parallelism** (the parallel alignment of the axis throughout the year), and sphericity. Earth rotates about its **axis**, an imaginary line extending through the planet from the geographic North Pole to the South Pole. As it rotates, the travelling boundary that divides daylight and darkness is called the **circle of illumination**. Earth's **axial tilt** is 23.5° from a perpendicular to the plane of the ecliptic and it remains oriented to the stars in the same direction throughout the year, or axial parallelism. Daylength is the interval between **sunrise**, the moment when the disk of the Sun first appears above the horizon in the east, and **sunset**, the moment when it totally disappears below the horizon in the west.

On December 21 or 22, at the moment of the **winter solstice** ("winter Sun stance"), or **December solstice**, the circle of illumination excludes the North Pole but includes the South Pole. The subsolar point is at 23.5° S latitude, the parallel called the Tropic of Capricorn. The moment of the **vernal equinox**, or **March equinox**, occurs on March 20 or 21. At that time, the circle of illumination passes through both poles so that all locations on Earth experience a 12-hour day and a 12-hour night.

June 20 or 21 is the moment of the **summer solstice**, or **June solstice**. The subsolar point now has shifted from the equator to 23.5° N latitude, the Tropic of Cancer. Because the circle of illumination now includes the North Polar region, everything north of the Arctic Circle receives 24 hours of daylight—the "midnight Sun." September 22 or 23 is the time of the **autumnal equinox**, or **September equinox**, when Earth's orientation is such that the circle of illumination again passes through both poles so that all parts of the globe experience a 12-hour day and a 12-hour night.

altitude (p. 53)
declination (p. 53)
daylength (p. 53)
revolution (p. 53)
rotation (p. 54)
axis (p. 54)
circle of illumination (p. 54)
axial tilt (p. 54)
axial parallelism (p. 55)
sunrise (p. 55)
sunset (p. 55)
winter solstice, December solstice (p. 56)
vernal equinox, March equinox (p. 57)
summer solstice, June solstice (p. 57)
autumnal equinox, September equinox (p. 57)

16. The concept of seasonality refers to what specific phenomena? How do these two aspects of seasonality change during a year at 0° latitude? At 40°? At 90°?
17. Differentiate between the Sun's altitude and its declination at Earth's surface.
18. For the latitude at which you live, how does daylength vary during the year? How does the Sun's altitude vary? Does your local newspaper publish a weather calendar containing such information?
19. List the five physical factors that operate together to produce seasons.
20. Describe Earth's revolution and rotation, and differentiate between them.
21. Define Earth's present tilt relative to its orbit about the Sun.
22. Describe seasonal conditions at each of the four key seasonal anniversary dates during the year. What are the solstices and equinoxes, and what is the Sun's declination at these times?

Critical Thinking

A. Using the concepts in Figure 2.16, use a protractor and stick or ruler to measure the angle of the Sun's altitude at noon (or 1 P.M., if in daylight saving time). Do not look at the Sun; rather, with your back to the Sun, align the stick so that it casts no shadow as you measure its rays against the protractor. Record this measurement in your notebook and affix a sticky note in the textbook to remind you to repeat the measurement near the end of the semester. Compare and analyze seasonal change using your different measurements of the Sun's altitude.

B. Also, in reference to the concepts in Figure 2.16, post a reminder in your notebook to check the position of sunrise and sunset at least twice during the semester. If you have a magnetic compass, note the degrees from north for sunrise and sunset (*azimuth* is read from north in a clockwise direction—0° and 360° being the same point, north). Find some place where you can see the horizon. If you are new to such observations, you will be surprised at the degree of location change over the span of months in a school term.

C. The variability of Earth's axial tilt, orbit about the Sun, and wobble to the axis is described in Figure 17.31. Please refer to this figure and compare these changing conditions to the information in Table 2.1 and the related figures in this chapter. Speculate on the effects of these changes on the annual march of the seasons.

Rain clouds over the upper Midwest cast shadows toward a full-Moon rise. Some of the droplets trailing from the clouds are virga, which evaporate before reaching the ground. Such scenes are the continuous beauty of our atmosphere, yet the atmosphere provides important functions that protect and sustain our lives. [Photo by Bobbé Christopherson.]

3 Earth's Modern Atmosphere

Key Learning Concepts

After reading the chapter, you should be able to:

- *Construct* a general model of the atmosphere based on the criteria of composition, temperature, and function, and *diagram* this model in a simple sketch.
- *List* the stable components of the modern atmosphere and their relative percentage contributions by volume, and *describe* each.
- *Describe* the conditions within the stratosphere; specifically, *review* the function and status of the ozonosphere (ozone layer).
- *Distinguish* between natural and anthropogenic variable gases and materials in the lower atmosphere.
- *Describe* the sources and effects of carbon monoxide, nitrogen dioxide, and sulphur dioxide, and *construct* a simple equation that illustrates photochemical reactions that produce ozone, peroxyacetyl nitrates, nitric acid, and sulphuric acid.

Earth's atmosphere is a unique reservoir of gases, the product of nearly 5 billion years of development. It sustains us and protects us from hostile radiation and particles from the Sun and beyond—the atmosphere serves as an efficient filter. When astronauts work in space, they must wear bulky spacesuits that do everything to sustain and protect them that the atmosphere does for us all the time.

In this chapter: We examine the modern atmosphere through its composition, temperature, and function. Our consideration of the atmosphere also includes the spatial aspects of human-induced inputs, such as air pollution. We all participate in the atmosphere with each breath we take, the energy we consume, the travelling we do, and the products we buy. Human activities caused the stratospheric ozone predicament and the blight of acid deposition on the landscape. These topics are essential, for we are influencing the atmosphere of the future.

Atmospheric Composition, Temperature, and Function

The *modern* atmosphere probably is the fourth general atmosphere in Earth's history. Therefore, this modern atmosphere is a gaseous mixture of ancient origin, the sum of all the exhalations and inhalations of life on Earth throughout time. The principal substance of this atmosphere is air, the medium of life as well as a major industrial and chemical raw material. *Air* is a simple mixture of gases that is naturally odourless, colourless, tasteless, and formless, blended so thoroughly that it behaves as if it were a single gas.

In his book *The Lives of a Cell*, the late physician and self-styled "biology watcher" Lewis Thomas compared the atmosphere of Earth to an enormous cell membrane. The membrane around a cell regulates the interactions between the cell's delicate inner workings and the potentially disruptive outer environment. Each cell membrane is very selective as to what it will allow to pass through. The modern atmosphere acts as Earth's protective membrane, as Thomas described so vividly (Figure 3.1).

As a practical matter, we consider the top of our atmosphere to be around 480 km (300 mi) above Earth's surface, the same altitude we used in Chapter 2 for measuring the solar constant and insolation receipt. Beyond that altitude, the atmosphere is rarefied (nearly a vacuum) and is called the **exosphere**, which means "outer sphere." It contains scarce lightweight hydrogen and helium atoms, weakly bound by gravity as far as 32,000 km (20,000 mi) from Earth.

Atmospheric Profile

Earth's modern atmosphere is in a series of imperfectly shaped concentric "shells" or "spheres" that grade into one another, all bound to the planet by gravity. As critical as the atmosphere is to us, it represents only the thinnest envelope, amounting to less than one-millionth of Earth's total mass. We study the atmosphere by viewing it in layers that have distinctive properties and purposes. Figure 3.2 charts essential aspects of the atmosphere in a vertical cross section, or side view, and is key to the following discussion. We simplify this complexity by using three atmospheric criteria: *composition*, *temperature*, and *function*—noted along the left side of Figure 3.2a, with the relations among the criteria detailed in Table 3.1.

Earth's atmosphere exerts its weight, pressing downward under the pull of gravity. Air molecules create air pressure through their motion, size, and number. Pressure is exerted on all surfaces in contact with the air. The weight (force over a unit area) of the atmosphere, or **air pressure**,

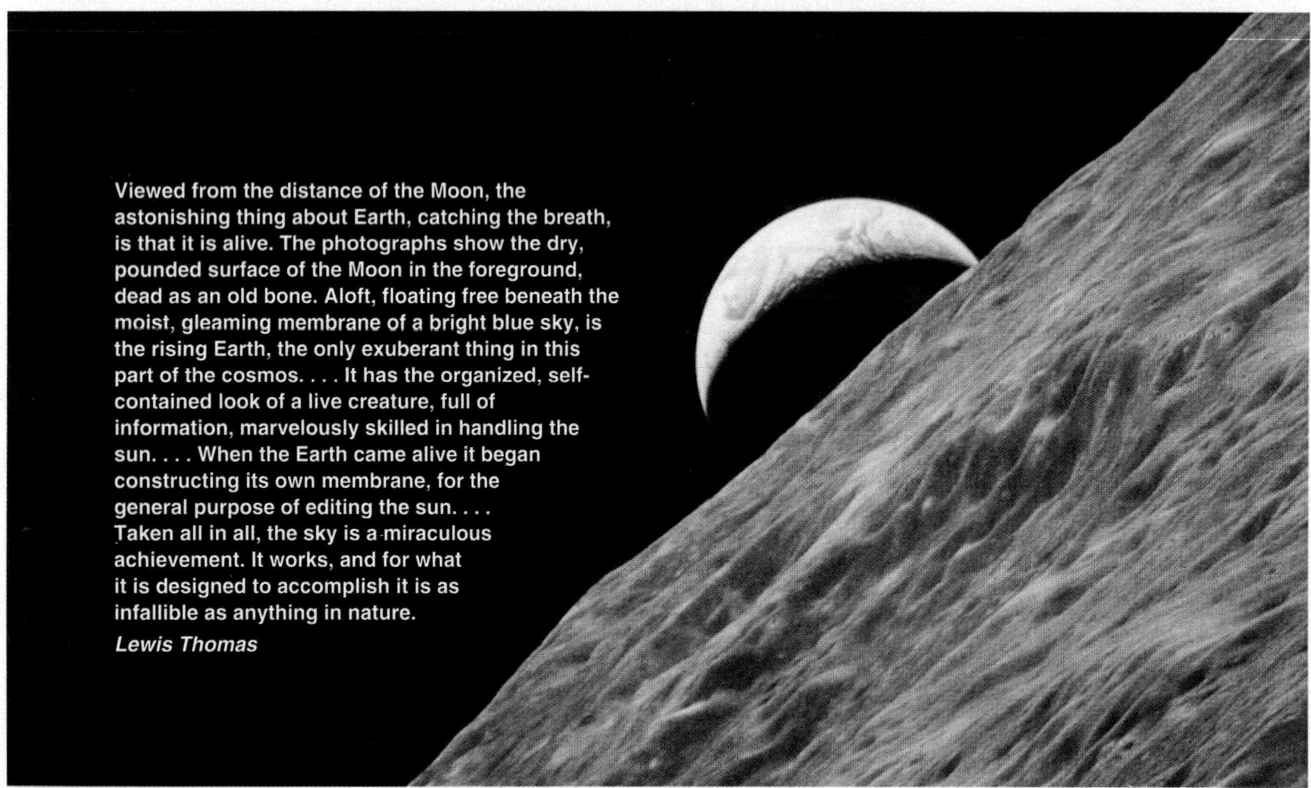

FIGURE 3.1 Earthrise.
Earthrise over the stark and lifeless lunar surface. [Photo by NASA; quotation from "The World's Biggest Membrane" from *The Lives of a Cell* by Lewis Thomas. Copyright © 1973 by the Massachusetts Medical Society. Originally published in the *New England Journal of Medicine*. Reprinted by permission of Viking Penguin, a division of Penguin Books USA, Inc.]

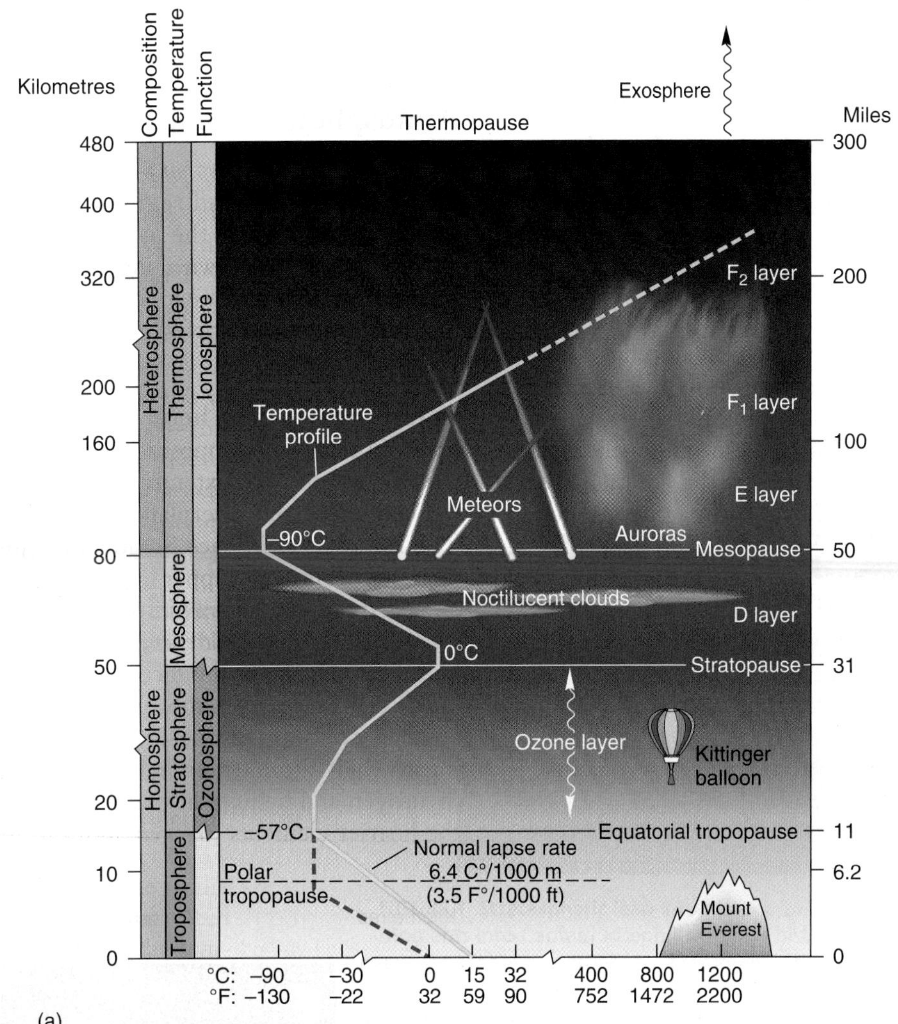

FIGURE 3.2 Profile of the modern atmosphere.
(a) An integrated chart of our modern atmosphere. The chart spans the atmosphere from Earth's surface to the top of the atmosphere at 480 km (300 mi). The columns on the left side show the division of the atmosphere by composition, temperature, and function. The plot of temperature and the scale along the bottom permit you to tell the temperature at any altitude. (The small balloon shows the height achieved by Kittinger discussed in News Report 3.1.)
(b) Space Shuttle astronauts captured a dramatic sunset through various atmospheric layers across the "edge" of our planet—called *Earth's limb*. A silhouetted cumulonimbus thunderhead cloud is seen topping out at the tropopause. [Space Shuttle photo from NASA.]

pushes in on all of us. Fortunately, that same pressure also exists inside us, pushing outward; otherwise we would be crushed by the mass of air around us.

The atmosphere exerts an average force of approximately 1 kg/cm^2 (14.7 lb/in.^{2}) at sea level. Gravity compresses air, making it denser near Earth's surface; it thins rapidly with increasing altitude (Figure 3.3a). Consequently, over half the total mass of the atmosphere is compressed below 5500 m (18,000 ft), 75% is compressed below 10,700 m (35,100 ft), and 90% is below 16,000 m (52,500 ft). All but

concentration of ozone (O_3) in the "ozone layer," from 19 to 50 km (12 to 31 mi), and the variations in water vapour, pollutants, and some trace chemicals in the lowest portion of the atmosphere.

The stable mixture of gases composing air in the homosphere evolved slowly. The present proportion, which includes oxygen, evolved approximately 500 million years ago. Table 3.2 lists by volume the stable ingredients that constitute dry, clean air in the homosphere.

The homosphere is a vast reservoir of relatively inert *nitrogen*, originating principally from volcanic sources. Nitrogen is a key element of life, yet we exhale all the nitrogen we inhale. The explanation for this contradiction is that nitrogen integrates into our bodies not from the air we breathe but through compounds in food. In the soil, nitrogen is bound to these compounds by nitrogen-fixing bacteria, and it returns to the atmosphere by denitrifying bacteria that remove nitrogen from organic materials. A complete discussion of the nitrogen cycle is in Chapter 19.

Oxygen, a by-product of photosynthesis, also is essential for life processes. Slight spatial variations occur in the percentage of oxygen in the atmosphere because of variations in photosynthetic rates with latitude, seasonal changes, and the lag time as atmospheric circulation slowly mixes the air. Although it forms about one-fifth of the atmosphere, oxygen forms compounds that compose about half of Earth's crust. Oxygen readily reacts with many elements to form these materials. Both nitrogen and oxygen reserves in the atmosphere are so extensive that, at present, they far exceed human capabilities to disrupt or deplete them.

The gas *argon*, constituting about 1% of the homosphere, is completely inert (an unreactive "noble" gas) and therefore is unusable in life processes. Argon is a residue from the radioactive decay of an isotope (form) of potassium called potassium-40 (symbolized ^{40}K). Slow accumulation over millions of years accounts for all the argon present in the modern atmosphere. Because industry has found uses for inert argon (in light bulbs, welding, and some lasers), it is extracted or "mined" from the atmosphere, in addition to nitrogen and oxygen, for commercial and industrial uses (Figure 3.4).

FIGURE 3.4 An air-mining operation.
Air is a major industrial and chemical raw material that is extracted from the atmosphere by air-mining companies. Nitrogen, oxygen, and argon are extracted using a cryogenic process (very low temperatures). [Photo by Robert W. Christopherson.]

Table 3.2 Stable Components of the Modern Homosphere

Gas (Symbol)	Percentage by Volume	Parts per Million (ppm)
Nitrogen (N_2)	78.084	780,840
Oxygen (O_2)	20.946	209,460
Argon (Ar)	0.934	9,340
Carbon dioxide (CO_2)*	0.038	375.6
Neon (Ne)	0.001818	18
Helium (He)	0.000525	5
Methane (CH_4)	0.00014	1.4
Krypton (Kr)	0.00010	1.0
Ozone (O_3)	Variable	
Nitrous oxide (N_2O)	Trace	
Hydrogen (H)	Trace	
Xenon (Xe)	Trace	

*2003 average measured at Mauna Loa, Hawai'i (see: http://cdiac.esd.ornl.gov/ftp/maunaloa-co2/maunaloa.co2).

Carbon dioxide is a natural by-product of life processes. It is essentially a stable atmospheric component, qualifying it for inclusion in Table 3.2. Although its present percentage in the atmosphere is small at 0.038%, it is important in maintaining global temperatures. Its percentage has increased over the past 200 years as a result of human activities. Chapter 10 discusses the implications of this increase in global warming and climate change.

Atmospheric Temperature Criterion

Shifting to temperature as a criterion, the atmosphere has four distinct temperature zones—the *thermosphere*, *mesosphere*, *stratosphere*, and *troposphere* (labelled in Figure 3.2).

Thermosphere We define the **thermosphere** ("heat sphere") as roughly corresponding to the heterosphere (80 km out to 480 km, or 50–300 mi). The upper limit of the thermosphere is called the **thermopause** (the suffix *-pause* means "to change"). During periods of a less active Sun (fewer sunspots and coronal bursts), the thermopause may lower in altitude from the average 480 km (300 mi) to only 250 km altitude (155 mi). An active Sun will cause the outer atmosphere to swell to an altitude of 550 km (340 mi), where it can create frictional drag on satellites in low orbit.

The temperature profile in Figure 3.2 (yellow curve) shows that temperatures rise sharply in the thermosphere, to 1200°C (2200°F) and higher. Despite such high temperatures, the thermosphere is not "hot" in the way you might expect. Temperature and heat are different concepts. The intense solar radiation in this portion of the atmosphere excites individual molecules (principally nitrogen and oxygen) to high levels of vibration. This **kinetic energy**, the energy of motion, is the vibrational energy that we measure as *temperature*.

However, the actual heat involved is very small. The reason is that the density of molecules is so low. There is little actual **heat** produced, or the flow of kinetic energy from one body to another because of a temperature difference between them. Heating in the atmosphere near Earth's surface is different because the greater number of molecules in the denser atmosphere transmits their kinetic energy as **sensible heat**, meaning that we can measure it. (Density, temperature, and heat capacity determine the sensible heat of a substance.) There is more on this topic in Chapters 4 and 5.

Mesosphere The **mesosphere** is the area from 50 to 80 km (30 to 50 mi) above Earth and is the highest in altitude of the three temperature regions within the homosphere. As Figure 3.2 shows, the mesosphere's outer boundary, the *mesopause*, is the coldest portion of the atmosphere, averaging −90°C (−130°F), although that temperature may vary considerably (25−30 C°, or 45−54 F°). Note in Figure 3.3b the extremely low pressures (low density of molecules) in the mesosphere.

The mesosphere sometimes receives cosmic or meteoric dust, acting as nuclei around which fine ice crystals form. At high latitudes, an observer may see these bands of crystals glow in rare and unusual night clouds called **noctilucent clouds**. For reasons not clearly understood, these unique clouds are on the increase. See, among several sites, **http://lasp.colorado.edu/noctilucent_clouds/**.

Stratosphere The **stratosphere** extends from 18 to 50 km (11 to 31 mi) from Earth's surface. Temperatures increase with altitude throughout the stratosphere, from −57°C (−70°F) at 18 km (tropopause), warming to 0°C (32°F) at 50 km at the stratosphere's outer boundary, the *stratopause*.

Troposphere The **troposphere** is the final layer encountered by incoming solar radiation as it surges through the atmosphere to the surface. It is the home of the biosphere, the atmospheric layer that supports life, and the region of principal weather activity.

Approximately 90% of the total mass of the atmosphere and the bulk of all water vapour, clouds, air pollution, and life forms are within the troposphere. The **tropopause**, its upper limit, is defined by an average temperature of –57°C (–70°F), but its exact elevation varies with the season, latitude, and surface temperatures and pressures. Near the equator, because of intense heating from the surface, the tropopause occurs at 18 km (11 mi); in the middle latitudes, it occurs at 12 km (8 mi); and at the North and South Poles it is only 8 km (5 mi) or less above Earth's surface.

Figure 3.5 illustrates the normal temperature profile within the troposphere during daytime. As the graph shows, temperatures decrease rapidly with increasing altitude at an average of 6.4 C° per kilometre (3.5 F° per 1000 ft), a rate known as the **normal lapse rate**. This temperature plot also appears in Figure 3.2.

The normal lapse rate is an average. The actual lapse rate at any particular time and place, which may deviate considerably because of local weather conditions, is called the **environmental lapse rate**. This variation in temperature gradient in the lower troposphere is central to our discussion of weather processes (Chapter 7).

In the stratosphere, the marked warming with increasing altitude causes the tropopause to act like a lid, essentially preventing whatever is in the cooler (denser) air below from mixing into the warmer (less dense) stratosphere. However, the tropopause may be disrupted above the midlatitudes wherever jet streams produce vertical turbulence and an interchange between the troposphere and the stratosphere (Chapter 6). Also, hurricanes occasionally inject moisture above this inverted temperature layer at the tropopause, and powerful volcanic eruptions may loft ash and sulphuric acid mists into the stratosphere, as the Mount Pinatubo eruptions did in 1991.

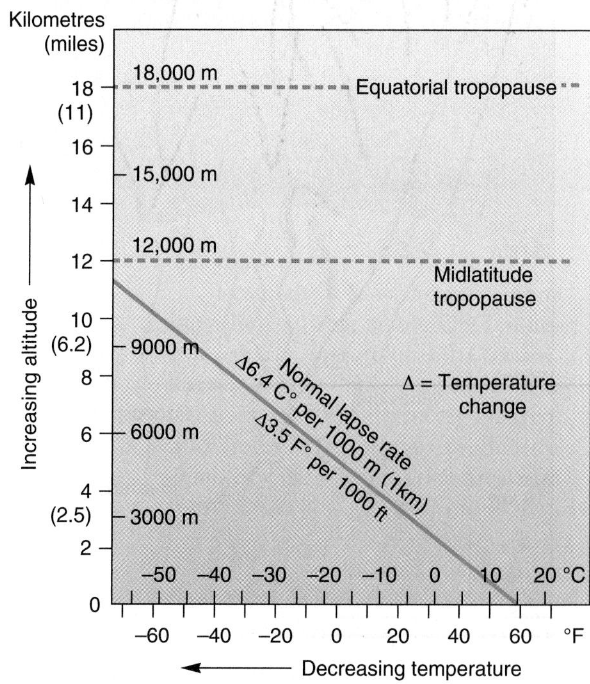

FIGURE 3.5 The temperature profile of the troposphere. During daytime, temperature decreases with increased altitude at a rate known as the *normal lapse rate*. Scientists use a concept called the *standard atmosphere* as an accepted description of air temperature and pressure changes with altitude. The values in this profile are part of the standard atmosphere. Note the approximate locations of the equatorial and midlatitude tropopauses.

(a)

(b)

(c)

(d)

FIGURE 3.8 Natural variable dust in the atmosphere. (a) A dust storm in central Nevada. (b) An orbital view of wind-blown silt and alkali dust rising from high interior-drainage basins in the Andes Mountains of Chile and Argentina and blowing far over the Atlantic Ocean. (c) A wall of dust from many kilometres distant blocks the sky as it moves over Melbourne, Australia. (d) Alkali dust, a serious air pollutant, rises from the exposed shorelines of Mono Lake, California. [(a) Photo by Robert W. Christopherson; (b) Space Shuttle photo from NASA; (c) photo by Bill Bachman/Photo Researchers, Inc.; (d) photo by Bobbé Christopherson.]

Temperature Inversion Vertical temperature and atmospheric density distribution in the troposphere also can worsen pollution conditions. A **temperature inversion** occurs when the normal temperature decrease with altitude (normal lapse rate) begins to *increase* at some altitude. This can happen at any point from ground level to several thousand metres. Figure 3.9 compares a normal temperature profile with that of a temperature inversion. The normal profile (Figure 3.9a) permits warmer (less dense) air at the surface to rise, ventilating the valley and moderating surface pollution. But the warm air inversion (Figure 3.9b) prevents the rise of cooler (denser) air beneath, halting the vertical mixing of pollutants with other atmospheric gases. Thus, instead of being carried away, pollutants are trapped under the *inversion layer*.

Inversions most often result from certain weather conditions, such as when the air near the ground is radiatively cooled on clear nights, or from topographic situations that

High Latitude Connection 3.1

Arctic Haze

Arctic haze is a term from the 1950s, when pilots noticed decreased visibility, either horizontally or at a slant angle from their planes. Since there is no heavy industry at these latitudes and sparse population, this seasonal haze (concentration of microscopic particles and air pollution that diminishes air clarity) was a mystery at first. When looking toward the Sun, the haze has a reddish-brown tint, especially when the polar air mass is dominated by stable high-pressure systems and calm weather conditions.

A remarkable attribute of industrialization in the Northern Hemisphere is the haze across the Arctic region, especially from November to April. This winter haze is worse toward Alaska's North Slope. Although the haze can extend up to 8 km (5 mi) in altitude, it sometimes appears layered since sources are at varying distances from the Arctic and the warmer transporting winds are variously lifted over the cold air mass that hugs the surface.

Simply, winds of atmospheric circulation transport pollution to sites far distant from points of origin. There is no comparable haze over the Antarctic continent. Based on this analysis, can you think of why Antarctica lacks such a condition?

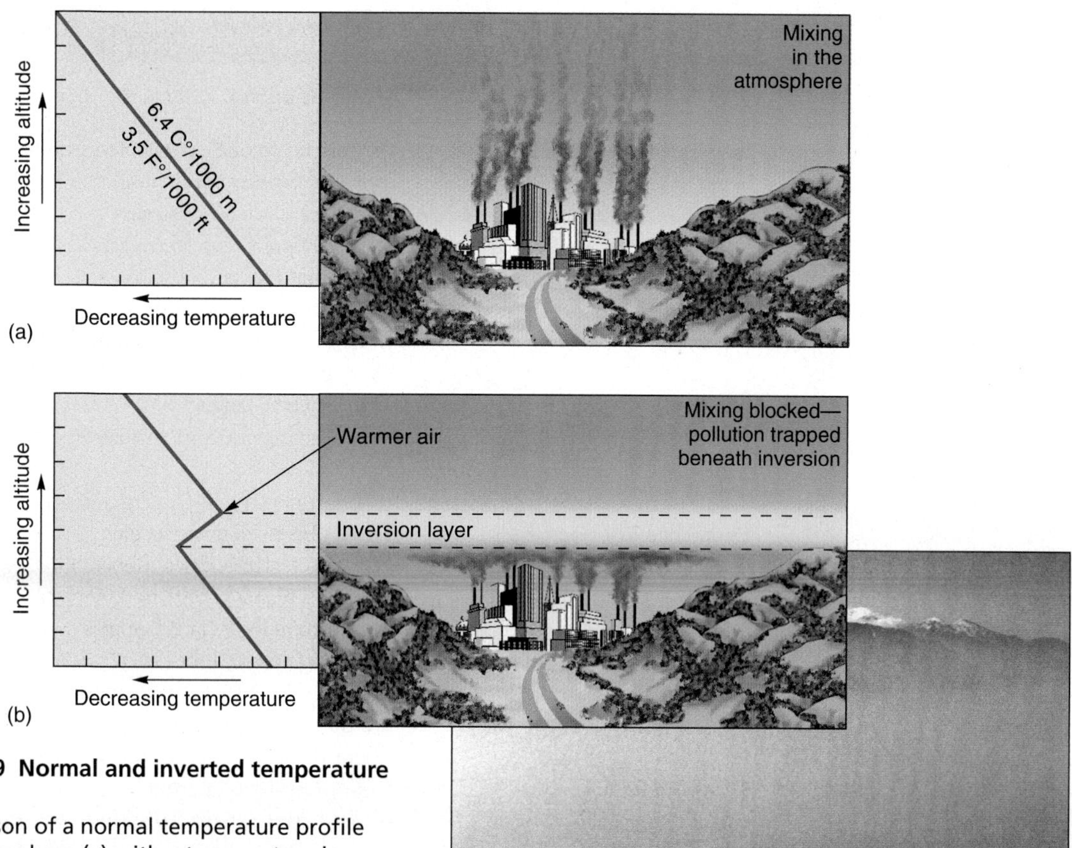

FIGURE 3.9 Normal and inverted temperature profiles.
A comparison of a normal temperature profile in the atmosphere (a) with a temperature inversion in the lower atmosphere (b). Note how the warmer air layer prevents mixing of the denser (cooler) air below the inversion, thereby trapping pollution. An inversion layer is visible in the morning hours over a valley (c). [Photo by Bobbé Christopherson.]

produce cold-air drainage into valleys. In addition, the air above snow-covered surfaces or beneath subsiding air in a high-pressure system may cause a temperature inversion. (The concepts of high- and low-pressure systems are discussed in Chapter 6.)

Anthropogenic Pollution

Anthropogenic, or human-caused, air pollution remains most prevalent in urbanized regions. Approximately 2% of annual deaths in the United States are attributable to air pollution—some 50,000 people. Comparable risks are identified in Canada, Europe, Mexico, Asia, and elsewhere.

The human population is moving to cities and is therefore coming in increasing contact with air pollution. By the year 2010, approximately 3.3 billion people (48% of world population) will live in metropolitan regions, some one-third with unhealthful levels of air pollution. This represents a potentially massive public health issue in this century.

Table 3.4 lists the names, chemical symbols, principal sources, and impacts of variable anthropogenic components in the air. The first seven pollutants in the table result from combustion of fossil fuels in transportation (specifically automobiles) and at stationary sources such as power plants and factories. Overall, automobiles contribute more than 60% of United States and 50% of Canadian human-caused air pollution. Figure 3.10 identifies the major human-caused pollutants and their proportional sources in the United States in 1999 (the latest report). The proportion of sources for these pollutants may be considered representative for most developed countries (see **http://www.epa.gov/**).

In the United States in 1999, transportation produced 77% of the carbon monoxide, 47% of volatile organic compounds (VOC), 56% of the nitrogen oxides, and 25% of particulates. Environment Canada reported in 1995 (latest available) that with Canada's smaller transportation fleet, Canadian automobile emissions contribute 40% of the carbon monoxide, 21% of the VOCs, and 60% of the nitrogen oxides in Canada (see **http://www.ec.gc.ca/**). Canada and the United States are negotiating an Air Quality Agreement, a process formally begun in 1991 and coordinated by an International Joint Commission. Acid deposition reduction is the main focus of the effort (see **http://www.ijc.org/**).

Table 3.4 Anthropogenic Gases and Materials in the Lower Atmosphere

Name	Symbol	Source	Description and Effects of Criteria Pollutants
Carbon monoxide	CO	Incomplete combustion of fuels	Odourless, colourless, tasteless gas Toxicity: affinity for hemoglobin Displaces O_2 in bloodstream 50 to 100 ppm causes headaches, vision and judgment losses
Nitrogen oxides	NO_x (NO, NO_2)	High temperature/pressure combustion	Reddish-brown choking gas Inflames respiratory system, destroys lung tissue Damages plants 3 to 5 ppm is dangerous
Volatile organic compounds	VOC	Incomplete combustion of fossil fuels such as gasoline; cleaning and paint solvents	Prime agents of ozone formation compounds
Ozone	O_3	Photochemical reactions	Highly reactive, unstable gas Oxidizes surfaces, dries rubber and elastic Damages plants at 0.01 to 0.09 ppm Agricultural losses at 0.1 ppm 0.3 to 1.0 ppm irritates eyes, nose, throat
Peroxyacetyl nitrates	PAN	Photochemical reactions	Produced by NO + VOC photochemistry No human health effects Major damage to plants, forests, crops
Sulphur oxides	SO_x (SO_2, SO_3)	Combustion of sulphur-containing fuels	Colourless; irritating smell 0.1 to 1 ppm impairs breathing, taste threshold Human asthma, bronchitis, emphysema Leads to acid deposition
Particulate matter	PM	Dust, dirt, soot, salt, metals, organics; fugitive dust from agriculture, construction, roads, and wind erosion	Complex mixture of solid and aerosol particles Dust, smoke, and haze affect visibility Various health effects: bronchitis, pulmonary function PM_{10} negative health effects established by researchers
Carbon dioxide	CO_2	Complete combustion, mainly from fossil fuel consumption	Principal greenhouse gas Atmospheric concentration increasing 64% of greenhouse warming effect
Methane	CH_4	Organic processes	Secondary greenhouse gas Atmospheric concentration increasing 19% of greenhouse warming effect
Water vapour	H_2O vapour	Combustion processes, steam	See Chapter 7 for more on the role of water vapour in the atmosphere.

The apparent manageability of this transportation-pollution problem is interesting. In one California study, only 7% of the vehicles contributed half of the carbon monoxide and only 10% contributed half of the VOC pollution. These "gross polluting" vehicles are not old cars—a common misconception—but include new cars! In random highway checks, 41% of vehicles had pollution equipment that was deliberately tampered with and 25% had defective or missing emission controls. Reducing air pollution from the transportation sector does not pose many mysteries.

Stationary sources, such as electric power plants and industrial plants that use fossil fuels, contribute the most sulphur oxides and particulates. For this reason, concentrations are focused in the Northern Hemisphere and the industrial, developed countries.

The last three gases shown in Table 3.4 are discussed elsewhere in this text: water vapour is examined with water and weather (Chapters 7 and 8); carbon dioxide and methane are discussed with greenhouse gases and climate (Chapters 4, 5, and 10).

Carbon Monoxide Pollution Carbon monoxide (CO) is a combination of one atom of carbon and one of oxygen. Carbon monoxide is produced by incomplete combustion (burning with limited oxygen) of fuels or other carbon-

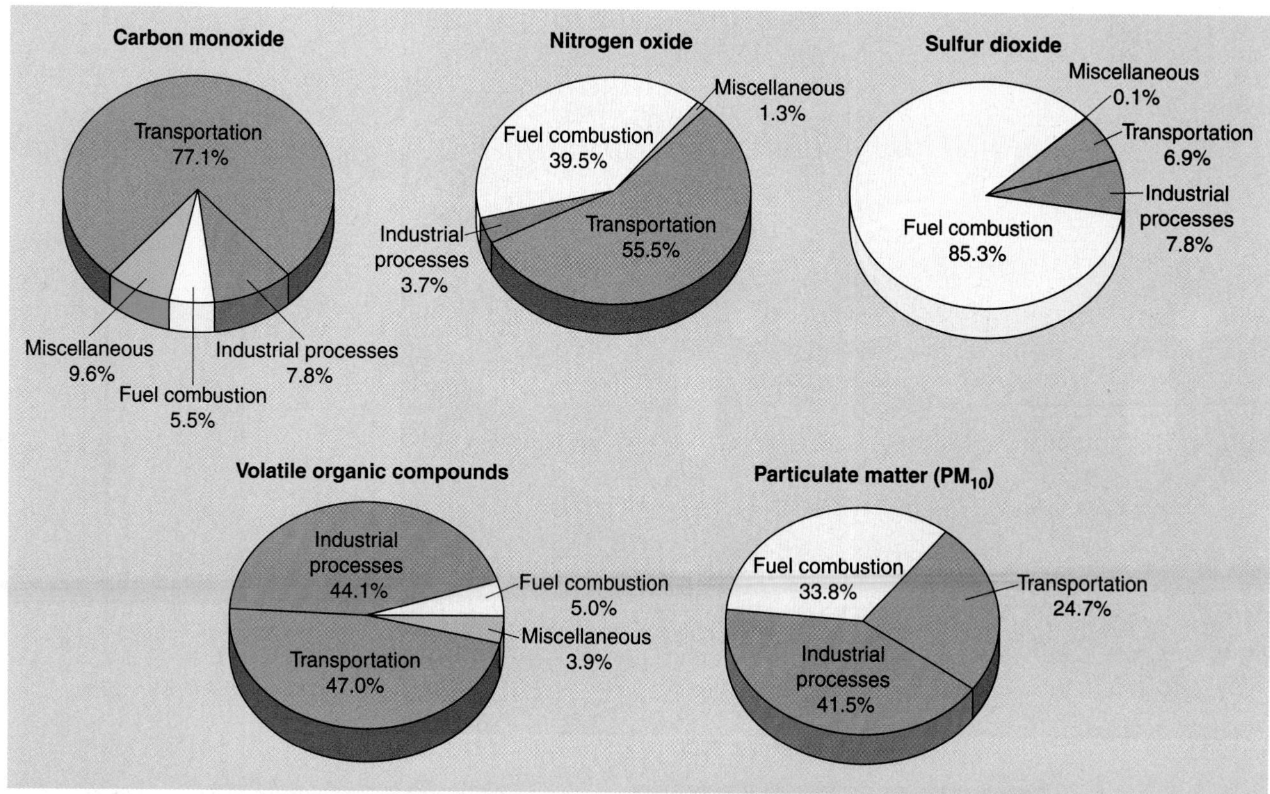

FIGURE 3.10 Human-caused air pollution and sources.
Major types of human-caused air pollution and their sources in the United States in 1999. These proportions are typical of developed, industrialized countries. [Adapted from Office of Air Quality, *National Air Quality and Emission Trends Report, 1999*, U.S. EPA (March 2001), Figures 2-4, 2-19, 2-33, 2-40, and 2-67, EPA 454/R-01-004.]

containing substances. A log decaying in the woods produces carbon monoxide, as does a forest fire or other organic decomposition. Natural sources produce up to 90% of existing carbon monoxide, whereas anthropogenic sources, principally transportation, produce the other 10%. A dangerous point source of carbon monoxide for individuals is from primary and secondary tobacco smoke.

In the tropics of south-central Africa and the Amazon region of South America, an interesting source of carbon monoxide is the widespread burning of biomass (trees, grasses, brush) from August to October. This carbon monoxide spreads throughout the Southern Hemisphere. Figure 3.11 compares carbon monoxide emissions from both human caused and wildfire biomass burning for March and September 2000 in South America. Generally, the carbon monoxide from human sources is concentrated in urban areas, where it directly affects human health (see Table 3.4).

Photochemical Smog Pollution Photochemical smog was not generally experienced in the past but developed with the advent of the automobile. Today it is the major component of anthropogenic air pollution (Figure 3.12). **Photochemical smog** results from the interaction of sunlight and the combustion products in automobile exhaust (nitrogen oxides and VOCs). Although the term *smog*—a combination of the words *sm*oke and f*og*—is a misnomer, it is generally used to describe this phenomenon. Smog is responsible for the hazy sky and reduced sunlight in many of our cities, as shown occurring in the contrasting photos in Figure 3.13.

Mexico City is notorious for poor air quality as its 22 million inhabitants and 3.5 million vehicles work, commute, and live in the world's second largest metropolitan region. In 1999 World Resources Institute named it as the unhealthiest city in the world for children; this was based on 1995 data. Conditions are worsened by frequent subtropical high-pressure systems (descending, stable air) that act as effective air traps over the Valley of Mexico, in which the city lies. The contrast between a rare, clear day and frequent polluted days in Mexico City is dramatic (Figure 3.13). Mexico enacted new laws in 1990 to reduce unhealthy photochemical smog conditions: more public rapid transportation, controls on automobiles, limitations on factory operations, and more pollution-absorbing park space and trees. Based on some success and an increase in clear days, a new 10-year plan began in 2000 directed at reducing ozone and particulates. The government has spent nearly $2 billion on pollution controls.

The connection between automobile exhaust and smog was not determined until 1953 in Los Angeles, long after society had established its dependence upon individualized

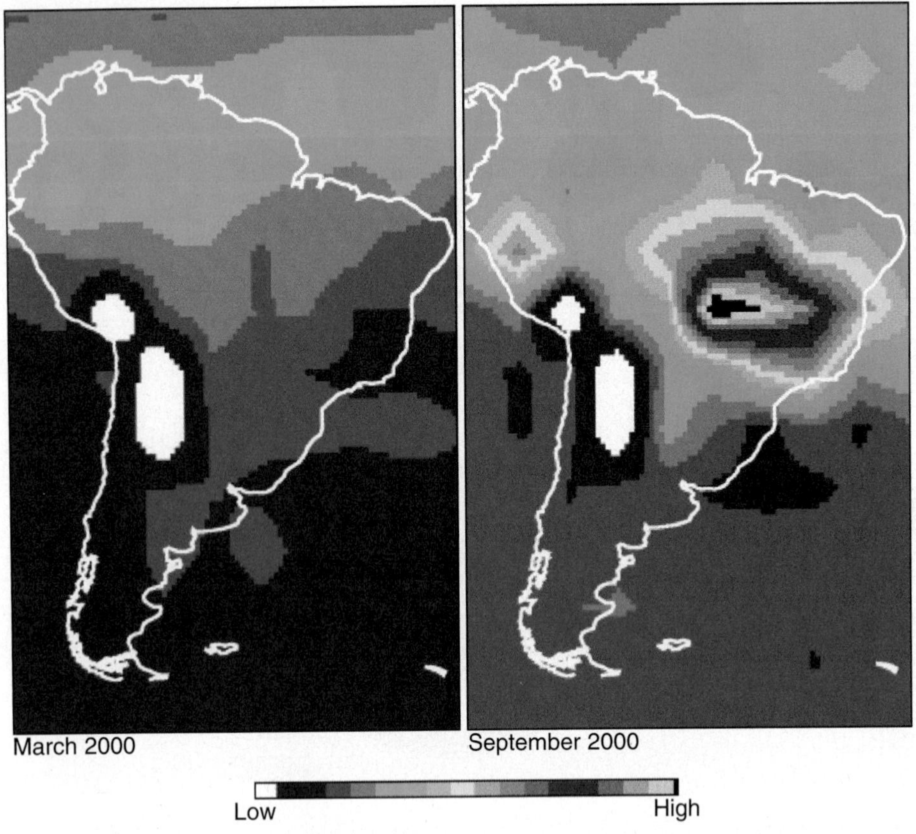

FIGURE 3.11 Biomass burning—a source of global carbon monoxide (CO). Images from March and September, 2000, show the onset of biomass burning. In March, the slightly higher CO levels over the equatorial latitudes are from African fires, transported by trade winds across the Atlantic. By September a large CO plume rises from Brazil, primarily from the burning of rain forest in the Amazon Basin. The soot and ash is lifted high in the atmosphere by strong cloud convection. Measurement is at the 700 millibar pressure level, approximately 3650 m (12,000 ft). [Images from MOPITT (Measurement of Pollution in the Troposphere) sensor aboard the *Terra* satellite courtesy of David Edwards, John Gille, and the MOPITT Science Team, UCAR.]

FIGURE 3.12 Photochemical smog near Denver. Photochemical reactions in the skies over Denver, Colorado, produce the blanket of smog that moves over mountains and forest. What do you notice about air pollution conditions where you live or go to university? [Photo by Bobbé Christopherson.]

transportation. Despite this discovery, widespread mass transit declined, the railroads dwindled, and the polluting individual automobile remains America's preferred transportation. Strangely, the U.S. fleet of 2004 model cars and trucks worsened in gas mileage from 2001. This poor showing is principally due to gas-guzzling sport-utility

(a)

(b)

FIGURE 3.13 Contrasts in the air over Mexico City.
A day of clear air (a) in contrast to a more typical day of photochemical smog pollution (b) in the skies over Mexico City. [Photos by Larry Reider/Sipa Press.]

vehicles and pickups that account for more than half of new sales. Efficiency standards for this class of vehicles have not changed since 1975; they are set lower than for cars.

Figure 3.14 summarizes how car exhaust is converted into major air pollutants—ozone, **peroxyacetyl nitrates (PAN)**, and nitric acid. PAN produces no known health effect in humans, but it is particularly damaging to plants, including both agricultural crops and forests. Damage in California is estimated to exceed $1 billion a year and several billion dollars nationwide in the farming and forestry sectors.

Worldwide, the problem with **nitrogen dioxide** production is its concentration in metropolitan regions. North American urban areas may have from 10 to 100 times higher nitrogen dioxide concentrations than nonurban areas. Nitrogen dioxide interacts with water vapour to form nitric acid (HNO_3), a contributor to acid deposition by precipitation, the subject of Focus Study 3.2.

Ozone is the primary ingredient in photochemical smog. (This is the same gas that is beneficial to us in the stratosphere in absorbing ultraviolet radiation.) The reactivity of ozone causes health concerns, for it damages biological tissues. For several reasons children are at greatest risk from ozone pollution—one in four children in U.S. cities is at risk of developing health problems from ozone pollution. This ratio is significant; it means that more than 12 million children are vulnerable in those cities with the worst polluted air (Los Angeles, New York City, Atlanta, Houston, and Detroit).

The **volatile organic compounds (VOCs)**, including hydrocarbons from gasoline, surface coatings, and combustion at electric utilities, are important factors in ozone formation. States such as California base their standards for control of ozone pollution on VOC emission controls—a scientifically accurate emphasis.

Industrial Smog and Sulphur Oxides Over the past 300 years, except in some developing countries, coal slowly replaced wood as the basic fuel used by society. The Industrial Revolution required high-grade energy to run machines. The changes involved conversion from *animate* energy (energy from animal sources, such as animal-powered farm equipment) to *inanimate* energy (energy from nonliving sources, such as coal, steam, and water). The air pollution associated with coal-burning industries is known as **industrial smog** (Figure 3.15). A London physician coined the term smog at the turn of the twentieth century

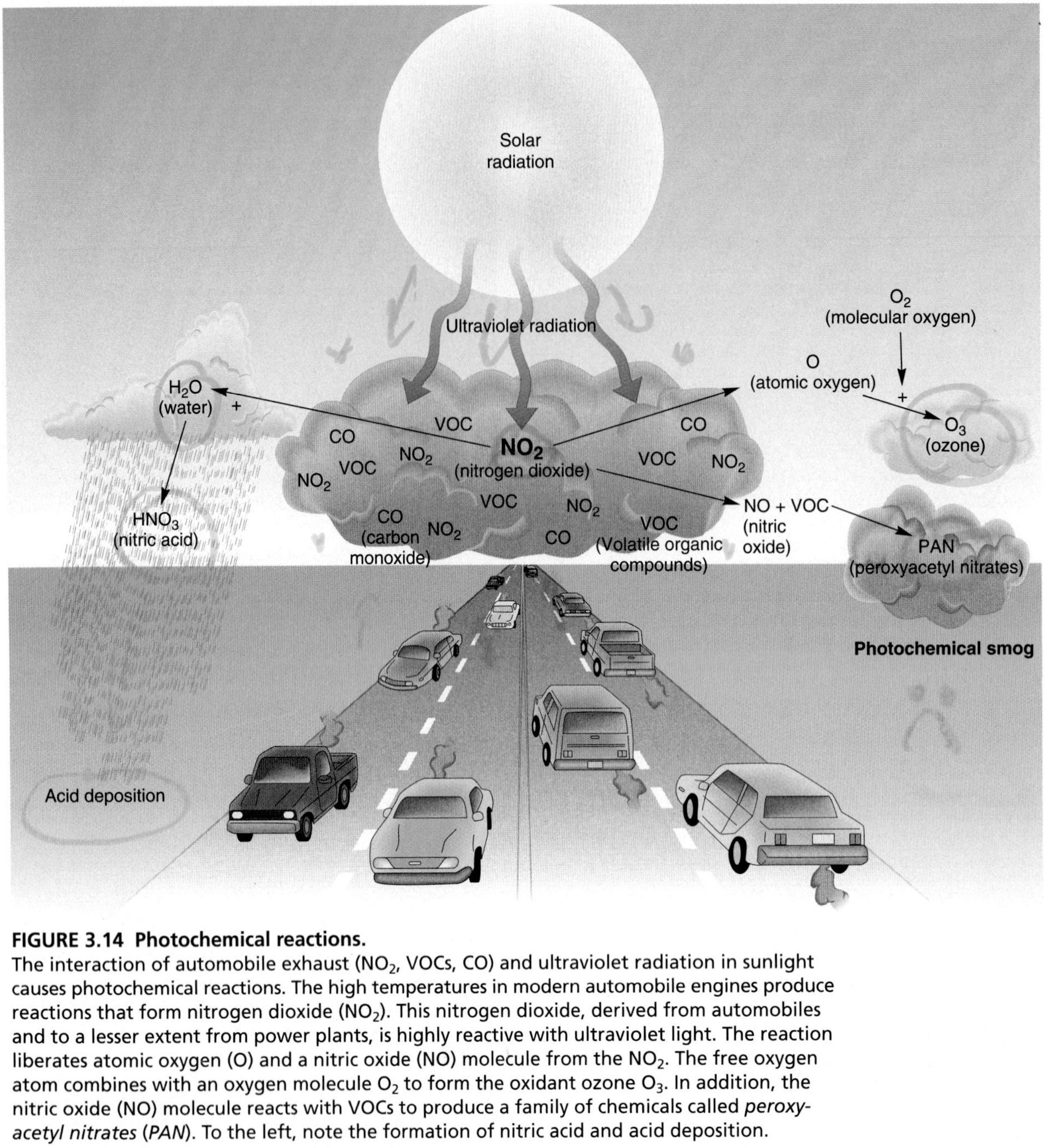

FIGURE 3.14 Photochemical reactions.
The interaction of automobile exhaust (NO_2, VOCs, CO) and ultraviolet radiation in sunlight causes photochemical reactions. The high temperatures in modern automobile engines produce reactions that form nitrogen dioxide (NO_2). This nitrogen dioxide, derived from automobiles and to a lesser extent from power plants, is highly reactive with ultraviolet light. The reaction liberates atomic oxygen (O) and a nitric oxide (NO) molecule from the NO_2. The free oxygen atom combines with an oxygen molecule O_2 to form the oxidant ozone O_3. In addition, the nitric oxide (NO) molecule reacts with VOCs to produce a family of chemicals called *peroxyacetyl nitrates* (*PAN*). To the left, note the formation of nitric acid and acid deposition.

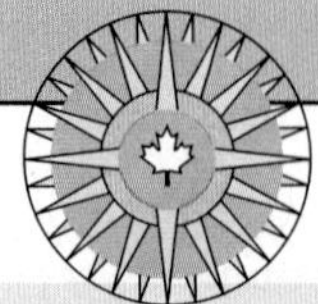

Focus Study 3.2

Acid Deposition: A Continuing Blight on the Landscape

Acid deposition is a major environmental problem in some areas of Canada, the United States, Europe, and Asia. Such deposition is most familiar as "acid rain," but it also occurs as "acid snow" and in dry form as dust or aerosols. (Aerosols are tiny liquid droplets or solid particles.) In addition, winds can carry the acid-producing chemicals many kilometres from their sources before they settle on the landscape, where they enter streams and lakes as runoff and groundwater flows.

Acid deposition is causally linked to serious problems: declining fish populations and fish kills in the northeastern United States, southeastern Canada, Sweden, and Norway; widespread forest damage in these same places and Germany; widespread changes in soil chemistry; and damage to buildings, sculptures, and historic artifacts. In New Hampshire's Hubbard Brook Experimental Forest, a study covering 1960 to the present found half the nutrient calcium and magnesium base cations (see Chapter 18) were leached from the soil. Excess acids are the cause of the decline.

Despite scientific agreement about the problem, which the U.S. General Accounting Office calls a "combination of meteorological, chemical, and biological phenomena," corrective action was delayed by its complexity and politics.

The acidity of precipitation is measured on the pH scale, which expresses the relative abundance of free hydrogen ions (H^+) in a solution. Free hydrogen ions in a solution are what make an acid corrosive, for they easily combine with other ions. The pH scale is logarithmic: each whole number represents a 10-fold change. A pH of 7.0 is neutral (neither acidic nor basic). Values less than 7.0 are increasingly *acidic*, and values greater than 7.0 are increasingly *basic*, or *alkaline*. (A pH scale for soil acidity and alkalinity is portrayed graphically in Chapter 18.)

Natural precipitation dissolves carbon dioxide from the atmosphere to form carbonic acid. This process releases hydrogen ions and produces an average pH reading for precipitation of 5.65. The normal range for precipitation is 5.3–6.0. Thus, normal precipitation is always slightly acidic.

Some anthropogenic gases are converted to acids in the atmosphere and then are removed by wet and dry deposition processes. Specifically, nitrogen and sulphur oxides released in the combustion of fossil fuels can produce nitric acid (HNO_3) and sulphuric acid (H_2SO_4) in the atmosphere.

Acid Precipitation Damage

Precipitation as acidic as pH 2.0 has fallen in the eastern United States, Scandinavia, and Europe. By comparison, vinegar and lemon juice register slightly less than 3.0. Aquatic plant and animal life perishes when lakes drop below pH 4.8.

More than 50,000 lakes and some 100,000 km (62,000 mi) of streams in the United States and Canada are at a pH level below normal (i.e., below 5.3), with several hundred lakes incapable of supporting any aquatic life—15% of the lakes in New England and 41% in the Adirondack Mountains. Acid deposition causes the release of aluminum and magnesium from clay minerals in the soil, and both of these are harmful to fish and plant communities.

Also, relatively harmless mercury deposits in lake-bottom sediments convert in acidified lake waters into highly toxic *methylmercury*, which is deadly to aquatic life. Local health advisories in two provinces and 22 U.S. states are regularly issued to warn those who fish of the methylmercury problem. Mercury atoms rapidly bond with carbon and move through biological systems as an *organometallic compound*.

Damage to forests results from the rearrangement of soil nutrients, the death of soil microorganisms, and an aluminum-induced calcium deficiency that is currently under investigation. The most advanced impact is seen in forests in Europe, especially in eastern Europe, principally because of its long history of burning coal and the density of industrial activity. In Germany and Poland up to 50% of the forests are dead or damaged; in Switzerland 30% are afflicted (Figure 1a).

In the United States, regional-scale decline in forest cover is significant, especially red spruce and sugar maples. In some maples, aluminum is collecting around rootlets; in spruce, acid fogs

(continued)

(a)

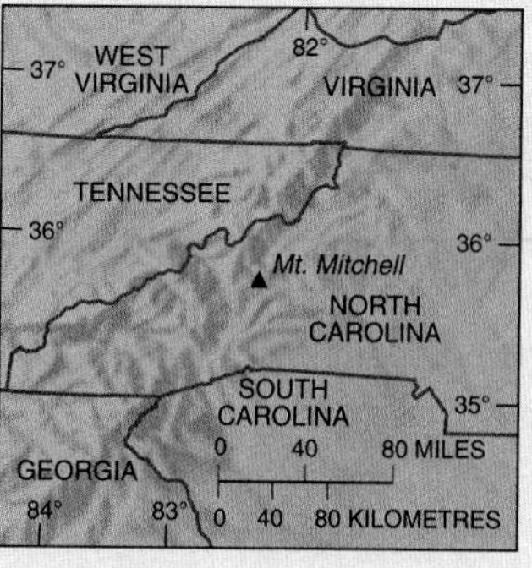

(b)

FIGURE 1 The blight of acid deposition.
The harm done to forests and crops by acid deposition is well established, especially in Europe, here in the Czech Republic (a) and in the forests of the Appalachian Mountains in the United States, here in the forests on Mount Mitchell (b). [Photos by (a) Simon Fraser/Science Photo Library/Photo Researchers, Inc.; (b) Will and Deni McIntyre/Photo Researchers, Inc.]

Focus Study 3.2 *(continued)*

and rains leach calcium from needles directly. Affected trees are susceptible to winter cold, insects, and droughts. In New England, some stands of spruce are as much as 75% affected, as evidenced through analysis of tree-growth rings, which become narrower in adverse growing years. An indicator of forest damage is the reduction by almost half of the annual production of U.S. and Canadian maple sugar. Trees at higher elevations in the Appalachians are injured by acid-laden cloud cover (Figure 1b).

Government estimates of damage in Canada, the United States, and Europe exceed $50 billion annually. Because wind and weather patterns are international, efforts at reducing acidic deposition also must be international in scope. The decline of sulphur dioxide by more than 40% between 1973 and the present is a result of the U.S. *Clean Air Act*. If goals are met, by 2010 sulphur dioxide emissions should be less than half this earlier level. Researchers found a correlation between these reductions and a reduction in the geographic area affected by wet deposition of sulphur. Figure 2 maps the reduction in sulphate deposition between the 1990–1994 and 1996–2000 periods. However, this progress is only a beginning. According to a study in *BioScience*, power plants and other sources must cut emissions 80% beyond the *Clean Air Act* mandate.

Steps can be taken to deal with acid precipitation damage. The Sudbury, Ontario, region has a history of high local SO_2 emissions from industrial activity and associated acid deposition. Industry and the Government of Ontario took measures to mitigate acid damage.

More than 7000 lakes in the area southwest and northeast of Sudbury suffered acid damage. Acidification resulted in large losses of sport fish—comparable to large losses in Nova Scotia rivers and portions of Québec. Long-term studies of the lakes and ponds near Sudbury (carried out for over 35 years) clearly established chemical and biological damage to water bodies resulting from smelter emissions. Area lakes responded rapidly to reductions in local smelter emissions. Environment Canada's Acid Rain Web page, **http://www.ec.gc.ca/acidrain/acidcase.html**, uses Sudbury as a case study and states that the two major producers of emissions, Inco and

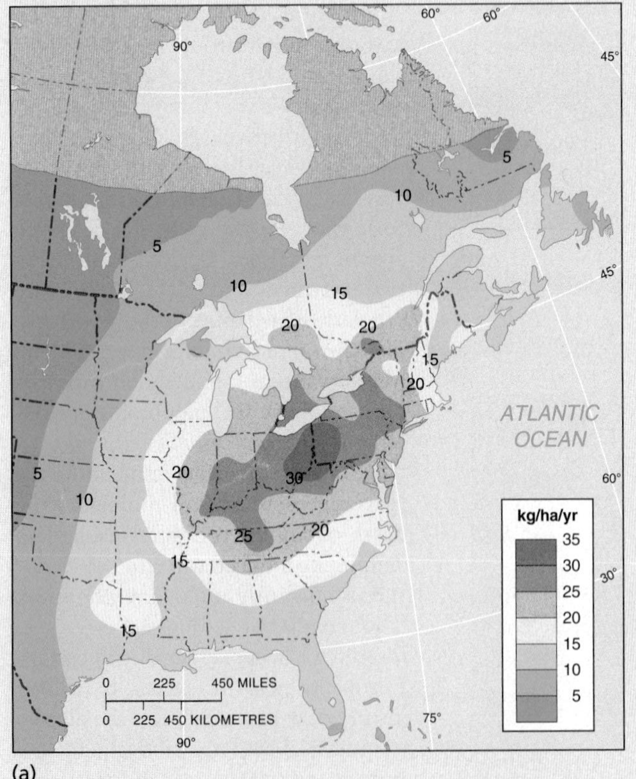

(a)

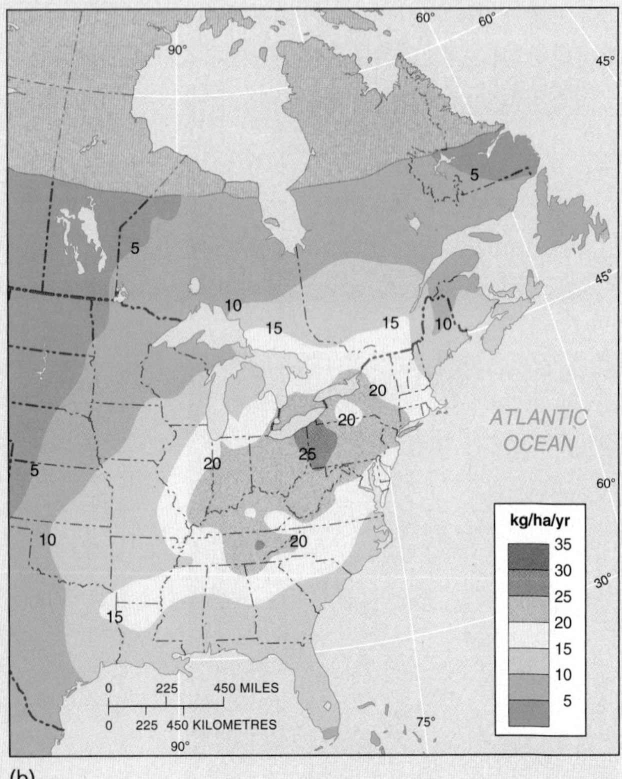

(b)

FIGURE 2 Improvement in wet sulphate deposition rate.
Spatial portrayal of annual sulphate (principally SO_4) wet deposition on the landscape, (a) 1990 to 1994, and, (b) 1996 to 2000 in kilograms per hectare per year. The Canadian *Environmental Protection Act*, the Canada–United States Border Air Quality Strategy, and the U.S. *Clean Air Act* regulations lowered levels of emissions that add acid to the environment. Improvement is still necessary to help ecosystems recover. [Maps from *Cleaner Air through Cooperation, Canada–United States, Progress under the Air Quality Agreement—2003, Environment Canada, 2003.* Reproduced with the permission of the Minister of Public Works and Government Services Canada.]

Falconbridge, reduced releases of SO_2 by 75% and 56% respectively.

Ten leading acid deposition researchers reported in an extensive study in *BioScience*, March 2001,

> Model calculations suggest that the greater the reduction in atmospheric sulfur deposition. . ., the greater the magnitude and rate of chemical recovery. Less aggressive proposals for controls of sulfur emissions will result in slower chemical and biological recovery and in delays in regaining the services of a fully functional ecosystem. . . . North America and Europe are in the midst of a large-scale experiment. Sulfuric and nitric acids have acidified soils, lakes, and streams, thereby stressing or killing terrestrial and aquatic biota.*

At best, acid deposition is an issue of global spatial significance for which science is providing strong incentives for action. Reductions in troublesome emissions are closely tied to energy conservation and therefore directly related to production of greenhouse gases and global warming concerns—thus linking these environmental issues.

*Driscoll, C. T., *et al.*, "Acidic deposition in the northeastern United States: Sources and Inputs, Ecosystems Effects, and Management Strategies," *BioScience* 51 (March 2001): 195.

to describe the combination of fog and smoke containing sulphur gases (sulphur is an impurity in fossil fuels).

Once in the atmosphere, **sulphur dioxide (SO_2)** reacts with oxygen (O) to form sulphur trioxide (SO_3), which is highly reactive and, in the presence of water or water vapour, forms **sulphate aerosols**, tiny particles about 0.1 to 1 μm in diameter. Sulphuric acid (H_2SO_4) can form in even moderately polluted air at normal temperatures. Sulphur dioxide–laden air is dangerous to health, corrodes metals, and deteriorates stone building materials at accelerated rates. Focus Study 3.2 discusses this vital atmospheric issue.

In the United States, coal-burning electric utilities and steel manufacturing are the main sources of sulphur dioxide, principally in the East and Midwest. And, because of the prevailing movement of air masses, they are the main sources of sulphur dioxide in adjacent Canadian regions. As much as 70% of Canadian sulphur dioxide is initiated within the United States.

FIGURE 3.15 Typical industrial smog. Pollution generated by industry differs from that produced by transportation. Industrial pollution has high concentrations of sulphur oxides, particulates, and carbon dioxide. [Photo by Robert W. Christopherson.]

Particulates **Particulate matter (PM)** is a diverse mixture of fine particles, both solid and aerosol, that impact human health. Haze, smoke, and dust are visible reminders of particulate material in the air we breathe. PM_{10}, particulate smaller than 10 microns (10 μm or less) in diameter, was designated a matter for concern in 1987. $PM_{2.5}$ is currently being debated as an appropriate standard for human health. Studies in Provo and Orem, Utah (1989), Philadelphia (1992), and other cities, and by the American Cancer Society (1995), established links between PM pollution and health. Nationally, a study of major cities disclosed a 26% greater risk of premature death due to respirable particulate pollution as compared with non-polluted air—further driving up medical costs and related expenses.

In Utah County, Utah, researchers correlated PM_{10} concentrations with increased rates of hospitalization for bronchitis, asthma, pneumonia, and pleurisy (especially in children), and greatly increased medical costs. Similar studies of children affected by related illnesses in seven other cities revealed sickness rates twice as high for the city having the dirtiest air as for the city having the cleanest air. Pollution sources dispute these findings and the concern generated by such studies.

Certainly, society cannot simply halt two centuries of industrialization to slow air pollution; the resulting economic chaos would be devastating. But neither can it permit pollution production to continue unabated, for catastrophic environmental and human health damage, and continued climate changes, inevitably will result. We are now contributing significantly to the creation of the **anthropogenic atmosphere**, a tentative label for Earth's next atmosphere. The urban air we breathe today may be just a preview. What is the air quality like where you live, work, and go to school? Where could you go to find out its status?

Benefits of the U.S. *Clean Air Act*

Concentration of many air pollutants declined over the past several decades because of U.S. *Clean Air Act* legislation (1970, 1977, 1990), resulting in the saving of trillions of dollars in avoided health, economic, and environmental losses. These benefits were shared with Canadian citizens as well. Despite this reality, air pollution controls are subject to a continuing political debate and threats to weaken standards. According to a report prepared by the EPA, *National Air Pollutant Emission Trends, 1999*, the 1999 emissions of five primary pollutants totalled 162 million metric tons (178 million tons), compared to 224 million metric tons (246 million tons) in 1970, the first year of the *Clean Air Act* (CAA). Figure 3.16 illustrates the trends in CO, NO_x, VOCs, SO_2, PM_{10}, and lead (Pb). Only nitrogen oxides increased between 1970 and 1999. In Canada, between 1980 and 1997, sulphur dioxide emissions decreased 44%.

Significant lead (Pb) reductions have global beneficial impact. Prior to the CAA, lead was added to gasoline, emitted in the exhaust, travelled great distances, and settled in living tissues, especially in children.

To be justified and worthwhile, abatement (mitigation and prevention) costs must not exceed the financial benefits derived from reducing pollution damage. Compliance with the CAA affected patterns of industrial production, employment, and capital investment. Although these expenditures must be viewed as investments that generated benefits and opportunities, the dislocation and job loss in some regions was severe: reductions in high-sulphur coal mining and cutbacks in polluting industries such as steel, for example.

In 1990, the U.S. Congress requested the Environmental Protection Agency (EPA) to answer the question: How do the overall health, welfare, ecological, and economic benefits of CAA programs compare with the costs of these programs? In response, the EPA performed an exhaustive cost-benefit analysis and published a report in 1997. *The Benefits of the* Clean Air Act, *1970 to 1990* (Office of Policy, Planning, and Evaluation, U.S. EPA) calculated the following:

- The *total direct cost* to implement the *Clean Air Act* for all federal, state, and local rules from 1970 to 1990 was *$523 billion* (in 1990-value dollars). This cost was borne by businesses, consumers, and government entities.
- The estimate of *direct monetized benefits* from the *Clean Air Act* from 1970 to 1990 falls in a range from $5.6 to $49.4 trillion with a central mean of *$22.2 trillion*. (The uncertainty of the assessment is indicated by the range of benefit estimates.)
- Therefore, the estimated *net financial benefit* of the *Clean Air Act* is *$21.7 trillion!* "The finding is overwhelming. The benefits far exceed the costs of the CAA in the first 20 years," said Richard Morgenstern, associate administrator for policy planning and evaluation at the EPA.

The benefits to society, directly and indirectly, have been widespread across the entire population, including improved health and environment, less lead to harm children, lowered cancer rates, less acid deposition, and an estimated 206,000 fewer deaths related to air pollution in 1990 alone. These benefits took place during a period in which the U.S. population grew by 22% and the economy expanded by 70%. The benefits continued between 1990 and 2000 as air quality continued to improve.

Canada benefits from the *Clean Air Act* because transboundary pollutants are reduced. Additionally, Canada is active in addressing clean air. The Government of Canada has made significant progress in tackling air pollution problems since 2000. This progress has come from cooperation and joint projects with the United States under the

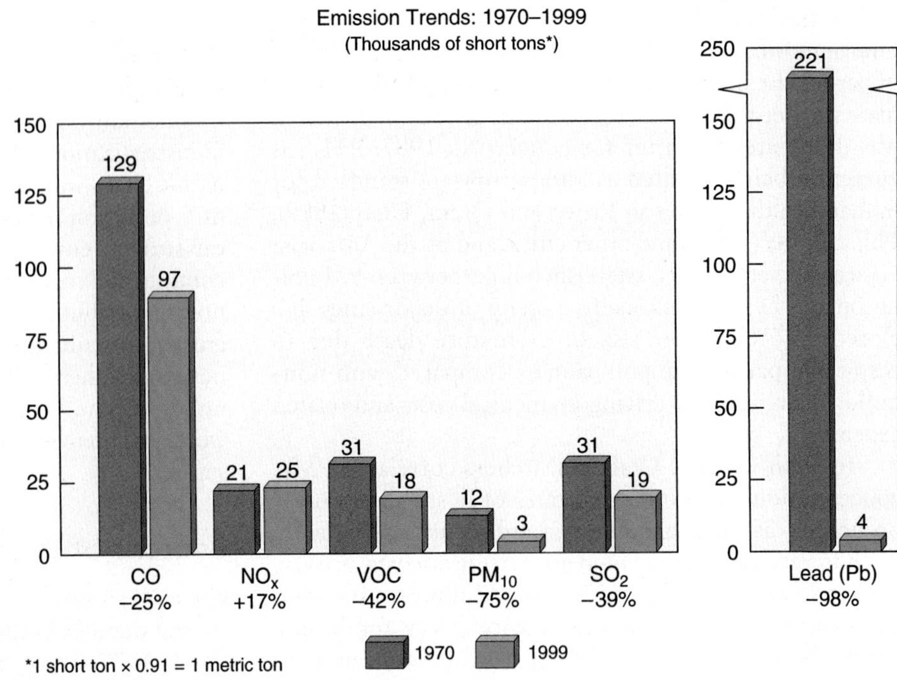

FIGURE 3.16 Trends in air pollutants.
Air pollution trends between 1970 and 1999: sulphur dioxide, −39% (due to scrubbers on smokestacks and emission controls); particulate matter, −75%; nitrogen oxide increased, +17%; volatile organic compounds, −42%; carbon monoxide, −25% (the last three involve exhaust emission controls); and a huge lead reduction of −98%, or 197,000 metric tons (217,000 tons) (as a result of unleaded gas and reduced industrial emissions). [Adapted from Office of Air Quality, *National Air Quality and Emission Trends Report, 1999*, U.S. EPA (March 2001), from Data Tables, Appendix A, EPA 454/R-01-004.]

Canada–U.S. Air Quality Agreement, working with the provinces to implement the *Canada-wide Standards*, and meeting commitments to reduce pollution from all vehicle engines and the fuels that power them. The Government of Canada introduced *The Interim Plan 2001 on Particulate Matter and Ozone* to address obligations to clean the air. In 2003, Canada acted to regulate vehicle emissions, install more air quality monitoring stations, and better track smog pollutants, in the hope of slowing human-induced climate change and cleaning the air we breathe. For a summary of these efforts, see the *Climate Change Plan for Canada* at **http://www.climatechange.gc.ca/plan_for_canada/plan/index.html**.

As you reflect on this chapter and our modern atmosphere, the treaties to protect stratospheric ozone, and the EPA study of benefits from the CAA, you should feel encouraged. Scientists did the research, society knew what to do, took action, and reaped enormous economic and health benefits. An important role for physical geographers is to explain these global impacts through spatial analysis and to guide an informed citizenry toward a better understanding.

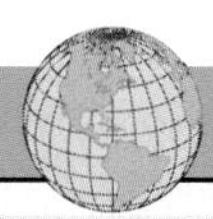

Applied Physical Geography

Radiation and Temperature

Radiation laws are the set of rules that summarize the way that matter interacts with the electromagnetic spectrum. We can think of radiation, energy, and temperature—the hotter a body, the more energy it radiates, and the shorter the wavelength of energy it radiates. Two laws are particularly useful in an examination of energy.

First is the Stefan-Boltzmann Law that gives the total amount of energy being emitted at all wavelengths by a body.

$$E = \sigma T^4$$

where E is the energy measured in W/m^2, σ is the Stefan-Boltzmann constant (5.6705×10^{-8} W/ m^2/K^4), and T is the temperature of the surface measured in the Kelvin scale. Kelvin is a scale of temperature that has an absolute zero: Zero Kelvin means there is no temperature. The measurement units are the same distance apart as on the Celsius scale—a relative temperature scale. To change from Kelvin to Celsius use the following conversion:

$$K = C + 273.$$

Second is the Wien Displacement Law that gives the wavelength of the peak of the radiation distribution.

$$\lambda_{MAX} = c/T$$

where λ_{MAX} is the wavelength in μm that is the maximum radiation at a given temperature, c is a constant (2898 μm), and T is the surface temperature in K. The numerator is a constant measured in angstroms (one ten billionth of a metre).

These laws apply only to something known as a blackbody—a perfectly radiating surface. Most surfaces are not perfect radiators, but the differences in radiation are not significant enough to discount the laws.

To see how these laws are applied, consider normal room temperature of 20°C. Convert this temperature to Kelvin by adding 273 to 20. Room temperature in Kelvin is 293K. How much energy is being emitted by a surface at room temperature?

$$\begin{aligned} E &= \sigma T^4 \\ &= (5.6705 \times 10^{-8}\ \text{W/m}^2/\text{K}^4) \times (293\text{K})^4 \\ &= (5.6705 \times 10^{-8}\ \text{W/m}^2/\text{K}^4) \times 7.37 \times 10^9\text{K}^4 \\ &= 417.9\ \text{W/m}^2 \end{aligned}$$

What is the wavelength of the maximum emission?

$$\begin{aligned} \lambda_{MAX} &= c/T \\ &= 2898/293\text{K} \\ &= 9.89\ \mu\text{m} \end{aligned}$$

At room temperature, a surface emits 417.9 W/m^2 of energy at a wavelength of 9.89 μm.

Summary and Review—Earth's Modern Atmosphere

- ***Construct* a general model of the atmosphere based on the criteria of composition, temperature, and function, and *diagram* this model in a simple sketch.**

Our modern atmosphere is a gaseous mixture so evenly mixed it behaves as if it were a single gas. It is naturally odourless, colourless, tasteless, and formless. The principal substance of this atmosphere is air—the medium of life.

Above 480 km (300 mi) altitude, the atmosphere is rarefied (nearly a vacuum) and is called the **exosphere**, which means "outer sphere." The weight (force over a unit area) of the atmosphere, exerted on all surfaces, is termed **air pressure**. It decreases rapidly with altitude.

By *composition*, we divide the atmosphere into the **heterosphere**, extending from 480 km (300 mi) to 80 km (50 mi), and the **homosphere**, extending from 80 km to Earth's surface. Within the heterosphere and using *temperature* as a criterion, we identify the **thermosphere**. Its upper limit, called the **thermopause**, is at approximately 480 km altitude. **Kinetic energy**, the energy of motion, is the vibrational energy that we measure and call temperature. The actual amount of heat produced in the thermosphere is very small. The density of the molecules is so low that little actual **heat**, the flow of kinetic energy from one body to another because of a temperature difference between them, is produced. Nearer Earth's surface the greater number of molecules in the denser atmosphere transmits their kinetic energy as **sensible heat**, meaning that we can feel it.

The homosphere includes the **mesosphere, stratosphere,** and **troposphere**, as defined by temperature criteria. Within the mesosphere, cosmic or meteoric dust acts as nuclei around which fine ice crystals form to produce rare and unusual night clouds called **noctilucent clouds.**

The normal temperature profile within the troposphere during the daytime decreases rapidly with increasing altitude at an average of 6.4 C° per kilometre (3.5 F° per 1000 ft), a rate known as the **normal lapse rate**. The top of the troposphere is wherever a temperature of –57°C (–70°F) is recorded, a transition known as the **tropopause**. The actual lapse rate at any particular time and place may deviate considerably because of local weather conditions and is called the **environmental lapse rate**.

We distinguish a region in the heterosphere by its *function*. The **ionosphere** absorbs cosmic rays, gamma rays, X-rays, and shorter wavelengths of ultraviolet radiation and converts them into kinetic energy. A functional region within the stratosphere is the **ozonosphere**, or **ozone layer**, which absorbs life-threatening ultraviolet radiation, subsequently raising the temperature of the stratosphere.

exosphere (p. 66)
air pressure (p. 66)
heterosphere (p. 68)
homosphere (p. 69)
thermosphere (p. 70)
thermopause (p. 70)
kinetic energy (p. 71)
heat (p. 71)
sensible heat (p. 71)
mesosphere (p. 71)
noctilucent clouds (p. 71)
stratosphere (p. 71)
troposphere (p. 71)
tropopause (p. 71)
normal lapse rate (p. 71)
environmental lapse rate (p. 71)
ionosphere (p. 72)
ozonosphere, ozone layer (p. 72)

1. What is air? Where did the components in Earth's present atmosphere originate?
2. In view of the analogy by Lewis Thomas, characterize the various functions the atmosphere performs that protect the surface environment.
3. What three distinct criteria are employed in dividing the atmosphere for study?
4. Describe the overall temperature profile of the atmosphere, and list the four layers defined by temperature.
5. Describe the two divisions of the atmosphere on the basis of composition.
6. What are the two primary functional layers of the atmosphere and what does each do?

List the stable components of the modern atmosphere and their relative percentage contributions by volume, and _describe_ each.

Even though the atmosphere's density decreases with increasing altitude in the homosphere, the blend (proportion) of gases is nearly uniform. This stable mixture of gases has evolved slowly.

The homosphere is a vast reservoir of relatively inert *nitrogen*, originating principally from volcanic sources and from bacterial action in the soil; *oxygen*, a by-product of photosynthesis; *argon*, constituting about 1% of the homosphere and completely inert; and *carbon dioxide*, a natural by-product of life processes and fuel combustion.

7. Name the four most prevalent stable gases in the homosphere. Where did each originate? Is the prevalence of any of these changing at this time?

Describe the conditions within the stratosphere; specifically, _review_ the function and status of the ozonosphere (ozone layer).

The overall reduction of the stratospheric ozonosphere, or ozone layer, during the past several decades represents a hazard for society and many natural systems and is caused by chemicals introduced into the atmosphere by humans. Since World War II quantities of human-made **chlorofluorocarbons (CFCs)** and bromine-containing compounds have made their way into the stratosphere. The increased ultraviolet light at those altitudes breaks down these stable chemical compounds, thus freeing chlorine and bromine atoms. These atoms act as catalysts in reactions that destroy ozone molecules.

chlorofluorocarbons (CFCs) (p. 73)

8. Why is stratospheric ozone (O_3) so important? Describe the effects created by increases in ultraviolet light reaching the surface.
9. Summarize the ozone predicament and present trends and any treaties that intend to protect the ozone layer.
10. Evaluate Crutzen, Rowland, and Molina's use of the scientific method in investigating stratospheric ozone depletion.

Distinguish between natural and anthropogenic variable gases and materials in the lower atmosphere.

Within the troposphere, both natural and human-caused variable gases, particles, and other chemicals are part of the atmosphere. We coevolved with natural "pollution" and thus are adapted to it. But we are not adapted to cope with our own anthropogenic pollution. It constitutes a major health threat, particularly where people are concentrated in cities.

Vertical temperature and atmospheric density distribution in the troposphere can worsen pollution conditions. A **temperature inversion** occurs when the normal temperature decrease with altitude (normal lapse rate) reverses. In other words, temperature begins to increase at some altitude.

temperature inversion (p. 78)

11. Why are anthropogenic gases more significant to human health than are those produced from natural sources?
12. In what ways does a temperature inversion worsen an air pollution episode? Why?

Describe the sources and effects of carbon monoxide, nitrogen dioxide, and sulphur dioxide, and _construct_ a simple equation that illustrates photochemical reactions that produce ozone, peroxyacetyl nitrates, nitric acid, and sulphuric acid.

Odourless, colourless, and tasteless, **carbon monoxide (CO)** is produced by incomplete combustion (burning with limited oxygen) of fuels or other carbon-containing substances. Transportation is the major human-caused source for carbon monoxide. The toxicity of carbon monoxide is due to its affinity for blood hemoglobin, which is the oxygen-carrying pigment in red blood cells. In the presence of carbon monoxide, the oxygen is displaced and the blood becomes deoxygenated (Table 3.4).

Photochemical smog results from the interaction of sunlight and the products of automobile exhaust, the single largest contributor of pollution that produces smog. Car exhaust, containing *nitrogen dioxide* and *volatile organic compounds* (*VOCs*), in the presence of ultraviolet light in sunlight converts into major air pollutants—*ozone*, *peroxyacetyl nitrates* (*PAN*), and *nitric acid*. The principal photochemical by-products include *ozone* (O_3), which causes negative health effects, oxidizes surfaces, and kills or damages plants; and **peroxyacetyl nitrates (PAN)**, which produce no known health effects in humans but are particularly damaging to plants, including both agricultural crops and forests. **Nitrogen dioxide (NO_2)** damages and inflames human respiratory systems, destroys lung tissue, and damages plants. Nitric oxides participate in reactions that form nitric acid (HNO_3) in the atmosphere, forming both wet and dry acidic deposition. The **volatile organic compounds (VOCs)**, including hydrocarbons from gasoline, surface coatings, and electric utility combustion, are important factors in ozone formation.

The distribution of human-produced **industrial smog** over North America, Europe, and Asia is related to transportation and electrical production. Such characteristic pollution contains **sulphur dioxide**. Sulphur dioxide in the atmosphere reacts to produce **sulphate aerosols**, which produce sulphuric acid (H_2SO_4) deposition, which can be dangerous to health, and affect Earth's energy budget by scattering and reflecting solar energy. **Particulate matter (PM)** consists of dirt, dust, soot, and ash from industrial and natural sources.

Energy conservation and efficiency and reducing emissions are essential strategies for abating air pollution. Earth's next atmosphere most accurately may be described as the **anthropogenic atmosphere** (human-influenced atmosphere).

carbon monoxide (CO) (p. 80)
photochemical smog (p. 81)
peroxyacetyl nitrates (PAN) (p. 83)
nitrogen dioxide (p. 83)
volatile organic compounds (VOCs) (p. 83)
industrial smog (p. 83)
sulphur dioxide (p. 87)
sulphate aerosols (p. 87)
particulate matter (PM) (p. 87)
anthropogenic atmosphere (p. 87)

13. What is the difference between industrial smog and photochemical smog?
14. Describe the relationship between automobiles and the production of ozone and PAN in city air. What are the principal negative impacts of these gases?
15. How are sulphur impurities in fossil fuels related to the formation of acid in the atmosphere and acid deposition on the land?
16. In summary, what are the results from the first 20 years under *Clean Air Act* regulations?
17. Summarize the commitments Canada has made to improve air quality.

Critical Thinking

A. Read the 2003 progress report on "Particulate Matter and Ozone" found at **http://www.ec.gc.ca/CEPARegistry/documents/agree/PM_resp_03/toc.cfm**. Do you think the Canadian government is making enough progress to improve air quality? What are the economic costs of meeting the tougher standards? How do the costs balance against the benefits to health, the environment, and lower energy costs through efficiency and conservation? The U.S. Environmental Protection Agency Study described in this chapter estimated a benefit-to-cost ratio of 42 to 1. Should this influence a decision as to whether to strengthen the Canadian *Environmental Protection Act*?

B. Relative to item A: In your opinion, why is the public generally unaware of the details regarding costs and benefits? What are the difficulties in instructing the public? Why is there such media attention given to antiscience and nonscientific opinions? Take a moment and brainstorm recommendations for action, education, and public awareness on these issues.

C. To determine the total ozone column at your present location, go to the TOMS home page at **http://toms.gsfc.nasa.gov/teacher/ozone_overhead.html**, "What was the total ozone column at your house?" Select a point on the map or enter your latitude and longitude, and the date you want to check. The ozone column refers principally to stratospheric ozone and not to the photochemical pollutant in the lower troposphere. Note the instrument and satellite platform used. (Note also the limitations listed on the extent of data availability.) For several different dates, when do the lowest values occur? The highest values? Briefly explain what your results mean. How do you interpret the values found?

Surface energy budgets in a metropolitan area differ from the surrounding countryside, creating an urban heat island. Park space such as the Don Valley, one of many ravines that winds through Toronto, Ontario, offers some relief. [Photo by Marisa D'Andrea.]

4 Atmosphere and Surface Energy Balances

Key Learning Concepts

After reading the chapter, you should be able to:

- *Identify* the pathways of solar energy through the troposphere to Earth's surface: transmission, scattering, diffuse radiation, refraction, albedo (reflectivity), conduction, convection, and advection.
- *Describe* what happens to insolation when clouds are in the atmosphere and *analyze* the effect of clouds and air pollution on solar radiation received at ground level.
- *Review* the energy pathways in the Earth–atmosphere system, the greenhouse effect, and the patterns of global net radiation.
- *Plot* the daily radiation curves for Earth's surface and *label* the key aspects of incoming radiation, air temperature, and the daily temperature lag.
- *Portray* typical urban heat island conditions and *contrast* the microclimatology of urban areas with that of surrounding rural environments.

Earth's biosphere pulses with flows of solar energy that sustain our lives and empower natural systems. Changing seasons, Earth's variety of climates, and daily weather fluctuations remind us of this constant flow of energy cascading through the atmosphere. Earth's shifting seasonal rhythms are covered in Chapter 2. Energy and moisture exchanges between Earth's surface and the atmosphere are essential elements of weather and climate, and these are discussed in later chapters.

In this chapter: This chapter follows solar energy through the troposphere to Earth's surface. The *input* of insolation is countered by the *outputs* of reflected light and emitted infrared energy from the atmosphere and surface environment. Together, this input and output determines the net energy available to perform work. We examine surface energy budgets and analyze how net radiation is spent. The chapter concludes with a look at the unique energy and moisture environment in our cities. The view across a hot parking lot in summer, of cars and pavement, is all too familiar—the air shimmers as heat energy is radiated skyward. The climate of our urban areas differs measurably from that of surrounding rural areas. Focus Study 4.1 discusses solar energy, a renewable energy resource of great potential.

Energy Essentials

When you look at a photograph of Earth taken from space, you can clearly see the surface receipts of incoming insolation (see Earth on the back cover of this book). Land and water surfaces, clouds, and atmospheric gases and dust intercept solar energy. The flows of energy are manifest in swirling weather patterns, powerful oceanic currents, and the varied distribution of vegetation. Specific energy patterns differ for deserts, oceans, mountaintops, plains, rain forests, and ice-covered landscapes. In addition, the presence or absence of clouds may make a 75% difference in the amount of energy that reaches the surface, because clouds reflect incoming energy.

Energy Pathways and Principles

Earth's atmosphere and surface are heated by solar energy, which is unevenly distributed by latitude and which fluctuates seasonally. Figure 4.1 is a simplified flow diagram of shortwave and longwave radiation in the Earth–atmosphere system, discussed in the pages that follow. You will find it helpful to refer to this figure, and the more detailed energy balance illustration in Figure 4.13, as you read through the following section. We first look at some important pathways and principles for insolation as it passes through the atmosphere to Earth's surface.

Transmission The passage of shortwave and longwave energy through either the atmosphere or water is **transmission**. Our budget of atmospheric energy comprises shortwave radiation *inputs* (ultraviolet light, visible light, and near-infrared wavelengths) and longwave radiation *outputs* (thermal infrared) that pass through the atmosphere by transmission. Atmospheric gases and dust physically interact with insolation through processes of scattering, a redirection of energy through refraction and reflection.

Scattering (Diffuse Radiation) Insolation encounters an increasing density of atmospheric gases as it travels toward the surface. The gas molecules redirect radiation, changing the direction of the light's movement *without altering its wavelengths*. This phenomenon is known as **scattering** and represents 7% of Earth's reflectivity, or albedo (see Figure 4.13). Dust particles, pollutants, ice, cloud droplets, and water vapour produce further scattering.

Have you wondered why Earth's sky is blue? And why sunsets and sunrises are often red? These simple questions have an interesting explanation, based upon a principle known as Rayleigh scattering (named for English physicist Lord Rayleigh, who stated the principle in 1881). This principle relates wavelength to the size of molecules or particles that cause the scattering. The general rule is: *The shorter the wavelength, the greater the scattering, and the longer the wavelength, the less the scattering.* Small gas molecules in the air scatter shorter wavelengths of light. Thus, the shorter wavelengths of visible light—the blues and violets—scatter the most and dominate the lower atmosphere. And, because there are more blue than violet wavelengths in sunlight, a blue sky prevails. A sky filled with smog and haze appears almost white because the larger particles associated with air pollution act to scatter all wavelengths of visible light.

The angle of the Sun's rays determines the thickness of atmosphere they must pass through to reach the surface. Therefore, direct rays (from overhead) experience less

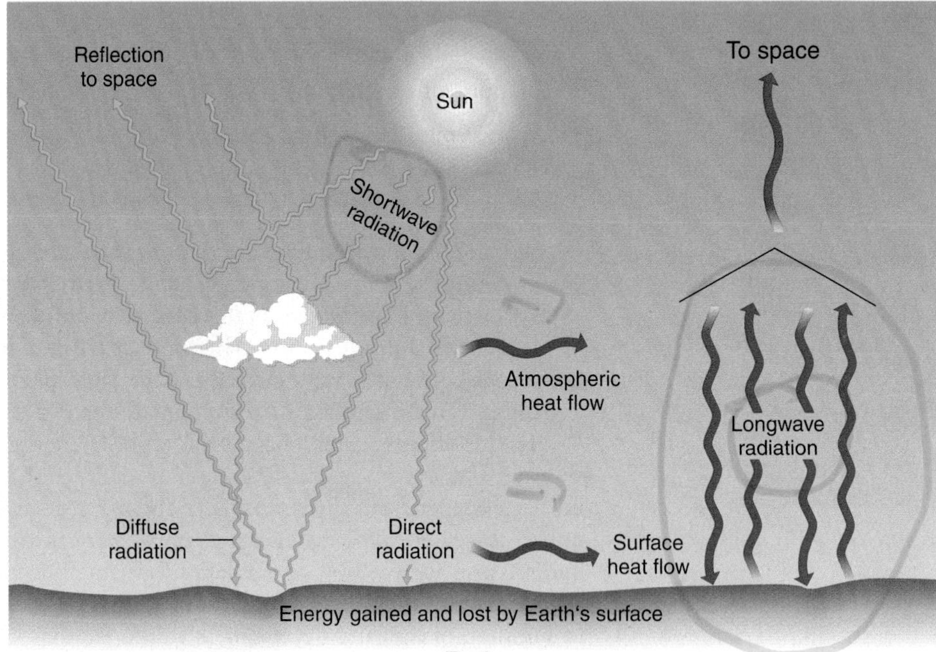

FIGURE 4.1 Energy gained and lost by Earth's surface and atmosphere.
Simplified view of the Earth–atmosphere energy system. Circuits include incoming shortwave insolation, reflected shortwave radiation, and outgoing longwave radiation.

ANIMATION Global Warming, Climate Change

scattering and absorption than do low, oblique-angle rays that must travel farther through the atmosphere. Insolation from the low-altitude Sun undergoes more scattering of shorter wavelengths, leaving only the residual oranges and reds to reach the observer at sunset or sunrise.

Some incoming insolation is diffused by clouds and atmosphere and is transmitted to Earth as **diffuse radiation**, the downward component of scattered light (labelled in Figure 4.13). This light is multidirectional and thus casts shadowless light on the ground.

Refraction As insolation enters the atmosphere, it passes from one medium to another, from virtually empty space into atmospheric gases, or from air into water. This transition subjects the insolation to a change of speed, which also shifts its direction, a bending action called **refraction**. In the same way, a crystal or prism refracts light passing through it, bending different wavelengths to different angles, separating the light into its component colours to display the spectrum. A rainbow is created when visible light passes through myriad raindrops and is refracted and reflected toward the observer at a precise angle (see Figure 4.2).

FIGURE 4.2 A rainbow.
Raindrops refract and reflect light to produce a primary rainbow. Note that the colour order in the rainbow is distributed with the shortest wavelengths on the inside of the bow and the longest wavelengths on the outside of the bow. [Photo by Robert W. Christopherson.]

Another example of refraction is a *mirage*, an image that appears near the horizon where light waves are refracted by layers of air of different temperatures (and consequently of different densities) on a hot day. The atmospheric distortion of the setting Sun in Figure 4.3 is also a product of refraction—light from the Sun low in the sky must penetrate more air than when the Sun is high; it is refracted through air layers of different densities on its way to the observer.

An interesting function of refraction is that it adds approximately 8 minutes of daylight that we would lack if Earth had no atmosphere. Sunlight refracts in its passage from space through the atmosphere, and so, at sunrise, we see the Sun's image about 4 minutes before the Sun actually peeks over the horizon. Similarly, the Sun actually sets at sunset but refracts its image from over the horizon for about 4 minutes afterward, so we see sunset later than it truly happens. To this day, science cannot predict the exact time of visible sunrise or sunset within these 4 minutes because the degree of refraction continually varies with atmospheric temperature, moisture, and pollutants.

Insolation Input *Insolation* is the single energy input driving the Earth–atmosphere system. The world map in Figure 4.4 shows the distribution of average annual solar energy received at Earth's surface. It includes all the radiation that arrives at Earth's surface, both direct and diffuse (scattered by the atmosphere).

Several patterns are notable on the map. Insolation decreases poleward from about 25° latitude in both the Northern and Southern Hemispheres. Consistent daylength and high Sun altitude produce average annual values of 180–220 W/m^2 throughout the equatorial and tropical latitudes. In general, greater insolation of 240–280 W/m^2 occurs in low-latitude deserts worldwide because of frequently cloudless skies. Note this energy pattern in the cloudless subtropical deserts in both hemispheres (for example, the Sonoran, Saharan, Arabian, Gobi, Atacama, Namib, Kalahari, and Australian deserts).

Albedo and Reflection A portion of arriving energy bounces directly back into space without being absorbed or performing any work. This returned energy is called **reflection. Albedo** is the reflective quality (intrinsic brightness) of a surface. It is an important control over the

FIGURE 4.3 Sun refraction.
The distorted appearance of the Sun nearing sunset over the ocean is produced by refraction of the Sun's image in the atmosphere. Have you ever noticed this effect? [Photo by Robert W. Christopherson.]

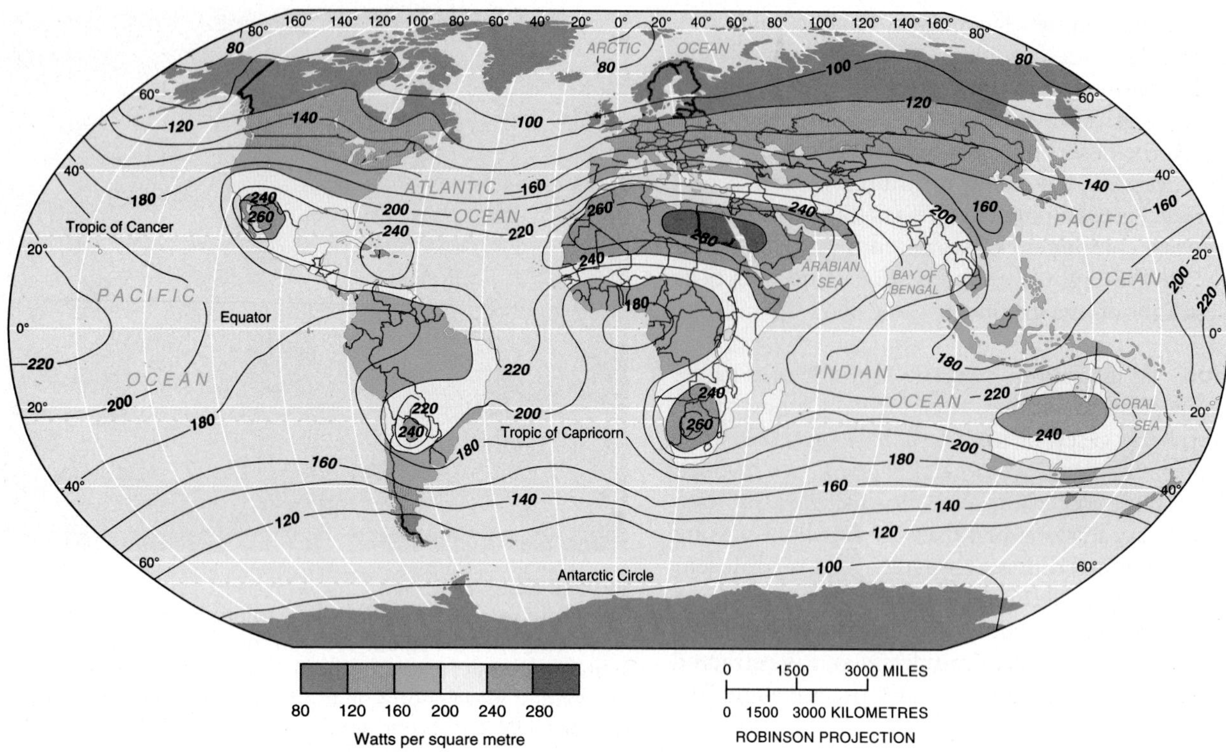

FIGURE 4.4 Insolation at Earth's surface.
Average annual solar radiation received on a horizontal surface at ground level in watts per square metre (100 W/m^2 = 75 kcal/cm^2/year). [After M. I. Budyko, *The Heat Balance of the Earth's Surface* (Washington, DC: U.S. Department of Commerce, 1958), p. 99.]

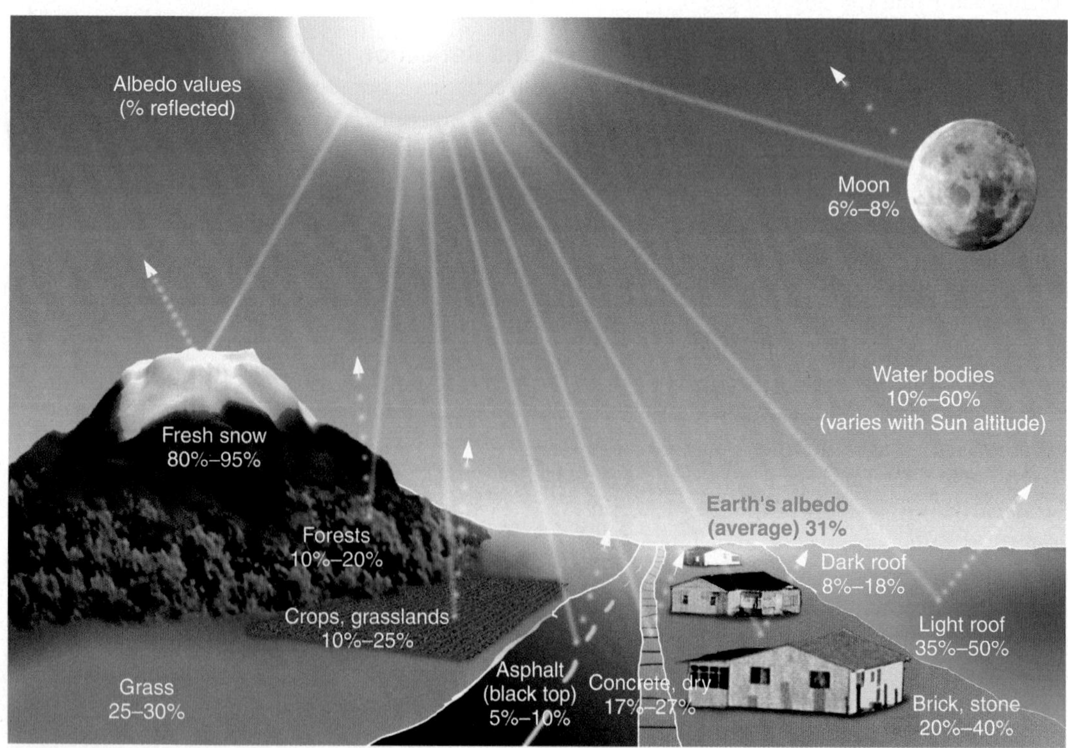

FIGURE 4.5 Various albedo values.
Different surfaces have different albedo values. In general, light surfaces are more reflective than dark surfaces and thus have higher albedo values. [Data from M. I. Budyko, *The Heat Balance of the Earth's Surface* (Washington, DC: U.S. Department of Commerce, 1958), p. 36.]

Global Albedo Values,
Global Shortwave Radiation

amount of insolation that is available for absorption by a surface. We state albedo as the percentage of insolation that is reflected (zero percent is total absorption; 100% is total reflectance). Examine the different surfaces and their albedo values in Figure 4.5.

In the visible wavelengths, darker colours have lower albedos, and lighter colours have higher albedos. On water surfaces, the angle of the solar rays also affects albedo values; lower angles produce a greater reflection than do higher angles (Figure 4.6). In addition, smooth surfaces increase albedo, whereas rougher surfaces reduce it. Specific locations experience highly variable albedo values during the year in response to changes in cloud and ground cover. Earth Radiation Budget (ERB) sensors aboard the *Nimbus*-7 satellite measured average albedos of 19%–38% for all surfaces between the tropics (23.5° N to 23.5° S) and as high as 80% in the polar regions.

Earth and its atmosphere reflect 31% of all insolation when averaged over a year. Looking ahead to Figure 4.13, you can see that Earth's average albedo is a combination of 21% reflected by clouds, 3% reflected by the ground (combined land and ocean surfaces), and 7% reflected and scattered by the atmosphere. By comparison, a full Moon, which is bright enough to read by under clear skies, has only a 6%–8% albedo value. Thus, with *earthshine* being four times brighter than moonlight (four times the albedo), and with Earth four times greater in diameter than the Moon, it is no surprise that astronauts report how startling our planet looks from space. News Report 4.1 presents information on earthshine output changes.

Figure 4.7 portrays total albedos for July 1985 and January 1986 as measured by the Earth Radiation Budget experiments aboard several satellites. These patterns are typical of most years. As compared with July albedos, January albedos are higher poleward of 40° N, because of the snow and ice that cover the ground. Tropical forests are characteristically low in albedo (15%), whereas generally cloudless deserts have high albedos (35%). The southward-shifting cloud cover over equatorial Africa is quite apparent on the January map. What other seasonal changes do you see on these ERB albedo maps?

Clouds, Aerosols, and the Atmosphere's Albedo An unpredictable factor in the tropospheric energy budget, and therefore in refining climatic models, is the role of clouds. Clouds reflect insolation and thus cool Earth's surface. An *increase in albedo* caused by clouds is described by the term **cloud-albedo forcing**. Yet clouds act as insulation, trapping longwave radiation from Earth and raising minimum temperatures. An *increase in greenhouse warming* caused by clouds is described as **cloud-greenhouse forcing**. Figure 4.8 illustrates the general effects of clouds on shortwave radiation and longwave radiation. More on clouds is presented later in this chapter and in a detailed section in Chapter 7.

FIGURE 4.6 Sunlight reflected off the ocean.
An astronaut's view of reflected sunlight off the Mozambique Channel, between the East coast of Africa and the island country of Madagascar. Ocean surface albedo values increase with lower Sun angles and calmer seas. [Space Shuttle photo from NASA.]

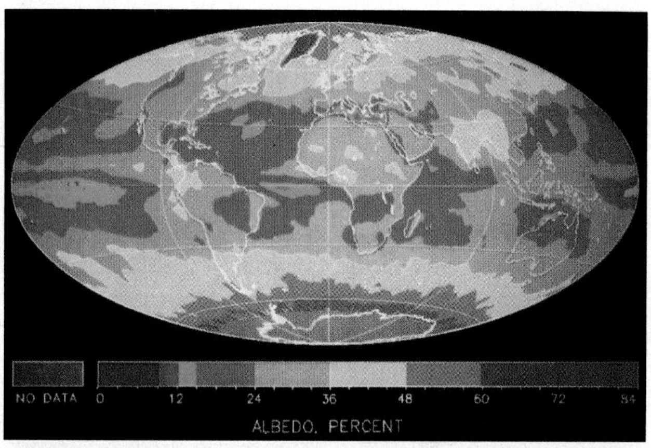

(a) July

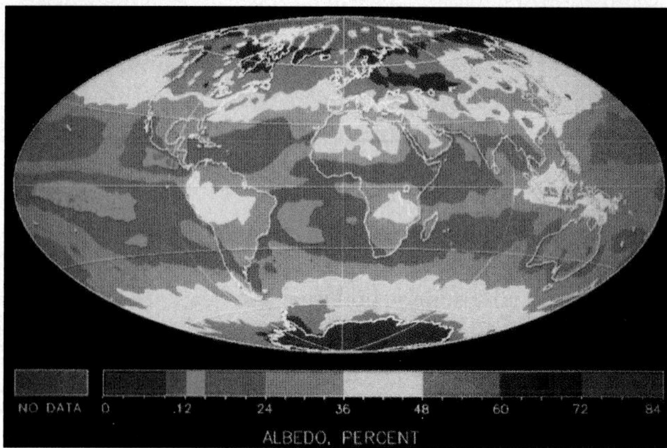

(b) January

FIGURE 4.7 Total albedos for July and January.
Total albedos for July 1985 (a) and January 1986 (b) as measured by the Earth Radiation Budget experiments (ERB) aboard satellites *Nimbus-7, NOAA-9,* and *ERBS* (*ERB Satellite*). Each colour represents a 12% interval in albedo values. (The map base is a modified elliptical equal-area projection.) [Courtesy of Radiation Services Branch, Langley Research Center, NASA.]

News Report 4.1

Earthshine Studies—Possible Energy Budget Diagnostic

Earth's reflection of light to space might prove to be a useful tool in analyzing energy budgets and climate. Earth's average albedo is 31%—that is, 31% of all incoming insolation returns to space without being absorbed. We have all seen the effect of *earthshine*—Earth's total albedo reflectance to space—a faint illumination of the dark portion of the Moon, especially in crescent phase, when the dark portion of the lunar disk is barely visible (Figure 1).

In contrast, the Moon reflects only 6% to 8% of the sunlight that hits its surface, producing the "moonlight" familiar to everyone on Earth. Despite the bright, white appearance of the Moon, the lunar surface albedo is about the same as that of asphalt pavement. Because Earth reflects about 400% as much light as the Moon, and is about 400% as great in diameter, it is a startling presence in space.

FIGURE 1 Earthshine illuminates the Moon. Our Moon intercepts some of Earth's shortwave reflectance to space. Earthshine is most visible when the Moon is in a crescent phase. Check this out next time you see the Moon in its crescent to half phase. [Composite photos courtesy of Earthshine Project, Big Bear Solar Observatory.]

Earthshine, if properly analyzed, is a proxy (substitute, representative) measure of Earth's shortwave reflectance and an important diagnostic tool in climate change studies. The significance of measuring earthshine is this: An approximate 1% change in albedo will produce about a 1 C° (2 F°) change in average atmospheric temperature. Thus, an albedo change can produce a temperature change, which can produce further albedo change and further alter climate. The solar-constant 11-year cycle produces about a 0.1% variation in earthshine and is counted out as a cause for present global warming.

Cloud cover is the significant factor that drives changes in Earth's shortwave reflectance, although surface changes and atmospheric pollution also are important. Increases in cloud cover are an indicator of increasing atmospheric temperatures. Relative to surface changes, imagine the impact on global albedo values if there were an increase in snow-free landscapes.

Scientists from the New Jersey Institute of Technology and California Institute of Technology now measure earthshine at the Big Bear Solar Observatory during the Moon's crescent phase when Earth's sunlight hemisphere is toward the Moon. These data are then compared to the International Satellite Cloud Climatology Project (ISCCP) record. André Danjon of France began earthshine studies in 1925. Current research shows Earth's average albedo was on a steady decline from 1984–2000 (less cloudy), whereas 2001–2004 (more clouds) demonstrated a complete reversal with increasing Earth reflectance. These large variations in reflectance imply climatologically significant cloud-driven changes in Earth's radiation budget, which is consistent with the large tropospheric warming that has occurred over the most recent decades. Moreover, if the observed reversal in Earth's reflectance trend is sustained during the next few years, it might also play a very important role in future climate change.*

A lot remains to be learned about this yardstick for Earth's energy balance. Think about earthshine the next time you take a moonlight walk.

*E. Pallé et al., "Changes in Earth Reflectance over the Past Two Decades," *Science* 304 (May 28, 2004): 1299–1301.

Other mechanisms affect atmospheric albedo and therefore atmospheric and surface energy budgets. Industrialization is producing a haze of pollution that is increasing the reflectivity of the atmosphere, including sulphate aerosols, soot and fly-ash, and black carbon. Emissions of sulphur dioxide and the subsequent chemical reactions in the atmosphere form *sulphate aerosols*. These aerosols act as an insolation-reflecting haze in clear-sky conditions. The result is both an atmospheric warming through absorption by the pollutants and a surface cooling through reduction in insolation reaching ground and water surfaces.

Figure 4.9 is from the CERES (Clouds and the Earth Radiant Energy System) sensors aboard satellite *Terra* and

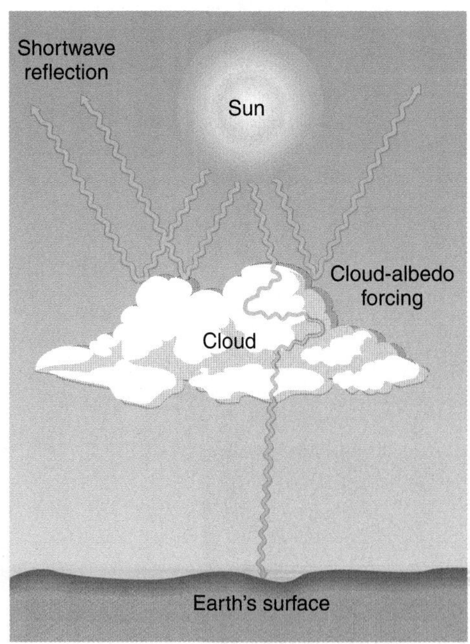

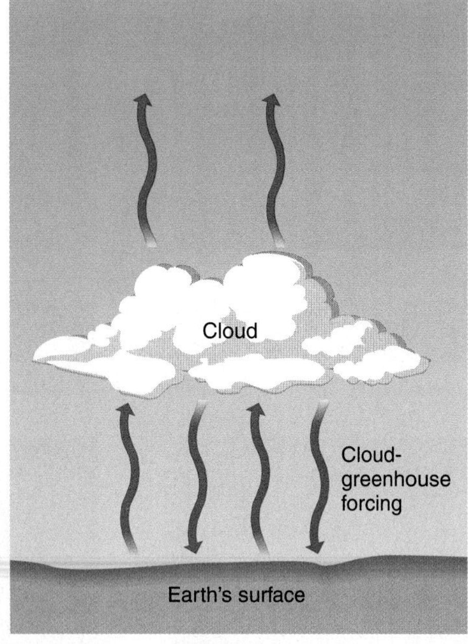

FIGURE 4.8 The effects of clouds on shortwave and longwave radiation. Shortwave radiation is reflected and scattered by clouds; a high percentage is returned to space (a). Longwave radiation emitted by Earth is absorbed and emitted by clouds; some infrared energy is radiated to space and some back toward the surface (b).

shows these effects on the atmospheric energy budget. The increased aerosols, containing black carbon, cause higher albedos (reflection off the atmosphere), an increase in atmospheric warming (absorption of energy by aerosols), and an increase in surface cooling (less insolation reaching Earth's surface). These aerosols reduce surface insolation by 10% and increase energy absorption in the atmosphere by 50%. Such pollution effects in southern Asia will affect the dynamics of the Asian monsoon through alteration of the region's Earth–atmosphere energy budget (see monsoons in Chapter 6). A weakening monsoonal flow will negatively impact regional water resources and agriculture. This research is part of the international, multi-agency Indian Ocean Experiment (INDOEX, see **http://www-indoex.ucsd.edu/**).

The eruption of Mount Pinatubo in the Philippines, beginning explosively during June 1991, illustrates how Earth's internal processes affect the atmosphere. Approximately 13–18 million metric tons (15–20 million tons) of sulphur dioxide were injected into the stratosphere; winds rapidly spread this aerosol (tiny droplets) worldwide (see the images in Figure 6.1). As a result, atmospheric albedo increased worldwide and produced a temporary average cooling of 0.5 C° (0.9 F°).

Absorption **Absorption** is the assimilation of radiation by molecules of matter and its conversion from one form of energy to another. Insolation (both direct and diffuse) that is not part of the 31% reflected from Earth's surface and atmosphere is absorbed. It is converted into either infrared radiation or chemical energy (by plants in photosynthesis). The temperature of the absorbing surface is raised in the process, and that warmer surface radiates more total energy at shorter wavelengths—thus, *the hotter the surface, the shorter the wavelengths that are emitted.* In addition to absorption by land and water surfaces (about 45% of incoming), absorption also occurs in atmospheric gases, dust, clouds, and stratospheric ozone (about 24% of incoming insolation). Figure 4.13 summarizes the pathways of insolation and the flow of heat in the atmosphere and at the surface.

Conduction, Convection, and Advection Several means transfer heat energy in a system. **Conduction** is the molecule-to-molecule transfer of heat energy as it diffuses through a substance. As molecules warm, their vibration increases, causing collisions that produce motion in neighbouring molecules, thus transferring heat from warmer to cooler materials.

Different materials (gases, liquids, and solids) conduct sensible heat directionally from areas of higher temperature to those of lower temperature. This heat flow transfers energy through matter at varying rates, depending on the conductivity of the material—Earth's land surface is a better conductor than air; moist air is a slightly better conductor than dry air.

Gases and liquids also transfer energy by movements called **convection**, when the physical mixing involves a strong vertical motion. When a lateral (horizontal) motion dominates, the term **advection** applies. In the atmosphere or in bodies of water, warmer (less dense) masses tend to rise and cooler (denser) masses tend to sink, establishing patterns of convection. Sensible heat transports physically through the medium in this way.

You commonly experience such energy flows in the kitchen: Energy is conducted through the handle of a pan, or boiling water bubbles in the saucepan in convective motions (Figure 4.10). Also in the kitchen you may use a convection oven that uses a fan to circulate heated air to uniformly cook food.

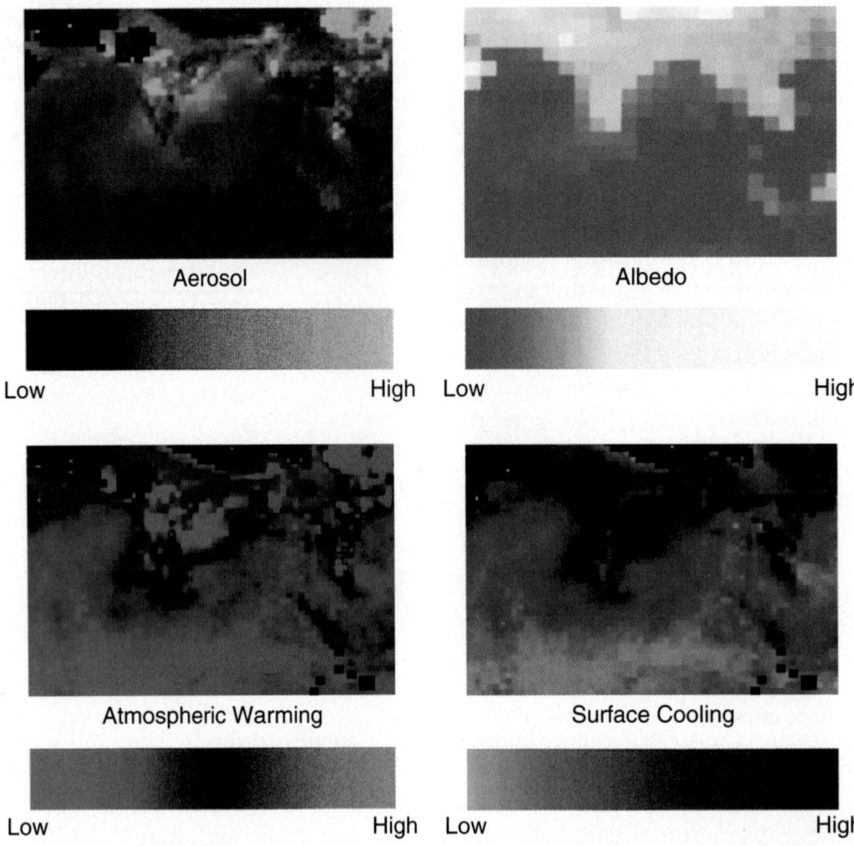

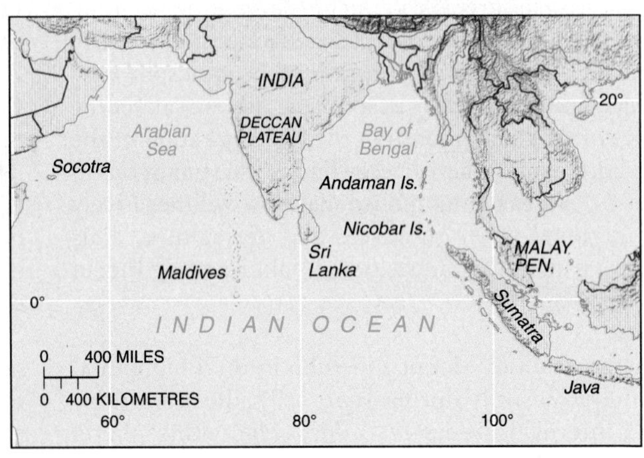

FIGURE 4.9 Aerosols impact Earth–atmosphere energy budgets.
Aerosols including black carbon both reflect and absorb incoming insolation as identified in these four images by the CERES sensors aboard satellite *Terra*, taken between January and March 2001 over southern Asia and the Indian Ocean. Note the colour scale for each image rating from low to high aerosol levels, albedo values, amount of atmospheric warming, and resultant surface cooling. The increased aerosol levels from human activities produce higher albedos and atmospheric absorption of energy, resulting in a lowering of surface temperatures. [CERES images aboard *Terra* courtesy of Goddard Space Flight Center, NASA.]

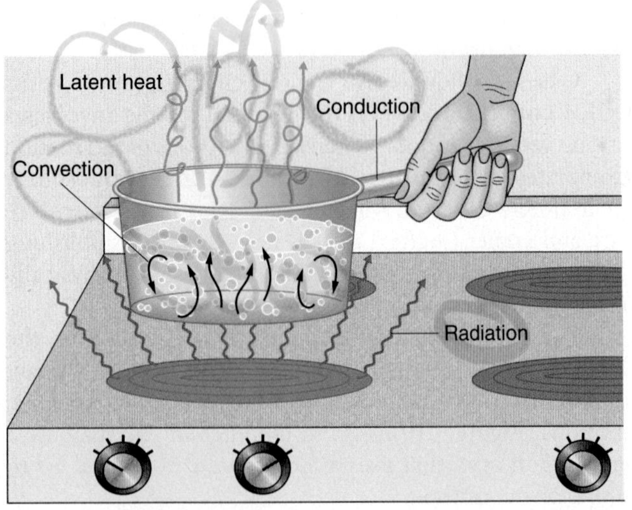

FIGURE 4.10 Heat energy transfer processes.
A pan of water on the stove illustrates heat transfer. Infrared energy *radiates* from the burner to the saucepan and the air. Energy *conducts* through the molecules of the pan and the handle. The water physically mixes, carrying heat energy by *convection*. The energy in the water and handle is measurable as *sensible heat*. The vapour leaving the surface of the water contains the *latent heat* absorbed in the change of water to a vapour.

In physical geography, we find many examples of each physical transfer mechanism.

- *Conduction* examples include surface energy budgets, temperature differences between land and water bodies, the heating of surfaces and overlying air, soil temperatures;
- *Convection* includes atmospheric and oceanic circulation, air mass movements and weather systems, internal motions deep within Planet Earth that produce a magnetic field, and movements in the crust; and
- *Advection* includes horizontal movement of winds from land to sea and back, fog that forms and moves to another area, air mass movements from source regions.

Now with these pathways and principles in mind, we put it all together in the energy budgets of the lower atmosphere.

Energy Balance in the Troposphere

The Earth–atmosphere energy system budget naturally balances itself in a steady-state equilibrium. The atmosphere and surface eventually radiate infrared energy back to space, and this energy, together with reflected energy, equals the initial solar input—think of cash flows into and out of a chequing account and the desired balance when deposits and withdrawals are equal.

Greenhouse gases in the atmosphere effectively delay losses to space and act to warm the lower atmosphere. We examine this effect, and then develop an overall budget for the troposphere.

The Greenhouse Effect and Atmospheric Warming

Previously, we characterized Earth as a cool-body radiator, emitting energy in infrared wavelengths from its surface and atmosphere toward space. (In contrast, the Sun is a hot-body radiator, emitting shorter wavelengths from its surface.) However, some of this infrared radiation is absorbed by carbon dioxide, water vapour, methane, nitrous oxide, chlorofluorocarbons (CFCs), and other gases in the lower atmosphere and then emitted back toward Earth. This absorption and emission delays energy loss to space and is an important factor in warming the troposphere. The rough similarity between this process and the way a greenhouse operates gives the process its name—the **greenhouse effect**.

In a greenhouse, the glass is transparent to shortwave insolation, allowing light to pass through to the soil, plants, and materials inside, where absorption and conduction take place. The absorbed energy is then radiated as thermal infrared back toward the glass, but the glass physically traps both the longer infrared wavelengths and the warmed air inside the greenhouse. Thus, the glass acts as a one-way filter, allowing the light energy in but not allowing the heat energy out, except through conduction. The same process also is quite evident in a car parked in direct sunlight.

Opening the greenhouse roof vent, or the car windows, allows the air inside to mix with the outside environment, thereby removing heat by moving air physically from one place to another—the process of convection. It is surprising how hot the interior of a car gets, even on a day with mild temperatures outside. Many people place an opaque sunscreen across the windshield to prevent shortwave energy from entering the car to begin the greenhouse process. Have you taken steps to reduce the insolation input into your car's interior or into windows at home?

In the atmosphere, the greenhouse analogy does not fully apply because infrared radiation is not trapped as it is in a greenhouse. Rather, its passage to space is *delayed* as the infrared radiation is absorbed by certain gases, clouds, and dust in the atmosphere and is emitted to Earth's surface. According to scientific consensus, today's increasing carbon dioxide concentration is forcing more infrared radiation absorption in the lower atmosphere, thus producing a warming trend and changes in the Earth–atmosphere energy system.

Clouds and Earth's "Greenhouse"

Clouds affect the heating of the lower atmosphere in several ways, depending on cloud type. Not only is the percentage of cloud cover important, but the cloud type, height, and thickness (water content and density) also has an effect. High-altitude, ice-crystal clouds reflect insolation with albedos of about 50%, whereas thick, lower cloud cover reflects about 90% of incoming insolation.

To understand the actual effects on the atmosphere's energy budget, however, we must consider both transmission of shortwave and longwave radiation and cloud type. Figure 4.11a portrays the *cloud-greenhouse forcing* caused by high clouds (warming, because their greenhouse effects exceed their albedo effects); and Figure 4.11b portrays the *cloud-albedo forcing* produced by lower, thicker clouds (cooling, because albedo effects exceed greenhouse effects). Understanding the nature of global cloud cover is crucial in refining computer models that forecast global climate change.

Jet contrails (condensation trails) produce high cirrus clouds (Figure 4.11c)—sometimes called *false cirrus clouds*. Scientists were suspicious that these clouds affected atmospheric and surface temperatures. The tragedy that struck the World Trade Center, and humanity, on 9/11/2001, inadvertently provided researchers with a chance to study these effects. Following 9/11, there was a three-day grounding of all commercial airline traffic and therefore no contrails across the United States. Weather data from 4000 stations over 30 years were compared with data during the three-day shutdown. *Diurnal temperature range* (DTR)—the difference between daytime maximum and nighttime minimum temperatures—increased during the three days. Specifically, maximum temperatures were more responsive to the missing clouds than minimums.

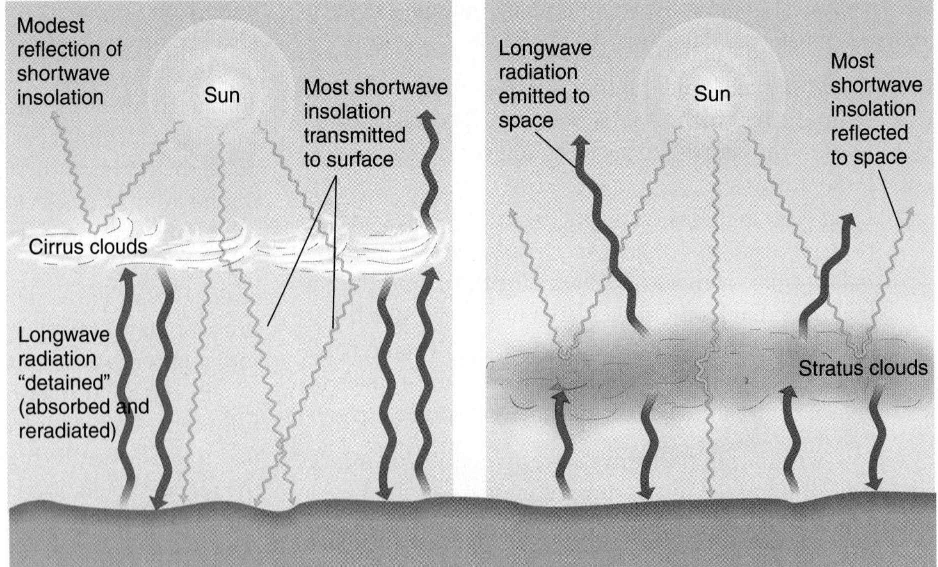

(a) High clouds: net greenhouse forcing and atmospheric warming

(b) Low clouds: net albedo forcing and atmospheric cooling

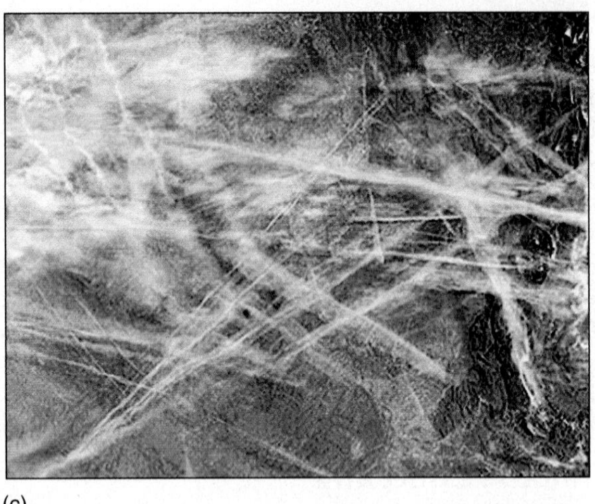

(c)

FIGURE 4.11 Energy effects of two cloud types. Cloud effects vary depending on cloud type. (a) High, ice-crystal clouds (called *cirrus*) transmit most of the insolation. However, they absorb and delay losses of outgoing longwave infrared, producing a greater greenhouse forcing and a net warming of Earth. (b) Low, thick clouds (stratus) reflect most of the incoming insolation and radiate longwave infrared to space, producing a greater albedo forcing and a net cooling of Earth. (c) Jet airliner exhaust triggers cirrus cloud development. Newer, thinner contrails spread to form cloud cover. [(c) Astronaut photo May 15, 2002, courtesy of NASA-JSC.]

Later study of synoptic conditions (air pressure, humidity, air masses data, all gathered at a specific time), analysis of Canadian air space, a check on conditions during adjacent three-day periods, and a look at the few military flights that took place during the halt of air travel served to verify the initial findings and strengthen the conclusion.* The elimination of contrail-stimulated clouds produced an increase in DTR—slightly higher afternoon and slightly lower nighttime temperature readings across the United States. The largest effects were in those regions where the greatest number of flights occur in the fall. This ongoing study is helpful in the spatial analysis of possible impacts of future aircraft design on the Earth–atmosphere energy budget.

*See David J. Travis et al., "Contrails reduce daily temperature range," *Nature* 418 (August 8, 2002): 601, from the Department of Geography and Geology, University of Wisconsin–Whitewater; and, D. J. Travis, A. M. Carleton, and, R. G. Lauritsen, "Regional variations in U.S. diurnal temperature range for the 9/11–14/2001 aircraft groundings: Evidence of jet contrail influence on climate," *Journal of Climate* 17 (March 1, 2004): 1123–34.

To better understand the role of clouds, NASA is operating the CERES program, an acronym for Clouds and Earth's Radiant Energy System. CERES sensors aboard satellites began operating in 1997 (*TRMM*) and the newest in 2000 (*Terra*). In addition to understanding natural clouds, the role of jet contrails (soot, oxidized sulphur, nitrogen oxides, mixed in hot and humid exhaust gases) is also important for they cause the formation of high ice-crystal cirrus clouds. CERES data are an important part of the study of aerosols and the monsoons in Figure 4.9. (See **http://asd-www.larc.nasa.gov/ceres/ASDceres.html**.)

Collection of data by CERES sensors covers both reflected and emitted radiation. Figure 4.12 shows the first global monthly images from satellite *Terra* for March 2000 in W/m^2 flux (meaning energy "flow"). In Figure 4.12a lighter regions indicate where more sunlight is reflected into space than is absorbed—for example, by light land surfaces such as deserts, or by cloud cover such as over tropical lands. Green and blue areas illustrate where less light was reflected.

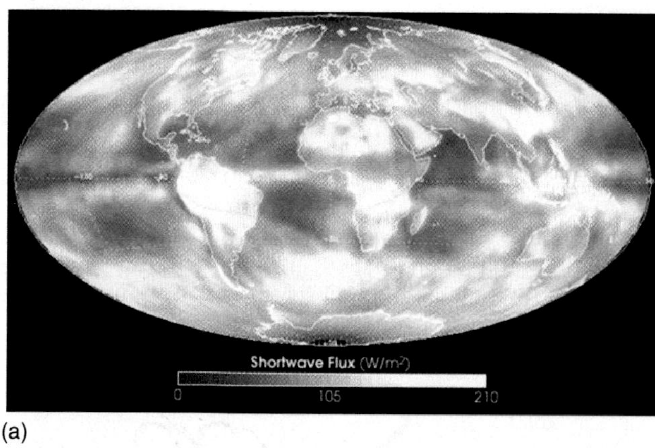

(a)

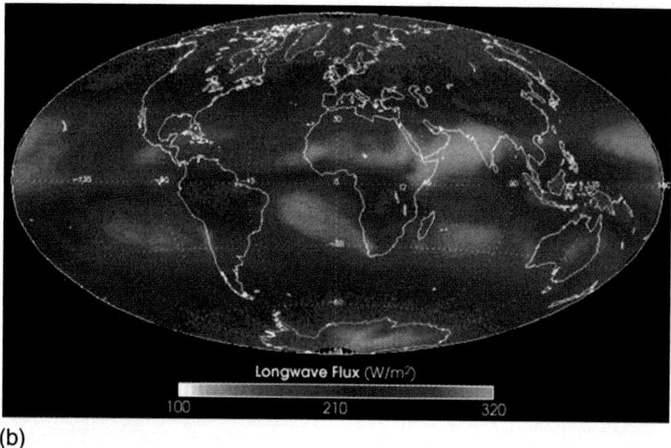

(b)

FIGURE 4.12 Shortwave and longwave images show Earth's radiation budget components. The CERES sensors aboard *Terra* made these portraits in March 2000, capturing (a) outgoing shortwave energy flux reflected from clouds, land, and water—Earth's albedo; and, (b) longwave energy flux emitted by surfaces back to space. The scale beneath each image displays value gradations in watts per square metre. [Images courtesy of CERES Instrument Team, Langley Research Center, NASA.]

In Figure 4.12b orange and red pixels indicate regions where more heat was absorbed and emitted to space, whereas less heat energy is escaping in the blue and purple regions. Those blue regions of lower longwave emissions over tropical lands are due to tall, thick clouds along the equatorial convergence (Amazon, equatorial Africa, and Indonesia); these clouds also caused higher shortwave reflection. Subtropical desert regions exhibit greater longwave radiation emissions owing to the presence of little cloud cover and greater radiative energy losses from surfaces that have absorbed a lot of energy, as we saw in Figure 4.4.

Earth–Atmosphere Radiation Balance

If Earth's surface and its atmosphere are considered separately, neither exhibits a balanced radiation budget. The average annual energy distribution is positive (an energy surplus) for Earth's surface and negative (an energy deficit) for the atmosphere as it radiates energy to space. Considered together, these two equal each other, making it possible for us to construct an overall energy balance. However, regionally and seasonally Earth absorbs more energy in the tropics and less in the polar regions, establishing the imbalance that drives global circulation patterns.

Figure 4.13 summarizes the Earth–atmosphere radiation balance. It brings together all the elements discussed to this point in the chapter by following 100% of arriving insolation through the troposphere. The shortwave portion of the budget is on the left in the illustration; the longwave part of the budget is on the right. Of 100% of solar energy arriving, Earth's average albedo is 31%. Figure 4.12a shows this shortwave radiation reflected from the Earth–atmosphere system during March 2000. Absorption by atmospheric clouds, dust, and gases involves another 21% and accounts for the atmospheric heat input. Stratospheric ozone absorption and radiation accounts for another 3% of the atmospheric budget. About 45% of the incoming insolation transmits through to Earth's surface as direct and diffuse radiation.

The natural energy balance occurs through energy transfers from the surface that are both *nonradiative* (physical motion) and *radiative*. Nonradiative transfers include convection, conduction, and the latent heat of evaporation (energy that is absorbed and dissipated by water as it evaporates and condenses). Radiative transfer is by infrared radiation between the surface, the atmosphere, and space, as illustrated on the right in Figure 4.13's depiction of the greenhouse effect.

In summarizing the thermal infrared part of the budget, Earth eventually emits the remaining 69% into space: 21% (atmospheric heating) + 45% (surface heating) + 3% (ozone emission) = 69%. This longwave radiation from the Earth–atmosphere system (net outgoing longwave) is shown in Figure 4.12b.

Figure 4.14 summarizes the radiation balance for all shortwave and longwave energy by latitude:

- Between the tropics, the angle of incoming insolation is high and daylength is consistent, with little seasonal variation, so more energy is gained than lost—*energy surpluses dominate*.
- In the polar regions, the Sun is low in the sky, surfaces are light (ice and snow) and reflective, and for up to 6 months during the year no insolation is received, so more energy is lost than gained—*energy deficits prevail*.
- At around 36° latitude, a balance exists between energy gains and losses for the Earth–atmosphere system.

The imbalance of net radiation from tropical surpluses to the polar deficits drives a vast global circulation of both energy and mass. The meridional (north–south) transfer agents are winds, ocean currents, dynamic weather systems, and related phenomena. Dramatic examples of such energy and mass transfers are tropical cyclones—hurricanes and typhoons. Forming in the tropics, these powerful storms

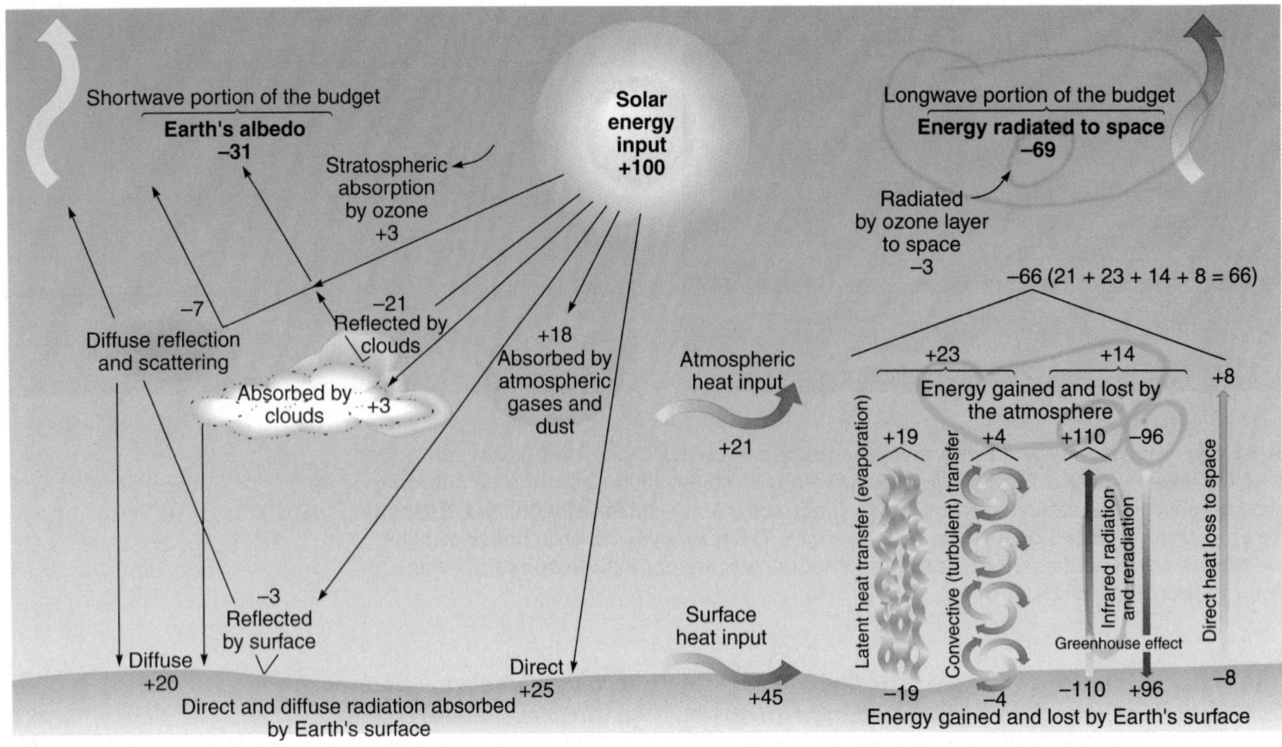

FIGURE 4.13 Details of the Earth–atmosphere energy balance.
Solar energy cascades through the lower atmosphere (left-hand portion of the illustration), where it is absorbed, reflected, and scattered. Clouds, atmosphere, and the surface reflect 31% of this insolation back to space. Atmospheric gases and dust and Earth's surface absorb energy and radiate infrared radiation. Earth and atmosphere exchange energy through latent heat transfer in water vapour, convective transfer (moving air), and infrared radiation (right-hand portion of the illustration). Over time, Earth emits, on average, 69% of incoming energy to space. When added to Earth's average albedo (31%, reflected energy), this equals the total energy input from the Sun.

Global Warming, Climate Change, Earth–Atmosphere Energy Balance

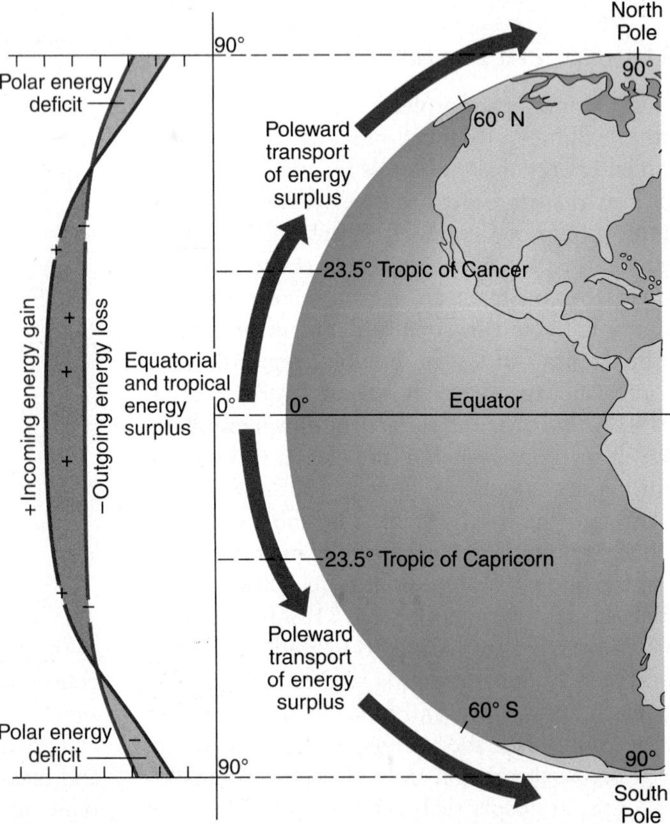

FIGURE 4.14 Energy budget by latitude.
Earth's energy surpluses and deficits by latitude produce poleward transport of energy and mass in each hemisphere—atmospheric circulation and ocean currents.

mature and migrate to higher latitudes, carrying with them energy, water, and water vapour.

Having established the Earth–atmosphere radiation balance, we next focus on energy characteristics at Earth's surface. Essentially, we want to examine energy budgets along the ground level as portrayed in Figure 4.13.

Energy Balance at Earth's Surface

Solar energy is the principal heat source at Earth's surface. The direct and diffuse radiation and infrared radiation arriving at the ground surface are shown in Figure 4.13. These radiation patterns at Earth's surface are of great interest to geographers and should be of interest to everyone because these are the surface environments where we live.

Daily Radiation Patterns

The fluctuating daily pattern of incoming shortwave energy absorbed and the resultant air temperature is shown in Figure 4.15. This graph represents idealized conditions for bare soil on a cloudless day in the middle latitudes. Incoming energy arrives during daylight, beginning at sunrise, peaking at noon, and ending at sunset.

The shape and height of this insolation curve vary with season and latitude. The highest trend for such a curve occurs at the time of the summer solstice (around June 21 in the Northern Hemisphere and December 21 in the Southern Hemisphere). The air temperature plot also responds to seasons and variations in insolation input. Within a 24-hour day, air temperature generally peaks between 3:00 and 4:00 P.M. and dips to its lowest point right at or slightly after sunrise.

The relationship between the insolation curve and the air temperature curve on the graph is interesting—they do not align; there is a *lag*. The warmest time of day occurs not at the moment of maximum insolation but at the moment when a *maximum of insolation is absorbed* and emitted to the atmosphere from the ground. As long as the incoming energy exceeds the outgoing energy, air temperature continues to increase, not peaking until the incoming energy begins to diminish in the afternoon as the Sun's altitude decreases. In contrast, if you have ever gone camping in the mountains, you no doubt experienced the coldest time of day with a wake-up chill at sunrise!

The annual pattern of insolation and air temperature exhibits a similar lag. For the Northern Hemisphere, January is usually the coldest month, occurring after the December solstice and the shortest days. Similarly, the warmest months of July and August occur after the June solstice and the longest days. Figure 4.16 shows how patterns of bright sunshine vary across the country.

Simplified Surface Energy Balance

Earth's surface is supplied with energy that varies daily and seasonally. Energy and moisture are continually

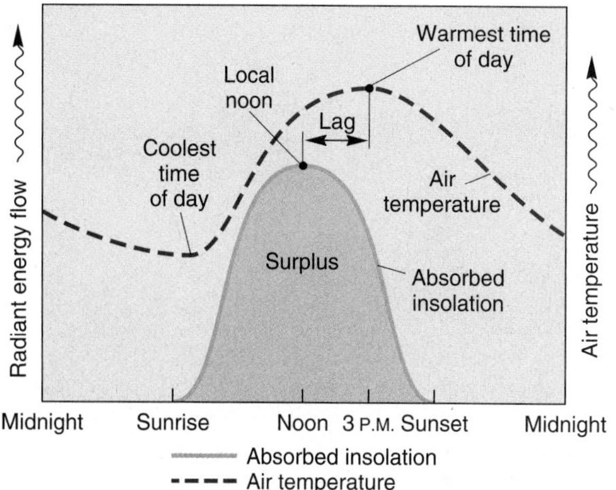

FIGURE 4.15 Daily radiation curves.
Sample radiation plot for a typical day shows the changes in insolation (orange line) and air temperature (dashed line). Comparing the curves demonstrates a lag between local noon (the insolation peak for the day) and the warmest time of day.

exchanged at the surface, creating worldwide "boundary layer climates" of great variety. Physical conditions at or near Earth's surface are studied in **microclimatology**—the science of this lowest portion of the atmosphere. The following discussion is more meaningful if you visualize an actual surface—perhaps a park, a front yard, or a place on campus.

The surface receives visible light and infrared radiation, and it reflects light and radiates infrared according to the following simple scheme:

$+SW\downarrow$	$-SW\uparrow$	$+LW\downarrow$	$-LW\uparrow$	$=$	NET R
(Insolation)	(Reflection)	(Infrared)	(Infrared)		(Net Radiation)

We use SW for shortwave, LW for longwave for simplicity. You may come acro ss other symbols in the microclimatology literature, such as Q* (pronounced Q-star) for NET R, K for shortwave, and L for longwave.

Figure 4.17 shows the components of a surface energy balance. The soil column shown continues to a depth at which energy exchange with surrounding materials or with the surface becomes negligible, usually less than a metre. Sensible heat transfer in the soil is through conduction, predominantly downward during the day or in summer, and toward the surface at night or in winter. Energy from the atmosphere that is moving toward the surface is regarded as positive (a gain), and energy that is moving away from the surface, through sensible and latent heat transfers, is considered negative (a loss) to the surface account.

Adding and subtracting the energy flow at the surface completes the calculation of **net radiation (NET R)**, or the balance of all radiation at Earth's surface. As the components of this simple equation vary with daylength through the seasons, cloudiness, and latitude, NET R varies. Figure 4.18 illustrates the components of a surface energy balance for a typical summer day at a midlatitude location showing the daily change in the components of

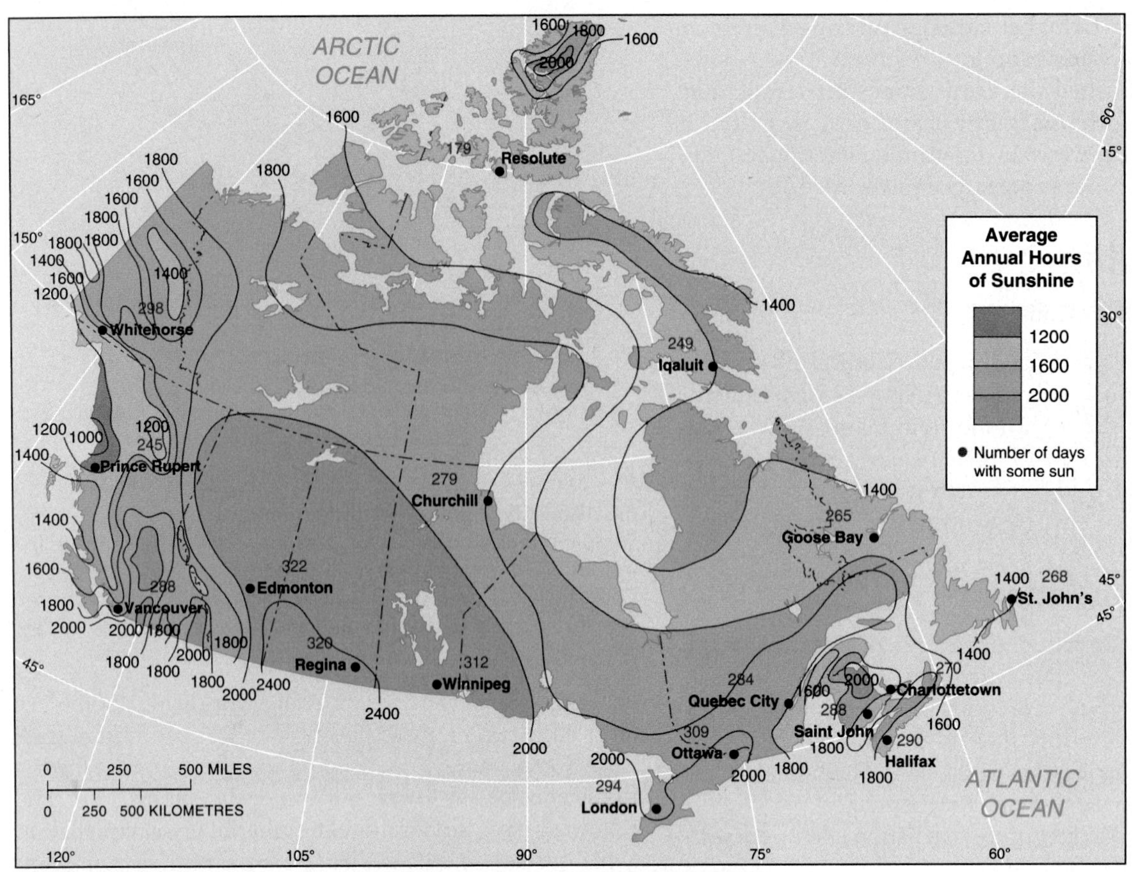

Sunniest Places in Canada			
Sunniest month	Eureka, N.W.T.	621 hours	May 1973
Greatest average annual number of sunny hours	Estevan, Sask.	2537	
Major city with greatest annual average number of sunny hours	Saskatoon	2450	
Sunniest small town under 10,000 population	Coronation, Alta.	2490	
Sunniest provincial capital	Regina	2331	
Sunniest year on record	Manyberries, Alta.	2785	1976
Shortest spell of consecutive days without sun	Charlottetown	10 days	
Sunniest summer on average	Yellowknife	1065 hours	June, July, August
Sunniest winter on average	Gimli, Man.	376 hours	December, January, February
Greatest annual number of hours of possible sunshine	Alert, N.W.T.	4580	
Greatest annual average number of sunny days	Calgary	329	
Greatest number of sunny days in one year	Medicine Hat	346	1976
Greatest number of sunshine recorder sites	Quebec	84	

FIGURE 4.16 Average annual hours of sunshine received across Canada. The greatest amounts of bright sunshine are received on the prairies even though these areas are farther north than southern Ontario and Québec. What factors influence this pattern of sunshine? [*The Climates of Canada*, David Phillips, Senior Climatologist, Environment Canada, 1990. Used by permission, the Minister of Public Works and Government Services Canada.]

FIGURE 4.17 Surface energy budget. Idealized input and output energy budget components for a surface and a soil column. Sensible heat transfer in the soil is through conduction, predominantly downward during the day or in summer, and toward the surface at night or in winter. (SW = shortwave, LW = longwave.)

net radiation. The items plotted are direct and diffuse insolation (+SW↓), reflected energy (surface albedo value, −SW↑), and infrared radiation arriving at (+LW↓) and leaving from (−LW↑) the surface.

Surface albedo values (−SW↑) dictate the amount of insolation reflected, and therefore not absorbed, at the surface. As an example, imagine a snow-covered landscape as a surface energy system. Snow has high reflectivity, sending sunlight back to space and reducing the amount of insolation absorbed. Consequently, surfaces and air temperatures are lower, and thus the snow cover does not melt. This is a system with positive feedback. (Remember from Chapter 1 that *positive feedback* increases response in the system: more cooling-more snow-increasing albedo-more cooling-then colder, drier air-then less snow-and so on.)

At night, the net radiation value becomes negative because the SW component ceases at sunset and the surface continues to lose infrared energy to the atmosphere. The surface rarely reaches a zero net radiation value—a perfect balance—at any one moment, but over time, Earth's surface naturally balances incoming and outgoing energies.

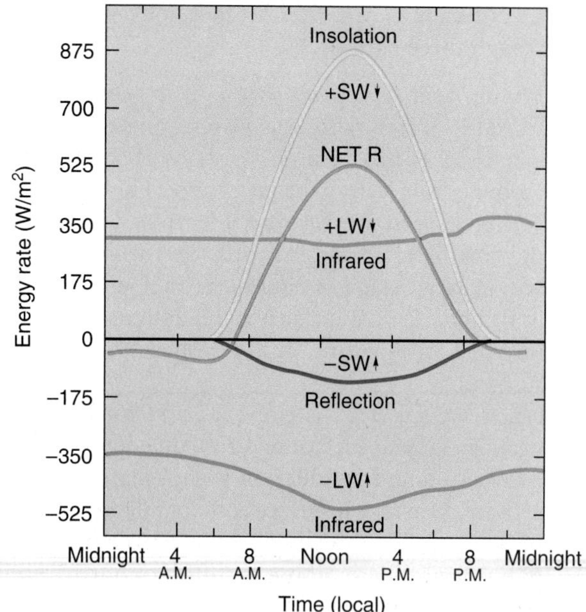

FIGURE 4.18 A day's radiation budget.
Radiation budget components and resulting net radiation (NET R) on a typical summer day for a midlatitude location (Matador in southern Saskatchewan, about 51° N, on July 30, 1971). [Adapted by permission from T. R. Oke, *Boundary Layer Climates* (New York: Methuen & Co., 1978), p. 21.]

Net Radiation The net radiation (NET R of all wavelengths) available at Earth's surface is the final outcome of the entire radiation-balance process discussed in this chapter. Figure 4.19 displays the global mean annual net radiation at ground level. The abrupt change in radiation balance from ocean to land surfaces is evident on the map. Note that all values are positive; negative values probably occur only over ice-covered surfaces poleward of 70° latitude in both hemispheres. The highest net radiation occurs north of the equator in the Arabian Sea at 185 W/m^2 per year. Aside from the obvious interruption caused by landmasses, the pattern of values appears generally zonal, or parallel, decreasing away from the equator.

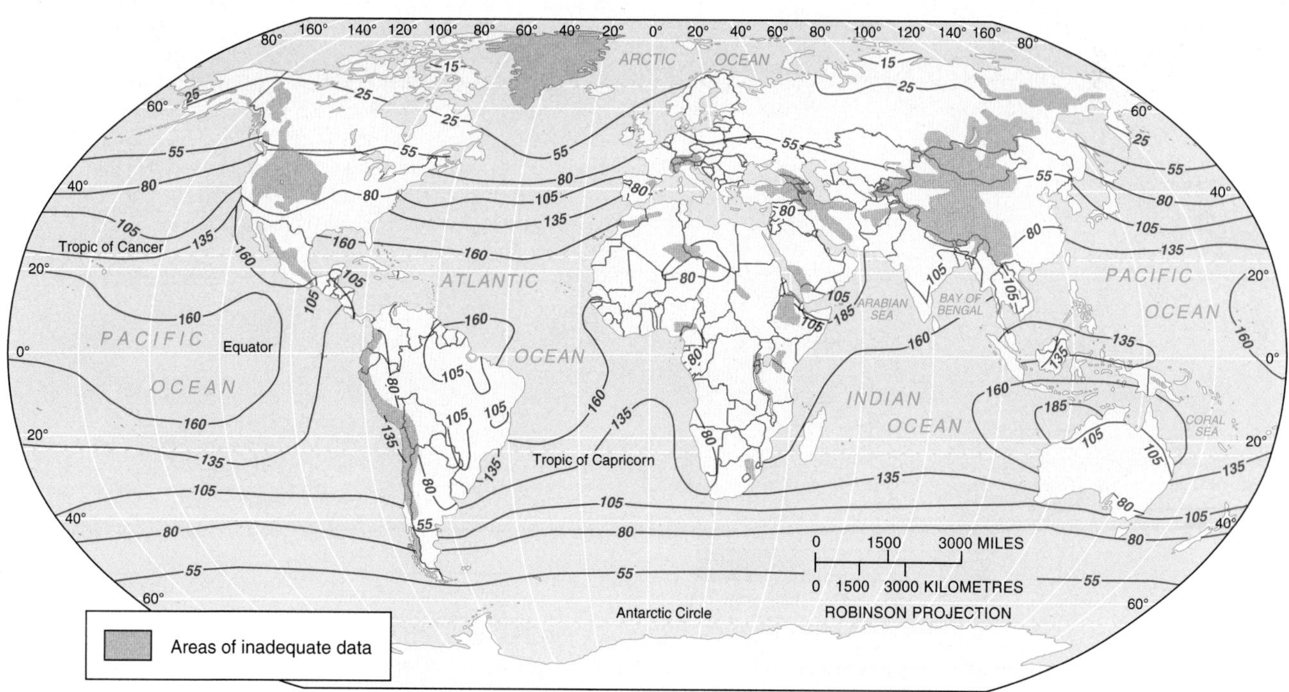

FIGURE 4.19 Global net radiation (NET R).
Distribution of global mean annual net radiation (NET R) at surface level in watts per square metre (100 W/m^2 = 75 kcal/cm^2/year). [After M. I. Budyko, *The Heat Balance of the Earth's Surface* (Washington, DC: U.S. Department of Commerce, 1958), p. 106.]

Net radiation is expended from a nonvegetated surface through three pathways:

- *LE*, or *latent heat of evaporation*, is the energy that is stored in water vapour as water evaporates. Large quantities of this *latent heat* are absorbed into water vapour during water's change of state. This heat energy is thereby removed from the surface. Conversely, this heat energy releases to the environment when water vapour changes state back to a liquid (discussed in Chapter 7). Latent heat is the dominant expenditure of Earth's entire NET R, especially over water surfaces.
- *H*, or *sensible heat*, is the back-and-forth transfer between air and surface in turbulent eddies, through convection and conduction within materials. This activity depends on surface and boundary-layer temperatures and on the intensity of convective motion in the atmosphere. About one-fifth of Earth's entire NET R is mechanically radiated as sensible heat from the surface, especially over land.
- *G*, or *ground heating and cooling*, is the energy that flows into and out of the ground surface (land or water) by conduction. During a year, the overall *G* value is zero because the stored energy from spring and summer is equalled by losses in fall and winter.

Another factor in ground heating is energy absorbed at the surface to melt snow or ice. In snow- or ice-covered landscapes, most available energy is in sensible and latent heat used in the melting and warming process.

On land, the highest annual values for latent heat of evaporation (*LE*) occur in the tropics and decrease toward the poles (Figure 4.20). Over the oceans, the highest *LE* values are over subtropical latitudes, where hot, dry air comes into contact with warm-ocean water.

The values for sensible heat (*H*) are distributed differently, being highest in the subtropics (Figure 4.20). Here, vast regions of subtropical deserts feature nearly waterless surfaces, cloudless skies, and almost vegetation-free landscapes. The bulk of NET R is expended as sensible heat in these dry regions. Moist and vegetated surfaces expend less in *H* and more in *LE*, as you can see by comparing the maps in Figures 4.20 and 4.21.

Understanding net radiation is essential to solar energy technologies that concentrate shortwave energy for use. Solar energy offers great potential worldwide and is presently the fastest-growing form of energy conversion by humans, although still decades away from its possibilities. Focus Study 4.1 briefly reviews direct application of surface energy budgets.

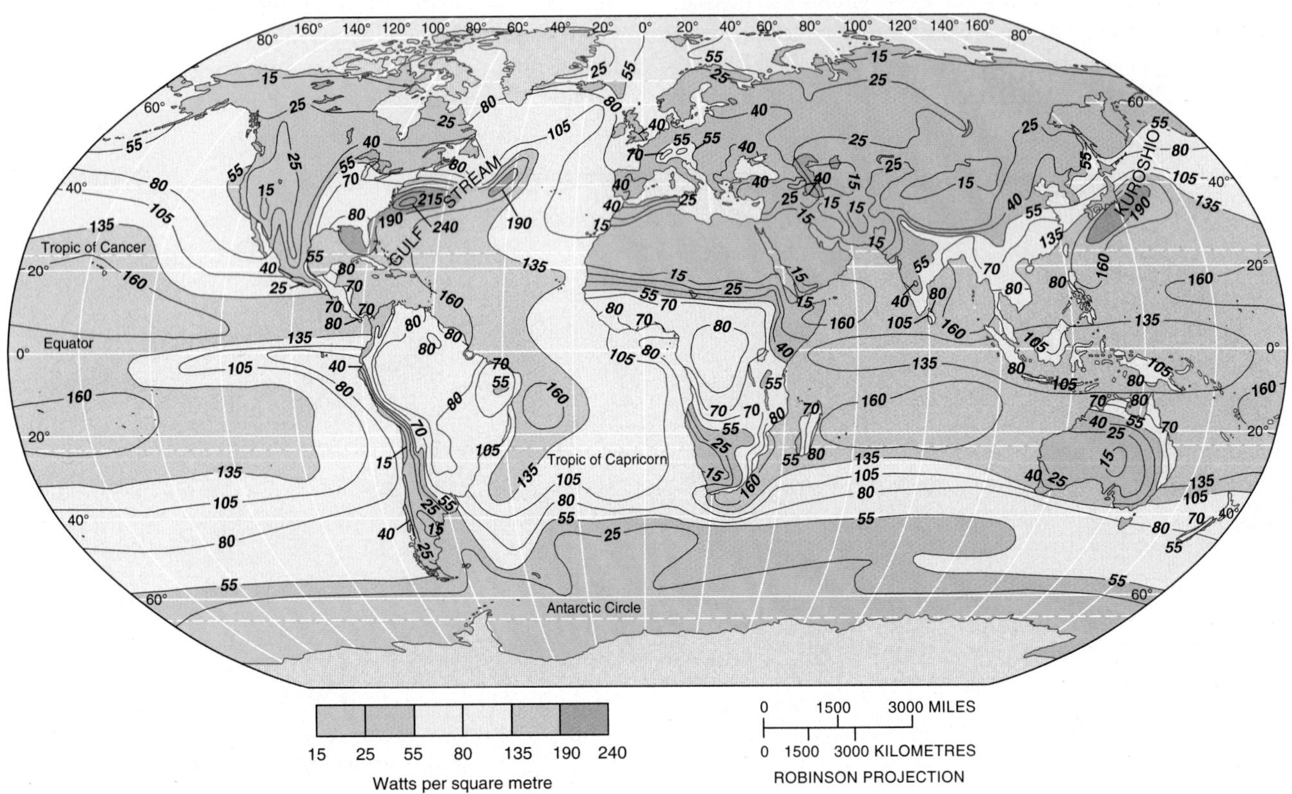

FIGURE 4.20 Global latent heat of evaporation (*LE*).
Distribution of annual energy expenditure as the latent heat of evaporation (*LE*) at surface level in watts per square metre (100 W/m^2 = 75 kcal/cm^2/year). Note the high values associated with high sea-surface temperatures in the area of the Gulf Stream and Kuroshio currents. [Adapted by permission from M. I. Budyko, *The Earth's Climate Past and Future* (New York: Academic Press, 1982), p. 56.]

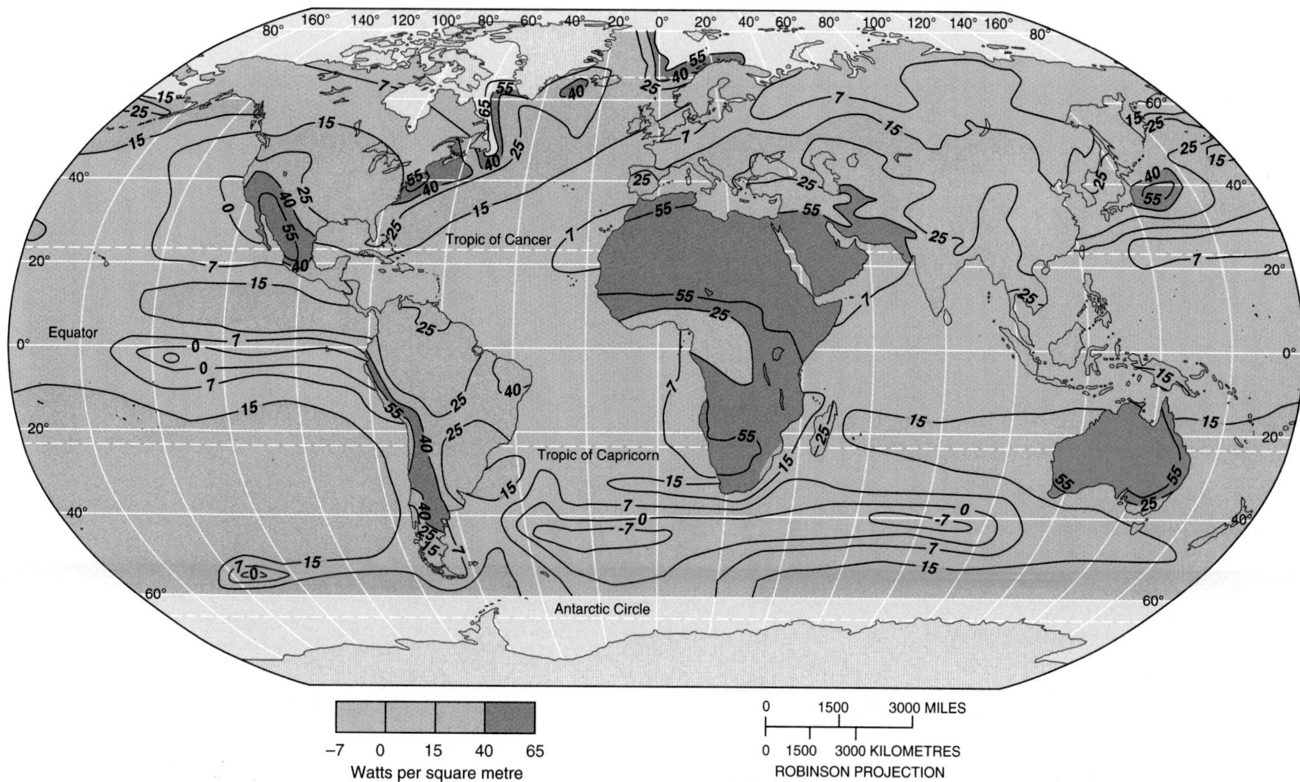

FIGURE 4.21 Global sensible heat (*H*).
Distribution of annual energy expenditure as sensible heat (*H*) at surface level in watts per square metre (100 W/m^2 = 75 kcal/cm^2/year). [Adapted by permission from M. I. Budyko, *The Earth's Climate Past and Future* (New York: Academic Press, 1982), p. 59.]

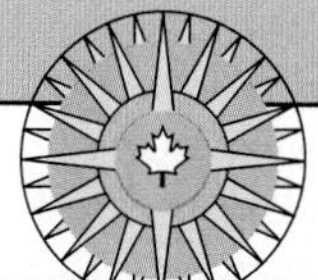

Focus Study 4.1

Solar Energy Collection and Concentration

Consider the following:

- Old photographs of residences in southern California and Florida show solar (flat-plate) water heaters on many rooftops. Early twentieth-century newspaper ads and merchandise catalogues featured the Climax solar water heater (1905) and the Day and Night water heater (1909). Applied solar energy principles and technologies are well established! However, low-priced natural gas and oil displaced many of these early applications.
- The insolation receipt in just 35 minutes at the surface of the United States exceeds the amount of energy derived from the burning of fossil fuels (coal, oil, natural gas) in a year.
- An average building in the United States receives 6 to 10 times more energy from the Sun hitting its exterior than is required to heat the inside.
- A 500-watt photovoltaic system that converts sunlight directly into electricity (including batteries) is cheaper to install at a rural site than a 2 km (1.2 mi) power line bringing in electricity. Such a system supplies more than enough electricity for lights, television, computer, a water pump, and some appliances. Photovoltaic prices dropped from $75 per watt in 1975 to $US 3.00 per watt in 2004.
- Installed photovoltaic capacity jumped 43% in 2000 (87 new megawatts in one year), worldwide capacity is now estimated at 288 megawatts. This production tripled 1996 levels.

Not only does insolation warm Earth's surface, it also provides an inexhaustible supply of energy far into the future for humanity. Sunlight is direct, pervasive (spreading widely), and renewable and has been collected for centuries through various technologies. Yet it is underutilized.

Rural villages in developing countries could benefit greatly from the simplest, most cost-effective solar application—the *solar-panel cooker*. For example, people in Kenya walk many kilometres collecting fuelwood for cooking fires (Figure 1a). Each village and refugee camp is surrounded by impoverished land, stripped of wood. Using solar cookers, villagers are able to cook meals and sanitize their drinking water without scavenging for wood (Figure 1b). (See Solar Cookers

(continued)

Focus Study 4.1 *(continued)*

(a)

(b)

FIGURE 1 The solar-cooking solution.
(a) Five women haul firewood many miles to the Dadaab refugee camp in northeastern Kenya. (b) Kenyan women in training to use their solar-panel cookers, which do not require scavenging the countryside for scarce fuelwood. These simple cookers collect direct and diffuse insolation through transparent glass or plastic and trap infrared radiation in an enclosed box or cooking bag. (This is a small-scale, efficient application of the greenhouse effect.) Construction is easy, using cardboard components. Temperatures easily exceed 105°C (220°F) for baking, boiling, purifying water, and sterilizing instruments. [Photos by Solar Cookers International, Sacramento, California.]

International at **http://solarcooking.org/**.)

In less-developed countries, the money for electrification (a *centralized* technology) is not available despite the push from more developed countries and energy corporations for large capital-intensive power projects. In such countries, the pressing need is for *decentralized* energy sources, appropriate in scale to everyday needs, such as cooking, heating water, and pasteurization. Net per capita (per person) cost for solar cookers is far less than for centralized electrical production, regardless of fuel source.

Collecting and Concentrating Solar Energy

Any surface that receives light from the Sun is a *solar collector*. But the diffuse nature of solar energy received at the surface requires that it be collected, concentrated, transformed, and stored to be useful. Space heating is the simplest application. Windows that are carefully designed and placed allow sunlight to shine into a building, where it is absorbed and converted into sensible heat. Here we have an everyday application of the greenhouse effect.

A *passive solar system* captures heat energy and stores it in a "thermal mass," such as water-filled tanks, adobe, tile, or concrete. Three key features of passive solar design are (1) large areas of glass facing south toward the Sun (facing north in the Southern Hemisphere), (2) a thermal storage medium, and (3) shades or screens to prevent light entry in the warm summer months. At night, shades or other devices can cover glass areas to prevent energy loss from the structure. An *active solar system* involves heating water or air in a collector and then pumping it through a plumbing system to a tank where it can provide hot water for direct use or for space heating.

Solar energy systems can generate heat energy of an appropriate scale for approximately half the present domestic applications in the United States (space heating and water heating). In marginal climates, solar-assisted water and space heating is feasible as a backup; even in New England and the Northern Plains states, solar collection systems prove effective. (See the National Solar Radiation Data Base at **http://rredc.nrel.gov/solar/**.)

Focusing (concentrating) mirrors, such as Fresnel lenses, or parabolic (curved surface) troughs and dishes can be used to attain very high temperatures to heat water or other heat-storing fluids. Kramer Junction, California, about 225 km (140 mi) northeast of Los Angeles, in the Mojave Desert near Barstow, has the world's largest operating solar electric-generating facility. A capacity of 150 MWe (megawatts electric; 150 million watts) operates at the plant. This is a moderate-sized power plant. Long troughs of computer-guided curved mirrors concentrate sunlight to create temperatures of 390°C (735°F) in vacuum-sealed tubes filled with synthetic oil. The heated oil heats water; the heated water produces steam that rotates turbines to generate cost-effective electricity. The facility converts 23% of the sunlight it receives into electricity during peak hours (Figure 2a) and operation and maintenance costs continue to decrease.

The U.S. National Renewable Energy Laboratory (NREL, **http://www.nrel.gov** and the U.S. National Center for Photovoltaics at **http://www.nrel.gov/ncpv/**) was established in 1974 to coordinate solar energy research, development, and testing in partnership with private industry. NREL's headquarters building in Golden, Colorado, features the latest in passive and active solar design. At NREL's Outdoor Test Facility, successful tests continue on arrays of prototype solar cells. Some of

(a)

(b)

(c)

FIGURE 2 Solar thermal and photovoltaic energy production.
(a) Kramer Junction solar thermal energy installation in southern California. (b) NREL Outdoor Test Facility in Golden, Colorado, where a variety of photovoltaic cell arrays successfully convert sunlight directly into electricity. (c) The Sacramento Municipal Utility District installed a PV array that doubles as parking lot cover. [Photos by (a) Kramer Junction Operating Company, Los Angeles; (b) and (c) Bobbé Christopherson.]

these panels have been in operation for more than 10 years (Figure 2b).

Electricity Directly from Sunlight

Producing electricity by *photovoltaic cells* (PVs) is a technology that has been used in spacecraft since 1958. Familiar to us all are the solar cells in pocket calculators (more than 100 million units now in use). When light shines upon a semiconductor material in these cells, it stimulates a flow of electrons (an electrical current) in the cell. PV cells are arranged in modules that can be assembled in large arrays.

The efficiency of these cells has improved to the level that they are generally cost-competitive, especially if government policies and subsidies were to be balanced evenly among energy sources. NREL developed a copper-indium-gallium solar cell that achieves an astonishing 18.8% conversion rate of sunlight to electricity. New cells that are 50% more efficient than crystalline silicon cells are now available for satellites.

Rooftop photovoltaic electrical generation is now cheaper than power line construction to rural sites. As of 1998, some 250,000 homes in Mexico, Indonesia, South Africa, India, and elsewhere have PV roof systems. A solar power project in the Philippines will bring electricity to 150 remote villages when completed. Norway, at the same high latitudes as Alaska, has 60,000 units operating and is adding about 8000 new PV systems a year. Some 200 photovoltaic power systems are operating in the Navajo Nation of northeastern Arizona. Innovative uses abound as shown in Figure 2c. (See the U.S. Department of Energy's "Photovoltaic Home Page," at **http://www.eere.energy.gov/**.)

Total production in 2003 was 744 MW, an astonishing increase of more than 1200% since 1993. In 2003, Japan still led the world in PV cells and module production at 360 MW, followed by Europe and Germany (200 MW), then the United States and the rest of the world. U.S. production lagged behind at 100 MW, mostly for export to Japan and Europe. Despite this international boom in photovoltaic electrical power generation, the U.S. administration continued with budget cuts in its photovoltaic program in 2004. In 2003 dollars, module costs average $3 per watt. Growth between 1997 and 2004 averaged 35% per year.

Obvious drawbacks of both solar-heating and solar-electric systems are periods of cloudiness and night, which inhibit operations. Research is under way to enhance energy-storage technologies, such as hydrogen fuel production (using energy to extract hydrogen from water for later use in producing more energy) and to improve battery technology.

The Promise of Solar Energy

Solar energy is a wise choice for the future. It is directly available to the consumer; it is based on a renewable energy source of an appropriate scale for end-use needs (it matches them well); and most solar strategies are labour-intensive (rather than capital-intensive as in centralized power production). Solar is preferable to further development of our decreasing fossil fuel reserves, further increases in oil imports and tanker spills, investment in foreign military incursions, or to adding more troubled nuclear power.

Whether or not we follow the alternative path of solar energy is a matter of political control and not technological innovation. Much of the technology is ready for installation and is cost-effective when all direct and indirect costs are considered for all the alternatives. NREL asserts in its mission statement that the laboratory wants to "lead the nation toward a sustainable energy future by developing renewable energy technologies, improving energy efficiency, advancing related science, and engineering commercialization." Unfortunately, political decisions slow progress, cut budgets, and create uneven investment incentives weighted toward fossil fuels.

Sample Stations A couple of real locations bring what you just read into meaningful perspective. Variation in the expenditure of NET R among sensible heat (*H*, energy we can feel), latent heat (*LE*, energy for evaporation), and ground heating and cooling (*G*) produces the variety of environments we experience in nature. Let us examine the daily energy balance at two locations, El Mirage in California and Pitt Meadows in British Columbia.

El Mirage, at 35° N, is a hot desert location characterized by bare, dry soil with sparse vegetation (Figure 4.22a, b). Our sample is a clear summer day, with a light wind in the late afternoon. The NET R-value is lower than might be expected, considering the Sun's position close to zenith (June solstice) and the absence of clouds. But the income of energy at this site is countered by surfaces of higher albedo than forest or cropland and by hot soil surfaces that radiate infrared back to the atmosphere throughout the afternoon.

El Mirage has little or no energy expenditure for evaporation (*LE*). With little water and sparse vegetation, most of the available radiant energy dissipates through turbulent transfer of sensible heat (*H*), warming air and soil to high temperatures. Over a 24-hour period, *H* is 90% of NET R; the remaining 10% is for ground heating (*G*). The *G* component is greatest in the morning, when winds are light and turbulent transfers are lowest. In

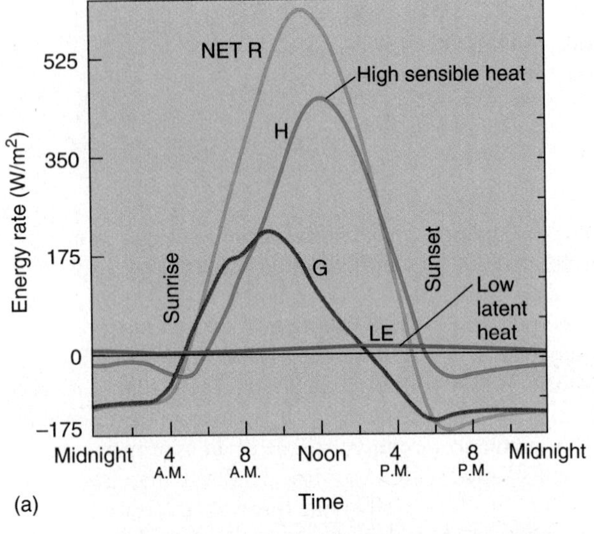

(b)

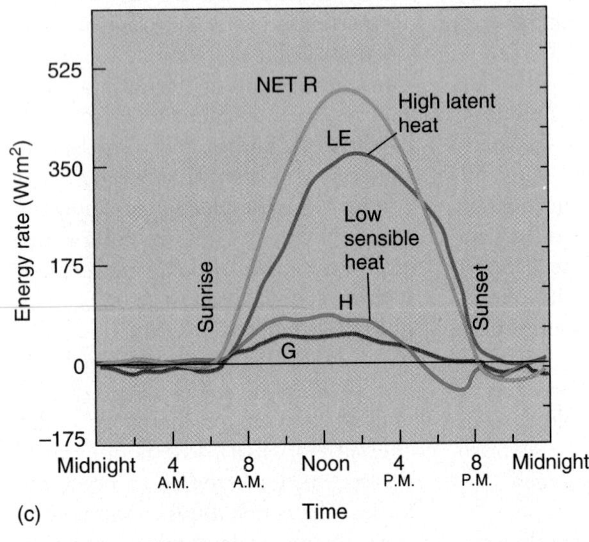

(d)

FIGURE 4.22 Radiation budget comparison for two stations.
(a) Graph shows daily net radiation expenditure for El Mirage, California, east of Los Angeles, at about 35° N. (b) Photo of the typical desert landscape near the site. (c) Graph of the daily net radiation expenditure for Pitt Meadows in southern British Columbia, at about 49° N. (d) Photo of irrigated blueberry orchards characteristic of the agricultural activity in this moist environment of moderate temperatures. (*H* = turbulent sensible heat transfer; *LE* = latent heat of evaporation; *G* = ground heating and cooling.) [(a) Adapted by permission from William D. Sellers, *Physical Climatology,* fig. 33, copyright 1965 by The University of Chicago. All rights reserved. (c) Adapted by permission from T. R. Oke, *Boundary Layer Climates* (New York: Methuen & Co., 1978), p. 23. Photos (b) and (d) by Robert W. Christopherson.]

the afternoon, heated air rises off the hot ground, and convective heat expenditures are accelerated as winds increase.

Compare El Mirage (Figure 4.22a) and Pitt Meadows (Figure 4.22c). Pitt Meadows is midlatitude (49° N), vegetated, and moist, and its energy expenditures differ greatly from those at El Mirage. The Pitt Meadows landscape is able to retain much more of its energy because of lower albedo values (less reflection), the presence of more water and plants, and lower surface temperatures than those of El Mirage.

The graph plots the energy balance data for Pitt Meadows for a cloudless summer day. Higher *LE* values result from the moist environment of rye grass and irrigated mixed-orchard ground cover for the sample area (Figure 4.22d), contributing to the more moderate sensible heat (*H*) levels during the day.

The Urban Environment

For most of you reading this book, an urban landscape produces the temperatures you feel each day. Urban microclimates generally differ from those of nearby nonurban areas. In fact, the surface energy characteristics of urban areas are similar to desert locations. Because almost 50% of the world's population will live in cities by the year 2010, urban microclimatology and other specific environmental effects related to cities are important topics for physical geographers.

The physical characteristics of urbanized regions produce an **urban heat island** that has on average both maximum and minimum temperatures higher than nearby rural settings. Table 4.1 lists five urban characteristics and the resulting temperature and moisture effects produced. Figure 4.23 illustrates these traits. Every major city produces its own **dust dome** of airborne pollution, which can be blown from the city in elongated plumes; as noted in the table, such domes affect urban energy budgets.

Table 4.2 compares climatic factors of rural and urban environments. The worldwide trend toward greater urbanization is placing more and more people on urban heat islands. NASA launched its Urban Heat Island Pilot Project (UHIPP) in 1997, through its Global Hydrology and Climate Center, to better understand the role of cities in climate. If ways can be found to make cities cooler, this will reduce energy consumption and fossil fuel use, thus reducing greenhouse gas emissions.

Thermal infrared measurements were made in 1998 from NASA's research jet over Atlanta, Georgia; Sacramento,

Table 4.1 Urban Physical Characteristics and Conditions

Urban characteristics	Results and conditions
Urban surfaces typically are metal, glass, asphalt, concrete, or stone, and their energy characteristics respond differently from natural surfaces	Albedos of urban surfaces are lower, leading to higher net radiation values Urban surfaces expend more energy as sensible heat than do nonurban areas (70% of the net radiation to *H*) Surfaces conduct up to three times more energy than wet, sandy soil and thus are warmer During the day and evening, temperatures above urban surfaces are higher than those above natural areas
Irregular geometric shapes in a city affect radiation patterns and winds	Incoming insolation is caught in mazelike reflection and radiation "canyons" Delayed energy is conducted into surface materials, thus raising temperatures Buildings interrupt wind flows, diminishing heat loss through advective (horizontal) movement Maximum heat island effects occur on calm, clear days and nights
Human activity alters the heat characteristics of cities	In summer, urban electricity production and use of fossil fuels releases energy equivalent to 25%–50% of insolation In winter, urban-generated sensible heat averages 250% greater than arriving insolation, reducing winter heating requirements
Many urban surfaces are sealed (built on and paved), so water cannot reach the soil	Central business district surfaces average 50% sealed, suburbs average 20% sealed, producing more water runoff Urban areas respond like a desert landscape: A storm may cause a flash flood over the hard, sparsely vegetated surfaces, to be followed by dry conditions a few hours later
Air pollution, including gases and aerosols, is greater in urban areas than in comparable natural settings; increased convection and precipitation are possible	Pollution increases the atmosphere's reflectivity above a city, reducing insolation and absorbing infrared radiation, reradiating infrared downward Increased particulates in pollution are condensation nuclei for water vapour, increasing cloud formation and precipitation Urban-stimulated increases in precipitation may occur downwind from cities

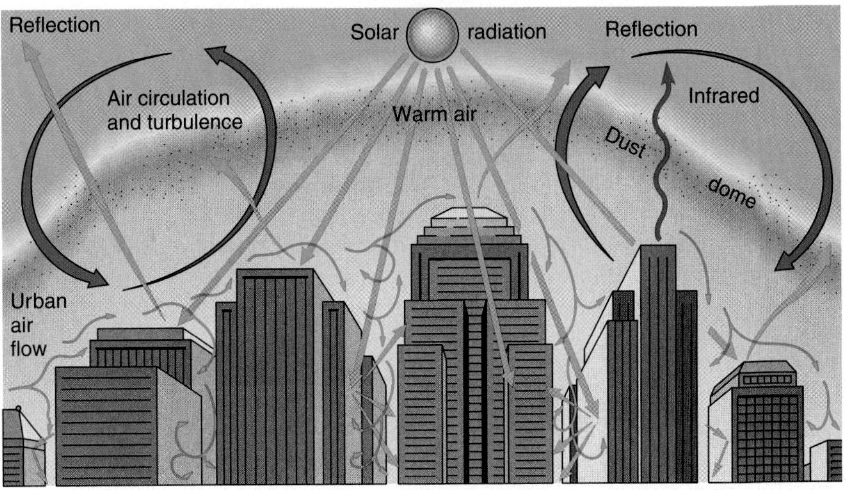

FIGURE 4.23 The urban environment. Insolation, wind movements, and dust dome in city environments.

California; Baton Rouge, Louisiana; and Salt Lake City, Utah. Teachers and students on the ground assisted efforts by making temperature measurements at the same time as the flights. Instruments carried by balloons tracked vertical temperature, relative humidity, and air pressure profiles. (See **http://www.ghcc.msfc.nasa.gov/urban/** for an update of this project.)

Figure 4.24 illustrates a generalized cross section of a typical urban heat island, showing increasing temperatures toward the downtown central business district. Note that temperatures drop over areas of trees and parks. Sensible heat is lessened because of latent heat of evaporation and plant effects (transpiration and shade). Urban forests are important factors in cooling cities. NASA measurements in an outdoor mall parking lot found temperatures of 48°C (118°F), but a small planter with trees in the same lot was significantly cooler at 32°C (90°F)—16 C° (29 F°) lower in temperature! In Central Park in New York City daytime temperatures average 5–10 C° (9–18 F°) cooler than urban areas outside the park.

Figure 4.25 is a thermal infrared image of a portion of Sacramento, California (midday). The false colours of red

Table 4.2 Average Differences in Climatic Elements Between Urban and Rural Environments

Element	Urban Compared with Rural Environs	Element	Urban Compared with Rural Environs
Contaminants		**Temperature**	
Condensation nuclei	10 times more	Annual mean	0.5–3.0 C° (0.9–5.4 F°) more
Particulates	10 times more	Winter minima (average)	1.0–2 C° (1.8–3.6 F°) more
Gaseous admixtures	5–25 times more	Summer maxima	1.0–3 C° (1.8–3.0 F°) more
Radiation		Heating degree days	10% less
Total on horizontal surface	0%–20% less	**Relative Humidity**	
Ultraviolet, winter	30% less	Annual mean	6% less
Ultraviolet, summer	5% less	Winter	2% less
Sunshine duration	5%–15% less	Summer	8% less
Cloudiness		**Wind Speed**	
Clouds	5%–10% more	Annual mean	20%–30% less
Fog, winter	100% more	Extreme gusts	10%–20% less
Fog, summer	30% more	Calm	5%–20% more
Precipitation			
Amounts	5%–15% more		
Days with <5 mm (0.2 in.)	10% more		
Snowfall, inner city	5%–10% less		
Snowfall, downwind (lee) of city	10% more		
Thunderstorms	10%–15% more		

Source: H. E. Landsberg, *The Urban Climate*, International Geophysics Series, vol. 28 (1981), p. 258. Reprinted by permission from Academic Press.

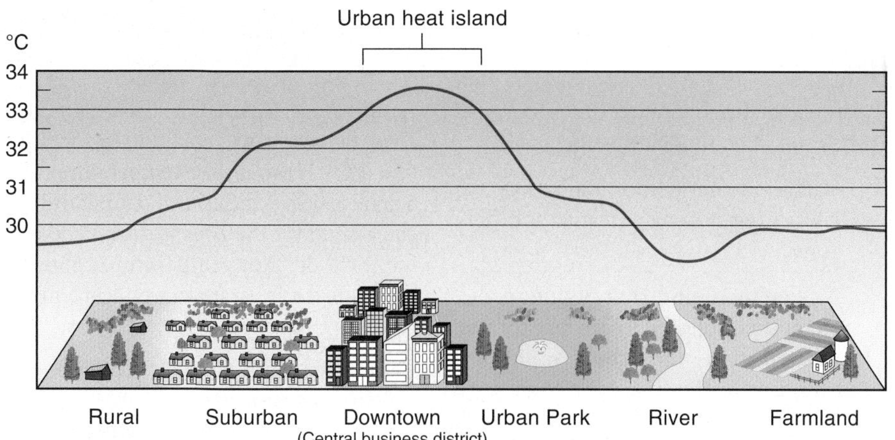

FIGURE 4.24 Typical urban heat island profile. Generalized cross section of a typical urban heat island. The trend of the temperature gradient from rural to downtown is measurable. Temperatures rise steeply in urban settings, plateau over the suburban built-up area, and peak where temperature is highest at the urban core. Note the cooling over the park area and river.

and white are relatively hot areas (60°C, 140°F), blues and greens are relatively cool areas (29°–36°C, 85°–96°F); clearly buildings are the hottest objects in the scene. As you look across this landscape, what strategies do you think would reduce the urban heat island effect? Possibilities include lighter-coloured surfaces for buildings, streets, and parking lots, more reflective roofs; and more trees, parks, and open space. (The images from all the test cities are available at **http://science.nasa.gov/newhome/headlines/essd01jul98%5F1.htm**.)

FIGURE 4.25 Heat island exposed. Urban Heat Island Pilot Project (UHIPP) thermal infrared image of Sacramento, California, taken June 29, 1998, at 1 P.M. PDT from a NASA jet at 2000 m (6600 ft). The Sacramento River runs from north to south to the left of centre of the frame, the American River is to the upper right, and the California state capitol building is the red dot in the green rectangle right of centre from the river. False colour tags white and red as relatively hot sites; greens and blues are relatively cool on this preliminary image. [Image courtesy of UHIPP, Marshall Space Flight Center, Global Hydrology and Climate Center, Huntsville, Alabama.]

Sacramento urban heat island in the distance.

Applied Physical Geography

Energy Balance Model

Energy balance models attempt to account for all incoming and outgoing energy of the Earth. In a simple global energy balance, the only variable is the temperature of the Earth, signified T_e. The term "balance" suggests that the system is at equilibrium—no energy is accumulated. See the Shodor Education Foundation Web site for an energy balance computer model (**http://www.shodor.org/**).

This energy balance model can be described mathematically as follows:

$$\text{Energy absorbed} = \text{energy emitted}$$
$$\pi r_E^2(1 = \alpha)H_0 = 4\pi\, r_E^2 \sigma T_e^4$$

where r is the radius of Earth, H_0 is the extraterrestrial solar flux in W/m^2, α is the albedo or reflectivity of the planet, σ is the Stefan-Boltzmann constant ($5.67 \times 10^{-8}\ W/m^2K^{-4}$), and T_e is the effective temperature of Earth (the temperature of the planet as it appears from space).

The above model aims to calculate the effective temperature, T_e. We are interested in the temperature at the surface, or T_s. The following calculation is used:

$$T_s\!: T_s = T_e + dT$$

where dT is the greenhouse increment. At this time, the greenhouse increment is about 33 K, and is a function of the efficiency of the infrared absorption.

This would be fairly simple except that most energy balance models are zonal, not global, models. They focus on the energy balance for a chosen latitude. As such, an equation that accounts for the flow of energy from one latitudinal zone to the next must be used. The model must become:

Radiation energy in = Radiation energy out + transport into another zone.

The incoming energy due to the Sun must be adjusted to account for the spherical shape and orbital variations of the Earth. Because each zone usually has its own albedo, or reflectivity, each zone also has its own zonal surface temperature (including the greenhouse increment). The zonal model calculates total energy received from the Sun per unit time as given by

$$r^2 H_0$$

where r is Earth's radius and H_0 is the solar constant.

Given that the Earth's total area can be calculated by $4r^2$, we can propose the equation:

$$(1 - \alpha)H_0 = \sigma T_e^4$$

The average extraterrestrial solar flux over the entire surface can be calculated by $H_0/4$.

Because all zones do not receive the same amount of incoming radiation (due to the variation of the incident angle of the Sun to a particular zone), a ratio, γ_i, can be used that corrects the average incoming radiation for a given zone. We can then calculate the incoming solar radiation for a given zone as:

$$\text{incoming radiation} = \gamma_i H_0/4.$$

Also, the surface albedo of each zone must be considered. Remember that the albedo depends upon the type of landcover and the varying amounts of land and water on the surface. A critical temperature, T_c, exists below which the land becomes ice covered (typically −10.0°C). If the surface temperature for a zone is below the critical temperature, the albedo for the zone is the albedo of ice, or 0.68. For temperatures above the critical temperature, a typical equation is:

albedo of the zone = (1 − fractional cloud cover for the zone) + (fractional cloud cover × albedo of the clouds).

Cloud albedo is typically specified as 0.5. Fractional cloud cover values are a typical input for a standard energy balance model. The transport of energy between zones is given by:

$$F_i = C(T_i - T_s)$$

where C is a constant equal to $3.80\ W/m^2/C$, T_i is the average temperature of the zone, and T_s is the mean global surface temperature.

More complicated methodologies exist, but this equation represents the fundamental parameters in an energy balance model.

Again, the purpose of the energy balance model is to calculate the temperature of the zone. A final equation for calculating temperatures is as follows:

$$T_i = (\gamma_i(H_0/4)(1 - \alpha_i) + CT_s$$
$$= A + 5\phi_i B)/B + C$$

where γ_i is the ratio correcting incoming radiation, H_0 is the solar constant, α_i is the surface albedo for the zone, T_s is the average surface temperature, A is a constant ($204\ W/m^{2)}$, B is a constant ($2.17\ W/m^2/C$), and ϕ_i is the fractional cloud cover in each zone.

The equation is repeated for each zone to reach a global energy balance.

Summary and Review—Atmosphere and Surface Energy Balances

Identify the pathways of solar energy through the troposphere to Earth's surface: transmission, scattering, diffuse radiation, refraction, albedo (reflectivity), conduction, convection, and advection.

Earth's biosphere is powered by radiant energy from the Sun that cascades through complex circuits to the surface. Our budget of atmospheric energy comprises shortwave radiation *inputs* (ultraviolet light, visible light, and near-infrared wavelengths) and longwave radiation *outputs* (thermal infrared).

Transmission refers to the passage of shortwave and longwave energy through either the atmosphere or water. The gas molecules redirect radiation, changing the direction of the light's movement *without altering its wavelengths*. This phenomenon is known as **scattering** and represents 7% of Earth's reflectivity, or albedo. Dust particles, pollutants, ice, cloud droplets, and water vapour produce further scattering. Some incoming insolation is diffused by clouds and atmosphere and is transmitted to Earth as **diffuse radiation**, the downward component of scattered light. The speed of insolation entering the atmosphere changes as it passes from one medium to another; the change of speed causes a bending action called **refraction**.

A portion of arriving energy bounces directly back into space without being converted into heat or performing any work. This returned energy is called **reflection. Albedo** is the reflective quality (intrinsic brightness) of a surface. It is an important control over the amount of insolation that is available for absorption by a surface. We state albedo as the percentage of insolation that is reflected. Earth and its atmosphere reflect 31% of all insolation when averaged over a year.

An increase in albedo and reflection of shortwave radiation caused by clouds is described by the term **cloud-albedo forcing**. Also, clouds can act as insulation, thus trapping longwave radiation and raising minimum temperatures. An increase in greenhouse warming caused by clouds is described by the term **cloud-greenhouse forcing**.

Absorption is the assimilation of radiation by molecules of a substance and its conversion from one form to another—for example, visible light to infrared radiation. **Conduction** is the molecule-to-molecule transfer of energy as it diffuses through a substance.

Energy also is transferred in gases and liquids by **convection** (when the physical mixing involves a strong vertical motion) or **advection** (when the dominant motion is horizontal). In the atmosphere or bodies of water, warmer portions tend to rise (they are less dense) and cooler portions tend to sink (they are more dense), establishing patterns of convection.

transmission (p. 94)
scattering (p. 94)
diffuse radiation (p. 95)
refraction (p. 95)
reflection (p. 95)
albedo (p. 95)
cloud-albedo forcing (p. 97)
cloud-greenhouse forcing (p. 97)
absorption (p. 99)
conduction (p. 99)
convection (p. 99)
advection (p. 99)

1. Diagram a simple energy balance for the troposphere. Label each shortwave and longwave component and the directional aspects of related flows.
2. Define refraction. How is it related to daylength? To a rainbow? To the beautiful colours of a sunset?
3. List several types of surfaces and their albedo values. Explain the differences among these surfaces. What determines the reflectivity of a surface?
4. Using Figure 4.7, explain the seasonal differences in albedo values for each hemisphere. Be specific, using the albedo values given in Figure 4.5 where appropriate.
5. What would you expect the sky colour to be at 50 km (30 mi) altitude? Why? Why is the lower atmosphere blue?
6. Define the concepts transmission, absorption, diffuse radiation, conduction, and convection.

Describe what happens to insolation when clouds are in the atmosphere and *analyze* the effect of clouds and air pollution on solar radiation received at ground level.

Clouds reflect *insolation*, thus cooling Earth's surface—*cloud-albedo forcing*. Yet clouds also act as insulation, thus trapping longwave radiation and raising minimum temperatures—*cloud-greenhouse forcing*. Clouds affect the heating of the lower atmosphere, depending on cloud type, height, and thickness (water content and density). High-altitude, ice-crystal clouds reflect insolation with albedos of about 50%, producing a net cloud-greenhouse forcing (warming); thick, lower cloud cover reflects about 90%, producing a net cloud-albedo forcing (cooling).

Emissions of sulphur dioxide and the subsequent chemical reactions in the atmosphere form *sulphate aerosols*, which act either as insolation—reflecting haze in clear-sky conditions or as a stimulus to condensation in clouds that increases reflectivity.

7. What role do clouds play in the Earth–atmosphere radiation balance? Is cloud type important? Compare high, thin cirrus clouds and lower, thick stratus clouds.
8. In what way does the presence of sulphate aerosols affect solar radiation received at ground level? How does it affect cloud formation?

Review the energy pathways in the Earth–atmosphere system, the greenhouse effect, and the patterns of global net radiation.

The Earth–atmosphere energy system naturally balances itself in a steady-state equilibrium. It does so through energy transfers that are *nonradiative* (convection, conduction, and the latent heat of evaporation) and *radiative* (by infrared radiation between the surface, the atmosphere, and space).

Some infrared radiation is absorbed by carbon dioxide, water vapour, methane, CFCs (chlorofluorocarbons), and other gases in the lower atmosphere and is then emitted to Earth, thus delaying energy loss to space. This process is the **greenhouse effect**. In the atmosphere, infrared radiation is not actually trapped, as it would be in a greenhouse, but its passage to space is delayed (heat energy is detained in the atmosphere) through absorption and counterradiation.

Between the tropics, high insolation angle and consistent daylength cause more energy to be gained than lost (there are energy surpluses). In the polar regions, an extremely low insolation angle, highly reflective surfaces, and up to 6 months of no insolation annually cause more energy to be lost (there are energy deficits). This imbalance of net radiation from tropical surpluses to the polar deficits drives a vast global circulation of both energy and mass.

Surface energy balances are used to summarize the energy expenditure for any location. Surface energy measurements are used as an analytical tool of **microclimatology**. Adding and subtracting the energy flow at the surface lets us calculate **net radiation (NET R)**, or the balance of all radiation at Earth's surface-shortwave (SW) and longwave (LW).

greenhouse effect (p. 101)
microclimatology (p. 105)
net radiation (NET R) (p. 105)

9. What are the similarities and differences between an actual greenhouse and the gaseous atmospheric greenhouse? Why is Earth's greenhouse changing?
10. In terms of energy expenditures for latent heat of evaporation, describe the annual pattern as mapped in Figure 4.20.
11. Generalize the pattern of global net radiation. How might this pattern drive the atmospheric weather machine? (See Figures 4.14 and 4.19.)
12. In terms of surface energy balance, explain the term *net radiation* (NET R).
13. What are the expenditure pathways for surface net radiation? What kind of work is accomplished?
14. What is the role played by latent heat in surface energy budgets?
15. Compare the daily surface energy balances of El Mirage, California, and Pitt Meadows, British Columbia. Explain the differences.

Plot the daily radiation curves for Earth's surface and _label_ the key aspects of incoming radiation, air temperature, and the daily temperature lag.

The greatest insolation input occurs at the time of the summer solstice in each hemisphere. Air temperature responds to seasons and variations in insolation input. Within a 24-hour day, air temperature peaks between 3:00 and 4:00 P.M. and dips to its lowest point right at or slightly after sunrise.

Air temperature lags behind each day's peak insolation. The warmest time of day occurs not at the moment of maximum insolation but at that moment when a maximum of insolation is absorbed.

16. Why is there a temperature lag between the highest Sun altitude and the warmest time of day? Relate your answer to the insolation and temperature patterns during the day.

Portray typical urban heat island conditions and _contrast_ the microclimatology of urban areas with that of surrounding rural environments.

A growing percentage of Earth's people live in cities and experience their unique set of altered microclimatic effects: increased conduction, lower albedos, higher NET R values, increased water runoff, complex radiation and reflection patterns, anthropogenic heating, and the gases, dusts, and aerosols of urban pollution. Urban surfaces of metal, glass, asphalt, concrete, and stone conduct up to three times more energy than wet sandy soil and thus are warmed as described by the term **urban heat island**. Air pollution, including gases and aerosols, is greater in urban areas than in rural ones. Every major city produces its own **dust dome** of airborne pollution.

urban heat island (p. 113)
dust dome (p. 113)

17. What is the basis for the urban heat island concept? Describe the climatic effects attributable to urban as compared with nonurban environments.
18. Which of the items in Table 4.2 have you yourself experienced? Explain.
19. Assess the potential for solar energy applications in our society. What are some negatives? What are some positives?

Critical Thinking

A. Given what you now know about reflection, albedo, absorption, and net radiation expenditures, assess your wardrobe (fabrics and colours), house or apartment (colours of walls, especially south and west facing; or, in the Southern Hemisphere, north and west facing), and roof (orientation relative to the Sun), automobile (colour, use of sun shades), bicycle seat (colour), and other aspects of your environment to determine a personal "Energy IQ." What grade do you give yourself? Be cool!

B. In Focus Study 4.1, "Solar Energy Collection and Concentration," there are several listings of URLs relating to solar energy applications. Take some time to explore the Internet for a personal assessment of these necessary technologies (solar thermal, solar electric, photovoltaic cells, solar-panel cookers, and the like). As we near the climatic limitations of the fossil fuel era, and the depletion of the resource itself, these available technologies will become part of the fabric of our lives. Briefly describe your search results. Given these findings, determine if there is availability of solar technology in your area.

C. Examine the following photograph. In Antarctica, on Petermann Island off the Graham Land Coast, we noticed this piece of kelp (a seaweed) dropped by a passing bird. The kelp was resting about 10 cm (4 in.) deep in the snow, in a hole about the shape of the kelp. In your opinion, what factors operated to make this scene? Now, expand your conclusion to the issue of mining in Antarctica. There are coal deposits and other minerals in Antarctica. The international Antarctic Treaty (1959, additional measures in 1972, 1982, 1991) blocks mining exploitation, although reconsideration is possible after 2048. Given your analysis of the kelp in the snow, information on surface energy budgets in this chapter, the dust and particulate output of mining, and the importance of a stable sea level, construct a case opposed to such mining activities based on these factors.

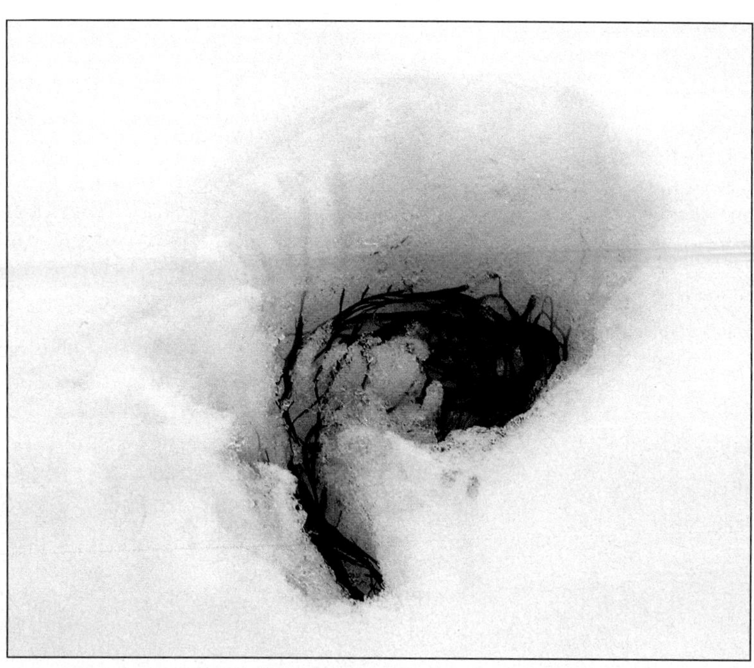

An autumn sunset bathes these prairie farms in Alberta, Canada. Warmer average temperatures are extending the growing season in Canada and melting permafrost soil in the far north. Conditions of drought are a concern.
[Photo by John Eastcott/Yva Momatiuk, DRK Photo.]

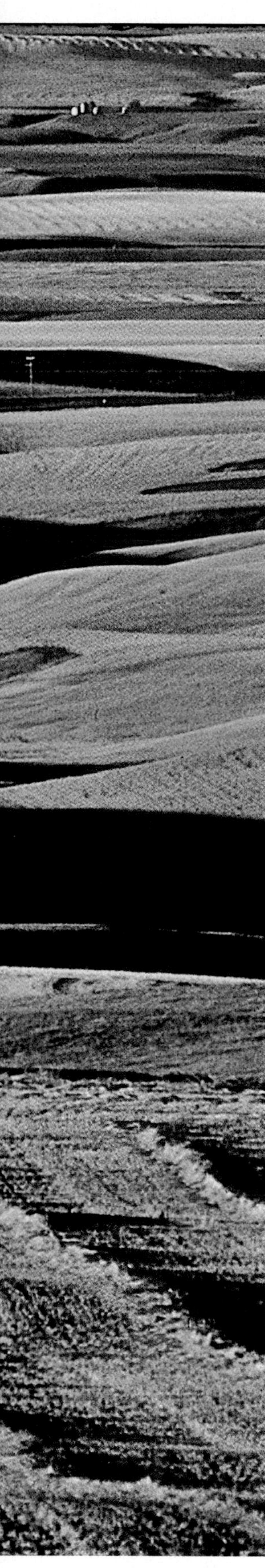

5 Global Temperatures

Key Learning Concepts

After reading the chapter, you should be able to:

- *Define* the concepts of temperature, kinetic energy, and sensible heat, and *distinguish* among Kelvin, Celsius, and Fahrenheit scales and how they are measured.
- *List* and *review* the principal controls and influences that produce global temperature patterns.
- *Review* the factors that produce different marine effects and continental effects as they influence temperatures and *utilize* several pairs of stations to illustrate these differences.
- *Interpret* the pattern of Earth's temperatures from their portrayal on January and July temperature maps and on a map of annual temperature ranges.
- *Describe* the human body's response to wind (wind chill) and heat and humidity (Humidex).

What is the temperature now—both indoors and outdoors—as you read these words? How is it measured, and what does the value mean? How is air temperature influencing your plans for the day? Air temperature plays a remarkable role in our lives, both at the micro level and at the macro level. Our bodies subjectively sense temperature and judge comfort and react to changing temperatures.

We read of heat waves and cold spells affecting people, crops, events, and energy consumption. For example, in summer 2003, heat, humidity, and drought led to the deaths of an estimated 20,000 people in Europe. Record warmth is reaching into the Arctic. Tree-ring analysis, ice cores, and other proxy measures indicate that present temperatures are warmer than Earth has experienced for the last 1000 years. This warming trend is the subject of much scientific, geographic, and political interest.

In this chapter: A variety of temperature regimes affect cultures, decision making, and resources consumed across the globe. Understanding some temperature concepts and measurements helps us begin our study of these Earth systems. We look at principal temperature controls of latitude, altitude, cloud cover, and land–water heating differences as they interact to produce Earth's temperature patterns. We end by examining the effect of temperature on the human body and the resultant spatial aspects of heat and cold on human experience.

Temperature Concepts and Measurement

Heat and temperature are not the same. *Heat* is a form of energy that flows from one system or object to another because the two are at different temperatures. **Temperature** is a measure of the average kinetic energy (motion) of individual molecules in matter. We feel the effect of temperature as the *sensible heat* transfer from warmer objects to cooler objects. For instance, when you jump into a cool lake you can sense the heat transfer from your skin to the water as kinetic energy leaves your body and flows to the water—a chill develops.

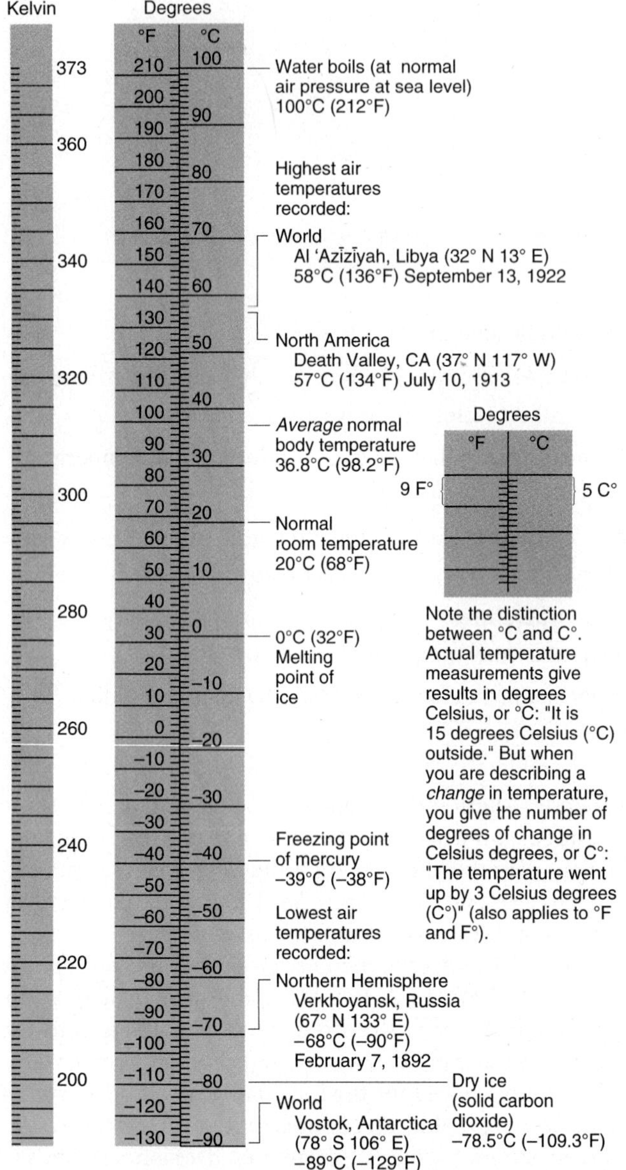

FIGURE 5.1 Temperature scales.
Scales for expressing temperature in Kelvin (K) and degrees Celsius (°C) and Fahrenheit (°F).

Temperature and heat are related because changes in temperature are caused by the absorption or emission (gain or loss) of heat energy. The term *heat energy* is frequently used to describe energy that is added to or removed from a system or substance.

Temperature Scales

The temperature at which all atomic and molecular motion in matter completely stops is called 0° *absolute temperature* (commonly, "absolute zero"). Its value on the different temperature-measuring scales is –273° Celsius (C), –459.4° Fahrenheit (F), and 0 Kelvin (K). Figure 5.1 compares these three scales. Formulas for converting between Celsius, SI (Système International), and English units are in Appendix C of this text.

The Fahrenheit scale places the melting point of ice at 32°F and the boiling point of water at 212°F. The scale is named for Daniel G. Fahrenheit, a German physicist (1686–1736). He used these odd values based on the coldest temperature he could achieve in his laboratory (which he called 0°F) and on the approximate temperature of the human body, thought to be about 100°F. His estimates placed the melting point of ice at 32°F, with 180 subdivisions in his scale to the boiling point of water at 212°F. (Note that there is only one melting point for ice, but there are many freezing points for water ranging from 32°F down to –40°F, depending on its purity and volume and certain conditions in the atmosphere.)

About a year after the adoption of the Fahrenheit scale, Swedish astronomer Anders Celsius (1701–1744) developed the Celsius scale (formerly called centigrade). He placed the melting point of ice at 0° and boiling temperature of water at sea level at 100°, dividing his scale into 100 degrees using a decimal system.

British physicist Lord Kelvin (born William Thomson, 1824–1907) proposed the Kelvin scale in 1848. Science uses this scale because temperature readings start at absolute zero and thus are proportional to the actual kinetic energy in a material. The Kelvin scale's melting point for ice is 273 K, and its boiling point of water is 373 K.

Canada, like most countries, uses the Celsius scale to express temperature. The United States is the only major country still using the Fahrenheit scale. This textbook presents Celsius (with Fahrenheit equivalents in parentheses) throughout.

Measuring Temperature

A *mercury thermometer* or *alcohol thermometer* is a sealed glass tube that measures outdoor temperatures. (Fahrenheit invented the alcohol and mercury thermometers.) Cold climates demand alcohol thermometers because alcohol freezes at –112°C (–170°F), whereas mercury freezes at –39°C (–38.2°F). The principle of these thermometers is simple: When fluids are heated, they expand; upon cooling, they contract. A thermometer stores fluid in a small reservoir at one end and is marked with calibrations to measure the expansion or contraction of the fluid, which reflects the temperature of the thermometer's environment. *Thermistors* measure temperature by sensing the electrical resistance of a semi-conducting material. Resistance changes at 4% per C° (a thermistor is in the shelter in Figure 5.3a).

Figure 5.2 shows a mercury minimum–maximum thermometer. It preserves readings of the day's highest and lowest temperatures until reset (by moving the markers with a magnet). Another type, the recording thermometer, creates an inked record on a turning drum; it is usually set for one full rotation every 24 hours or every 7 days.

Thermometers for standardized official readings are placed outdoors, in small Instrument Shelters (Figure 5.3a) or Stephenson Screen shelters (Figure 5.3b) that are white (for high albedo) and louvred (for ventilation) to avoid overheating the instruments. They are placed 1.2 m (4 ft) above the ground surface, usually over turf. The placement of thermometers in shade prevents the effect of direct insolation.

Temperature readings are taken daily, sometimes hourly, at more than 15,400 weather stations worldwide. One of the goals of the Global Climate Observing System (GCOS) is to establish a reference network of one station per 250,000 km^2 (95,800 mi^2). Some stations with recording equipment also report the duration of temperatures, rates of rise or fall, and variation over time throughout the day and night. (See the World Meteorological Organization at **http://www.wmo.ch/**.)

The *daily mean temperature* is an average of daily minimum–maximum readings. The *monthly mean temperature* is the total of daily mean temperatures for the month divided by the number of days in the month. An *annual temperature range* expresses the difference between the lowest and highest monthly mean temperatures for a given year. If you install a thermometer for outdoor temperature reading, be sure to avoid direct sunlight on the instrument

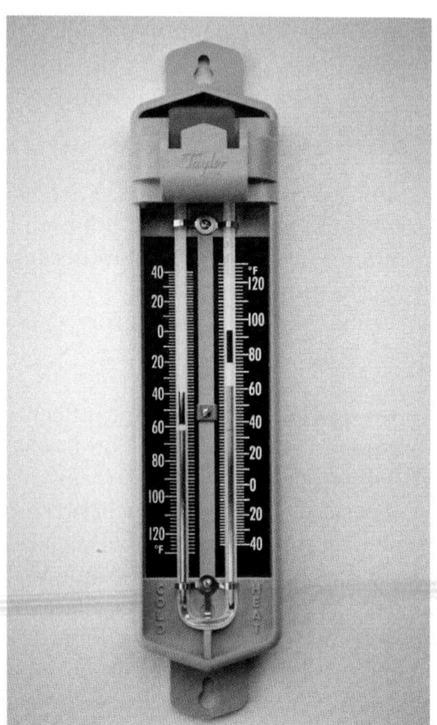

FIGURE 5.2 A minimum–maximum thermometer. [Photo by Bobbé Christopherson.]

(a)

(b)

FIGURE 5.3 Instrument shelter. (a) This standard thermometer shelter is white (for high albedo) and louvred (for ventilation). (b) The Stephenson Screen, a louvered wooden box that houses a minimum and maximum thermometer or a wet bulb thermometer apparatus, provides protection from direct insolation. [(a) Photo by Bobbé Christopherson; (b) Photo by Dick Hemingway.]

and place it in an area of good ventilation, and at least 1.2 m off the ground.

Principal Temperature Controls

The interaction of complex control variables produces Earth's temperature patterns. These principal influences upon temperatures include latitude, altitude, cloud cover, and land–water heating differences.

Latitude

Insolation is the single most important influence on temperature variations. Figure 2.9 shows how insolation intensity decreases as one moves away from the subsolar point—a point that migrates annually between the Tropic of Cancer and Tropic of Capricorn (between 23.5° N and 23.5° S). In addition, daylength and Sun angle change throughout the year, increasing seasonal effect with increasing latitude. The five cities graphed in Figure 5.4 demonstrate the effects of latitudinal position. From equator to poles, Earth ranges from continually warm to seasonally variable to continually cold.

Altitude

Within the troposphere, temperatures decrease with increasing altitude above Earth's surface. (Recall that the *normal lapse rate* of temperature change with altitude is 6.4 C°/1000 m, or 3.5 F°/1000 ft; see Figure 3.5). Thus, worldwide, mountainous areas experience lower temperatures than do regions nearer sea level, even at similar latitudes. The density of the atmosphere also diminishes with increasing altitude. In fact, the density of the atmosphere at an elevation of 5500 m (18,000 ft) is about half of that at sea level. As the atmosphere thins, its ability to absorb and radiate sensible heat is reduced.

The consequences are that, at high elevations, average air temperatures are lower, nighttime cooling is greater, and the temperature range between day and night is greater than at low elevations. The temperature difference between areas of sunlight and shadow is greater than at sea level. You may have felt temperatures decrease noticeably in the shadows and shortly after sunset when you were in the mountains. Surfaces both gain energy rapidly and lose energy rapidly to the thinner atmosphere.

Also, at higher elevations, the insolation received is more intense because of the reduced mass of atmospheric gases. As a result of this intensity, the ultraviolet energy component makes sunburn a distinct hazard.

The snowline seen in mountain areas indicates where winter snowfall exceeds the amount of snow lost through summer melting and evaporation. The snowline's location is a function both of elevation and latitude, so glaciers can exist even at equatorial latitudes if the elevation is high enough. In equatorial mountains, the snowline occurs at approximately 5000 m (16,400 ft) because of the latitude (more insolation in the tropics produces temperatures that place the snowline at higher altitude). Permanent ice fields and glaciers exist on equatorial mountain summits in the Andes and East Africa. With increasing latitude, snowlines gradually lower in elevation from 2700 m (8850 ft) in the midlatitudes to lower than 900 m (2950 ft) in southern Greenland.

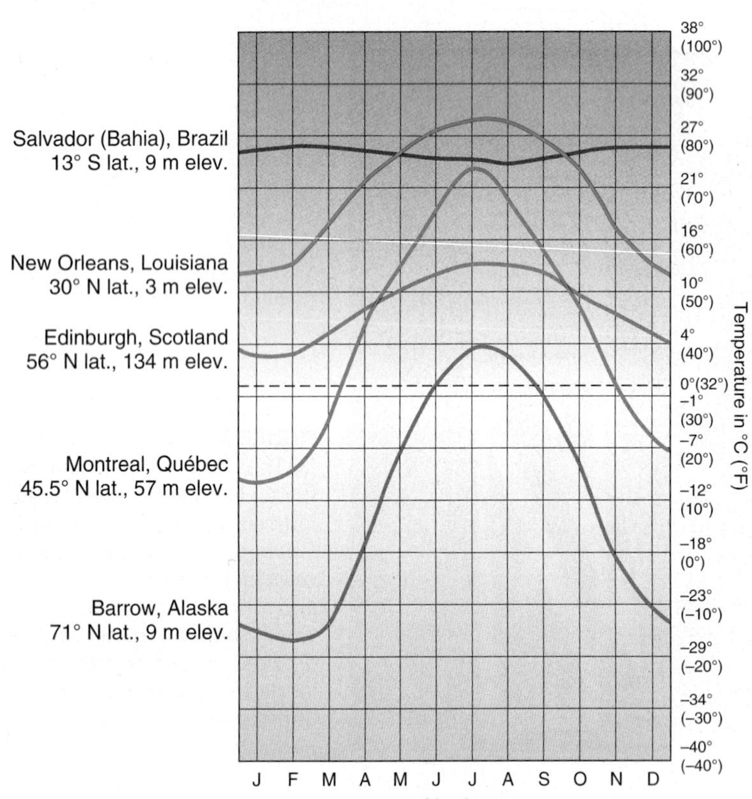

FIGURE 5.4 Latitude affects temperatures.
A comparison of five cities from near the equator to above the Arctic Circle demonstrates changing seasonality and increasing differences between average minimum and maximum temperatures.

Two cities in Bolivia illustrate the interaction of the two temperature controls, latitude and altitude. Figure 5.5 displays temperature data for the cities of Concepción and La Paz, which are near the same latitude (about 16° S). Note the elevation, average annual temperature, and precipitation for each location noted on the figure.

The hot, humid climate of Concepción at its much lower elevation stands in marked contrast to the cool, dry climate of highland La Paz. People living around La Paz actually grow wheat, barley, and potatoes—crops characteristic of the cooler midlatitudes—despite the fact that La Paz is 4103 m (13,461 ft) above sea level (Figure 5.6). (For comparison, the summit of Mount Waddington is at 4016 m (13,176 ft) and Fairweather Mountain is at 4663 m (or 15,298 ft). Both mountains are on the British Columbia–Alaska border).

The combination of elevation and low-latitude location guarantees La Paz nearly constant daylength and moderate temperatures, averaging about 9°C (48°F) every month. Such moderate temperature and moisture conditions lead to the formation of more fertile soils than those found in the warmer, wetter climate of Concepción.

Cloud Cover

Orbiting satellites reveal that approximately 50% of Earth is cloud covered at any given moment. Clouds moderate temperature, and their effect varies with cloud type, height, and density. Because their moisture reflects, absorbs, and liberates large amounts of energy, clouds reduce the insolation that reaches the surface. In general, they lower daily maximum temperatures and raise nighttime minimum temperatures. Clouds also reduce latitudinal and seasonal temperature differences.

At night, clouds act as insulation and radiate longwave energy, preventing rapid energy loss. During the day, clouds reflect insolation as a result of their high albedo values. In the last chapter, Figures 4.8 and 4.11 portrayed cloud-albedo forcing and cloud-greenhouse forcing as they relate to the presence of clouds and cloud types.

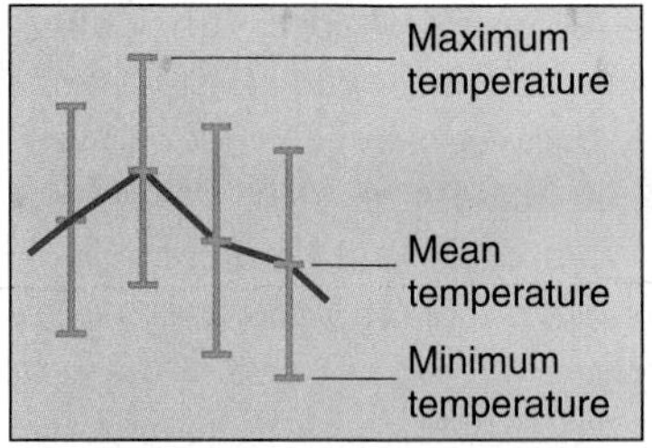

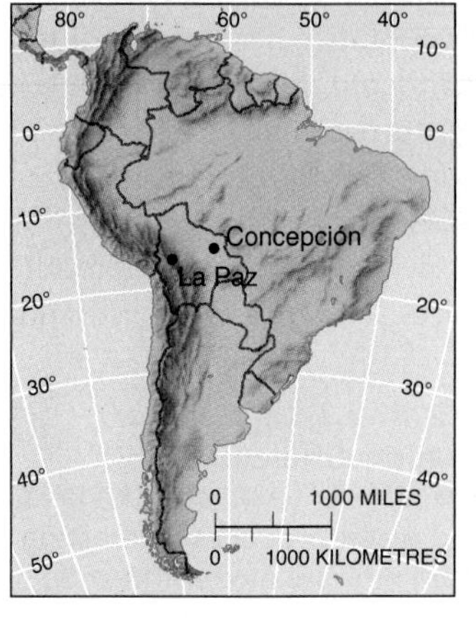

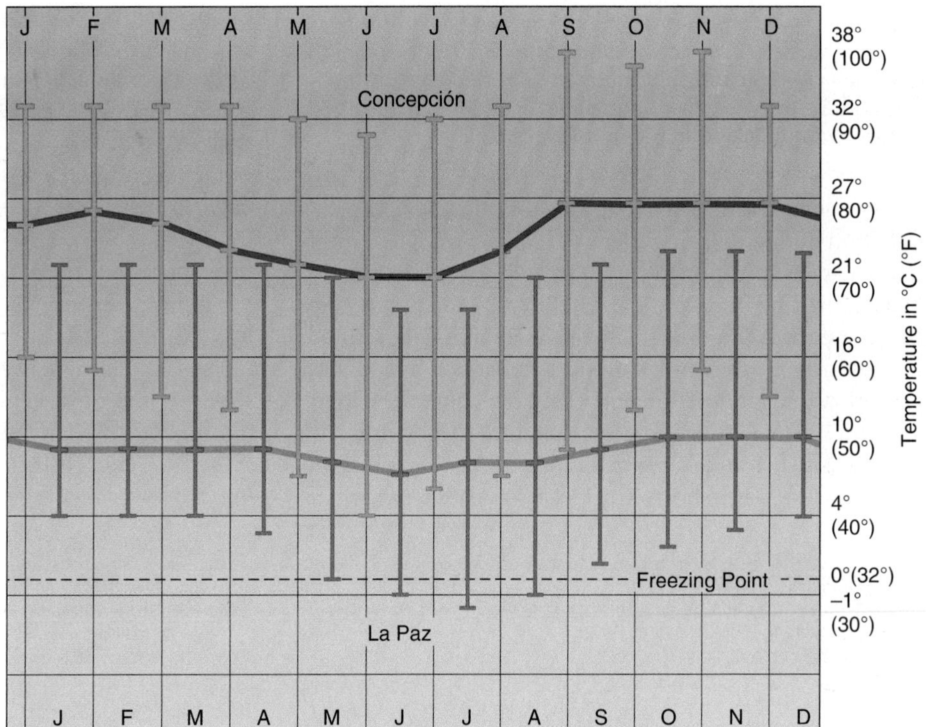

	Station	
	Concepción, Bolivia	**La Paz, Bolivia**
Latitude/longitude	16° 15′ S 62° 03′ W	16° 30′ S 68° 10′ W
Elevation	**490 m (1608 ft)**	**4103 m (13,461 ft)**
Avg. ann. temperature	24°C (75.2°F)	9°C (48.2°F)
Ann. temperature range	5 C° (9 F°)	3 C° (5.4 F°)
Ann. precipitation	121.2 cm (47.7 in.)	55.5 cm (21.9 in.)
Population	10,000	810,300 (Administrative division 1.6 million)

FIGURE 5.5 Effects of latitude and altitude.
Comparison of temperature patterns in two Bolivian cities: La Paz (4103 m, 13,461 ft) and Concepción (490 m, 1608 ft).

FIGURE 5.6 High-elevation farming.
People in these high-elevation villages grow potatoes and wheat in view of the permanent ice-covered peaks of the Andes Mountains. The combination of low latitude and high elevation creates consistent but moderate temperatures throughout the year, averaging about 9°C (48°F). [Photo by Mireille Vautier/Woodfin Camp & Associates.]

Clouds are the most variable factor influencing Earth's radiation budget, making them the subject of much investigation and simulation in computer models of atmospheric behaviour. The International Satellite Cloud Climatology Project, part of the World Climate Research Programme, is presently in the midst of such research. The Earth Radiation Budget experiments (ERB), including the Clouds and the Earth Radiant Energy System (CERES) sensors aboard *TRMM* and *Terra* satellites, are assessing cloud effects on longwave, shortwave, and net radiation patterns as never before possible. (For more about clouds, see the ISCCP and WCRP Home Pages at **http://isccp.giss.nasa.gov/** and **http://www.wmo.ch/web/wcrp/wcrp-home.html**.)

Land–Water Heating Differences

Another major control over temperature is the pronounced difference in the heating of land and water by insolation. Earth presents these two surfaces in an irregular arrangement of continents and oceans. Each absorbs and stores energy differently than the other and therefore contributes to the global pattern of temperature. Moderate temperature patterns are associated with water bodies; extreme temperatures occur inland.

The physical nature of land (rock and soil) and water (oceans, seas, and lakes) is the reason for these **land–water heating differences**—land heats and cools faster than water. Figure 5.7 visually summarizes the following discussion of the five land–water temperature controls: evaporation, transparency, specific heat, movement and ocean currents, and sea-surface temperatures.

Evaporation Evaporation consumes more of the energy arriving at the ocean's surface than is expended over a comparable area of land, simply because so much water is available. An estimated 84% of all evaporation on Earth is from the oceans. When water evaporates and thus changes to water vapour, *heat energy is absorbed in the process and is stored in the water vapour as latent heat*. We saw this process in Figure 4.20, the map of energy expended for the latent heat of evaporation. Latent heat is discussed fully in Chapter 7.

You can experience this evaporative heat loss (cooling) by wetting the back of your hand and then blowing on the moist skin. Sensible heat energy is drawn from your skin to supply some of the energy for evaporation, and you feel the cooling. Similarly, as surface water evaporates, it absorbs substantial energy from the immediate environment, resulting in a lowering of temperatures. Temperatures over land,

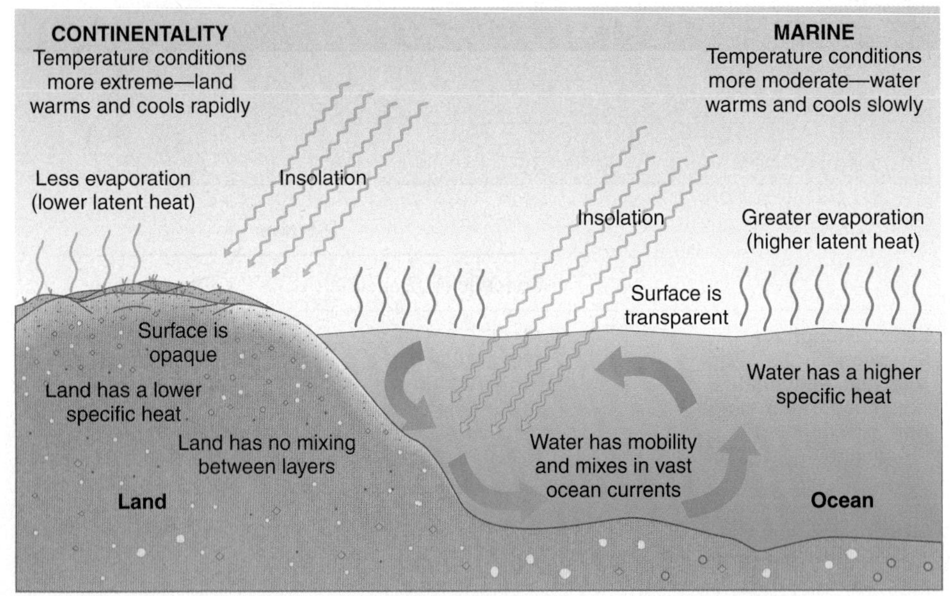

FIGURE 5.7 Land–water heating differences.
The differential heating of land and water produces contrasting marine (more moderate) and continental (more extreme) temperature regimes. (*LE*, latent heat of evaporation, is the energy stored in water vapour.)

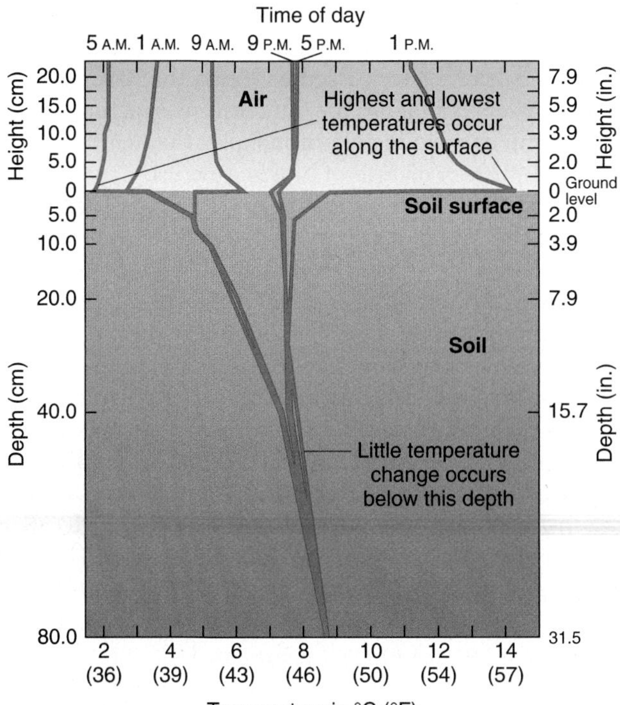

FIGURE 5.8 Land is opaque.
Profile of air and soil temperatures in Seabrook, New Jersey. Note that little temperature change occurs throughout the year at depths beyond a metre, whereas the daily extremes of temperature register along the surface, where insolation is absorbed. [Adapted from John R. Mather, *Climatology: Fundamentals and Applications* (New York: McGraw-Hill, 1974), p. 36. Adapted by permission.]

with far less water, are not as moderated by evaporative cooling as are marine locations.

Transparency The transmission of light obviously differs between soil and water: Solid ground is opaque; water is transparent. Consequently, light striking a soil surface does not penetrate but is absorbed, heating the ground surface. That energy is accumulated during times of exposure and is rapidly lost at night or in shadows.

Figure 5.8 shows the profile of diurnal (daily) temperatures for a column of soil and the atmosphere above it at a midlatitude location. You can see that maximum and minimum temperatures generally are experienced right at ground level. Below the surface, even at shallow depths, temperatures remain about the same throughout the day. This situation often exists at a beach, where surface sand may be painfully hot to your feet, but dig in your toes and you feel the sand a few centimetres below the surface is cooler, offering relief.

In contrast, when light reaches a body of water, it penetrates the surface because of water's **transparency**—water is clear and light transmits through it to an average depth of 60 m (200 ft) in the ocean (Figure 5.9). This illuminated zone is known as the *photic layer* and has been recorded in some ocean waters to depths of 300 m (1000 ft). This characteristic of water results in the distribution of available heat energy over a much greater depth and volume, forming a larger energy reservoir than that of the surface layers of the land.

Specific Heat When comparing equal volumes of water and land, water requires far more energy to increase its temperature than does land. In other words, *water can hold more heat than can soil or rock*, and therefore water is said to have a higher **specific heat**, the heat capacity of a substance. On the average, the specific heat of water is about four times that of soil. A given volume of water represents a more substantial energy reservoir than an equal volume of land, so changing the temperature of the oceanic energy reservoir is a slower process than changing the temperature of land.

Likewise, for that oceanic heat reservoir to lose heat energy requires more time than would a similar volume of land. The temperature response of water bodies is "sluggish" in comparison with land surfaces. For this reason, day-to-day temperatures near a substantial body of water tend to be moderated.

Movement Land is a rigid, solid material, whereas water is a fluid and is capable of movement. Differing temperatures and currents result in a mixing of cooler and warmer waters, and that mixing spreads the available energy over an even greater volume than if the water were still. Surface water and deeper waters mix, redistributing energy. Both

FIGURE 5.9 Ocean is transparent.
The transparency of the ocean at Taveuni Reef near Fiji permits insolation to penetrate to average depths of 60 m (200 ft), greatly increasing the volume of water that absorbs energy. [Photo by Copr. F. Stuart Westmorland/Photo Researchers, Inc.]

ocean and land surfaces radiate longwave radiation at night, but land loses its energy more rapidly than does the greater mass of the moving oceanic energy reservoir.

Ocean Currents and Sea-Surface Temperatures Warm water adds energy to overlying air through high evaporation rates and transfers of latent heat. Thus, in an air mass, the amount of water vapour that ocean temperature affects forms an interesting *negative feedback* mechanism. Across the globe, ocean water is rarely found warmer than 31°C (88°F). Higher ocean temperatures produce higher evaporation rates and more energy is lost from the ocean as latent heat. As water vapour content of the overlying air mass increases, the ability of the air to absorb longwave radiation also increases. Therefore, the air mass becomes warmer, enhancing the greenhouse effect. The warmer the air and the ocean become, the more evaporation will occur and the more water vapour will enter the air mass. More water vapour leads to cloud formation, which reflects insolation and produces lower temperatures. Lower temperatures of air and ocean reduce evaporation rates and the ability of the air mass to absorb water vapour.

As a specific example, the **Gulf Stream** (described in Chapter 6) moves northward off the east coast of North America, carrying warm water far into the North Atlantic (Figure 5.10). As a result, the southern third of Iceland experiences much milder temperatures than would be expected for a latitude of 65° N, just below the Arctic Circle (66.5°). In Reykjavík, on the southwestern coast of Iceland, monthly temperatures average above freezing during all months of the year. Similarly, the Gulf Stream moderates temperatures in coastal Scandinavia and northwestern Europe. In the western Pacific Ocean, the Kuroshio, or Japan Current, similar to the Gulf Stream, functions much the same in its warming effect on Japan, the Aleutians, and the northwestern margin of North America.

In contrast, along midlatitude and subtropical west coasts, cool ocean currents influence air temperatures. When conditions in these regions are warm and moist, fog frequently forms in the chilled air over the cooler currents. Ocean currents are detailed further in Chapter 6.

Remote sensing from satellites is providing sea-surface temperature (SST) data that are well-correlated with actual sea-surface measurements. This correlation permits a thorough global assessment of SSTs in programs such as Tropical Ocean Global Atmosphere (TOGA) and Coupled Ocean-Atmosphere Response Experiment (COARE). (See http://lwf.ncdc.noaa.gov/oa/coare/index.html.)

The Physical Oceanography Distributed Active Archive Center (PODAAC, http://podaac.jpl.nasa.gov/), part of the Earth Observing System Data Information System (EOSDIS, http://romulus.gsfc.nasa.gov/eosinfo/Welcome/), is responsible for storage and distribution of data relevant to the physical state of the ocean. Sea-level height, currents, and ocean temperatures are measured as part of the effort to understand oceans and climate interactions.

Figure 5.11 displays SST data for February and July 1999 from satellites in the NOAA/NASA Pathfinder AVHRR data set, aboard *NOAA-7*, *-9*, *-11*, and *-14*. The

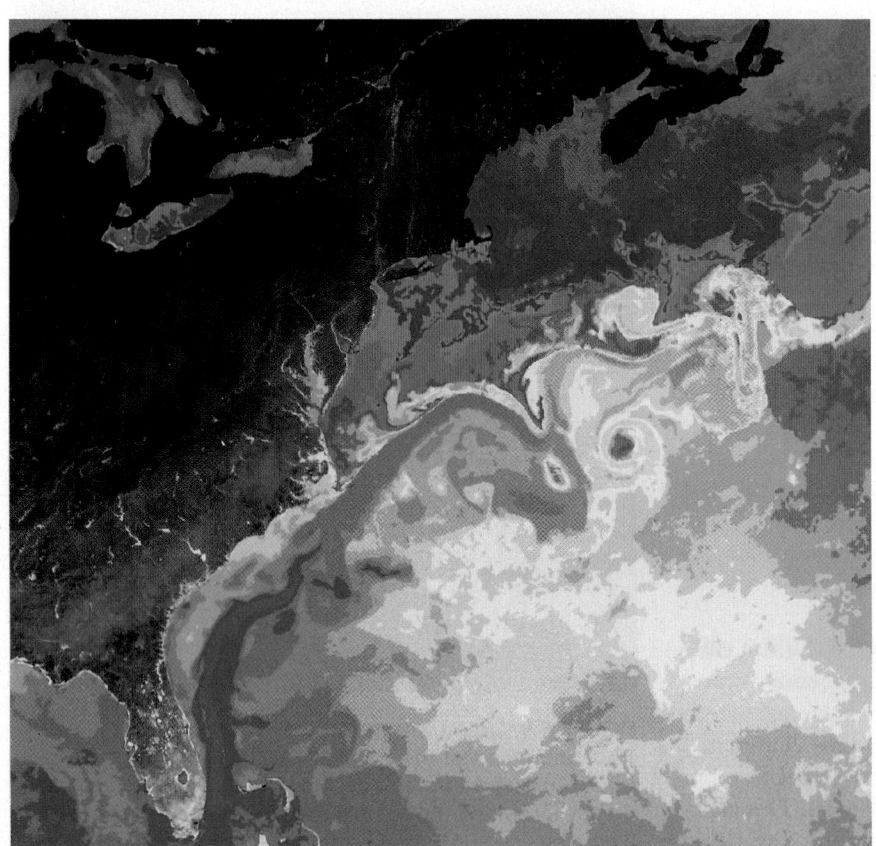

FIGURE 5.10 The Gulf Stream. Satellite image of the warm Gulf Stream as it flows northward along the North American eastern coast. It is the stream-like flow in red, orange, and yellow. Instruments sensitive to infrared wavelengths produced this remote-sensing image, which covers approximately 11.4 million square kilometres (4.4 million square miles). Temperature differences are distinguished by computer-enhanced coloration: reds/oranges = 25–29°C (76–84°F), yellows/greens = 17–24°C (63–75°F); blues = 10–16°C (50–61°F); and purples = 2–9°C (36–48°F). [Imagery by Rosenstiel School of Marine and Atmospheric Science, University of Miami.]

Western Pacific Warm Pool is the red and maroon area in the southwestern Pacific Ocean (north of New Guinea) with temperatures above 30°C (86°F). This region has the highest average ocean temperatures in the world. Note the seasonal change in ocean temperatures; for example compare the waters around Australia on the two images. Mean annual SSTs increased steadily from 1982 through 2000 to record levels for the past several hundred years.

Summary of Marine Effects vs. Continental Effects

As noted, Figure 5.7 summarizes the operation of the five land–water temperature controls presented: evaporation, transparency, specific heat, movement and ocean currents, and sea-surface temperatures. The term **marine effect**, or *maritime*, describes locations that exhibit the moderating influences of the ocean, usually along coastlines or on islands. **Continental effect**, a condition of *continentality*, refers to areas less affected by the sea and therefore having a greater range between maximum and minimum temperatures, daily and yearly.

Vancouver, British Columbia, and Winnipeg, Manitoba, exemplify marine and continental conditions (Figure 5.12). Both cities are at approximately 49° N latitude. However, Vancouver has a more moderate pattern of average maximum and minimum temperatures. Vancouver's annual range of 16.0 C° (28.8 F°) is far less than Winnipeg's 38.0 C° (68.4 F°) range. In fact, Winnipeg's continental temperature pattern is more extreme in every aspect than that of maritime Vancouver.

Earth's Temperature Patterns

Earth's temperature patterns result from the combined effect of the controlling factors in our discussion. Let us now look at temperatures portrayed on maps that show worldwide mean air temperatures for January (Figure 5.13) and July (Figure 5.15). To complete the analysis, Figure 5.16 presents the temperature range differences between the January and July maps, or the difference between averages of the coolest and warmest months.

We use maps for January and July instead of the solstice months of December and June because a lag occurs between insolation received and maximum or minimum temperatures experienced, as explained earlier in Chapter 4. The U.S. National Climate Data Center provided the data for this map preparation. Some ship reports go back to 1850 and land reports to 1890, although the bulk of the record is representative of conditions since 1950. An important

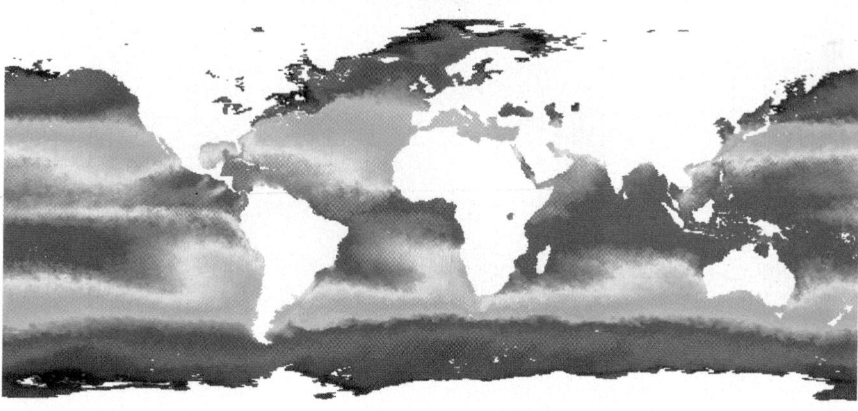

(a) February

(b) July

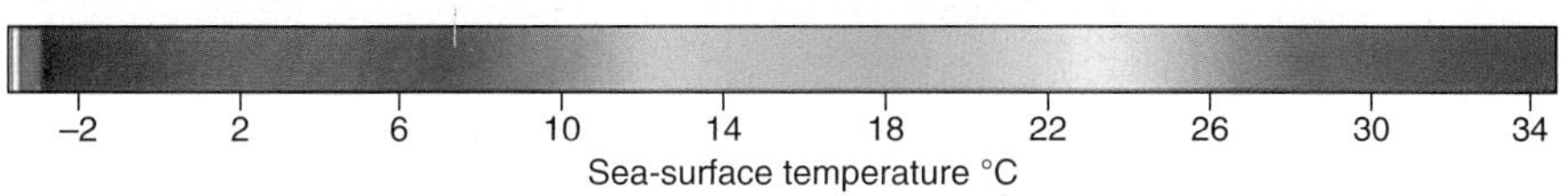

FIGURE 5.11 Sea-surface temperatures.
Average annual sea-surface temperatures for February (a) and July (b) 1999 from satellites in the NOAA/NASA Pathfinder AVHRR data set, aboard *NOAA-7*, *-9*, *-11*, and *-14*. The Western Pacific Warm Pool, the warmest area of all oceans, is well defined. These remotely sensed data are closely correlated with actual measurements of the ocean's surface temperature. [Satellite image data from the NASA Physical Oceanography Distributed Active Archive Center at the Jet Propulsion Laboratory, California Institute of Technology.]

Global Sea-surface Temperatures

FIGURE 5.12 Marine and continental cities—Canada.
Comparison of temperatures in coastal Vancouver, British Columbia, and continental Winnipeg, Manitoba. Note that the freezing levels on the two graphs are positioned differently to accommodate the contrasting data. [Vancouver waterfront photo by Robert W. Christopherson; Winnipeg photo by John Eastcott/Yva Momatiak/The Image Works.]

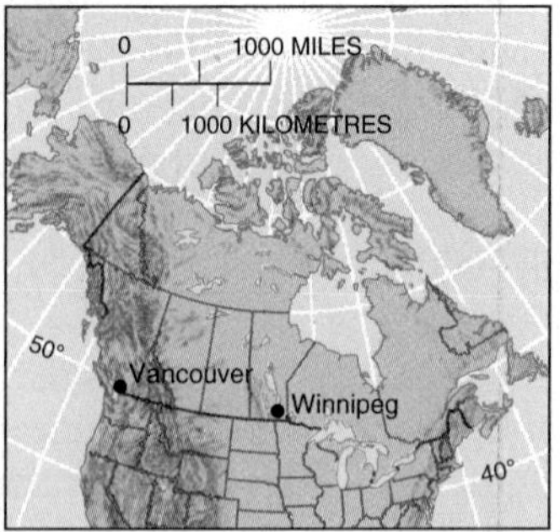

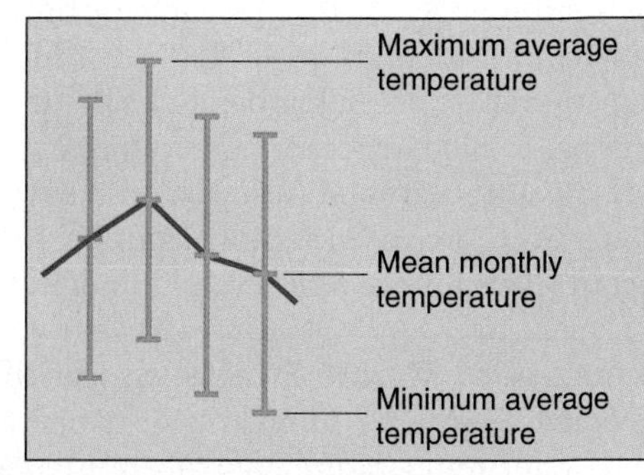

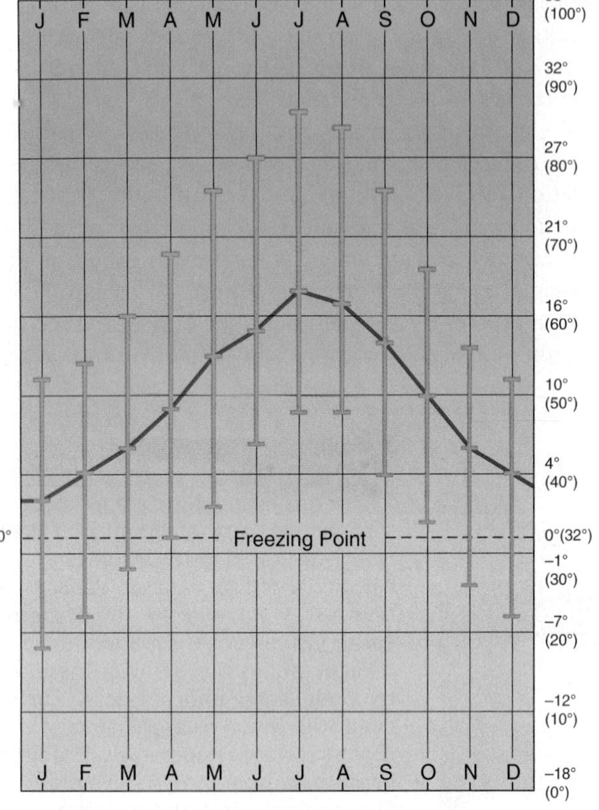

Station: Vancouver, British Columbia
Lat/long: 49° 11′ N 123° 10′ W
Avg. ann. temp.: 10°C (50°F)
Total ann. precip.: 104.8 cm (41.3 in.)
Elevation: sea level
Population: 520,000
Ann. temp. range: 16 C° (28.8 F°)

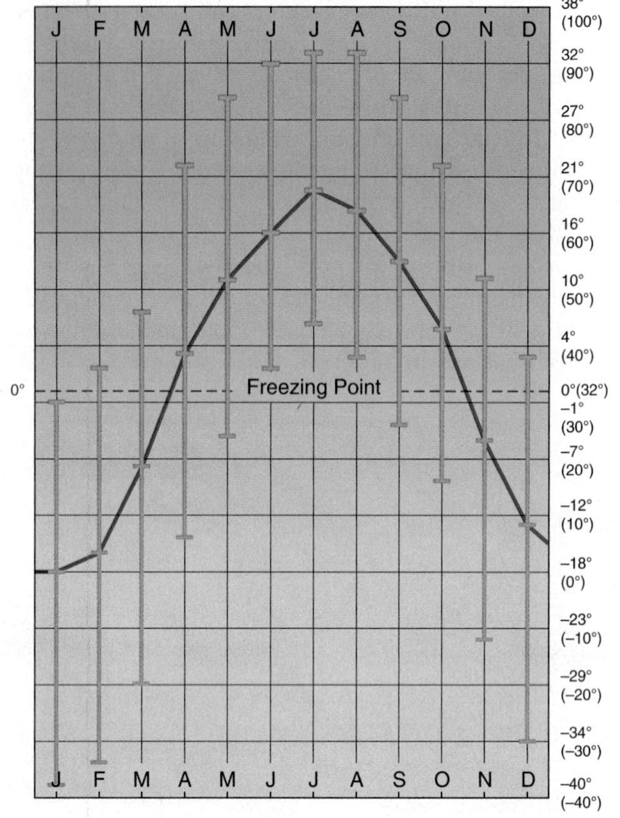

Station: Winnipeg, Manitoba
Lat/long: 49° 54′ N 97° 14′ W
Avg. ann. temp.: 2°C (35.6°F)
Total ann. precip.: 51.7 cm (20.3 in.)
Elevation: 248 m (813.6 ft)
Population: 620,000
Ann. temp. range: 38 C° (68.4 F°)

FIGURE 5.13 Global mean temperatures for January.
Temperatures are in Celsius (convertible to Fahrenheit by means of the scale) as taken from separate air temperature data bases for ocean and land. Note the inset map of North America and the equatorward-trending isotherms in the interior—(a) world map, (b) North Polar region, and (c) South Polar region. (Compare with Figure 5.15.) [Adapted from National Climatic Data Center, *Monthly Climatic Data for the World*, 47 (January 1994). Prepared in cooperation with the World Meteorological Organization. Washington, DC: National Oceanic and Atmospheric Administration.]

Global Surface Temperatures, Land and Ocean

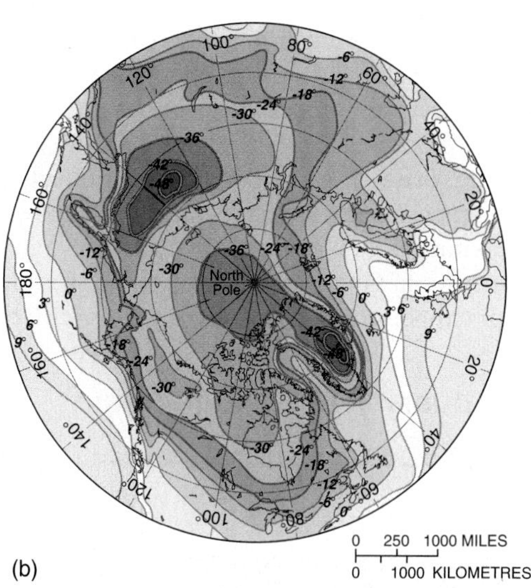

(b)

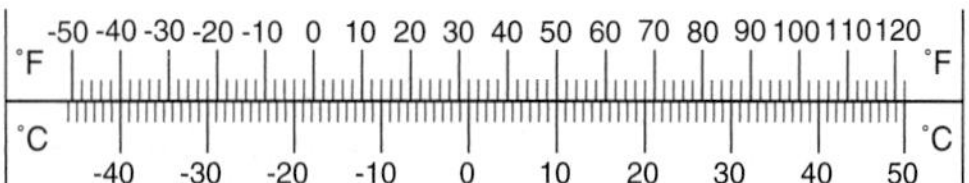

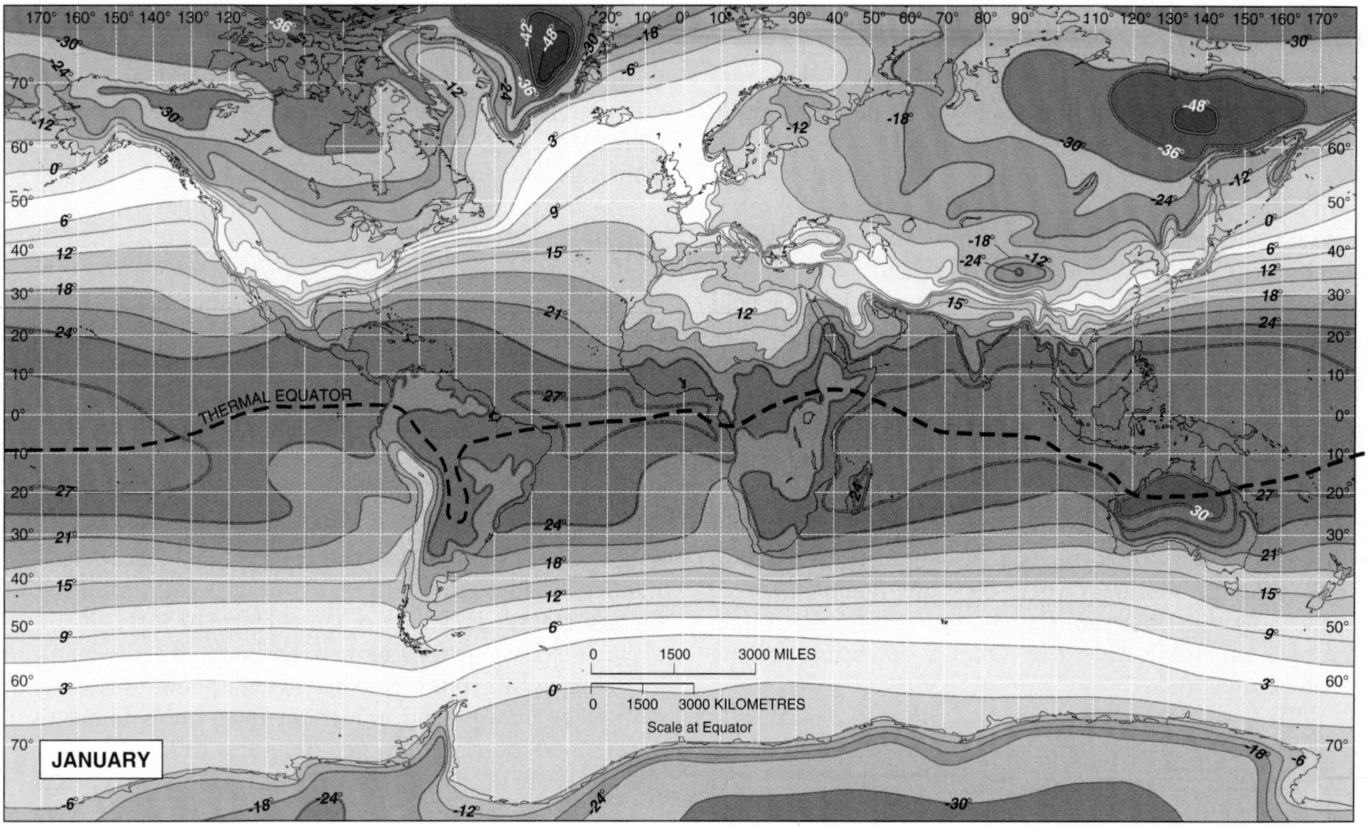

JANUARY

THERMAL EQUATOR

0 1500 3000 MILES
0 1500 3000 KILOMETRES
Scale at Equator

(a)

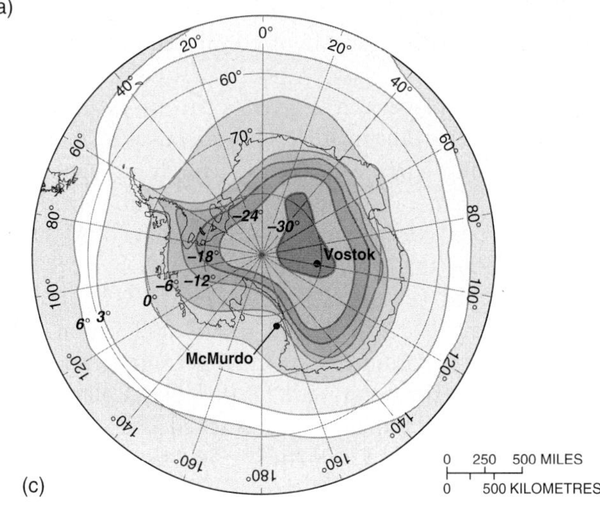

(c)

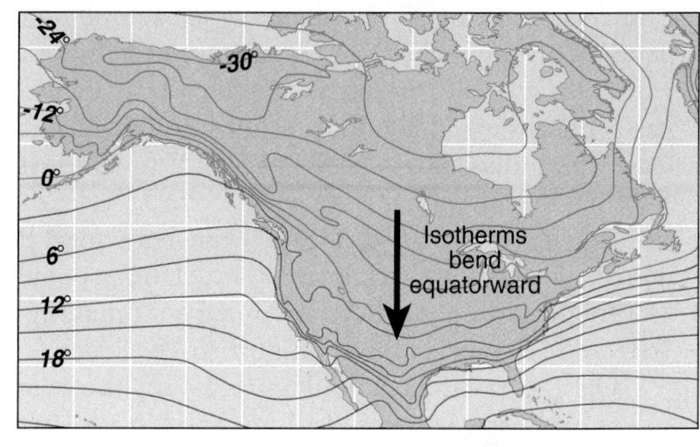

consideration in using these maps is to remember that their small scale permits only generalizations about actual temperatures at specific locations.

The lines on temperature maps are known as *isotherms*. An **isotherm** is an isoline that connects points of equal temperature and portrays the temperature pattern, just as a contour line on a topographic map illustrates points of equal elevation. Geographers are concerned with spatial analysis of temperatures, and isotherms help with this analysis.

January Temperature Map

Figure 5.13 maps January's mean temperatures for the world (a), North Polar region (b), and South Polar region (c). In the Southern Hemisphere the higher Sun altitude causes longer days and summer weather conditions; in the Northern Hemisphere the lower Sun angle causes the short days of winter. Isotherms generally are zonal, trending east-west, parallel to the equator, and they appear to be interrupted by the presence of landmasses. Isotherms mark the general decrease in insolation and net radiation with distance from the equator.

The **thermal equator** (an isoline connecting all points of highest mean temperature, roughly 27°C, 80°F) trends southward into the interior of South America and Africa, indicating higher temperatures over landmasses. In the Northern Hemisphere, isotherms shift equatorward as cold air chills the continental interiors. The oceans, on the other hand, are more moderate, with warmer conditions extending farther north than over land at comparable latitudes.

As an example, follow along 50° north latitude (the 50th parallel) and compare isotherms: 3° to 6°C in the North Pacific and 3° to 9°C in the North Atlantic, as contrasted to −18°C in the interior of North America and −24° to −30°C in central Asia. Also, note the orientation of isotherms over areas where there are mountain ranges and how they illustrate the cooling effects of altitude. Check the South American Andes as an example of the effects of altitude.

Russia is the coldest area on the map, specifically northeastern Siberia. The intense cold results from winter conditions of consistent clear, dry, calm air, small insolation input, and an inland location far from moderating maritime effects. Verkhoyansk, Russia (located within the −48°C isotherm on the map), actually recorded a minimum temperature of –68°C (90°F) and experiences a daily average of −50.5°C (−58.9°F) for January. Verkhoyansk (Figure 5.14) has 7 months of temperatures below freezing, including at least 4 months below −34°C (−30°F)! In contrast, this town has hit a maximum temperature of +37°C (+98°F) in July—an incredible 105 C° (189 F°) min–max range! People do live and work in Verkhoyansk, which has a population of 1400; the town has been occupied continuously since 1638 and is today a minor mining district.

On the polar map in Figure 5.13b, the island of Greenland has a summit elevation of 3240 m (10,630 ft) on Earth's second-largest ice sheet, the highest elevation north of the Arctic Circle. Two-thirds of the island is north of the Arctic Circle. Its north shore is only 800 km (500 mi) from the North Pole. This combination of high latitude and interior high altitude on the ice sheet produces cold midwinter temperatures.

In Antarctica, "summer" is underway in December. This is Earth's coldest and highest average elevation landmass (Figure 5.13c). January average temperatures for the three scientific bases noted on the map are: McMurdo Station, at the coast on Ross Island, averages −3°C; the Admundsen–Scott Station at the South Pole (elevation 2835 m, 9301 ft) averages −28°C; and the Russian Vostok Station at its more continental location (elevation 3420 m, 11,220 ft) averages −32°C.

Trondheim, Norway, is near the latitude of Verkhoyansk and at a similar elevation. But Trondheim's coastal location moderates its annual temperature regime (see Figure 5.14). January minimum and maximum temperatures range between −17° and +8°C (+1.4° and +46°F), and the minimum-maximum range for July is from +5° to +27°C (+41° to +81°F). The most extreme minimum and maximum temperatures ever recorded in Trondheim are −30° and +35°C (−22° and +95°F)—quite a large difference from the continental extremes at Verkhoyansk.

July Temperature Map

Average July temperatures are presented in Figure 5.15a for the world, North Polar region (b), and South Polar region (c). The longer days of summer and higher Sun altitude are in the Northern Hemisphere. Winter dominates the Southern Hemisphere, although it is milder than winters north of the equator because continental landmasses are smaller and the dominant oceans and seas store and release more energy. The thermal equator shifts northward with the high summer Sun and reaches the Persian Gulf-Pakistan-Iran area. The Persian Gulf is the site of the highest recorded sea-surface temperature of 36°C (96°F), difficult to imagine for a large water body.

During July in the Northern Hemisphere, isotherms shift poleward over land, as higher temperatures dominate continental interiors. July temperatures in Verkhoyansk average more than 13°C (56°F), which represents a 63 C° (113 F°) seasonal range between winter and summer averages. The Verkhoyansk region of Siberia is probably Earth's most dramatic example of continental effects on temperature.

The hottest places on Earth occur in Northern Hemisphere deserts during July. The reasons are simple: clear skies, strong surface heating, virtually no surface water, and few plants. Prime examples are portions of the Sonoran Desert of North America and the Sahara of Africa. Africa recorded a shade temperature higher than 58°C (136°F), a record set on September 13, 1922, at Al 'Azīzīyah, Libya (32° 32' N; 112 m, or 367 ft elevation).

The highest maximum and annual average temperatures in North America occurred in Death Valley, California, where the Greenland Ranch Station reached 57°C (134°F) in 1913. (The station is at 37° N and is −54.3 m, or −178 ft,

FIGURE 5.14 Marine and continental cities—Eurasia. Comparison of temperatures in coastal Trondheim, Norway, and continental Siberian Russia. Note that the freezing levels on the two graphs are positioned differently to accommodate the contrasting data. [Trondheim photo by Norman Benton/Peter Arnold, Inc.; Verkhoyansk photo by TASS/Sovfoto/Eastfoto.]

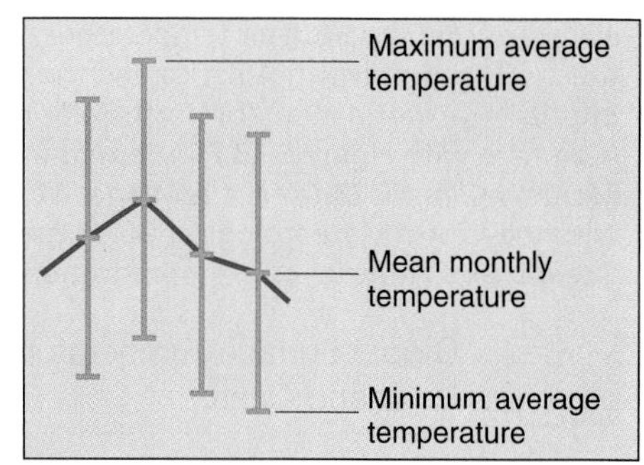

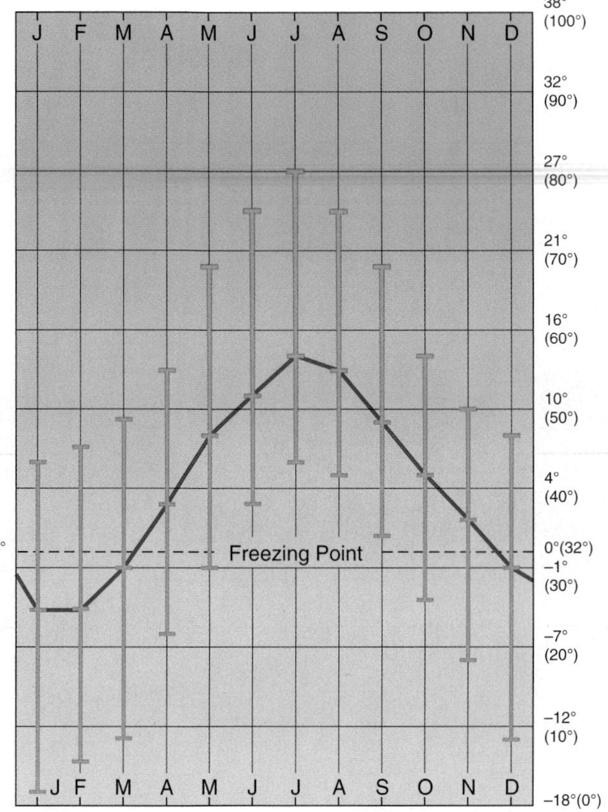

Station: Trondheim, Norway
Lat/long: 63° 25′ N 10° 27′ E
Avg. ann. temp.: 5°C (41°F)
Total ann. precip.: 85.7 cm (33.7 in.)
Elevation: 115 m (377.3 ft)
Population: 139,000
Ann. temp. range: 17 C° (30.6 F°)

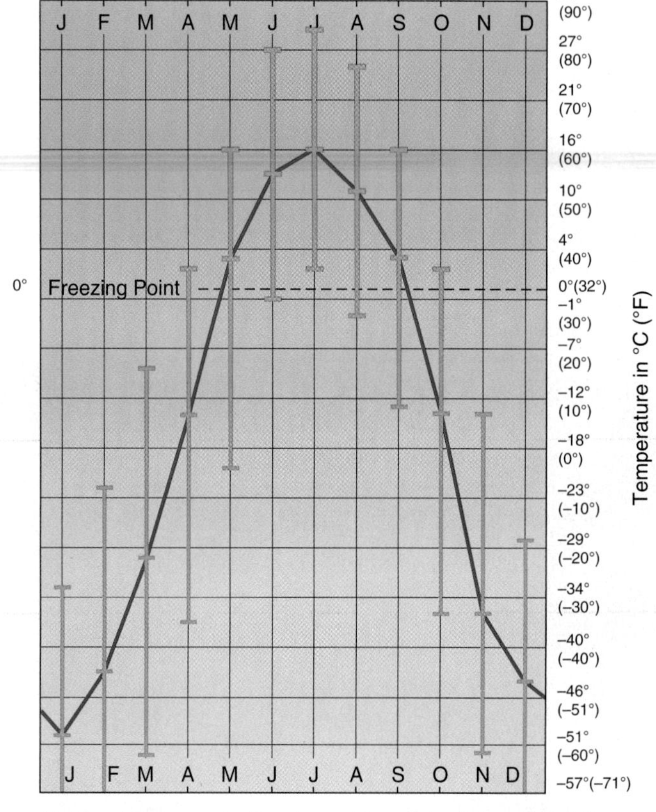

Station: Verkhoyansk, Russia
Lat/long: 67° 35′ N 135° 23′ E
Avg. ann. temp.: –15°C (5°F)
Total ann. precip.: 15.5 cm (6.1 in.)
Elevation: 137 m (449.5 ft)
Population: 1400
Ann. temp. range: 63 C° (113.4 F°)

FIGURE 5.15 Global mean temperatures for July. Temperatures are in Celsius (convertible to Fahrenheit by means of the scale) as taken from separate air temperature data bases for ocean and land. Note the inset map of North America and the poleward-trending isotherms in the interior—(a) world map, (b) North Polar region, and (c) South Polar region. (Compare with Figure 5.13.) [Adapted from National Climatic Data Center, *Monthly Climatic Data for the World*, 47 (July 1994). Prepared in cooperation with the World Meteorological Organization. Washington, DC: National Oceanic and Atmospheric Administration.]

Global Surface Temperatures, Land and Ocean

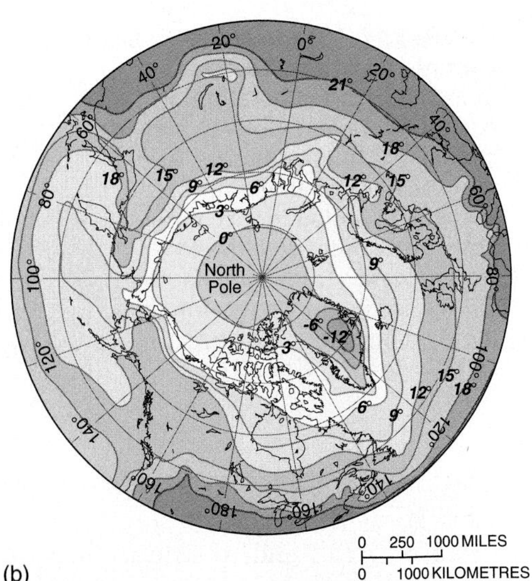

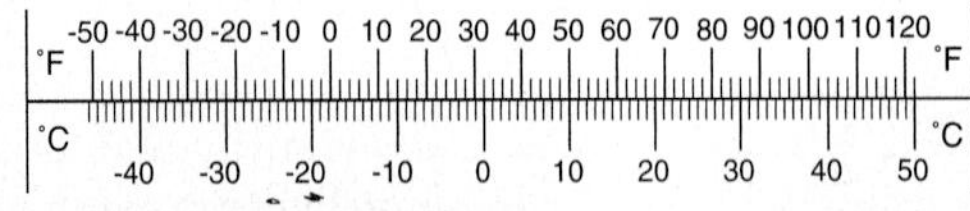

(b)

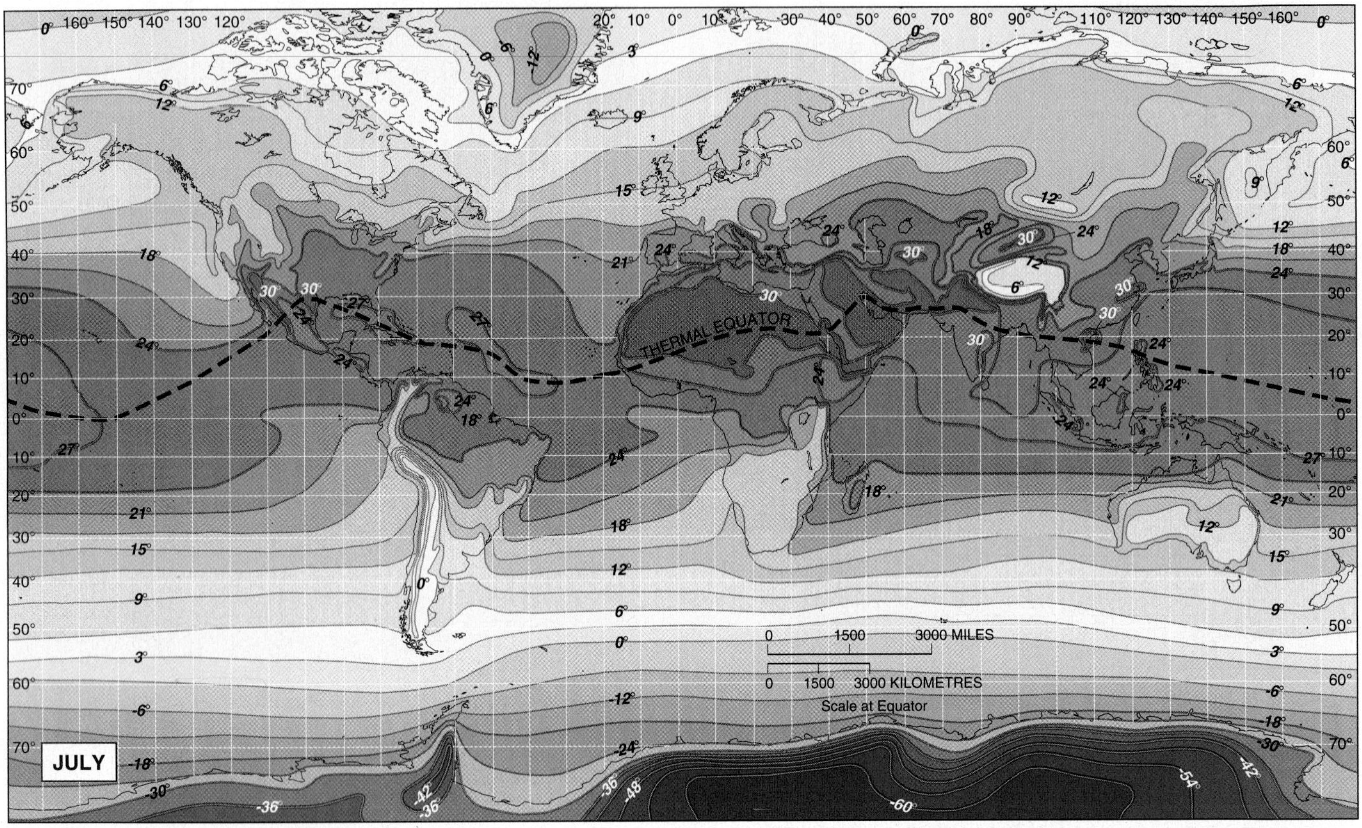

JULY

THERMAL EQUATOR

0 1500 3000 MILES

0 1500 3000 KILOMETRES

Scale at Equator

(a)

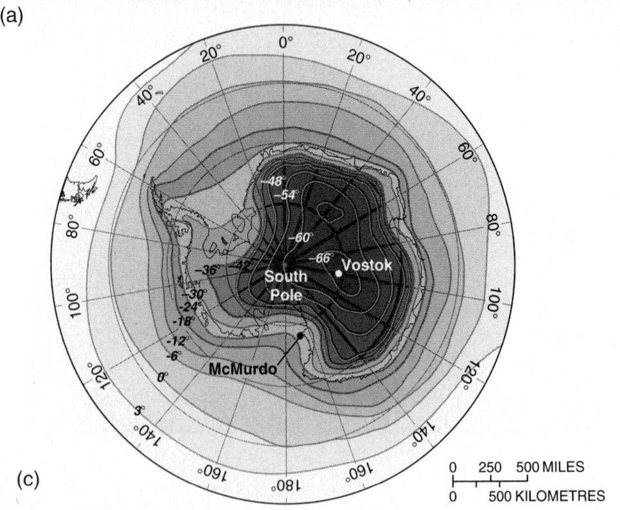

(c)

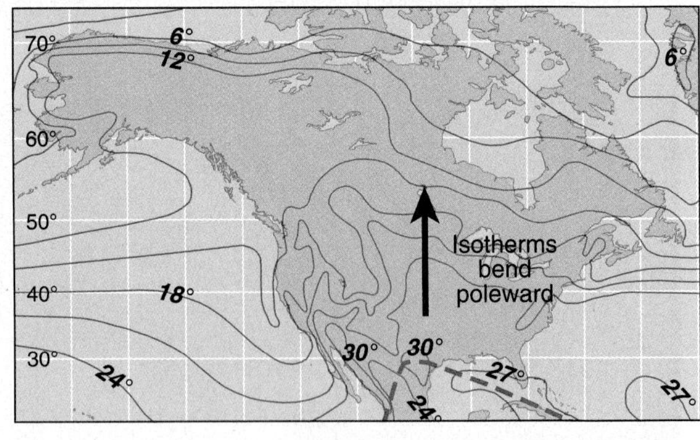

below sea level). Such hot, arid lands are discussed further in Chapter 15.

July is a time when nights in Antarctica are 24 hours long. This lack of insolation results in the lowest natural temperature reported on Earth, a frigid −89.2°C (−128.6°F), recorded on July 21, 1983, at the Russian Vostok Station, Antarctica (Figure 5.15c). Such a temperature is 11 C° (19.8 F°) colder than the freezing point of dry ice (solid carbon dioxide)! If the concentration of carbon dioxide were large enough, such a cold temperature would theoretically freeze tiny carbon dioxide dry-ice particles out of the sky.

The average July temperature around Vostok is −68°C (−90.4°F). For average temperature comparisons, the Admundsen-Scott Station at the South Pole experiences −60°C (−76°F) and McMurdo Station has a −26°C (−14.8°F) reading. Note that the coldest temperatures in Antarctica are usually in August, not July, just before the equinox sunrise in September at the end of the long polar night. High Latitude Connection 5.1 presents an overview of temperature trends in the polar regions.

Annual Temperature Range Map

The temperature range map helps identify areas that experience the greatest annual extremes (continental locations) and the most moderate temperature regimes (marine locations), as demonstrated in Figure 5.16. As you might expect, the largest temperature ranges occur in subpolar locations in North America and Asia, where average ranges of 64 C° (115 F°) are recorded. The Southern Hemisphere, on the other hand, has little seasonal variation in mean temperatures, owing to the lack of large landmasses and vast expanses of water to moderate temperature extremes.

For example, in January (Figure 5.13), Australia is dominated by isotherms of 20–30°C (68–86°F), whereas in July (Figure 5.15), Australia is crossed by the 12°C (54°F) isotherm. Southern Hemisphere temperature patterns are generally maritime, and Northern Hemisphere patterns feature continentality. The Northern Hemisphere, with greater land area overall, registers a slightly higher average surface temperature than does the Southern Hemisphere.

Imagine living in some of these regions and the degree to which your personal wardrobe and other comfort adaptations would need to adjust. See Focus Study 5.1 for more on air temperature and the human body.

There is a distinct possibility that in the future humans may experience greater temperature-related challenges owing to complex changes now under way in the lower atmosphere. See page 140 for an introduction to some of these global changes that are discussed more extensively in Chapter 10.

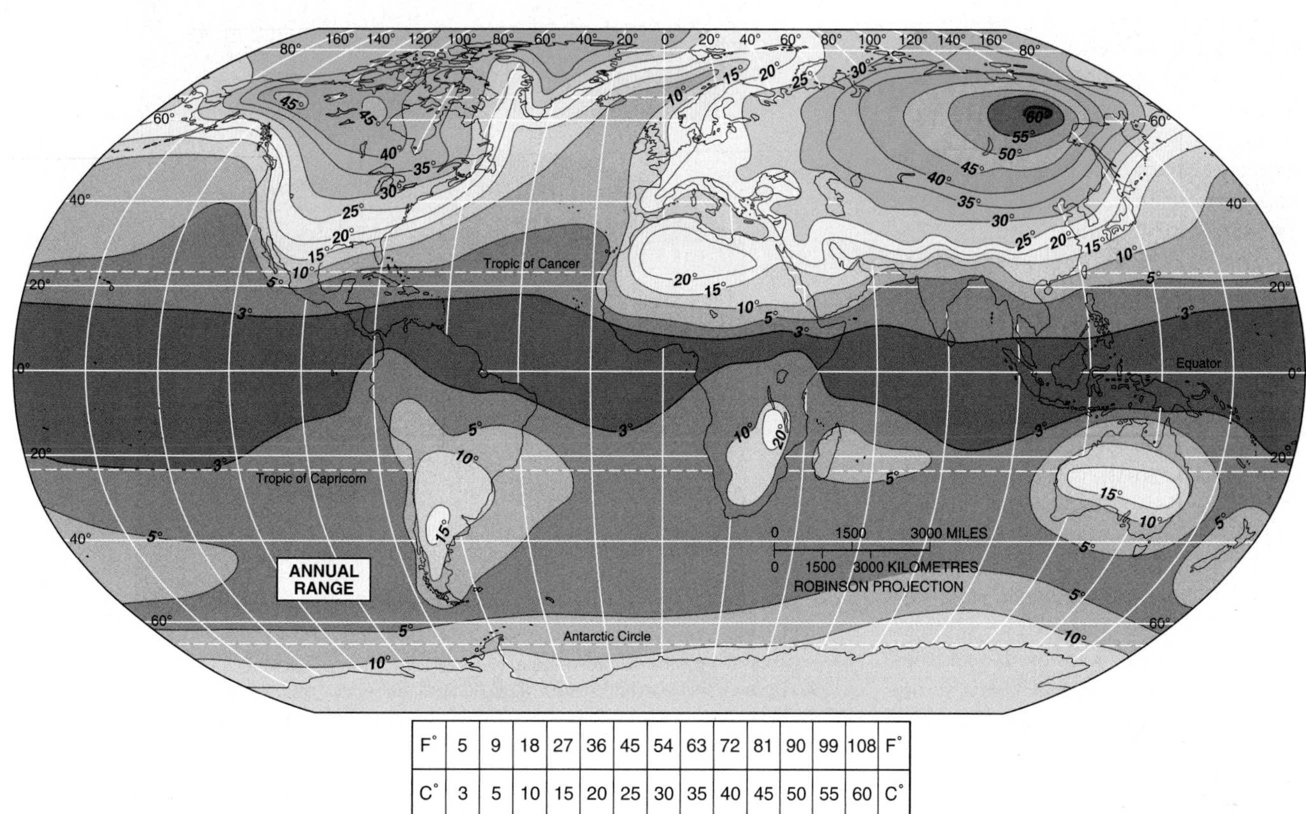

F°	5	9	18	27	36	45	54	63	72	81	90	99	108	F°
C°	3	5	10	15	20	25	30	35	40	45	50	55	60	C°

FIGURE 5.16 Global annual temperature ranges.
A generalized portrait of the annual range of global temperatures in Celsius degrees (conversions to Fahrenheit degrees shown on scale). The mapped data show the difference between January and July temperature means.

High Latitude Connection 5.1

Overview of Trends in the Polar Regions

Climate models used by scientists to predict and direct measurements show that the polar regions are experiencing some dramatic global climate change impacts. These changes lead some to say that the high latitudes are providing the global community an early warning signal. The question is, how do we read changing temperature signals, how do they relate to natural circulation cycles, and what are the spatial implications to the rest of the planet?

Arctic

Many proxy and direct measurements confirm that the twentieth century was a time of increasing temperatures at both middle and low latitudes and in the polar regions, especially during the last half century. Daily maximum and minimum temperatures show there is warming in the Arctic at a rate of about 5 C° (9 F°) per century. Since 1978, warming increased to a rate of 1.2 C° (2.2 F°) per decade, which means the last 20 years warmed at nearly 7 times the rate of the last 100 years. The trend is not uniform across the Arctic polar region, with areas of slight cooling in eastern Canada, the North Atlantic, and portions of Greenland, although an overall warming dominates.

In response to rising air and water temperatures, Arctic sea ice is on a significant decline. The sea ice is melting at a rate of about 9% per decade since 1978, especially in the eastern and central Arctic Ocean. Atmospheric pressure patterns cause sea ice to shift as well. Record losses marked 2002 and 2003, as sea ice reached its smallest spatial distribution in the satellite record. Figure 1 is a composite satellite image for 1979 and 2003 comparing sea-ice coverage in the Arctic. The sea ice thins as warmer air melts the surface and warmer waters attack the base of the ice. The summer melt period is increasing as spring arrives earlier and fall is delayed. Since 1970, about 43% of the Arctic sea ice has disappeared. More open water means darker surfaces that absorb more insolation that leads to more warming.

Chapters 1 and 17 discuss the 400% increase in meltponds on the surface of the Greenland ice sheet, ice shelves, and glaciers. This increase represents a significant positive feedback mechanism. In response to the increased discharge of freshwater in the Arctic, the northern oceans are freshening—actually, a lowering in salinity. There is valid concern that these meltwaters riding atop saline water can disrupt important circulation systems in the northern oceans.

In Alaska, temperatures rose over the past 30 years at a 3 C° (5 F°) per decade rate. All 11 mountain ranges experienced glacial ice losses. Glacial thinning reached 1.8 m per year by the late 1990s across Alaska. In response to this unloading of ice mass, the crust is

FIGURE 1 Loss of Arctic sea ice.
A composite of satellite data (DMSP, Special Sensor Microwave Imager) and surface data from 1979 and 2003 shows remarkable loss of Arctic sea ice. Each composite is a portrait of minimum sea-ice concentrations during summer months. For scale, the amount of sea-ice loss is approximately the size of Labrador, or 300,000 km^2 (116,000 mi^2)—approximately 43% of sea ice has disappeared since 1970. Not only did the atmosphere record increased warmth but the Arctic Ocean warmed as well. Another factor is atmospheric pressure patterns that cause sea ice to shift. [Images courtesy of Scientific Visualization Studio, GSFC/NASA.]

rebounding upward. A News Report in Chapter 17 explains the negative net mass balance of 67 Alaskan glaciers.

All of these changes are affecting living systems as specific high-latitude ecosystems shift across the landscape poleward at 6.1 km (3.8 mi) per decade and spring arrives earlier at a pace of 2.3 days per decade. Changes in tundra soils and the increased depth of active-layer melting in permafrost indicate regional warming, as discussed in Chapter 17. These thawing lands provide less nutrition to caribou and moose, worsen forest fire conditions, and are an additional source of carbon dioxide to the atmosphere.

By 2080, the Intergovernmental Panel on Climate Change (IPCC) forecasts increasing warmth in the Arctic ranging from 4.0° to 7.5 C° in summer and 2.5 to 14.0 C° in winter over land; and 0.5° to 4.5 C° in summer and 3.0 to 16.0 C° in winter over the Arctic Ocean. With these temperature changes, precipitation will increase since warmer air can contain more moisture.

Antarctica

In Antarctica and the Southern Ocean, the temperature records of the permanently occupied research stations over the last 45 years demonstrate an overall warming. This record includes periods of slight cooling within this time frame. The present warming rate is less than that of the Arctic, at about a 0.9° to 1.2 C° increase per century.

However, along the Antarctic Peninsula, the location of numerous ice-shelf collapses and disintegrations, the rate of warming is more than twice this rate, as the January 0° isotherm continues to shift southward. The exposed land is open to exotic plants and animals that move into these altered ecosystems. In terms of sea ice, the Antarctic trend is not as pronounced as that of the Arctic, with sea-ice extent reduced by 0.4–1.8° of latitude over the last century. Continued changes will affect marine life and birds.

By 2080, the IPCC forecasts increasing warmth in the Antarctic ranging from 1.0 to 4.8 C° in summer and 1.0 to 5.0 C° in winter over the continent; and 0.0 to 2.8 C° in summer and 0.5° to 5.0 C° in winter over the Southern Ocean.

For more information on both polar regions, please see: Chapter 16, "Polar Regions (Arctic and Antarctic)," in *Climate Change 2001, Impacts, Adaptation, and Vulnerability, Contribution of Working Group II to the Third Assessment Report of the Intergovernmental Panel on Climate Change* (New York: Cambridge University Press, © 2001), pp. 801–41. The Web site is at http://www.ipcc.ch/.

Focus Study 5.1

Air Temperature and the Human Body

We describe our perception of temperature with the term *apparent temperature*, or *sensible temperature*. This perception varies among individuals and cultures. Through complex mechanisms, our bodies maintain an average internal temperature within a degree of 36.8°C (98.2°F), slightly lower in the morning or in cold weather and slightly higher at emotional times or during exercise and work.*

The water vapour content of air, wind speed, and air temperature taken together affect each individual's sense of comfort. The most discomfort comes with high temperatures, high humidity, and low winds. More comfort comes with low humidity, moderate temperatures, and light winds.

Although modern heating and cooling systems, where available, reduce the impact of extreme temperatures indoors, the danger to human life from excessive heat or cold persists. A notable example is the deaths of more than 20,000 people in Europe during the summer heat wave of 2003.

When changes occur in the surrounding air, the human body reacts to maintain its core temperature and to protect the brain at all costs. Table 1 summarizes the human body's response to stress induced by exposure to *hypothermia* (low temperature) and *hyperthermia* (high temperature). Carefully review these two lists of responses for future reference.

Wind Chill

The wind-chill index is important to people who experience winters with freezing temperatures and was first proposed by Antarctic explorer Paul Siple in 1939. The *wind-chill factor* indicates the enhanced rate at which body heat is lost to the air and at best represents an estimate of heat energy loss. As wind speeds increase, heat loss from the skin increases. A formula for calculating these relationships was developed in 1945 and the U.S. National Weather Service (NWS) began reporting wind-chill temperatures in 1970. This older index tended to overestimate heat loss from skin.

The NWS and the Meteorological Service of Canada (MSC, http://www.msc-smc.ec.gc.ca/) revised the wind chill formula and standard assumptions for the 2001–2002 winter season. The new Wind Chill Temperature (WCT) Index is an effort to improve the

(continued)

*The traditional value for "normal" body temperature, 37°C (98.6°F), was set in 1868 using old methods of measurement. According to Dr. Philip Mackowiak of the University of Maryland School of Medicine, a more accurate modern assessment places the normal value at 36.8°C (98.2°F), with a range of 2.7 C° (4.8 F°), for the human population overall (*Journal of the American Medical Association*, September 23–30, 1992).

Focus Study 5.1 *(continued)*

Table 1 The Human Body's Response to Temperature Stress

At Low Temperatures (Heat-gaining mechanism)	At High Temperatures (Heat-dissipation mechanism)
Temperature Regulation Methods	
Constriction of surface blood vessels	Dilation of surface blood vessels
Concentration of blood	Dilution of blood
Flexing to reduce surface exposure	Extending to increase exposure
Increased muscle tone	Decreased muscle tone
Decrease in sweating	Sweating
Inclination to increase activity	Inclination to decrease activity
Shivering	
Increased cell metabolism	
Consequent Disturbances	
Increased urine volume	Decreased urine volume
Danger to inadequate blood supply to exposed parts; frostbite	Reduced blood supply to brain; dizziness, nausea, fainting
Discomfort leading to neuroses	Discomfort leading to neuroses
Increased appetite	Decreased appetite
	Mobilization of tissue fluid
	Thirst and dehydration
	Reduced chloride balance; heat cramps
Failure of Regulation	
Falling body temperature	Rising body temperature
Drowsiness	Impaired heat-regulating centre
Cessation of heartbeat and respiration	Failure of nervous regulation; cessation of breathing

Source: Climatology—Arid Zone Research X. © UNESCO 1958. Reproduced by permission of UNESCO.

accuracy of heat loss calculations. Computer modelling, clinical trials and testing, and advances in technology make this revision possible. Figure 1 is the new version that went into service November 2001.

For example, using the new chart, if the air temperature is −7°C (20°F) and the wind is blowing at 32 kmph (20 mph), skin temperatures will be at −16°C (4°F). The lower wind-chill values present a serious freezing hazard to exposed flesh. Imagine the wind chill experienced by a downhill ski racer going 130 kmph (80 mph)—frostbite is a definite possibility during a 2-minute run. The wind chill does omit consideration of sunlight intensity, a person's physical activity, and the use of protective clothing, such as a wind-breaker, that prevents the wind access to your skin.

Humidex

Humidex, a Canadian innovation first used in 1965, was devised to describe how hot, humid weather feels to the average person. It represents the heating effect felt as a result of a lack of evaporation from the skin surface and is only measured in the summer months. Humidex is reported as a temperature—not the recorded temperature, but how hot it "feels" based on humidity. In the United States, the effect of high heat and moisture on the human body is calculated in a similar way (**http://www.hpc.ncep.noaa.gov/heat_index.shtml**).

Humidex is a calculation based on air temperature and relative humidity (water vapour in the air—see Chapter 7) and, as mentioned, is reported as an equivalent temperature. Water vapour in the air is expressed as relative humidity, a concept presented in Chapter 7. Although it is used widely in Canada, the areas most affected by the Humidex readings are in southern Ontario and Québec. Here, in summer, the greatest impact of moist tropical air from the Gulf of Mexico is felt.

The following formula is a simplified method used to calculate Humidex:

$$\text{Humidex} = T + 5/9\,(e - 10)$$

where e = vapour pressure $(6.112 \times 10^{(7.5 \times T/(237.7 + T)) \times H/100})$,
T = air temperature (degrees Celsius), and
H = humidity (%).

Table 2 describes the comfort levels associated with Humidex levels as suggested by the Meteorological Service of Canada.

High Humidex values produce stifling conditions that can be serious, particularly to the sick and elderly. In the summer of 2003, Europe was paralysed by extreme temperatures that topped 40°C. Official estimates of deaths due to the extreme heat reached more than 20,000. The estimates were believed by many to be low and this controversy sparked demands for improved action plans for future heat wave catastrophes.

France was hardest hit, with a heat-related death toll of over 14,000—11,345 deaths in the first two weeks of August alone. The estimate was calculated by comparing the number of deaths to the statistical average for August. The timing of the heat wave was important—it began on August 1, the start of a typical summer holiday period when many leave home for vacation. A seasonal reduction of doctors, nurses, and in-service hospital beds resulted from this holiday period. By August 5, increased activity began for paramedics and hospital emergency rooms. As the heat wave continued, government officials were reluctant to cut their holidays short to deal with the problem. An emergency response was

Actual Air Temperature in °C (°F)

Wind speed, kmph (mph)									
Calm	4° (40°)	−1° (30°)	−7° (20°)	−12° (10°)	−18° (0°)	−23° (−10°)	−29° (−20°)	−34° (−30°)	−40° (−40°)
8 (5)	2° (36°)	−4° (25°)	−11° (13°)	−17° (1°)	−24° (−11°)	−30° (−22°)	−37° (−34°)	−43° (−46°)	−49° (−57°)
16 (10)	1° (34°)	−6° (21°)	−13° (9°)	−20° (−4°)	−27° (−16°)	−33° (−28°)	−41° (−41°)	−47° (−53°)	−54° (−66°)
24 (15)	0° (32°)	−7° (19°)	−14° (6°)	−22° (−7°)	−28° (−19°)	−36° (−32°)	−43° (−45°)	−50° (−58°)	−57° (−71°)
32 (20)	−1° (30°)	−8° (17°)	−16° (4°)	−23° (−9°)	−30° (−22°)	−37° (−35°)	−44° (−48°)	−52° (−61°)	−59° (−74°)
40 (25)	−2° (29°)	−9° (16°)	−16° (3°)	−24° (−11°)	−31° (−24°)	−38° (−37°)	−46° (−51°)	−53° (−64°)	−61° (−78°)
48 (30)	−2° (28°)	−9° (15°)	−17° (−1°)	−24° (−12°)	−32° (−26°)	−39° (−39°)	−47° (−53°)	−55° (−67°)	−62° (−80°)
56 (35)	−2° (28°)	−10° (14°)	−18° (0°)	−26° (−14°)	−33° (−27°)	−41° (−41°)	−48° (−55°)	−56° (−69°)	−63° (−82°)
64 (40)	−3° (27°)	−11° (13°)	−18° (−1°)	−26° (−15°)	−34° (−29°)	−42° (−43°)	−49° (−57°)	−57° (−71°)	−64° (−84°)
72 (45)	−3° (26°)	−11° (12°)	−19° (−2°)	−27° (−16°)	−34° (−30°)	−42° (−44°)	−50° (−58°)	−58° (−72°)	−66° (−86°)
80 (50)	−3° (26°)	−11° (12°)	−19° (−3°)	−27° (−17°)	−35° (−31°)	−43° (−45°)	−51° (−60°)	−59° (−74°)	−67° (−88°)

Frostbite times: 30 min. 10 min. 5 min.

FIGURE 1 Wind Chill Temperature Index.
WCT Index factor for various temperatures and wind speeds. A new version of the wind-chill chart—effective November 2001. For quick calculations see: http://www.nws.noaa.gov/om/windchill/index.shtml. (In English units the new formula is: Wind chill (F°) = $35.74 + 0.6125T - 35.75(V^{0.16}) + 0.4275T(V^{0.16})$; where T = air temperature in °F, V = wind speed in mph. In Canada, heat loss is expressed in watts per square metre.) [Adapted from the National Weather Service and Meteorological Services of Canada, version 11/01/01.]

Table 2 Comfort Levels and Suggested Activities for Ranges of Humidex

Range of Humidex	Degree of comfort
Less than 29	No discomfort
30 to 39	Some discomfort; tone down or modify strenuous outdoor activity
40 to 45	Great discomfort; avoid exertion, curtail activity
Above 45	Dangerous
Above 54	Heat stroke is imminent

Source: The Meteorological Service of Canada. Reproduced with the permission of Environment Canada, http://www.qc.ec.gc.ca/meteo/documentation/humidex_e.html.

launched August 13—the day temperatures began to fall. This response included calling hospital staff back to work and re-opening wards that had been closed for the August vacation season. This action was too late. The impact of the heat wave was felt across Europe: The United Kingdom counted 907 heat-related deaths, Portugal 545, Italy 4127, and Spain 112 official deaths, with estimates as high as 6000.

Global Temperatures Suggest a Greenhouse Warming

There is a distinct possibility that future humans may experience greater temperature-related challenges owing to complex changes now under way in the lower atmosphere. Scientists agree that human activities are enhancing Earth's natural greenhouse. Certain gases that absorb and emit radiation are increasing and are absorbing more longwave radiation and delaying losses of heat energy to space, thus changing the natural Earth–atmosphere energy equilibrium.

The Intergovernmental Panel on Climate Change (IPCC), through major reports in 1990, 1992, 1995, its *Third Assessment Report*, and summarizing *Synthesis Report* in 2001, confirms that global warming is occurring. Its latest report states, "... there is new and stronger evidence that most of the warming observed over the past 50 years is attributable to human activities.... Both temperature and sea level are projected to continue to rise throughout the twenty-first century for all scenarios studied." Uncertainty remains in forecasting the pace and implications of this warming for Earth systems.

The period from 1970 to 2003 registered the warmest years in the history of instrumental measurements. Effects of this warming are the subject of many scientific studies: melting and retreat of mountain glaciers worldwide, disintegration of coastal ice shelves around Antarctica, sea level rising at a faster rate than previously observed, more intense thunderstorms and weather extremes, changes in vegetation on land and the distribution of marine organisms in the oceans, and heat-wave effects on grain production. The snowline in portions of the European Alps has risen 100 m (330 ft) in elevation since 1980.

An array of sophisticated satellites, remote-sensing capabilities, and powerful computers equip scientists to run global circulation models and decipher the climate trends. With the blame resting on the exhaust from our fossil fuel consumption and our modern technological society, the political fallout and debate is intense. Chapter 10 discusses global warming and climate change. There we address what is known and unknown, how global models work, the radiatively active gases that are forcing the warming, the consequences to natural systems, the uncertainties, and what international action is under way to slow the effects of such change.

Applied Physical Geography

Humidex

Humidex, a calculated parameter that is based on temperature and humidity, can be easily calculated to determine the comfort level of the air at a specific temperature and humidity. It gives a measure of the amount of discomfort felt by the combined effect of the two elements. Humidex is calculated using the following formula:

$$\text{Humidex} = T + 5/9 \times (e - 10)$$

where e = vapour pressure $(6.112 \times 10^{(7.5 \times T/(237.7 + T)) \times H/100})$, T = air temperature (degrees Celsius), and H = humidity (%).

For example, given a temperature of 25°C with relative humidity of 82%, first determine the vapour pressure:

$$e = \text{vapour pressure } (6.112 \times 10^{(7.5 \times T/(237.7 + T)) \times H/100})$$

$$= 6.112 \times 10^{(7.5 \times 25/(237.7 + 25)) \times 82/100}$$

$$= 6.112 \times 10^{0.5852683}$$

$$= 23.52078.$$

Then use the vapour pressure value in the Humidex equation:

$$\text{Humidex} = T + 5/9 \times (e - 10)$$

$$= 25 + 5/9 \times (23.52078 - 10)$$

$$= 25 + 7.5115444$$

$$= 25 + 8$$

$$= 33.$$

So, on a day with a fairly moderate temperature, the humidity makes it feel much hotter.

Summary and Review—Global Temperatures

- ***Define* the concepts of temperature, kinetic energy, and sensible heat, and *distinguish* among Kelvin, Celsius, and Fahrenheit scales and how they are measured.**

Temperature is a measure of the average kinetic energy (motion) of individual molecules in matter. We feel the effect of temperature as the sensible heat transfer from warmer objects to cooler objects when these objects are touching. Temperature scales include:

- Kelvin scale: 100 units between ice's melting point (273 K) and water's boiling point (373 K).
- Celsius scale: 100 degrees between ice's melting point (0°C) and water's boiling point (100°C).

- Fahrenheit scale: 180 degrees between ice's melting point (32°F) and water's boiling point (212°F).

The Kelvin scale is used in scientific research because temperature readings start at absolute zero and thus are proportional to the actual kinetic energy in a material.

temperature (p. 122)

1. Distinguish between sensible heat and sensible temperature.
2. What does air temperature indicate about energy in the atmosphere?
3. Compare the three scales that express temperature. What is the basic assumption for each?
4. What is your source of daily temperature information? Describe the highest temperature you have experienced and the lowest temperature. From what we have discussed in this chapter, can you identify the factors that may have contributed to these temperatures?

List and *review* the principal controls and influences that produce global temperature patterns.

Principal controls and influences upon temperature patterns include latitude (the distance north or south of the equator), altitude (location above sea level), cloud cover (reflect, absorb, and reradiate energy), and land–water heating differences (the nature of evaporation, transparency, specific heat, movement, and ocean currents and sea-surface temperatures).

5. Explain the effect of altitude on air temperature. Why is air at higher altitudes lower in temperature? Why does it feel cooler standing in shadows at higher altitude than at lower altitude?
6. What noticeable effect does air density have on the absorption and radiation of energy? What role does altitude play in that process?
7. How is it possible to grow moderate-climate-type crops such as wheat, barley, and potatoes at an elevation of 4103 m (13,460 ft) near La Paz, Bolivia, so near the equator?
8. Describe the effect of cloud cover with regard to Earth's temperature patterns. From the last chapter, review the cloud-albedo forcing and cloud-greenhouse forcing of different cloud types and relate the concepts with a simple sketch.

Review the factors that produce different marine effects and continental effects as they influence temperatures and *utilize* several pairs of stations to illustrate these differences.

The physical nature of land (rock and soil) and water (oceans, seas, and lakes) is the reason for **land–water heating differences**, the fact that land heats and cools faster than water. Moderate temperature patterns are associated with water bodies, and extreme temperatures occur inland. The five controls that differ between land and water surfaces are evaporation, transparency, specific heat, movement and ocean currents, and sea-surface temperatures.

Light penetrates water because of its **transparency**. Water is clear and light transmits to an average depth of 60 m (200 ft) in the ocean. This penetration distributes available heat energy over a much greater volume than could occur on opaque land; thus, a larger energy reservoir is formed. When equal volumes of water and land are compared, water requires far more energy to increase its temperature than does land. In other words, water can hold more energy than can soil or rock, so water has a higher **specific heat**, the heat capacity of a substance, averaging about four times that of soil.

Ocean currents affect temperature. An example of the effect of ocean currents is the **Gulf Stream**, which moves northward off the east coast of North America, carrying warm water far into the North Atlantic. As a result, the southern third of Iceland experiences much milder temperatures than would be expected for a latitude of 65° N, just below the Arctic Circle (66.5°).

Marine effect, or maritime, describes locations that exhibit the moderating influences of the ocean, usually along coastlines or on islands. **Continental effect** refers to the condition of areas that are less affected by the sea and therefore have a greater range between maximum and minimum temperatures diurnally and yearly.

land–water heating differences (p. 126)
transparency (p. 127)
specific heat (p. 127)
Gulf Stream (p. 128)
marine effect (p. 129)
continental effect (p. 129)

9. List the physical aspects of land and water that produce their different responses to heating from absorption of insolation. What is the specific effect of transparency in a medium?
10. What is specific heat? Compare the specific heat of water and soil.
11. Describe the pattern of sea-surface temperatures (SSTs) as determined by satellite remote sensing. Where is the warmest ocean region on Earth?
12. What effect does sea-surface temperature have on air temperature? Describe the negative feedback mechanism created by higher sea-surface temperatures and evaporation rates.
13. Differentiate between marine and continental temperatures. Give geographic examples of each from the text: Canada, Norway, and Russia.

Interpret the pattern of Earth's temperatures from their portrayal on January and July temperature maps and on a map of annual temperature ranges.

Maps for January and July instead of the solstice months of December and June are used for temperature comparison because of the natural lag that occurs between insolation received and maximum or minimum temperatures experienced. Each line on these temperature maps is an **isotherm**, an isoline that connects points of equal temperature. Isotherms portray temperature patterns.

Isotherms generally are zonal, trending east–west, parallel to the equator. They mark the general decrease in insolation and net radiation with distance from the equator. The

thermal equator (isoline connecting all points of highest mean temperature) trends southward in January and shifts northward with the high summer Sun in July. In January it extends farther south into the interior of South America and Africa, indicating higher temperatures over landmasses.

In the Northern Hemisphere in January, isotherms shift equatorward as cold air chills the continental interiors. The coldest area on the map is in Russia, specifically northeastern Siberia. The intense cold experienced there results from winter conditions of consistent clear, dry, calm air, small insolation input, and an inland location far from any moderating maritime effects.

isotherm (p. 132)
thermal equator (p. 132)

14. What is the thermal equator? Describe its location in January and in July. Explain why it shifts position annually.
15. Observe trends in the pattern of isolines over North America and compare the January average temperature map with the July map. Why do the patterns shift locations?
16. Describe and explain the extreme temperature range experienced in north-central Siberia between January and July.
17. Where are the hottest places on Earth? Are they near the equator or elsewhere? Explain. Where is the coldest place on Earth?
18. From the maps in Figures 5.13, 5.15, and 5.16, determine the average temperature values and annual range of temperatures for your present location.

Describe the human body's response to wind (wind chill) and heat and humidity (Humidex).

19. Explain the principle behind the wind-chill concept. Give an example.
20. Explain how the Canadian Humidex measure tells us about sensible temperature and the human body. Give an example.

Critical Thinking

A. With each temperature map (Figures 5.13, 5.15, and 5.16), begin by finding your own city or town and noting the temperatures indicated by the isotherms for January and July and the annual temperature range. Record the information from these maps in your notebook. As you work through the different maps throughout this text, note atmospheric pressure and winds, annual precipitation, climate type, landforms, soil orders, vegetation, and terrestrial biomes. By the end of the course you will have recorded a complete physical geography profile for your regional environment.

B. Have you ever experienced any of the different responses of the human body to low-temperature or high-temperature stress noted in Focus Study 5.1, Table 1? Where were you at the time of each experience? Make copies of the wind-chill chart given in Focus Study 5.1. On an appropriate day, check air temperature and wind speed and determine the combined effect on skin chilling. In contrast, on an appropriate day, check air temperature and relative humidity values, and relate it to the comfort levels in the Humidex chart.

Career Link 5.1

Dr. Louwrens Hacquebord, Professor of Arctic and Antarctic Studies

The Hornsund fjord system is in southwestern Spitsbergen, the largest island of the Svalbard Archipelago in the Arctic Ocean, 965 km (600 mi) north of Norway. The surrounding mountains have a light covering of fresh snow; steep slopes sweep to the water's edge. The air is 4°C (39°F) with a brisk wind chill near 1°C and a cloudy, moody sky overhead. A weary eye for polar bears adds to the feel of the place. We are at 77° N latitude.

We walk inland along a curving, rocky shoreline toward a mound. Whalebones are stacked against the windward side of the ruins of a small dwelling. Here a cooper (a barrel maker) lived in A.D. 1618, and English whalers worked the waters for Greenland right whales. Many of these sites, and ones operated by the Dutch in the north, were abandoned by the nineteenth century.

We come upon four Dutch researchers excavating several sites in the area. Here we meet project leader Dr. Louwrens Hacquebord standing in a metre-deep excavation pit in a 400-year-old midden deposit (garbage dump) where the cooper threw his trash. Louwrens describes environmental conditions in 1618 and the changes in sea ice and climate that were just ahead in this cooper's life, as he carefully brushes soil away from a dark object emerging from the side of the pit.

You hear Louwrens' interdisciplinary perspective as he weaves physical geography, history, biology, and archeology together in recreating life at this site (Figure 1). He explains that with the eradication of the whales there was a population explosion of zooplankton. He wants to know how this affected bird life and impacted ecosystems—synthesizing the evidence he finds from the middens with past temperatures, climate, and ecosystems, to recreate the environment in which these whalers worked.

The moment arrives when he gently removes a leather shoe and places it on the ground, continuing to remove its earthen covering. The shoe's design is clearly visible. For 386 years, from the day the cooper discarded it, this shoe sat awaiting Louwrens' discovering hands. The heavy boots we wear are in stark contrast to this slipper of a shoe. Life was rough at these whaling stations. Louwrens explains that, "Some 80% of the men died of scurvy (lack of Vitamin C)."

Louwrens Hacquebord was born and raised in The Netherlands, a landscape partially reclaimed from the sea. He recalls, "I was Boy Scout between ages 12 and 16 and loved using maps and compasses. I loved to make maps, and when I was a boy, I created maps of imaginary countries, naming features, and cities, capitals. I noticed the artificial 'dwellings hills,' like bumps on the landscape on which houses were built, and wanted to know more; wanted to understand what they were for and who built them, and when they were built. I was interested in many aspects of my country, with its open delta and extensive ocean front."

By the time he went to high school he knew he was interested in landscape studies and maps. "When we went to outdoor camps, I realized I loved being out in the field, out in nature. I started my studies with physical geography."

At the University of Utrecht he majored in physical geography because it was an allied field for graduate-level studies in archeology, a field he wanted to pursue. But he explains, "As I studied more physical geography and completed more field work, I found that physical geography was simply too interesting to leave behind for archeology. I decided to stay in physical geography and do my Masters program in it." Louwrens was shaping a multidisciplinary program and career with geography at the core.

After earning his Masters' degree, he taught high school for six years before returning to graduate school for a Ph.D. at the University of Amsterdam. For his doctorate, Louwrens studied a seventeenth century Dutch whaling settlement at Smeerenburg, on Spitsbergen. He was able to bring in past environmental conditions as he reconstructed this relict whaling station. His Ph.D. was awarded with *cum laude* (highest honours) distinction for the nature of his multidisciplinary approach and synthesis of varied subject areas—he forged a new methodology with his work.

Dr. Hacquebord took a position at the University of Groningen in 1984 and was appointed head of the Arctic Centre. He achieved full professor status and assumed a newly created position as Chair in Arctic Studies in 1994. Describing his work at Groningen, he says, "I teach Arctic Studies, and physical geography is at the core of the discipline, along with history, geography, archeology, and biology."

His approach spread to the international stage: "I became the The Netherlands representative to the International Arctic Science Committee (IASC) and serve on the IASC Executive Committee. I asked all the human and social scientists to join in and meld with the physical and life scientists, for studies circum-Arctic in scope. IASC is an advisory board to the Arctic Council. I was there at the beginning of the Arctic Climate Impact Assessment (ACIA). I am now working on plans for the International Polar Year, which begins March 2007."

To a question about climate change, he replies, "The impact of climate change is much bigger in the polar region than the rest of the globe. I saw the latest scientific maps with temperature trends over the last 30 years in the Arctic and it was scary to see the magnitude of change! Especially in the Eurasian and American continents; the shifting of the tree line and the permafrost distribution is remarkable. This is why it is a key interest at IASC."

About students and teaching, "I encourage my students to use physical geography as a core and then move outward to bring in many approaches so they can get a complete view of the environment. You will be successful when you go over the borders of the discipline. However, it is important to never forget your starting point in physical geography."

FIGURE 1 Dr. Louwrens Hacquebord in the field.
Professor Hacquebord teaching us about an early 17th century English whaling station, which he is excavating on Spitsbergen Island, Arctic Ocean. [Photo by Bobbé Christopherson.]

As an example, Louwrens describes one of his Ph.D. students. She has taken old Antarctic maps from 1800 to 1957—the last International Geophysical Year—and digitized them to reconstruct ice shelf movement. She uses GIS to synthesize dynamic maps, linking past conditions with climate and other variables, to understand the patterns. Louwrens explains, "This is a first for this kind of mapping."

Louwrens concludes, "I want to write about how the Arctic makes us feel, how nature makes us feel, and how we respond. I want to see young people experiencing the Arctic, and deciphering what is occurring so dramatically in these polar regions." Just as Louwrens taught us on that cold morning in Spitsbergen, as he lifted the leather shoe from its four-century rest and described climatic conditions in 1618, we hear a calling for geographers to be the synthesizers. Louwrens is truly a scientist pushing the edges of the discipline.

The winds fill the sails of the *Bluenose II* off the shore of Nova Scotia. Serious questions arise about the feasibility of again harvesting the winds to assist in powering the world's merchant fleet and oil tankers. Estimates of fuel savings range from 15% to 50%. [Photo by © Sherman Hines/Masterfile.com.]

6 Atmospheric and Oceanic Circulations

Key Learning Concepts

After reading the chapter, you should be able to:

- *Define* the concept of air pressure and *describe* instruments used to measure air pressure.
- *Define* wind and *describe* how wind is measured, how wind direction is determined, and how winds are named.
- *Explain* the four driving forces within the atmosphere—gravity, pressure gradient force, Coriolis force, and friction force—and *describe* the primary high- and low-pressure areas and principal winds.
- *Describe* upper-air circulation and its support role for surface systems and *define* the jet streams.
- *Explain* several types of local winds: land–sea breezes, mountain–valley breezes, katabatic winds, and the regional monsoons.
- *Discern* the basic pattern of Earth's major surface and deep ocean currents.

Early in April 1815, on an island named Sumbawa in present-day Indonesia, the volcano Tambora erupted violently. It spewed an estimated 150 km^3 (36 mi^3) of material, 25 times the volume produced by the 1980 Mount St. Helens eruption in Washington State. Global atmospheric circulation carried material from Tambora worldwide, creating a stratospheric veil of dust and acid mist. Remarkable optical and meteorological effects troubled Earth's atmosphere years after the eruption—beautiful sunrises and sunsets and a temporary lowering of temperatures worldwide.

Scientists in 1815 lacked the remote-sensing capability of satellite technology, and they had no way of knowing the global impact of Tambora's eruption. Today, technology permits a depth of analysis unknown in the past—satellites now track the atmospheric effects from dust storms, forest fires, industrial haze, warfare, and the dispersal of volcanic explosions, among many other things.

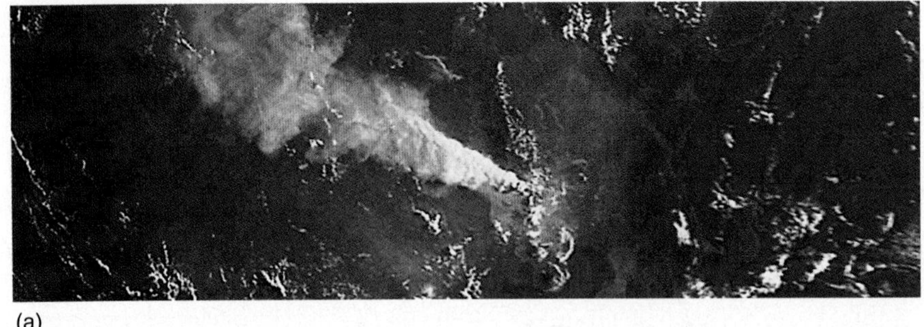

(a)

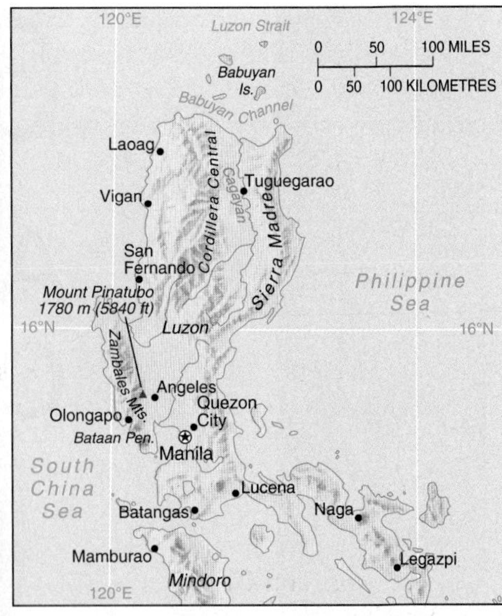

Luzon Island, Philippines

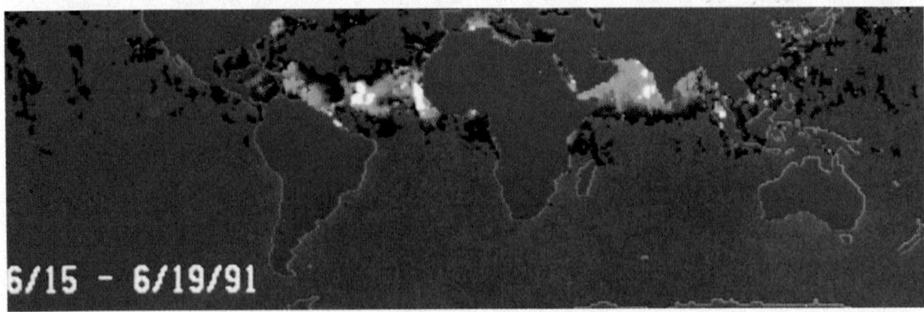

(b)

(c)

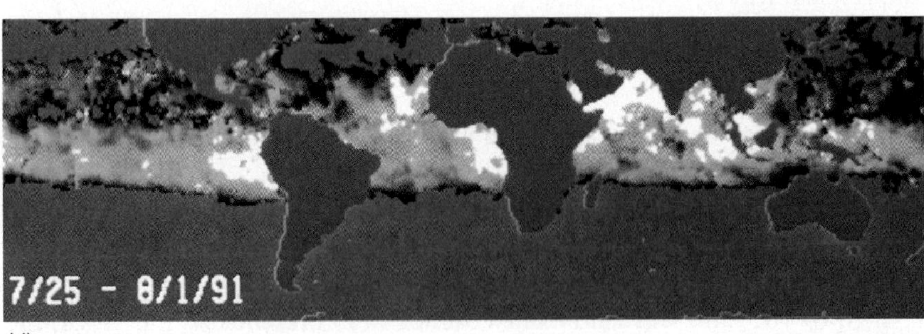

(d)

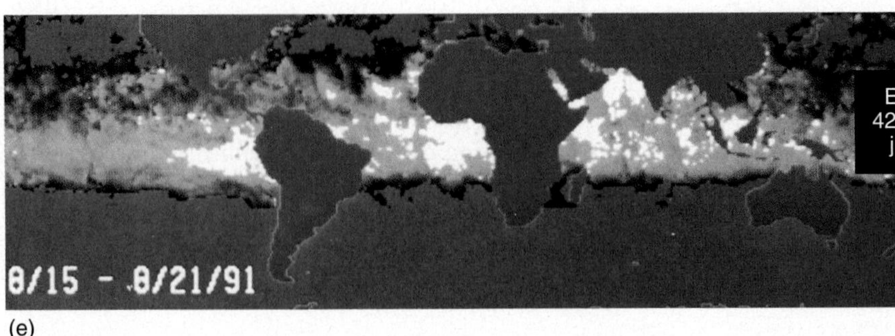

(e)

FIGURE 6.1 Volcanic eruption effects spread worldwide by winds. Satellite image shows Mount Pinatubo as it erupted (a). False-colour images (b-e) show aerosols from Mount Pinatubo, smoke from fires, and dust storms, all swept about the globe by the general atmospheric circulation. The dramatic increase in aerosols over the oceans from mid-June 1991 (b) to mid-August (e) is due to the Mount Pinatubo eruption on June 15. The false colour shows aerosol concentration, measured by the atmosphere's aerosol optical thickness (AOT): White is densest, dull yellow indicates medium values, and brown areas have the lowest aerosol concentration. In (b) note the dust moving westward from Africa, smoke from Kuwaiti oil well fires set during the Persian Gulf War, smoke from forest fires in Siberia, haze off the east coast of the United States, and the Pinatubo aerosol layer beginning to emerge north of Indonesia and expanding globally in (c) through (e). [(a) *AVHRR* satellite eruption image courtesy of U.S. Geological Survey, EROS Data Center. *AVHRR* satellite images of aerosols courtesy of Dr. Larry L. Stowe, National Environmental Satellite, Data, and Information Service, National Oceanic and Atmospheric Administration. Used by permission.]

After 635 years of dormancy, Mount Pinatubo in the Philippines erupted in 1991. This event had tremendous atmospheric impact, lofting 13 to 18 million metric tons (15–20 million tons) of ash, dust, and sulphur dioxide (SO_2) into the atmosphere. As the sulphur dioxide rose into the stratosphere, it quickly formed sulphuric acid (H_2SO_4) aerosols, which became concentrated at 16–25 km (10–15.5 mi) altitude. This debris increased atmospheric albedo about 1.5%, giving scientists an estimate of the aerosol volume generated by the eruption (see Figure 1.7).

The AVHRR instrument aboard *NOAA-11* monitored the reflected solar radiation from Mount Pinatubo's aerosols as global winds swept them around Earth. Figure 6.1 shows images made at three-week intervals that clearly track the spread of the debris worldwide (Figure 6.1b–d). Some 60 days after the eruption (the last satellite image in the sequence), the aerosol cloud spanned about 42% of the globe from 20° S to 30° N. Again, for almost 2 years colourful sunrises and sunsets and a small lowering of average temperatures followed. The eruption provided a unique insight into the dynamics of atmospheric circulation.

Global winds are certainly an important reason why the United States, the former Soviet Union, and Great Britain signed the 1963 Limited Test Ban Treaty. That treaty banned above-ground testing of nuclear weapons because atmospheric circulation spread radioactive contamination worldwide. Such agreements illustrate how the fluid movement of the atmosphere socializes humanity more than any other natural or cultural factor. Our atmosphere makes the world a spatially linked society—one person's or country's exhalation is another's inhalation.

In this chapter: We begin with a discussion of wind essentials, consisting of air pressure and its measurement and a description of wind. The driving forces that produce surface winds are pressure gradient, Coriolis, and friction. We examine the circulation of Earth's atmosphere and the patterns of global winds, including principal pressure systems and winds. We also consider Earth's wind-driven oceanic currents. The energy driving all this movement comes from one source: the Sun.

Wind Essentials

Earth's atmospheric circulation transfers both energy and mass on a grand scale. In the process, the imbalance between equatorial energy surpluses and polar energy deficits (Chapter 4) is partly resolved, Earth's weather patterns formed, and ocean currents produced. Air pollutants, whether natural or human-caused, are spread worldwide by atmospheric circulation, far from their point of origin.

Atmospheric circulation is generally categorized at three levels: *primary circulation* (general worldwide circulation), *secondary circulation* of migratory high-pressure and low-pressure systems, and *tertiary circulation* that includes local winds and temporal weather patterns. Winds that move principally north or south along meridians are known as *meridional flows*. Winds moving east or west along parallels of latitude are called *zonal flows*.

Air Pressure and Its Measurement

Important to an understanding of wind is the concept of air pressure, its measurement and expression. The molecules that constitute air create *air pressure* through their motion, size, and number—the factors that determine the temperature and density of the air. Air pressure, then, is a product of the temperature and density of a mass of air. Pressure is exerted on all surfaces in contact with the air.

In 1643, Galileo's pupil Evangelista Torricelli was working on a mine-drainage problem. His work led him to discover a method for measuring air pressure (Figure 6.2a). He knew that pumps in the mine were able to "pull" water upward about 10 m (33 ft), but no higher, and he did not know why. Careful observation led him to discover that this limitation was caused not by weak pumps but by the atmosphere itself. Torricelli noted that the water level in the vertical pipe fluctuated from day to day. He figured out that air pressure varies with weather conditions.

To simulate the problem at the mine, Torricelli devised an instrument at Galileo's suggestion, using a much denser fluid than water—mercury (Hg)—in a glass laboratory tube only 1 m high. Torricelli sealed the glass tube at one end, filled it with mercury, and inverted it into a dish of mercury (Figure 6.2b). He determined that the average height of the column of mercury in the tube was 760 mm (29.92 in.) and that it did vary day to day as the weather changed. He concluded that the mass of surrounding air was exerting pressure on the mercury in the dish that counterbalanced the column of mercury.

Using similar instruments, scientists set a standard of *normal sea-level pressure* at 1013.2 millibars (mb). A millibar expresses force per square metre of surface area. In Canada, we officially measure pressure in millibars, which the media weather reports in kilopascals (kPa) where 1 kPa = 10 mb. Normal sea-level pressure is therefore 101.32 kPa.

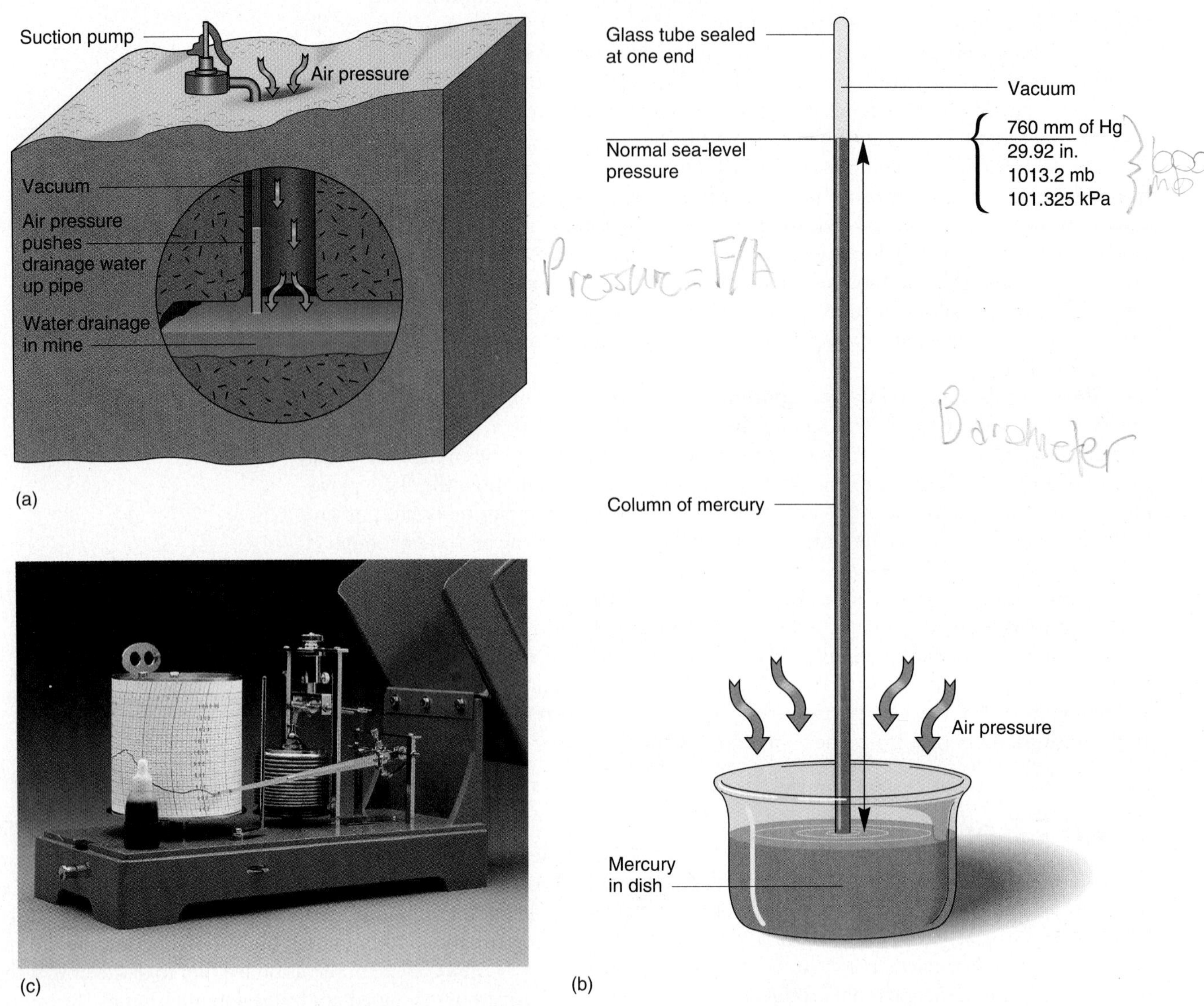

FIGURE 6.2 Developing the barometer.
Evangelista Torricelli developed the barometer to measure air pressure as a by-product of trying to solve a mine-drainage problem (a). Two types of instruments are used to measure atmospheric pressure: (b) an idealized sketch of a mercury barometer, and (c) an aneroid barometer. Have you used a barometer? If so, what type is it? Have you tried to reset it using a local weather information source? [(c) Courtesy of Qualimetrics, Inc., Sacramento, California.]

Any instrument that measures air pressure is called a *barometer* (from the Greek *baros*, meaning "weight"). Torricelli developed a **mercury barometer**. A more compact barometer design, which works without a metre-long tube of mercury, is the aneroid barometer, shown in Figure 6.2c. *Aneroid* means "using no liquid." The **aneroid barometer** principle is simple: Imagine a small chamber, partially emptied of air, which is sealed and connected to a mechanism attached to a needle on a dial. As air pressure increases, it presses on the chamber; as air pressure decreases, it relieves pressure from the chamber. The chamber responds to these changes in air pressure and moves the needle. An aircraft altimeter is a type of aneroid barometer. It accurately measures altitude because air pressure diminishes with elevation above sea level. For accuracy the altimeter must be adjusted for temperature changes.

Figure 6.3 illustrates comparative scales in kilopascals and millibars used to express air pressure and its relative force. The normal range of Earth's atmospheric pressure from strong high pressure to deep low pressure is about 105.0 to 98.0 kPa. The figure also indicates the extreme highest and lowest pressures ever recorded in Canada, the United States, and on Earth. Air pressure differences between places produce wind.

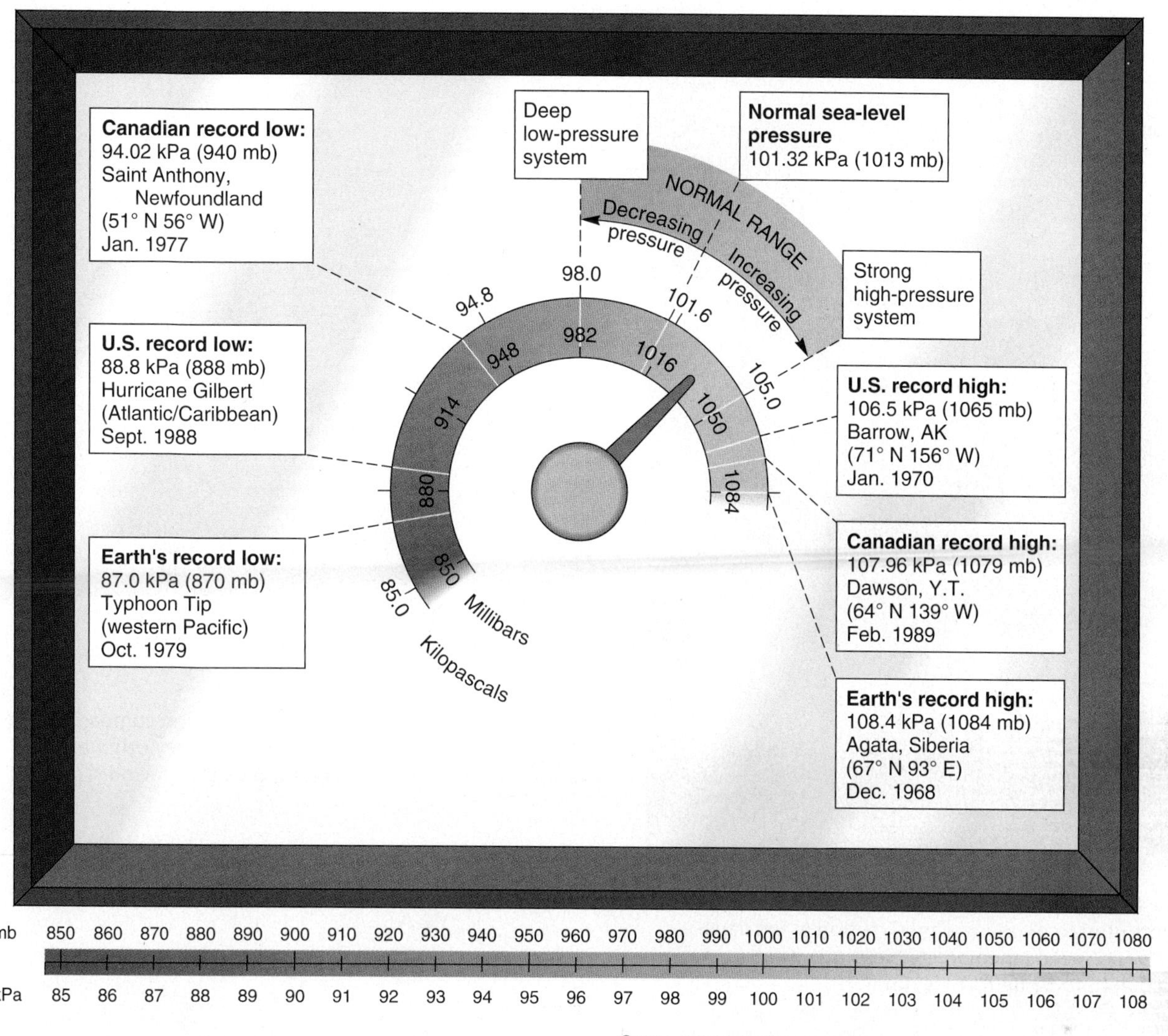

FIGURE 6.3 Air pressure readings and conversions.
Scales for expressing barometric air pressure in kilopascals and millibars, with average air pressure values and recorded pressure extremes (10 mb = 1 kPa).

Wind: Description and Measurement

Simply stated, **wind** is generally the horizontal motion of air across Earth's surface. Turbulence adds wind updrafts and downdrafts and a vertical component to this definition. *Differences in air pressure from one location to another produce wind.* Wind's two principal properties are speed and direction, and instruments measure each. An **anemometer** measures wind speed in kilometres per hour (kmph), miles per hour (mph), metres per second (mps), or knots. (A *knot* is a nautical mile per hour, covering 1 minute of Earth's arc in an hour, equivalent to 1.85 kmph, or 1.15 mph.) A **wind vane** determines wind direction; the standard measurement is taken 10 m (33 ft) above the ground to reduce the effects of local topography on wind direction (Figure 6.4).

Winds are named for the direction *from which they originate*. For example, a wind from the west is a *westerly* wind (it blows eastward); a wind out of the south is a *southerly* wind (it blows northward). Figure 6.5 illustrates a simple wind compass, naming 16 principal wind directions used by meteorologists.

The traditional *Beaufort wind scale* is a descriptive scale useful in visually estimating wind speed. In 1806, Admiral Beaufort of the British Navy introduced his wind scale. In 1926, G. C. Simpson expanded Beaufort's scale to include wind speeds on land. The scale is still referenced on ocean charts, enabling estimation of wind speed without instruments, although most ships use sophisticated equipment to perform such measurements. Using no instruments, try using the Beaufort scale in Table 6.1 to estimate wind

FIGURE 6.4 Wind vane and anemometer.
Instruments used to measure wind direction (wind vane, right) and wind speed (anemometer, left) at a weather station installation. [Photo by Belfort Instruments.]

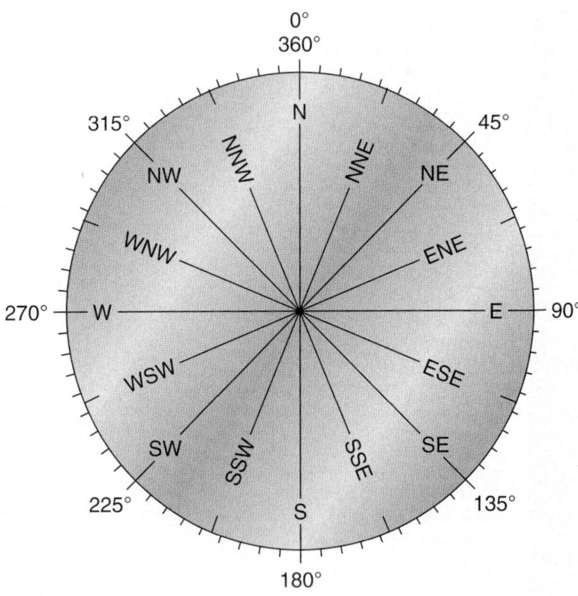

FIGURE 6.5 A wind compass.
Sixteen wind directions identified on a wind compass. Winds are named for the direction from which they originate. For example, a wind from the west is a westerly wind.

speed as you walk across campus today; moisten your finger to sense cooling and from which direction the wind is blowing.

Global Winds

The primary circulation of winds across Earth has fascinated travellers, sailors, and scientists for centuries, although only in the modern era is a true picture emerging of the pattern and causes of global winds. Breakthroughs in space-based observations and Earth-bound computer technology are refining models that simulate total atmospheric and oceanic circulation.

A remarkable portrait of surface winds across the Pacific Ocean was painstakingly assembled by scientists at the Jet Propulsion Laboratory and the University of California, Los Angeles (Figure 6.6). The *Seasat* satellite produced the image using radar to measure the motion and direction of ocean waves. Because wind drives waves on the ocean surface, wave patterns indicate winds.

The patterns in the figure are the result of specific forces at work in the atmosphere: *pressure gradient force*, *Coriolis force*, *friction force*, and *gravity*. These forces are our next topic. As we progress through this chapter, you may want to refer to this *Seasat* image to identify the winds, eddies, and vortexes it portrays.

Driving Forces Within the Atmosphere

Four forces determine both speed and direction of winds:

- Earth's *gravitational force* on the atmosphere is virtually uniform. Gravity equally compresses the atmosphere worldwide, with the density decreasing as altitude increases. Without gravity, there would be no atmospheric pressure—or atmosphere, for that matter.
- **Pressure gradient force** drives air from areas of higher barometric pressure (more dense air) to areas of lower barometric pressure (less dense air), thereby causing winds. Without a pressure gradient force, there would be no wind.
- The **Coriolis force**, a deflective force, makes wind that travels in a straight path appear to be deflected in relation to Earth's rotating surface. The Coriolis force

Table 6.1 Beaufort Wind Scale

Wind Speed			Beaufort Wind Scale			
kmph	**mph**	**knots**	**Beaufort Number**	**Wind Description**	**Observed Effects at Sea**	**Observed Effects on Land**
<1	<1	<1	0	Calm	Glassy calm, like a mirror	Calm, no movement of leaves
1–5	1–3	1–3	1	Light air	Small ripples; wavelet scales; no foam on crests	Slight leaf movement; smoke drifts; wind vanes still
6–11	4–7	4–6	2	Light breeze	Small wavelets; glassy look to crests, which do not break	Leaves rustling; wind felt; wind vanes moving
12–19	8–12	7–10	3	Gentle breeze	Large wavelets; dispersed whitecaps as crests break	Leaves and twigs in motion; small flags and banners extended
20–29	13–18	11–16	4	Moderate breeze	Small, longer waves; numerous whitecaps	Small branches moving; raising dust, paper, litter, and dry leaves
30–38	19–24	17–21	5	Fresh breeze	Moderate, pronounced waves; many whitecaps; some spray	Small trees and branches swaying; wavelets forming on inland waterways
39–49	25–31	22–27	6	Strong breeze	Large waves, white foam crests everywhere; some spray	Large branches swaying; overhead wires whistling; difficult to control an umbrella
50–61	32–38	28–33	7	Moderate (near) gale	Sea mounding up; foam and sea spray blown in streaks in the direction of the wind	Entire trees moving; difficult to walk into wind
62–74	39–46	34–40	8	Fresh gale (or gale)	Moderately high waves of greater length; breaking crests forming sea spray; well-marked foam streaks	Small branches breaking; difficult to walk; moving automobiles drifting and veering
75–87	47–54	41–47	9	Strong gale	High waves; wave crests tumbling and the sea beginning to roll; visibility reduced by blowing spray	Roof shingles blown away; slight damage to structures; broken branches littering the ground
88–101	55–63	48–55	10	Whole gale (or storm)	Very high waves and heavy, rolling seas; white appearance to foam-covered sea; overhanging waves; visibility reduced	Uprooted and broken trees; structural damage; considerable destruction; seldom occurring
102–116	64–73	56–63	11	Storm (or violent storm)	White foam covering a breaking sea of exceptionally high waves; small- and medium-sized ships lost from view in wave troughs; wave crests frothy	Widespread damage to structures and trees, a rare occurrence
>117	>74	>64	12–17	Hurricane	Driving foam and spray filling the air; white sea; visibility poor to nonexistent	Severe to catastrophic damage; devastation to affected society

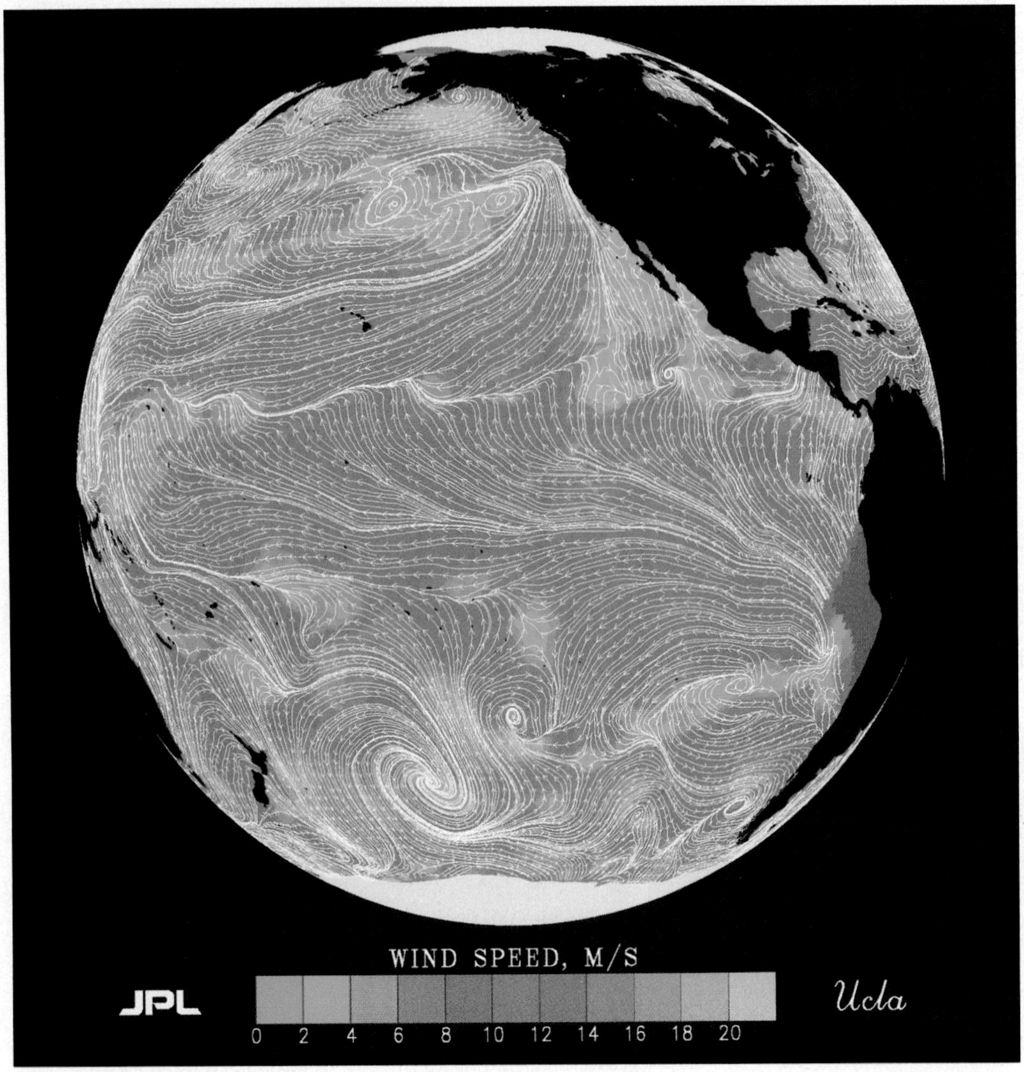

(a)

(b)

FIGURE 6.6 Wind portrait of the Pacific Ocean.
Surface wind measured by radar scatterometer aboard the *Seasat* satellite on a September day. Scientists analyzed 150,000 measurements to produce this image (a). Colours are correlated with wind speeds, and the white arrows denote wind direction. Try comparing the wind patterns with a visible-light image of the same region (b). Can you identify the pattern of trade winds, westerlies, high-pressure cells, and low-pressure cells from the cloud patterns on the image? [Wind portrait courtesy of Dr. Peter Woiceshyn, Jet Propulsion Laboratory, Pasadena, California. Satellite image inset from Laboratory of Planetary Studies, Cornell University. Used by permission.]

deflects wind to the right in the Northern Hemisphere and to the left in the Southern Hemisphere. Without Coriolis force, winds would move along straight paths between high- and low-pressure areas.

- The **friction force** drags on the wind as it moves across surfaces; it decreases with height above the surface. Without friction, winds would simply move in paths parallel to isobars and at high rates of speed.

All four of these forces operate on moving air and ocean currents at Earth's surface and influence global wind circulation patterns. The following sections describe the actions of the pressure gradient, Coriolis, and friction forces. (The gravitational force operates uniformly worldwide.)

Pressure Gradient Force

High- and low-pressure areas exist in the atmosphere principally because Earth's surface is unequally heated. For example, cold, dense air at the poles exerts greater pressure than warm, less dense air along the equator. These pressure differences establish a *pressure gradient force*.

An **isobar** is an *isoline* (a line along which there is a constant value) plotted on a weather map to connect points of equal pressure. A pattern of isobars on a weather map provides a portrait of the pressure gradient between an area of higher pressure and one of lower pressure. The spacing between isobars indicates the intensity of the pressure difference, or *pressure gradient*.

Just as closer contour lines on a topographic map indicate a steeper slope on land, so do closer isobars denote a steepness in the pressure gradient. In Figure 6.7a, note the spacing of the isobars (green lines). A steep gradient causes faster air movement from a high-pressure area to a low-pressure area. Isobars spaced wider apart from one another mark a more gradual pressure gradient, one that creates a slower airflow. Along a horizontal surface, the pressure gradient force alone acts at right angles to the isobars, so wind blows across them at right angles. Note the location of steep ("strong winds") and gradual ("light winds") pressure gradients and their relationship to wind intensity on the map in Figure 6.7b.

Figure 6.8 illustrates the forces that direct the wind. Figure 6.8a shows the pressure gradient force acting alone. In a high-pressure area, as air descends, a field of subsiding, or sinking, air develops. Air diverges out of the high-pressure area at the surface, moving outward in all directions. On the other hand, in a low-pressure area, as air rises, it converges from all directions into the area of lower pressure at the surface. For instance, on a warm day, the temperature of the air is less dense and more buoyant, so it rises. In contrast on a cold day, the temperature of the air is lower, the air is

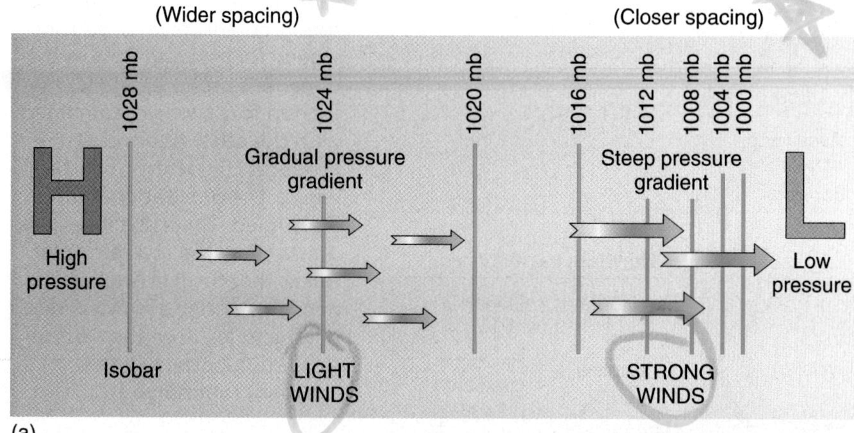

(a)

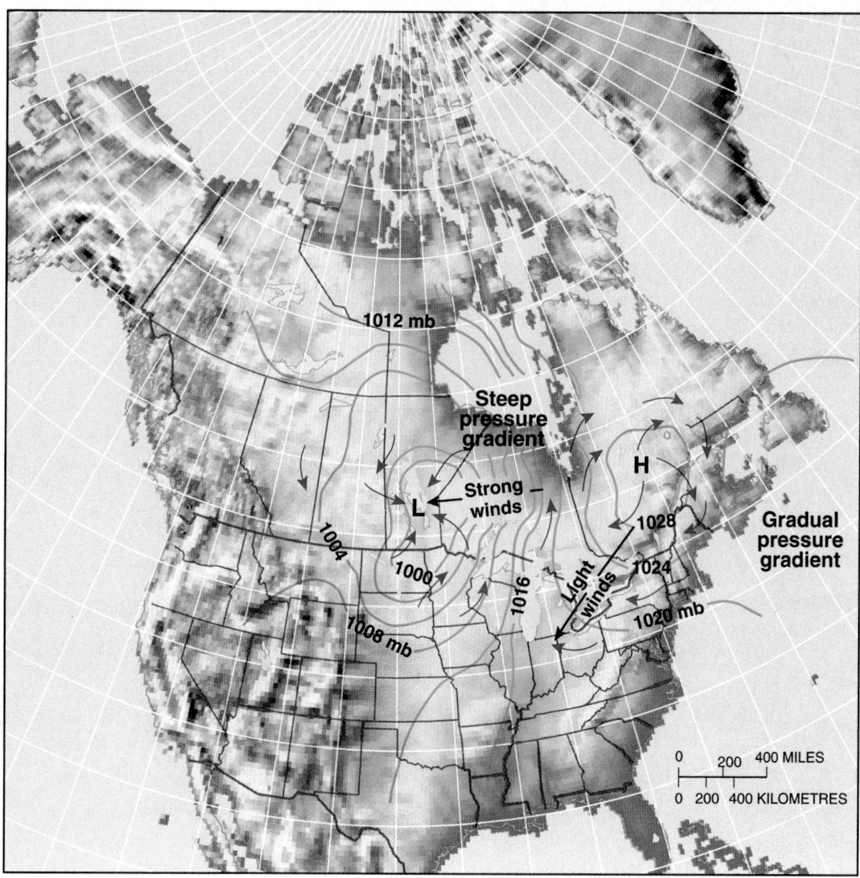

(b)

FIGURE 6.7 Pressure gradient determines wind speed.
Pressure gradient (a). On a weather map (b), the closer spacing of isobars represents a steeper pressure gradient that produces stronger winds; wider spacing of isobars denotes a gradual pressure gradient that leads to lighter winds. Here we see surface winds spiralling clockwise out of a high-pressure system and spiralling counterclockwise into a low-pressure system.

denser and less buoyant, so it descends. This behaviour of a parcel of air is discussed further in Chapter 7.

Coriolis Force

You might expect surface winds to move in a straight line from areas of higher pressure to areas of lower pressure. On a nonrotating Earth, they would. But on our rotating planet, the Coriolis force deflects anything that flies or flows across Earth's surface—wind, an airplane, or ocean currents—from a straight path. This force is an effect of Earth's rotation.

Earth's rotational speed varies with latitude, increasing from 0 kmph at the poles to 1675 kmph (1041 mph) at the equator (see Table 2.2). The Coriolis force is zero along the equator, increases to half the maximum deflection at

Top view and side view of air movement in an idealized high-pressure area and low-pressure area on a nonrotating Earth.

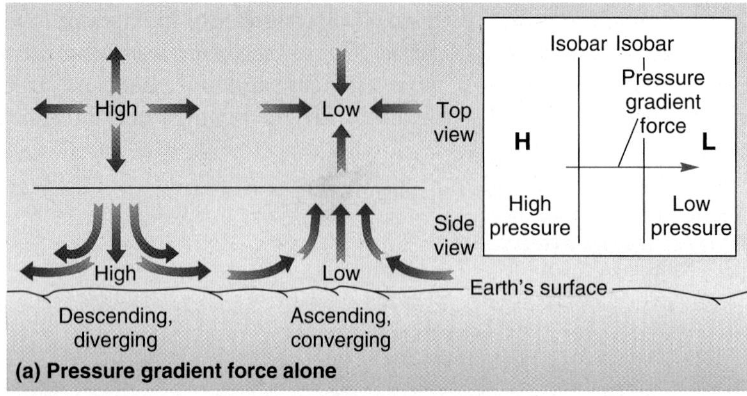

(a) Pressure gradient force alone

Earth's rotation adds the Coriolis force and a "twist" to air movements. High-pressure and low-pressure areas develop a rotary motion, and wind flowing between highs and lows flows parallel to isobars.

Upper-level geostrophic winds–Northern Hemisphere

Upper-level geostrophic winds–Southern Hemisphere

(b) Pressure gradient + Coriolis forces (upper-atmosphere winds)

Surface friction adds a countering force to Coriolis, producing winds that spiral out of a high-pressure area and into a low-pressure area. Surface winds cross isobars at an angle.

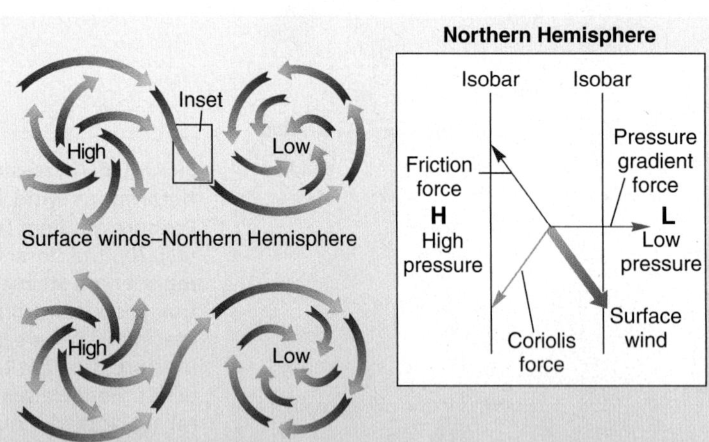

(c) Pressure gradient + Coriolis + friction forces (surface winds)

Air flows into low pressure cyclones and turns to the left. However note that the Coriolis force is still deflecting winds to the right in the Northern Hemisphere (left in the S.H.) from the pressure gradient.

FIGURE 6.8 Three physical forces that produce winds. Three physical forces integrate to produce wind patterns at the surface and aloft: (a) the pressure gradient force; (b) the Coriolis force counters the pressure gradient force, producing a geostrophic wind flow in the upper atmosphere; and (c) the friction force, which, combined with the other two forces, produces characteristic surface winds. The gravitational force is assumed. The three inset diagrams show the interaction of forces that form prevailing geostrophic and surface winds. In (b) and (c), note the reverse circulation pattern in the Southern Hemisphere.

30° N and 30° S latitudes, and reaches maximum deflection flowing away from the poles.

The deflection occurs regardless of the direction in which the object is moving. Because Earth rotates eastward, objects that move in an absolute straight line over a distance (such as winds and ocean currents) appear to curve to the right in the Northern Hemisphere and to the left in the Southern Hemisphere (Figure 6.9a). The effect of the Coriolis force increases as the speed of the moving object increases; thus, the faster the wind speed, the greater its apparent deflection. The Coriolis force does not normally affect small-scale motions that cover insignificant distance and time (see News Report 6.1).

The key to understanding Coriolis force is one's viewpoint. From the viewpoint of an airplane that is passing over Earth's surface, the surface can be seen to rotate slowly below. But, looking from the surface at the airplane, the surface seems stationary, and the airplane appears to curve off course. The airplane does not actually deviate from a straight path, but it *appears* to do so because we are standing on Earth's rotating surface beneath the airplane. Because of this apparent deflection, the airplane must make constant corrections in flight path to maintain its "straight" heading.

As an example of the effect of this force, see Figure 6.9b. A pilot leaves the North Pole and flies due south toward Quito, Ecuador. If Earth were not rotating, the aircraft would simply travel along a meridian of longitude and arrive at Quito. But Earth is rotating eastward beneath the aircraft's flight path. If the pilot does not allow for this rotation, the plane will reach the equator over the ocean along an apparently curved path far to the west of the intended destination. Pilots must correct for this Coriolis deflection in their navigational calculations.

This effect is in force regardless of the direction of the moving object. A flight from Vancouver to Gander is shown in Figure 6.9c. The Coriolis deflection occurs because, as the airplane flies to Gander, Earth continues to rotate eastward, so the destination moves farther to the east. The pilot must correct for Earth's rotational motion to end up in Gander, and not farther to the south.

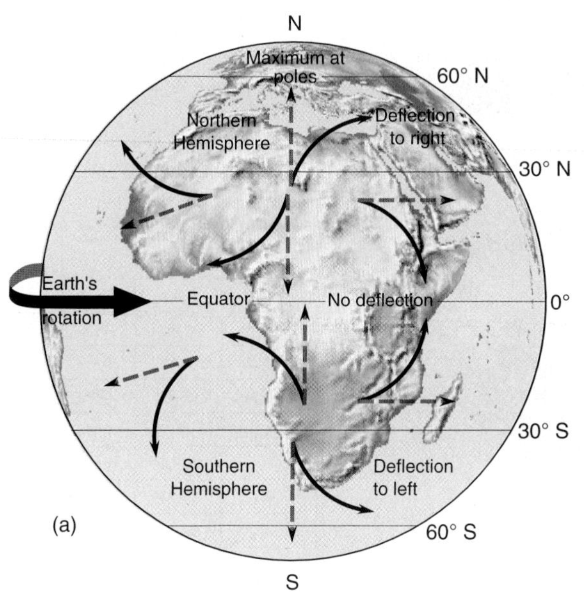

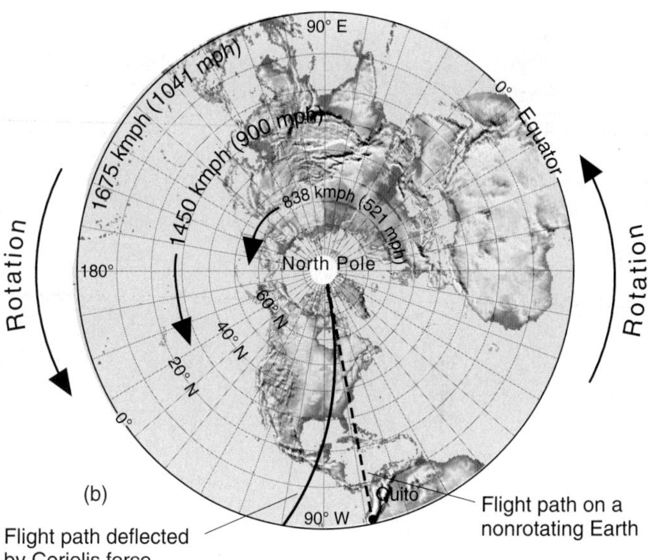

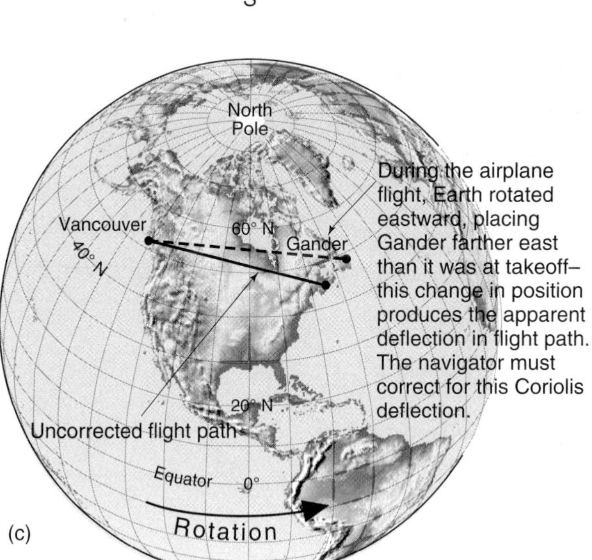

FIGURE 6.9 The Coriolis force—an apparent deflection. Distribution of the Coriolis force on Earth: (a) apparent deflection to the right of a straight line in the Northern Hemisphere and apparent deflection to the left in the Southern Hemisphere; (b) Coriolis deflection of a flight path between the North Pole and Quito, Ecuador, which is on the equator; (c) deflection of a flight path between Vancouver and Gander. Deflection from a straight path occurs regardless of the direction of movement.

Coriolis Force

How does the Coriolis force affect wind? As air rises from the surface through the lowest levels of the atmosphere, leaving the drag of surface friction behind, its speed increases. This increase in speed increases the Coriolis force, spiralling the winds to the right in the Northern Hemisphere or to the left in the Southern Hemisphere, generally producing upper-air westerly winds from the subtropics to the poles. In the upper troposphere, the Coriolis force just balances the pressure gradient force. Consequently, the winds between higher-pressure and lower-pressure areas aloft flow parallel to the isobars.

Figure 6.8b illustrates the combined effect of the pressure gradient force and the Coriolis force on air currents aloft. Together, they produce winds that do not flow directly from high to low, but *around* the pressure areas, remaining parallel to the isobars. Such winds are called **geostrophic winds** and are characteristic of upper tropospheric circulation. (The suffix *-strophic* means "to turn.") Geostrophic winds produce the characteristic pattern shown on the upper-air weather map in Figure 6.10. Note the inset illustration showing the effects of the pressure gradient and Coriolis forces that produce a geostrophic flow of air.

Friction Force

Figure 6.8c adds the effect of friction to the Coriolis and pressure gradient forces on wind movements; combining all three forces produces the wind patterns we see along Earth's surface. The effect of surface friction extends to a height of about 500 m (around 1600 ft) and varies with surface texture, wind speed, time of day and year, and atmospheric conditions. In general, rougher surfaces produce more friction.

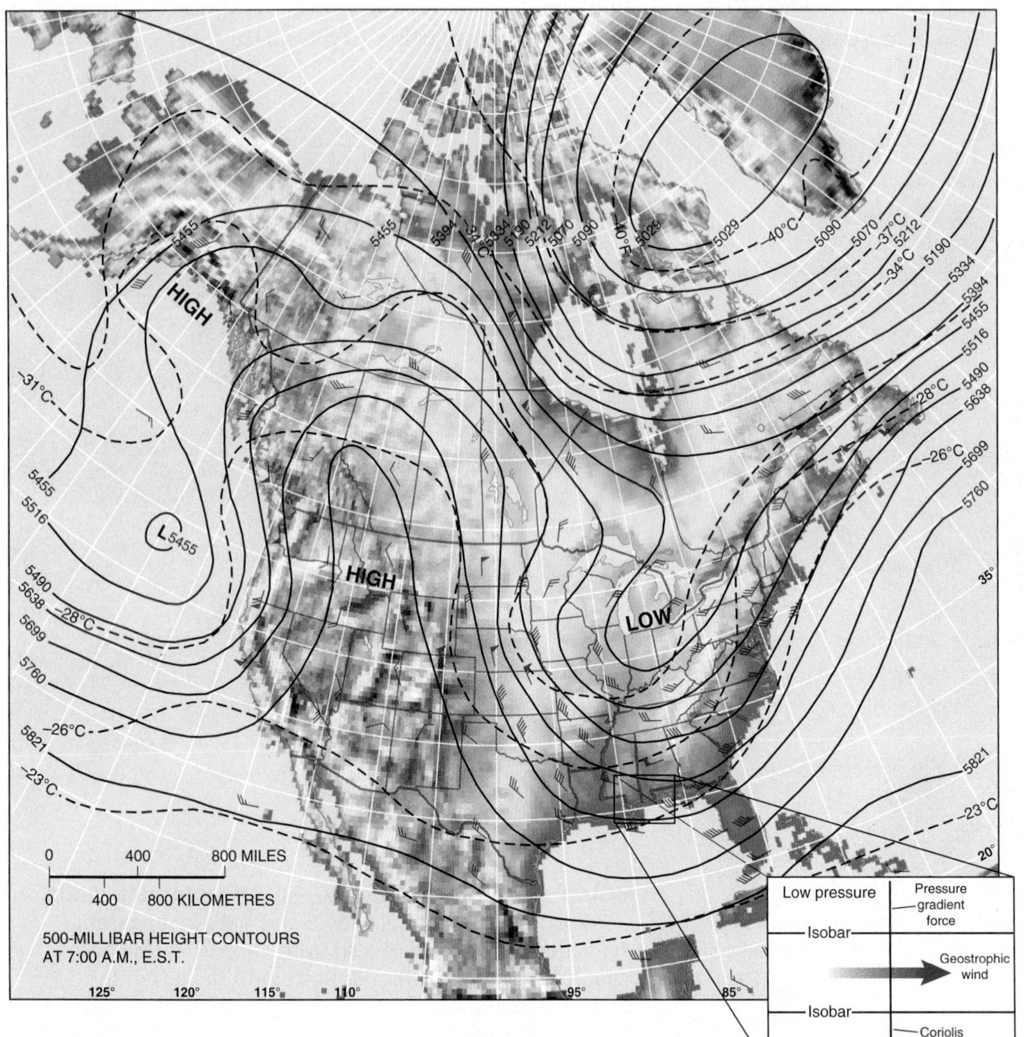

Wind Speed Symbol	Kilometres per Hour	Knots
◎	Calm	Calm
	1–5	1–3
	6–11	4–6
	12–19	7–10
	20–28	11–15
	29–38	16–21
	36–49	22–27
	50–61	28–33
	62–74	34–40
	75–88	41–47
	89–102	48–55
	103–117	56–63
	118–133	64–71
	134–145	72–78
	146–157	79–85
	158–169	86–91
	170–181	92–98
	182–194	99–105

FIGURE 6.10 A 500-mb pressure map and geostrophic winds aloft.
Isobaric chart for an April day. Contours show elevation (in metres) at which 500-mb pressure occurs. The pattern of contours reveals geostrophic wind patterns in the troposphere at approximately 5500 m (18,000 ft) altitude. Note the "ridge" of high pressure over the Intermountain West (through the Rockies) and the "trough" of low pressure over the Great Lakes region. The inset diagram shows the interaction of forces that form prevailing geostrophic winds. [Data provided by Meteorological Service of Canada and the National Weather Service, NOAA.]

News Report 6.1

Coriolis, a Forceful Effect on Drains?

A common misconception about the Coriolis force is that it affects water draining out of a sink, tub, or toilet. Can the Coriolis force cause this twist? When a ship crosses the equator, does the direction of a draining spiral of water in a sink suddenly reverse?

Moving water or air must cover some distance across space and time before the Coriolis force noticeably deflects it. Long-range artillery shells and guided missiles do exhibit small amounts of deflection that must be corrected for accuracy. But water movements down a drain are too small in spatial extent to be noticeably affected by this force.

Note that we call Coriolis a *force*. The label force is appropriate because, as the physicist Sir Isaac Newton (1643–1727) stated, when something is accelerating over a space, a force is in operation (mass times acceleration). This *apparent force* (in classical mechanics, an inertial force) acts as an effect on moving objects. It is named for Gaspard Coriolis, a French mathematician and researcher of applied mechanics, who first described the phenomenon in 1831.

Near the surface, friction disrupts the equilibrium established in geostrophic wind flows between the pressure gradient and Coriolis forces—note the inset illustration in Figure 6.8c. Because surface friction decreases wind speed, it reduces the effect of the Coriolis force and causes winds to move across isobars at an angle.

In Figure 6.8c, you can see that the Northern Hemisphere winds spiral out from a high-pressure area *clockwise* to form an **anticyclone** and spiral into a low-pressure area *counterclockwise* to form a **cyclone**. (In the Southern Hemisphere these circulation patterns are reversed, flowing out of high-pressure cells counterclockwise and into low-pressure cells clockwise.)

Atmospheric Patterns of Motion

With these forces and motions in mind, we are ready to build a general model of total atmospheric circulation. The warmer, less-dense air along the equator rises, creating low pressure at the surface, and the colder, denser air at the poles sinks, creating high pressure. If Earth did not rotate, the result would be a simple wind flow from the poles to the equator (a meridional flow), caused solely by pressure gradient.

However, Earth does rotate, creating a more complex flow system. On a rotating Earth the poles-to-equator flow is predominantly zonal (latitudinal), both at the surface and aloft. Winds are westerly (eastward-moving) in the middle and high latitudes and easterly (westward-moving) in the low latitudes toward the equator in both hemispheres. This system transfers thermal energy and air and water masses from equatorial energy surpluses to polar energy deficits, using waves, streams, and eddies on a planetary scale.

Primary High-Pressure and Low-Pressure Areas

The following discussion of Earth's pressure and wind patterns refers often to Figure 6.11, isobaric maps showing average surface barometric pressure in January and July. Indirectly, these maps indicate prevailing surface winds, which are suggested by the isobars.

The primary high- and low-pressure areas of Earth's general circulation appear on these maps as cells or uneven belts of similar pressure that stretch across the face of the planet, interrupted by landmasses. Between these areas flow the primary winds, which have been noted in adventure stories and hero myths throughout human history.

Secondary highs and lows, from a few hundred to a few thousand kilometres in diameter and hundreds to thousands of metres high, are formed within these primary pressure areas. The secondary systems seasonally migrate to produce changing weather patterns in the regions over which they pass.

Four broad pressure areas cover the Northern Hemisphere and a similar set exists in the Southern Hemisphere. In each hemisphere, two of the pressure areas are stimulated by thermal (temperature) factors. These are the **equatorial low-pressure trough** (marked by the ITCZ line on the maps) and the weak **polar high-pressure cells** at the North and South Poles (not shown, as the maps are cut off at 80° N and 80° S). The other two pressure areas are formed by dynamic (mechanical) factors: the **subtropical high-pressure cells** (H) and **subpolar low-pressure cells** (L). Table 6.2 summarizes the characteristics of these pressure areas. We now examine each principal pressure region.

Equatorial Low-Pressure Trough—ITCZ: Clouds and Rain Figure 6.12 is a satellite image showing the equatorial low-pressure trough. The broken band of clouds that straddles the equator across the middle of the image reveals this low-pressure system. The equatorial low-pressure trough is an elongated, undulating narrow band of low pressure (converging, ascending airflow) that nearly encircles the planet.

Constant high Sun altitude and consistent daylength (12 hours a day, year-round) make large amounts of energy available in this region throughout the year. The warming creates lighter, less-dense, ascending air, with surface winds converging along the entire extent of the low-pressure

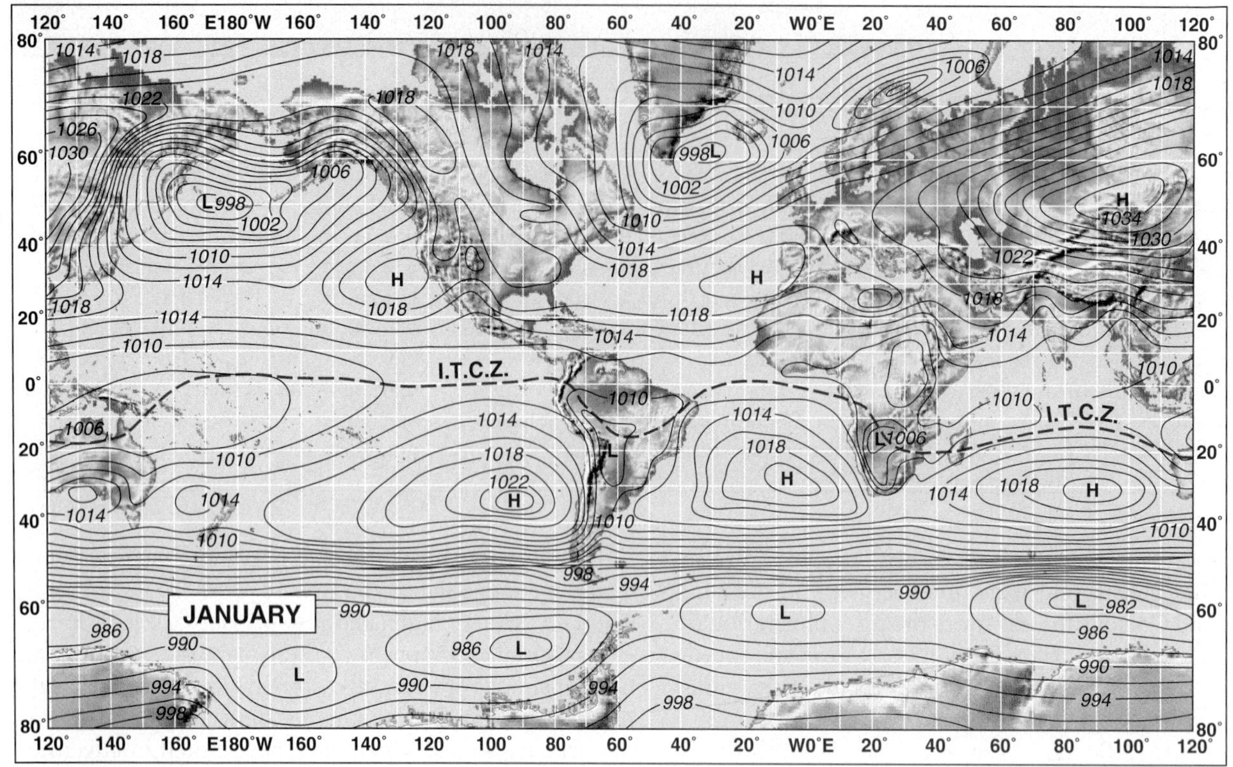

(a)

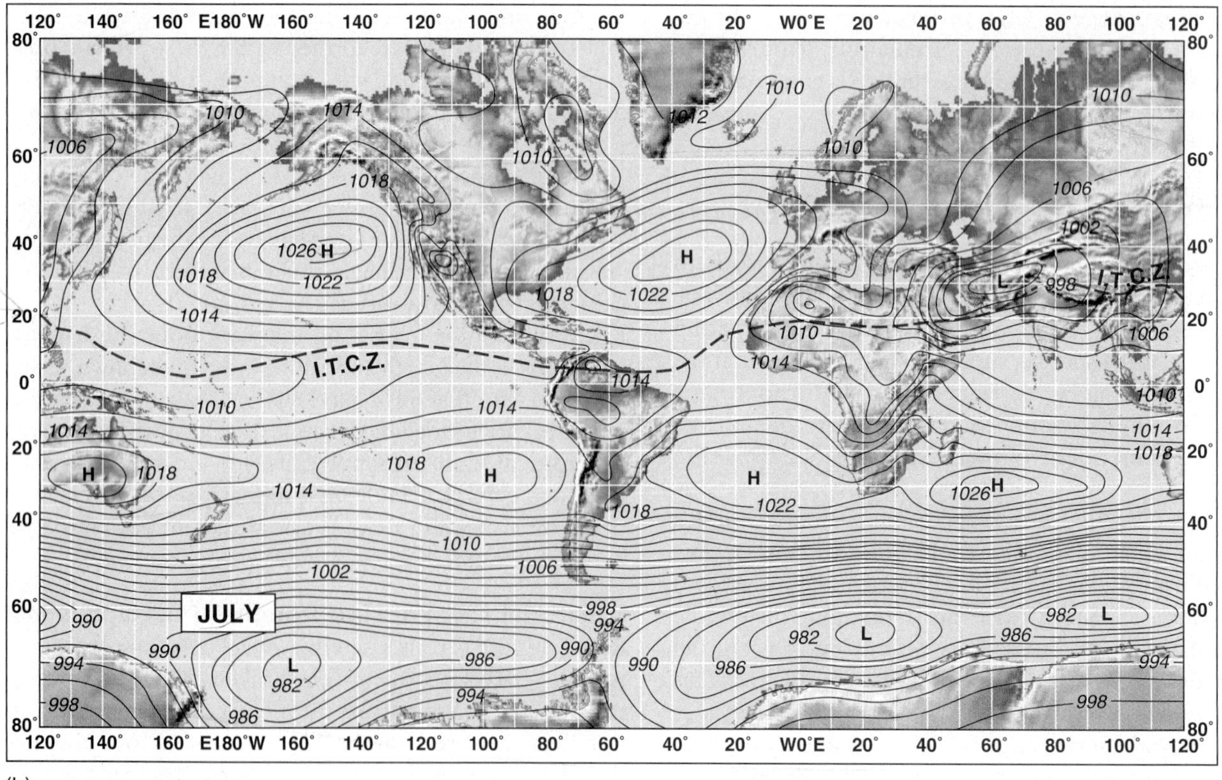

(b)

FIGURE 6.11 Global barometric pressures.
Average surface barometric pressure (millibars) for January and July. Dashed red line marks the intertropical convergence zone (ITCZ). [Adapted from the National Climatic Data Center, Monthly Climatic Data for the World, 46, no. 1, January and July 1993. Prepared in cooperation with the WMO and NOAA.]

Global Patterns of Pressure

Global Sea-level Pressure

Table 6.2 Four Hemispheric Pressure Areas

Name	Cause	Location	Air Temperature/Moisture
Polar high-pressure cells	Thermal	90° N 90° S	Cold/dry
Subpolar low-pressure cells	Dynamic	60° N 60° S	Cool/wet
Subtropical high-pressure cells	Dynamic	20° to 35° N and S	Hot/dry
Equatorial low-pressure trough	Thermal	10° N to 10° S	Warm/wet

trough. This converging air is extremely moist and full of latent heat energy. As it rises, the air expands and cools, producing condensation; consequently, rainfall is heavy throughout this zone. Vertical cloud columns frequently reach the tropopause, in thunderous strength and intensity.

The combination of heating and convergence forces air aloft and forms the **intertropical convergence zone (ITCZ)**. The ITCZ is identified by bands of clouds associated with the convergence of winds along the equator and is noted on the January and July pressure maps (see Figure 6.11). During summer, a marked wet season accompanies the shifting ITCZ over various regions. The maps in Figure 6.11 show the ITCZ as a dashed line.

In January, the zone crosses northern Australia and dips southward in eastern Africa and South America. Note this ITCZ location on the spacecraft image in Figure 6.12 using cloud patterns; for example, compare Australia in both figures. By July the zone shifts northward with the Sun, as far north as Pakistan and southern Asia. You easily can identify this ITCZ cloudiness on the *GOES* images in Figure 1.27.

Figure 6.13 shows two views of Earth's general circulation. The winds converging on the equatorial low-pressure trough are known generally as the **trade winds**, or *trades*. *Northeast trade winds* blow in the Northern Hemisphere and *southeast trade winds* in the Southern Hemisphere. These are labelled in Figure 6.13a. The trade winds were named during the era of sailing ships carrying trade across the seas.

The trade winds pick up large quantities of moisture as they return through the Hadley circulation cell for another cycle of uplift and condensation (shown in cross section in Figure 6.13b). These *Hadley cells* in each hemisphere, named for the eighteenth-century English scientist who

FIGURE 6.12 Clouds portray equatorial and subtropical circulation patterns on a *Galileo* spacecraft image.
An interrupted band of clouds along the equator denotes the intertropical convergence zone (ITCZ), flanked to the north and south by several subtropical high-pressure systems and clear skies. Note the greater cloud development over land. This natural-colour image was taken by the solid-state imaging instrument aboard the *Galileo* spacecraft during its December 1990 flyby of Earth on its successful mission to the planet Jupiter in 1995. [The Solid State Imaging instrument (violet, green, and red filters) image courtesy of Dr. W. Reid Thompson, Laboratory of Planetary Studies, Cornell University. Used by permission.]

(a)

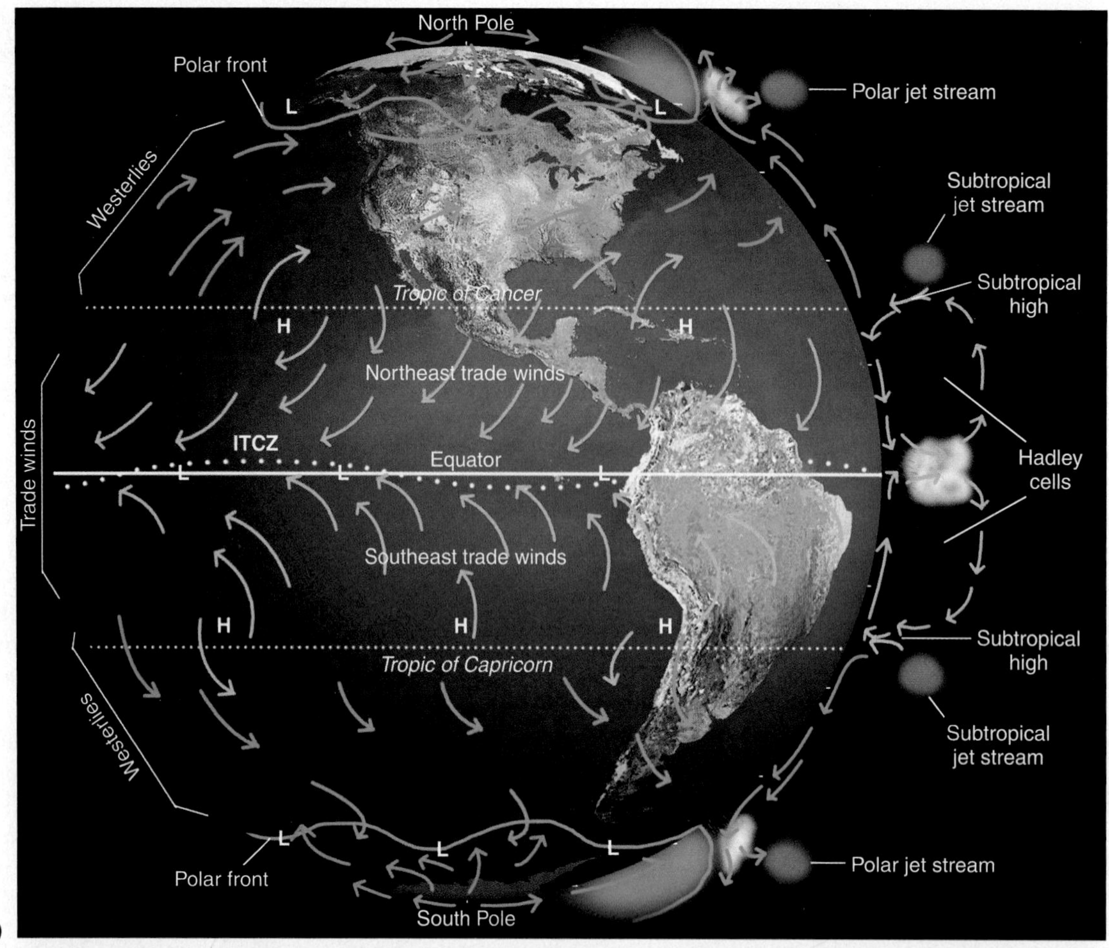

(b)

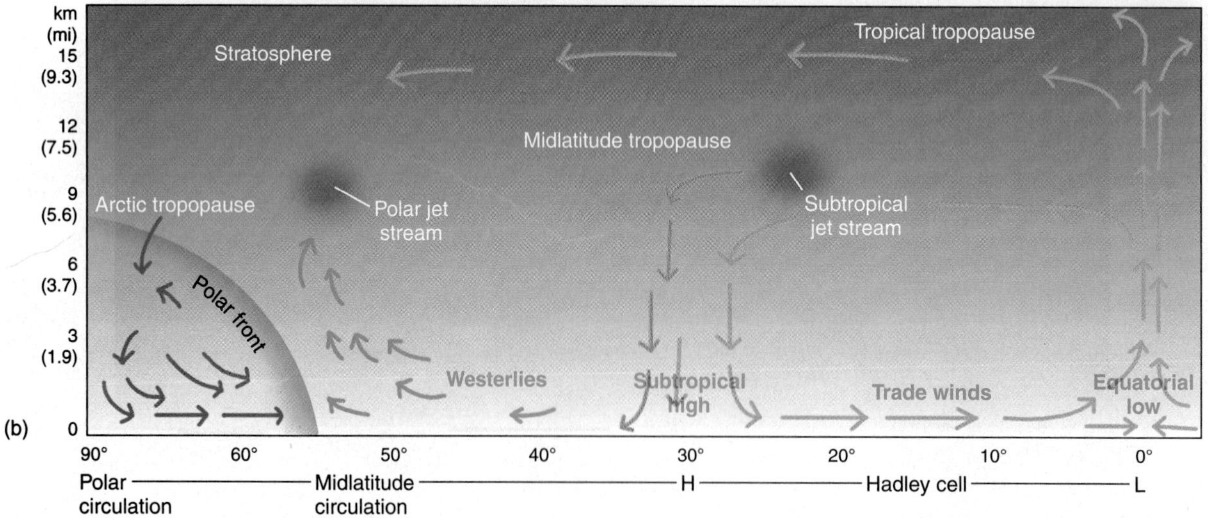

FIGURE 6.13 General atmospheric circulation model.
Two views of the general atmospheric circulation: (a) general circulation schematic; (b) equator-to-pole cross section of the Northern Hemisphere. Both views show Hadley cells, subtropical highs, polar front, the subpolar low-pressure cells, and approximate locations of the subtropical and polar jet streams.

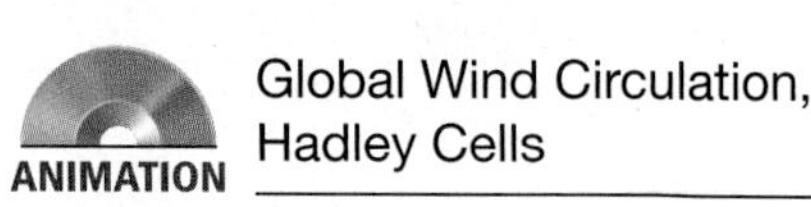

Global Infrared

described the trade winds, denote the circuit completed by winds rising along the ITCZ, moving northward and southward into the subtropics, descending to the surface, and returning to the ITCZ as the trade winds. During the year in each hemisphere, this circulation pattern appears most vertically symmetrical near the equinoxes.

Within the ITCZ, winds are calm or mildly variable because of the even pressure gradient and the vertical ascent of air. These equatorial calms are the *doldrums*, a name formed from an older English word meaning "foolish," because of the difficulty sailing ships encountered when attempting to move through this zone. The rising air from the equatorial low-pressure area spirals upward into a geostrophic flow to the north and south. These upper-air winds turn eastward, flowing from west to east, beginning at about 20° N and 20° S, and form descending masses of air and high-pressure systems in the subtropical latitudes.

Subtropical High-Pressure Cells: Hot, Dry, Desert Air Between 20° and 35° latitude in both hemispheres, a broad high-pressure zone of hot, dry air is evident across the globe (see Figures 6.11, 6.13). Clear, frequently cloudless skies over the Sahara and Arabian Desert and portions of the Indian Ocean dominate these regions. Can you identify these desert regions on the *Galileo* spacecraft image in Figure 6.12?

The dynamic cause of these subtropical anticyclones is too complex to detail here, but they generally form as air above the subtropics is mechanically pushed downward and heats by compression on its descent to the surface, as in Figure 6.13. Warmer air has a greater capacity to absorb evaporation than does cooler air, making this descending warm air relatively dry (large water vapour holding capacity, low water vapour content). The air is also dry because heavy precipitation along the equatorial portion of the circulation removes moisture.

Surface air diverging from the subtropical high-pressure cells generates Earth's principal surface winds: the westerlies and the trade winds. The **westerlies** are the dominant surface winds from the subtropics to high latitudes. They diminish somewhat in summer and are stronger in winter.

As you examine the global pressure maps in Figure 6.11, you find several high-pressure areas. In the Northern Hemisphere, the Atlantic subtropical high-pressure cell is called the **Bermuda high** (in the western Atlantic) or the **Azores high** (when it migrates to the eastern Atlantic in winter). The area in the Atlantic under this subtropical high features clear, warm waters and large quantities of *Sargassum* (a seaweed), which gives the area its name—the Sargasso Sea.

The **Pacific high**, or *Hawaiian high*, dominates the Pacific in July, retreating southward in January. In the Southern Hemisphere, three large high-pressure centres dominate the Pacific, Atlantic, and Indian Oceans, especially in January, and tend to move along parallels of latitude in shifting zonal positions.

The entire high-pressure system migrates with the summer high Sun, fluctuating about 5–10° in latitude. The *eastern sides* (right-hand side) of these anticyclonic systems are drier and more stable (less convective activity) and feature cooler ocean currents than do the *western sides* (left-hand side). The drier eastern side of these systems and dry-summer conditions influence climate along subtropical and midlatitude west coasts (Figure 6.14). In fact, Earth's major deserts generally occur within the subtropical belt

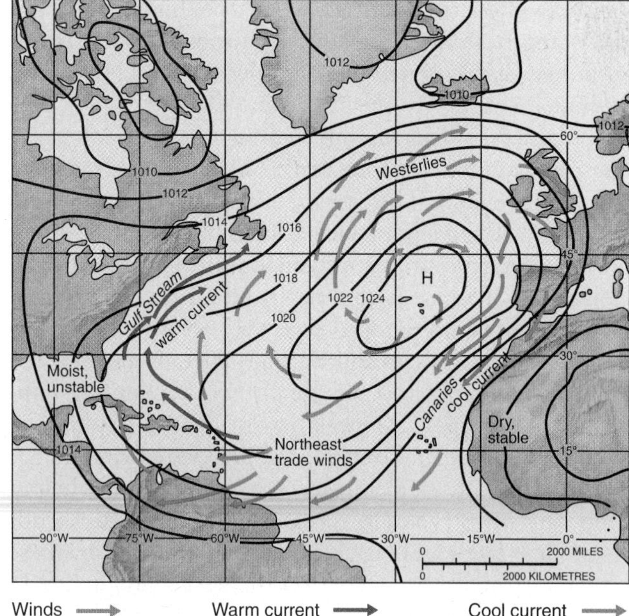

FIGURE 6.14 Subtropical high-pressure system in the Atlantic.
Characteristic circulation and climate conditions related to the Atlantic subtropical high-pressure anticyclone in the Northern Hemisphere. Note deserts extending to the shores of Africa with offshore cool currents, whereas the southeastern United States is moist and humid, with offshore warm currents.

and extend to the west coast of each continent except Antarctica. In the figure, the desert regions of Africa come right to the shore in both hemispheres, with the cool, southward flowing *Canaries Current* offshore in the north, and the cool, northward flowing *Benguela* current offshore in the south.

The western sides of subtropical high-pressure cells tend to be moist and unstable. These conditions cause warm, moist weather in Hawai'i, Japan, southeastern China, and the southeastern United States characterized in Figure 6.14.

Because the location of the subtropical belts are near 25° N and 25° S latitudes, these areas sometimes are known as the *calms of Cancer* and the *calms of Capricorn*. These zones of windless, hot, dry desert air, so deadly in the era of sailing ships, earned the name *horse latitudes*. The origin of this term is popularly attributed to becalmed and stranded sailing crews of past centuries, who destroyed the horses on board, not wanting to share food or water with the livestock. The term's true origin may never be known; the *Oxford English Dictionary* calls it "uncertain."

Subpolar Low-Pressure Cells: Cool and Moist Air In January, two low-pressure cyclonic cells exist over the oceans around 60° N latitude, near their namesakes: the North Pacific **Aleutian low** and the North Atlantic **Icelandic low** (see Figure 6.11a). Both cells are dominant in winter and weaken or disappear in summer with the strengthening of high-pressure systems in the subtropics.

The area of contrast between cold (from higher latitudes) and warm (from lower latitudes) air forms the **polar front**, an air mass battleground that encircles Earth and is focused in these low-pressure areas.

Figure 6.13 illustrates this confrontation between warm, moist air from the westerlies and cold, dry air from the polar and Arctic regions. The upward displacement of the warm air forces cooling and condensation in the lifted air. Low-pressure cyclonic storms migrate out of the Aleutian and Icelandic frontal areas and may produce precipitation in North America and Europe, respectively. Northwestern sections of North America and Europe generally are cool and moist as a result of the passage of these cyclonic systems onshore—consider the weather in British Columbia, Washington, Oregon, Ireland, and the United Kingdom.

In the Southern Hemisphere, a noncontinuous belt of subpolar low cyclonic pressure systems surrounds Antarctica. The spiralling cloud patterns produced by these cyclonic systems are visible on the spacecraft image in Figure 6.15. Severe cyclonic storms can cross Antarctica, producing strong winds and new snowfall. How many cyclonic systems can you identify on the image?

Polar High-Pressure Cells: Frigid, Dry Deserts Polar high-pressure cells are weak. The polar atmospheric mass is small, receiving little energy to put it into motion. Variable winds, cold and dry, move away from the polar region in an anticyclonic direction. They descend and diverge clockwise in the Northern Hemisphere (counterclockwise in the Southern Hemisphere) and form weak, variable winds named **polar easterlies**.

Of the two polar regions, the **Antarctic high** is stronger and more persistent, forming over the Antarctic landmass. Over the Arctic Ocean, a polar high-pressure cell is less pronounced. When it does form, it tends to locate over the colder northern continental areas in winter (Canadian and Siberian highs) rather than directly over the relatively warmer Arctic Ocean.

Upper Atmospheric Circulation

Circulation in the middle and upper troposphere is an important component of the atmosphere's general circulation. Just as sea level is a reference datum for evaluating air pressure at the surface, we use a pressure level such as 500 mb as a **constant isobaric surface** for a pressure-reference datum in the upper atmosphere.

On upper-air pressure maps, we plot the height above sea level at which an air pressure of 500 mb occurs. In contrast, on surface weather maps we plot different pressures at the fixed elevation of sea level—a *constant height surface*. Using the isobaric chart for an April day (see Figure 6.10), Figure 6.16a and b illustrate such an undulating isobaric surface, upon which all points have the same pressure.

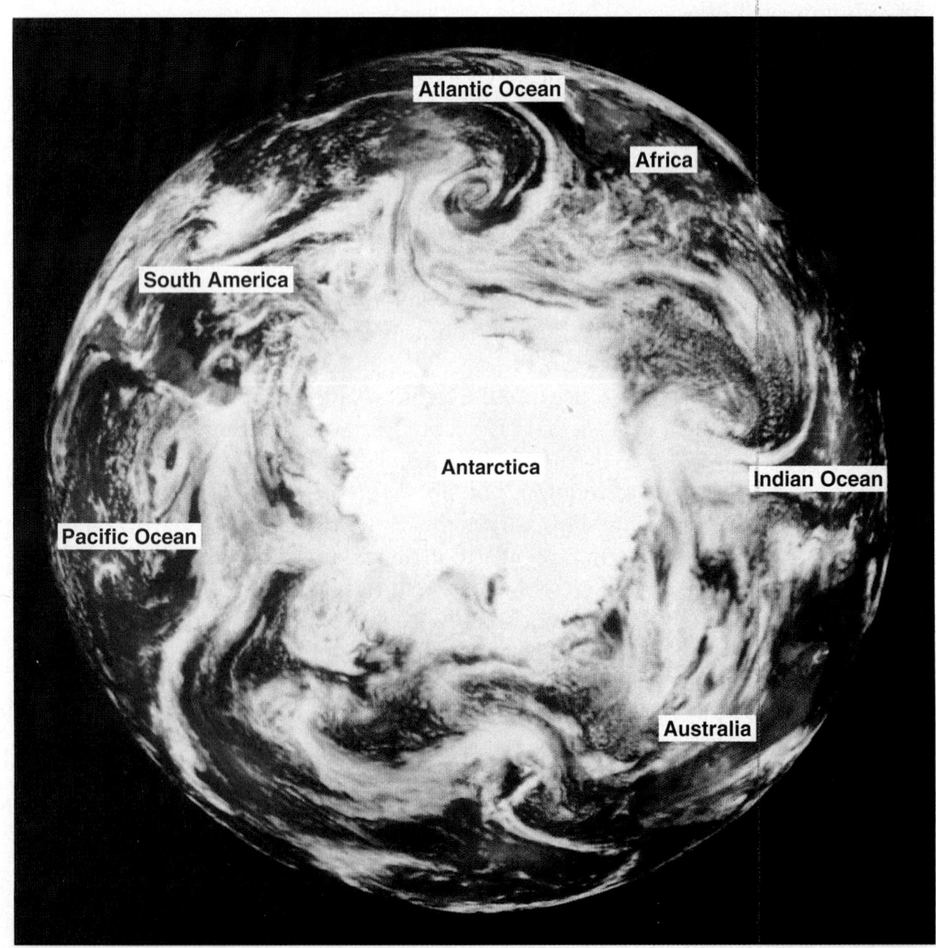

FIGURE 6.15 Clouds portray subpolar and polar circulation patterns.
Centred on Antarctica, this image shows a series of subpolar low-pressure cyclones in the Southern Hemisphere. Antarctica is fully illuminated by a midsummer Sun as the continent approaches the December solstice. Imaging instrument aboard the *Galileo* spacecraft made this image during its December 1990 flyby of Earth. [The Solid State Imaging instrument (violet, green, and red filters) image courtesy of Dr. W. Reid Thompson, Laboratory of Planetary Studies, Cornell University. Used by permission.]

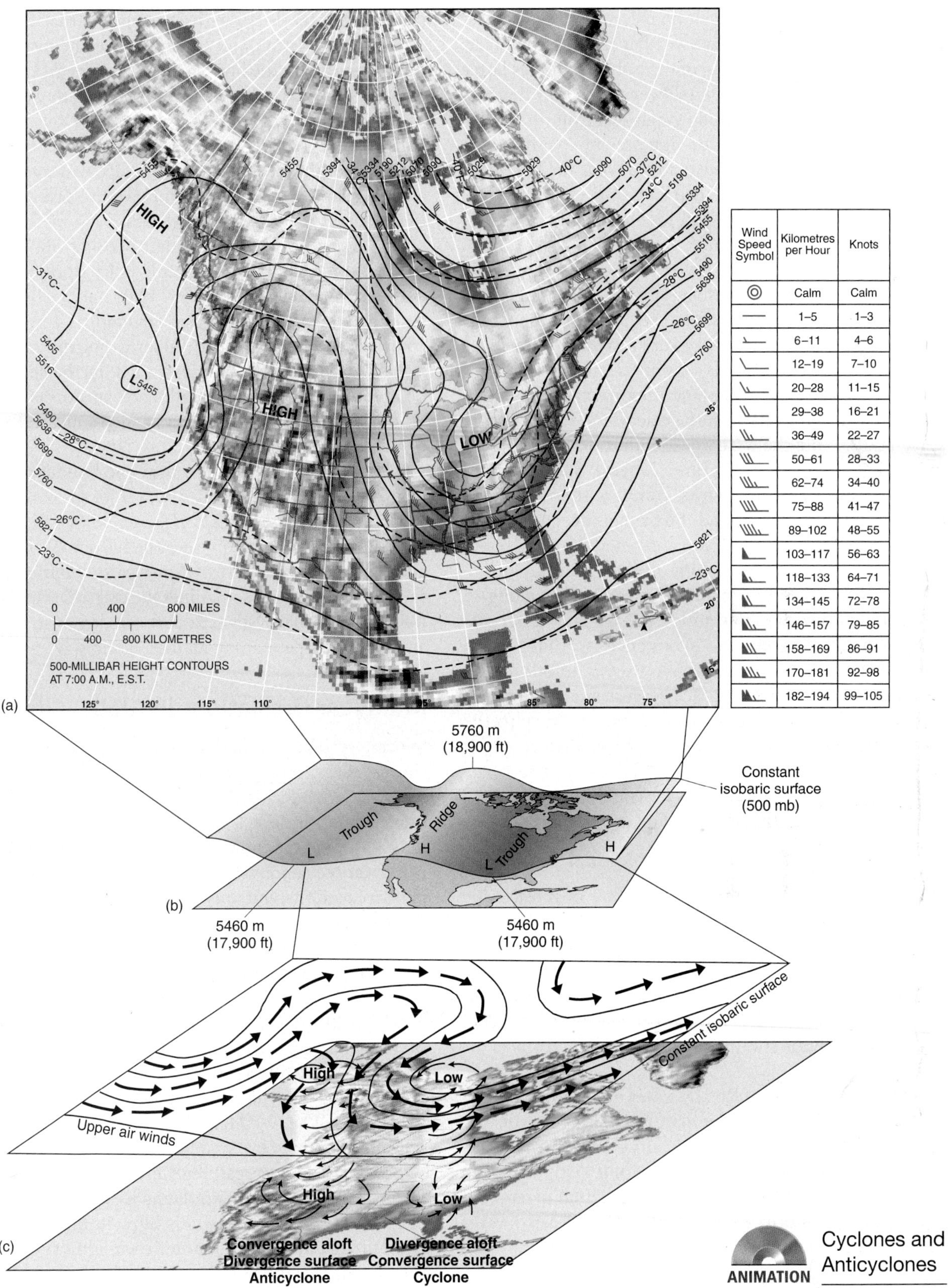

Wind Speed Symbol	Kilometres per Hour	Knots
◎	Calm	Calm
	1–5	1–3
	6–11	4–6
	12–19	7–10
	20–28	11–15
	29–38	16–21
	36–49	22–27
	50–61	28–33
	62–74	34–40
	75–88	41–47
	89–102	48–55
	103–117	56–63
	118–133	64–71
	134–145	72–78
	146–157	79–85
	158–169	86–91
	170–181	92–98
	182–194	99–105

FIGURE 6.16 Analysis of a constant isobaric surface.
Isobaric chart for an April day. (a) Contours show elevation (in metres) at which 500-mb pressure occurs—a constant isobaric surface. The pattern of contours reveals a 500-mb isobaric surface and geostrophic wind patterns in the troposphere ranging from 5029 to 5821 m (16,500 to 19,100 ft) elevation. (b) Note the "ridge" of high pressure over the Intermountain West, at 5760 m altitude, and the "trough" of low pressure over the Great Lakes region and off the Pacific Coast on the map, also at 5460 m altitude, and in the sketch beneath the chart. (c) Note areas of convergence aloft (corresponding to surface divergence) and divergence aloft (corresponding to surface convergence)—upper atmosphere conditions at the 500-mb level support surface cyclones and anticyclones. [Data for map in (a) from the National Weather Service, NOAA.]

We use this 500-mb level to analyze upper-air winds and possible support for surface weather conditions. Similar to surface maps, closer spacing of the isobars indicates faster winds; wider spacing indicates slower winds. On this isobaric pressure surface, altitude variations from the reference datum are called *ridges* for high pressure (with isobars on the map bending poleward) and *troughs* for low pressure (with isobars on the map bending equatorward). Looking at the figure, can you identify such ridges and troughs in the isobaric surface?

The pattern of ridges and troughs in the upper-air wind flow is important in sustaining surface cyclonic (low) and anticylonic (high) circulation. Frequently, the upper-air wind flow generates surface pressure systems. Near ridges in the isobaric surface, winds slow and converge (pile-up), whereas winds near the area of maximum wind speeds along the trough in the isobaric surface accelerate and diverge (spread out). Note the wind-speed indicators and labels in Figure 6.16a near the ridge (over Alberta, Saskatchewan, Montana, and Wyoming); now compare these with the wind-speed indicators around the trough (over Kentucky, West Virginia, the New England states, and the Maritimes). Also, note the wind relationships off the Pacific Coast.

Now look at Figure 6.16c. As wind moves along in geostrophic flow, it is constantly experiencing horizontal convergence (piling up) and divergence (spreading out). This divergence in the upper-air flow is important to cyclonic circulation at the surface because it creates an outflow of air aloft that stimulates an inflow of air into the low-pressure cyclone (such as what happens when you open a chimney damper to create an upward draft). Convergence aloft, on the other hand, drives descending airflows and divergent winds at the surface, moving out from high-pressure anticyclones.

Rossby Waves Within the westerly flow of geostrophic winds are great waving undulations called **Rossby waves**, named for meteorologist Carl G. Rossby who first described them mathematically in 1938. The polar front is the line of conflict between colder air to the north and warmer air to the south (Figure 6.17). Rossby waves bring tongues of cold air southward, with warmer tropical air moving northward.

The development of Rossby waves in the upper-air circulation is shown in the three-part figure. As these disturbances mature, distinct cyclonic circulation forms, with warmer air and colder air mixing along distinct fronts. These wave-and-eddy formations and upper-air divergence support cyclonic storm systems at the surface. Rossby waves develop along the flow axis of a jet stream.

Jet Streams The most prominent movement in these upper-level westerly wind flows is the **jet stream**, an irregular, concentrated band of wind occurring at several different locations that supports surface weather systems. (Figure 6.13a shows the location of four jet streams.) Rather flattened in vertical cross section, the jet streams normally are 160–480 km (100–300 mi) wide by 900–2150 m (3000–7000 ft) thick, with core speeds that can exceed 300 kmph (190 mph). Jet streams in each hemisphere tend to weaken during the hemisphere's summer and strengthen during winter as the streams shift closer to the equator. The pattern of ridges and troughs causes variation in jet stream speeds (convergence and divergence). These upper-level westerly wind systems also affect air transportation, allowing shorter flight times from west to east and causing longer flight times from east to west.

The *polar jet stream* meanders between 30–70° N latitude, at the tropopause along the polar front, at altitudes between 7600 and 10,700 m (24,900 and 35,100 ft). The polar jet stream can migrate as far south as Texas, steering colder air masses into North America and influencing surface storm paths travelling eastward. In the summer, the polar jet stream exerts less influence on storms by staying far poleward. Figure 6.18 shows a map and a stylized view of a polar jet stream flow.

In subtropical latitudes, near the boundary between tropical and midlatitude air, another jet stream flows near the tropopause, the *subtropical jet stream* (see Figure 6.13). The subtropical jet stream meanders from 20–50° latitude and may occur over North America simultaneously with the polar jet stream—sometimes the two will actually merge for brief episodes. News Report 6.2 demonstrates upper air circulation patterns in an interesting way.

Multiyear Oscillations in Global Circulation

Several system fluctuations that occur in multiyear or shorter periods are important in the global circulation picture, yet an understanding of them is just emerging. The most famous of these is the El Niño–Southern Oscillation (ENSO) phenomenon discussed later in Chapter 10. Multiyear oscillations affect temperatures, air masses, and air pressure patterns, and thus affect global winds and climates. These air masses, discussed in Chapter 7, have distinctive characteristics of moisture and temperature. Here we briefly overview three of these hemisphere-scale oscillations.

North Atlantic Oscillation A north–south fluctuation of atmospheric variability marks the North Atlantic Oscillation (NAO) as pressure differences between the Icelandic low and the Azores high in the Atlantic alternate in strength. The *NAO Index* is in its *positive phase* when the Icelandic low-pressure system is lower than normal and the Azores (west of Portugal) high-pressure cell is higher than normal. Strong westerly winds and jet stream cross the eastern Atlantic. Northerly winds blow in the Labrador Sea (west of Greenland) and southerly winds move through the Norwegian Sea (east of Greenland). In the eastern United States, winters tend to be less severe in contrast to the strong warm, wet storms hitting northern Europe; however, the Mediterranean region is dry.

In its *negative phase*, the NAO features a weaker pressure gradient than normal between Iceland and the Azores and reduced westerlies and jet stream. Storm tracks shift southward in Europe, bringing moist conditions to the

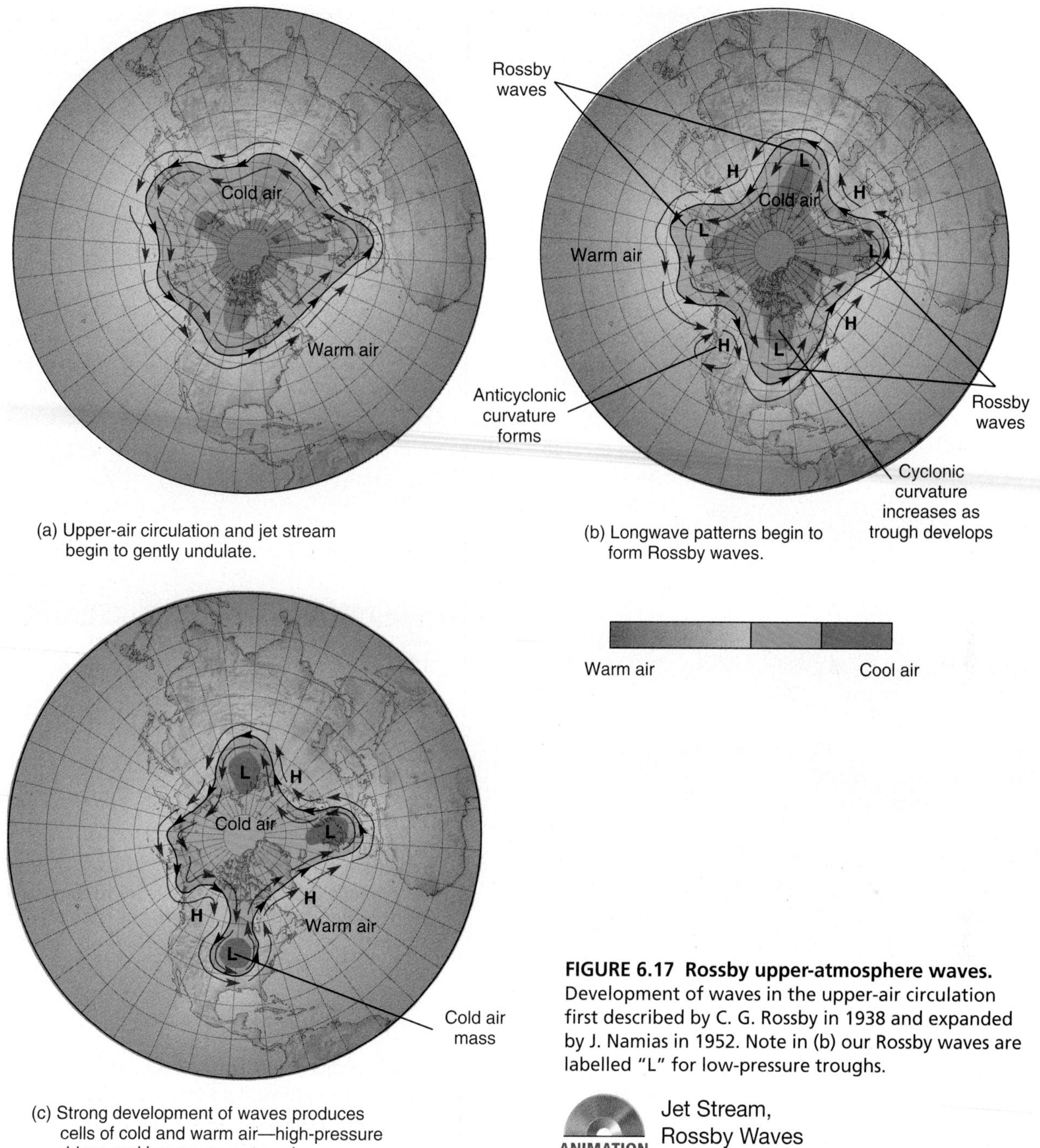

FIGURE 6.17 Rossby upper-atmosphere waves. Development of waves in the upper-air circulation first described by C. G. Rossby in 1938 and expanded by J. Namias in 1952. Note in (b) our Rossby waves are labelled "L" for low-pressure troughs.

ANIMATION Jet Stream, Rossby Waves

Mediterranean and cold, dry winters to northern Europe. The eastern United States experiences cold, snowy winters as Arctic air masses plunge to lower latitudes.

With unpredictable flips between positive and negative phases, sometimes changing from week to week, a trend to a more positive phase than negative has emerged since 1960. Since 1980, the NAO has been predominately positive (see **http://www.ldeo.columbia.edu/NAO/**).

Arctic Oscillation Variable fluctuations between middle- and high-latitude air mass conditions over the Northern Hemisphere produce the Arctic Oscillation (AO). The AO is associated with the NAO, especially in winter, and the two phases of the *AO Index* correlate to the two-phased *NAO Index*. In the *warm phase* of the AO Index (positive NAO), the pressure gradient is affected by lower pressure than normal over the North Pole region and relatively higher pressures at lower latitudes. This sets up stronger westerly winds and a flow of warmer Atlantic water currents into the Arctic Ocean. Cold air masses do not migrate as far south in winter, whereas winters are colder than normal in Greenland.

In the *cold phase* of the AO Index (negative NAO), the pattern is reversed, with higher-than-normal pressure over the North Pole region and relatively lower pressure in the central Atlantic. Here the air masses of winter bring cold

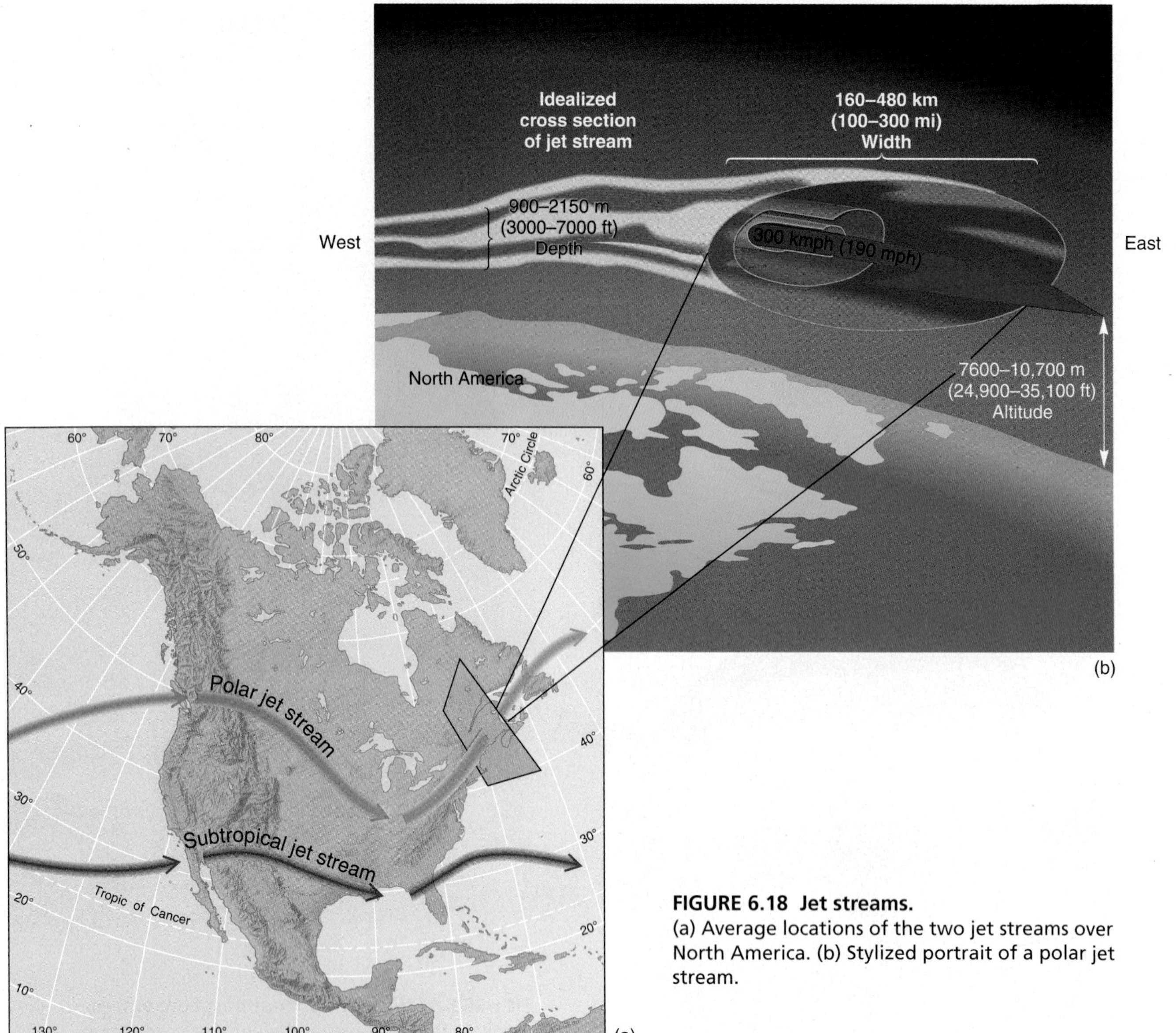

FIGURE 6.18 Jet streams.
(a) Average locations of the two jet streams over North America. (b) Stylized portrait of a polar jet stream.

conditions to the eastern United States, northern Europe, and Asia and sea ice in the Arctic Ocean becomes a bit thicker. Greenland is warmer than normal.

Since the 1980s, the NAO and AO indices are in a strong positive, warm phase. In response, the ice drift in the eastern Arctic Ocean is counterclockwise and air pollution from Europe and Russia moves across the region to Canada. Since the expected variability in these oscillations is essentially random, the emergence of a strong positive, warm phase is challenging to understand. Scientists are examining correlations with changes in sea-surface temperatures to understand what is happening and perhaps develop a forecast capability. For instance, researchers have discovered linkages between the behaviour of the NAO and the increasingly warm Indian Ocean.

Given the warming of ocean temperatures and the present trends of freshening in the northern ocean and increasing salinity in the tropical ocean, there is concern about a further strengthening of these oscillations and what effects this might have on weather and climate. Such is the excitement of physical geography and Earth systems science, as global connections are found linking diverse physical systems.

Pacific Decadal Oscillation Across the Pacific Ocean, the Pacific Decadal Oscillation (PDO) is longer-lived, at 20 to 30 years in duration, than the 2-to 12-year variation in the ENSO. The PDO term came into use in 1996. Involved are two regions of sea-surface temperatures and related air pressure: the northern and tropical western Pacific (region #1), and the area of the eastern tropical Pacific, along the West Coast (region #2).

Between 1947 and 1977, higher-than-normal temperatures dominated region #1, and lower temperatures were in region #2; this is the PDO *negative phase* (or cool phase). A switch to a *positive phase* (or warm phase) in the PDO ran from 1977 to the 1990s, when lower temperatures were in region #1 and higher-than-normal temperatures dominated

News Report 6.2

MANTRA's Big Balloon—Blowing in the Wind

A 25-story balloon named MANTRA (Middle Atmosphere Nitrogen Trend Assessment) launched from Vanscoy, Saskatchewan, August 24, 1998. The unpiloted mission was intended to measure concentrations of human-made chemicals and ozone in the stratosphere using a sophisticated instrument array.

After its 3:25 A.M. lift off, the balloon rose to a planned 38-km altitude and collected valuable data throughout the day. Upon mission completion, explosive charges were designed to release the instrument payload and a parachute for a safe landing in nearby Manitoba. However, a malfunction left the payload attached to the balloon, adrift in the stratosphere in the tow of upper wind streams. An unexpected voyage was underway.

The balloon's path traced upper-atmospheric wind circulation and the flowing polar jet stream across Manitoba, northern Ontario and Québec, Labrador, the tip of Newfoundland, and out over the Atlantic (Figure 1). Realizing the potential threat to commercial jets, Canadian military jets were dispatched to shoot MANTRA down. Thousands of rounds of ammunition were fired into the balloon to no avail because MANTRA was a zero-pressure balloon. The helium was not under pressure in the plastic, so the holes created by the ammunition merely produced slow leaks. American and British military radar tracked MANTRA's continuing voyage. Imagine this balloon adrift in the Rossby waves depicted in Figure 6.17.

The upper winds drove MANTRA northeastward over the Denmark Straits between Greenland and Iceland, across the Norwegian Svalbard Islands, poleward of 80° N, and over the Russian Franz Josef Land and Novaya Zemlya islands groups. Then winds took the balloon south over the Russian coast and westward across Finland. The depleted balloon began its descent September 2, after a 9-day odyssey, eventually settling to Earth in

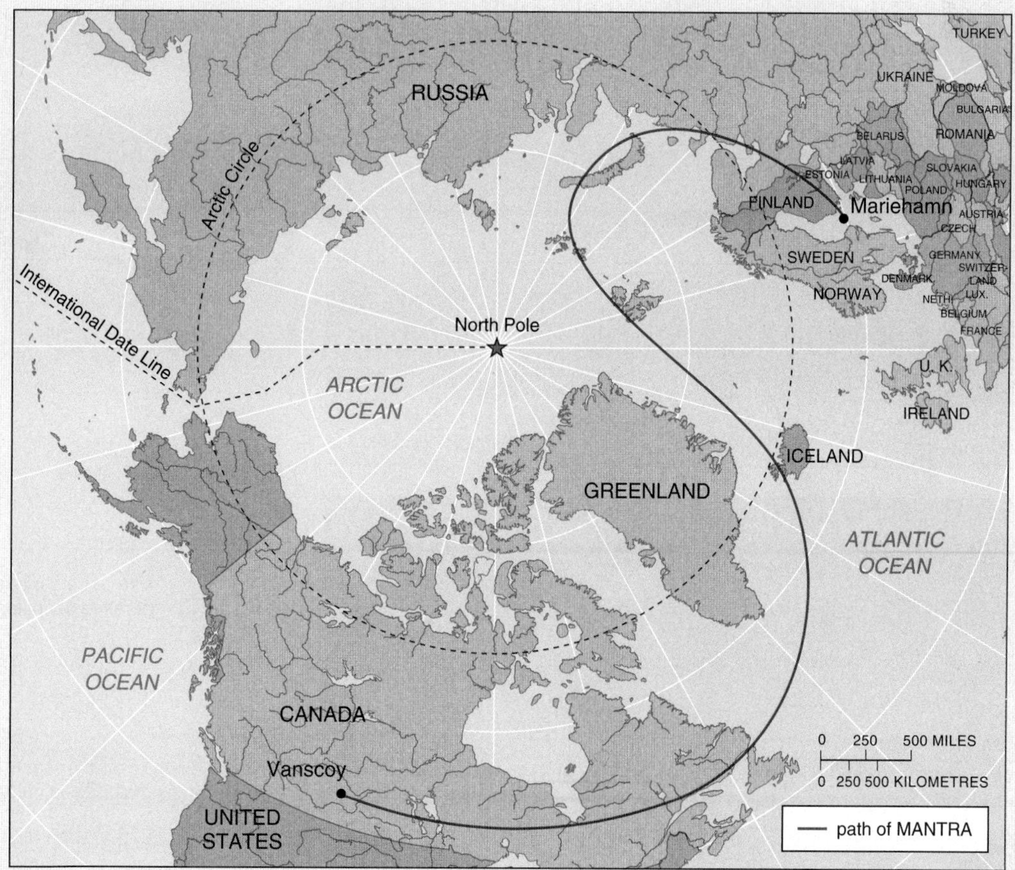

FIGURE 1 Flight path of MANTRA 1998's big balloon.
Westerly winds carried the balloon east from Vanscoy, Saskatchewan, over Manitoba, northern Ontario, Québec, Labrador, and the tip of Newfoundland. The path turned northeastward and passed between Iceland and Greenland. It then veered northward toward the Svalbard Islands and then south to Russia. Finally the balloon headed west to land in Finland. [Used by permission of the Minister of Public Works and Government Services Canada; Natural Resources Canada, Geological Survey of Canada.]

(continued)

News Report 6.2 *(continued)*

Mariehamn, a city on Aland Island, in the Gulf of Bothnia. Finnish meteorologists gathered the payload and shipped it back to Canada.

The mission was repeated two years later, again with successful data gathering, only this time it ended at the correct landing site. MANTRA's 1998 unscheduled voyage to Europe dramatically demonstrated the course of the polar jet stream within Earth's upper atmospheric circulation.

region #2, coinciding with a time of more intense ENSO events. In 1999, a switch to a *negative phase* began. Unfortunately for the U.S. Southwest, this PDO negative phase can mean a decade or more of drier conditions for the already drought-plagued region.

Causes of the PDO and its cyclic variability over time are unknown. Scientists monitor conditions in the Pacific and look for patterns. A better understanding of the PDO will help scientists predict ENSO events as well as regional drought cycles (see **http://topex-www.jpl.nasa.gov/science/pdo.html**).

Local Winds

Several winds form in response to local terrain. Weather systems passing through an area can, of course, overwhelm such local effects.

Land–sea breezes occur on most coastlines (Figure 6.19). Different heating characteristics of land and water surfaces create these breezes. During the day, land gains heat energy faster and becomes warmer than the water offshore. Because warm air is less dense, it rises and triggers an onshore flow of cooler marine air to replace the rising

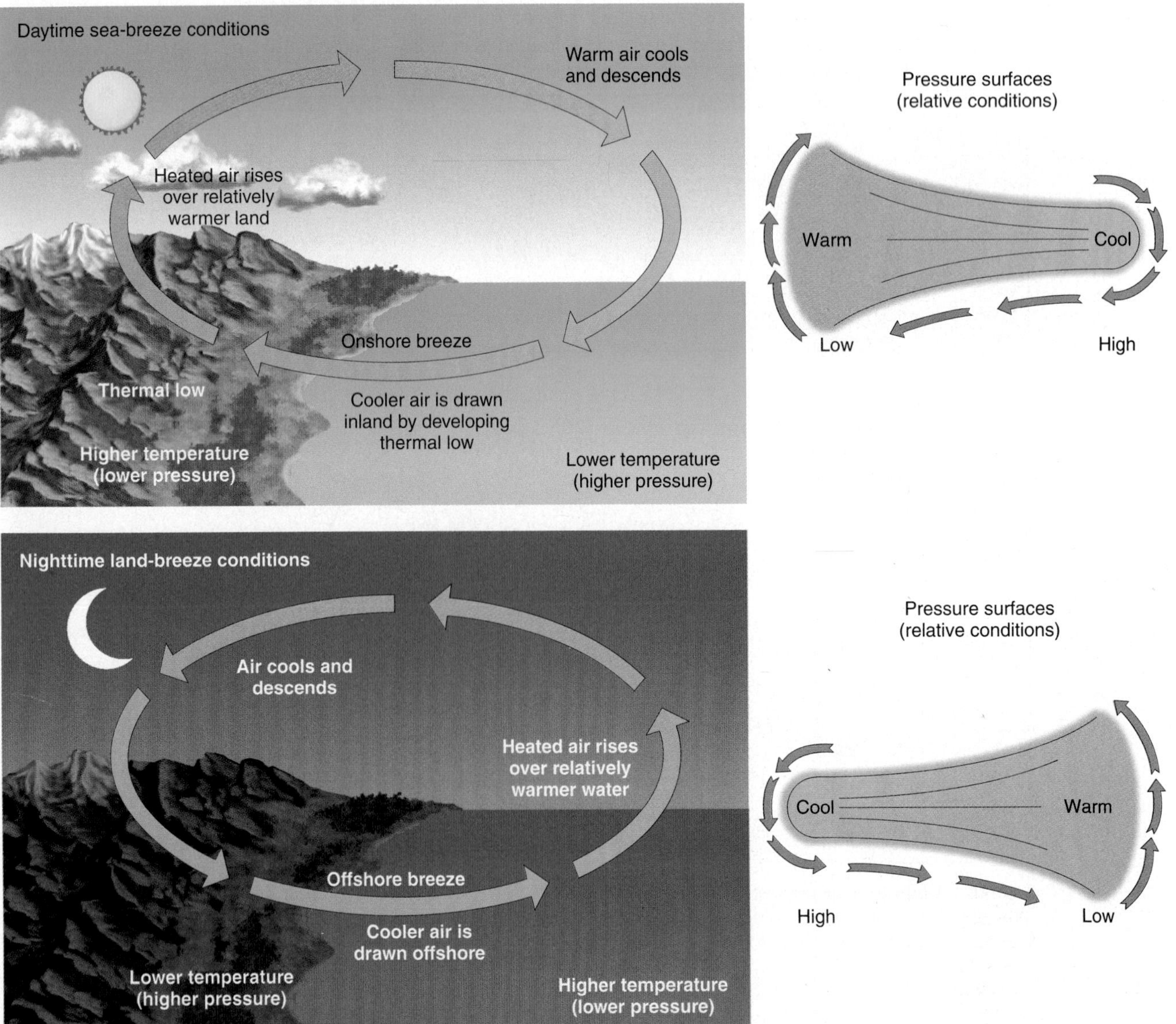

FIGURE 6.19 Land–sea breezes characteristic of day and night.

warm air—the flow is usually strongest in the afternoon. At night, inland areas cool (radiate heat energy) faster than offshore waters. As a result, the cooler air over the land subsides and flows offshore over the warmer water, where the air is lifted. This night pattern reverses the process that developed during the day.

Mountain–valley breezes result when mountain air cools rapidly at night, whereas valley air gains heat energy rapidly during the day (Figure 6.20). Thus, warm air rises upslope during the day, particularly in the afternoon; at night, cooler air subsides downslope into the valleys.

Katabatic winds, or gravity drainage winds, are of larger regional scale and usually stronger than mountain–valley breezes, under certain conditions. An elevated plateau or highland is essential, where layers of air at the surface cool, become denser, and flow downslope. The ferocious winds that can blow off the ice sheets of Antarctica and Greenland are katabatic in nature.

Worldwide, a variety of terrains produce such winds and bear many local names. The *mistral* of the Rhône Valley in southern France can cause frost damage to vineyards as the cold north winds move over the region to the Gulf of Lions and the Mediterranean Sea. The frequently stronger *bora*, driven by the cold air of winter high-pressure systems inland, flows across the Adriatic Coast to the west and south. In Alaska such winds are called the *taku*.

Chinooks are another type of local wind. They occur when a mountain range is exposed to a strong prevailing crosswind. Moist air is forced up the mountains bringing both cloud and precipitation to the *windward* side. The descending air then warms by compression and becomes drier as it is forced down the *leeward* side of the mountains. The relatively warm, dry, gusty winds that periodically occur to the leeward side of mountain ranges around the world are known by many names. In Canada and the northern United States, they are referred to as *chinooks*, thought to be a native word meaning snow eater. In parts of Europe they are known as *foehn* or *föhn*, winds.

Regionally, wind represents a significant source of renewable energy of great promise. Focus Study 6.1 briefly explores the potential for development of wind resources.

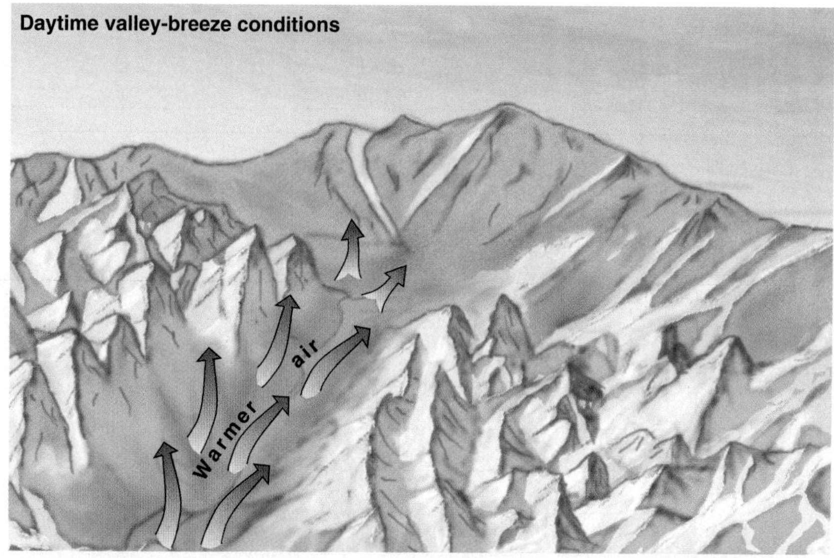

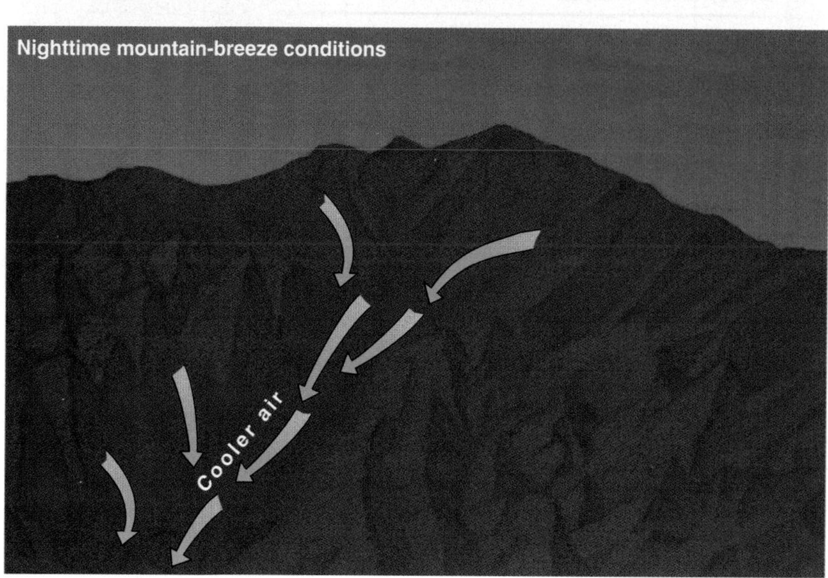

FIGURE 6.20 Pattern of mountain–valley breezes during day and night.

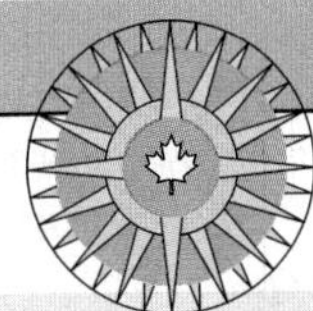

Focus Study 6.1

Wind Power: An Energy Resource for the Present and Future

The principles of wind power are ancient, but the technology is modern and the benefits are worth pursuing. In more-developed countries, energy sources are dominated by the use of nonrenewable fuels—coal, gas, oil, nuclear—and centralized energy production. In less-developed countries, however, many rely on renewable energy—small hydroelectric plants, wind-power systems, diminishing wood supplies, and solar energy—for cooking, heating, and pumping water. These resources are considered renewable because they are not depleted in the span of a human lifetime.

Rough estimates place the global wind resource at 500% more than present global energy use. The Financial Times World Renewable Energy Conference held in Brussels, Belgium, in 1999, proclaimed that wind power could supply 10% of world energy needs and create 1.7 million new jobs by the year 2020.

A Brief Assessment

Wind-generated energy resources are the fastest-growing energy technology, in terms of new capacity. By the end of 2003, world wind energy generating capacity had reached almost 39,294 MW, an 8133 MW increase over 2002. Most of this wind generated power capacity is installed in Europe, with Germany leading the way with 11,994 MW installed in 2002 and an additional 2645 in 2003. Table 1 summarizes the 15 countries leading installed capacity at the end of 2003. The rate of installed wind generating capacity is illustrated in Figure 1. The European Wind Energy Association announced an installed capacity goal of 60,000 MW by 2010, more than two times the worldwide total in 2002. As of 2004, Canada produces approximately 320 MW of wind-generated electricity. The Canadian Wind Energy Association has stated a goal of 10,000 MW of installed electricity capacity by 2010.

There are wind energy generation installations in seven provinces and

Table 1 Leading Wind Power Generating Installations by the End of 2003

Country	Installed by end of 2002	Installed during 2003	Total Installations by end of 2003
Germany	11,994	2,615	14,609
U.S.A	4,685	1,689	6,374
Spain	4,825	1,377	6,202
Denmark	2,889	221	3,110
India	1,702	1,408	3,110
Austria	140	1,970	2,110
Netherlands	693	219	912
Italy	788	116	904
Japan	414	272	686
U.K.	552	97	649
China	468	100	568
Sweden	345	54	399
Greece	297	78	375
Canada	236	81	317
Portugal	195	104	299

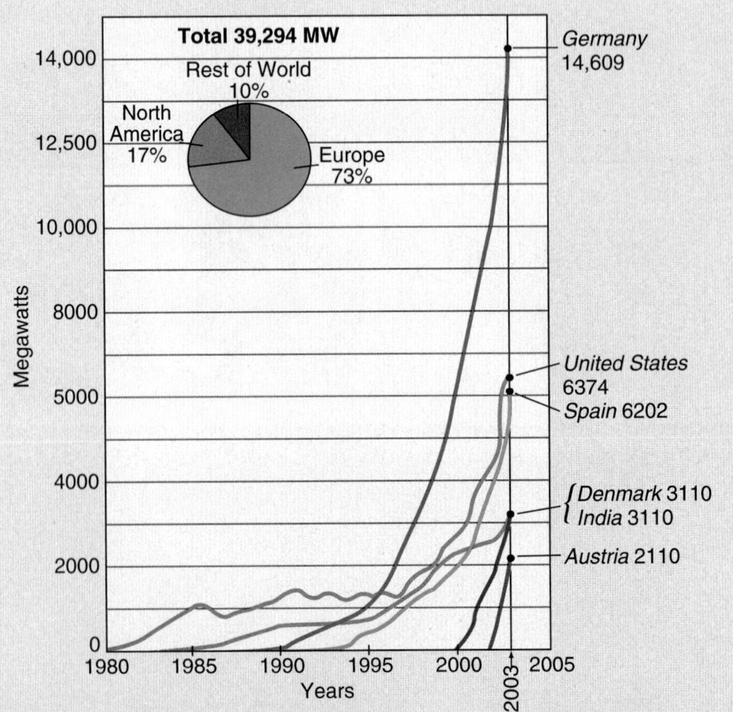

FIGURE 1 Installed wind-generating capacity.
In 1980, only 10 MW of wind-generated capacity was in operation in the world. By 1997 it had risen to 7630 MW, and by 2003, it surged to 39,294 MW worldwide. New capacity is growing at record rates in Germany, Denmark, Spain, India, and to a lesser extent, in the United States. [Sources: the American Wind Energy Association (AWEA) and the European Wind Energy Association (EWEA) annual reports.]

territories. In Yukon Territory, renewable energy programs fund pilot projects. In Alberta and Ontario, private for-profit power developers operate wind farms to supply electricity to competitive wholesale markets. In other regions, partnerships between private companies and provincial crown corporations are developing wind-power generation. Table 2 presents the active wind-power generation capacity by province and territory as of August 2004.

To put these numbers in meaningful perspective, every 10,000 MW of wind-generation capacity reduces carbon dioxide emissions by 33 million metric tons if it replaces coal, or 21 million metric tons if it replaces mixed fossil fuels. As an example, if countries rally and create a proposed US$400-billion-dollar industry by installing 500,000 MW of worldwide wind capacity by 2020, as much as a quarter of carbon dioxide emissions would be avoided. For the United States, 225,000 wind turbines would reduce coal emissions of carbon dioxide by 59%. For comparison, in the 1997 Kyoto Protocol the United States proposed reducing greenhouse gas emissions by just 7% below 1990 levels.

Table 2 Installed Wind-power in Canada

Province/Territory	Number of installed sites	Total Power (kW)
Prince Edward Island	2	13,560
Nova Scotia	3	4,860
Québec	5	113,250
Ontario	6	14,610
Saskatchewan	2	21,760
Alberta	10	170,670
Yukon	1	810
Total:	**27**	**339,520**

Source: Canadian Wind Energy Association, http://www.canwea.ca.

The Nature of Wind Energy

Power generation from wind is site-specific, because conditions that produce adequate winds are limited to certain areas. Figure 2 shows such farms in California, Germany, and Alberta. Wind resources are greatest in three basic settings: (1) along coastlines

(a)

(b)

(c)

FIGURE 2
(a) Wind farm near the Cajon Pass in southern California, along Interstate 15. (b) Wind farms near Harle, East Friesland, Germany. (c) Wind farm in Alberta. [Photos by (a) Bobbé Christopherson; (b) © Uwe Walz/CORBIS; (c) © Ed Gifford/Masterfile.com.]

(continued)

Focus Study 6.1 *(continued)*

that are influenced by trade winds and westerly winds; (2) where mountain passes constrict air flow and interior valleys develop thermal low-pressure areas, thus drawing air across the landscape; or (3) where localized winds occur, such as katabatic or monsoonal flows. Cash-short developing countries are generally located in areas blessed by such steady winds. Where wind is reliable less than 25%–30% of the time, only small-scale uses are economically feasible. Improvement in energy storage strategies, such as the production of hydrogen from water, could cover windless days.

The Benefits of the Wind Resource

Economic reality will perhaps override further delaying actions, especially where peak winds are in concert with peak electrical demand for air cooling, space heating, or agricultural water pumping. Needless to say, whether or not governments and transnational energy corporations begin full-scale planning and implementation of renewable resources, international realities of the near future will necessitate expansion. By the middle of this century, wind-generated electricity will be routine, along with other renewable energy sources, conservation, and energy efficiency. Germany, Spain, and Denmark in the European Union are leading the way for now.

Monsoonal Winds

Some regional wind systems seasonally change direction. Intense, seasonally shifting wind systems occur in the tropics over Southeast Asia, Indonesia, India, northern Australia, and equatorial Africa. A milder version of such monsoonal-type flows affects the extreme southwestern United States. These winds involve an annual cycle of returning precipitation with the summer Sun. The Arabic word for season, *mausim*, or **monsoon**, names them. (Specific monsoonal weather, associated climate types, and vegetation regions are discussed in Chapters 8, 10, and 20.) The location and size of the Asian landmass and its proximity to the Indian Ocean drive the monsoons of southern and eastern Asia (Figure 6.21). Also important to the generation of monsoonal flows are wind and pressure patterns in the upper-air circulation.

The extreme temperature range from summer to winter over the Asian landmass is due to its continentality (isolation from the modifying effects of the ocean). An intense high-pressure anticyclone dominates this continental land-

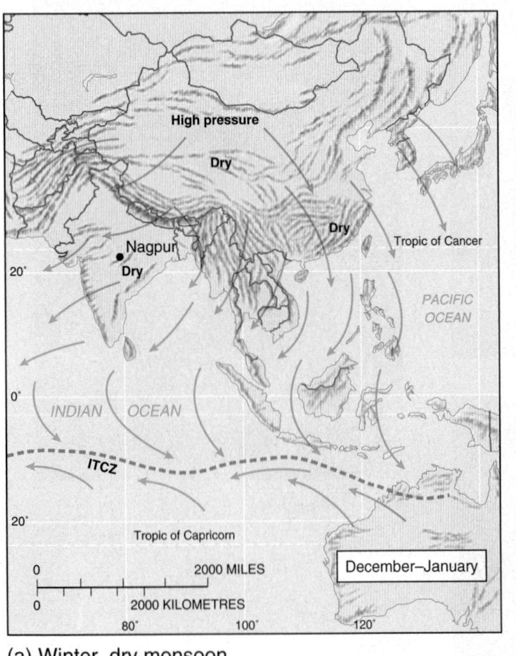

(a) Winter, dry monsoon

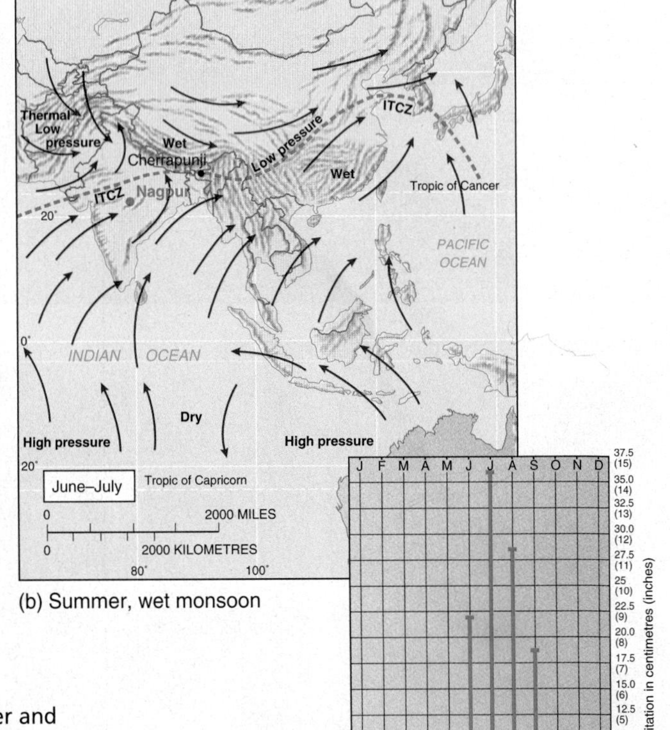

(b) Summer, wet monsoon

(c) Precipitation at Nagpur, India

FIGURE 6.21 The Asian monsoons.
Asian monsoon pressure and wind patterns during (a) winter and (b) summer. Note the shifting location of the ITCZ, the changing pressures over the Indian Ocean, and the different conditions over the Asian landmass. The inset climograph for Nagpur shows the severe contrast in seasonal precipitation (c). [Adapted from Joseph E. Van Riper, *Man's Physical World*, p. 215. Copyright 1971 by McGraw-Hill. Adapted by permission.]

mass in winter (see Figures 6.11a and 6.21a), whereas the equatorial low-pressure trough (ITCZ) dominates the central area of the Indian Ocean. This pressure gradient produces cold, dry winds from the Asian interior over the Himalayas, downslope and across India. Average temperatures range between 15–20°C (60–68°F) at lower elevations. These winds desiccate (dry out) the landscape and then give way to hot weather from March through May. Figure 2 in News Report 1.3 was made May 20, 1998, 18 m (60 ft) below the summit of Mount Everest—the monsoons dictate climbing schedules.

During the June–September wet period, the subsolar point (direct overhead rays of sunlight) shifts northward to the Tropic of Cancer, near the mouths of the Indus and Ganges Rivers. The ITCZ shifts northward over southern Asia, and the Asian continental interior develops a thermal low pressure, associated with high average temperatures (remember the summer warmth in Verkhoyansk, Siberia, from Chapter 5). Meanwhile, subtropical high pressure dominates the Indian Ocean, with a surface temperature of 30°C (86°F). As a result of this reversed pressure gradient, hot, dry subtropical air sweeps over the warm ocean, producing extremely high evaporation rates (Figure 6.21b).

By the time this air mass reaches India and the convergence zone, it is laden with moisture in thunderous, dark clouds. The warmth of the land lends additional lifting to the incoming air, as do the Himalayas, which force the air mass to higher altitudes. When the monsoonal rains arrive from June to September, they are welcome relief from the dust, heat, and parched land of Asia's springtime. Likewise, the annual monsoon is an integral part of Indian music, poetry, and life.

World-record rainfalls of the wet monsoon drench India. Cherrapunji, India, received both the second-highest average annual rainfall (1143 cm, or 450 in.) and the highest single-year rainfall (2647 cm, or 1042 in.).

The fact that the monsoons of southern Asia involve vast global pressure systems leads us to ask whether future climate change might affect present monsoonal patterns. Researchers are conducting a field experiment in the Indian Ocean, the Indian Ocean Experiment (INDOEX) to examine this question (**http://www-indoex.ucsd.edu/ProjDescription.html**). Their model projections forecast higher rainfall if consideration is given to increases in carbon dioxide and its greenhouse warming alone. However, when consideration is given to increases in aerosols—principally sulphur compounds and black carbon—then a drop in precipitation of 7%–14% appears in the model. Air pollution reduces surface heating and therefore decreases the pressure differences at the heart of monsoonal flows. Considering that 70% of the annual precipitation for the entire region comes during the wet monsoon, such changes will force difficult societal adjustments to changing water resources. (See the satellite images in Figure 4.9 and review the text discussion.)

Oceanic Currents

The driving force for ocean currents is the frictional drag of the winds, thus linking the atmospheric and oceanic systems. Also important in shaping these currents is the interplay of the Coriolis force, density differences caused by temperature and salinity, the configuration of the continents and ocean floor, and astronomical forces (the tides).

Surface Currents

Figure 6.22 portrays the general patterns of major ocean currents. Because ocean currents flow over distance and

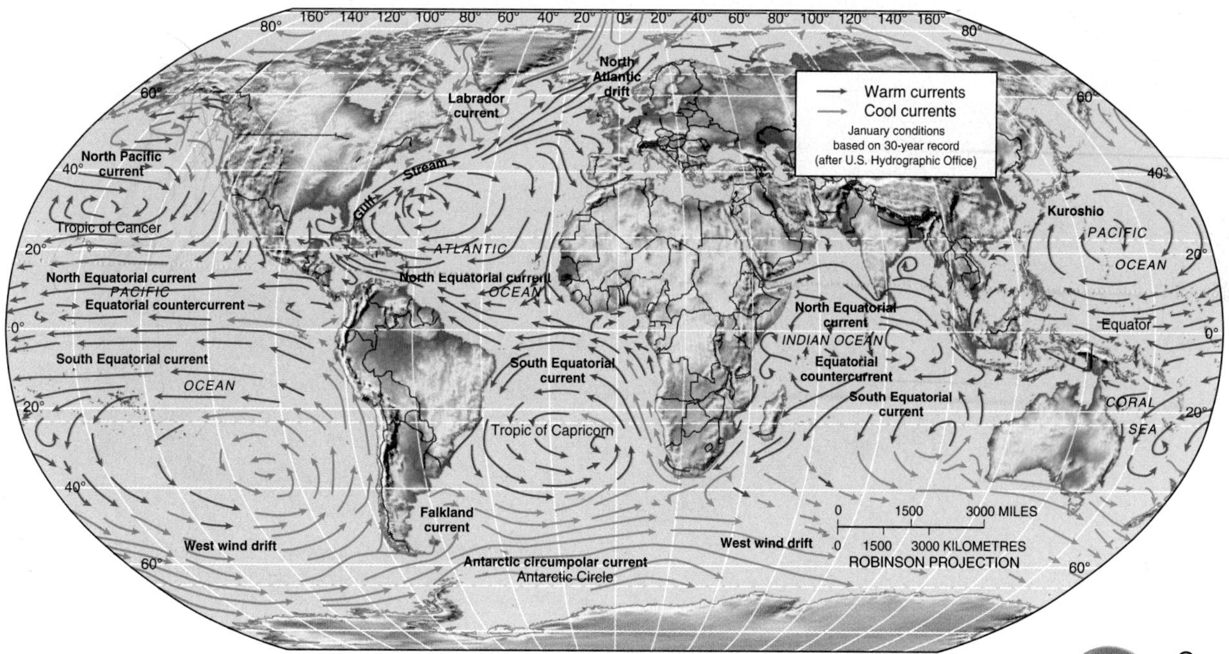

FIGURE 6.22 Major ocean currents.
[After the U. S. Navy Hydrographic Office.]

ANIMATION Ocean Circulation

through time, the Coriolis force deflects them. However, their pattern of deflection is not as tightly circular as that of the atmosphere. Compare this ocean-current map with the map showing Earth's pressure systems (see Figure 6.11) and you can see that ocean currents are driven by the circulation around subtropical high-pressure cells in both hemispheres. These circulation systems are known as *gyres* and generally appear to be offset toward the western side of each ocean basin. (Remember, in the Northern Hemisphere, winds and ocean currents move *clockwise* about high-pressure cells—note the currents in the North Pacific and North Atlantic on the map. In the Southern Hemisphere, circulation is *counterclockwise* around high-pressure cells, evident on the map.)

In sailing days the Spanish galleons (the *Manila Galleons*) would leave San Blas and Acapulco, Mexico (16.5° N), and sail southwest, catching the northeast trade winds across the Pacific to the Philippines and Manila (14° N). Goods would be traded and new commodities obtained, and the ships would move northward to catch the westerlies in the midlatitudes to be blown across the ocean to the shores of present-day Alaska or British Columbia down to Northern California. The galleons would sail south, fighting the rain, frequent fog, and the right-hand Coriolis deflection pushing them away from the coast. The journey would end back in Mexico with cargo from the Orient. Thus the history of the *Manila Galleons* is a lesson in oceanic currents around the Pacific gyre.

Equatorial Currents In Figure 6.22, you can see that trade winds drive the ocean surface waters westward in a concentrated channel along the equator. These currents, called *equatorial currents*, are kept near the equator by the Coriolis force, which diminishes to zero at the equator. As these surface currents approach the western margins of the oceans, the water actually piles up against the eastern shores of the continents. The average height of this pileup is 15 cm (6 in.). This phenomenon is the **western intensification**.

The piled-up ocean water then goes where it can, spilling northward and southward in strong currents, flowing in tight channels along the eastern shorelines. In the Northern Hemisphere, the *Gulf Stream* and the *Kuroshio* (current east of Japan) move forcefully northward as a result of western intensification. Their speed and depth are increased by the constriction of the area they occupy. The warm, deep, clear water of the ribbonlike Gulf Stream (Figure 5.10) usually is 50–80 km (30–50 mi) wide and 1.5–2.0 km (0.9–1.2 mi) deep, moving at 3–10 kmph (1.8–6.2 mph). In 24 hours, ocean water can move 70–240 km (40–150 mi) in the Gulf Stream.

Deep Currents

Where surface water is swept away from a coast, either by surface divergence (induced by the Coriolis force) or by offshore winds, an **upwelling current** occurs. This cool water generally is nutrient-rich and rises from great depths to replace the vacating water. Such cold upwelling currents exist off the Pacific coasts of North and South America and the subtropical and midlatitude west coast of Africa. These areas are some of Earth's prime fishing regions.

In other regions where there is an accumulation of water—such as the western end of an equatorial current, or the Labrador Sea, or along the margins of Antarctica—the excess water gravitates downward in a **downwelling current**. These currents flow along the ocean floor and travel the full extent of the ocean basins, carrying heat energy and salinity.

To picture such a deep current, imagine a continuous channel of water beginning with cold water downwelling in the North Atlantic, flowing deep, and upwelling in the

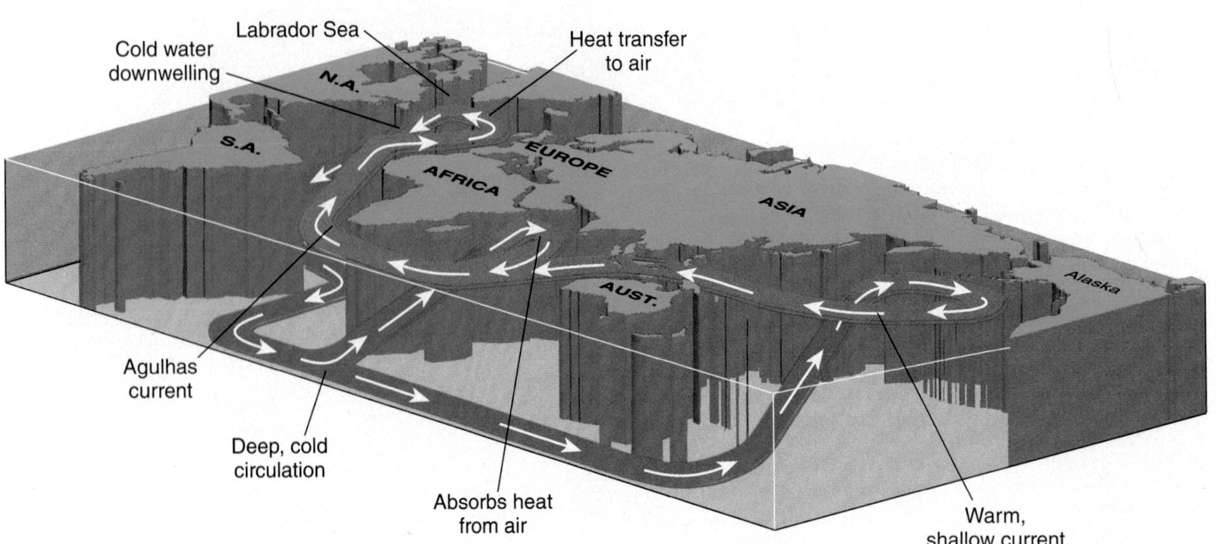

FIGURE 6.23 Deep-ocean circulation.
Scientists are deciphering centuries-long deep circulation in the oceans. This global circulation mimics a vast conveyor belt of water, drawing heat energy from some regions and transporting it for release in others.

Ocean Circulation

Indian Ocean and North Pacific (Figure 6.23). Here it warms and then is carried in surface currents back to the North Atlantic. A complete circuit of the current may require 1000 years from downwelling in the Labrador Sea off Greenland to its reemergence in the southern Indian Ocean and return. Even deeper Antarctic bottom water flows northward in the Atlantic Basin beneath these currents. These current systems appear to play a profound role in global climate; in turn, global warming has the potential to disrupt the downwelling in the North Atlantic.

News Report 6.3

A Message in a Bottle and Rubber Duckies

To give you an idea of the dynamic circulation of the ocean, consider the following examples. A 9-year-old child at Dana Point, California (33.5° N), a small seaside community south of Los Angeles, placed a letter in a glass juice bottle in July 1992 and tossed it into the waves. Thoughts of distant lands and fabled characters filled the child's imagination as the bottle disappeared. The vast circulation around the Pacific high, clockwise-circulating gyre, now took command (Figure 1).

Three years passed before ocean currents carried the message in a bottle to the coral reefs and white sands of Mogmog, a small island in Micronesia (7° N). A 7-year-old child there had found a pen pal from afar and immediately sent a photo and card to the sender of the message. Imagine the journey of that note from California—travelling through storms and calms, clear moonlit nights and typhoons, as it floated on ancient currents as the galleons once had.

In January 1994, a large container ship from Hong Kong loaded with toys and other goods was ravaged by a powerful storm. One of the containers on board split apart in the wind off the coast of Japan, dumping nearly 30,000 rubber ducks, turtles, and frogs into the North Pacific. Westerly winds and the North Pacific current swept this floating cargo across the ocean to the coast of Alaska, Canada, Oregon, and California. Other toys, still adrift, went through the Bering Sea and into the Arctic Ocean (this route is indicated by the dashed line in Figure 1). These will eventually end up in the Atlantic Ocean as they drift around the Arctic Ocean frozen into pack ice.

The high-floating message bottle and rubber ducks offered a much better opportunity to study winds than did an earlier spill of 60,000 athletic shoes near Japan. The low-floating shoes tracked across the Pacific Ocean until they landed in the Pacific Northwest. By the way, the shoes that did not make landfall headed (or footed) back around the Pacific gyre into the tropics and westward, back toward Japan! Scientists are using incidents such as these to learn more about wind systems and ocean currents.

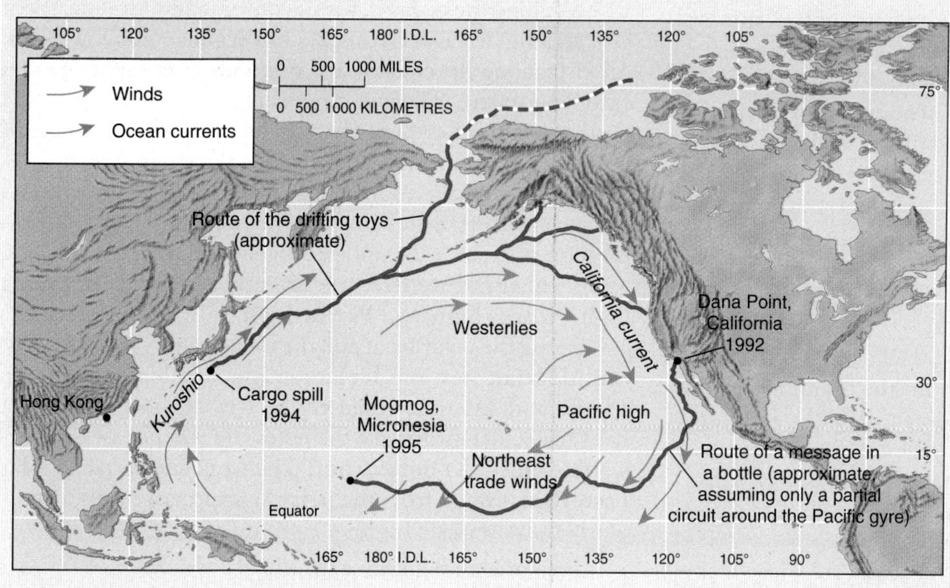

FIGURE 1 Pacific Ocean currents transport human artifacts.
The approximate route of a message in a bottle from Dana Point, California, to Mogmog, Micronesia, assumes a partial circuit around the Pacific gyre. Given the 3-year travel time, we do not know if the message circumnavigated the Pacific Ocean more than once. The rubber duckies voyaged eastward across the Pacific and beyond.

Summary and Review—Atmospheric and Oceanic Circulations

Define the concept of air pressure and *describe* instruments used to measure air pressure.

The weight (created by motion, size, and number of molecules) of the atmosphere is *air pressure*, which exerts an average force of approximately 1 kg/cm^2 (14.7 $lb/in.^2$). A **mercury barometer** measures air pressure at the surface (mercury in a tube—closed at one end and open at the other, with the open end placed in a vessel of mercury—that changes level in response to pressure changes); so does an **aneroid barometer** (a closed cell, partially evacuated of air, that detects changes in pressure).

mercury barometer (p. 148)
aneroid barometer (p. 148)

1. How does air exert pressure? Describe the basic instrument used to measure air pressure. Compare the operation of two different types of instruments discussed.
2. What is normal sea-level pressure in millimetres? Millibars? Inches? Kilopascals?

Define wind and *describe* how wind is measured, how wind direction is determined, and how winds are named.

Volcanic eruptions such as those of Tambora in 1815 and Mount Pinatubo in 1991 dramatically demonstrate the power of global winds to disperse aerosols and pollution worldwide in a matter of weeks. Atmospheric circulation facilitates important transfers of energy and mass on Earth, thus maintaining Earth's natural balances. Earth's atmospheric and oceanic circulations represent a vast heat engine powered by the Sun.

Wind is the horizontal movement of air across Earth's surface. Its speed is measured with an **anemometer** (a device with cups that are pushed by the wind) and its direction with a **wind vane** (a flat blade or surface that is directed by the wind). A descriptive scale useful in visually estimating wind speed is the traditional *Beaufort wind scale*.

wind (p. 149)
anemometer (p. 149)
wind vane (p. 149)

3. What is a possible explanation for the beautiful sunrises and sunsets during the summer of 1992 in North America? Relate your answer to global circulation.
4. Explain this statement: "The atmosphere socializes humanity, making all the world a spatially linked society." Illustrate your answer with some examples.
5. Define wind. How is it measured? How is its direction determined?
6. Distinguish among primary, secondary, and tertiary general classifications of global atmospheric circulation.
7. What is the purpose of the Beaufort wind scale? Characterize winds given Beaufort numbers of 4, 8, and 12, giving effects over both water and land.

Explain the four driving forces within the atmosphere—gravity, pressure gradient force, Coriolis force, and friction force—and *describe* the primary high- and low-pressure areas and principal winds.

Earth's gravitational force on the atmosphere operates uniformly worldwide. Winds are driven by the **pressure gradient force** (air moves from areas of high pressure to areas of low pressure), deflected by the **Coriolis force** (an apparent deflection in the path of winds or ocean currents caused by the rotation of Earth; deflecting objects to the right in the Northern Hemisphere and to the left in the Southern Hemisphere), and dragged by the **friction force** (Earth's varied surfaces exert a drag on wind movements in opposition to the pressure gradient). Maps portray air pressure patterns using the **isobar**—an isoline that connects points of equal pressure. A combination of the pressure gradient and Coriolis forces alone produces **geostrophic winds**, which move parallel to isobars, characteristic of winds above the surface frictional layer.

Winds descend and diverge, spiralling outward to form an **anticyclone** (clockwise in the Northern Hemisphere), and they converge and ascend, spiralling upward to form a **cyclone** (counterclockwise in the Northern Hemisphere). The pattern of high and low pressures on Earth in generalized belts in each hemisphere produces the distribution of specific wind systems. These primary pressure regions are the **equatorial low-pressure trough**, the weak **polar high-pressure cells** (at both the North and South Poles), and the **subtropical high-pressure cells** and **subpolar low-pressure cells**.

All along the equator, winds converge into the equatorial low, creating the **intertropical convergence zone (ITCZ)**. Air rises along the equator and descends in the subtropics in each hemisphere. The winds returning to the ITCZ from the northeast in the Northern Hemisphere and from the southeast in the Southern Hemisphere produce the **trade winds**.

Winds flowing out of the subtropics to higher latitudes produce the **westerlies** in either hemisphere. The subtropical high-pressure cells on Earth, generally between 20° and 35° in either hemisphere, are variously named the **Bermuda high**, **Azores high**, and **Pacific high**.

Along the polar front and the series of low-pressure cells, the **Aleutian low** and **Icelandic low** dominate the North Pacific and Atlantic, respectively. This region of contrast between colder air toward the poles and warmer air equatorward is called the **polar front**. The weak and variable **polar easterlies** diverge from the polar high-pressure cells, particularly the **Antarctic high**.

pressure gradient force (p. 150)
Coriolis force (p. 150)
friction force (p. 152)
isobar (p. 152)
geostrophic winds (p. 156)
anticyclone (p. 157)
cyclone (p. 157)
equatorial low-pressure trough (p. 157)

polar high-pressure cells (p. 157)
subtropical high-pressure cells (p. 157)
subpolar low-pressure cells (p. 157)
intertropical convergence zone (ITCZ) (p. 159)
trade winds (p. 159)
westerlies (p. 161)
Bermuda high (p. 161)
Azores high (p. 161)
Pacific high (p. 161)
Aleutian low (p. 161)
Icelandic low (p. 161)
polar front (p. 162)
polar easterlies (p. 162)
Antarctic high (p. 162)

8. What does an isobaric map of surface air pressure portray? Contrast pressures over North America for January and July.
9. Describe the effect of the Coriolis force. Explain how it apparently deflects atmospheric and oceanic circulations.
10. What are geostrophic winds, and where are they encountered in the atmosphere?
11. Describe the horizontal and vertical air motions in a high-pressure anticyclone and in a low-pressure cyclone.
12. Construct a simple diagram of Earth's general circulation, including the four principal pressure belts or zones and the three principal wind systems.
13. How is the intertropical convergence zone (ITCZ) related to the equatorial low-pressure trough? How might it appear on a satellite image?
14. Characterize the belt of subtropical high pressure on Earth: Name the specific cells. Describe the generation of westerlies and trade winds. Discuss sailing conditions.
15. What is the relation among the Aleutian low, the Icelandic low, and migratory low-pressure cyclonic storms in North America? In Europe?

Describe **upper-air circulation and its support role for surface systems and *define* the jet streams.**

Air pressure in the middle and upper troposphere is described using a **constant isobaric surface**, or surface along which the same pressure, such as 500 mb, is recorded regardless of altitude. The height of this surface above the ground is described in ridges and troughs that support the development of and help sustain surface pressure systems; lows are sustained by divergence aloft, and highs are sustained by convergence aloft.

Vast, flowing longwave undulations in these upper-air westerlies form wave motions called **Rossby waves**. Prominent streams of high-speed westerly winds in the upper-level troposphere are called the **jet streams**. Depending on their latitudinal position in either hemisphere, they are termed the *polar jet stream* or the *subtropical jet stream*.

constant isobaric surface (p. 162)
Rossby waves (p. 164)
jet streams (p. 164)

16. What is the relation between wind speed and the spacing of isobars?
17. How is the constant isobaric surface (ridges and troughs) related to surface pressure systems? To divergence aloft and surface lows? To convergence aloft and surface highs?
18. Relate the jet-stream phenomenon to general upper-air circulation. How is the presence of this circulation related to airline schedules from Halifax to Vancouver and the return trip to Halifax?

Explain **several types of local winds: land–sea breezes, mountain–valley breezes, katabatic winds, and the regional monsoons.**

Different heating characteristics of land and water surfaces create **land–sea breezes. Mountain–valley breezes** are caused by temperature differences during the day and evening between valleys and mountain summits. **Katabatic winds**, or gravity drainage winds, are of larger regional scale and are usually stronger than mountain–valley breezes, under certain conditions. An elevated plateau or highland is essential, where layers of air at the surface cool, become denser, and flow downslope.

Intense, seasonally shifting wind systems occur in the tropics over Southeast Asia, Indonesia, India, northern Australia, equatorial Africa, and southern Arizona. These winds involve an annual cycle of returning precipitation with the summer Sun and are named after the Arabic word for season, *mausim*, or **monsoon**. The monsoons of southern and eastern Asia are driven by the location and size of the Asian landmass and its proximity to the Indian Ocean.

land–sea breezes (p. 168)
mountain–valley breezes (p. 169)
katabatic winds (p. 169)
monsoon (p. 172)

19. People living along coastlines generally experience variations in winds from day to night. Explain the factors that produce these changing wind patterns.
20. The arrangement of mountains and nearby valleys produces local wind patterns. Explain the day and night winds that might develop.
21. Describe the seasonal pressure patterns that produce the Asian monsoonal wind and precipitation patterns. Contrast January and July conditions.

Discern **the basic pattern of Earth's major surface and deep ocean currents.**

Ocean currents are primarily caused by the frictional drag of wind and occur worldwide at varying intensities, temperatures, and speeds, both along the surface and at great depths in the oceanic basins. The circulation around subtropical high-pressure cells in both hemispheres is notable on the ocean circulation map—these *gyres* are usually offset toward the western side of each ocean basin.

The trade winds converge along the ITCZ and push enormous quantities of water in a process known as the **western intensification**. Where surface water is swept away from a coast, either by surface divergence (induced by the Coriolis force) or by offshore winds, an **upwelling current** occurs. This cool water generally is nutrient-rich and rises from great depths to replace the vacating water. In other portions of the sea where there is an accumulation of water, the excess water gravitates downward in a **downwelling current**. These currents generate important mixing currents that flow along the ocean floor and travel the full extent of the ocean basins, carrying heat energy and salinity.

western intensification (p. 174)
upwelling current (p. 174)
downwelling current (p. 174)

22. What is the relationship between global atmospheric circulation and ocean currents? Relate oceanic gyres to patterns of subtropical high pressure.
23. Define the western intensification. How is it related to the Gulf Stream and Kuroshio currents?
24. Where on Earth are upwelling currents experienced? What is the nature of these currents?
25. What is meant by deep-ocean circulation? At what rates do these currents flow? How might this circulation be related to the Gulf Stream in the western Atlantic Ocean?

Critical Thinking

A. Using Table 6.1 and Figure 6.5, on a day with wind, estimate wind speed and wind direction at least twice during the day and record them in your notebook. If possible, check these against the reports from some local source of weather information. What changes do you notice over several days? How did these changes relate to the weather you experienced?

B. Visit the Canadian Wind Energy Association Web site, **http://www.canwea.ca/**, and the American Wind Energy Association Web site, **http://www.awea.org**. Sample the materials presented as you assess Focus Study 6.1 and the potential for wind-generated electricity. What are your thoughts concerning this resource—its potential, reasons for delays, and the competitive economics presented? What countries are leading the way? Propose a brief action plan for more rapid progress, or for more delays, depending on your point of view.

Career Link 6.1

Nathan Badger, GIS/GPS and Environmental Specialist

Nathan Badger describes himself as "a very visual person." Growing up in a family that travelled extensively and spent a lot of time outdoors, he was fascinated by new places and maps. It was in his final year in high school in Brantford, Ontario, that Nathan—inspired by a teacher with an infectious love for geography—decided to pursue geography at university.

In his first year at Wilfrid Laurier University in Waterloo, Ontario, Nathan learned how computers could be used in geographic analysis and became hooked on GIS (geographic information systems). He combined his two majors of geography and general biology while writing his Honours thesis. The project was a study on river water quality using GIS in the analysis of "spatial and temporal phosphorus trends."

Nathan earned a Master's Degree after continuing with an environmental studies program jointly offered by Wilfrid Laurier and the University of Waterloo. His thesis was titled "Shoreline bluff failures: A GIS assessment of susceptibility and risk for Lake Erie's north central shore."

Nathan is currently a GIS/GPS and environmental specialist with Superior Wind Energy Inc. (SWEI). "Most of my work focuses on GIS, GPS, geospatial database development, and use of proprietary wind modelling software. It includes a mix of fieldwork and in-office computer time. I am responsible for building, managing, and improving SWEI's geospatial technology and data related to research and development for wind farms across Canada." SWEI is currently developing a 100-megawatt wind farm in Prince Township near Sault Ste. Marie, Ontario. When completed, it will be Ontario's largest wind farm.

Nathan's work has specific applications for wind farming, like "spatial analysis, which involves the layout of wind turbines based on a number of factors such as wind direction, elevation, obstructions, proximity to residential areas, environmental issues,

FIGURE 1 Nathan Badger, GIS/GPS and environmental specialist. Nathan's job takes him out in the field to collect information on wind energy, and back to the computer to analyze the data using various wind-modelling software. His work with geospatial technology and data relates to the development of wind farms across Canada. [Photo by Nathan Badger.]

decibel level of turbines, and 'flicker' or 'shadow' of turbine blades." His job also requires "plenty of data collection, research, organization, and analysis. On the ground this can mean GPS fieldwork, site audits of leased lands, and identification of environmental entities that could affect a wind farm. Back in the office it means, among many other things, developing databases and creating maps."

Before starting his current job in the renewable energy and environmental field, Nathan applied GIS techniques to utilities, real estate, and remote sensing. Nathan also started his own consulting business. His work took him from Ontario to California, Colorado, and Alberta before he returned to Ontario, where SWEI operates out of Stoney Creek, near Hamilton on Lake Ontario. Nathan has been involved in analyzing a global fibre optic network, analyzing special data for the multi-family housing industry, and acquiring, processing, and distributing high-resolution radar images of the Earth's surface taken from a fleet of Lear jets.

In his private life, Nathan is involved with his church and youth groups. He loves to travel and has been to South America, Europe, and Australia. Even off the job he is "intensely interested in maps and remotely sensed images. The book *Earth from Above* (by Yann Arthus-Bertrand) is one of my favourites," he says.

Nathan likes the variety of his work—the combination of environmental issues with high technology. "GIS is very multidisciplinary, so it is a constant challenge to work with. I enjoy being challenged and having my brain stimulated. It is hard not to be stimulated in geography, GIS, and environmental studies. Besides," he says, "I love computers, high technology, and the new geospatial tools. I get to play every day on cool software, developing things (software and databases, maps, reports), and be at the front of the technology wave. It's a lot of fun!"

Nathan is excited by his latest career move. "Wind energy is fascinating. I remember hearing about it in public school as this Star Trekkie thing of the future—a pipe dream. And now I'm working with it! I'm also helping to develop and forward renewable energy in Ontario and Canada," he goes on to say. "I'm proud and excited about that. The appearance of wind turbines on the landscape will force people to think about the way they use energy and responsible ways of producing it."

Nathan sees part of his role as an educator. "I am helping to promote the importance of place and geography both in our company and in our province. Geography is undervalued as a discipline, and GIS has been slow to make its way into the classroom—yet it is becoming an integral part of our lives, from emergency response to wind energy, from MapQuest to GPS in cars."

"The inner workings of GIS can be complex," Nathan explains. "Without formal training and hands-on experience you can become lost. The technology requires people to change their approach to work—they need to think spatially and think about organizing data and research in a new way. Part of my role as a GIS person is to understand and keep up with the rapidly growing technology, but also to educate those around me as to how it works and how it can benefit their own work."

Nathan Badger has one word of advice to future geographers: *computers*. "If you are going into geography," he advises, "be sure to get computer experience. It is now an essential tool in all aspects of this field—from GIS and maps to document writing to data analysis."

PART TWO

The Water, Weather, and Climate Systems

Ice, water, and water vapour in the Arctic region comprise features of Earth's water, weather, and climate system. These huge icebergs are about 86% more massive beneath the ocean's surface than what you see. The mirrored reflections with cloud-diffused evening light create a scene of great beauty. The polar regions are the scientific focus of the International Polar Year 2007–2008 that will involve topics from PART TWO. [Photo by Bobbé Christopherson.]

Earth is the water planet. Surface water in such quantity is unique in the solar system. Chapter 7 explains why water covers more than two-thirds of the globe and describes the remarkable qualities and properties it possesses. We see the daily dynamics of the atmosphere—the powerful interaction of moisture and energy and the resulting stability and instability, and the variety of cloud forms—as a preamble to understanding weather.

Chapter 8 examines weather and its causes. Topics include the interaction of air masses, understanding the daily weather map, and the violent phenomena of thunderstorms, tornadoes, and hurricanes and the recent trends for each of these.

Chapter 9 explains water circulation on and over Earth in the hydrologic cycle. We examine the water-budget concept, which is useful in understanding soil-moisture and water-resource relationships at all levels—global, regional, and local. In Chapter 10, we see the spatial implications over time of the energy–atmosphere and water–weather systems and the generation of Earth's climatic patterns. In this way Chapter 10 interconnects all the system elements from Chapters 2 through 9. Part 2 closes with a discussion of global climate change and future climate trends.

reverses and a gram of water freezes. The *latent heat of freezing* or the *latent heat of melting* involves 80 calories.

To raise the temperature of 1 g of water at 0°C (32°F) to boiling at 100°C (212°F), we must add 100 calories, gaining an increase of 1 C° (1.8 F°) for each calorie added.

Water Vapour, the Gas Phase Water vapour is an invisible and compressible gas in which each molecule moves independently of the others (Figure 7.4a). The phase change from liquid to vapour at boiling temperature, under normal sea-level pressure, requires the addition of a much greater amount of heat energy than the phase change from solid to liquid: each gram of water changed to water vapour requires 540 calories (Figure 7.6). Those calories are the **latent heat of vaporization**. When water vapour condenses to a liquid, each gram gives up its hidden 540 calories as the **latent heat of condensation**. Perhaps you have felt the liberation of the latent heat of condensation on your skin from steam, as when you drain steamed vegetables or pasta or fill a hot teakettle.

In summary, taking 1 g of ice at 0°C and changing its phase to water, then to water vapour at 100°C—from a solid to a liquid to a gas—*absorbs* 720 calories (80 cal + 100 cal + 540 cal). Reversing the process, or changing the phase of 1 g of water vapour at 100°C to water, then to ice at 0°C, *liberates* 720 calories into the surrounding environment.

Heat Properties of Water in Nature

In a lake or stream or in soil water, at 20°C (68°F), every gram of water that breaks away from the surface through evaporation must absorb from the environment approximately 585 calories as the *latent heat of evaporation* (see the natural scene in Figure 7.6). This is slightly more energy than would be required if the water were at a higher temperature such as boiling (540 cal). You can feel this absorption of latent heat as evaporative cooling on your skin when it is wet. This latent heat exchange is the dominant cooling process in Earth's energy budget.

The process reverses when air cools and water vapour condenses back into the liquid state, forming moisture droplets and thus liberating 585 calories for every gram of water as the *latent heat of condensation*. When you realize that a small, puffy, fair-weather cumulus cloud holds 450–900 metric tons (500–1000 tons) of moisture droplets, think of the tremendous latent heat released when water vapour condensed to droplets! Government meteorologists estimated that the moisture in Hurricane Andrew (1992) weighed nearly 30 trillion metric tons at its maximum power and mass. With 585 calories released for every gram as the latent heat of condensation, you can see that a weather event such as a hurricane involves a staggering amount of energy.

The **latent heat of sublimation** absorbs 680 calories as a gram of ice transforms into vapour. Water vapour freezing directly to ice releases a comparable amount of energy.

Humidity

Humidity refers to water vapour in the air. The capacity of air to hold water vapour is primarily a function of temperature—the temperatures of both the air and the water vapour, which are usually the same. Warmer air has a greater capacity for holding water vapour than cooler air.

We are all aware of humidity in the air, for its relationship to air temperature determines our sense of comfort. North Americans spend billions of dollars a year to adjust humidity, either with air conditioning (extracting water vapour and cooling) or with air humidifying (adding water vapour). We discussed the relation between humidity and temperature and the Humidex in Chapter 5. To determine the energy available for powering weather, one has to know the water-vapour *content* of air and relate this in a ratio to the air's *saturation equilibrium* at a given temperature.

Relative Humidity

After air temperature and barometric pressure, the most common piece of information in local weather broadcasts is relative humidity. **Relative humidity** is a ratio (expressed as a percentage) of the amount of water vapour that is *actually* in the air (content) compared to the maximum water vapour possible in the air at a given temperature. Warmer air increases the evaporation rate from water surfaces, whereas cooler air tends to increase the condensation rate of water vapour to water surfaces. Because there is a maximum amount of water vapour that can exist in a volume of air at a given temperature, the rates of evaporation and condensation can reach equilibrium at some point; the air is then saturated with humidity. Relative humidity tells us how near the air is to saturation and is an expression of an ongoing process of water molecules moving between air and moist surfaces, for condensation and evaporation operate continuously.

If air is relatively dry, the relative humidity percentage is low; if the air is relatively moist, the relative humidity percentage is higher. If the air is saturated with maximum water vapour for its temperature, the relative humidity percentage is 100% (Figure 7.7). Figure 7.7 shows that at 5 P.M. the evaporation rate exceeds condensation at these higher temperatures. At 11 A.M. the evaporation rate still exceeds condensation, though not by as much, since daytime temperatures at 5 P.M. are not as high. At 5 A.M., in the cooler morning air, saturation equilibrium exists and any further cooling or addition of water vapour will produce net condensation. The formula to calculate the relative humidity ratio and express it as a percentage is simply:

$$\text{Relative humidity} = \frac{\text{actual water vapour content of the air}}{\text{maximum water vapour possible in the air at that temperature}} \times 100$$

Relative humidity varies because of evaporation, condensation, or temperature changes. All three affect both the moisture content (the numerator) and the water vapour possible (the denominator) of the air. Relative humidity is an expression of an ongoing process between air and moist surfaces, for condensation and evaporation operate continuously—water molecules move back and forth between the air and bodies of water or ice.

Saturation As stated, air is **saturated** when the rate of evaporation and the rate of condensation reach equilibrium—that is, 100% relative humidity. In saturated air, the net transfer of water molecules between a moist surface and the air reaches equilibrium. Saturation indicates that any further addition of water vapour or any decrease in temperature that reduces the evaporation rate will result in active condensation (clouds, fog, or precipitation). Therefore, relative humidity indicates the nearness of air to a saturated condition and when active condensation will begin.

The temperature at which a given mass of air becomes saturated is termed the **dew-point temperature**. In other words, *air is saturated when the dew-point temperature and the air temperature are the same*. A cold drink in a glass provides a common example of these conditions. The water droplets that form on the outside of the glass condense from the air because the air layer next to the glass is chilled to below its dew-point temperature and thus becomes saturated (Figure 7.8). Figure 7.8 shows two additional examples of saturated air and active condensation—above a rock surface and in a fog formation overlying a cool ocean surface.

Satellites now routinely sense water vapour content of the lower atmosphere. Water vapour absorbs infrared wavelengths, making it possible to distinguish areas of relatively high water-vapour content from areas of low water-vapour content, using infrared sensors. Figure 7.9 includes images of Hurricane Michelle and the Western Hemisphere showing water-vapour content recorded by sensors of the "water-vapour channel." This knowledge is important to forecasting because it shows the moisture available to weather systems and therefore the energy available (latent heat) and precipitation potential of those systems.

Daily and Seasonal Relative Humidity Patterns An inverse relation occurs during a typical day between air temperature and relative humidity—as temperature rises, relative humidity falls (Figure 7.10a). Relative humidity is highest at dawn, when air temperature is lowest. If you park outdoors, you know about the wetness of the dew that condenses on the car overnight. Relative humidity is lowest in the late afternoon, when higher air temperatures increase the capacity of the air to hold water vapour. The actual water-vapour content in the air may remain the same throughout the day, but because the temperature varies, relative humidity changes from morning to afternoon, as shown in Figure 7.7.

Weather records for Sacramento, California, show the seasonal variation in relative humidity by time of day, confirming the relationship of temperature and relative humidity (Figure 7.10b). January readings are higher than July readings because air temperatures are lower overall in winter. Similar relative humidity records at most weather stations demonstrate the same relation among season, temperature, and relative humidity. In your own experience, you probably have noticed this pattern—the morning dew on windows, cars, and lawns evaporates by late morning as the capacity of the air to hold water vapour increases with air temperature.

Expressions of Relative Humidity

There are several ways to express humidity and relative humidity. Each has its own utility and application. Two measures involve vapour pressure and specific humidity.

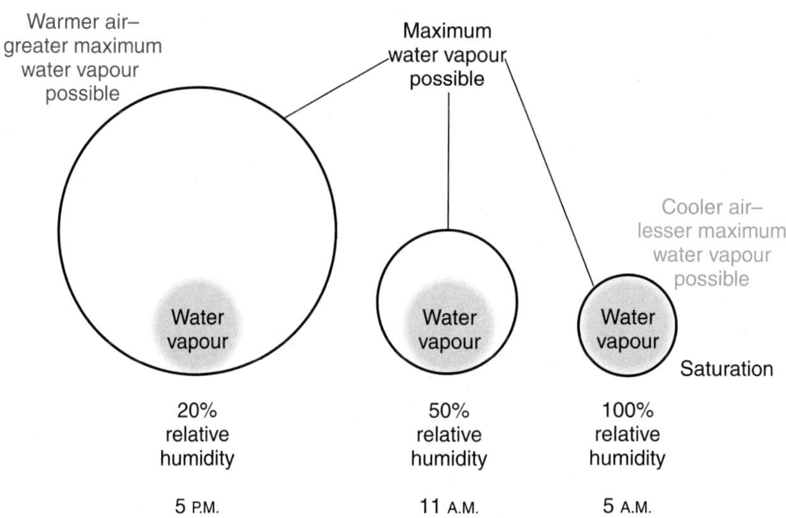

FIGURE 7.7 Water vapour, temperature, and relative humidity.
The maximum water vapour possible in warm air is greater (net evaporation) than that of cold air (net condensation), so relative humidity changes with temperature, even though in this example the actual water vapour in the air stays the same during the day.

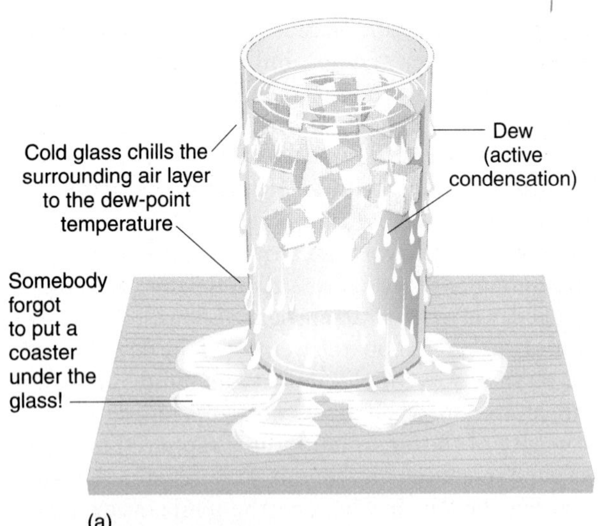

(a)

(b)

(c)

FIGURE 7.8 Dew-point temperature examples. (a) The low temperature of the glass chills the surrounding air layer to the dew-point temperature and saturation. Thus, water vapour condenses out of the air and onto the glass as dew. (b) Cold air above the rain-soaked rocks is at the dew point and is saturated. Condensation of water shrouds the rock in a changing veil of clouds. (c) The cold ocean surface chills the moist air layer to the dew point and saturation. As water vapour condenses, a dense fog forms. In the evening when temperatures drop over coastal lands, fog forms there too, giving the appearance of moving inland. [Photos by Robert W. Christopherson.]

Vapour Pressure As free water molecules evaporate from surfaces into the atmosphere, they become water vapour. Now part of the air, water vapour molecules become a part of the air pressure measurement, for they exert a portion of the air pressure. The share of air pressure that is made up of water vapour molecules is **vapour pressure**. Millibars (mb) express vapour pressure, the same as air pressure.

Water-vapour molecules continue to evaporate from a moist surface, slowly diffusing into the air, until the increasing vapour pressure in the air causes some molecules to return to the surface. As explained earlier, *saturation* is reached when the movement of water molecules between surface and air is in equilibrium. The maximum capacity of the air at a given temperature is the *saturation vapour pressure* and indicates the maximum pressure that water vapour molecules can exert. Any temperature increase or decrease will change the saturation vapour pressure.

Figure 7.11 (p. 194) graphs the saturation vapour pressure at various air temperatures. The graph illustrates that, for every temperature increase of 10 C° (18 F°), the vapour pressure capacity of air nearly doubles. This relation explains why warm tropical air over the ocean can hold so much water vapour, thus providing great latent heat to power tropical storms. It also explains why cold air is "dry" and why cold air toward the poles does not produce a lot of precipitation (it holds too little water vapour).

As the graph shows, air at 20°C (68°F) has a saturation vapour pressure of 24 mb; that is, the air is saturated if the water-vapour portion of the air pressure is at 24 mb. Thus, if the water-vapour content actually present is exerting a vapour pressure of only 12 mb in 20°C air, the relative humidity is 50% (12 mb ÷ 24 mb = 0.50 × 100 = 50%). The inset in Figure 7.11 compares saturation vapour pressure over water and over ice surfaces at subfreezing temperatures. You can see that saturation vapour pressure is greater above a water surface than over an ice surface—that is, it takes more water-vapour molecules to saturate air above water than it does above ice. This fact is important to condensation processes and rain-droplet formation, both of which appear later in this chapter.

Specific Humidity A useful humidity measure is one that remains constant as temperature and pressure change. **Specific humidity** is the mass of water vapour (in grams) per mass of air (in kilograms) at any specified temperature. Because it is measured in mass, specific humidity is not

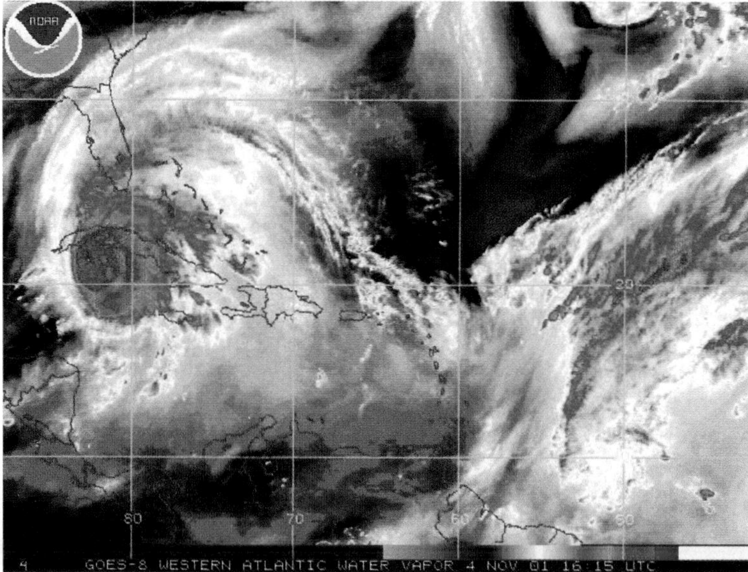

(a)

(b)

FIGURE 7.9 Images of water vapour in the atmosphere.
Water-vapour content of the atmosphere as disclosed in a *GOES-8* infrared image. (a) On the colour scale used for this image, the lighter-grey tones denote higher water-vapour content, and colour denotes high-altitude cloud tops that are cooler. Over the Gulf of Mexico and Caribbean, Hurricane Michelle and its strong vertical development is clearly visible heading toward western Cuba and near Florida, November 4, 2001. (b) Water-vapour content over the full Western Hemisphere; note subpolar low-pressure circulation. [*GOES* images courtesy of NESDIS Satellite Services Division NOAA.]

affected by changes in temperature or pressure, such as when an air parcel rises to higher elevations. Specific humidity stays constant despite volume changes.

The maximum mass of water vapour that a kilogram of air can hold at any specified temperature is termed the *maximum specific humidity*, plotted in Figure 7.12 (p. 195). The graph shows that a kilogram of air could hold a maximum specific humidity of 47 g of water vapour at 40°C (104°F), 15 g at 20°C (68°F), and about 4 g at 0°C (32°F). Therefore, if a kilogram of air at 40°C has a specific humidity of 12 g, its relative humidity is 25.5% (12 g ÷ 47 g = 0.255 × 100 = 25.5%). Specific humidity is useful in describing the moisture content of large air masses that are interacting in a weather system, and it is necessary information for weather forecasting.

Instruments for Measuring Humidity Various instruments measure relative humidity. The **hair hygrometer** uses the principle that human hair changes as much as 4% in length between 0 and 100% relative humidity. The instrument connects a standardized bundle of human hair through a mechanism to a gauge. As the hair absorbs or loses water in the air, it changes length, indicating relative humidity (Figure 7.13a, p. 195).

Another instrument used to measure relative humidity is a **sling psychrometer**. Figure 7.13b shows this device, which has two thermometers mounted side by side on a metal holder. One is the *dry-bulb thermometer*; it simply records the ambient (surrounding) air temperature. The other thermometer is the *wet-bulb thermometer*; it is set lower in the holder and a moistened cloth wick covers its

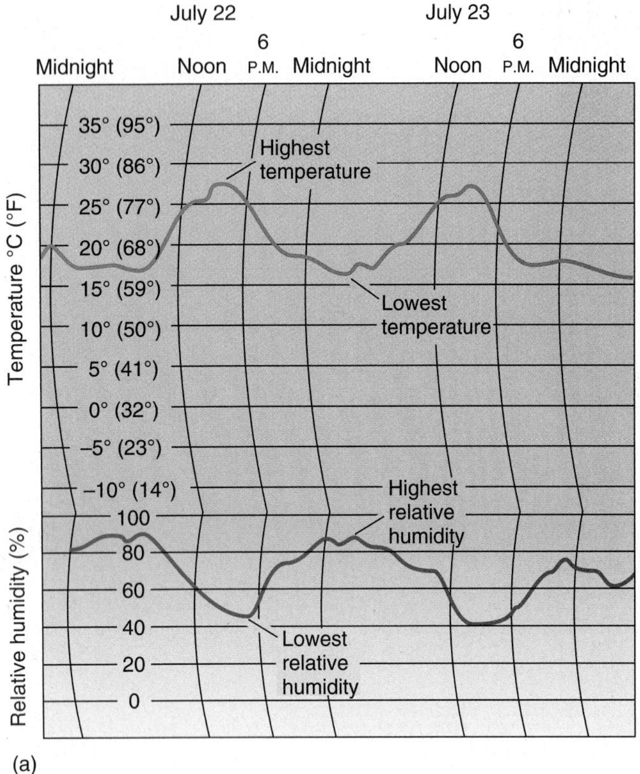

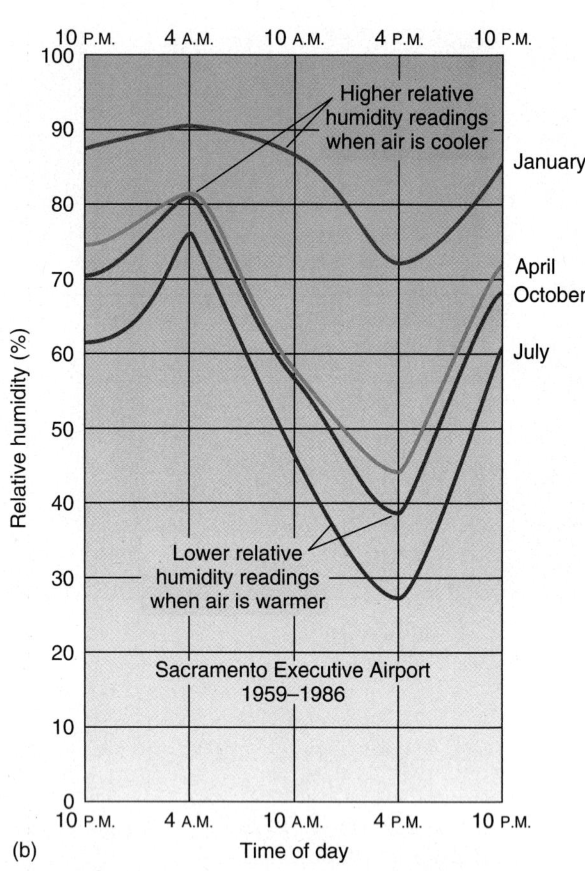

FIGURE 7.10 Daily and seasonal relative humidity patterns. (a) Typical daily variations in temperature and relative humidity; (b) seasonal variations in daily relative humidity.

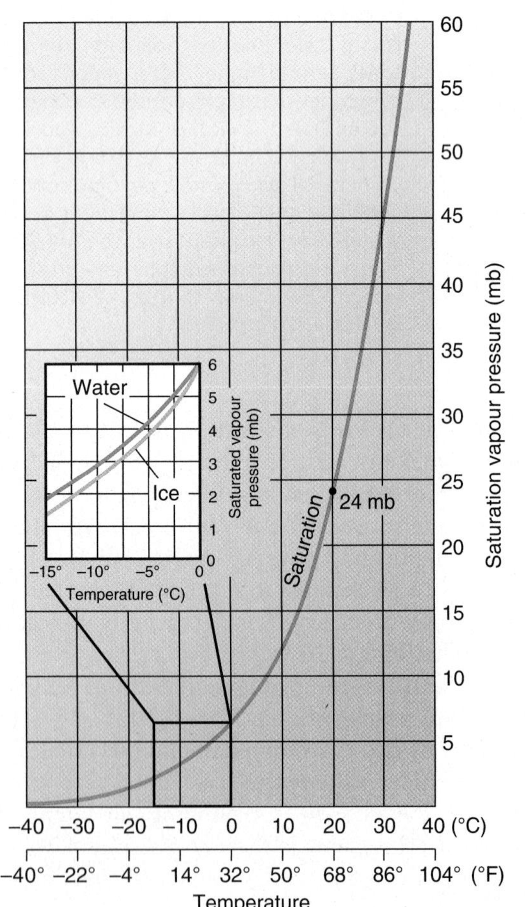

FIGURE 7.11 Saturation vapour pressure.
Saturation vapour pressure of air at various temperatures—the maximum possible water vapour as measured by the pressure it exerts. Inset compares saturation vapour pressures over water surfaces with those over surfaces at subfreezing temperatures. Note the 24 mb label for the text discussion.

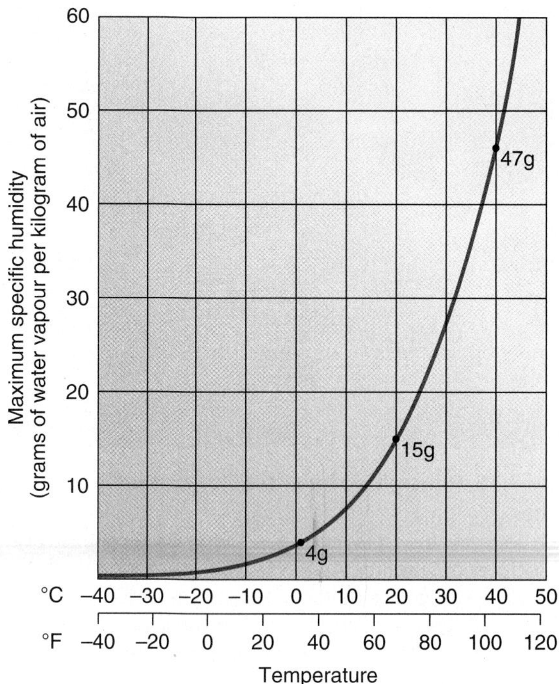

FIGURE 7.12 Maximum specific humidity.
Maximum specific humidity for a mass of air at various temperatures—the maximum possible water vapour in mass of water vapour per unit of mass of air (g/kg). Note the 47 g, 15 g, and 4 g labels for the text discussion.

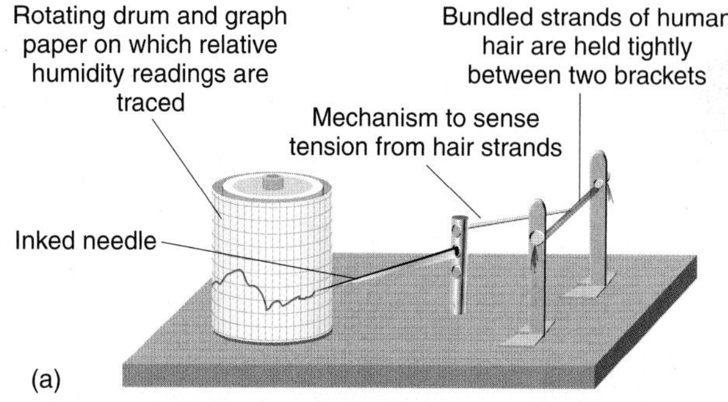

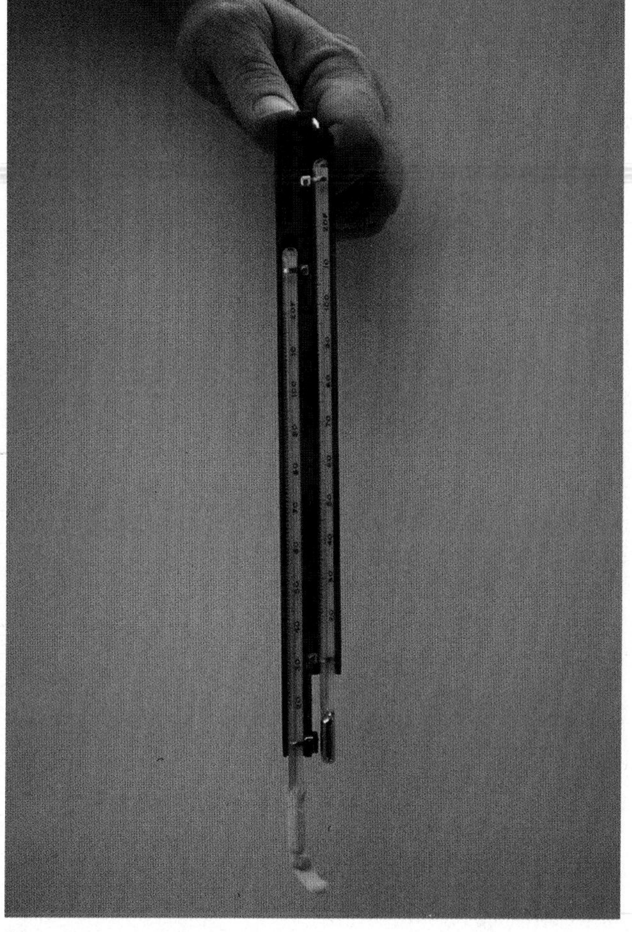

(b)

FIGURE 7.13 Instruments that measure relative humidity. (a) The principle of a hair hygrometer. (b) Sling psychrometer with wet and dry bulbs. [Photo by Bobbé Christopherson.]

bulb. The psychrometer is then spun ("slung") by its handle or placed where a fan forces air over the wet bulb.

The rate at which water evaporates from the wick depends on the relative saturation of the surrounding air. If the air is dry, water evaporates quickly, *absorbing the latent heat of evaporation from the wet-bulb thermometer and its wick*, cooling the thermometer and causing its temperature to drop (the *wet-bulb depression*). In conditions of high humidity, little water evaporates from the wick; in low humidity, more water evaporates. After being spun a minute or two, the temperature on each bulb is compared on a relative humidity (psychrometric) chart, from which relative humidity can be determined.

Now that you know something about atmospheric moisture, dew point, and relative humidity, let us examine the concept of stability in the atmosphere.

Atmospheric Stability

Meteorologists use the term *parcel* to describe a body of air that has specific temperature and humidity characteristics. Think of an air parcel as a volume of air, perhaps 300 m (1000 ft) in diameter, or more. Differences in temperature create changes in density within the parcel. Warm air produces a lower density in a given volume of air; cold air produces a higher density. Two opposing forces work on a parcel of air: an upward *buoyant force* and a downward *gravitational force*. A parcel of lower density rises (is more buoyant); a rising parcel expands as external pressure decreases. A parcel of higher density descends (is less buoyant); a falling parcel compresses as external pressure increases. Figure 7.14 shows air parcels and illustrates these relationships. (In Chapter 8, we discuss air masses, which are larger parcels and regional in extent.)

An indication of weather conditions is the relative stability of air parcels and air masses in the atmosphere. **Stability** refers to the tendency of an air parcel, with its water-vapour cargo, either to remain in place or to change vertical position by ascending (rising) or descending (falling). An air parcel is *stable* if it resists displacement

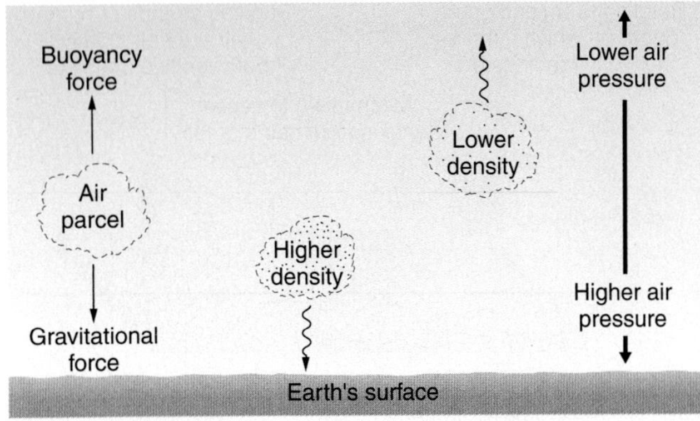

FIGURE 7.14 The forces acting on an air parcel.
Buoyancy and gravitational forces work on an air parcel. Different densities produce rising or falling parcels in response to imbalance in these forces.

ANIMATION Atmospheric Stability

FIGURE 7.15 Principles of air stability and balloon launches.
Hot-air balloons being launched in the Swiss Alps illustrate the principles of stability. As the temperature inside a balloon increases, the air in the balloon becomes less dense than the surrounding air and the buoyancy force causes the balloon to rise, acting like a warm air parcel. [Photo by Bap Vandystadt/Photo Researchers, Inc.]

upward or, when disturbed, it tends to return to its starting place. An air parcel is *unstable* if it continues to rise until it reaches an altitude where the surrounding air has a density (air temperature) similar to its own.

To visualize this, imagine a hot-air balloon launch. The air-filled balloon sits on the ground with the same air temperature inside as in the surrounding environment, like a stable air parcel. As the burner ignites, the balloon fills with hot (less-dense) air and rises buoyantly (Figure 7.15), like an unstable parcel of air. The concepts of stable and unstable air allow us to examine the specific temperature characteristics that produce these conditions.

Adiabatic Processes

Determining the degree of stability or instability requires measuring two temperatures: the temperature inside an air parcel and the temperature in the air surrounding the parcel. The contrast of these two temperatures determines stability. Such temperature measurements are made daily with instrument packages called *radiosondes* carried aloft by helium-filled balloons at thousands of weather stations.

The *normal lapse rate*, introduced in Chapter 3, is the average decrease in temperature with increasing altitude, a value of 6.4 C°/1000 m (3.5 F°/1000 ft). This rate of temperature change is for still, calm air, and it can vary greatly under different weather conditions. Consequently, the *environmental lapse rate* is the actual lapse rate at a particular place and time. It can vary by several degrees per thousand metres.

An ascending (rising) parcel of air cools by expansion, an expansion resulting from the reduced air pressure surround-

FIGURE 7.16 Vertically moving air experiences temperature changes.
(a) A rising air parcel cools by expansion. (b) A falling air parcel heats by compression.

ANIMATION Atmospheric Stability

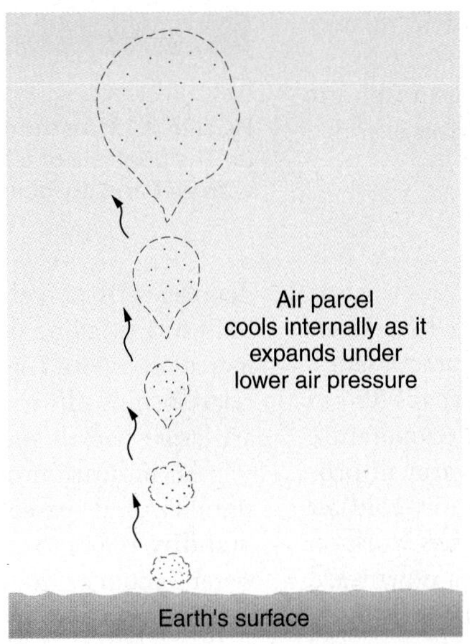

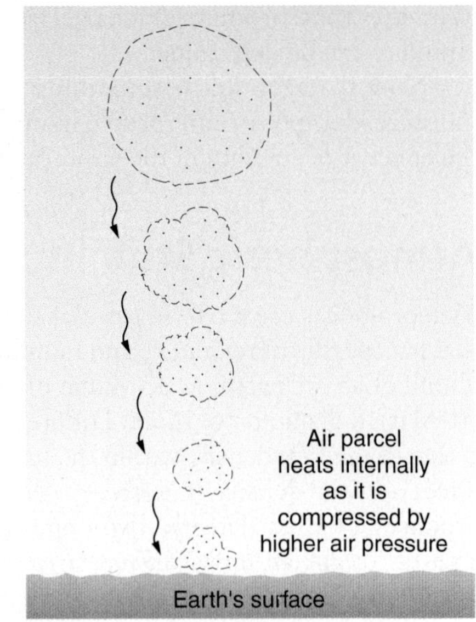

ing the parcel at higher altitudes (Figure 7.16a). A descending (falling) parcel heats by compression (Figure 7.16b). Physical laws that govern the behaviour of gases explain these temperature changes internal to a moving air parcel.

When pressure on a parcel decreases as it rises to higher altitudes, the parcel expands and its temperature and density decrease (the expansion process consumes sensible heat). Conversely, as an air parcel sinks toward the surface, air pressure increases, causing the parcel to compress. Compression increases the temperature and density in the parcel (compression produces sensible heat).

Temperature changes in both ascending and descending air occur *without any significant heat exchange between the surrounding environment and the vertically moving parcel of air*. The warming and cooling rates for a parcel of expanding or compressing air are termed **adiabatic**. (*Diabatic* means occurring with an exchange of heat; *adiabatic* means occurring *without a loss or gain* of heat energy to or from the environment.) There are two adiabatic rates, depending on moisture conditions in the vertically moving air parcel: a dry adiabatic rate (DAR) and a moist adiabatic rate (MAR).

Dry Adiabatic Rate The **dry adiabatic rate (DAR)** is the rate at which "dry" air cools by expansion (if ascending) or heats by compression (if descending). "Dry" refers to air that is less than saturated (relative humidity is less than 100%). The average DAR is 10 C°/1000 m (5.5 F°/1000 ft).

The rising parcel at the left in Figure 7.17a illustrates the principle. To see how a specific example of dry air behaves, consider an unsaturated parcel of air at the surface

(a) Air parcel *cools* adiabatically at the DAR

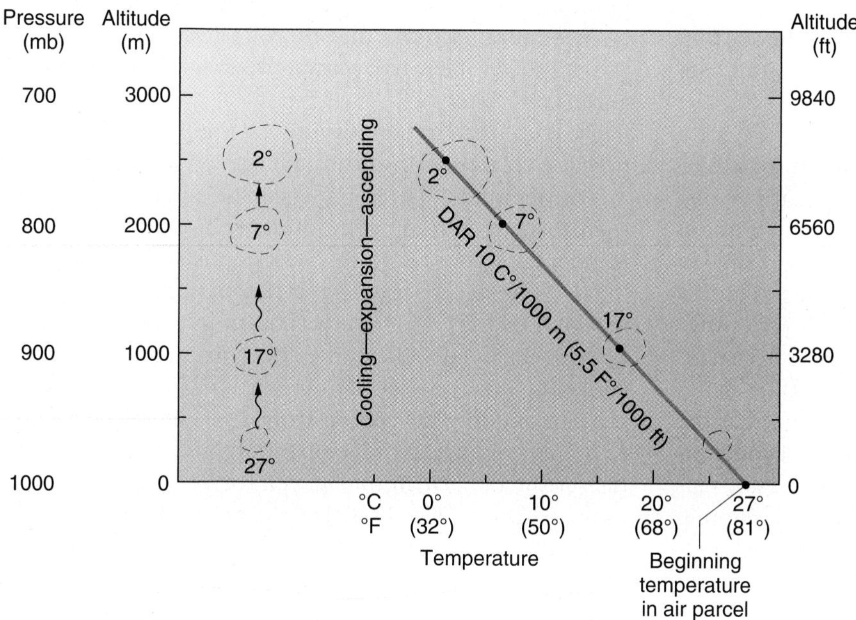

(b) Air parcel *heats* adiabatically at the DAR

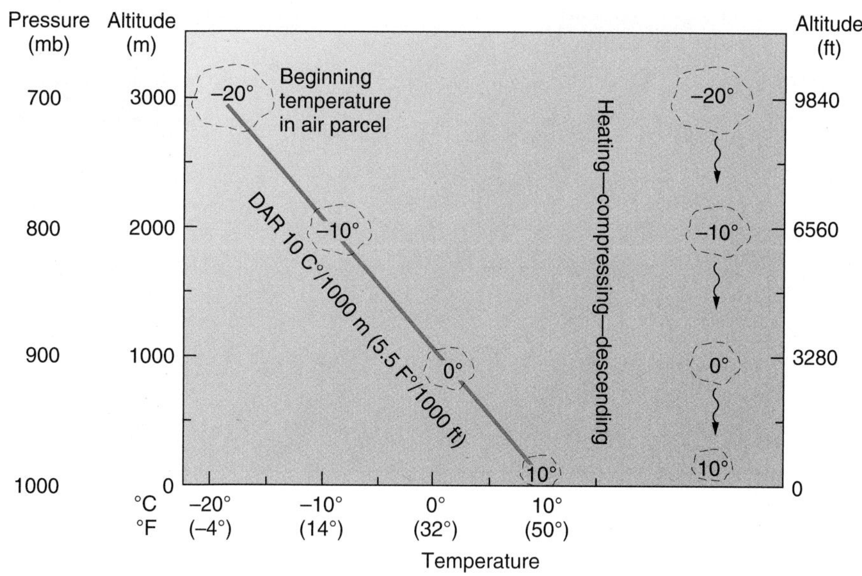

FIGURE 7.17 Adiabatic cooling and heating.
Vertically moving air parcels expand when they rise (because air pressure is less with increasing altitude) and are compressed when they descend. (a) An air parcel that is less than saturated cools adiabatically at the dry adiabatic rate (DAR). (b) A descending air parcel that is less than saturated heats adiabatically by compression at the DAR.

Atmospheric Stability

with a temperature of 27°C (81°F). It rises, expands, and cools adiabatically at the DAR as it rises to 2500 m (approximately 8000 ft). What happens to the temperature of the parcel? Calculate the temperature change in the parcel, using the dry adiabatic rate:

$$(10\ C°/1000\ m) \times 2500\ m = 25\ C° \text{ of total cooling}$$
$$(5.5\ F°/1000\ ft) \times 8000\ ft = 44\ F° \text{ of total cooling}$$

Subtracting the 25 C° (45 F°) of adiabatic cooling from the starting temperature of 27°C (81°F) gives the temperature in the air parcel at 2500 m of 2°C (36°F).

In Figure 7.17b, assume that an unsaturated air parcel with a temperature of –20°C is at 3000 m (–4°F at 9800 ft) descends to the surface, heating adiabatically. Using the dry adiabatic lapse rate, we determine the temperature of the air parcel when it arrives at the surface:

$$(10\ C°/1000\ m) \times 3000\ m = 30\ C° \text{ of total warming}$$
$$(5.5\ F°/1000\ ft) \times 9800\ ft = 54\ F° \text{ of total warming}$$

Adding the 30 C° of adiabatic warming from the starting temperature of –20°C gives the temperature in the air parcel at the surface of 10°C (50°F).

Moist Adiabatic Rate The **moist adiabatic rate (MAR)** is the rate at which an ascending air parcel that is moist (saturated) cools by expansion or that a descending parcel warms by compression. The average MAR is 6 C°/1000 m (3.3 F°/1000 ft). This is roughly 4 C° (2 F°) less than the dry adiabatic rate. From this average, the MAR varies with moisture content and temperature and can range from 4 C° to 10 C° per 1000 m (2 F° to 5.5 F° per 1000 ft).

The cause of this variability, and the reason that the rate is lower than the DAR, is the latent heat of condensation. As water vapour condenses in the saturated air, sensible heat is liberated and the adiabatic rate of cooling lowers. The release of latent heat may vary with temperature and water vapour content. The MAR is much lower than the DAR in warm air, whereas the two rates are more similar in cold air.

Stable and Unstable Atmospheric Conditions

Now we bring this discussion together to determine atmospheric stability. The relation among the dry adiabatic rate (DAR), moist adiabatic rate (MAR), and the environmental (actual) lapse rate at a given time and place determines the stability of the atmosphere over an area. You see examples of possible stability relationships in Figure 7.18. Let's examine what produces this variation in atmospheric stability.

Temperature relationships in the atmosphere produce the three different conditions: unstable, conditionally unstable, and stable. For the sake of illustration, the three examples in Figure 7.19 begin with an air parcel at the surface at 25°C (77°F). In each example, compare the temperatures of the air parcel and the surrounding environment. Assume that there is a lifting mechanism present to get the parcel started (we examine lifting mechanisms in Chapter 8).

Given unstable conditions in Figure 7.19a, the air parcel continues to rise through the atmosphere because it is warmer (and, therefore, less dense and more buoyant) than the surrounding environment. Note that the environmental lapse rate on this occasion is at 12 C°/1000 m (6.6 F°/1000 ft). That is, the air surrounding the air parcel is cooler by 12 C° for every 1000-m increase in altitude. By 1000 m (about 3300 ft), the lifting air parcel adiabatically cooled by expansion at the DAR from 25° to 15°C, while the surrounding air cooled from 25°C at the surface to 13°C. By comparing the temperature in the air parcel and the surrounding environment, you see that the temperature in the parcel is 2 C° (3.6 F°) warmer than the surrounding air at 1000 m. *Unstable* describes this condition because the less dense air parcel will continue to lift.

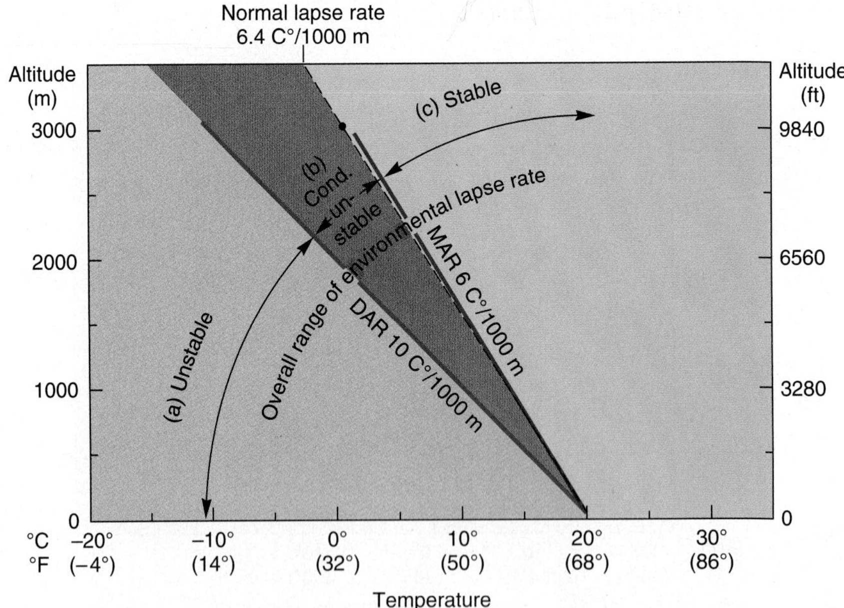

FIGURE 7.18 Temperature relationships and atmospheric stability.
The relationship between dry and moist adiabatic rates and environmental lapse rates produces three atmospheric conditions: (a) unstable (environmental lapse rate exceeds the DAR), (b) conditionally unstable (environmental lapse rate is between the DAR and MAR), and (c) stable (environmental lapse rate is less than DAR and MAR).

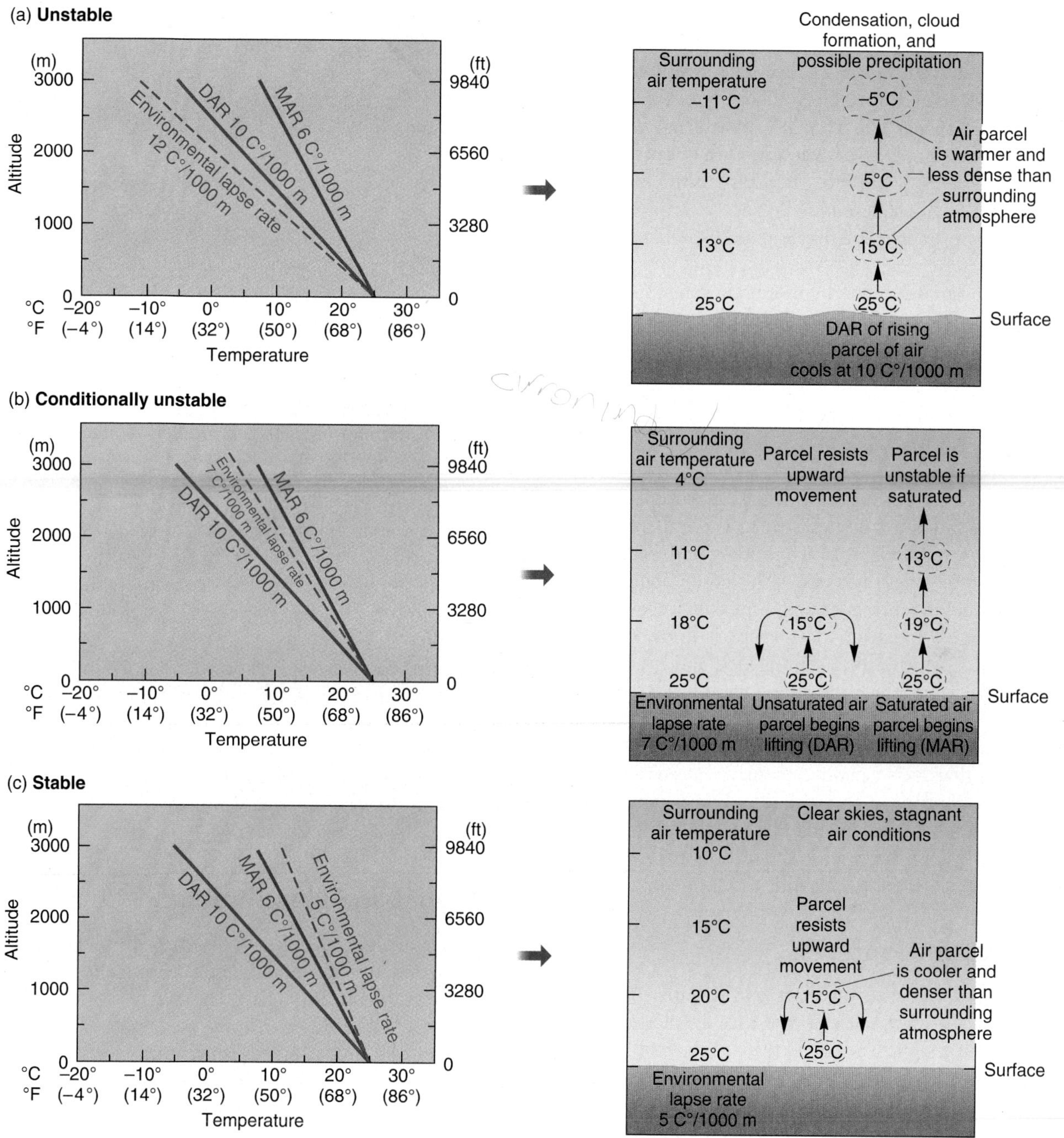

FIGURE 7.19 Stability—three examples.
Specific examples of (a) unstable, (b) conditionally unstable, and (c) stable conditions in the lower atmosphere. Note the response to these three conditions in the air parcel on the right side of each diagram.

Eventually, as the air parcel continues lifting and cooling, it may achieve the dew-point temperature, saturation, and active condensation. This point of saturation forms the *lifting condensation level* that you see in the sky as the flat bottoms of clouds.

On the other hand, if the environmental lapse rate is at only 5 C°/1000 m (3 F°/1000 ft) on another day, stable conditions result, as shown in Figure 7.19c. An environmental lapse rate of 5 C°/1000 m is less than both the DAR and the MAR. This environmental lapse rate sets a condition in which the air parcel has a lower temperature (higher density, less buoyant) than in the surrounding environment. The relatively cooler air parcel settles back to its original position—it is *stable*. The denser air parcel resists lifting and the sky remains generally cloud-free. In regions experiencing air pollution, stable conditions in the atmosphere worsen the pollution by slowing down exchanges in the surface air.

You may be wondering what stability condition exists if the environmental lapse rate is somewhere between the DAR and MAR and conditions, therefore, are neither unstable nor stable. In Figure 7.19b, the environmental lapse rate is measured at 7 C°/1000 m. Under these conditions, the air parcel resists upward movement if it is less than saturated. But, if the air parcel becomes saturated and cools at the MAR, it acts unstable and continues to rise.

One example of such conditionally unstable air occurs when stable air lifts as it passes over a mountain range. As the air parcel lifts and cools to the dew point, the air becomes saturated and condensation begins. Now the MAR is in effect and the air parcel behaves in an unstable manner. The sky may be clear and without a cloud, yet huge clouds may develop over a nearby mountain range.

With these stability relationships in mind, let us look at the most visible expressions of stability and humidity in the atmosphere: clouds and fog.

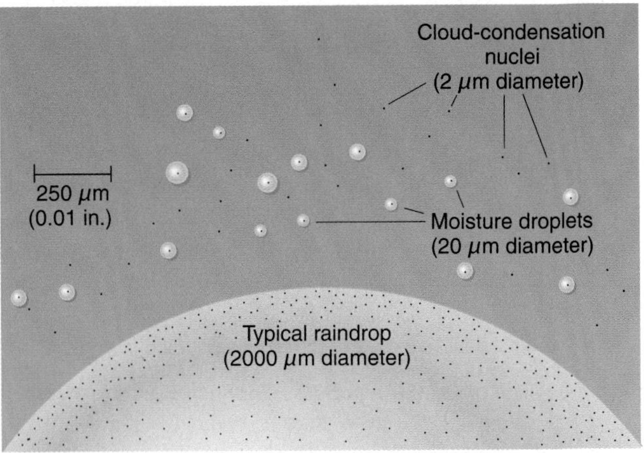

FIGURE 7.20 Moisture droplets and raindrops. Cloud-condensation nuclei, moisture droplets, and a raindrop enlarged many times—compared at roughly the same scale.

Clouds and Fog

Clouds are more than whimsical, beautiful decorations in the sky; they are fundamental indicators of overall atmospheric conditions: stability, moisture content, and weather. They form as air becomes saturated with water. Clouds are the subject of much scientific inquiry, especially regarding their effect on net radiation patterns, as discussed in Chapters 4 and 5. With a little knowledge and practice, you can learn to "read" the atmosphere from its signature clouds.

A **cloud** is an aggregation of tiny moisture droplets and ice crystals that are suspended in air, great enough in volume and concentration to be visible. Fog is simply a cloud in contact with the ground. Cloud types are too numerous to fully describe here, so the text offers the most common examples in a simple classification scheme.

Cloud Formation Processes

Clouds may contain raindrops, but not initially. At the outset, clouds are a great mass of moisture droplets, each invisible without magnification. A **moisture droplet** is approximately 20 μm (micrometres) in diameter (0.002 cm, or 0.0008 in.). It takes a million or more such droplets to form an average raindrop of 2000 μm in diameter (0.2 cm, or 0.078 in.), as shown in Figure 7.20.

Given unstable conditions an air parcel rises until it becomes saturated—that is, until the air cools to the dew-point temperature and relative humidity is 100%. (Under certain conditions, condensation may occur at slightly less than 100% relative humidity.) More lifting of the air parcel cools it further, producing condensation of water vapour into water. Water does not just condense among the air molecules. Condensation requires **cloud-condensation nuclei**, microscopic particles that always are present in the atmosphere.

Continental air masses average 10 billion cloud-condensation nuclei per cubic metre. Ordinary dust, soot, and ash from volcanoes and forest fires and particles from burned fuel, such as sulphate aerosols, typically provide these nuclei. The air over cities contains great concentrations of such nuclei. In maritime air masses, a high concentration of sea salts derived from ocean sprays, which average 1 billion nuclei per cubic metre, supply the needed nuclei. The lower atmosphere never lacks cloud-condensation nuclei.

Given the conditions of saturated air, availability of cloud-condensation nuclei, and the presence of cooling (lifting) mechanisms in the atmosphere, condensation occurs. Two principal processes account for the majority of the world's raindrops and snowflakes: the *collision-coalescence process* and the *Bergeron ice-crystal process*. Figure 7.21 summarizes these.

Cloud Types and Identification

As noted, a cloud is a collection of moisture droplets and ice crystals suspended in air in sufficient volume and concentration to be visible. In 1803, English biologist and amateur meteorologist Luke Howard, in his article "On the Modification of Clouds," established a classification system for clouds and coined Latin names for them that we still use. About Howard's accomplishment his biographer stated,

> Clouds were no longer exempt from human comprehension, and Howard, in contributing both a system of analysis and a full Latin nomenclature covering their families and genera, had contributed more than anyone to easing the path of understanding. . . . But the naming of clouds was a different kind of gesture for the hand of classification to have made. Here was the naming not of a solid, stable thing but of a series of self-canceling evanescences [disappearing entities]. Here was the naming of a fugitive presence that hastened to its onward dissolution. Here was the naming of clouds.*

*R. Hamblyn, *The Invention of Clouds, How an Amateur Meteorologist Forged the Language of the Skies* (New York: Farrar, Straus, and Giroux, 2001), pp. 165, 171.

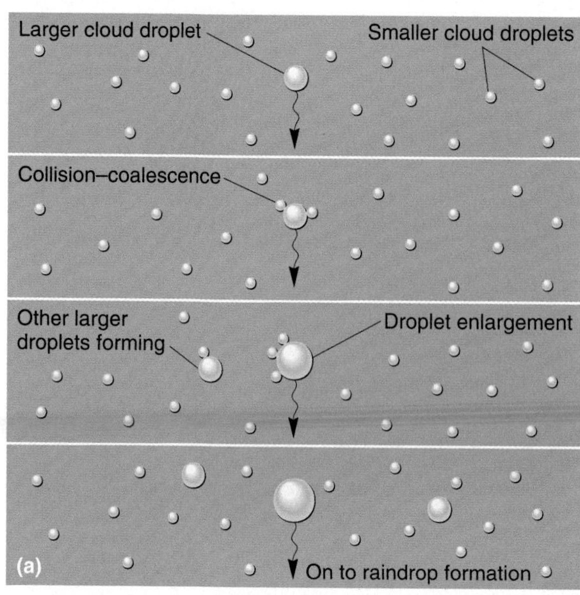

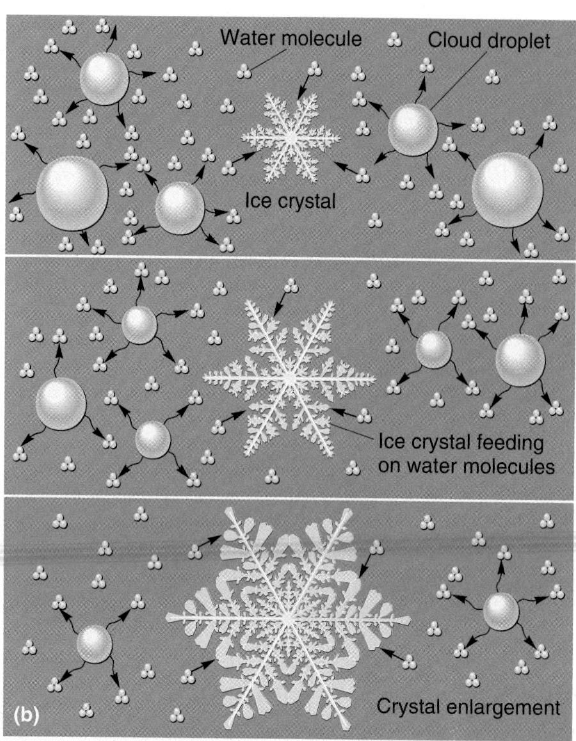

FIGURE 7.21 Raindrop formation.
Principal processes for raindrop and snowflake formation: the *collision-coalescence process* and the *ice-crystal process.* (a) The collision-coalescence process predominates in clouds that form at above-freezing temperatures, principally in the warm clouds of the tropics. Initially, simple condensation takes place on small nuclei, some of which are larger and produce larger water droplets. As those larger droplets respond to gravity and fall through a cloud, they combine with smaller droplets, gradually coalescing into a raindrop. (b) Supercooled water droplets (minute droplets of water that are below freezing and still in liquid form) will evaporate rapidly near ice crystals, which then absorb the vapour. The ice crystals feed on the supercooled cloud droplets, grow in size, and eventually fall as snow or rain. Precipitation in middle and high latitudes begins as ice and snow high in the clouds, then melts and gathers moisture as it falls through the warmer portions of the cloud. [Adapted from Frederick K. Lutgens and Edward J. Tarbuck, *The Atmosphere: An Introduction to Meteorology*, 3d. ed., copyright © 1986, p. 127. Reprinted by permission of Prentice Hall, Inc., Englewood Cliffs, NJ.]

Altitude and *shape* are key to cloud classification. Clouds occur in three basic forms—flat, puffy, and wispy—and in four primary altitude classes and ten basic cloud types. Horizontally developed clouds—flat and layered—are *stratiform* clouds. Vertically developed clouds—puffy and globular—are *cumuliform* clouds. Wispy clouds usually are quite high in altitude and are made of ice crystals; these are *cirroform*.

These three basic forms occur in four altitudinal classes: low, middle, high, and those vertically developed through the troposphere. Table 7.2 on p. 204 presents the basic cloud classes and types. The symbols noted were of Luke Howard's invention. Figure 7.22 illustrates the general appearance of each type and includes representative photographs.

Low clouds, ranging from the surface up to 2000 m (6500 ft) in the middle latitudes, are simply called *stratus* or *cumulus* (Latin for "layer" and "heap," respectively). **Stratus** clouds appear dull, grey, and featureless. When they yield precipitation, they become **nimbostratus** (*nimbo-* denotes stormy or rainy), and their showers typically fall as drizzling rain (Figure 7.22e).

Cumulus clouds appear bright and puffy, like cotton balls. When they do not cover the sky, they float by in infinitely varied shapes. Vertically developed cumulus clouds are in a separate class in Table 7.2 because further vertical development can produce cumulus clouds that extend beyond low altitudes into middle and high altitudes (illustrated at the far right in Figure 7.22 and 7.22d).

Sometimes near the end of the day **stratocumulus** may fill the sky in patches—lumpy, greyish, low-level clouds. Near sunset, these spreading puffy stratiform remnants may catch and filter the Sun's rays, sometimes indicating clearing weather.

The prefix *alto-* (meaning "high") denotes middle-level clouds. They are made of water droplets and, when cold enough, can be mixed with ice crystals. **Altocumulus** clouds, in particular, represent a broad category that occurs in many different styles: patchy rows, wave patterns, a "mackerel sky," or lens-shaped (lenticular) clouds.

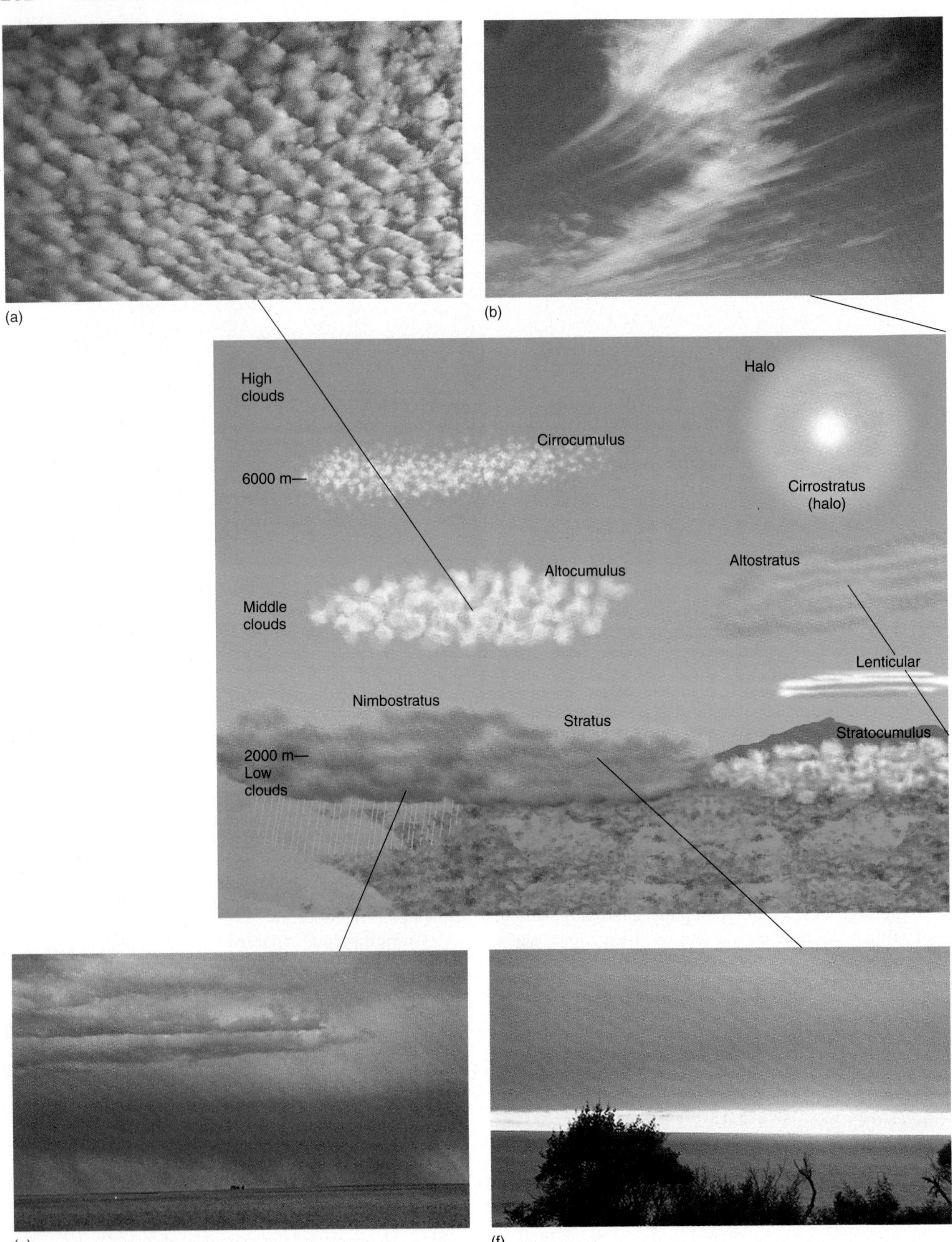

FIGURE 7.22 Principal cloud types.
Principal cloud types, classified by form (cirroform, stratiform, and cumuliform) and altitude (low, middle, high, and vertically developed across altitude): (a) altocumulus, (b) cirrus, (c) cirrostratus, (d) cumulonimbus, (e) nimbostratus, (f) stratus, (g) altostratus, and (h) cumulus. [Photos by Robert W. Christopherson, except (b), (d), and (h) by Bobbé Christopherson.]

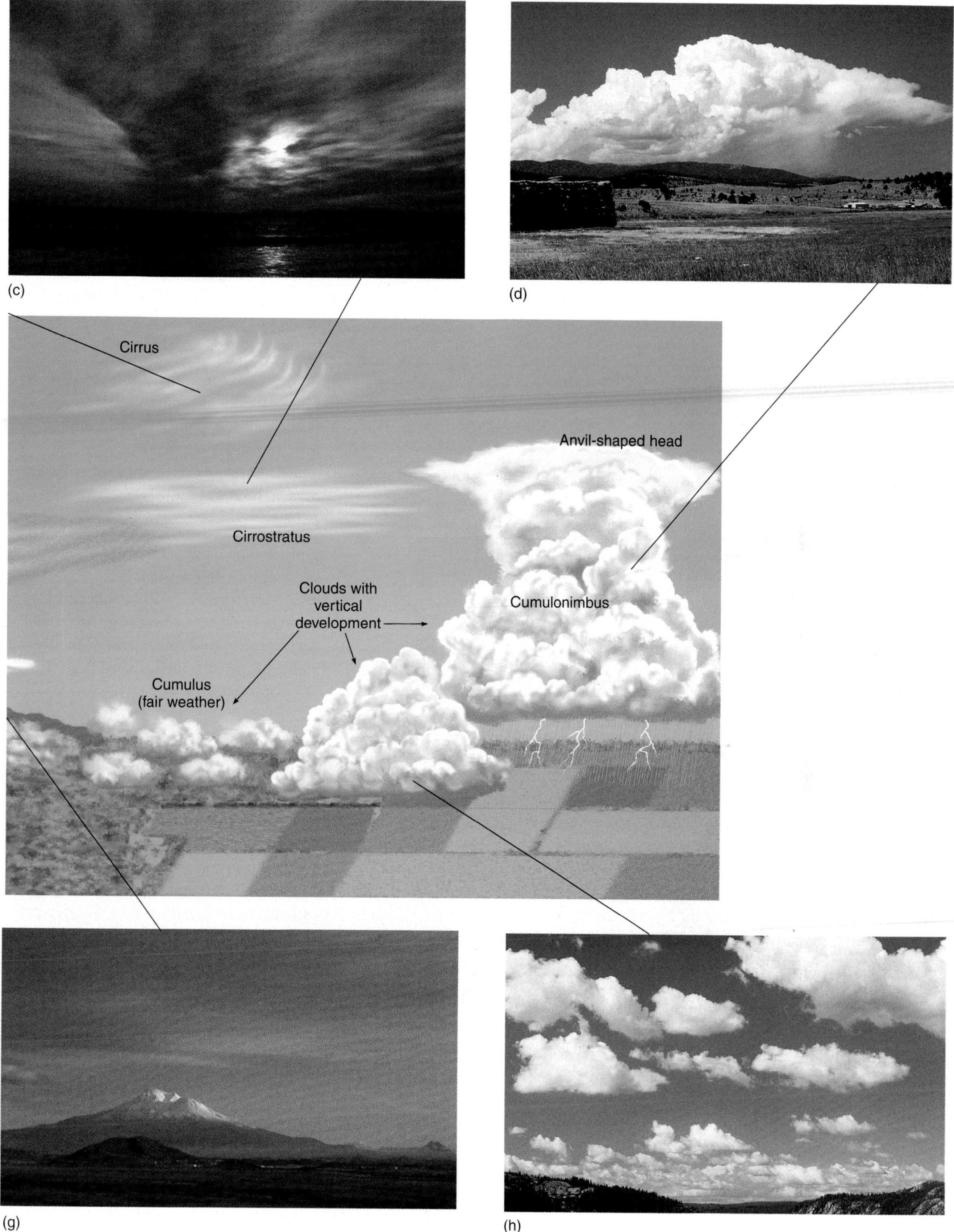
Cirrus
Cirrostratus
Anvil-shaped head
Clouds with vertical development
Cumulonimbus
Cumulus (fair weather)

(c)

(d)

(g)

(h)

Table 7.2 Cloud Classes and Types

Class	Altitude/Composition at Midlatitudes	Type	Symbol	Description
Low clouds (C_L)	Up to 2000 m (6500 ft) Water	Stratus (St)		Uniform, featureless, grey, like high fog
		Stratocumulus (Sc)		Soft, grey, globular masses in lines, groups, or waves, heavy rolls, irregular overcast patterns
		Nimbostratus (Ns)		Grey, dark, low, with drizzling rain
Middle clouds (C_M)	2000–6000 m (6500–20,000 ft) Ice and water	Altostratus (As)		Thin to thick, no halos, Sun's outline just visible, grey day
		Altocumulus (Ac)		Patches of cotton balls, dappled, arranged in lines or groups, rippling waves, the lenticular clouds associated with mountains
High clouds (C_H)	6000–13,000 m (20,000–43,000 ft) Ice	Cirrus (Ci)		Mares'-tails, wispy, feathery, hairlike, delicate fibres, streaks, or plumes
		Cirrostratus (Cs)		Veil of fused sheets of ice crystals, milky, with Sun and Moon halos
		Cirrocumulus (Cc)		Dappled, "mackerel sky," small white flakes, tufts, in lines or groups, sometimes in ripples
Vertically developed clouds	Near surface to 13,000 m (43,000 ft) Water below, ice above	Cumulus (Cu)		Sharply outlined, puffy, billowy, flat-based, swelling tops, fair weather
		Cumulonimbus (Cb)		Dense, heavy, massive, dark thunderstorms, hard showers, explosive top, great vertical development, towering, cirrus-topped plume blown into anvil-shaped head

Ice crystals in thin concentrations compose clouds occurring above 6000 m (20,000 ft). These wispy filaments, usually white except when coloured by sunrise or sunset, are **cirrus** clouds (Latin for "curl of hair"), sometimes dubbed mares'-tails. Cirrus clouds look as though an artist took a brush and added delicate feathery strokes high in the sky. Cirrus clouds indicate an oncoming storm, especially if they thicken and lower in elevation. The prefix *cirro-*, as in cirrostratus and cirrocumulus, indicates other high clouds that form a thin veil or puffy appearance, respectively.

A cumulus cloud can develop into a towering giant called **cumulonimbus** (again, *-nimbus* in Latin denotes rain storm or thundercloud; Figure 7.23). Such clouds are called *thunderheads* because of their shape and associated lightning and thunder. Note the surface wind gusts, updrafts and downdrafts, heavy rain, and the presence of ice crystals at the top of the rising cloud column. High-altitude winds may then shear the top of the cloud into the characteristic anvil shape of the mature thunderhead.

Fog

By international definition, **fog** is a cloud layer on the ground, with visibility restricted to less than 1 km (3300 ft). The presence of fog tells us that the air temperature and the dew-point temperature at ground level are nearly identical, indicating saturated conditions. An inversion layer generally caps a fog layer, with as much as 22 C° (40 F°) difference in air temperature between the cool ground under the fog and the warmer, sunny skies above.

Most fog is warm—that is, its moisture droplets are above freezing. Supercooled fog, which occurs when the moisture droplets are below freezing, is special because it can be dispersed by means of artificial seeding with ice crystals or other crystals that mimic ice, following the principles of the ice-crystal formation process described earlier. Let's briefly look at several types of fog.

Advection Fog **Advection fog** forms when air in one place *migrates* to another place where conditions are right for saturation. For example, when warm, moist air overlays cooler ocean currents, lake surfaces, or snow masses, the layer of migrating air directly above the surface becomes chilled to the dew point, and fog develops. Off all subtropical west coasts in the world, summer fog forms in the manner just described (Figure 7.24). Some coastal desert communities actually extract usable water from such fog formations, as described in News Report 7.1.

Another type of advection fog forms when cold air lies over the warm water of a lake, ocean surface, or even a swimming pool. This wispy **evaporation fog**, or *steam fog*, may form as water molecules evaporate from the water sur-

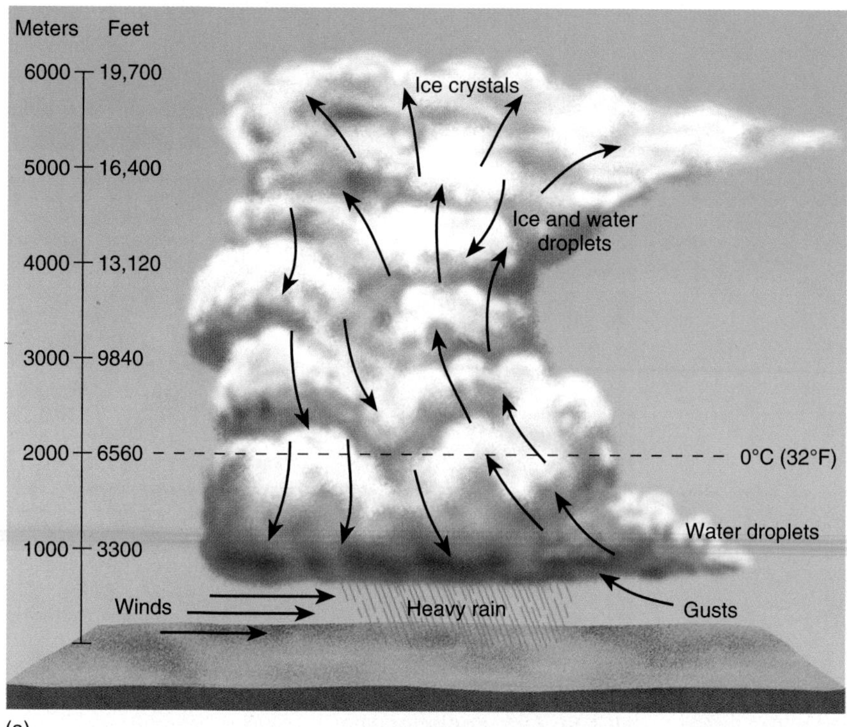

(a)

(b)

(c)

FIGURE 7.23 Cumulonimbus thunderhead. (a) Structure and form of a cumulonimbus cloud. Violent updrafts and downdrafts mark the circulation within the cloud. Blustery wind gusts occur along the ground. (b) Space shuttle astronauts capture a dramatic cumulonimbus thunderhead as it moves over Galveston Bay, Texas. (c) Few acts of nature can match the sheer power released by an intense thunderstorm. [(b) Space Shuttle photo from NASA; (c) photo by Bobbé Christopherson.]

face into the cold overlying air, effectively humidifying the air, on to saturation and then condensation to form fog. When evaporation fog happens at sea, it is a shipping hazard called *sea smoke*.

A type of advection fog forms when moist air flows to higher elevations along a hill or mountain. This upslope lifting leads to adiabatic cooling by expansion as the air rises. The resulting **upslope fog** forms a stratus cloud at the condensation level of saturation. Along the Appalachians and the eastern slopes of the Rockies such fog is common in winter and spring. Another advection fog associated with topography is **valley fog**. Because cool air is denser than warm air, it settles in low-lying areas, producing a fog in the chilled, saturated layer near the ground (Figure 7.25).

Radiation Fog **Radiation fog** forms when radiative cooling of a surface chills the air layer directly above that surface to the dew-point temperature, creating saturated conditions and fog. This fog occurs over moist ground especially on clear nights; it does not occur over water, because water does not cool appreciably overnight. Slight movements of air deliver even more moisture to the cooled area for more fog formation of greater depth (Figure 7.26).

Rime Fog Similar to radiation fog, **rime fog** consists mostly of tiny supercooled droplets that turn into rime frost on contact with freezing objects. It is very common in cold weather, when the air temperature near the surface is below freezing and the air is fairly moist. Rime fog usually happens when the sky is clear on cold mornings. When this type of fog occurs at airports, aircraft have to de-ice before takeoff.

Ice-crystal Fog At low temperatures in a continental arctic air mass, **ice-crystal fog** may develop (Figure 7.27); for example, when the air becomes full of ice crystals that

FIGURE 7.24 Advection fog.
San Francisco's Golden Gate Bridge shrouded by an invading advection fog characteristic of summer conditions along a western coast. [Photo by Robert W. Christopherson.]

FIGURE 7.26 Radiation fog.
Satellite image of a radiation fog in the southern Great Valley of Central California, November 20, 2002. This fog is locally known as a tule fog (pronounced "toolee") because of its association with the tule (bulrush) plants that line the low-elevation islands and marshes of the Sacramento River and San Joaquin River delta regions. [*Terra* MODIS image courtesy of MODIS Rapid Response Team, GSFC/NASA.]

FIGURE 7.25 Valley fog.
Cold air settles in the valleys of the Appalachian Mountains, chilling the air to the dew point and forming a valley fog. [Photo by Robert W. Christopherson.]

FIGURE 7.27 Ice-crystal fog in Whitehorse.
Fog of ice crystals that forms at extremely low temperatures. In this photograph, the air temperature is –42°C without windchill. [Photo courtesy of Pathfinder Publications.]

formed by sublimation. Such an ice-crystal fog seriously limits visibility.

Every year the media carry stories of multi-car pileups on stretches of highway where tailgating vehicles continued to speed in foggy conditions. These totally avoidable crash scenes can involve dozens of cars and trucks. Fog is a hazard to drivers, pilots, sailors, pedestrians, and cyclists, and its conditions of formation are quite predictable. The spatial aspects of fog occurrence should be a planning element for any proposed airport, harbour facility, or highway. The prevalence of fog throughout Canada and the United States is shown in Figure 7.28.

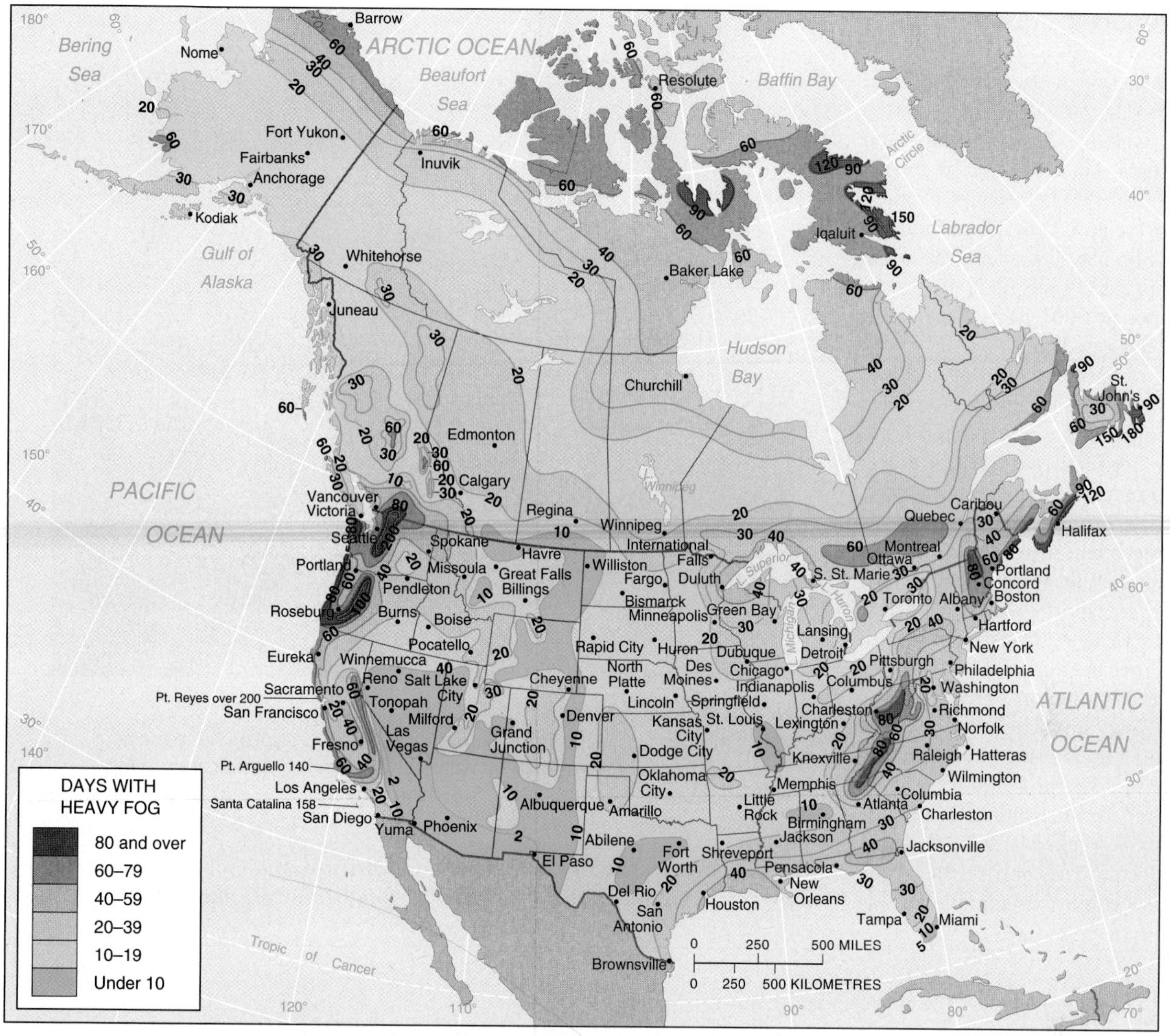

FIGURE 7.28 Fog incidence map.
Mean annual number of days with heavy fog in the United States and Canada. Officially, fog is declared if visibility is less than 1 km (3300 ft). The foggiest spot in the United States is the mouth of the Columbia River where it enters the Pacific Ocean at Cape Disappointment, Washington. One of the foggiest places in the world is Newfoundland's Avalon Peninsula, specifically Argentia and Belle Isle, which regularly exceed 200 days of fog each year. [Data courtesy of National Weather Service; Map Series 3, *Climatic Atlas of Canada*, Atmospheric Environment Service Canada, and *The Climates of Canada*, compiled by David Philips, Senior Climatologist, Environment Canada, 1990.]

News Report 7.1

Harvesting Fog

In 1985, a group of scientists approached Canada's International Development Research Centre (IDRC) with a proposal to collect advection fog to supplement the water supply of a remote Chilean village, Chungungo. The scientists were supported by the United Nations Educational, Scientific, and Cultural Organization (UNESCO) to develop fog-catcher technology. By 1992, water harvested from the fog was flowing to homes and businesses. This simple technology more than doubled Chungungo's per capita water supply and inspired other communities around the world to try this new technology.

The First International Conference on Fog & Fog Collection was held in Vancouver, British Columbia in 1998. Scientists and water managers from around the world shared their research

(continued)

News Report 7.1 *(continued)*

on fog collection in places ranging from Hawai'i to the Sultanate of Oman, the Canary Islands, Croatia, Peru, and South Africa. The conference was organized by Robert Schemenauer, a retired research scientist at Environment Canada who played a role in the in the Chilean project. A second international conference in 2001 took place at St. John's, Newfoundland.

The technology of the fogcatcher is simple (Figure 1). Ultraviolet-resistant polypropylene mesh, stretched horizontally between two upright poles, at right angles to the prevailing wind, catches fog droplets that grow larger on the mesh and drip into gutters. In Chungungo, the gutters empty into pipes for transport to a 100,000-litre reservoir. Over 40 litres of water are supplied per person in the village per day from 88 collectors. There is a low fee for each household to use the water and a local committee manages the resource. The project was designed to supplement the original water supply that was trucked to the village. At least 30 countries across the globe experience conditions suitable for this water resource technology (see **http://www.wssd-smdd.gc.ca/sd_action/stories/water_e.cfm** and **http://www.fogquest.org/index.shtml**).

FIGURE 1 Fog harvesting.
In the mountains inland from Chungungo, Chile, polypropylene mesh stretched between two posts captures advection fog for local drinking water supplies. [Photo by Robert S. Schemenauer.]

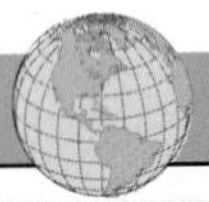

Applied Physical Geography

Measuring Relative Humidity

How humid is it? Measuring the level of relative humidity is actually a simple matter of reading the temperature simultaneously shown by two ordinary mercury-in-glass thermometers mounted side by side (Figure 7.13b). One is just a regular thermometer from which we read the temperature of the air. The other is the same type of thermometer, but with a cloth sleeve that can be wetted for the wet bulb. On a warm, dry day the thermometer with the wet sleeve measures a lower temperature than the dry bulb. This results because moisture evaporates from the cloth sleeve and cools the bulb. The lower the relative humidity, the more rapid the evaporation, the greater the cooling, and the greater the difference in temperatures.

Because the device described above works well only if air is moving rapidly past the wet bulb, a fan can be installed to create a strong air flow. In a sling psychrometer, two thermometers are mounted side by side and are linked to a handle. After wetting the cloth sleeve, the psychrometer is moved rapidly in a circle to get the maximum evaporation rate. When the psychrometer stops, the two temperatures, one dry bulb and one wet bulb, are recorded and compared. The difference is found on a relative humidity table (Table 1).

To use the tables to determine relative humidity (RH, %) and dew point (°C), for a pair of numbers from the sling psychrometer, take the difference between the wet bulb and the dry bulb. Table 2 gives examples of relative humidity and dew-point temperature based on the differences between wet-bulb and dry-bulb readings. Fill in the spaces in the last two rows using the tables.

Table 1 Relative Humidity Table

Psychrometric chart of relative humidity (in percent)
(a) Depression of the wet bulb (dry-bulb temperature minus wet-bulb temperature in °C)

Dry-bulb temperature (air temperature °C)	0.5	1.0	1.5	2.0	2.5	3.0	3.5	4.0	4.5	5.0	7.5	10.0	12.5	15.0	17.5	20.0	22.5	25.0
20	70	41	11															
–17.5	75	51	26	2														
–15	79	58	38	18														
–12.5	82	65	47	30	13													
–10	85	69	54	39	24	10												
–7.5	87	73	60	48	35	22	10											
–5	88	77	66	54	43	32	21	11	1									
–2.5	90	80	70	60	50	42	37	22	12	3								
0	91	82	73	65	56	47	39	31	23	15								
2.5	92	84	76	68	61	53	46	38	31	24								
5	93	86	78	71	65	58	51	45	38	32	1							
7.5	93	87	80	74	68	62	56	50	44	38	11							
10	94	88	82	76	71	65	60	54	49	44	19							
12.5	94	89	84	78	73	68	63	58	53	48	25	4						
15	95	90	85	80	75	70	66	61	57	52	31	12						
17.5	95	90	86	81	77	72	68	64	60	55	36	18	2					
20	95	91	87	82	78	74	70	66	62	58	40	24	8					
22.5	96	92	87	83	80	76	72	68	64	61	44	28	14	1				
25	96	92	88	84	81	77	73	70	66	63	47	32	19	7				
27.5	96	92	89	85	82	78	75	71	68	65	50	36	23	12	1			
30	96	93	89	86	82	79	76	73	70	67	52	39	27	16	6			
32.5	97	93	90	86	83	80	77	74	71	68	54	42	30	20	11	1		
35	97	93	90	87	84	81	78	75	72	69	56	44	33	23	14	6		
37.5	97	94	91	87	85	82	79	76	73	70	58	46	36	26	18	10	3	
40	97	94	91	88	85	82	79	77	74	72	59	48	38	29	21	13	6	
42.5	97	94	91	88	86	83	80	78	75	72	61	50	40	31	23	16	9	2
45	97	94	91	89	86	83	81	78	76	73	62	51	42	33	26	18	12	6
47.5	97	94	92	89	86	84	81	79	76	74	63	53	44	35	28	21	15	9
50	97	95	92	89	87	84	82	79	77	75	64	54	45	37	30	23	17	11

Psychrometric chart of dew-point temperature (in °C)
(b) Depression of the wet bulb (dry-bulb temperature minus wet-bulb temperature in °C)

Dry-bulb temperature (air temperature °C)	0.5	1.0	1.5	2.0	2.5	3.0	3.5	4.0	4.5	5.0	7.5	10.0	12.5	15.0	17.5	20.0
–20	–25	–33														
–17.5	–21	–27	–38													
–15	–19	–23	–28													
–12.5	–15	–18	–22	–29												
–10	–12	–14	–18	–21	–27	–36										
–7.5	–9	–11	–14	–17	–20	–26	–34									
–5	–7	–8	–10	–13	–16	–19	–24	–31								
–2.5	–4	6	–7	–9	–11	–14	–17	–22	–28	–41						
0	–1	–3	–4	–6	–8	–10	–12	–15	–19	–24						
2.5	1	0	–1	–3	–4	–6	–8	–10	–13	–16						
5	4	3	2	0	–1	–3	–4	–6	–8	–10	–48					
7.5	6	6	4	3	2	1	–1	–2	–4	–6	–22					
10	9	8	7	6	5	4	2	1	0	–2	–13					
12.5	12	11	10	9	8	7	6	4	3	2	–7	–28				
15	14	13	12	12	11	10	9	8	7	5	–2	–14				
17.5	17	16	15	14	13	12	12	11	10	8	2	–7	–35			
20	19	18	18	17	16	15	14	14	13	12	6	–1	–15			
22.5	22	21	20	20	19	18	17	16	16	15	10	3	6	–38		
25	24	24	23	22	21	21	20	19	18	18	13	7	0	–14		
27.5	27	26	26	25	24	23	23	22	21	20	16	11	5	–5	–32	
30	29	29	28	27	27	26	25	25	24	23	19	14	9	2	–11	
32.5	32	31	31	30	29	29	28	27	26	26	22	18	13	7	–2	
35	34	34	33	32	32	31	31	30	29	28	25	21	16	11	4	
37.5	37	36	36	35	34	34	33	32	32	31	28	24	20	15	9	0
40	39	39	38	38	37	36	36	35	34	34	30	27	23	18	13	6
42.5	42	41	41	40	40	39	38	38	37	36	33	30	26	22	17	11
45	44	44	43	43	42	42	41	40	40	39	36	33	29	25	21	15
47.5	47	46	46	45	45	44	44	43	42	42	39	35	32	28	24	19
50	49	49	48	48	47	47	46	45	45	44	41	38	35	31	28	23

(continued)

Applied Physical Geography *(continued)*

Table 2

Dry Bulb Temperature (°C)	Wet Bulb Temperature (°C)	Difference (°C)	Relative Humidity (%)	Dew Point Temperature (°C)
31	14	17	16	–11
35	25	10	44	21
1	–3	4	31	–15
41	28	13	29	23
17.5	___	___	86	___
–10	–12	___	___	___

Summary and Review—Water and Atmospheric Moisture

■ *Describe* the origin of Earth's waters, *define* the quantity of water that exists today, and *list* the locations of Earth's freshwater supply.

The next time it rains where you live, pause and reflect on the journey each of those water molecules has made. Water molecules came from within Earth over a period of billions of years, in a process called **outgassing**. Thus began the endless cycling of water through the hydrologic system of evaporation–condensation–precipitation. Water covers about 71% of Earth. Approximately 97% of it is salty seawater, and the remaining 3% is freshwater—most of it frozen.

The present volume of water on Earth is estimated to be 1.36 billion cubic kilometres (326 million cubic miles), an amount reached roughly 2 billion years ago. This overall steady-state equilibrium might seem in conflict with the many changes in sea level that have occurred over Earth's history, but is not. Worldwide changes in sea level are called **eustasy** and are related to the change in volume of water in the oceans. Some of these changes are explained by the amount of water stored in glaciers and ice sheets, called **glacio-eustatic** factors. At present, sea level is rising because of increases in the temperature of the oceans and the record melting of glacial ice.

outgassing (p. 184)
eustasy (p. 184)
glacio-eustatic (p. 184)

1. Approximately where and when did Earth's water originate?
2. If the quantity of water on Earth has been quite constant in volume for at least 2 billion years, how can sea level have fluctuated? Explain.
3. Describe the locations of Earth's water, both oceanic and fresh. What is the largest repository of freshwater at this time? In what ways is this distribution of water significant to modern society?
4. Why might you describe Earth as the water planet? Explain.

■ *Describe* the heat properties of water and *identify* the traits of its three phases: solid, liquid, and gas.

Water is the most common compound on the surface of Earth, and it possesses unusual solvent and heat characteristics. Part of Earth's uniqueness is that its water exists naturally in all three states—solid, liquid, and gas—owing to Earth's temperate position relative to the Sun. A change from one state to another is a **phase change**. The change from solid to vapour is **sublimation**; from liquid to solid, freezing; from solid to liquid, melting; from vapour to liquid, condensation; and from liquid to vapour, vaporization, or evaporation.

The heat energy required for water to change phase is **latent heat**, because, once absorbed, it is hidden within the structure of the water, ice, or water vapour. For 1 g of water to become 1 g of water vapour at boiling requires addition of 540 calories, or the **latent heat of vaporization**. When this 1 g of water vapour condenses, the same amount of heat energy is liberated, as 540 calories of the **latent heat of condensation**. The **latent heat of sublimation** is the energy exchanged in the phase change from ice to vapour and vapour to ice. Weather is powered by the tremendous amount of latent heat energy involved in the phase changes between the three states of water.

phase change (p. 188)
sublimation (p. 188)
latent heat (p. 189)
latent heat of vaporization (p. 190)
latent heat of condensation (p. 190)
latent heat of sublimation (p. 190)

5. Describe the three states of matter as they apply to ice, water, and water vapour.
6. What happens to the physical structure of water as it cools below 4°C (39°F)? What are some visible indications of these physical changes?
7. What is latent heat? How is it involved in the phase changes of water?
8. Take 1 g of water at 0°C and follow it through to 1 g of water vapour at 100°C, describing what happens along the way. What amounts of energy are involved in the changes that take place?

● *Define* humidity and the expressions of the relative humidity concept, and *explain* dew-point temperature and saturated conditions in the atmosphere.

The amount of water vapour in the atmosphere is **humidity**. The ability of air to hold water vapour is principally a function of the temperature of the air and of the water vapour (usually the same). **Relative humidity** is a percentage expression of the humidity content of the air compared with the capacity of the air to hold water vapour at a given temperature—content compared with capacity. Relatively dry air has a lower relative humidity value; relatively moist air a higher percentage. Air is said to be **saturated**, or filled to capacity, if it contains all the water vapour it can hold at a given temperature (100% relative humidity). The temperature at which air achieves saturation is the **dew-point temperature**.

Among the various ways to express humidity and relative humidity are vapour pressure and specific humidity. **Vapour pressure** is that portion of the atmospheric pressure that is produced by the presence of water vapour. A comparison of vapour pressure with the saturation vapour pressure at any moment produces a relative humidity percentage. **Specific humidity** is the mass of water vapour (in grams) per mass of air (in kilograms) at any specified temperature. Because it is measured as a mass, specific humidity does not change as temperature or pressure changes, making it a valuable measurement in weather forecasting. A comparison of specific humidity with the maximum specific humidity at any moment produces a relative humidity percentage.

Two instruments that are used to measure relative humidity, and indirectly the actual humidity content of the air, are the **hair hygrometer** and the **sling psychrometer**.

humidity (p. 190)
relative humidity (p. 190)
saturated (p. 191)
dew-point temperature (p. 191)
vapour pressure (p. 192)
specific humidity (p. 192)
hair hygrometer (p. 193)
sling psychrometer (p. 193)

9. What is humidity? How is it related to the energy present in the atmosphere? To our personal comfort and how we perceive apparent temperatures?
10. Define relative humidity. What does the concept represent? What is meant by the terms *saturation* and *dew-point temperature*?
11. Using different measures of humidity in the air given in the chapter, derive relative humidity values (vapour pressure/saturation vapour pressure; specific humidity/maximum specific humidity).
12. How do the two instruments described in this chapter measure relative humidity?
13. How does the daily distribution of relative humidity compare with the daily distribution of air temperature?

● *Define* atmospheric stability and *relate* it to a parcel of air that is ascending or descending.

Meteorologists use the term *parcel* to describe a body of air that has specific temperature and humidity characteristics. Think of a parcel of air as a volume of air, perhaps 300 m (1000 ft) in diameter, that is subjected to temperature differences that create changes in density within the parcel. Warm air has a lower density in a given volume of air; cold air has a higher density.

Stability refers to the tendency of an air parcel, with its water-vapour cargo, either to remain in place or to change vertical position by ascending (rising) or descending (falling). An air parcel is *stable* if it resists displacement upward or, when disturbed, it tends to return to its starting place. An air parcel is *unstable* if it continues to rise until it reaches an altitude where the surrounding air has a density (air temperature) similar to its own.

stability (p. 195)

14. Differentiate between stability and instability relative to a parcel of air rising vertically in the atmosphere.
15. What are the forces acting on a vertically moving parcel of air? How are they affected by the density of the air parcel?

● *Illustrate* three atmospheric conditions—unstable, conditionally unstable, and stable—with a simple graph that relates the environmental lapse rate to the dry adiabatic rate (DAR) and moist adiabatic rate (MAR).

An ascending (rising) parcel of air cools by expansion, responding to the reduced air pressure at higher altitudes. A descending (falling) parcel heats by compression. These temperature changes internal to a moving air parcel are explained by physical laws that govern the behaviour of gases. Temperature changes in both ascending and descending air parcels occur without any significant heat exchange between the surrounding environment and the vertically moving parcel of air. The warming and cooling rates for a parcel of expanding or compressing air are termed **adiabatic**.

The **dry adiabatic rate (DAR)** is the rate at which "dry" air cools by expansion (if ascending) or heats by compression (if descending). The term *dry* is used when air is less than saturated (relative humidity less than 100%). The DAR is 10 C°/1000 m (5.5 F°/1000 ft). The **moist adiabatic rate (MAR)** is the average rate at which ascending air that is moist (saturated) cools by expansion, or descending air warms by compression. The average MAR is 6 C°/1000 m (3.3 F°/1000 ft). This is roughly 4 C° (2 F°) less than the dry rate. The MAR, however, varies with moisture content and temperature and can range from 4 to 10 C° per 1000 m (2 to 5.5 F° per 1000 ft).

A simple comparison of the dry adiabatic rate (DAR) and moist adiabatic rate (MAR) in a vertically moving parcel of air with that of the environmental lapse rate in the surrounding air determines the atmosphere's stability—whether it is unstable (lifting of air parcels continues), stable (air parcels resist vertical displacement), or conditionally unstable (air parcel behaves as though unstable if the MAR is in operation and stable otherwise).

adiabatic (p. 197)
dry adiabatic rate (DAR) (p. 197)
moist adiabatic rate (MAR) (p. 198)

16. How do the adiabatic rates of heating or cooling in a vertically displaced air parcel differ from the normal lapse rate and environmental lapse rate?
17. Why is there a difference between the dry adiabatic rate (DAR) and the moist adiabatic rate (MAR)?
18. What would atmospheric temperature and moisture conditions be on a day when the weather is unstable? When it is stable? Relate in your answer what you would experience if you were outside watching.

Identify the requirements for cloud formation and *explain* the major cloud classes and types, including fog.

A **cloud** is an aggregation of tiny moisture droplets and ice crystals suspended in the air. Clouds are a constant reminder of the powerful heat-exchange system in the environment. **Moisture droplets** in a cloud form when saturated air and the presence of **cloud-condensation nuclei** lead to *condensation*. Raindrops are formed from moisture droplets through either the *collision-coalescence process* or the *Bergeron ice-crystal process*.

Low clouds, ranging from the surface up to 2000 m (6500 ft) in the middle latitudes, are **stratus** (flat clouds, in layers) or **cumulus** (puffy clouds, in heaps). When stratus clouds yield precipitation, they are **nimbostratus**. Sometimes near the end of the day, lumpy, greyish, low-level clouds called **stratocumulus** may fill the sky in patches. Middle-level clouds are denoted by the prefix *alto-*. **Altocumulus** clouds, in particular, represent a broad category that occurs in many different styles. Clouds at high altitude, principally composed of ice crystals, are called **cirrus**. A cumulus cloud can develop into a towering giant **cumulonimbus** cloud (*-nimbus* in Latin denotes rain storm or thundercloud). Such clouds are called *thunderheads* because of their shape and their associated lightning, thunder, surface wind gusts, updrafts and downdrafts, heavy rain, and hail.

Fog is a cloud that occurs at ground level. **Advection fog** forms when air in one place migrates to another place where conditions exist that can cause saturation—for example, when warm, moist air moves over cooler ocean currents. Another type of advection fog forms when cold air flows over the warm water of a lake, ocean surface, or swimming pool. This **evaporation fog**, or steam fog, may form as the water molecules evaporate from the water surface into the cold overlying air. **Upslope fog** is produced when moist air is forced to higher elevations along a hill or mountain. Another fog caused by topography is **valley fog**, formed because cool, denser air settles in low-lying areas, producing fog in the chilled, saturated layer near the ground. Radiative cooling of a surface chills the air layer directly above the surface to the dew-point temperature, creating saturated conditions and a **radiation fog**. **Rime fog**, similar to radiation fog, consists mostly of tiny supercooled droplets that turn into rime frost on contact with freezing objects. It is very common in cold weather, when the air temperature near the surface is below freezing and the air is fairly moist. **Ice-crystal fog** develops at low temperatures, for example in a continental arctic air mass, when the air becomes full of ice crystals that formed by sublimation. Ice-crystal fog seriously limits visibility.

cloud (p. 200)
moisture droplet (p. 200)
cloud-condensation nuclei (p. 200)
stratus (p. 201)
nimbostratus (p. 201)
cumulus (p. 201)
stratocumulus (p. 201)
altocumulus (p. 201)
cirrus (p. 204)
cumulonimbus (p. 204)
fog (p. 204)
advection fog (p. 204)
evaporation fog (p. 204)
upslope fog (p. 205)
valley fog (p. 205)
radiation fog (p. 205)
rime fog (p. 205)
ice-crystal fog (p. 205)

19. Specifically, what is a cloud? Describe the droplets that form a cloud.
20. Explain the condensation process: What are the requirements? What two principal processes are discussed in this chapter?
21. What are the basic forms of clouds? Using Table 7.2, describe how the basic cloud forms vary with altitude.
22. Explain how clouds might be used as indicators of the conditions of the atmosphere and of expected weather.
23. What type of cloud is fog? List and define the principal types of fog.
24. Describe the occurrence of fog in Canada and the United States. Where are the regions of highest incidence?

Critical Thinking

A. Examine the iceberg photograph in Figure 7.5b. The photo was taken in Scoresby Sund, East Greenland. Determine what caused the "shoreline" watermark above the ocean surface around the iceberg (near the top of the photo). Why do you think the iceberg appears to be riding higher in the water than several weeks earlier? In rough terms, how much ice (in percent) do you think is beneath the surface in comparison to the amount you see above sea level? Explain why this physical trait can be a hazard to shipping.

B. Using Figure 7.22, begin to observe clouds on a regular basis. See if you can relate the cloud type to particular weather conditions at the time of observation. You may want to keep a log in your notebook during this physical geography course. Seeing clouds in this way will help you to understand weather and make learning Chapter 8 easier.

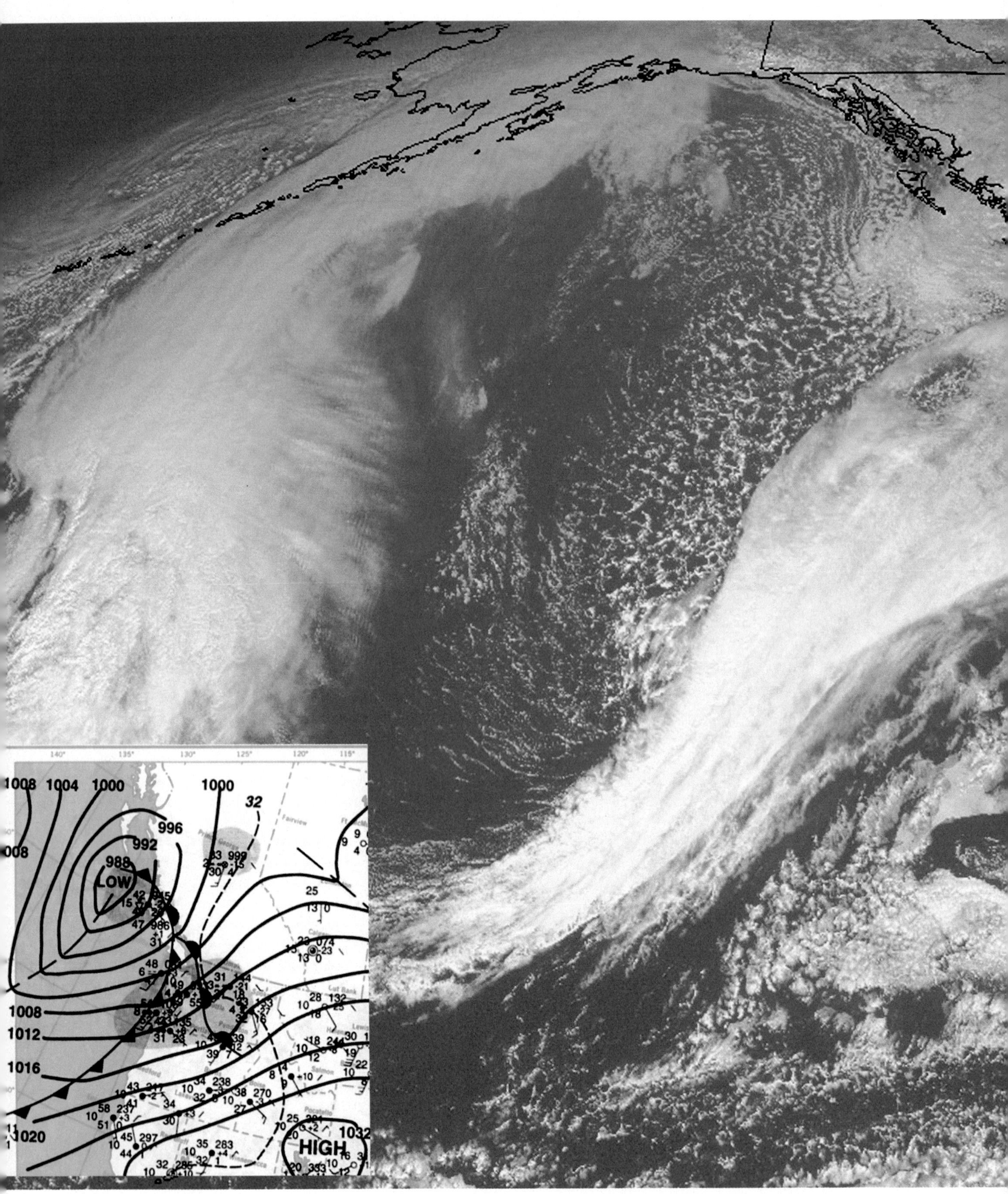

February 1, 2000: Parts of British Columbia, Washington, and Oregon receive heavy snow in the mountains and rain elsewhere from a jet-stream-guided storm system. Wind gusts reach 110 kmph (70 mph) along the Oregon Coast as air rushes into the low-pressure centre. The next system is far to the west over the Pacific Ocean. [*Goes-10* image courtesy of NESDIS/NOAA; weather map inset courtesy of "Daily Weather Maps," National Weather Service, NOAA.]

8 Weather

Key Learning Concepts

After reading the chapter, you should be able to:

- *Describe* air masses that affect North America and *relate* their qualities to source regions.
- *Identify* types of atmospheric lifting mechanisms and *describe* four principal examples.
- *Analyze* the pattern of orographic precipitation and *describe* the link between this pattern and global topography.
- *List* the measurable elements that contribute to weather and *describe* the life cycle of a midlatitude cyclonic storm system.
- *Analyze* various forms of violent weather and the characteristics of each.

Water has a leading role in the vast drama played out daily on Earth's stage. It affects the stability of air masses and their interactions and produces powerful and beautiful special effects in the lower atmosphere. Air masses come into conflict; they move and shift, dominating now one region then another, varying in strength and characteristics. Think of the weather as a play, North America the stage, and the air masses as actors of varying ability.

Weather is the short-term, day-to-day condition of the atmosphere, contrasted with *climate*, which is the long-term average (over decades) of weather conditions and extremes in a region. Weather is, at the same time, both a "snapshot" of atmospheric conditions and a technical status report of the Earth–atmosphere heat–energy budget. Important elements that contribute to the weather are temperature, air pressure, relative humidity, wind speed and direction, and insolation receipt related to daylength and Sun angle—in other words, the seasons.

We turn for the weather forecast to the Weather Office of the Canadian Meteorological Centre (http://weatheroffice.ec.gc.ca), a branch of the Meteorological Service of Canada, Environment Canada, or in the United States to the National Weather Service (http://www.nws.noaa.gov), to see current satellite images and to hear weather analysis. Internationally, the World Meteorological Organization coordinates weather information (see http://www.wmo.ch/index-en.html). Many sources of weather information and related topics are found in the "Destinations" section for this chapter on the Companion Website.

Meteorology is the scientific study of the atmosphere. (*Meteor* means "heavenly" or "of the atmosphere.") Meteorologists study the atmosphere's physical characteristics and motions, related chemical, physical, and geologic processes, the complex linkages of atmospheric systems, and weather forecasting. Computers handle volumes of data for accurate forecasting of near-term weather and for studying trends in long-term weather, climatology, and climatic change.

New developments in supercomputing, an Earth-bound instrument network in the Automatic Weather Observation System (AWOS; in Canada) and Automated Surface Observing System (ASOS; in the U.S.) arrays, orbiting observation systems, and Doppler radar installations are rapidly advancing the science of the atmosphere. By the end of 2004, 158 WSR-88D (*W*eather *S*urveillance *R*adar) Doppler radar systems as part of the NEXRAD (Next Generation Weather Radar) program were operational through the U.S. National Weather Service (125 systems), in conjunction with the U.S. Federal Aviation Administration (12) and the U.S. Department of Defense (21). In Canada, the National Radar Project will have 30 CWSR-98 radars in service (Figure 8.1).

FIGURE 8.1 Weather installation. Doppler radar installation at Exeter, Ontario, operated by the Meteorological Service of Canada. The radar antenna is sheltered within the dome structure. [Photo by Mary-Louise Byrne.]

Doppler radar detects the direction of moisture droplets toward or away from the radar, indicating wind direction and speed. This information is critical to weather forecasting and severe storm warnings. An essential part of this modernization in Canada is the deployment of the Weather Workstation, and in the U.S., the deployment of the Advanced Weather Interactive Processing System (AWIPS). AWIPS will eventually include 148 stations.

Weather-related destruction has risen more than 500% over the past two decades, from an average of $2 billion to $10 billion annually—considering storms, floods, droughts, and wildfires. For instance, 1998 weather damage alone topped $90 billion worldwide, which exceeds the total for all the 1980s, even when adjusted for inflation! Floods, droughts, ice storms, tropical cyclones and hurricanes, tornadoes, coastal storm surges, and heat waves all contribute to these totals.

In this chapter: We follow huge air masses across North America, observe powerful lifting mechanisms in the atmosphere, revisit the concepts of stable and unstable conditions, examine migrating cyclonic systems with attendant cold and warm fronts, and conclude with a portrait of violent and dramatic weather. Water, with its ability to absorb and release vast quantities of heat energy, drives this daily drama in the atmosphere. The spatial implications of these weather phenomena and their relationship to human activities strongly link meteorology to physical geography and this chapter.

Air Masses

Each area of Earth's surface imparts its temperature and moisture characteristics to the air it touches. The effect of the surface on the air creates regional masses of air having specific conditions of temperature, humidity, and stability. These masses of air interact to produce weather patterns—in essence, they are the actors in our weather drama. Such a distinctive body of air is called an **air mass**, and it initially reflects the characteristics of its *source region*. For example, weather forecasters speak of a "cold Canadian air mass" and "moist tropical air mass."

The longer an air mass remains stationary over a region, the more definite its physical attributes become. Within each air mass there is a homogeneous mix of temperature and humidity that sometimes extends through the lower half of the troposphere. Such masses of air possess all the physical characteristics of the atmosphere discussed in earlier chapters and thus link the Earth–atmosphere energy budget and water–weather systems.

Air Masses Affecting North America

Air masses generally are classified according to the moisture and temperature characteristics of their source regions:

1. *Moisture*—designated **m** for maritime (wet) and **c** for continental (dry).
2. *Temperature* (latitude)—designated **A** (arctic), **P** (polar), **T** (tropical), **E** (equatorial), and **AA** (Antarctic).

The principal air masses that affect North America in winter and summer are mapped in Figure 8.2.

Continental arctic (**cA**) air masses originate in Siberia and northern Canada. These cA air masses dominate the extreme north in winter when they cross over the North Pole and spill into the North American continent. Arctic air, colder than polar air and with a lower dew point, often forms when a high-pressure area becomes nearly stationary over northern Canada, Eastern Alaska, the Yukon, or Siberia. The small amount of winter solar radiation, abundant surface snow/ice cover, and the continuous emission of radiation from Earth's surface cause the air to become increasingly colder. If the jet stream becomes meridional during the time the air is stationary, very cold air spreads into southern Canada and the U.S. where it modifies to continental polar air.

Continental polar (**cP**) air masses form only in the Northern Hemisphere and are most developed in winter when they dominate cold weather conditions. These cP air masses are major players in middle- and high-latitude weather. The cold, dense cP air lifts moist, warm air in its path, producing lifting, cooling, and condensation. As we will see, the greater the temperature difference between this cold air mass and warmer air masses, the more dramatic is the weather produced. An area covered by cP air in winter experiences cold, stable air, clear skies, high pressure, and anticyclonic wind flow, all visible on the weather map in Figure 8.3. The Southern Hemisphere lacks the necessary landmasses (continentality) at high latitudes to produce continental polar characteristics.

Maritime polar (**mP**) air masses in the Northern Hemisphere exist northwest and northeast of the North American continent over the northern oceans. Within them, cool, moist, unstable conditions prevail throughout the year. The Aleutian and Icelandic subpolar low-pressure cells reside within these mP air masses, especially in their well-developed winter pattern (see the chapter-opening satellite image).

Two maritime tropical (**mT**) air masses—the *mT Gulf/Atlantic* and the *mT Pacific*—influence North America. The humidity experienced in the East and Midwest is created by the mT Gulf/Atlantic air mass, which is particularly unstable and active from late spring to early fall (Figure 8.4). In contrast, the mT Pacific is stable to conditionally unstable and generally lower in moisture content and available energy. As a result, the western United States, influenced by this weaker Pacific air mass, receives lower average precipitation than the rest of the country.

Please review Figure 6.14 and the discussion of subtropical high-pressure cells off the coast of North America—the moist, unstable conditions on the western

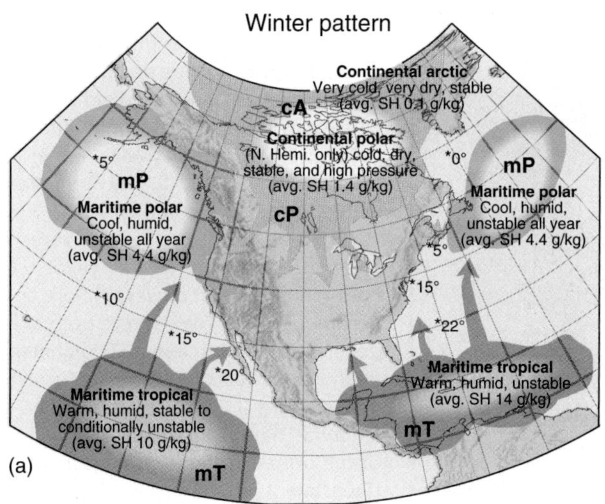

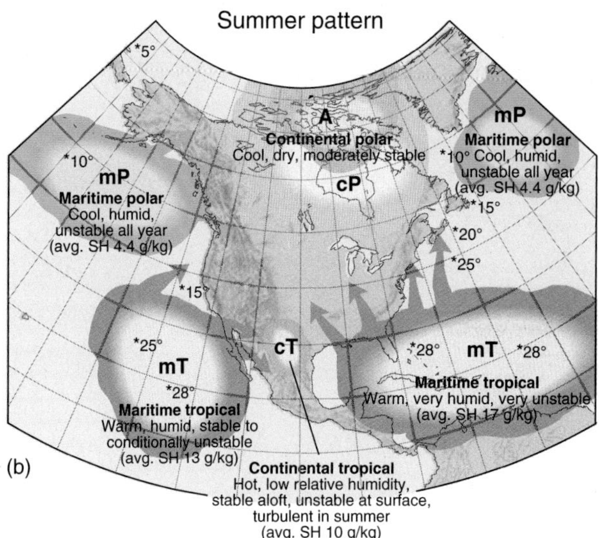

FIGURE 8.2 Principal air masses.
Air masses that influence North America in winter and summer. (*Sea-surface temperature in °C; SH = specific humidity.)

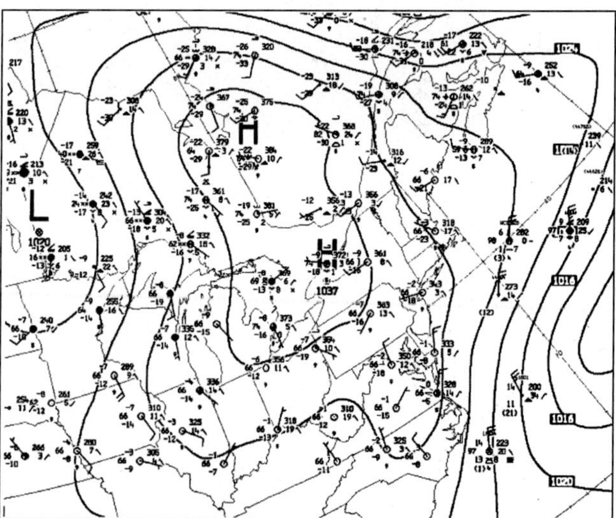

FIGURE 8.3 Winter high-pressure system.
A cP air mass with two high-pressure centres merging over the Great Lakes Region. One high pressure system of 1037.2 mb (103.72 kPa) has a temperature of –9°C and a dew-point temperature of –18°C. The northern high-pressure centre has a pressure of 1038.4 mb (103.84 kPa) with a temperature of –22°C and a dew point of –29°C. Associated with these centres are clear, calm stable conditions that dominate a large area. [Map courtesy of Environment Canada. Used by permission of the Minister of Public Works and Government Services Canada.]

edge of the Atlantic (east coast), and the drier, stable conditions on the eastern edge of the Pacific (west coast). These conditions, coupled respectively with ocean currents that are warmer (Gulf Stream) and cooler (California Current), produce the characteristics of each source region for these different maritime air masses.

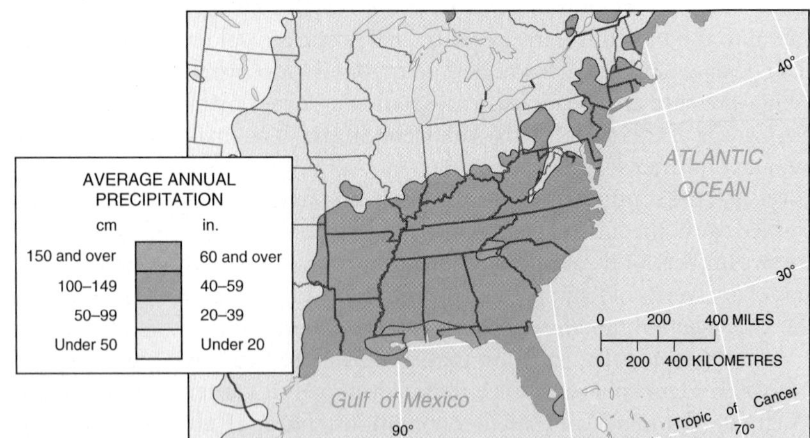

FIGURE 8.4 Influence of mT Gulf/Atlantic air mass.
The pattern of precipitation over the southeastern United States shows the influence of the warm, moist, and generally unstable mT Gulf/Atlantic air mass. Precipitation decreases with distance inland from the source region over the Gulf of Mexico and Atlantic Ocean.

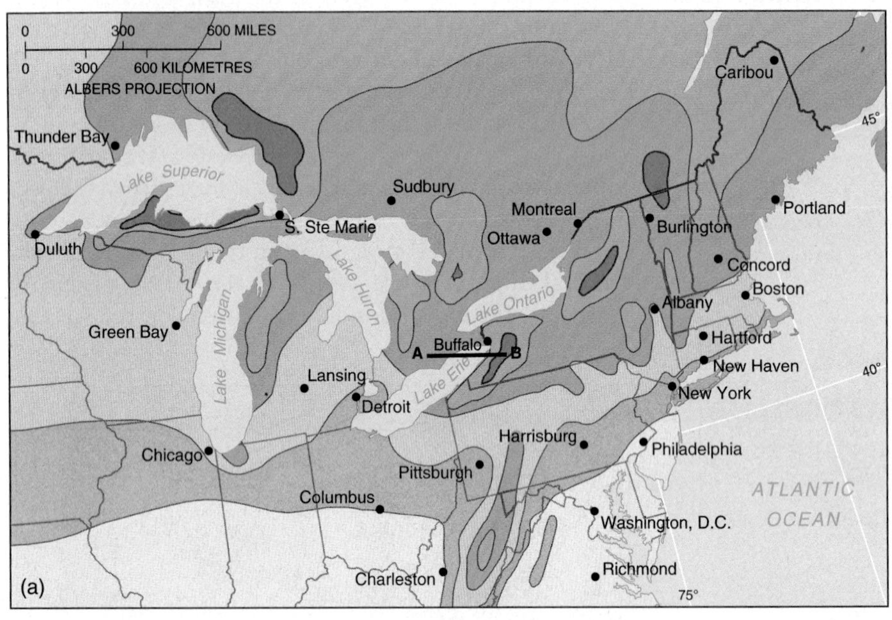

FIGURE 8.5 Lake-effect snowbelts of the Great Lakes.
(a) Locally, heavy areas of snowfall are associated with the lee side of each of the Great Lakes. In winter, cold cP and cA air masses pass from colder land surfaces across the relatively warmer water of these lakes. (b) The air masses are warmed and humidified (water vapour is added) from the lake water. The humid, now-unstable air yields heavy snowfall as it moves onshore and becomes chilled. The strongest effect is generally limited to about 50 km (30 mi) inland up to 100 km (60 mi). (c) Satellite image shows the lake-effect weather. [Snowfall data from the *Climatic Atlas of the United States* (Washington, DC: Department of Commerce, NOAA, 1983), p. 53; (c) MODIS sensor satellite *Terra* image, December 7, 2002, courtesy of the Rapid Response Team, NASA/GSFC.]

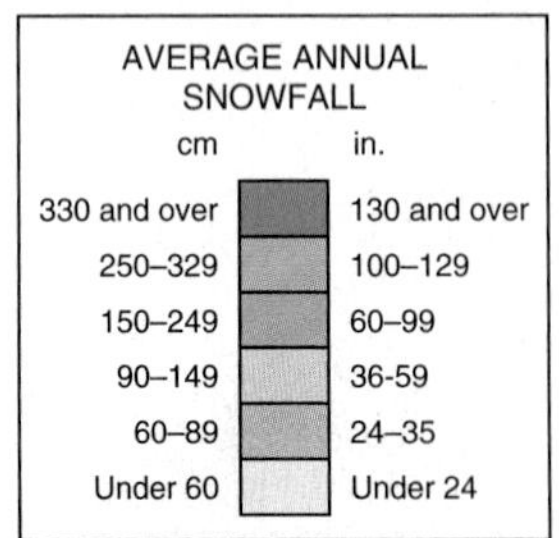

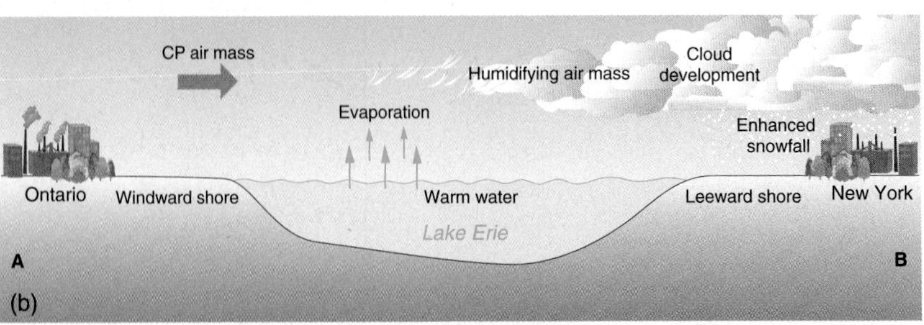

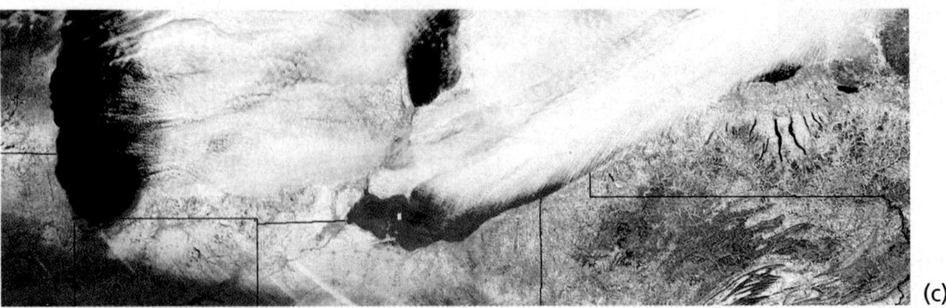

Air Mass Modification

As air masses migrate from their source regions, their temperature and moisture characteristics modify and slowly take on the characteristics of the land over which they pass. For example, an mT Gulf/Atlantic air mass may carry humidity to Chicago and on to Winnipeg but gradually will lose its initial characteristics of high humidity and warmth with each day's passage northward.

Similarly, below-freezing temperatures occasionally reach into southern Texas and Florida, brought by an invading winter cP air mass from the north. However, that air mass warms from the –50°C (–58°F) of its source region in central Canada. In winter, as a cP air mass moves southward over warmer land, it moderates, warming especially after it leaves areas covered by snow (the snowline).

Modification of cP air as it moves south and east produces snowbelts that lie to the east of each of the Great Lakes. As below-freezing cP air passes over the warmer Great Lakes, it absorbs heat energy and moisture from the lake surfaces (is *humidified*). This enhancement produces heavy lake-effect snowfall downwind into Ontario, Québec, Michigan, Pennsylvania, and New York—some areas receiving in excess of 250 cm (100 in.) in average snowfall a year (Figure 8.5). Lake effect snowfall is not limited to the Great Lakes—any large body of open water will produce this effect. Lake effect snowfall continues until lakes completely freeze over. Generally, the greatest accumulations of snow associated with lake effect occur in fall and early winter when storms are most intense.

Atmospheric Lifting Mechanisms

For air masses to cool adiabatically (by expansion) and to reach the dew-point temperature and saturate, condense, form clouds, and perhaps precipitate, they must lift and rise in altitude. Four principal lifting mechanisms operate in the atmosphere: convergent lifting (air flows toward an area of low pressure), convectional lifting (stimulated by local surface heating), orographic lifting (air is forced over a barrier such as a mountain range), and frontal lifting (along the leading edges of contrasting air masses). Descriptions of all four mechanisms follow and are summarized in Figure 8.6.

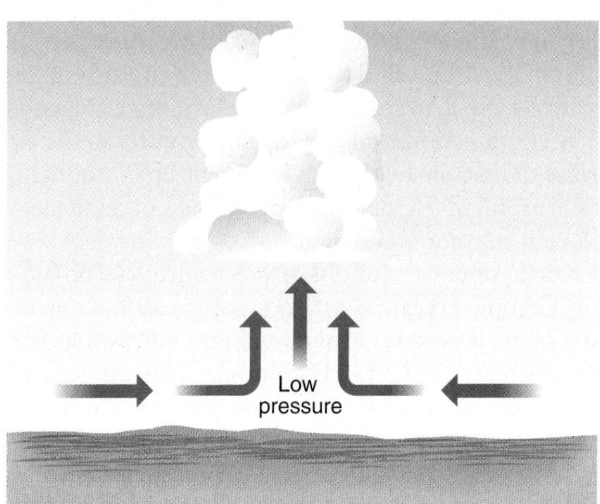

(a) Convergent

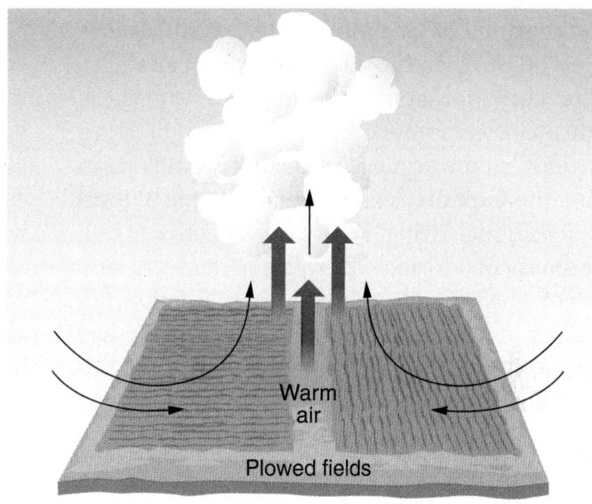

(b) Convectional (local heating)

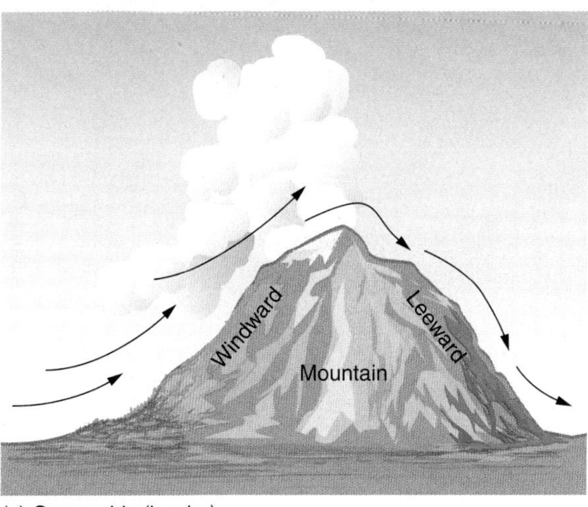

(c) Orographic (barrier)

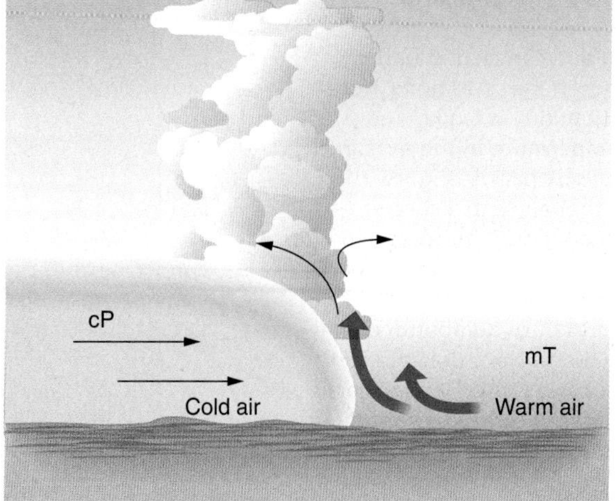

(d) Frontal (e.g., cold front)

FIGURE 8.6 Four atmospheric lifting mechanisms.
(a) Convergent lifting. (b) Convectional lifting. (c) Orographic lifting. (d) Frontal lifting.

Convergent Lifting

Air flowing from different directions into the same low-pressure area is converging, displacing air upward in **convergent lifting**. In the tropics, convergent lifting of warm, moist air produces disturbances that can lead to the development of a tropical storm. All along the equatorial region, the southeast and northeast trade winds converge, forming the intertropical convergence zone (ITCZ) and areas of extensive uplift, towering cumulonimbus cloud development, and high average annual precipitation (see Figures 6.12 and 6.13b).

Convectional Lifting

When an air mass passes from a maritime source region to a warmer continental region, heating from the warmer land causes lifting and convection in the air mass. Other sources of surface heating might include an urbanized area (heat island) or an area of dark soil in a ploughed field—the warmer surfaces produce **convectional lifting**. If conditions are unstable, initial lifting sustains and clouds develop. Figure 8.7 illustrates convectional action stimulated by local heating, with unstable conditions present in the atmosphere. The rising parcel of air continues its ascent because it is warmer (less dense) than the surrounding environment.

Florida's precipitation generally illustrates both these lifting mechanisms: convergence and convection. Heating of the land produces convergence of onshore winds from the Atlantic and the Gulf of Mexico. As an example of local heating and convectional lifting, Figure 8.8 depicts a day on which the landmass of Florida was warmer than the surrounding Gulf of Mexico and Atlantic Ocean. Because the Sun's radiation gradually heats the land throughout the day and warms the air above it, convectional showers tend to form in the afternoon and early evening, causing the highest frequency of days with thunderstorms in the United States. Florida appears highlighted and painted with clouds.

Towering cumulonimbus clouds are summertime features in the regions of North America that experience the mT Gulf/Atlantic air mass and, to a lesser extent, by the weaker mT Pacific air mass. Convectional precipitation also dominates along the ITCZ, over tropical islands, and anywhere that moist, unstable air is heated from below or where the inflowing trade winds produce a dynamic convergence.

Orographic Lifting

The physical presence of a mountain acts as a topographic barrier to migrating air masses. **Orographic lifting** (*oro* means "mountain") occurs when air is forcibly lifted upslope as it is pushed against a mountain. The lifting air cools adiabatically. Stable air forced upward in this manner may produce stratiform clouds, whereas unstable or conditionally unstable air usually forms a line of cumulus and cumulonimbus clouds. An orographic barrier enhances convectional activity and causes additional lifting during the passage of weather fronts and cyclonic systems, thereby extracting more moisture from passing air masses.

Figure 8.9a illustrates the operation of orographic lifting under unstable conditions. The wetter intercepting slope is termed the *windward slope*, as opposed to the drier far-side slope, known as the *leeward slope*. Moisture is condensed from the lifting air mass on the windward side of the mountain; on the leeward side, the descending air mass is heated by compression, and any remaining water in the air evaporates. Thus, air beginning its ascent up a mountain can be warm and moist, but finishing its descent on the leeward slope it becomes hot and dry.

In North America, **chinook winds** (called *föhn* or *foehn* winds in Europe) are the warm, downslope airflows characteristic of the leeward side of mountains. Such winds can bring as much as a 20 C° (36 F°) jump in temperature and greatly reduced relative humidity on the lee side of the mountains. The warm, descending wind is strong and creates a suitable environment for wind-power generation. In

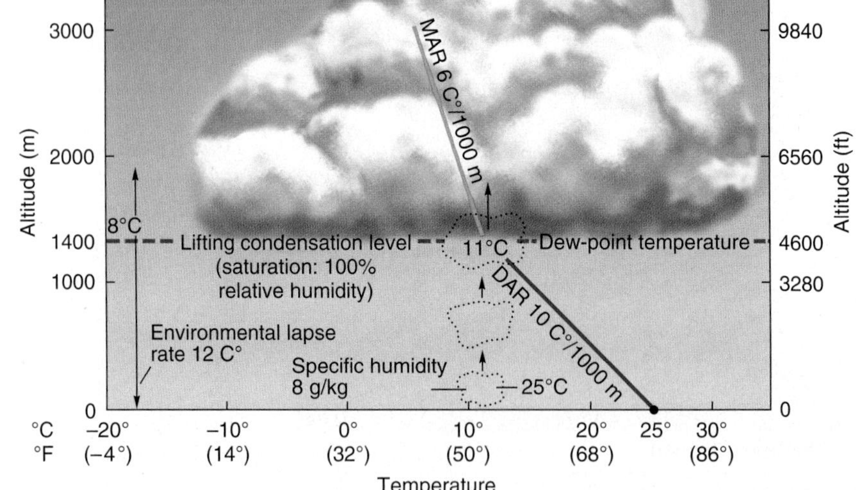

FIGURE 8.7 Local heating and convection.
Local heating and convection under unstable atmospheric conditions. Note that specific humidity is 8 g/kg and beginning temperature in the air parcel is 25°C. If you look back to Figure 7.12, you will find that air with a specific humidity of 8 g/kg must be cooled to 11°C to achieve the dew-point temperature. In the example, this temperature is reached after 14 C° of adiabatic cooling at 1400 m (4600 ft). Note that the DAR (dry adiabatic rate) is used when the air parcel is less than saturated, changing to the MAR (moist adiabatic rate) above the lifting-condensation level at 1400 m.

Atmospheric Stability

FIGURE 8.8 Convectional activity over the Florida Peninsula. Cumulus clouds cover Florida with several cells developing into cumulonimbus thunderheads. Warm, moist air from the Gulf of Mexico and Atlantic Ocean is lifted by local heating as it passes over the land. The remnants of Tropical Storm Edouard are slightly to the east. [*Terra* image from 9/3/2002, courtesy of the MODIS Land Rapid Response Team, NASA/GSFC.]

addition, there is turbulence associated with the descent of the chinook.

The term **rain shadow** is applied to dry conditions experienced in regions leeward of mountains. East of the Coast and Rocky Mountains in Canada and in the United States, and east of the Cascade Range, and Sierra Nevada, such rain-shadow patterns predominate (Figure 8.9b). In fact, the precipitation pattern of windward and leeward slopes persists worldwide, as confirmed by the precipitation maps for North America (Figure 9.6) and the world (Figure 10.2). See News Report 8.1 for more about the role of orographic barriers in setting precipitation records.

The province of British Columbia provides an excellent example of this concept, as shown in Figure 8.10. The Coast Mountains and the Rocky Mountains orographically lift invading mP air masses from the North Pacific Ocean,

News Report 8.1

Mountains Set Precipitation Records

Because orographic lifting is limited in areal extent to locations where a topographic barrier exists, it is the least dominant lifting mechanism worldwide. But mountain ranges are the most consistent of all the precipitation-inducing mechanisms. Both the greatest average annual precipitation and the greatest maximum annual precipitation on Earth occur on the windward slopes of mountains that intercept moist tropical trade winds.

The world's greatest average annual precipitation occurs in the United States on Mount Waialeale, on the island of Kaua'i, Hawai'i. This mountain rises 1569 m (5147 ft) above sea level. On its windward slope, rainfall averaged 1234 cm (486 in., or 40.5 ft) a year for the years 1941–1992 (topping the previous average of 460 in. and other lower values). In contrast, the rain-shadow side of Kaua'i receives only 50 cm (20 in.) of rain annually. If no islands existed at this location, this portion of the Pacific Ocean would receive only an average 63.5 cm (25 in.) of precipitation a year.

Another place receiving world-record precipitation is Cherrapunji, India, 1313 m (4309 ft) above sea level at 25° N latitude, in the Assam Hills south of the Himalayas. Because of the summer monsoons that pour in from the Indian Ocean and the Bay of Bengal, Cherrapunji has received 930 cm (366 in., or 30.5 ft) of rainfall in one month and a total of 2647 cm (1042 in., or 86.8 ft) in one year! Not surprisingly, Cherrapunji is the all-time precipitation record holder for a single year and for every other time interval from 15 days to 2 years. The average annual precipitation there is 1143 cm (450 in., 37.5 ft), placing it second only to Mount Waialeale. Record precipitation occurrences in Canada exist for locations along the Pacific Coast, on the windward side of the mountains. Henderson Lake, on Vancouver Island, is the wettest location in Canada with an average annual precipitation of 665.5 cm (262 in.).

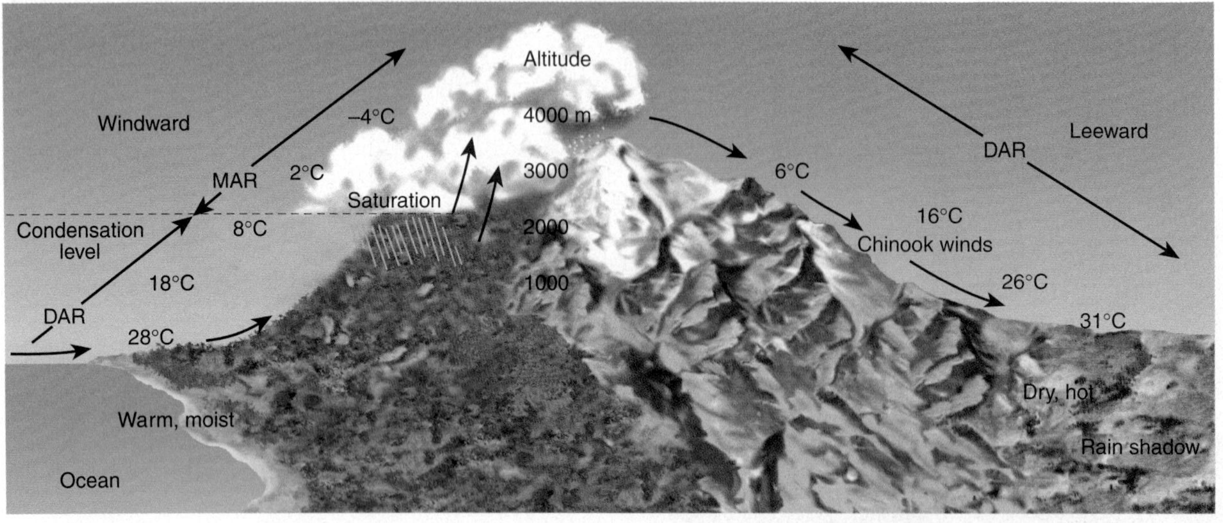

(a)

(b)

FIGURE 8.9 Orographic precipitation.
(a) Orographic barrier and precipitation patterns—unstable conditions assumed. Prevailing winds force warm, moist air upward against a mountain range, producing adiabatic cooling, eventual saturation, cloud formation, and precipitation. On the leeward slope, as the "dried" air descends, compressional heating warms it, creating the hot, relatively dry rain shadow of the mountain. (b) Rain shadow produced by descending, warming air contrasts with the clouds of the windward side. Dust is stirred up by leeward slope winds. [(b) Photo by Robert W. Christopherson.]

squeezing precipitation onto the windward sides of the mountains and allowing dry air to descend the leeward sides. The Egg Island Weather Station demonstrates precipitation on the windward slope of the Coast Mountains, and the Mount Fidelity Station on the edge of Glacier National Park demonstrates the windward slope for the Rockies. The leeward slopes are represented by 100 Mile House in the Caribou (leeward of the Coast Mountains) and Calgary International Airport, both of which show the lesser annual precipitation of the mountain rain-shadow zone.

Frontal Lifting (Cold and Warm Fronts)

The leading edge of an advancing air mass is called its *front*. Vilhelm Bjerknes (1862–1951) first applied the term while working with a team of meteorologists in Norway during World War I. Weather systems seemed to them to be migrating air-mass "armies," doing battle along fronts. A front is a place of atmospheric discontinuity, a narrow zone forming a line of conflict between two air masses of different temperature, pressure, humidity, wind direction and speed, and cloud development. The leading edge of a cold air mass is a **cold front**, whereas the leading edge of a warm air mass is a **warm front**.

Cold Front On weather maps, such as those shown later in Figure 8.14 and in Figure 8.17e, a cold front is a line with triangular spikes drawn that point in the direction of frontal movement along an advancing cP or mP air mass. The steep face of the cold air mass suggests its

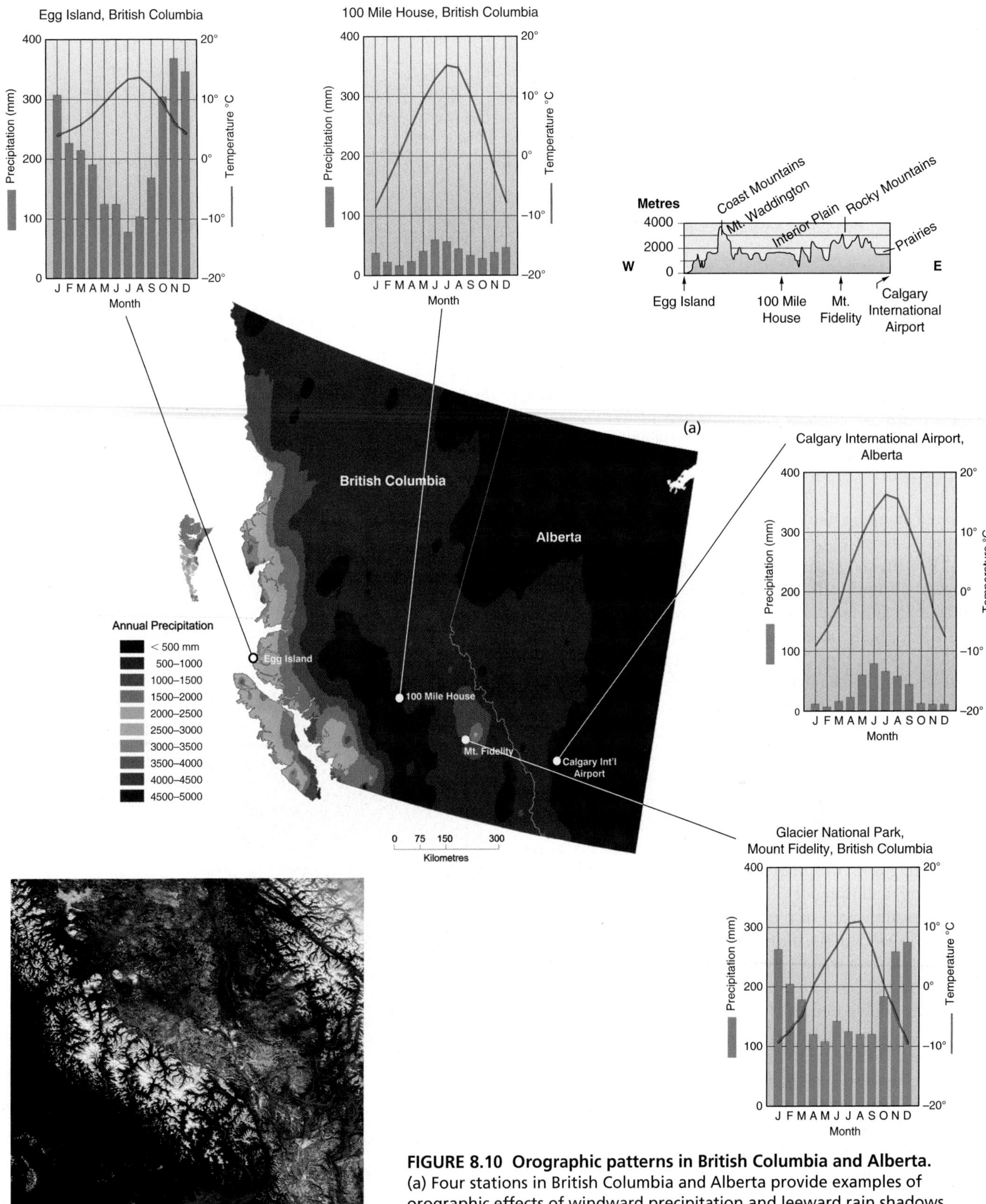

FIGURE 8.10 Orographic patterns in British Columbia and Alberta. (a) Four stations in British Columbia and Alberta provide examples of orographic effects of windward precipitation and leeward rain shadows. Isohyets (lines connecting points of equal precipitation) that form the boundaries between the colours on the map indicate precipitation (in mm). (b) The windward slopes of the Coast Mountain Range and leeward rain shadow conditions of the Interior Dry Plateau are clearly visible despite the light dusting of snow in this true-colour MODIS image from the *Aqua* satellite. [(a) Data courtesy of Meteorological Service of Canada, and map by Jessica Mueller and Pam Schaus; (b) Image courtesy of NASA/GSFC.]

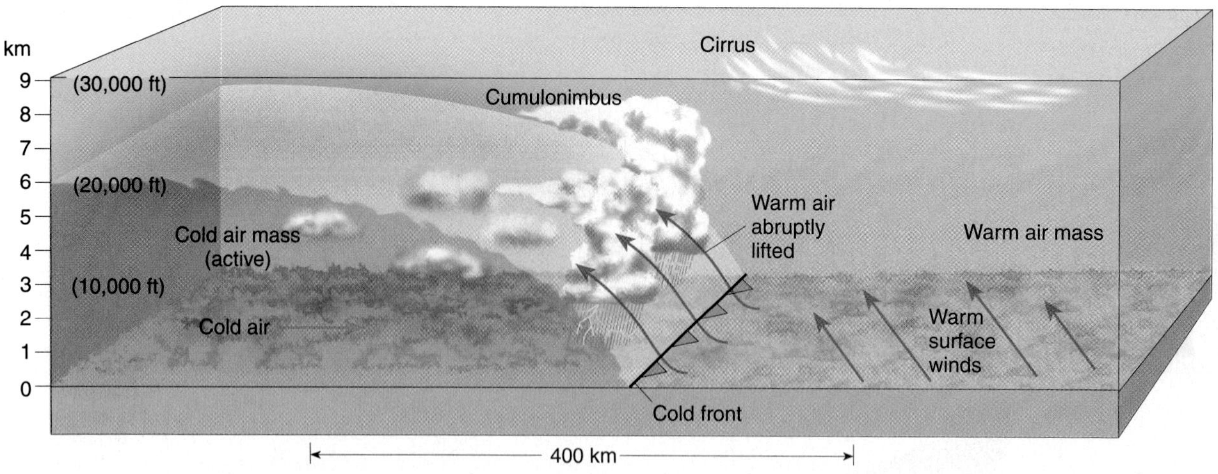

FIGURE 8.11 A typical cold front.
Denser, advancing cold air forces warm moist air to lift abruptly. As the air is lifted, it cools by expansion at the DAR, cooling to the dew-point temperature as it rises to a level of condensation and cloud formation. Cumulonimbus clouds may produce large raindrops, heavy showers, lightning and thunder, and hail.

Cold and Warm Fronts

ground-hugging nature, caused by its density and uniform physical character (Figure 8.11).

Warm, moist air in advance of the cold front lifts upward abruptly and experiences the same adiabatic rates of cooling and factors of stability or instability that pertain to all lifting air parcels. A day or two ahead of the cold front's passage, high cirrus clouds appear, telling observers that a lifting mechanism is on the way.

The cold front's advance is marked by a wind shift, temperature drop, and lowering barometric pressure due to lifting along the front. Air pressure reaches a local low as the line of most intense lifting passes, usually just ahead of the front itself. Clouds may build along the cold front into characteristic cumulonimbus form and may appear as an advancing wall of clouds. Precipitation usually is heavy, containing large droplets, and can be accompanied by hail, lightning, and thunder.

The aftermath of a cold front passage usually brings northerly winds in the Northern Hemisphere as anticyclonic high-pressure advances (southerly winds in the Southern Hemisphere); lower temperatures; increasing air pressure from the cooler, denser air; and broken cloud cover.

The particular shape and size of the North American landmass and its latitudinal position present conditions where cP and mT air masses are best developed and have the most direct access to each other. The resulting contrast can lead to dramatic weather, particularly in late spring, with sizable temperature differences from one side of a cold front to the other.

A fast-advancing cold front can cause violent lifting and create a zone right along or slightly ahead of the front called a **squall line**. Along a squall line, such as the one in the Gulf of Mexico shown in Figure 8.12, wind patterns are turbulent and wildly changing, and precipitation is intense. The well-defined frontal clouds in the photograph rise abruptly to almost 17,000 m (56,000 ft), with new thunderstorms forming along the front. Tornadoes also may develop along such a squall line.

Warm Front A line with semicircles facing in the direction of frontal movement denotes a warm front on weather maps (see Figure 8.14). The leading edge of an advancing warm air mass is unable to displace cooler, passive air, which

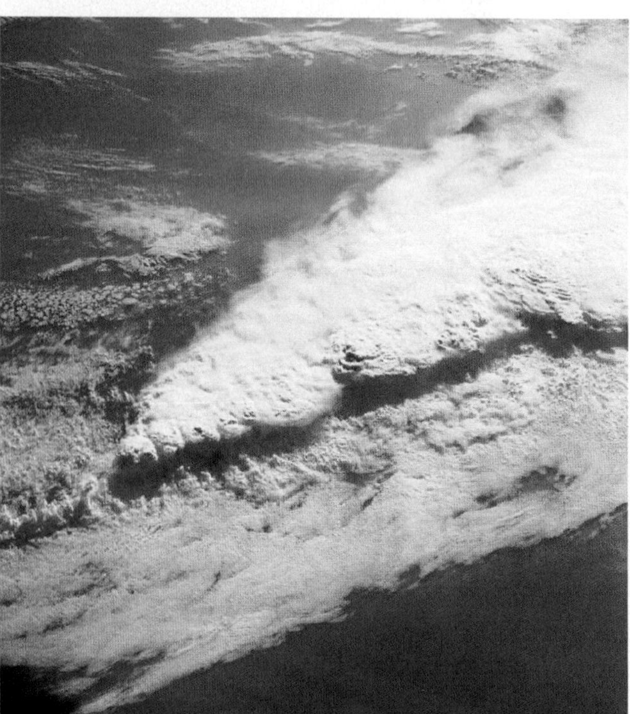

FIGURE 8.12 Cold front and squall line.
Cold front and squall line are marked by a sharp line of cumulonimbus clouds in the Gulf of Mexico. The cloud formation rises to 17,000 m (56,000 ft). The passage of such a frontal system over land often produces strong winds and possibly tornadoes. [Space Shuttle photo from NASA.]

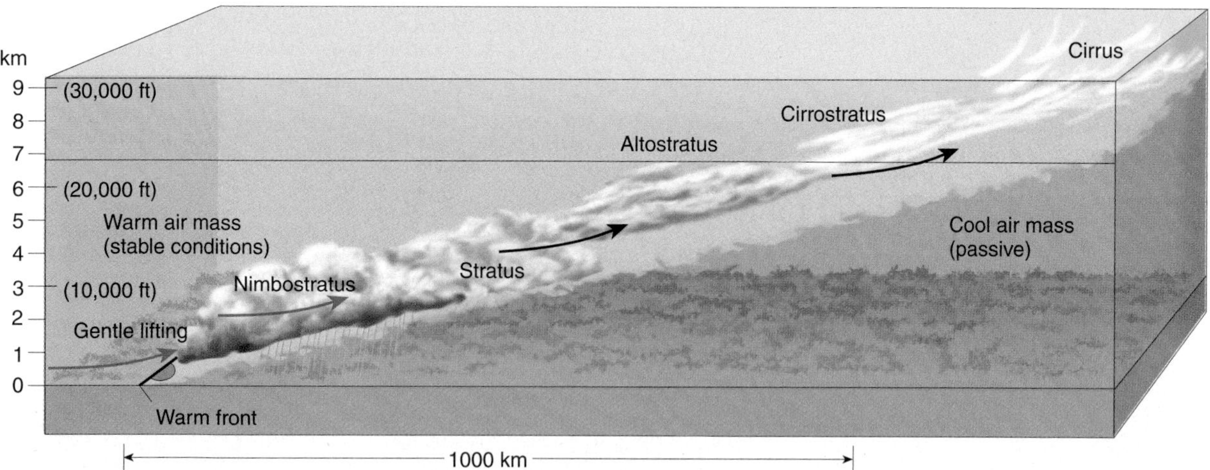

FIGURE 8.13 A typical warm front.
Note the sequence of cloud development as the warm front approaches. Warm air slides upward over a wedge of cooler, passive air near the ground. Gentle lifting of the warm, moist air produces nimbostratus and stratus clouds and drizzly rain showers, in contrast to the more dramatic precipitation associated with the passage of a cold front.

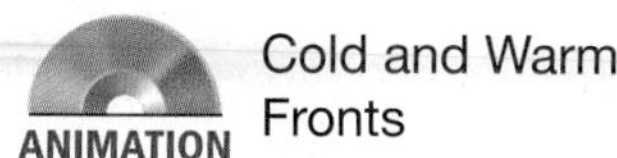

is denser. Instead, the warm air tends to push the cooler, underlying air into a characteristic wedge shape, with the warmer air sliding up over the cooler air. Thus, in the cooler-air region a temperature inversion is present, sometimes causing poor air drainage and stagnation.

Figure 8.13 illustrates a typical warm front in which mT air is gently lifted, leading to stratiform cloud development and characteristic nimbostratus clouds and drizzly precipitation. A warm front produces a progression of cloud development: High cirrus and cirrostratus clouds announce the advancing frontal system; then clouds lower and thicken to altostratus; and finally the clouds lower and thicken to stratus within several hundred kilometres of the front.

Midlatitude Cyclonic Systems

The conflict between contrasting air masses can develop a **midlatitude cyclone**, or **wave cyclone**. This migrating low-pressure centre with converging, ascending air, spirals inward counterclockwise in the Northern Hemisphere (or inward clockwise in the Southern Hemisphere). Because of the undulating nature of frontal boundaries and the steering flow of the jet streams, the term *wave* is appropriate. The combination of the *pressure gradient force*, *Coriolis force*, and *surface friction* generates this cyclonic motion (see discussion in Chapter 6).

Before World War I, weather maps displayed only pressure and wind patterns. V. Bjerknes added the concept of fronts, and his son Jacob contributed the concept of migrating centres of cyclonic low-pressure systems.

Wave cyclones dominate weather patterns in the middle and higher latitudes of both the Northern and Southern Hemispheres and act as a catalyst for air mass conflict. Such a midlatitude cyclone can initiate along the polar front, particularly in the region of the Icelandic and Aleutian subpolar low-pressure cells in the Northern Hemisphere. The intense high-speed winds of the jet streams guide cyclonic systems along their tracks (see Figures 6.17 and 6.18).

Life Cycle of a Midlatitude Cyclone

Figure 8.14 shows the birth, maturity, and death of a typical midlatitude cyclone in several stages, along with an idealized weather map. On the average, a midlatitude cyclone takes 3–10 days to progress through these stages from the area where it develops to the area where it finally dissolves. However, chaos rules and every day's weather map departs from the ideal in some manner.

Cyclogenesis **Cyclogenesis** is the atmospheric process in which low-pressure systems develop and strengthen. Along the polar front, cold and warm air masses converge and conflict.

The polar front is a discontinuity of temperature, moisture, and winds that establishes potentially unstable conditions. For a wave cyclone to form along the polar front, a point of air *convergence* at the surface must be matched by a compensating area of air *divergence* aloft. Even a slight disturbance along the polar front, perhaps a small change in the path of the jet stream, can initiate the converging, ascending flow of air and thus a surface low-pressure system (illustrated in Figure 8.14a).

In addition to the polar front, certain other areas are associated with wave cyclone development and intensification: the eastern slope of the Rockies and other north-south mountain barriers, the Gulf Coast, and the east coasts of North America and Asia.

Open Stage To the east of the developing low-pressure centre, warm air begins to move northward along an advancing front, while cold air advances southward to the west of the centre. See this movement on Figure 8.14b as

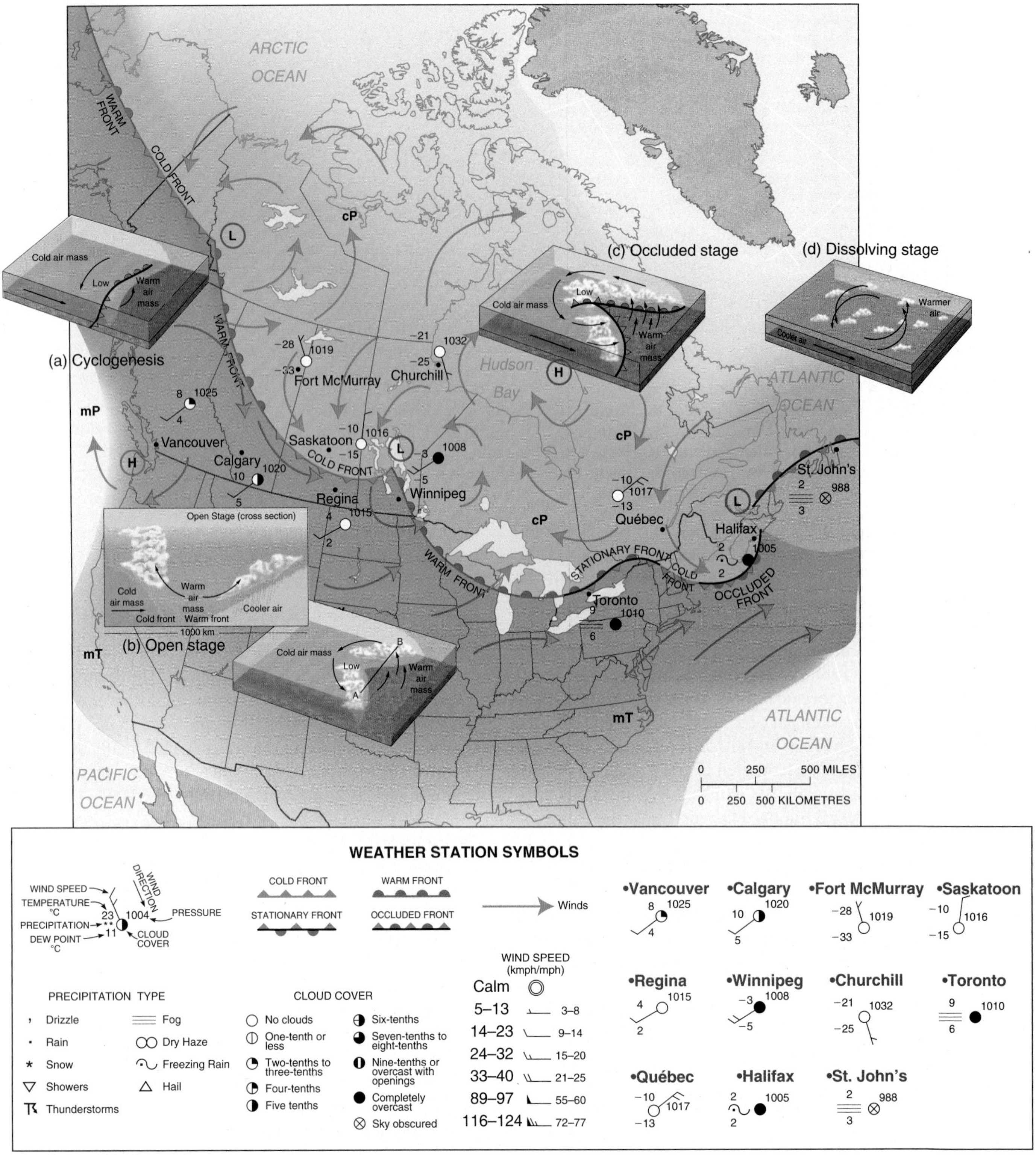

FIGURE 8.14 Idealized stages of a midlatitude wave cyclone.
(a) Cyclogenesis is noted where surface convergence and lifting begin. (b) The open stage. (c) The occluded stage. (d) The dissolving stage is reached at the end of the storm track as the cyclone spins down, no longer energized by the latent heat from condensing moisture. Standard weather symbols are in the inset box. After studying the text and the map, can you describe conditions in Vancouver, Calgary, Fort McMurray, Saskatoon, Regina, Winnipeg, Churchill, Toronto, Québec, Halifax, and St. John's depicted on this weather map?

a trough, or area of beginning convergence. The growing circulation system then vents into upper-level winds. As the midlatitude cyclone matures, the counterclockwise flow (in the Northern Hemisphere) draws the cold air mass from the north and west and the warm air mass from the south (here centred over Manitoba). In the cross section, you can see the profiles of both a cold front and a warm front and each air mass segment.

On the map, the cold front has passed over Saskatchewan. The wind symbol in Regina clearly shows winds are from the southwest. After the passage of the cold front, winds shift to northwest. Temperature and humidity are also affected. To the south of the low-pressure centre, southern Manitoba is experiencing temperatures of –3°C with a dew point of –5°C, while to the west of the centre, the temperature is –10°C with a dew point of –15°C.

Such an open stage of a midlatitude cyclone occurred February 19, 2004, with a low pressure centred over Nova Scotia. Figure 8.15 shows you a portion of a daily weather map for that day and an image from the *GOES-12* weather satellite for eastern North America. Note how the isobars portray the cyclone and the low of 996.2 mb (99.62 kPa) on the map. Also note the cloud pattern stretching along the cold front and swirling around the low. Compare the cold front and warm front and overall patterns with Figure 8.14b. This storm dumped over 1 metre of snow on Halifax in a 24-hour period—the largest one-day snow accumulation recorded in Atlantic Canada.

Occluded Stage Because the cP air mass is cooler in temperature and higher in pressure than the mT air mass, the cold air is denser and heavier. The cooler, more unified, air mass acts like a bulldozer blade and, therefore, moves faster than the warm front. Cold fronts can travel at an average 40 kmph (25 mph), whereas warm fronts average roughly half that at 16–24 kmph (10–15 mph). Thus, a cold front often overtakes the cyclonic warm front, wedging beneath it, producing an **occluded front** (*occlude* means "to close"). The cold front is occluding with the warm front just southwest of the low-pressure system. Precipitation may be moderate to heavy initially and then taper off as the warmer air wedge is lifted higher by the advancing cold air mass. On this idealized map a cold front and a warm front remain active to the south of the occluded area.

Also note the designation of a **stationary front** on the weather map (over the Great Lakes). This frontal symbol tells you that there is a stalemate between cooler and warmer air masses where airflow on either side is almost parallel to the front, although in opposite directions. Some gentle lifting is producing light to moderate precipitation. Eventually the stationary front will begin to move, as one of the air masses assumes dominance, evolving into a warm or a cold front.

Dissolving Stage The final, dissolving, stage of the midlatitude cyclone occurs when its lifting mechanism is completely cut off from the warm air mass, which was its source of energy and moisture. Remnants of the cyclonic system then dissipate in the atmosphere, perhaps after passage across the country (Figure 8.14d).

Storm Tracks Cyclonic storms—1600 km (1000 mi) wide—and their attendant air masses move across the continent along **storm tracks**, which shift latitudinally with the Sun and the seasons. Typical storm tracks that cross North America are farther northward in summer and farther

(a)

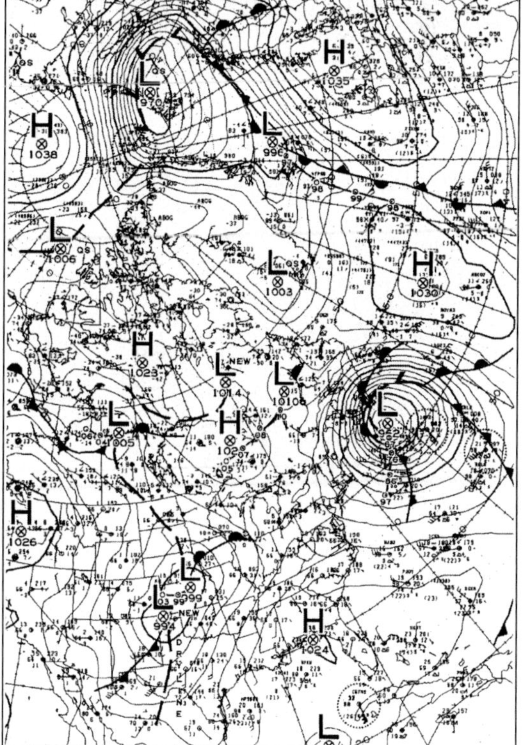

(b)

FIGURE 8.15 Open stage of a midlatitude cyclone.
(a) *GOES-12* infrared image of a cyclonic system over Nova Scotia. The cloud patterns are areas of precipitation; clear skies are behind the cold front as cP air mass covers the landscape. (b) A segment from the February 19, 2004 daily weather map at approximately the same time as the image showing the low pressure system centred on 996.2 mb (99.62 kPa). Counterclockwise winds circulate around the low. [Satellite *GOES-12* images courtesy of Environment Canada. Used by permission of the Minister of Public Works and Government Services Canada.]

southward in winter (Figure 8.16). As the storm tracks begin to shift northward in the spring, cP and mT air masses are in their clearest conflict. This is the time of strongest frontal activity, featuring thunderstorms and tornadoes. Storm tracks follow the path of upper-air winds, which direct storm systems across the continent.

A map of actual storm tracks for March 1991 in Figure 8.16b demonstrates several areas of cyclogenesis: the northwest over the Pacific Ocean, the Gulf of Mexico, the eastern seaboard, and the Arctic. Cyclonic circulation also frequently develops on the lee side of mountain ranges, as along the Rockies from Alberta south to Colorado. By moving eastward, such systems gain access to the moisture-laden, energy-rich mT air masses from the Gulf of Mexico.

The pattern of storm tracks has important implications for Canadian weather. During winter, when storm tracks are shifted south, much of Canada experiences weather associated with the northern half of low-pressure systems. "Northeasters" affect the Maritimes, Québec, and many of the American northeast coastal states. These are storm conditions generated in the northeastern quadrant of the advancing low-pressure system. Northeasters pull in moisture from the Atlantic Ocean and can result in large amounts of precipitation.

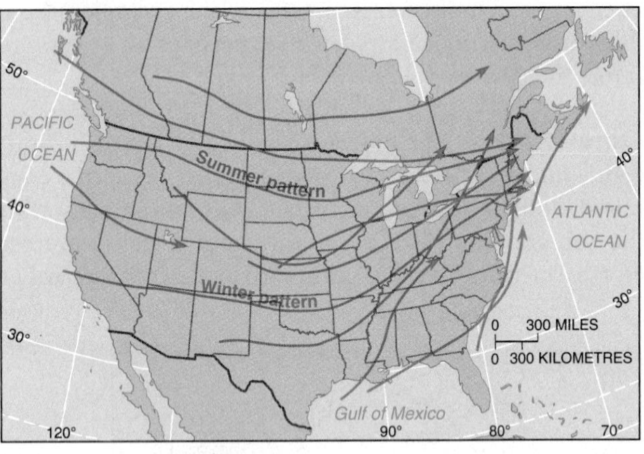

(a) Average storm tracks

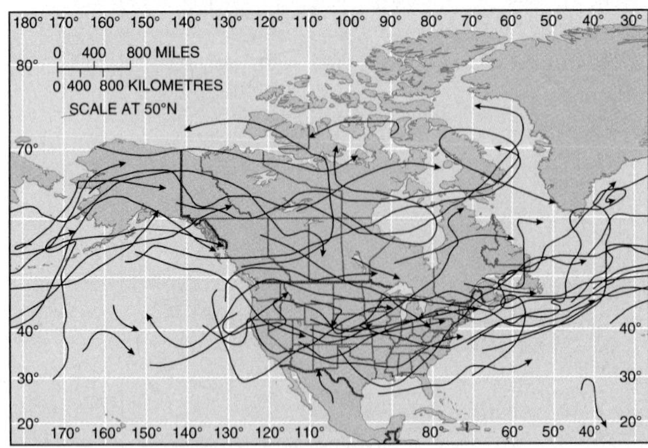

(b) Actual storm tracks in March 1991

FIGURE 8.16 Typical and actual storm tracks.
(a) Cyclonic storm tracks over North America vary seasonally. The tracks indicate several locations of cyclogenesis. (b) Actual cyclonic tracks during March 1991 over North America. [(b) From *Storm Data* 33, no. 3 (March 1991); Asheville, NC: NOAA, (NESDIS), National Climatic Data Center.]

The Canadian Prairies experience weather associated with expansion and contraction of continental high-pressure systems. The boundary of a strengthening Arctic high-pressure air mass can expand westward, pushing cold air up mountain slopes and resulting in light precipitation from orographic lifting of the dry, cold air. The weather thus approaches from the East or Northeast, contrary to the usual west to east movement of frontal weather.

On the West Coast, extreme weather develops when arctic outflow conditions develop. Normally, mild, moist air comes inland off the Pacific Ocean and flows from west to east. During an arctic outflow, cold arctic air moves from the north and gets trapped on the western side of the Rockies. Valleys with a west to east orientation, normally filled with mild moist air off the Pacific, are filled with cold, dry arctic air, and drastic temperature changes result.

Analysis of Daily Weather Maps—Forecasting

Synoptic analysis is the evaluation of weather data collected at a selected time. Building a database of wind, pressure, temperature, and moisture conditions is key to *numerical* (computer-based) *weather prediction* and the development of weather-forecasting models. Development of numerical models is a great challenge because the atmosphere operates as a nonlinear (irrational) system, tending toward chaotic behaviour. Slight variations in input data or slight changes in the basic assumptions of the model's behaviour can produce widely varying forecasts. As our knowledge of the interactions that produce weather and our instruments and software improve, so too will the accuracy of our forecasts.

Weather data necessary for the preparation of a synoptic map and forecast include:

- Barometric pressure (sea level and altimeter setting)
- Pressure tendency (steady, rising, falling)
- Surface air temperature
- Dew-point temperature
- Wind speed, direction, and character (gusts, squalls)
- Type and movement of clouds
- Current weather
- State of the sky (current sky conditions)
- Visibility; vision obstruction (fog, haze)
- Precipitation since last observation

For links to weather maps, current forecasts, satellite images, and the latest radar, please go to the Companion Website, to Chapter 8, "Destinations," and you will find many related links to the Internet. With the Internet, there is no need to wait for television or the newspaper to bring you the latest satellite image.

The Meteorological Service of Canada (MSC; **http://www.msc-smc.ec.gc.ca/msc/contents_e.html**) is responsible for collecting, recording, and reporting accurate and accessible daily weather, water, and ice information. MSC is composed of six directorates, one of which, the Atmospheric Environment Prediction Directorate (AEPD), provides leadership for all prediction activities of the Atmospheric Environment Program.

The Canadian Meteorological Centre (CMC) carries out synoptic analysis. Its three branches—Informatics, Operations, and Development—provide forecast guidance to regional prediction centres. The Informatics Branch provides centralized computing and telecommunications services and operates and maintains the supercomputer facility in Dorval, Québec, and various telecommunications networks. The Operations Branch is responsible for the meteorological operations of numerous production systems for weather, climate, air quality, and environmental programs at the CMC. The Development Branch is responsible for developing new systems and for technology transfer from research to operations of the Canadian environmental prediction effort.

Typical instrumentation and displays are illustrated by Figure 8.17. Automated stations use the Automatic Weather Observation System (AWOS) developed in partnership between the Atmospheric Environment Service and a private corporation. Canada currently has 31 upper air stations that send two radiosondes up each day at 1200 UTC and 0000 UTC. Additionally, there are six emergency stations and five Department of National Defence stations that occasionally produce upper air soundings. Nationally, there are 31 Doppler weather radar installations and 770 hourly weather observation sites across the country. This includes 261 NAV Canada aviation observation sites, the Department of National Defence sites, and differing types of automated observation sites that have various types of observation equipment. There are 298 Reference Climate Stations (RCS sites) that record maximum and minimum temperatures and precipitation amounts twice a day. Finally, there are 1425 climate stations operated by volunteers. The numbers of hourly observations, reference climate stations, and volunteer climate stations changes frequently.

AWOS sensor instrument arrays are a primary surface weather-observing network (Figure 8.17a). An AWOS installation includes rain gauge (tipping bucket), temperature/dew-point sensor, barometer, present weather identifier, wind speed indicator, direction sensor, cloud height indicator, freezing rain sensor, thunderstorm sensor, and visibility sensor, among other items.

The sequence in Figure 8.14 illustrates an ideal midlatitude cyclone model. The actual pattern of cyclonic passage over North America is not so tidy; it is widely varied in shape and duration. Regardless, you can apply this general model, along with your understanding of warm and cold fronts, to the actual midlatitude cyclone shown in the weather map and infrared satellite image in Figure 8.15. Preparing a weather report and forecast requires analysis of such daily weather maps and satellite images and the use of the standard weather symbols.

On the weather map in Figure 8.15, you can identify the temperatures reported by various stations, the patterns created, and the location of warm and cold fronts. The distribution of air pressure is defined by *isobars*, lines that connect points of equal pressure on the map. Although the low-pressure centre over northern Québec is not intense, it is well defined, with winds following in a counterclockwise, cyclonic path around the low pressure. This pattern is clear on the satellite image. A high-pressure cP air mass dominates central Canada. Note the dryness in western Ontario where the air temperature is –11.0°C (12.2°F) and the dew point is –14.0°C (6.8°F)!

Violent Weather

Weather provides a continuous reminder of the flow of energy across the latitudes that at times can set into motion destructive, violent weather conditions. In dollar value, weather-related damage is increasing each year, as population increases and people settle in hazardous areas. Environment Canada issues severe weather warnings, watches, and advisories to the public via the media, weather outlets, and Weatheradio Canada (see **http://www.msc-smc.ec.gc.ca/cd/brochures/warning_e.cfm** for a summary of different types of warnings, watches, and advisories). MSC includes a branch responsible for weather and climate research and a branch responsible for severe weather (**http://www.msc-smc.ec.gc.ca/acsd/mrb/severe_e.html**). In the United States, government research and monitoring of violent weather is centred at NOAA's National Severe Storms Laboratory and Storm Prediction Center in several cities (see **http://www.nssl.noaa.gov**; consult this site for each of the topics that follow). As mentioned earlier, 1998 broke all records for weather-related damage worldwide. We focus on ice storms, thunderstorms, tornadoes, and hurricanes.

Ice Storms

Ice storms (freezing rain, ice glaze, and ice pellets), snow blizzards, and low temperatures are forms of violent weather. Freezing precipitation occurs when *supercooled* moisture freezes on contact with a surface. The most common types of freezing precipitation are *freezing rain* and *freezing drizzle*, both of which can accumulate on surfaces and cause great damage (Figure 8.18a). Ice storms are a hazard in all parts of Canada except for the far north. They are especially common in the southern and eastern parts of the country, in a swath from southern Ontario to Newfoundland (Figure 8.18b). The thickness of ice accumulation associated with a storm, the storm's duration, and the extent of area affected determine the severity of the event. Typically, an ice storm lasts for 45 to 65 hours and deposits, at most, 30 to 40 mm (1.2 to 1.6 in.) of ice.

The ice storm of 1998 was an exceptional event that knocked out power for several weeks over a wide area—affecting eastern Ontario, southern Québec, the Fundy coast of New Brunswick and Nova Scotia, and the American northeast. During the 1998 storm there were over 80 hours of freezing rain and drizzle, and in some

Prairie irrigation in the Frenchman River valley south of the Cypress Hills in southwestern Saskatchewan. A field of hay is having its annual water balance augmented by a rolling sprinkler system. [Photo by David Sauchyn.]

9 Water Resources

Key Learning Concepts

After reading the chapter, you should be able to:

- *Illustrate* the hydrologic cycle with a simple sketch and *label* it with definitions for each water pathway.
- *Relate* the importance of the water-budget concept to your understanding of the hydrologic cycle, water resources, and soil moisture for a specific location.
- *Construct* the water-balance equation as a way of accounting for the expenditures of water supply and *define* each of the components in the equation and their specific operation.
- *Describe* the nature of groundwater and *define* the elements of the groundwater environment.
- *Identify* critical aspects of freshwater supplies for the future and *cite* specific issues related to sectors of use, regions and countries, and potential remedies for any shortfalls.

The physical reality of life is defined by water. Our lives are bathed and infused with water. Our own bodies are about 70% water, as are plants and animals. We use water to cook, bathe, wash clothing, and dilute our wastes. We water small gardens and vast agricultural tracts. Most industrial processes would be impossible without water. It is the essence of our existence and is therefore the most critical resource supplied by Earth systems—the essential resource for life.

Fortunately, water is a renewable resource, constantly cycling through the environment, endlessly renewed. Even so, some 80 countries face impending water shortages, either in quantity or quality, or both. Approximately 2.4 billion people lack adequate sanitary facilities. This translates to approximately 1.75 million deaths due to lack of water and 5 million deaths a year from water-borne infections and disease. During the first half of the new century, water availability per person will drop by 74%, as population increases and adequate quality water decreases. In the foreword to the United Nations World Water Development Report, *Water for People, Water for Life*, Kofi Annan stated:

> The centrality of freshwater in our lives cannot be overestimated. Water has been a major factor in the rise and fall of civilizations. It has been a source of tensions and fierce competition between nations that could become even worse if present trends continue. Lack of access to water for meeting basic needs such as health, hygiene, and food security undermines development and inflicts enormous hardship on more than a billion members of the human family. And its quality reveals everything, right or wrong, that we do in safeguarding the global environment.*

In the last two chapters, we saw how the exchanges of energy between water and the atmosphere drive Earth's weather systems. The flow of water links the atmosphere, ocean, land, and living things through exchanges of energy and matter. In particular, the energy and moisture exchange between plants and the atmosphere is important to the status of the climate system and the range of responses from plant communities to climate change.

Water is not always naturally available where and when we want it. Consequently, we rearrange surface-water resources to suit our needs. We drill wells, build cisterns and reservoirs, and dam and divert streams to redirect water either spatially (geographically, from one area to another) or temporally (over time, from one part of the calendar to another). All of this activity constitutes water-resource management.

In this chapter: The hydrologic cycle and global water balance give us a model for understanding the global plumbing system, so this important cycle begins the chapter. Water spends time in the ocean, in the air, on the surface, and underground as groundwater. Water availability to plants from precipitation and from the soil is critical to water-resource issues.

We look at the water resource using a water-budget approach—similar in many ways to a money budget—in which we examine water "receipts" and "expenses" at specific locations. Precipitation provides the principal receipt of moisture, whereas evaporation and plant transpiration are the principal expenditures. This budget approach can be applied at any scale, from a small garden, to a farm, to a regional landscape.

About half the population draws freshwater from the groundwater resource, yet groundwater is tied to surface water supplies for recharge. There are finite limits to groundwater. We discuss groundwater resources, overuse through groundwater mining, the irreversibility of groundwater pollution, and future prospects.

This chapter concludes by considering the quantity and quality of the water we withdraw and consume for irrigation, industrial, and municipal uses—our specific water supply. Adequate water supplies in terms of quantity and quality loom as *the resource issue* for many parts of the world in this century. Ismail Serageldin, chair of the World Water Commission, is quoted bluntly in a recent book on water issues: ". . . the wars of the twenty-first century will be fought over water. . . . Water is the most critical issue facing human development."**

The Hydrologic Cycle

Vast currents of water, water vapour, ice, and energy are flowing about us continuously in an elaborate, open global plumbing system. Together they form the **hydrologic cycle**, which has operated for billions of years, from the lower atmosphere to several kilometres beneath Earth's surface. The cycle involves the circulation and transformation of water throughout Earth's atmosphere, hydrosphere, lithosphere, and biosphere. (See the Canada Water Survey Web site, at http://www.wsc.ec.gc.ca/, and NASA's Global Hydrology and Climate Center site, at http://www.ghcc.msfc.nasa.gov/ for a combined government and academic effort to study the global hydrologic cycle and related climatic effects.)

Modern study of the hydrologic cycle involves computer modelling, direct observation, and remote sensing. A better understanding of the hydrologic cycle is central to understanding water resources and global climate change. Such systems as the hydrologic cycle operate in a chaotic manner, making model building difficult.

A Hydrologic Cycle Model

Figure 9.1 is a simplified model of this complex system. Let's use the ocean as a starting point for our discussion,

*World Water Assessment Programme, *Water for People, Water for Life* (UNESCO Publishing, 2003), Joint report by the UN agencies concerned with freshwater. (http://www.unesco.org/water/wwap)

**M. De Villiers, *Water, The Fate of Our Most Precious Resource* (New York: Houghton Mifflin Co., 2000), p. 13–14.

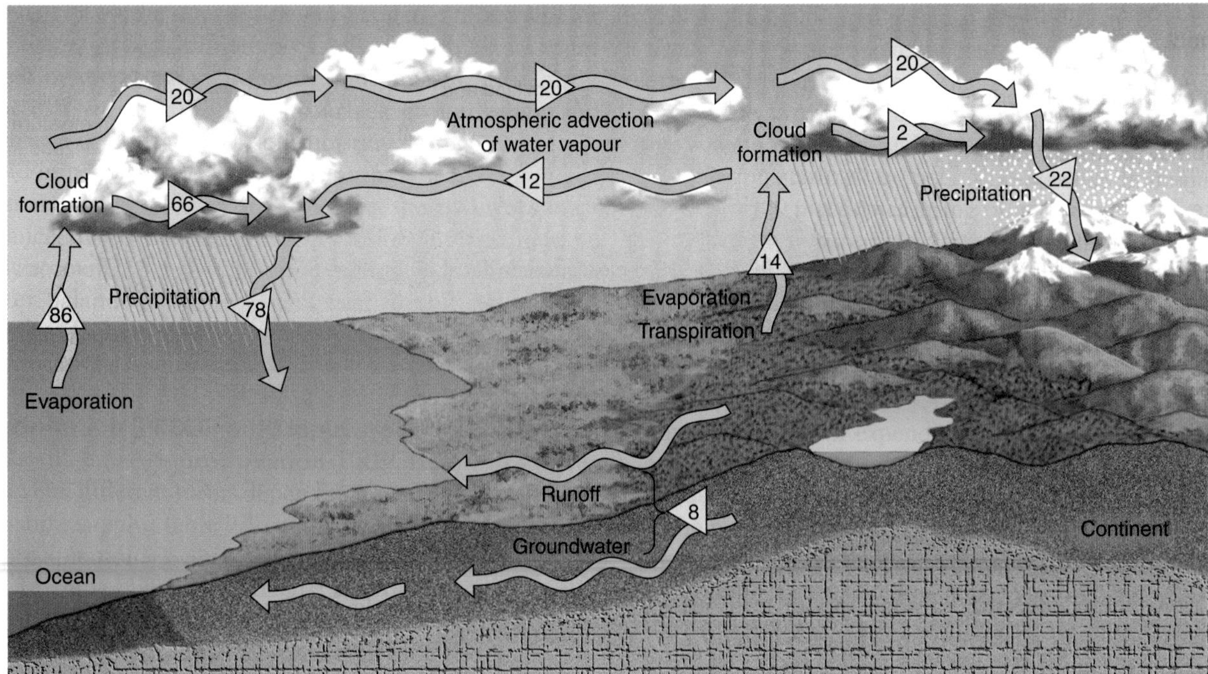

FIGURE 9.1 The hydrologic cycle model.
The model shows how water travels endlessly through the hydrosphere, atmosphere, lithosphere, and biosphere. The triangles show global average values as percentages. Note that all evaporation (86% + 14% = 100%) equals all precipitation (78% + 22% = 100%), when all of Earth is considered. Regionally, various parts of the cycle will vary, creating imbalances and, depending on climate, surpluses in one region and shortages in another.

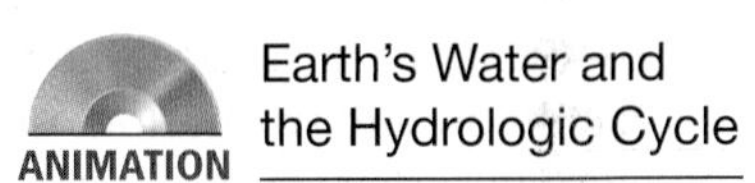

although we could jump into the model at any point. More than 97% of Earth's water is in the ocean, and here most evaporation and precipitation occur. We can trace 86% of all evaporation to the ocean. The other 14% is from the land, including water moving from the soil into plant roots and passing through their leaves (a process called *transpiration*, described later in this chapter).

In the figure, you can see that, of the 86% of evaporation rising from the ocean, 66% combines with 12% advected (moving horizontally) from the land to produce the 78% of all precipitation that falls back into the ocean. The remaining 20% of moisture evaporated from the ocean, plus 2% of land-derived moisture, produces the 22% of all precipitation that falls over land. Clearly, the bulk of continental precipitation comes from the oceanic portion of the cycle.

Figure 9.2 presents a global water balance in the hydrologic cycle. The percentages from Figure 9.1 are given with the volume (in 1000 km^3) of water flowing along these pathways.

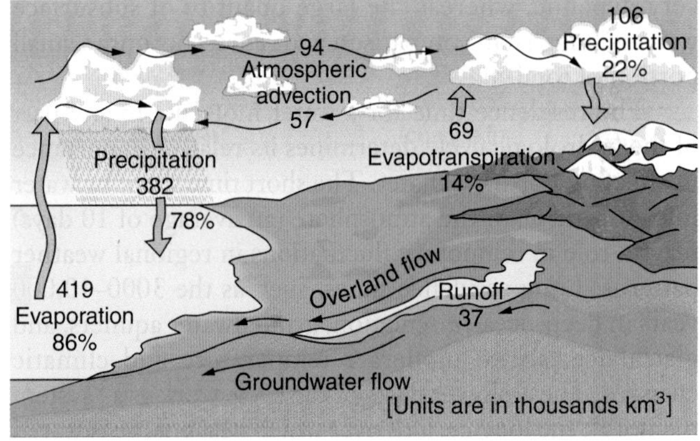

FIGURE 9.2 The global water balance in the hydrologic cycle.
The annual volume of water in all parts of the hydrologic cycle as measured in thousands of cubic kilometres. A balance exists between total evaporation and transpiration and precipitation and between advection in the atmosphere and surface runoff of water (1 $km^3 \times 0.24 = 1$ mi^3). Percentages are drawn from Figure 9.1, as given in the small directional arrows.

Surface Water

Precipitation that reaches Earth's surface follows two basic pathways: It either flows overland or soaks into the soil. Along the way **interception** occurs when precipitation strikes vegetation or other ground cover. Intercepted water that drains across plant leaves and down their stems to the ground is *stem flow* and can be an important moisture route to the ground surface. Precipitation that falls directly to the ground, coupled with drips onto the ground from vegetation (excluding stem flow), constitutes *throughfall*. Water soaks into the subsurface through **infiltration**, or penetration of the soil surface. It further permeates soil or rock through downward movement called **percolation**. These concepts are shown in Figure 9.3.

Overuse of Groundwater

As water is pumped from a well, the surrounding water table within an unconfined aquifer may experience **drawdown**, or become lowered. Drawdown occurs if the pumping rate exceeds the replenishment flow of water into the aquifer, or the horizontal flow around the well. The resultant lowering of the water table around the well is called a **cone of depression** (see Figure 9.16, left).

Overpumping Aquifers frequently are pumped beyond their flow and recharge capacities, a condition known as **groundwater mining**. The major area of overuse of groundwater in Canada is the Region of Waterloo in Ontario. Here, nearly a half a million people rely on groundwater for municipal supplies. The depletion of groundwater aquifers has led to extensive conservation efforts and exploration of other water sources.

In the United States, chronic groundwater overdrafts occur in large tracts of land in the Midwest, West, lower Mississippi Valley, Florida, and the intensely farmed Palouse region of eastern Washington State. In many places, the water table or artesian water level has declined more than 12 m (40 ft). In the United States, groundwater mining is of special concern in the great High Plains aquifer, which is the topic of Focus Study 9.1. About half of India's irrigated water and half of industrial and urban water needs are met by the groundwater reserve. And, in approximately 20% of India's agricultural districts, groundwater mining through more than 17 million wells is beyond recharge rates.

In the Middle East, conditions are even more severe, as detailed in News Report 9.1. The groundwater resource beneath Saudi Arabia accumulated over tens of thousands of years, forming "fossil aquifers," but the increasing withdrawals are not being naturally recharged to any appreciable degree at present due to the desert climate—in essence, it is now a nonrenewable groundwater resource. Some researchers suggest that groundwater in the region will be depleted in a decade, although worsening water-quality problems will no doubt arise before this date. Desalination of seawater to augment diminishing groundwater supplies is becoming increasingly important as a freshwater source (Figure 9.19).

> Like any renewable resource, groundwater can be tapped indefinitely as long as the rate of extraction does not exceed the rate of replenishment. But just like a bank account, a groundwater reserve will dwindle if withdrawals exceed deposits. Few governments have established and enforced rules and regulations to insure that groundwater sources are exploited at a sustainable rate.... No government has yet adequately tackled the issue of groundwater depletion, but it is at least getting more attention.*

Collapsing Aquifers A possible effect of water removal from an aquifer is that the aquifer, which is a layer of rock

*L. Brown et al., and the Worldwatch Institute, *Vital Signs, The Environmental Trends That Are Shaping Our Future* (New York: W. W. Norton & Co., 2000), pp. 122, 123.

Focus Study 9.1

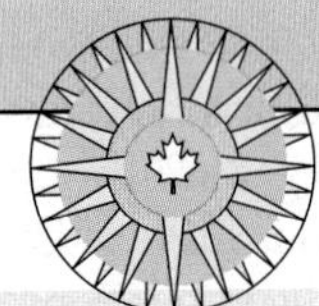

High Plains Aquifer Overdraft

Earth's largest known aquifer is the High Plains aquifer. It lies beneath the American High Plains, an eight-state, 450,600-km^2 (174,000-mi^2) area from southern South Dakota to Texas (Figure 1a). Precipitation over the region varies from 30 cm in the southwest to 60 cm in the northeast (12 to 24 in.). For several hundred thousand years, the aquifer's sand and gravel were charged with meltwaters from retreating glaciers. However, heavy mining of High Plains groundwater has occurred for the past 100 years, and mining intensified after World War II with the introduction of centre-pivot irrigation (Figure 2). These large circular devices provide vital water to wheat, sorghums, cotton, corn, and about 40% of the grain fed to cattle in the United States. The USGS began monitoring this groundwater mining in 1988. (See **http://ne.water.usgs.gov/** for links or **http://webserver.cr.usgs.gov/nawqa/hpgw/HPGW_home.html** for a study.)

The High Plains aquifer irrigates about one-fifth of all U.S. cropland: 120,000 wells provide water for 5.7 million hectares (14 million acres). This is down from the peak of 170,000 wells in 1978. In 1980, water was pumped from the aquifer at the rate of 26 billion cubic metres (21 million acre-feet) a year, an increase of more than 300% since 1950. By 1995 withdrawals had decreased 10% due to declining well yields and increasing pumping costs.

During the past five decades, the water table in the aquifer dropped more than 30 m (100 ft), and throughout the 1980s it has averaged a 2-m (6-ft) drop each year. The USGS estimates that recovery of the High Plains aquifer (those portions that have not collapsed) would take at least 1000 years if groundwater mining stopped today!

Figure 1b maps changes in water levels from 1980 to 1995. Declining water levels are most severe in northern Texas where the saturated thickness of the aquifer is least, through the Oklahoma panhandle and into Kansas. Rising water levels are noted in portions of south-central Nebraska and a portion of Texas owing to recharge from surface irrigation, a period of above-normal precipitation years, and downward percolation from canals and reservoirs.

Obviously, billions of dollars of agricultural activity cannot be abruptly halted, but neither can profligate water mining continue. This issue raises tough questions: How best to manage cropland? Can extensive irrigation continue? Can the region continue to meet the demand to produce commodities for export? Should we continue high-volume farming of certain crops that are in chronic oversupply? Should we rethink federal policy on crop subsidies and price supports? What would be the impact on farmers and rural communities of any changes to the existing system?

Present irrigation practices, if continued, will destroy about half of the High Plains aquifer resource (and two-thirds of the Texas portion) by the year 2020. Add to this the approximate 10% loss of soil moisture due to increased evapotranspiration demand caused by climatic warming, as forecast by computer models for this region by 2050, and we have a portrait of a major regional water problem and a challenge for society.

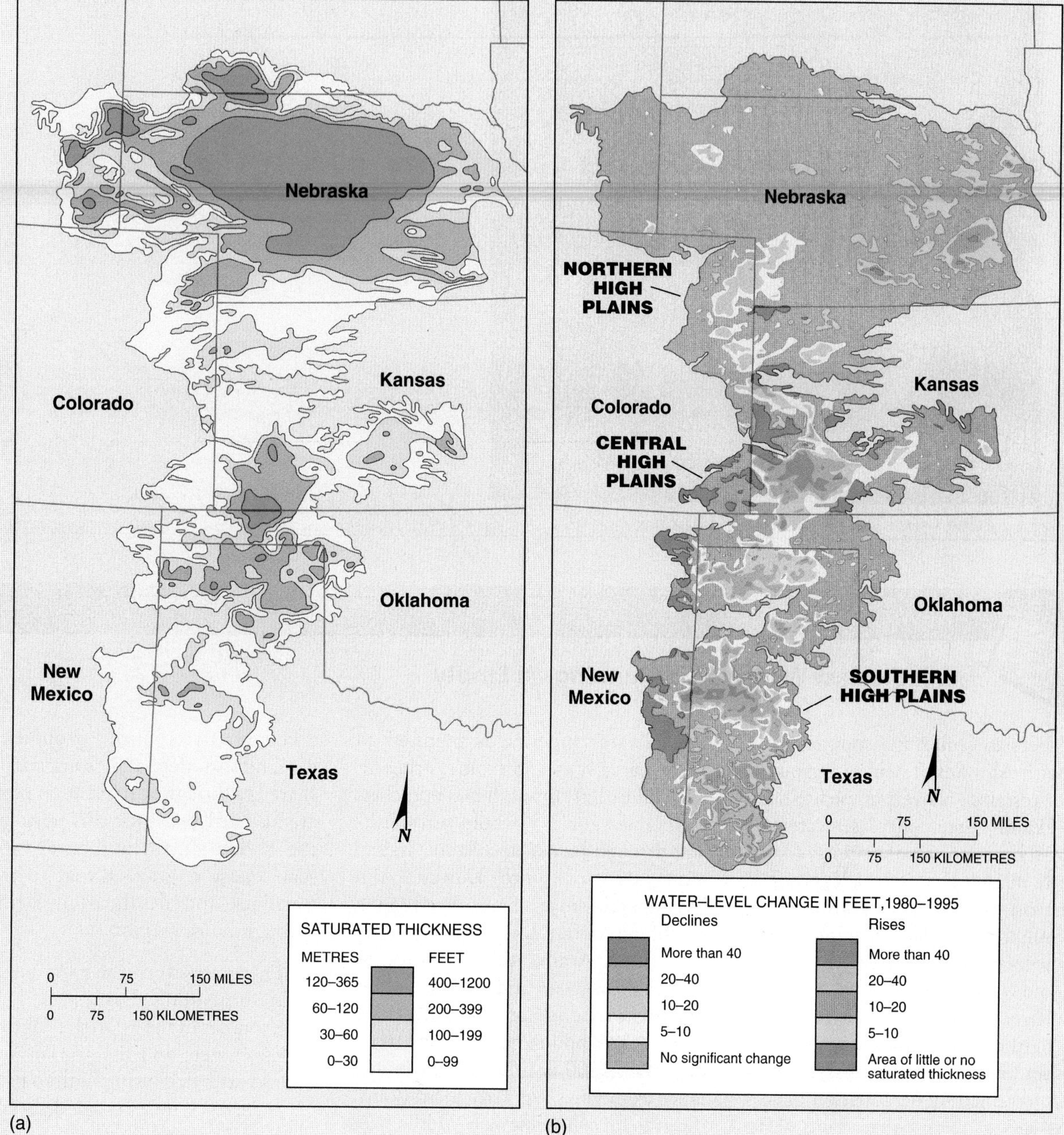

FIGURE 1 High Plains aquifer.
(a) The High Plains is the largest known aquifer in North America, mapped here showing its average saturated thickness. (b) Water-level changes in the aquifer from 1980 to 1995, given in feet. [(a) After D. E. Kromm and S. E. White, "Interstate groundwater management preference differences: The High Plains region," *Journal of Geography* 86, no. 1 (January–February 1987): 5. (b) USGS "Water-Level Changes in the High Plains Aquifer, 1980 to 1995," Fact Sheet FS-068-97, Lincoln, Nebraska: 1998.]

(continued)

Focus Study 9.1 *(continued)*

FIGURE 2 Central-pivot irrigation.
Myriad central-pivot irrigation systems water crops in north-central Nebraska. A growing season for corn requires from 10 to 20 revolutions of the sprinkler arm, depending on the weather. The arm delivers about 3 cm (1.18 in.) of water per revolution (rainfall equivalent). The High Plains aquifer is at depths of more than 76 m (250 ft) in this part of Nebraska. [Photo by Comstock.]

News Report 9.1

Middle East Water Crisis: Running on Empty

The Persian Gulf states soon may run out of freshwater. Their vast groundwater resource is overpumped to such an extent that salty seawater is encroaching into aquifers tens of kilometres inland! In this decade, groundwater on the Arabian Peninsula may become undrinkable. Imagine having the hottest issue in the Middle East become water, not oil!

Remedies for groundwater overuse are neither easy nor cheap. In the Persian Gulf area, additional freshwater is obtained by desalination of seawater, using desalination plants along the coasts. These processing plants remove salt from seawater by distillation and evaporation processes. In fact, approximately 60% of the world's 4000 desalination plants are presently operating in Saudi Arabia and other Persian Gulf states (see Figure 9.19).

A water pipeline is planned to carry water overland from Turkey in the Middle East through two branches. The Gulf water line would run southeast through Jordan and Saudi Arabia, with extensions into Kuwait, Abu Dhabi, and Oman. The other branch would run south through Syria, Jordan, and Saudi Arabia to the cities of Makkah (Mecca) and Jeddah. This pipeline would import 6 million cubic metres (1.68 billion gallons) of water a day some 1500 km (930 mi), the distance from New York City to St. Louis! (See the links listed under Middle East Water Information Network at **http://www.columbia.edu/cu/lweb/indiv/mideast/cuvlm/water.html**.)

Other remedies are possible. Traditional agricultural practices could be modernized to use less water. Urban water use could be made more efficient to reduce groundwater demand. Aquifers and rivers could be shared, although at present no negotiated accords exist for this purpose in the Middle East. Conflicts at various scales pose a grave threat to water pipelines and desalination facilities throughout the region.

> There are severe water shortages in the Middle East. . . . The resources of the Nile, the Tigris-Euphrates, and the Jordan are overextended owing both to natural causes and to those deriving from human behavior. . . . In addition to a severe shortage in the quantity of water, there is a growing concern over water quality.*

*N. Kliot, *Water Resources and Conflict in the Middle East* (London: Routledge, 1994), p. 1.

FIGURE 9.19 Water desalination.
Freshwater is supplied to Saudi Arabia from the Jabal water desalination plant along the Red Sea. Saudi Arabia obtains a significant amount of its water from desalination of seawater. [Photo by Liaison Agency.]

or sediment, will lose its internal support. Water in the pore spaces between rock grains is not compressible, so it adds structural strength to the rock. If the water is removed through overpumping, air infiltrates the pores. Air is readily compressible, and the tremendous weight of overlying rock may crush the aquifer. On the surface, the visible result may be land subsidence, cracked house foundations, and changes in drainage. Unfortunately, collapsed aquifers may not be rechargeable, even if surplus gravitational water becomes available, because pore spaces may be permanently collapsed. In the United States, the water-well fields that serve the Tampa Bay–St. Petersburg, Florida, area are a case in point. Pond and lake levels, swamps, and wetlands in the area are declining and land surfaces subsiding as the groundwater drawdown for export to the cities increases.

Houston, Texas, provides another example. The removal of groundwater and crude oil caused land within an 80-km (50-mi) radius of Houston to subside more than 3 m (10 ft) over the years. Yet another example is the Fresno area of California's San Joaquin Valley. After years of intensive pumping of groundwater for irrigation, land levels have dropped almost 10 m (33 ft) because of a combination of water removal and soil compaction from agricultural activity.

Surface mining ("strip mining") for coal in eastern Texas, northeastern Louisiana, Wyoming, Arizona, and other locales, also destroys aquifers. Aquifer collapse is an increasing problem in West Virginia, Kentucky, and Virginia, where low-sulphur coal is mined to meet current air-pollution requirements for coal-burning electric power plants.

Saltwater Encroachment When aquifers are over-pumped near the ocean, another problem arises. Along a coastline, fresh groundwater and salty seawater establish a natural interface or *contact surface*. But excessive withdrawal of freshwater can cause this interface to migrate inland. As a result, wells near the shore may become contaminated with saltwater, and the aquifer may become useless as a freshwater source. Figure 9.16 illustrates this seawater intrusion (far-right side). Pumping freshwater back into the aquifer may halt contamination by seawater, but once contaminated, the aquifer is difficult to reclaim.

Pollution of Groundwater

When surface water is polluted, groundwater inevitably becomes contaminated because it is recharged from surface-water supplies. Surface water flows rapidly and flushes pollution downstream, but slow-moving groundwater, once contaminated, remains polluted virtually forever.

Pollution can enter groundwater from industrial injection wells (wastes pumped into the ground), septic tank outflows, seepage from hazardous-waste disposal sites, industrial toxic waste, agricultural residues (pesticides, herbicides, fertilizers), and urban solid-waste landfills. Groundwater pollution from agricultural practices is the topic of Focus Study 9.2.

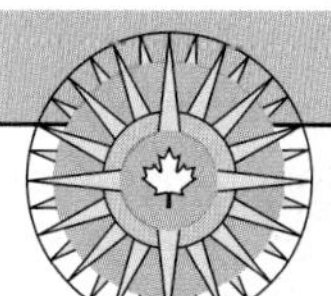

Focus Study 9.2

Walkerton, Ontario: Groundwater Contamination, Water System Mismanagement, and Tragedy

In May 2000 the town of Walkerton, Ontario (Figure 1) was the site of water resources mismanagement that ultimately led to the illnesses of 2300 residents and the deaths of seven people. In early May, there was a period of heavy precipitation that resulted in local flooding, which had a tragic impact on the drinking water supply.

The town of Walkerton is among many in a part of Ontario that relies heavily on groundwater. The town has six wells that supply its municipal water needs. During the May 2000 precipitation event, Well 5 became contaminated. Well 5 was an extremely shallow well, directly connected to surface water. Contamination may have entered the well via overland flow but is more likely to have been transported through boreholes (fence posts) and fractures in the bedrock. It is likely that the groundwater contamination occurred after rapid percolation of water through the thin soil that was spread with animal waste from feedlots. Rapid percolation is enhanced by the drawdown around the well when water is pumped. A secondary source of contamination was from Well 7. This artesian well had an overflow device, allowing excess water to run out when the well was not operating. During periods of heavy precipitation, as in May 2000, the excess water flows out of the wellhead and floods surrounding

(continued)

Focus Study 9.2 *(continued)*

depression areas. When Well 7 was turned on, the small plastic flap valve was not able to prevent water from flowing down the pipe into the well. In Figure 9.16 you can see how the surface water, seepage from pollution sources, and groundwater wells are interrelated.

On May 19, 2000, several people contacted the regional Medical Health Office (MHO) to relate symptoms including bloody diarrhea, vomiting, cramps, and fever. The MHO began to investigate a possible source of bacterial contamination—beginning with the water system. The Public Utilities Commission (PUC) that managed the water system assured the MHO that the water was fine and that wells were routinely sampled. As the MHO continued the investigation, more people became ill. Again, the PUC reassured officials that the water was safe. Regardless, the MHO issued a boil water advisory, took its own water sample, and found that the local drinking water was contaminated with *Escherichia coli*, more commonly known as E. coli. The bacteria had been washed into wells and seeped into the groundwater in the area. A judicial inquiry was called to investigate the event.

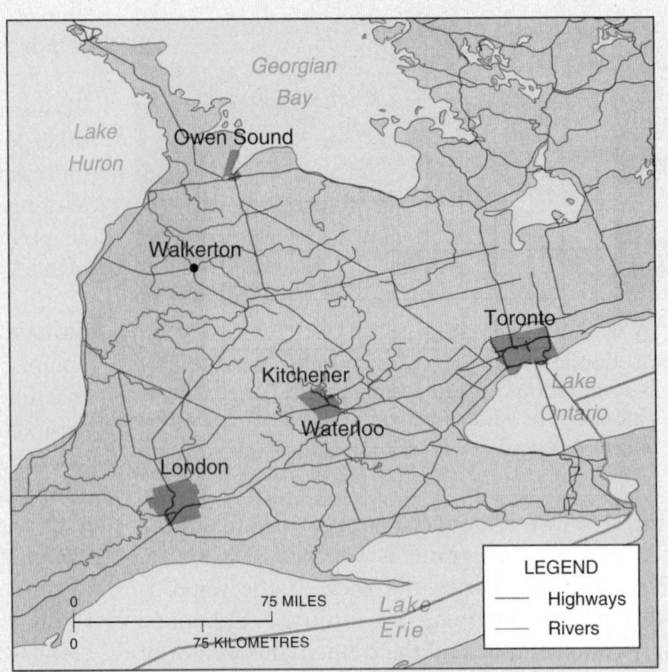

FIGURE 1 Walkerton, Ontario.
Walkerton is typical of the small towns in southern and south-central Ontario that rely on groundwater for freshwater supply. [Map created by Pam Schaus.]

The results of the Inquiry summarized that seven people died and more than 2300 became ill. Of those who became ill, many, especially children, will have lasting effects as a result of the E. coli contamination. The bacteria entered Municipal Well 5 on or about May 12, 2000 when heavy precipitation and local flooding resulted in runoff from fields spread with uncomposted manure. During the precipitation event, the well was not continuously monitored and chlorine levels were not measured. The results of the inquiry determined that the PUC had mismanaged the water system for years. Government budget cutbacks for water monitoring and minimizing water management standards compounded the problem.

Judicial inquiry recommendations included planning and standards for drinking water quality, the management of runoff and other contaminant pathways, increases in monitoring and licensing of water managers, and establishment of electronic access to drinking water information.

For management purposes, about 35% of pollution is *point source* (such as a gasoline tank or septic tank); 65% is *nonpoint source* (from a broad area, such as an agricultural field, or urban runoff). Nitrates contaminate nearly all the groundwater that underlies agricultural land in Canada. The levels are below the guidelines for Canadian drinking water quality but, while historical data suggest that nitrate levels have not changed in the last 50 years, the incidence of bacteria in well water has almost doubled in the same time period. The 1996 State of Canada's Environment Report (**http://www.ec.gc.ca/soer-ree/English/SOER/1996report/Doc/1-7-3-6-5-3-1.cfm**) noted that, in some areas, nitrate levels are more than four times greater than the Canadian drinking water guidelines. Regardless of the spatial nature of the source, pollution can spread over a great distance, illustrated in Figure 9.16. The extent of groundwater pollution is underestimated since aquifers are inaccessible except at well sites.

However, once identification of recharge areas of both confined and unconfined aquifers takes place, the prevailing government body should zone them to prohibit pollution discharges, septic and sewage-system installations, or hazardous-material dumping. An informed population should insist on such action because protection is cheaper than the nearly impossible cleanup or replacement of contaminated groundwater sources. In the illustration, note the improperly located disposal pond on the aquifer recharge area, contaminating wells to the right.

In the face of government inaction, and even attempts to reverse some protection laws, serious groundwater contamination continues nationwide, adding validity to a quote from more than 20 years ago:

> One characteristic is the practical irreversibility of groundwater pollution, causing the cost of clean-up to be prohibitively high. . . . It is a questionable ethical

practice to impose the potential risks associated with groundwater contamination on future generations when steps can be taken today to prevent further contamination.*

Our Water Supply

Human thirst for adequate water supplies, both in quantity and quality, will be a major issue in this century. Internationally, increases in per capita water use are double the rate of population growth. Since we are so dependent on water, it seems that humans should cluster where good water is plentiful. But accessible water supplies are not well correlated with population distribution or the regions where population growth is greatest.

Table 9.3 shows estimated world water supplies, present world population, estimated population figures for 2025, population change forecast between 2004 and 2050 at present growth rates, and a comparison of population and global runoff percentages for each continent. The table gives an idea of the unevenness of Earth's water supply, which is tied to climatic variability and water demand, which is tied to level of development, affluence, and per capita consumption.

For example, North America's mean annual discharge is 5960 km^3 and Asia's is 13,200 km^3. However, North America has only 4.8% of the world's population, whereas Asia has 61.4%, with a population doubling time less than half of North America's. In northern China, 550 million people living in approximately 500 cities lack adequate water supplies. For comparison, note that the 1990 floods cost China $10 billion, whereas water shortages are running at more than $35 billion a year in costs to their economy. The Yellow River, a water resource for many Chinese, runs dry every year and in 1997 it failed to reach the sea for almost 230 days! An analyst for the World Bank stated that China's water shortages pose a more serious threat than floods during this century.

*J. Tripp, "Groundwater protection strategies," in *Groundwater Pollution, Environmental and Legal Problems* (Washington, DC: American Association for the Advancement of Science, 1984), p. 137. Reprinted by permission.

Water is critical for survival. Just to produce our food requires enormous quantities of water, for growing, cleaning, processing, and waste disposal. Important to the assessment of water use is the measuring standards used for water resources. See News Report 9.2 for personal water use and water measurements. We take for granted the quality and quantity of our water supply, because it always seems to be there with little effort on our part.

At present, the world's people are withdrawing 30% of the runoff that is accessible. This idea of "accessibility" is important, because about 20% of global runoff is remote and not readily available to meet water demand. Timing of flows is also important, for approximately 50% of total runoff remains beyond use as uncaptured floodwater. For example, the greatest river in terms of runoff discharge on Earth—the Amazon—is about 95% remote from population centres, or not readily available.

Water resources differ from other resources in that there is no alternative substance to water. The World Water Assessment Program (UNESCO, 2003) summarized that more than 2 billion people in over 40 countries are affected by water shortages, 1.1 billion do not have sufficient drinking water, 2.4 billion have no provision for sanitation, and, by 2050, at least one in four people is likely to live in countries affected by chronic or recurring shortages of freshwater. Water shortages increase the probability for international conflict, endanger public health, reduce agricultural productivity, and damage life-supporting ecological systems. New dams and river-management schemes might increase runoff accessibility by 10% over the next 30 years, but population is projected to grow by 32% in the same time period.

Water Supply in Canada

The Canadian water supply derives from surface and groundwater sources. The supply of freshwater and some of

Table 9.3 Estimate of Available Global Water Supply Compared by Region and Population

Region (2004 population in millions)	Land Area in Thousands of km^2	(mi²)	Share of Mean Annual Discharge in km^3/year	(BGD)	Global Stream Runoff (%)	Projected Global Population, 2025 (%)	Projected Population, 2025 (millions)	Projected Population Change (+) 2004–2050 (%)
Africa (883)	30,600	(11,800)	4,220	(3,060)	11	16.3	1,323	119
Asia (3875)	44,600	(17,200)	13,200	(9,540)	36	60.5	4,778	39
Australia–Oceania (33)	8,420	(3,250)	1,960	(1,420)	5	0.5	41	43
Europe (728)	9,770	(3,770)	3,150	(2,280)	8.8	9.1	722	–8
North America (432) (Canada, Mexico, U.S.)	22,100	(8,510)	5,960	(4,310)	15	6.6	518	41
Central and South America (443)	17,800	(6,880)	10,400	(7,510)	26	7.0	553	54
Global (6396) (excluding Antarctica)	134,000	(51,600)	38,900	(28,100)	—	100.00	7,934	45

Note: BGD, billion gallons per day. Population data from *2004 World Population Data Sheet*, Washington, D.C: Population Reference Bureau, 2004.

News Report 9.2

Personal Water Use in Canada

Canadians are second only to the United States as the highest per capita users of water in the world. Water use for municipal supply stresses surface reservoirs and groundwater aquifers. Treating and distributing water uses energy and has a heavy economic cost. After use, the released water is usually poorer in quality, diminishing the condition of the downstream supply.

An Environment Canada national survey on water use, updated in 1999, emphasizes that more than 8 million Canadians rely solely on groundwater for their water needs. The communities that rely on groundwater (found in interior British Columbia, the southern Prairies, southern Ontario, and Prince Edward Island) have more frequent water shortages, and in 1999, approximately 26% reported water availability problems. Figure 1a illustrates how the demand per capita in Canada decreased through the 1990s. However, population growth during the same time meant that total water usage increased.

Infrastructure is deteriorating. The leaks in the waterworks create inefficiency in water and wastewater treatment with as much as 30% of municipal water wasted. Estimated costs of rebuilding this infrastructure in the next 10 years are between 40 and 70 billion Canadian dollars.

The direct costs of supplying water are often unnoticed by the average user. In the 1999 national water survey, unmetered households used 433 litres of water per person per day. In metered households where water was paid for by the volume used, the daily residential water use was 288 litres per person per day (Figure 1b). Water meters are clearly an effective conservation mechanism, saving the consumer money on water bills and future outlays for more waterworks.

A further breakdown of residential water use is shown in Figure 2. The largest share, about two-thirds, of water used in a household is for personal washing and toilet flushing. Water conservation programs encourage the use of water-saving showerheads and low-flow toilets.

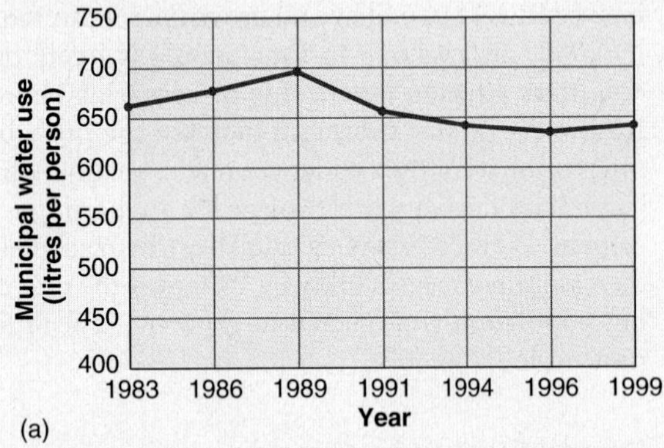

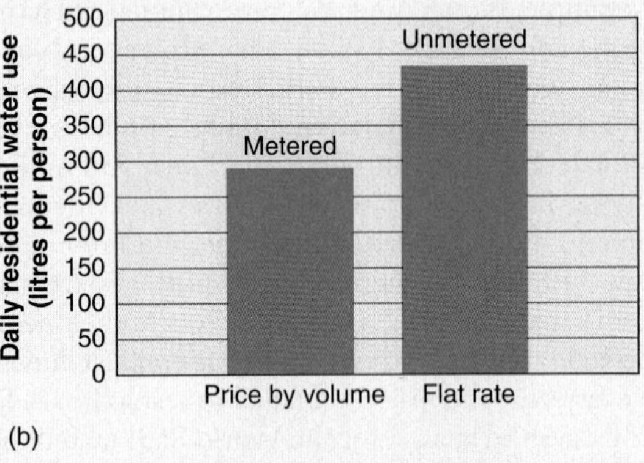

FIGURE 1 Indicators of daily municipal water use.
(a) Per capita daily municipal water use 1983 to 1999. Note the small declining trend in per capita consumption of water. Remember that overall population is rising and that the total demand for water is increasing. (b) The effect of metering water use is dramatic. The metered household uses one-third less water. [Graph data courtesy of Environment Canada's Freshwater Web site (http://www.ec.gc.ca/water). Used by permission of the Minister of Public Works and Government Services.]

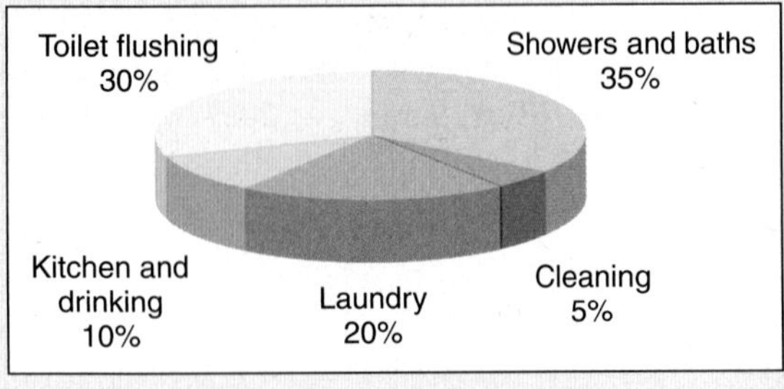

FIGURE 2 Water use in the home, 1999.
The greatest household demand for water is for showers and baths, followed closely by toilet-flushing. [Used by permission of the Minister of Public Works and Government Services.]

the threats to it are outlined on the National Water Research Institute's Web site (http://www.nwri.ca/threats2full/perspective-e.html). Canada has about 9% of Earth's renewable water distributed over 7% of Earth's landmass. Water is accessed through the rivers, lakes, ponds and reservoirs, groundwater aquifers, the snowpack, glaciers, ice fields, and the liquid and solid precipitation that replenishes all other sources. Measurements of precipitation recorded across the country are difficult to aggregate because the hydrology of the landmass varies so greatly.

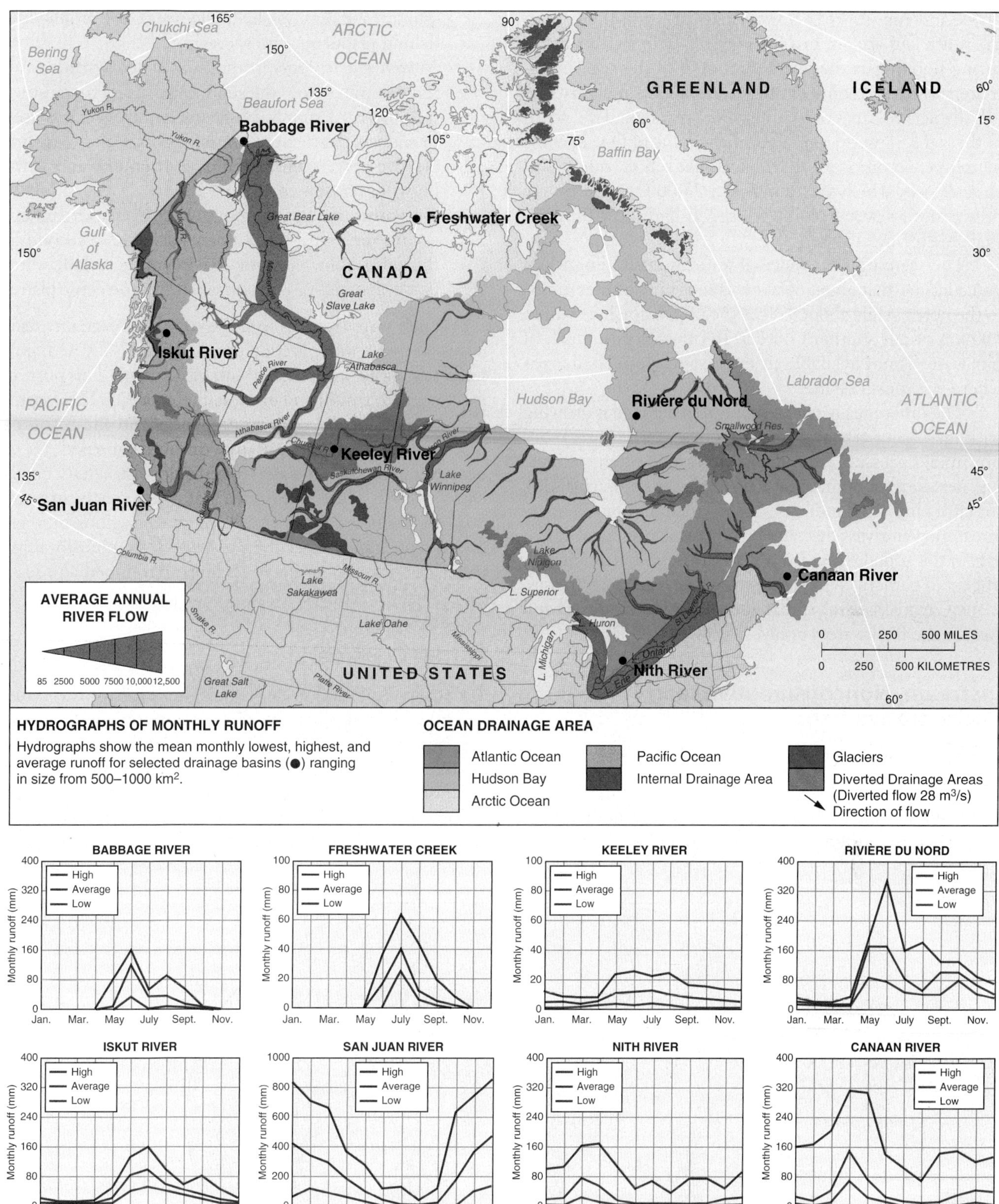

FIGURE 9.20 Streamflows in Canada.
The greatest volume of streamflow in Canada exits northward through the Mackenzie River. This streamflow represents the surface runoff from that drainage basin. Next in volume is the flow to the Atlantic from the Great Lakes through the St. Lawrence River. The hydrographs show the effects of seasonality on the timing of the melt. [Map and data used with permission of Natural Resources Canada.]

Figure 9.20 is a map of the streamflow in Canada found on the National Atlas Web site (**http://atlas.gc.ca/site/english/maps/archives/5thedition/environment/water/mcr4178**). Insets portray the distribution of low flows, peak flows, and runoff. Peak flows occur earlier in the year to the south and are later to the north. Often, this results in spring flooding as the northern mouth of the river is still frozen when the southern headwaters have melted. The map depicts volumes of flow in major streams and the width of the red coloration represents the volume of flow in cubic metres per second (m^3/sec). This surface runoff (runoff plus streamflow), which varies between 75,000 m^3/sec in low flow times to over 134,500 m^3/sec in high flow times, is available for use.

The seeming abundance of water is misleading when you consider that about 60% of Canada's freshwater drains to the north, while about 85% of the population lives within 300 km of our southern border. In other words, much of our water is not available in the heavily-populated areas where it is most needed.

The difference between supply and demand is growing with increasing urbanization. All sources of freshwater are now under pressure from the growing, and often conflicting, demands for domestic water supplies for municipalities, for agriculture and industry, and for maintaining adequate streamflow in rivers that support aquatic ecosystems. There is also the added stress from the uncertain, but predicted, effects of climate change. Despite these growing stresses, many Canadians assume that governments will protect and sustain the freshwater supply.

Instream, Nonconsumptive, and Consumptive Uses

Surface runoff available for use can be classified according to the type of use:

- *Instream uses* are those that use streamwater in place: navigation, wildlife and ecosystem preservation, waste dilution and removal, hydroelectric power production, fishing resources, and recreation.
- *Nonconsumptive uses*, sometimes called **withdrawal**, remove water from the supply, use it, and then return it to the same supply. Nonconsumptive water is used by industry, agriculture, municipalities, and in steam-electric power generation. A portion of water withdrawn is consumed.
- **Consumptive uses** remove water from a stream but do not return it, so it is not available for a second or third use. Some consumptive examples include water that evaporates or is vaporized in steam-electric plants.

When water returns to the system, water quality usually is altered—water is contaminated chemically with pollutants or waste or thermally with heat energy. This portion is returned to runoff and eventually the ocean. This wastewater represents an opportunity to extend the resource through reuse. Contaminated or not, returned water becomes a part of all water systems downstream. Canada uses only 9% of its withdrawn water for agriculture and 80% for industry. Figure 9.21 compares regions by their use of withdrawn water during 1998. It graphically illustrates the differences between more-developed and less-developed parts of the world.

Future Considerations

When precipitation is budgeted, the limits of the water resource become apparent. How can we satisfy the growing demand for water? Water availability per person declines as population increases, and individual demand increases with economic development, affluence, and technology. Thus, world population growth since 1970 reduced per capita water supplies by a third. Also, pollution limits

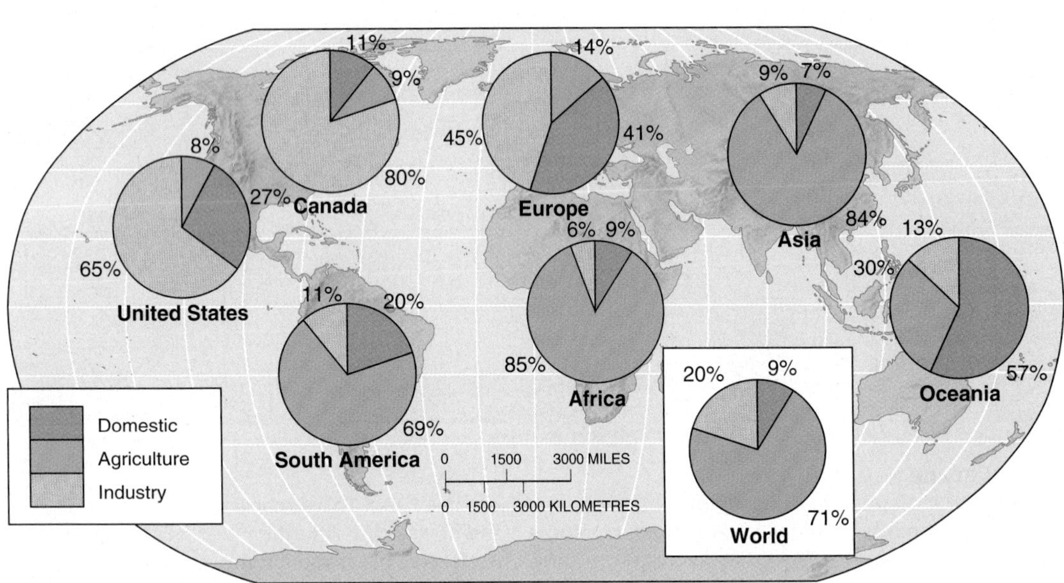

FIGURE 9.21 Water withdrawal by sector.
Compare industrial water use among the geographic areas, as well as agricultural and municipal uses. [After World Resources Institute, *World Resources 2000–2001*, Data Table FW.1, pp. 276–77.]

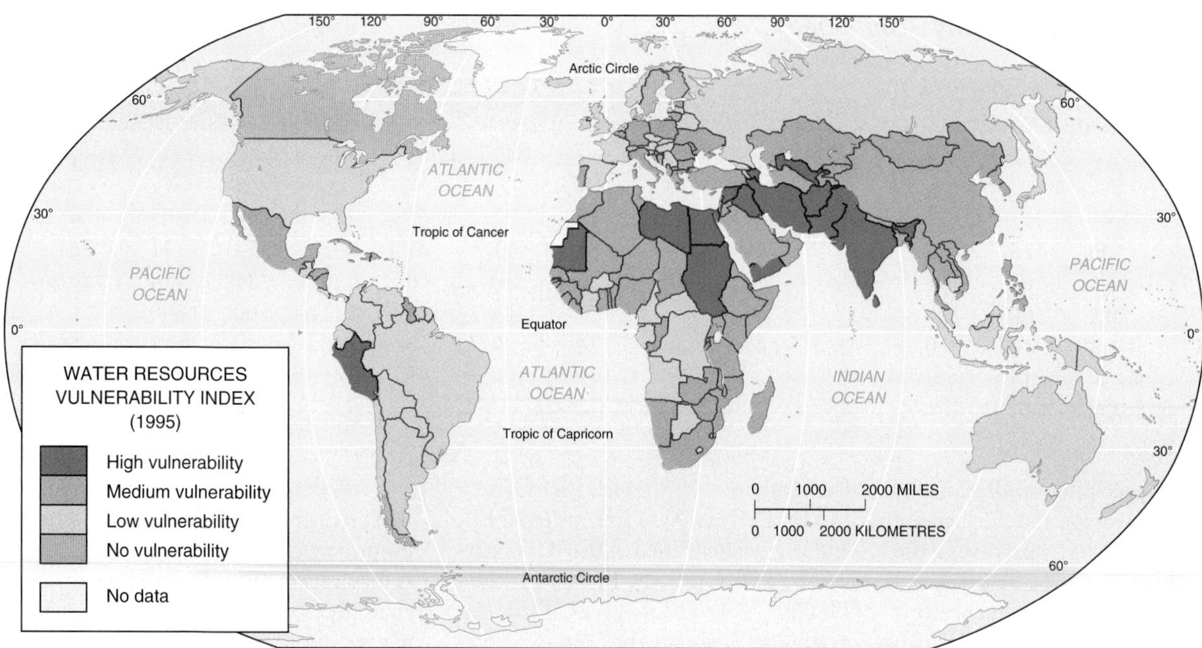

FIGURE 9.22 Global water scarcity.
Water resource vulnerability, a composite index. [Compiled by The World Resources Institute from data gathered by the Stockholm Environment Institute, *Comprehensive Assessment of the Freshwater Resources of the World*, 1997, appearing in *World Resources 1998–1999* (New York: The World Resources Institute, 1998), p. 223.]

the water-resource base, so that even before *quantity* constraints are felt, *quality* problems may limit the health and growth of a region. The international aspect of the problem is illustrated by the 200 major river drainage basins in the world (basins where rivers drain into an ocean, lake, or inland sea). One hundred and forty-five countries possess territory within an international river drainage basin—truly a global commons.

A composite index comparing available water resources to current use patterns, supplies, and national income reveals regional scarcities in Africa, the Middle East, Asia, Peru, and Mexico (Figure 9.22).

> Unlike other important commodities such as oil, copper, or wheat, freshwater has no substitutes for most of its uses. It is also impractical to transport the large quantities of water needed in agriculture and industry more than several hundred kilometres. Freshwater is now scarce in many regions of the world, resulting in severe ecological degradation, limits on agriculture and industrial production, threats to human health, and increased potential for international conflict.*

Clearly, cooperation is needed, yet we continue toward a water crisis without a concept of a *world water economy* as a frame of reference. When will more international coordination begin, and which country or group of countries will lead the way to sustain future water resources?

*S. L. Postal, and others, "Human appropriation of renewable fresh water," *Science* 271, no. 5250 (February 9, 1996): 785.

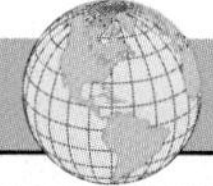

Applied Physical Geography

A Thornthwaite Water Balance Problem

Table 1 presents, in random order, data (in mm) for potential evapotranspiration (PE), precipitation (P), soil moisture storage (ST), actual evapotranspiration (AE), water deficit (D), and water surplus (S) for a Northern Hemisphere station. Determine the appropriate label for each of the rows and explain your reasoning. What type of climate is represented?

We are using the Thornthwaite water balance described earlier in this chapter. Although soil-moisture storage and field capacity can vary depending on soil type and the crop planted, we set it at 300 mm for this example. Therefore, Row #4 is storage because the number 300 does not change from January to April. It decreases from May to September and then increases through October to become recharged in November.

Now consider Row #5, immediately below the row identified as storage. When storage falls below 300 mm, water is being removed. Water is removed from storage only when there

(continued)

Applied Physical Geography *(continued)*

Table 1 Weather Station Data

	J	F	M	A	M	J	J	A	S	O	N	D	TOTAL
Row #1	147	117	94	61	48	45	30	37	61	122	141	165	1068
Row #2	8	15	30	48	72	89	85	71	64	45	23	11	561
Row #3	139	102	64	13	0	0	0	0	0	0	35	154	507
Row #4	300	300	300	300	276	232	177	143	140	217	300	300	—
Row #5	0	0	0	0	2	6	24	29	5	0	0	0	66
Row #6	8	15	30	48	74	95	109	100	69	45	23	11	627

is a deficit of precipitation. Because of the decrease in storage and the increase in values in Row #5, this row is the moisture deficit.

A deficit occurs when the precipitation decreases and there are only two rows that show a decrease in values. Row #1 has values across the year and shows a decrease that begins the month before the deficit appears. This decrease continues across the summer months and then increases into the fall when the deficit ends. Row #3 also shows a similar pattern, but does not have values across the year. Row #1 is therefore assumed to be precipitation and Row #3 surplus.

This leaves two rows to be labelled. These two rows contain values that are remarkably similar. They represent actual evapotranspiration and potential evapotranspiration. But which one is which? Remember, potential evapotranspiration is the amount of evapotranspiration (evaporation + transpiration) that would occur if the water supply were available. It represents the demand that the atmosphere makes on the available water supply.

Remember also that if PRECIP > POTET, then ACTET = POTET, and that water deficit (DEFIC) occurs when PRECIP < POTET, then DEFIC = POTET − ACTET. An examination shows that the two rows are equal January to April and October to December. When the deficit occurs in the summer months, Row #2 is less than Row #6. So, Row #6 is potential evapotranspiration and Row #2 is actual evapotranspiration.

To determine the type of climate depicted, graph precipitation, potential evapotranspiration, and actual evapotranspiration (Figure 1). Here we see that precipitation is greatest during winter months. Both potential and actual evapotranspiration increase in summer and both decrease in winter. This is typical of the Marine West Coast climate, with all months averaging above freezing, a cool summer, and abundant precipitation.

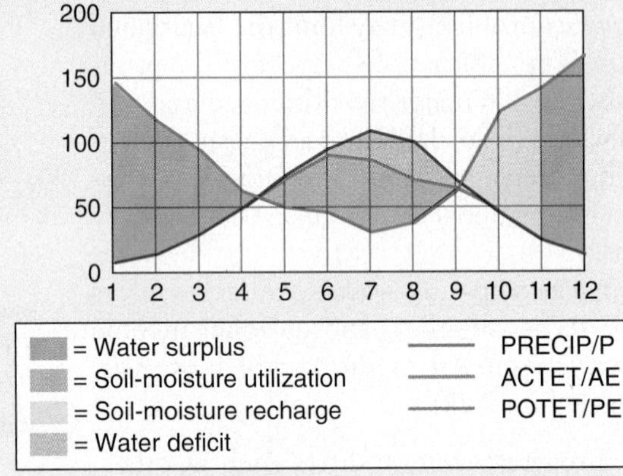

FIGURE 1 Sample graph.

Summary and Review—Water Resources

- ***Illustrate* the hydrologic cycle with a simple sketch and *label* it with definitions for each water pathway.**

The flow of water links the atmosphere, ocean, and land through energy and matter exchanges. The **hydrologic cycle** is a model of Earth's water system, which has operated for billions of years from the lower atmosphere to several kilometres beneath Earth's surface. **Interception** occurs when precipitation strikes vegetation or other ground cover. Water soaks into the subsurface through **infiltration**, or penetration of the soil surface. It further permeates soil or rock through vertical movement called **percolation**.

hydrologic cycle (p. 252)
interception (p. 253)
infiltration (p. 253)
percolation (p. 253)

1. Sketch and explain a simplified model of the complex flows of water on Earth—the hydrologic cycle.
2. What are the possible routes that a raindrop may take on its way to and into the soil surface?

3. Compare precipitation and evaporation volumes from the ocean with those over land. Describe advection flows of moisture and countering surface and subsurface runoff.

- ***Relate* the importance of the water-budget concept to your understanding of the hydrologic cycle, water resources, and soil moisture for a specific location.**

A **soil-water budget** can be established for any area of Earth's surface by measuring the precipitation input and the output of various water demands in the area considered. Understanding both the supply of the water resource and the natural demands on the resource is essential to sustainable human interaction with the hydrologic cycle. Water resources represent the ultimate output of Earth's water system. That portion of the water budget that enters soil moisture storage is critical to plant growth. Water resources require human management through water-budgeting techniques if they are to meet human needs of quantity and quality water.

Groundwater is the largest potential freshwater source in the hydrologic cycle and is tied to surface supplies. Streams represent only a tiny fraction of all water (1250 km^3, or 300 mi^3), the smallest volume of any of the freshwater categories. Yet streams represent four-fifths of all the water we use.

soil-water budget (p. 254)

4. How might an understanding of the hydrologic cycle in a particular locale, or a soil-moisture budget of a site, assist you in assessing water resources? Give some specific examples.

- ***Construct* the water-balance equation as a way of accounting for the expenditures of water supply and *define* each of the components in the equation and their specific operation.**

The moisture supply to Earth's surface is **precipitation** (PRECIP, or P), arriving as rain, sleet, snow, and hail. Precipitation is measured with the **rain gauge. Evaporation** is the net movement of free water molecules away from a wet surface into air. **Transpiration** is the movement of water through plants and back into the atmosphere; it is a cooling mechanism for plants. Evaporation and transpiration are combined into one term—**evapotranspiration**. The ultimate demand for moisture is **potential evapotranspiration** (POTET, or PE), the amount of water that *would* evaporate and transpire under optimum moisture conditions (adequate precipitation and adequate soil moisture). Evapotranspiration is measured with an **evaporation pan** (*evaporimeter*) or the more elaborate **lysimeter**.

Unsatisfied POTET is **deficit** (DEFIC). By subtracting DEFIC from POTET, we determine **actual evapotranspiration**, or ACTET. Ideally, POTET and ACTET are about the same, so that plants have sufficient water. If POTET is satisfied and the soil is full of moisture, then additional water input becomes **surplus** (SURPL), which may puddle on the surface, flow across the surface toward stream channels, or percolate underground through the soil. The **overland flow** to streams includes precipitation and groundwater flows into river channels to make up the **total runoff** from the area.

A "savings account" of water that receives deposits and provides withdrawals as water-balance conditions change is the **soil-moisture storage** (ΔSTRGE). This is the volume of water stored in the soil that is accessible to plant roots. In soil, **hygroscopic water** is inaccessible because it is a molecule-thin layer that is tightly bound to each soil particle by hydrogen bonding. As available water is utilized, soil reaches the **wilting point** (all that remains is unextractable water). **Capillary water** is generally accessible to plant roots because it is held in the soil by surface tension and hydrogen bonding between water and soil. Almost all capillary water that remains in the soil is **available water** in soil-moisture storage. After water drains from the larger pore spaces, the available water remaining for plants is termed **field capacity**, or storage capacity. When soil is saturated after a precipitation event, surplus water in the soil becomes **gravitational water** and percolates to groundwater. As **soil-moisture utilization** removes soil water, the plants work harder to extract the same amount of moisture; whereas **soil-moisture recharge** is the rate at which needed moisture enters the soil.

The texture and the structure of the soil dictate available pore spaces, or **porosity**. The soil's **permeability** is the degree to which water can flow through it. Permeability depends on particle sizes and the shape and packing of soil grains.

Drought does not have a simple water-budget definition, rather it can occur in at least four forms: *meteorological drought*, *agricultural drought*, *hydrologic drought*, and/or a *socioeconomic drought*.

precipitation (p. 255)
rain gauge (p. 255)
evaporation (p. 255)
transpiration (p. 255)
evapotranspiration (p. 256)
potential evapotranspiration (p. 256)
evaporation pan (p. 256)
lysimeter (p. 257)
deficit (p. 258)
actual evapotranspiration (p. 258)
surplus (p. 258)
overland flow (p. 258)
total runoff (p. 258)
soil-moisture storage (p. 258)
hygroscopic water (p. 258)
wilting point (p. 258)
capillary water (p. 259)
available water (p. 259)
field capacity (p. 259)
gravitational water (p. 259)
soil-moisture utilization (p. 260)
soil-moisture recharge (p. 260)
porosity (p. 260)
permeability (p. 260)

5. What does this statement mean? "The soil-water budget is an assessment of the hydrologic cycle at a specific site."
6. What are the components of the water-balance equation? Construct the equation and place each term's definition below its abbreviation in the equation.
7. Using the annual water-balance data for Hamilton, Ontario, work the values through the water-balance "bookkeeping" method. Does the equation balance?

8. Explain how to derive actual evapotranspiration (ACTET) in the water-balance equation.
9. What is potential evapotranspiration (POTET)? How do we go about estimating this potential rate? What factors did Thornthwaite use to determine this value?
10. Explain the operation of soil-moisture storage, soil-moisture utilization, and soil-moisture recharge. Include discussion of field capacity, capillary water, and wilting point concepts.
11. In the case of silt-loam soil from Figure 9.10, roughly what is the available water capacity? How is this value derived?
12. In terms of water balance and water management, explain the logic behind the Snowy Mountains Scheme in southeastern Australia.

Describe the nature of groundwater and *define* the elements of the groundwater environment.

Groundwater is a part of the hydrologic cycle, but it lies beneath the surface beyond the soil-moisture root zone. Groundwater does not exist independently because its replenishment is tied to surface surpluses. Excess surface water moves through the **zone of aeration**, where soil and rock are less than saturated. Eventually, the water reaches the **zone of saturation**, where the pores are completely filled with water.

The *permeability* of subsurface rocks depends on whether they conduct water readily (higher permeability) or tend to obstruct its flow (lower permeability). They can even be impermeable. An **aquifer** is a rock layer that is permeable to groundwater flow in usable amounts. An **aquiclude** (aquitard) is a body of rock that does not conduct water in usable amounts.

The upper limit of the water that collects in the zone of saturation is called the **water table**; it is the contact surface between the zones of saturation and aeration. A **confined aquifer** is bounded above and below by impermeable layers of rock or sediment. An **unconfined aquifer** has a permeable layer on top and an impermeable one beneath. The **aquifer recharge area** extends over an entire unconfined aquifer. Water in a confined aquifer is under the pressure of its own weight, creating a pressure level to which the water can rise on its own, called the **potentiometric surface**, which can be above ground level. Groundwater confined under pressure is **artesian water**; it may rise up in wells and even flow out at the surface without pumping, if the head of the well is below the potentiometric surface.

As water is pumped from a well, the surrounding water table within an unconfined aquifer will experience **drawdown**, or become lower, if the rate of pumping exceeds the horizontal flow of water in the aquifer around the well. This excessive pumping causes a **cone of depression**. Aquifers frequently are pumped beyond their flow and recharge capacities, a condition known as **groundwater mining**.

groundwater (p. 264)
zone of aeration (p. 264)
zone of saturation (p. 264)
aquifer (p. 264)
aquiclude (p. 264)
water table (p. 266)
confined aquifer (p. 266)
unconfined aquifer (p. 266)
aquifer recharge area (p. 266)
potentiometric surface (p. 266)
artesian water (p. 267)
drawdown (p. 268)
cone of depression (p. 268)
groundwater mining (p. 268)

13. Are groundwater resources independent of surface supplies, or are the two interrelated? Explain your answer.
14. Make a simple sketch of the subsurface environment, labelling zones of aeration and saturation and the water table in an unconfined aquifer. Then add a confined aquifer to the sketch.
15. At what point does groundwater utilization become groundwater mining? Use the High Plains aquifer example to explain your answer.
16. What is the nature of groundwater pollution? Can contaminated groundwater be cleaned up easily? Explain.

Identify critical aspects of freshwater supplies for the future and *cite* specific issues related to sectors of use, regions and countries, and potential remedies for any shortfalls.

Nonconsumptive uses, or water **withdrawal**, remove water from the supply, use it, and then return it to the stream. **Consumptive uses** remove water from a stream but do not return it, so the water is not available for a second or third use. Regional and global water-resource planning, using water-budget principles, is essential if Earth's societies are to have enough water of adequate quality.

withdrawal (p. 276)
consumptive uses (p. 276)

17. What is the difference between withdrawal and consumptive use of water resources? Compare these with instream uses.
18. Characterize each of the sectors withdrawing water: irrigation, industry, and municipalities. What are the present usage trends in more-developed and less-developed nations?
19. Briefly assess the status of world water resources. What challenges are there in meeting future needs of an expanding population and growing economies?

Critical Thinking

A. Select your campus, yard, or perhaps a house plant and apply the water-balance concepts. What is the supply of water? Estimate the ultimate water supply and demand for the area you selected. Estimate water needs and how they vary with season as components of the water budget change.

B. You have no doubt had several glasses of water between the time you awoke this morning and the time you are reading these words. Where did this water originate? Determine whether it is surface or groundwater to meet demands, and check how the water is metered and billed. If your province or state requires water quality reporting, obtain a copy of the analysis of your tap water.

C. What about the water on your campus? If the campus has its own wells, how is the quality tested? Who on campus is in charge of supervising these wells? Lastly, what is your subjective assessment of your water: taste, smell, hardness, clarity? Compare these perceptions with others in your class.

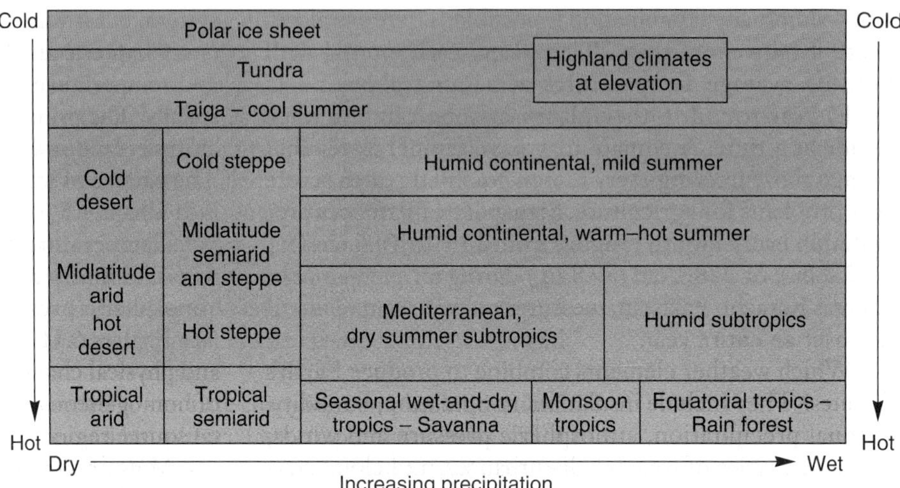

FIGURE 10.3 Climatic relationships. Temperature and precipitation schematic reveals climatic relationships. Based on general knowledge of your location, can you identify its approximate location on the schematic diagram? Now locate the region of your birthplace.

influenced by equatorial low pressure and the intertropical convergence zone (ITCZ, see Figure 6.11).

Simply relating the two principal climatic components—temperature and precipitation—reveals general climate types (Figure 10.3). Temperature and precipitation patterns, plus other weather factors, provide the key to climate classification.

Focus Study 10.1

The El Niño Phenomenon—Record Intensity, Global Linkages

Climate is the consistent behaviour of weather over time, but average weather conditions also include extremes that depart from normal. The El Niño–Southern Oscillation (ENSO) in the Pacific Ocean forces the greatest interannual variability of temperature and precipitation on a global scale. The two strongest ENSO events in 120 years hit in 1997–1998 and 1982–1983. The spring wildflower bloom in Death Valley in 1998 provides visible evidence of the resultant heavy rains (Figure 1). Peruvians coined the name El Niño ("the boy child") because these episodes seem to occur around the traditional December celebration time of Christ's birth. Actually El Niños can occur as early as spring and summer and persist through the year.

Revisit Figure 6.22 to see that the northward-flowing Peru Current dominates the region off South America's West Coast. These cold waters move toward the equator and join the westward movement of the south equatorial current.

(a) 1998

(b) 2002

FIGURE 1 El Niño's impact on the desert.
Death Valley, southeastern California, in (a) full spring bloom following record rains triggered by the 1997–1998 El Niño and (b) the same scene in spring 2002 in its stark desert grandeur. A dramatic effect caused by changes in the distant tropics of the Pacific Ocean. [Photos by Bobbé Christopherson.]

The Peru Current is part of the normal counterclockwise circulation of winds and surface ocean currents around the subtropical high-pressure cell dominating the eastern Pacific in the Southern Hemisphere. As a result, a location such as Guayaquil, Ecuador, normally receives 91.4 cm (36 in.) of precipitation each year under dominant high pressure, whereas islands in the Indonesian archipelago receive more than 254 cm (100 in.) under dominant low pressure. This normal alignment of pressure is shown in Figure 2a.

What Is ENSO?

Occasionally, for unexplained reasons, pressure patterns and surface ocean temperatures shift from their usual locations. Higher pressure than normal develops over the western Pacific, and lower pressure develops over the eastern Pacific. Trade winds normally moving from east to west weaken and can be reduced or even replaced by an eastward (west-to-east) flow. The shifting of atmospheric pressure and wind patterns across the Pacific is the *Southern Oscillation*.

Sea-surface temperatures increase, sometimes more than 8 C° (14 F°) above normal in the central and eastern Pacific, replacing the normally cold, upwelling, nutrient-rich water along Peru's coastline. Such ocean-surface warming, the "warm pool," may extend to the International Date Line. This surface pool of warm water is known as El Niño. Thus, the designation ENSO is derived—El Niño–Southern Oscillation. This condition is shown in Figure 2b in illustration and satellite image.

The thermocline (boundary of colder, deep-ocean water) lowers in depth in the eastern Pacific Ocean. The change in wind direction and warmer surface water slows the normal upwelling currents that control nutrient availability. This loss of nutrients affects the phytoplankton and food chain, depriving many fish, marine mammals, and predator birds of nourishment.

Scientists at the National Oceanographic and Atmospheric Administration (NOAA) speculate that ENSO events occurred nine times between 1896 and 1941–1942. They are certain that ENSO events occurred in 1953, 1957–1958, 1965, 1969–1970, 1972–1973, 1976–1977, 1982–1983 (second strongest event), 1986–1987, 1991–1993 (one of the longest), and the most intense episode in 1997–1998 that disrupted global weather.

The expected interval for recurrence is 3 to 5 years, but it may range from 2 to 12 years. The frequency and intensity of ENSO events increased through the twentieth century, a topic of much research by scientists to see if there is a relation to global climate change. Recent studies suggest ENSO might be more responsive to global change than previously thought. Surface temperatures in the central tropical Pacific returned to near normal (neutral) by mid-2001 (Figure 2e). Slight warming marked a weaker El Niño event in 2002–2003. Conditions in the Pacific were neutral into 2004.

La Niña—El Niño's Cousin

When surface waters in the central and eastern Pacific cool to below normal by 0.4 C° (0.7 F°) or more, the condition is dubbed La Niña, Spanish for "the girl." This is a weaker condition and less consistent than El Niño. There is no correlation in the strength or weakness of each. For instance, following the record 1997–1998 ENSO event, the subsequent La Niña was not as strong as predicted and shared the Pacific with lingering warm water.

Between 1900 and 1998 there were 13 La Niñas of note, the latest in 1988, 1995, and late 1998 to 2000 (Figure 2c and d). According to National Center for Atmospheric Research (NCAR) scientist Kevin Trenberth, El Niños occurred 31% and La Niñas 23% of the time between 1950 and 1997; during the remaining 46% of the time the Pacific was in a more neutral condition. Don't look for symmetry and opposite effects between the two events, for there is great variability possible, except perhaps in Indonesia where remarkable drought (El Niño) and heavy rain (La Niña) correlations seem strong.

Global Effects Related to ENSO and La Niña

Effects related to ENSO and La Niña occur worldwide: droughts in South Africa, southern India, Australia, and the Philippines; strong hurricanes in the Pacific, including Tahiti and French Polynesia; and flooding in the southwestern United States and mountain states, Bolivia, Cuba, Ecuador, and Peru. In India, every drought between 1525 and 1900 seems linked to ENSO events. The Atlantic hurricane season weakens during El Niño years and strengthens during La Niñas. (Refer back to the discussion in Focus Study 8.1 and review William Gray's Atlantic hurricane forecasting methods based on these linkages.) Increasing ocean temperatures also are tied to the record level of coral bleaching happening across the tropics, a subject addressed in Chapter 16.

Precipitation in the southwestern United States is greater in El Niño than La Niña years. The Pacific Northwest is wetter with La Niña than El Niño. The Colorado River flooding shown in Chapter 15's Focus Study 15.1 was in part attributable to the 1982–1983 El Niño. Yet, as conditions vary, other El Niños have produced drought in the very regions that flooded during a previous episode.

Since the 1982–1983 event, and with the development of remote-sensing satellites and computing capability, scientists now are able to identify the complex global interconnections among surface temperatures, pressure patterns in the Pacific, occurrences of drought in some places, excessive rainfall in others, and the disruption of fisheries and wildlife. Estimates place the overall damage from the 1982–1983 ENSO at more than $8 billion worldwide. Present estimates of weather-related costs for the ENSO in 1997–1998 exceed $80 billion, with some 300 million people displaced and 30,000 deaths.

Discovery of these truly Earth-wide relations and spatial impacts is at the heart of physical geography. The climate of one location is related to climates elsewhere, although it should be no surprise that Earth operates as a vast

(continued)

Focus Study 10.1 *(continued)*

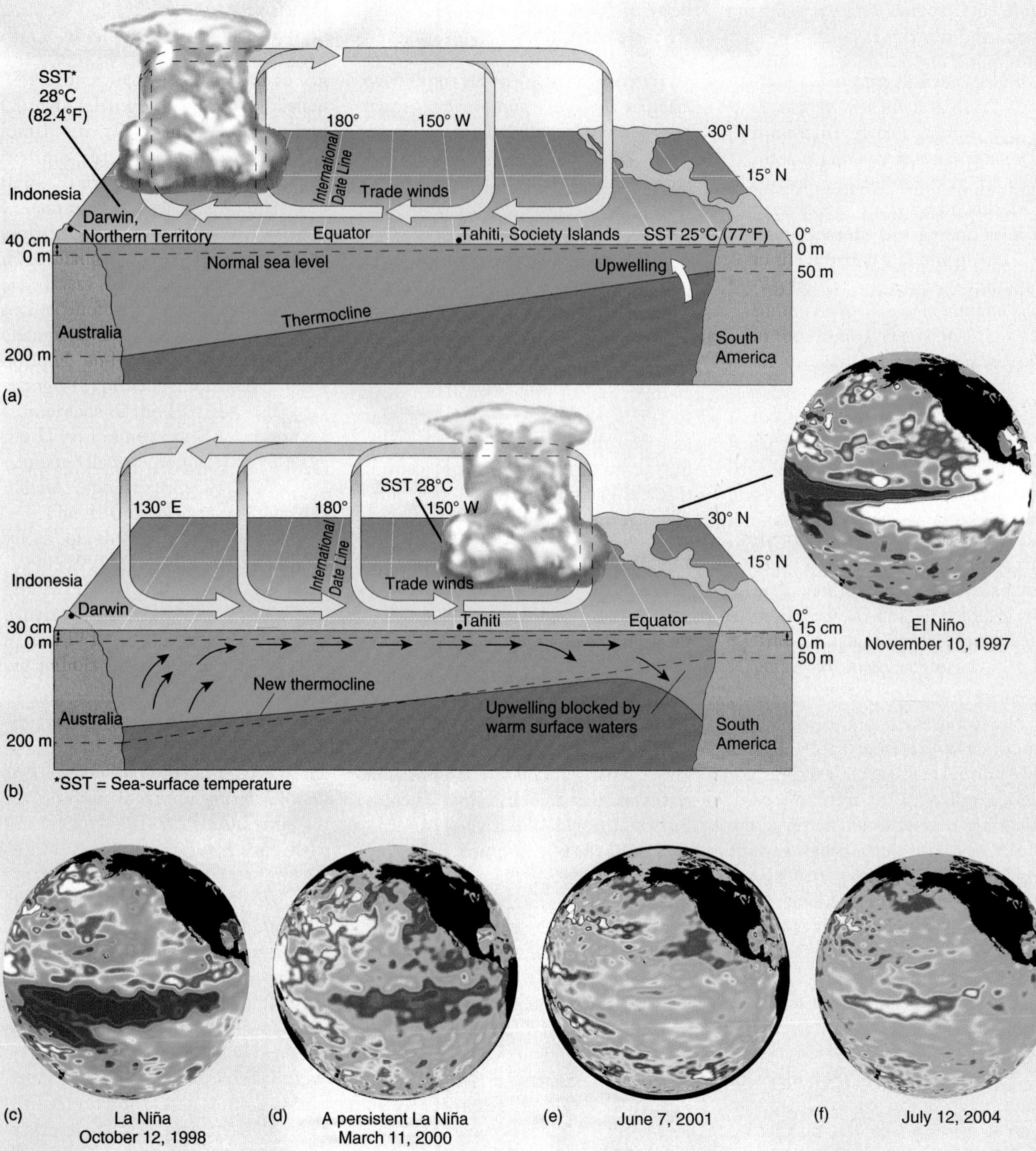

SST*
28°C
(82.4°F)
180°
150° W
30° N
15° N
International Date Line
Trade winds
Indonesia
Darwin,
Northern Territory
Equator
Tahiti, Society Islands
SST 25°C (77°F)
0°
40 cm
0 m
Normal sea level
Upwelling
0 m
50 m
Thermocline
Australia
200 m
South
America
(a)

130° E
180°
SST 28°C
150° W
30° N
15° N
International Date Line
Trade winds
Indonesia
Darwin
Tahiti
Equator
0°
30 cm
0 m
15 cm
0 m
50 m
New thermocline
Upwelling blocked by
warm surface waters
Australia
200 m
South
America
(b)
*SST = Sea-surface temperature

El Niño
November 10, 1997

(c) La Niña
October 12, 1998

(d) A persistent La Niña
March 11, 2000

(e) June 7, 2001

(f) July 12, 2004

FIGURE 2 Normal, El Niño, and La Niña changes in the Pacific.
(a) Normal patterns in the Pacific; (b) El Niño wind and weather patterns across the Pacific Ocean and *TOPEX/Poseidon* satellite image for November 10, 1997 (white and red colours indicate warmer surface water—a warm pool). (c) *TOPEX/Poseidon* image of La Niña conditions in transition in the Pacific on October 12, 1998 (purple and blue colours for cooler surface water—a cool pool). (d) A persistent La Niña in March 11, 2000 satellite image. (e) Image from June 7, 2001, showing no El Niño as equatorial waters slowly warm with sea-surface temperature near normal. (f) El Niño returns, August 2002, as the warm pool of waters moves eastward toward South America at more than 200 km (125 mi) per day, which by 2004 had returned westward leaving more neutral conditions off South America. [(a) and (b) Adapted and author corrected from C. S. Ramage, "El Niño." © 1986 by *Scientific American*, Inc.; (b)–(f) *TOPEX/Poseidon* images courtesy of Jet Propulsion Laboratory, NASA.]

El Niño/La Niña

integrated system. "It is fascinating that what happens in one area can affect the whole world. As to why this happens, that's the question of the century. Scientists are trying to make order out of chaos," says NOAA scientist Alan Strong. (For ENSO monitoring and forecasts, see Climate Prediction Center at **http://www.cpc.ncep.noaa.gov/** or the Jet Propulsion Laboratory at **http://www.jpl.nasa.gov/earth/ocean_motion/el_nino_index.cfm** or NOAA's El Niño Theme Page at **http://www.pmel.noaa.gov/toga-tao/el-nino/nino-home.html**.)

Classification of Climatic Regions

The ancient Greeks simplified their view of world climates into three zones: The "torrid zone" referred to warmer areas south of the Mediterranean; the "frigid zone" was to the north; and the area where they lived was labelled the "temperate zone," which they considered the optimum climate. They believed that travel too close to the equator or too far north would surely end in death. But the world is a diverse place and Earth's myriad climatic variations are more complex than these simple views.

Classification is the process of grouping data or phenomena in related categories. Such generalizations are important tools in science and are especially useful for the spatial analysis of climatic regions. Just as there is no agreed-upon climate classification system, neither is there a single set of empirical (data) or genetic (causal) criteria to which everyone agrees. Any classification system should be viewed as developmental, because it is always open to change and improvement.

A climate classification based on *causative* factors—for example, the interaction of air masses—is called a **genetic classification**. A climate classification based on *statistical data* of observed effects is an **empirical classification**. Climate classifications based on temperature and precipitation data are examples of empirical classifications. This chapter features descriptions of climatic regions that include both genetic factors of causal elements and empirical factors of statistical elements.

Genetic classifications explain climates in terms of net radiation, thermal regimes, or air mass dominance over a region. Empirical classifications are descriptive and single out selected weather data. One empirical classification system, published by C. W. Thornthwaite in 1948, identified moisture regions using aspects of the water-budget approach (Chapter 9) and vegetation types. Another empirical classification system, which forms the framework for our climate regions discussion, is the Köppen classification system.

A Climate Classification System

The Köppen classification system, widely recognized, was designed by Wladimir Köppen (1846–1940), a German climatologist and botanist. In 1928, after years of research and development, his first wall map showing world climates, coauthored with his student Rudolph Geiger, was widely adopted. Köppen continued to refine this system until his death. In Appendix C you find a description of his system and the detailed criteria he used to distinguish climatic regions.

In this chapter we use a system that is somewhat middle ground between genetic and empirical. This allows description of the climatic regions, yet gives you some ideas as to why such climates are found where they occur. The Köppen system provides us an outline and general base map.

Classification Categories The basis of any classification system is the choice of criteria or causative factors used to draw lines between categories. Some climate elements that could be used include average monthly temperatures, average monthly precipitation, total annual precipitation, air mass characteristics, ocean currents and sea-surface temperatures, moisture efficiency, insolation, and net radiation, among others. As we devise spatial categories and boundaries, we must remember that boundaries really are transition zones of gradual change. The trends and overall patterns of boundary lines are more important than their precise placement, especially with the small scales generally used for world maps.

Here we focus on temperature and precipitation measurements, and for the desert areas, moisture efficiency. Keep in mind these are measurable results produced by the climatic elements listed in the last paragraph. Figure 10.4 portrays six basic climate categories and their regional types that provide us a structure for our discussion.

- Tropical (equatorial and tropical latitudes)
  –rain forest (rainy all year)
  –monsoon (6 to 12 months rainy)
  –savanna (less than 6 months rainy)
- Mesothermal (midlatitudes, mild winters)
  –humid subtropical (hot summers)
  –marine west coast (warm to cool summers)
  –Mediterranean (dry summers)
- Microthermal (mid- and high latitude, cold winters)
  –humid continental (hot to warm summers)
  –subarctic regions (cool summers to very cold winters)
- Polar (high latitudes and polar regions)
  –tundra (high latitude or high altitude)
  –ice caps and ice sheets (perpetually frozen)
  –polar marine

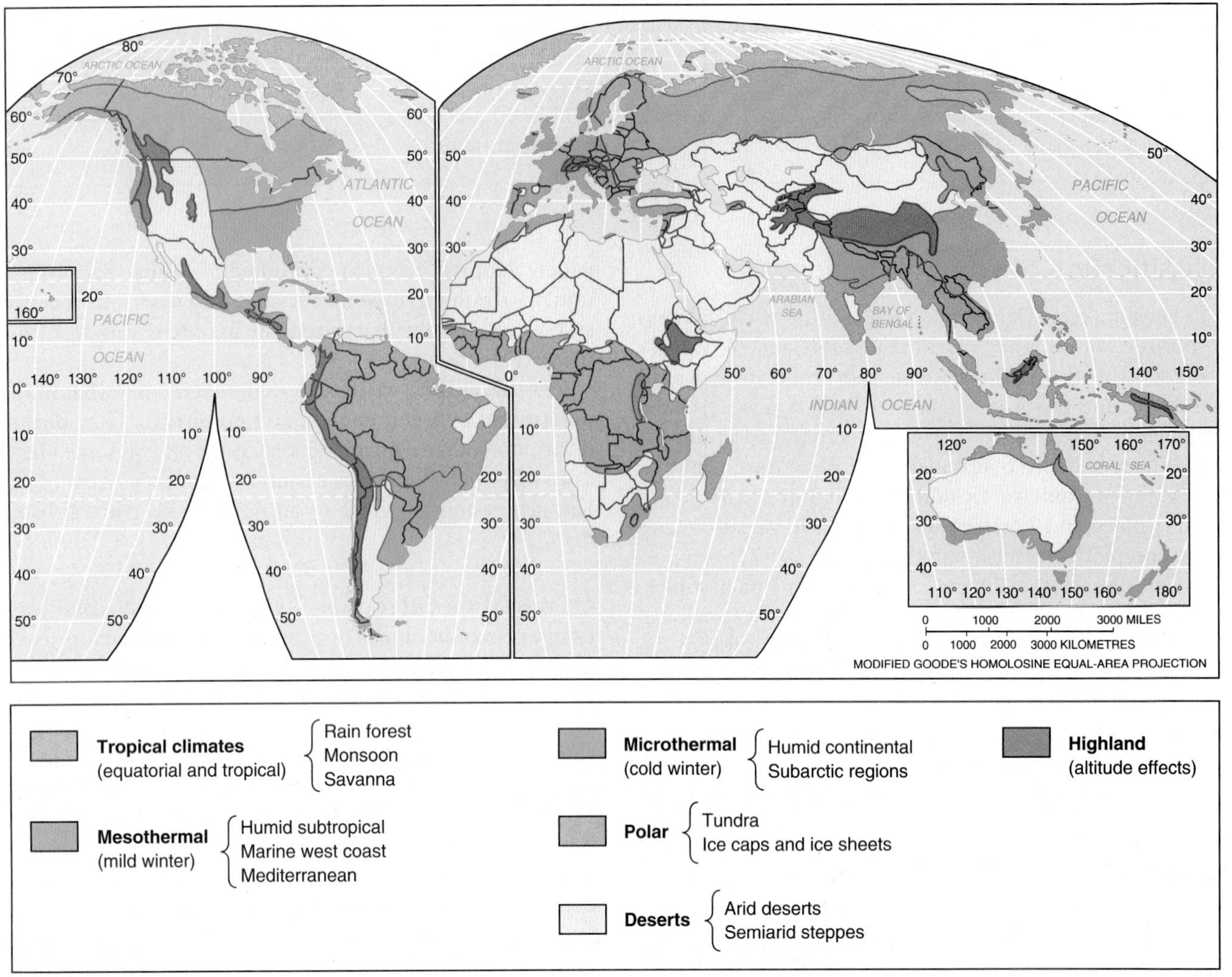

FIGURE 10.4 Climate regions generalized.
Six general climate categories. Relative to the question asked about your campus and birthplace in the caption to Figure 10.3, locate these two places on this map.

- Highland (compared to lowlands at the same latitude, highlands have lower temperatures—recall the normal lapse rate)

Only one climate category is based on moisture efficiency as well as temperature:

- Deserts (permanent moisture deficits)
  –arid deserts (tropical and midlatitudes)
  –semiarid steppes (tropical and midlatitudes)

Global Climate Patterns Adding detail to Figure 10.4, we develop the world climate map presented in Figure 10.5. The following sections describe specific climates, organized around each of the main climate categories listed previously. An opening box at the beginning of each climate section gives a simple description of the climate category and causal elements that are in operation. A world map showing distribution and the featured representative cities also is in the introductory box for each climate. In this discussion the names of the climates appear in italics.

Climographs exemplify particular climates for selected cities. A **climograph** is a graph that shows monthly temperature and precipitation, location coordinates, average annual temperature, total annual precipitation, elevation, the local population, annual temperature range, annual hours of sunshine (if available, as an indication of cloudiness), and a location map. Along the top of each climograph, find the dominant weather features that are influential in that climate.

Discussions of soils, vegetation, and major terrestrial biomes that fully integrate these global climate patterns are in Chapters 18, 19, and 20. Table 20.1 synthesizes all this information and will enhance your understanding of this chapter, so please place a tab on that page and refer to it as you read.

Tropical Climates (equatorial and tropical latitudes)

Tropical climates, the most extensive, occupy about 36% of Earth's surface, including both ocean and land areas. The tropical climates straddle the equator from about 20° N to 20° S, roughly between the Tropics of Cancer and Capricorn, thus the name. Tropical climates stretch northward to the tip of Florida and south-central Mexico, central India, Southeast Asia, and southward to northern Australia, Madagascar, central Africa, and southern Brazil. These climates truly are winterless. Important causal elements include:

- Consistent daylength and insolation input, which produce consistently warm temperatures.
- Intertropical convergence zone (ITCZ), which brings rains as it shifts seasonally with the high Sun.
- Warm ocean temperatures and unstable maritime air masses.

Tropical climates have three distinct regimes: *tropical rain forest* (ITCZ present all year), *tropical monsoon* (ITCZ present for 6 to 12 months), and *tropical savanna* (ITCZ present for less than 6 months).

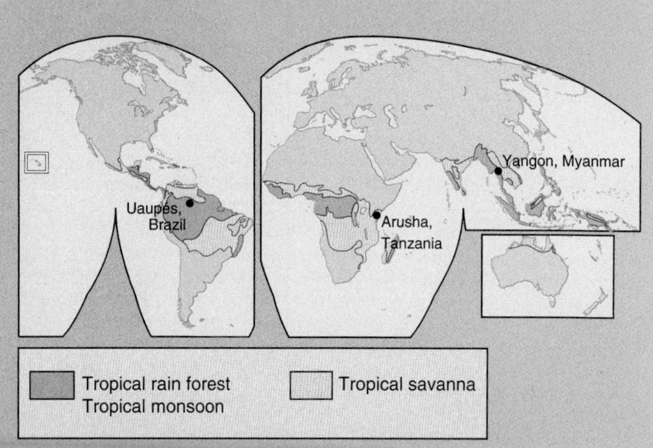

Tropical Rain Forest Climates

The *tropical rain forest* climate is constantly moist and warm. Convectional thunderstorms, triggered by local heating and trade-wind convergence, peak each day from midafternoon to late evening inland. These thunderstorms may hit earlier in the day where marine influence is strong. This precipitation follows the migrating intertropical convergence zone (ITCZ, Chapter 6). Its extreme positions for July and January are plotted in Figure 10.5. The ITCZ shifts northward and southward with the summer Sun throughout the year, but it influences *tropical rain forest* regions during all 12 months. Not surprisingly, water surpluses are enormous, creating the world's greatest stream discharges in the Amazon and Congo (Zaire) Rivers.

High rainfall sustains lush evergreen broadleaf tree growth, producing Earth's equatorial and tropical rain forests. Their leaf canopy is so dense that little light diffuses to the forest floor, leaving the ground surface dim and sparse in plant cover. Dense surface vegetation occurs along riverbanks, where light is abundant (see Figure 10.6b). Widespread deforestation of Earth's rain forest is detailed in Chapter 20.

High temperature promotes energetic bacterial action in the soil so that organic material is quickly consumed. Heavy precipitation washes away certain minerals and nutrients. The resulting soils are somewhat sterile and can support intensive agriculture only if supplemented by fertilizer.

Uaupés, Brazil (Figure 10.6, p. 294), is characteristic of *tropical rain forest*. On the climograph you see that the lowest-precipitation month receives nearly 15 cm (6 in.), and the annual temperature range is barely 2 C° (3.6 F°). The ITCZ is present all year. In all such climates, the diurnal (day to night) temperature range exceeds the annual average minimum-maximum (coolest to warmest) range: Day–night temperatures can range more than 11 C° (20 F°), more than five times the annual range of monthly averages.

The only interruption of *tropical rain forest* climates across the equatorial region is in the highlands of the South American Andes and in East Africa (see Figure 10.5). There, higher elevations produce lower temperatures; Mount Kilimanjaro is less than 4° S of the equator, but at 5895 m (19,340 ft) elevation it has permanent glacial ice on its summit, which is rapidly disappearing because of increasing air temperatures from global warming. Such mountainous sites fall within the highland climate designation.

Tropical Monsoon Climates

The *tropical monsoon* climates feature a dry season that lasts one or more months. Rainfall brought by the ITCZ affects these areas from 6 to 12 months of the year, with the dry season occurring when the convergence zone is not overhead. Yangon, Myanmar (formerly Rangoon, Burma), is an example of a monsoon climate in the tropics, as illustrated by the climograph and photograph in Figure 10.7, p. 295.

Tropical monsoon climates lie principally along coastal areas within the tropical rain forest climatic realm and experience seasonal variation of winds and precipitation. Evergreen trees grade into thorn forests on the drier margins near the adjoining tropical savannas.

(continued p. 295)

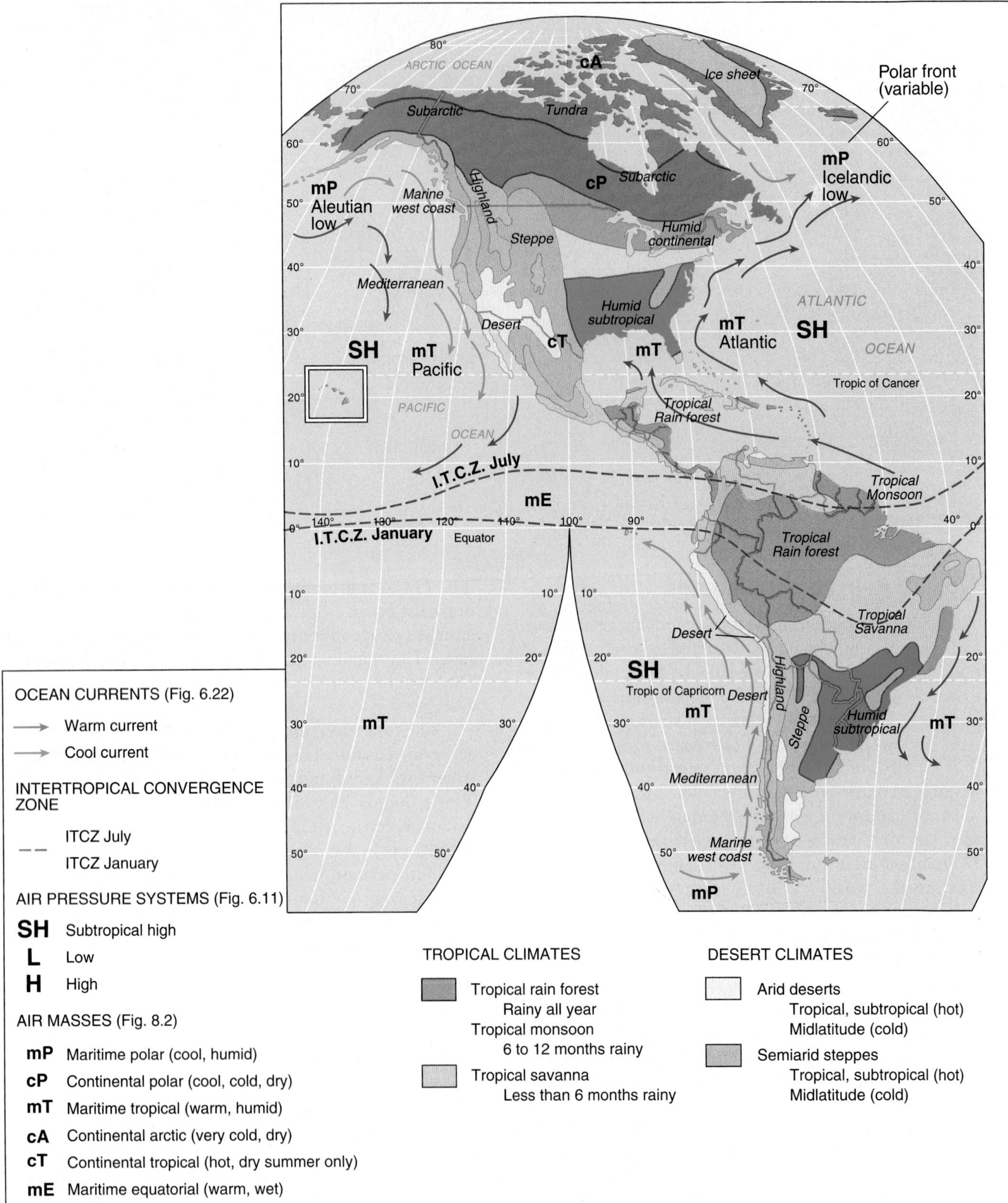

FIGURE 10.5 World climate classifications.
Annotated on this map are selected air masses, near shore ocean currents, pressure systems, and the January and July locations of the ITCZ. Use the colours in the legend to locate various climate types; some labels of the climate names appear in italics on the map to guide you.

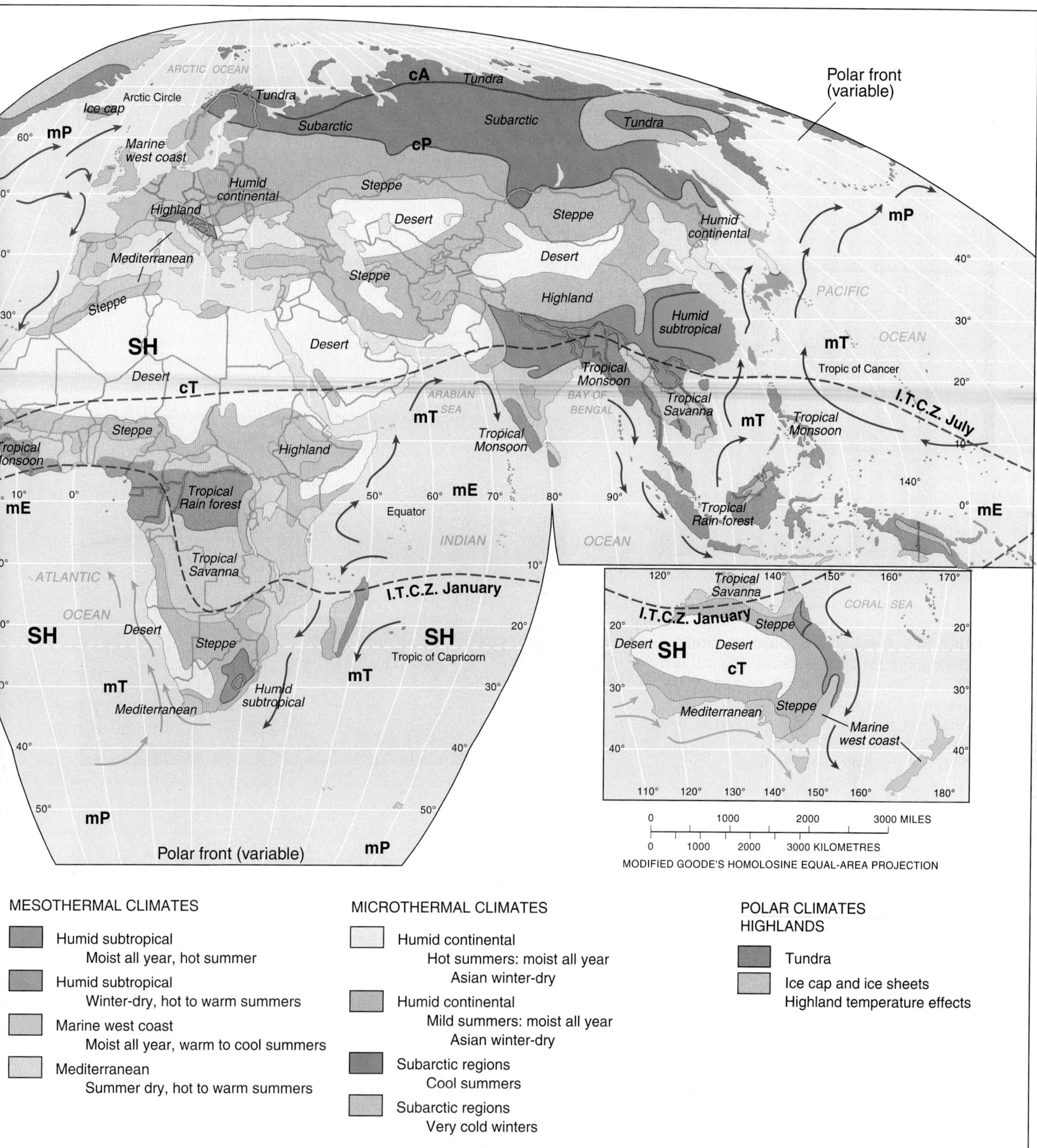
ARCTIC OCEAN
Arctic Circle
Ice cap
Tundra
cA
Subarctic
cP
Polar front (variable)
mP
Marine west coast
Humid continental
Highland
Mediterranean
Steppe
Desert
Humid subtropical
SH
cT
Tropical Monsoon
Tropical Savanna
ARABIAN SEA
BAY OF BENGAL
mT
mE
PACIFIC OCEAN
Tropic of Cancer
I.T.C.Z. July
Tropical Rain forest
Equator
INDIAN OCEAN
ATLANTIC OCEAN
I.T.C.Z. January
Tropic of Capricorn
CORAL SEA
Polar front (variable)
0 1000 2000 3000 MILES
0 1000 2000 3000 KILOMETRES
MODIFIED GOODE'S HOMOLOSINE EQUAL-AREA PROJECTION
MESOTHERMAL CLIMATES
Humid subtropical
Moist all year, hot summer
Humid subtropical
Winter-dry, hot to warm summers
Marine west coast
Moist all year, warm to cool summers
Mediterranean
Summer dry, hot to warm summers
MICROTHERMAL CLIMATES
Humid continental
Hot summers: moist all year
Asian winter-dry
Humid continental
Mild summers: moist all year
Asian winter-dry
Subarctic regions
Cool summers
Subarctic regions
Very cold winters
POLAR CLIMATES
HIGHLANDS
Tundra
Ice cap and ice sheets
Highland temperature effects

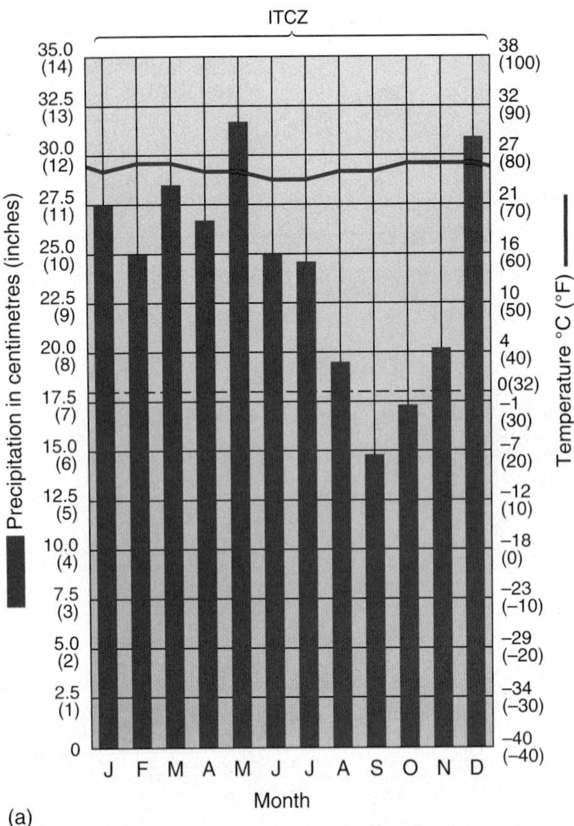

Station: Uaupés, Brazil
Lat/long: 0°08' S 67°05' W
Avg. Ann. Temp.: 25°C (77°F)
Total Ann. Precip.: 291.7 cm (114.8 in.)
Elevation: 86 m (282.2 ft)
Population: 10,000
Ann. Temp. Range: 2 C° (3.6 F°)
Ann. Hr of Sunshine: 2018

FIGURE 10.6 Tropical rain forest climate.
(a) Climograph for Uaupés, Brazil (*tropical rain forest*). (b) The rain forest near Uaupés along a tributary of the Rio Negro. (c) The lush equatorial rain forest and Sangha River, near Ouesso, Congo, Africa. [Photos by (b) Will and Deni McIntyre/Photo Researchers, Inc. and (c) BIOS M. Gunther/Peter Arnold, Inc.]

(b)

(c)

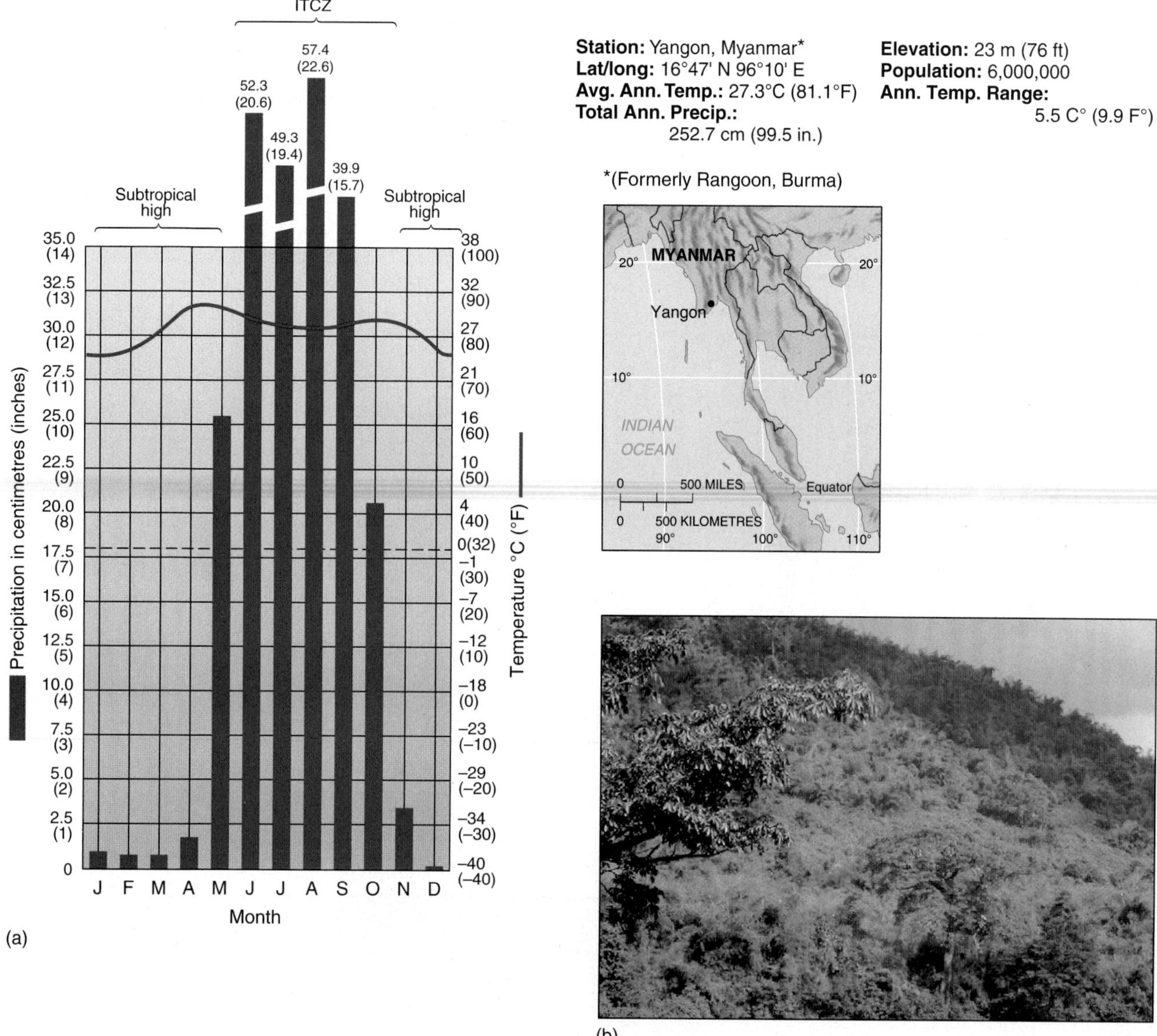

FIGURE 10.7 Tropical monsoon climate.
(a) Climograph for Yangon, Myanmar (formerly Rangoon, Burma) (*tropical monsoon*). (b) The monsoonal forest near Malang, Java, at the Purwodadi Botanical Gardens. [Photo by Tom McHugh/Photo Researchers, Inc.]

Tropical Savanna Climates

Tropical savanna climates occur poleward of the *tropical rain forest* climates. The ITCZ dominates these climates for 6 months or less of the year as it migrates with the summer Sun. Summers are wetter than winters because convectional rains accompany the shifting ITCZ when it is overhead. This produces a notable dry condition when the ITCZ is farthest away and high pressure dominates. Thus, the natural water demand exceeds the natural water supply in winter, causing soil-moisture shortages.

Temperatures vary more in *tropical savanna* climates than in *tropical rain forest* regions. The *tropical savanna* regime can have two temperature maximums because the Sun's direct rays are overhead twice during the year (before and after the summer solstice in each hemisphere as the Sun moves between the equator and the tropic). Dominant grasslands with scattered, drought-resistant trees, able to cope with the highly variable precipitation, characterize the *tropical savanna* regions (Figure 10.8b).

Arusha, Tanzania, is a characteristic *tropical savanna* city (Figure 10.8). This city of more than 1,368,000 people is east of the famous Serengeti plains savanna and Olduvai Gorge, site of human origins, and north of Tarangire National Park. Temperatures are consistent with tropical climates, despite the elevation of the station (1387 m, 4550 ft). Note the marked dryness from June to October, which defines changing dominant pressure systems rather than annual changes in temperature. This region is near the transition to the dryer hot-desert steppe climates to the northeast.

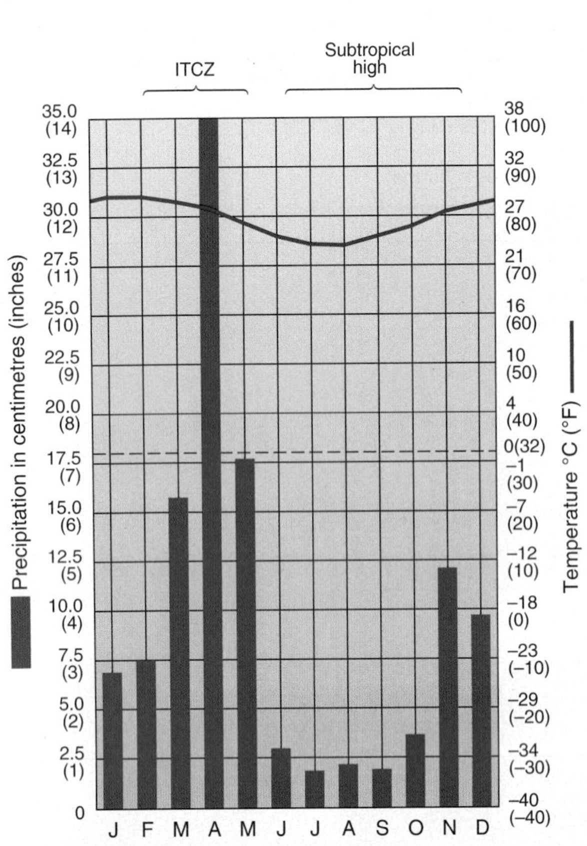

(a)

Station: Arusha, Tanzania
Lat/long: 3°24' S 36°42' E
Avg. Ann. Temp.: 26.5°C (79.7°F)
Total Ann. Precip.: 119 cm (46.9 in.)
Elevation: 1387 m (4550 ft)
Population: 1,368,000
Ann. Temp. Range: 4.1 C° (7.4 F°)
Ann. Hr of Sunshine: 2600

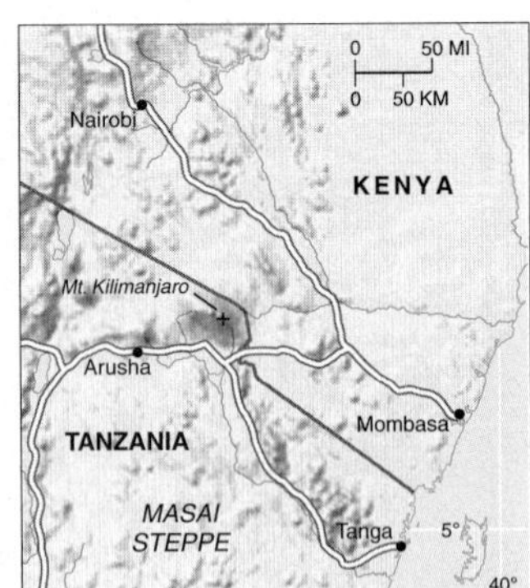

(b)

FIGURE 10.8 Tropical savanna climate.
(a) Climograph for Arusha, Tanzania (*tropical savanna*); note the intense dry period.
(b) Characteristic landscape in Kenya, with plants and animals adapted to seasonally dry water budgets. [Photo by Stephen J. Krasemann/DRK Photo.]

Mesothermal Climates (midlatitudes, mild winters)

Mesothermal, meaning "middle temperature," describes these warm and temperate climates, where true seasonality begins and seasonal contrasts in vegetation, soil, and human lifestyle adaptations are evident. More than half the world's population—approximately 55%—resides in these mesothermal climates. These climates occupy the second-largest percentage of Earth's land and sea surface behind the tropical climates, about 27%. Together, the tropical and mesothermal climates dominate over half of Earth's oceans and about one-third of its land area.

The mesothermal climates, and nearby portions of the microthermal (cold winter) climates, are regions of great weather variability, for these are the latitudes of greatest air mass interaction. Causal elements include:

- Shifting air masses of maritime and continental origin are guided by upper air westerly winds and undulating Rossby waves and jet streams.
- Migrating cyclonic (low pressure) and anticyclonic (high pressure) systems bring changeable weather conditions and air mass conflicts.
- Sea-surface temperatures of offshore ocean currents influence air mass strength: cooler water temperatures along west coasts (weaken) and warmer water along east coasts (strengthen).

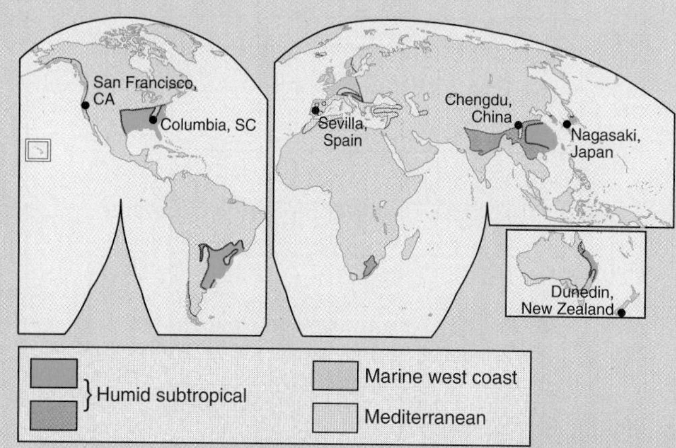

- Summers transition from hot to warm to cool as you move away from the tropics. Climates are humid, except where subtropical high pressure produces dry-summer conditions.

Mesothermal climates have four distinct regimes based on precipitation variability: *humid subtropical* hot summer (moist all year), *humid subtropical* winter dry (hot to warm summers, in Asia), *marine west coast* (warm to cool summers, moist all year), and *Mediterranean* (warm to hot summers, dry summers).

Humid Subtropical Climates

The *humid subtropical hot-summer* climates are either moist all year or have a pronounced winter-dry period as occurs in eastern and southern Asia. Maritime tropical air masses generated over warm waters off eastern coasts influence *humid subtropical hot-summer* climates during summer. This warm, moist, unstable air produces convectional showers over land. In fall, winter, and spring, maritime tropical and continental polar air masses interact, generating frontal activity and frequent midlatitude cyclonic storms. Overall, precipitation averages 100–200 cm (40–80 in.) a year. In North America, Columbia, South Carolina, is characteristic (Figure 10.9) of this climate regime, with precipitation totals of 126.5 cm (49.8 in.), hot, humid summers, and mild winters.

In eastern and southern Asia, winter precipitation is a bit less because of the effects of the Asian monsoon. These winter-dry climates relate to the seasonal pulse of the monsoons. They extend poleward from *tropical savanna* climates and have a summer month that receives 10 times more precipitation than their driest winter month. A representative station is Chengdu, China. Figure 10.10 demonstrates the strong correlation between precipitation and the high-summer Sun (review the monsoonal maps in Figure 6.21).

The concentration of people in north-central India, the bulk of China's 1.3 billion people, and the many who live in climatically similar portions of the United States, prove the habitability of the *humid subtropical* climates. The intense summer rains of the Asian monsoon can cause problems, as they did in the 2004 floods in India and Bangladesh. (See also News Report 10.1.)

Marine West Coast Climates

Marine west coast climates feature mild winters and cool summers and dominate Europe and other middle-to-high-latitude west coasts (see Figure 10.5). In Canada and the United States, these climates with their cooler summers are in contrast to the hot-summer humid climate of the southeastern United States.

Maritime polar air masses—cool, moist, unstable—control *marine west coast* climates. Weather systems forming along the polar front move into these regions throughout the year, making weather quite unpredictable. Coastal fog, annually totalling 30 to 60 days, is a part of the moderating marine influence. Frosts are possible and tend to shorten the growing season.

Marine west coast climates are unusually mild for their latitude owing to marine influences. They extend along the coastal margins of the Aleutian Islands in the North Pacific, cover the southern third of Iceland in the North Atlantic and coastal Scandinavia, and dominate the British Isles. To have average monthly temperatures that are above freezing throughout the year at such high-latitude locations is hard to imagine.

Unlike *marine west coast* climates in Europe, these climates in Canada, Alaska, Chile, and Australia are backed by mountains and remain restricted to coastal environs. The climograph for Vancouver demonstrates the moderate

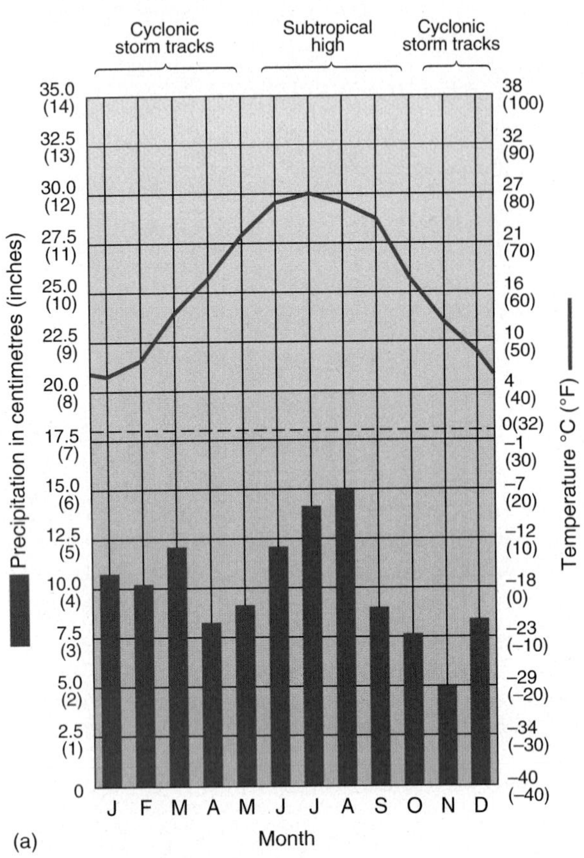

Station: Columbia, South Carolina
Lat/long: 34° N 81° W
Avg. Ann. Temp.: 17.3°C (63.1°F)
Total Ann. Precip.: 126.5 cm (49.8 in.)
Elevation: 96 m (315 ft)
Population: 116,000
Ann. Temp. Range: 20.7 C° (37.3 F°)
Ann. Hr of Sunshine: 2800

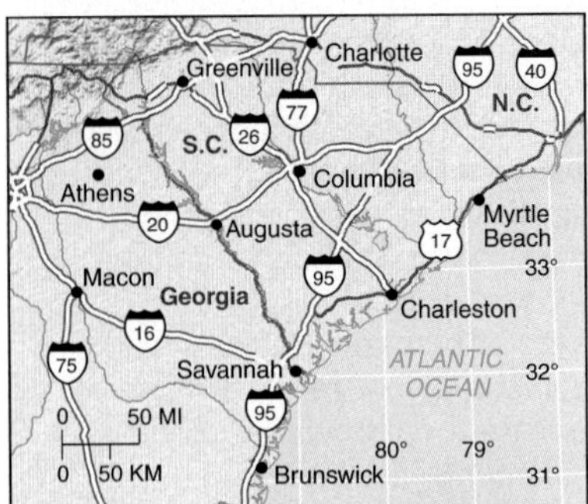

(b)

FIGURE 10.9 Humid subtropical climate, rainy all year.
(a) Climograph for Columbia, South Carolina (*humid subtropical*). Note the more consistent precipitation pattern, as Columbia receives seasonal cyclonic storm activity and summer convection showers within maritime tropical air. (b) The mixed deciduous and evergreen forest south of Atlanta, Georgia, typical of the humid subtropical southeastern United States. [Photo by Bobbé Christopherson.]

temperature patterns and the annual temperature range for a *marine west coast* city (Figure 10.11). The climograph for Dunedin, New Zealand, demonstrates the moderate temperature patterns and the annual temperature range for a *marine west coast* station in the Southern Hemisphere (Figure 10.12).

An interesting anomaly occurs in the eastern United States. In portions of the Appalachian highlands, increased elevation moderates summer temperatures in the surrounding *humid subtropical hot-summer* climate, producing a *marine west coast* cooler summer. The climograph for Bluefield, West Virginia (Figure 10.13, p. 301), reveals

News Report 10.1

Record Rains from the Asian Monsoons

The subtropical monsoonal winter-dry climates hold several precipitation records. Cherrapunji, India, in the Assam Hills south of the Himalayas, is the all-time precipitation holder for a single year and for every other time interval from 15 days to 2 years. Because of the summer monsoons that pour in from the Indian Ocean and the Bay of Bengal, Cherrapunji has received 930 cm (30.5 ft) of rainfall in one month and 2647 cm (86.8 ft) in one year—both world records. Because of extensive deforestation, these rains produce tremendous soil erosion. Sediments generated by this erosion are deposited in the Bay of Bengal as fragile, temporary islands that attract settlements. Floodwaters and heavy monsoonal downpours easily overwhelm these fertile islands. Two massive tropical cyclones struck the nearby coast of India in 1999, further worsening the fragile coastal conditions.

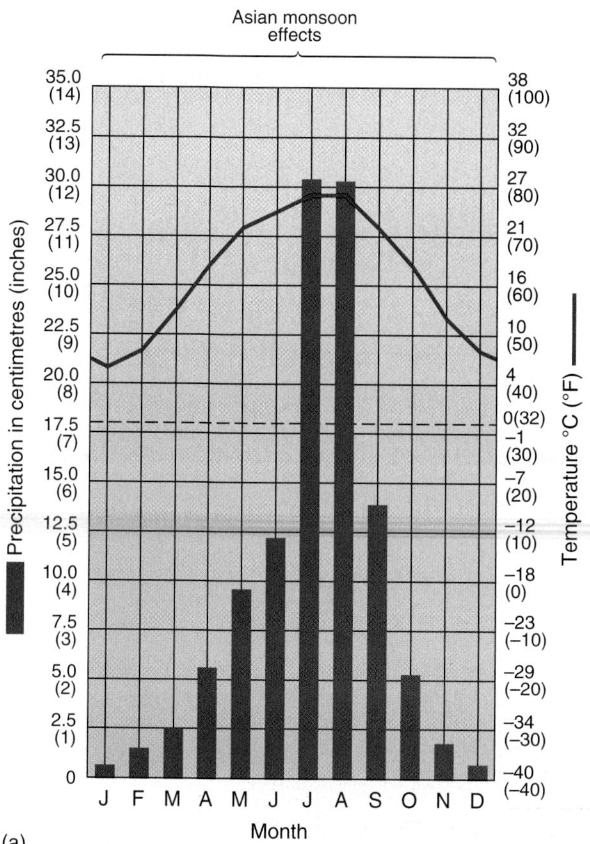

Station: Chengdu, China
Lat/long: 30°40' N 104°04' E
Avg. Ann. Temp.: 17°C (62.6°F)
Total Ann. Precip.: 114.6 cm (45.1 in.)
Elevation: 498 m (1633.9 ft)
Population: 2,500,000
Ann. Temp. Range: 20 C° (36 F°)
Ann. Hr of Sunshine: 1058

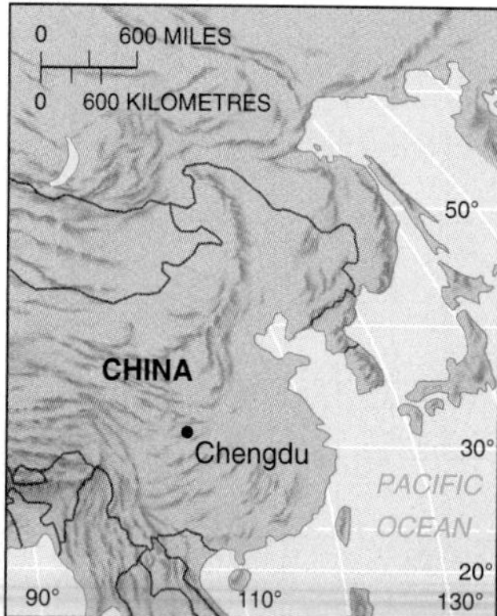

FIGURE 10.10 Humid subtropical winter-dry climate. (a) Climograph for Chengdu, China. (b) Landscape of southern interior China characteristic of this winter-dry climate. This valley is near Mount Daliang in Sichuan Province. [Photo by Jin Zuqi, Sovfoto/Eastfoto.]

marine west coast temperature and precipitation patterns, despite its location in the east. Vegetation similarities between the Appalachians and the Pacific Northwest are quite noticeable and have enticed many emigrants from the East to settle in these climatically familiar environments in the Northwest.

Mediterranean Dry-Summer Climates

Across the planet during summer months, shifting subtropical high-pressure cells block moisture-bearing winds from adjacent regions. For example, the continental tropical air mass over the Sahara in Africa shifts northward in summer over the Mediterranean region and blocks maritime air masses and cyclonic systems. The shifting of stable, warm-to-hot, dry air over an area in summer and away from these regions in the winter creates a unique dry-summer and wet-winter pattern. Mediterranean climates experience at least 70% of their annual precipitation during the winter months. This is in contrast to the majority of the world that experience summer-maximum precipitation.

Added to the high-pressure influence, cool offshore ocean currents (the California current, Canary current, Peru current, Benguela current, and West Australian current) produce stability in overlying air masses along west coasts, poleward of subtropical high pressure. The world climate map (Figure 10.5) shows these currents and *Mediterranean dry-summer* regions along the western margins of North America, central Chile, and the southwestern tip of Africa, as well as across southern Australia and the Mediterranean Basin—the climate's namesake region.

Figure 10.14 (p. 302) compares the climographs of *Mediterranean dry-summer* cities of San Francisco, California, and Sevilla (Seville), Spain. Coastal maritime effects moderate San Francisco's climate, producing a cool summer. The transition to hot summers occurs no more than 24–32 km (15–20 mi) inland from San Francisco.

Along these west coasts, the warm, moist air that contacts cool ocean water produces frequent summer fog, discussed in Chapter 7. However, this type of fog is not associated with the enclosed Mediterranean Sea region itself because offshore water temperatures there are higher

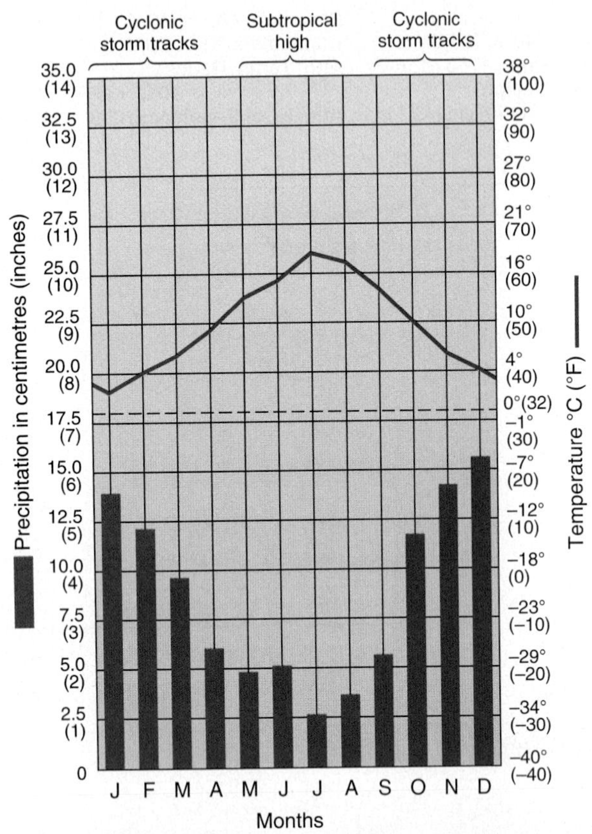

Station: Vancouver, British Columbia
Lat/long: 49°11' N, 123°10' W
Avg. Ann. Temp.: 10° C (50° F)
Total Annual Precipitation: 104.8 cm (41.3 in.)
Elevation: sea level
Population: 1,580,000
Ann. Temp. Range: 16 C° (28.8 F°)
Ann. Hrs. of Sunshine: 1723

(a)

(b)

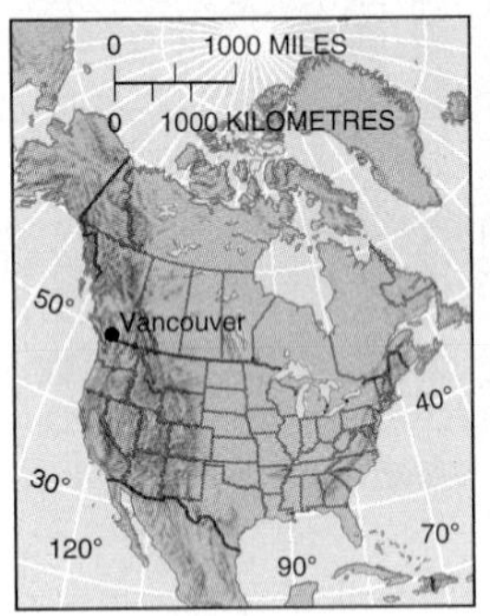

(c)

FIGURE 10.11 A marine west coast climate. (a) Climograph and locator map for Vancouver, British Columbia, a *marine west coast* climate. (b) The Vancouver waterfront and skyline. (c) The natural vegetation in the Channel Islands, Strait of Georgia, British Columbia (*marine west coast*). [Photos by (b) Robert W. Christopherson and (c) Bobbé Christopherson.]

than water temperatures near other similar climatic regions during the summer months. Instead, the Mediterranean regime features relatively high humidity values.

The *Mediterranean dry-summer* climate brings natural summer water-resource shortages. Winter precipitation recharges soil moisture, but water usage usually exhausts it by late spring. Large-scale agriculture requires irrigation; some subtropical fruits, nuts, and vegetables are uniquely suited to these conditions. Natural vegetation features a hard-leafed, drought-resistant variety known locally as *chaparral* in the western United States. (Chapter 20 discusses other local names for this type of vegetation in other parts of the world.)

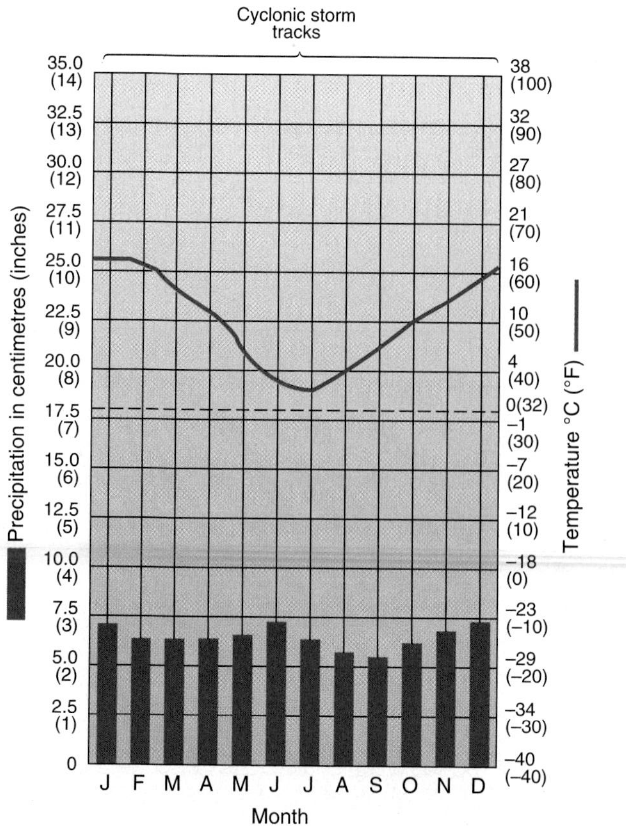

Station: Dunedin, New Zealand
Lat/long: 45°54' S 170°31' E
Avg. Ann. Temp.: 10.2°C (50.3°F)
Total Ann. Precip.: 78.7 cm (31.0 in.)
Elevation: 1.5 m (5 ft)
Population: 120,000
Ann. Temp. Range: 14.2 C° (25.5 F°)

(a)

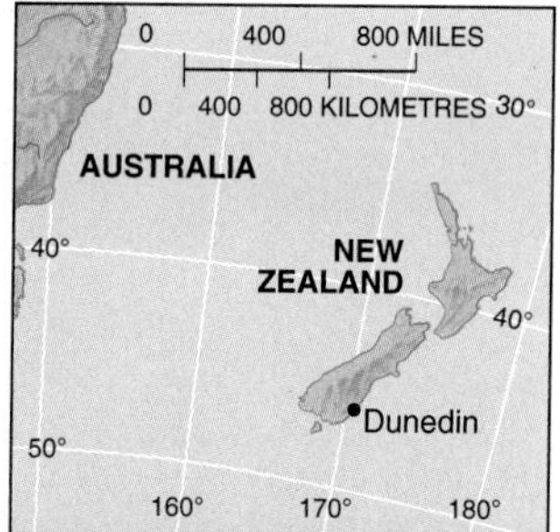

(b)

FIGURE 10.12 A Southern Hemisphere marine west coast climate.
(a) Climograph for Dunedin, New Zealand demonstrates a *marine west coast* climate with a mild summer. (b) Meadow, forest, and mountains on South Island, New Zealand. [Photo by Brian Enting/Photo Researchers, Inc.]

Cyclonic storms (summer convection)

Precipitation in centimetres (inches)

Temperature °C (°F)

J F M A M J J A S O N D

Month

Station: Bluefield, West Virginia
Lat/long: 37°16' N 81°13' W
Avg. Ann. Temp.: 12°C (53.6°F)
Total Ann. Precip.: 101.9 cm (40.1 in.)
Elevation: 780 m (2559 ft)
Population: 16,000
Ann. Temp. Range: 21 C° (37.8 F°)

(a)

(b)

FIGURE 10.13 Climate in the Appalachians.
(a) Climograph for Bluefield, West Virginia, exhibits *marine west coast* characteristics. (b) Characteristic mixed forest of Dolly Sods Wilderness in the Appalachian highlands. [Photo by David Muench Photography, Inc.]

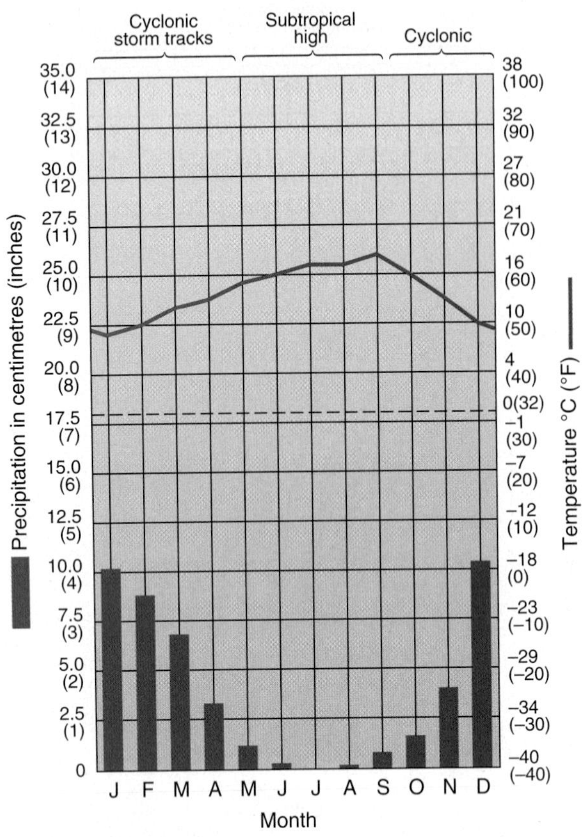

Station: San Francisco, California
Lat/long: 37°37' N 122°23' W
Avg. Ann. Temp.: 14°C (57.2°F)
Total Ann. Precip.: 47.5 cm (18.7 in.)
Elevation: 5 m (16.4 ft)
Population: 747,000
Ann. Temp. Range: 9 C° (16.2 F°)
Ann. Hr of Sunshine: 2975

(a)

Cyclonic storm tracks
Subtropical high
Cyclonic storm tracks
Precipitation in centimetres (inches)
Temperature °C (°F)
J F M A M J J A S O N D
Month

Station: Sevilla, Spain
Lat/long: 37°22' N 6°00' W
Avg. Ann. Temp.: 18°C (64.4°F)
Total Ann. Precip.: 55.9 cm (22 in.)
Elevation: 13 m (42.6 ft)
Population: 1,764,000
Ann. Temp. Range: 16 C° (28.8 F°)
Ann. Hr of Sunshine: 2862

(b)

(c)

(d)

FIGURE 10.14 Mediterranean climates. (a) Climographs for San Francisco (*Mediterranean cool-summer*) and (b) Sevilla, Spain (*Mediterranean hot-summer*). (c) Central California landscape of oak savanna. (d) The countryside around Olvera, Andalusia, Spain. [Photos by (c) Bobbé Christopherson; (d) Kaz Chiba/Gamma-Liaison Agency, Inc.]

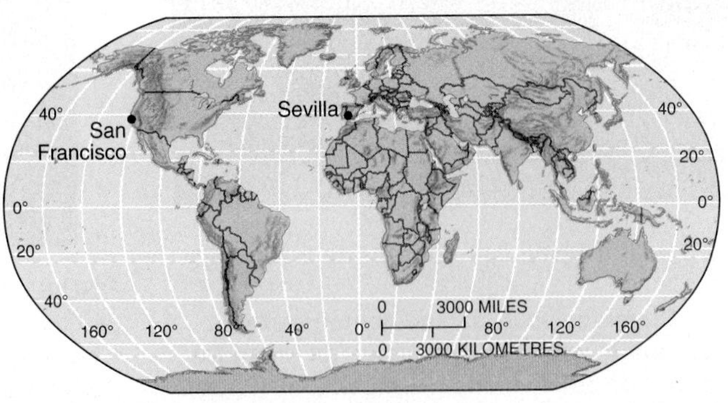

Microthermal Climates (mid- and high latitudes, cold winters)

Humid microthermal climates have a winter season with some summer warmth. Here the term *microthermal* means cool temperate to cold. Approximately 21% of Earth's land surface is influenced by these climates, equalling about 7% of Earth's total surface. These climates occur poleward of the mesothermal climates and experience great temperature ranges related to continentality and air mass conflicts.

Temperatures decrease with increasing latitude and toward the interior of continental landmasses, leading to intensely cold winters. Precipitation varies between moist-all-year regions (the northern tier across the United States and Canada, eastern Europe through the Ural Mountains) and winter-dry regions associated with the Asian monsoon.

In Figure 10.5, note the absence of microthermal climates in the Southern Hemisphere. Because the Southern Hemisphere lacks substantial landmasses, microthermal climates develop there only in highlands. Important causal elements include:

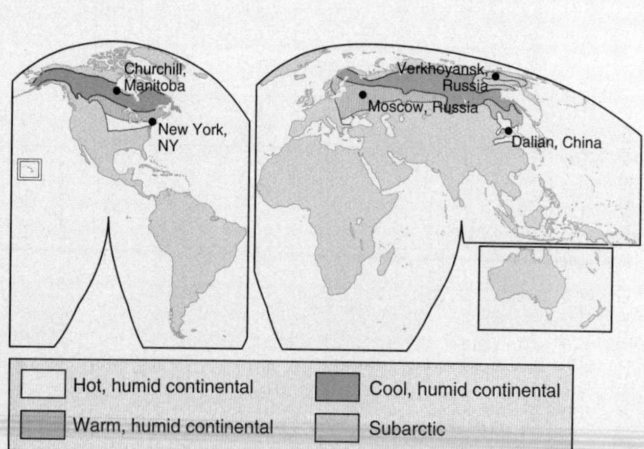

- Increasing seasonality (daylength and Sun altitude), and greater temperature ranges (daily and annually).
- Upper-air westerly winds and undulating Rossby waves, which bring warmer air northward and colder air southward for cyclonic activity; convectional thunderstorms from mT air masses in summer.
- Asian winter-dry pattern for the microthermal climates, increasing east of the Ural Mountains to the Pacific Ocean and eastern Asia.
- Hot summers cooling northward from the mesothermal climates; short spring and fall seasons surrounding winters that are cold to very cold.
- Continental interiors serving as source regions for intense continental polar (cP) air masses that dominate winter, blocking cyclonic storms.

Microthermal climates have four distinct regimes based on increasing cold with latitude and precipitation variability: *humid continental hot-summer* (Chicago, New York); *humid continental mild-summer* (Duluth, Toronto, Moscow); *subarctic* climates featuring cool summers (Churchill, Manitoba); and the formidable extremes of frigid *subarctic very cold winters* in Verkhoyansk and northern Siberia.

Humid Continental Hot-Summer Climates

Humid continental hot-summer climates are differentiated by their annual precipitation distribution. In the summer, maritime tropical air masses influence both humid continental moist-all-year and winter-dry climates. In North America frequent stormy weather is possible from conflicting air masses—maritime tropical and continental polar—especially in winter. The climographs for New York City, New York, and Dalian, China, illustrate these two humid, hot-summer regimes (Figure 10.15).

Before European settlement, forests covered the *humid continental hot-summer* region of the United States west to the Indiana–Illinois border. Beyond that approximate line, tall-grass prairies extended westward to about the 98th meridian (98° W) and the approximate location of the 51 cm (20 in.) isohyet (line of equal precipitation). The short-grass prairies extended to the west, where precipitation is less.

Deep sod made farming difficult for the first settlers, as did the climate. However, native grasses soon were replaced with domesticated wheat and barley. Various inventions brought from the East (barbed wire, the self-scouring steel plough, well-drilling techniques, and the railroads) helped open the region further. In the United States today, the *humid continental hot-summer* region is the location of corn, soybean, hog, and cattle production (Figure 10.15c).

The dry winter associated with the vast Asian landmass, specifically Siberia, results from a dry-winter high-pressure anticyclone. The dry monsoons of southern and eastern Asia are produced in the winter months by this system, as winds blow out of Siberia toward the Pacific and Indian Oceans. The Dalian, China, climograph demonstrates this dry-winter tendency. The intruding cold of continental air is a significant winter feature.

Humid Continental Mild-Summer Climates

Soils are thinner and less fertile in the cooler microthermal climates, yet agricultural activity is important and includes dairy cattle, poultry, flax, sunflowers, sugar beets, wheat, and potatoes. Frost-free periods range from fewer than 90 days in the north to as many as 225 days in the south. Overall, precipitation is less than in the hot-summer regions to the south. However, notably heavier snowfall is important to soil moisture recharge when it melts. Various snow–capturing strategies are used, including fences and tall stubble (plant stalks left standing after harvest) in fields to create snowdrifts and thus more moisture retention on the soil.

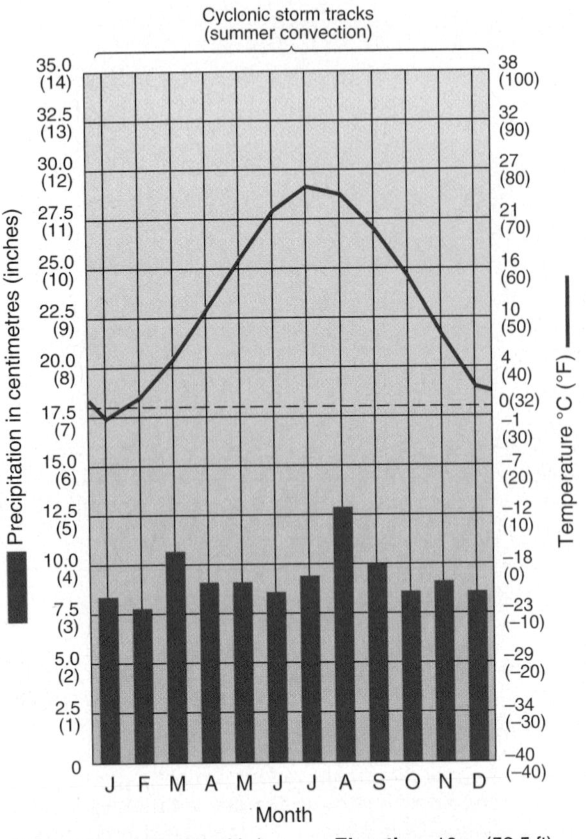

Station: New York, New York
Lat/long: 40°46' N 74°01' W
Avg. Ann. Temp.: 13°C (55.4°F)
Total Ann. Precip.: 112.3 cm (44.2 in.)
Elevation: 16 m (52.5 ft)
Population: 8,092,000
Ann. Temp. Range: 24 C° (43.2 F°)
Ann. Hr of Sunshine: 2564

(a)

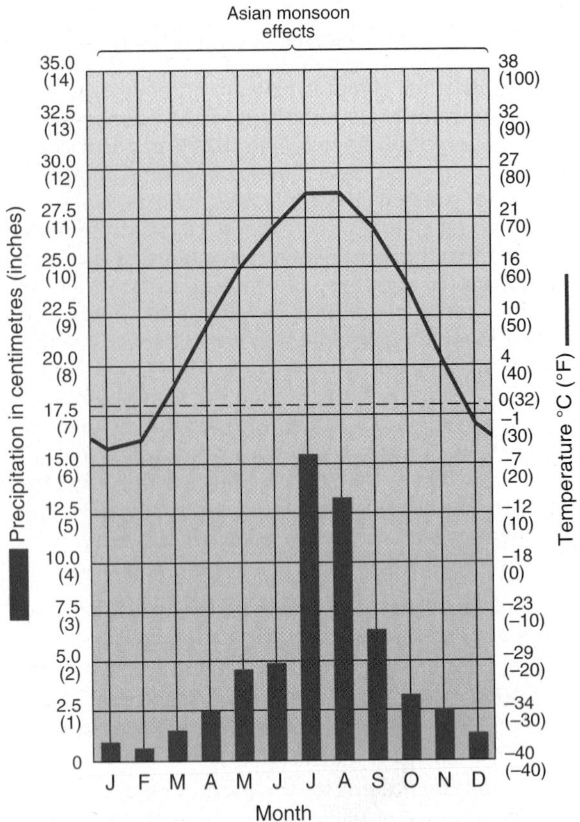

Station: Dalian, China
Lat/long: 38°54' N 121°54' E
Avg. Ann. Temp.: 10°C (50°F)
Total Ann. Precip.: 57.8 cm (22.8 in.)
Elevation: 96 m (314.9 ft)
Population: 5,550,000
Ann. Temp. Range: 29 C° (52.2 F°)
Ann. Hr of Sunshine: 2762

(b)

(c)

(d)

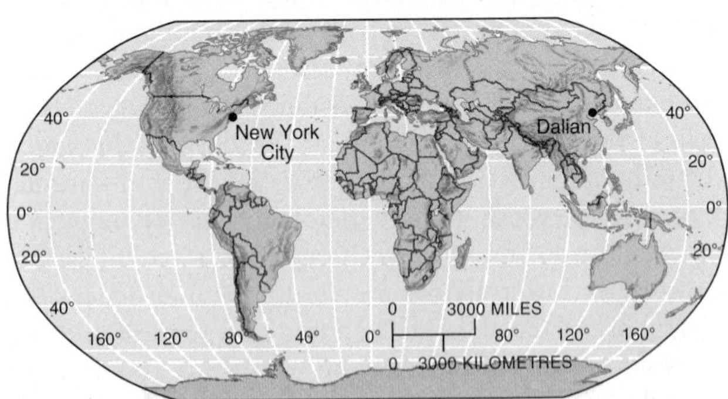

FIGURE 10.15 Humid continental hot-summer climate. Climographs for (a) New York City (*humid continental, moist all year*) and (b) Dalian, China (*humid continental winter-dry*). (c) Typical of this climate region, a deciduous forest and ready-to-harvest soybean field in central Indiana near Zelma. (d) New York City's Central Park emerging from winter just before spring and the return of leaves and warmth. [Photos (c) and (d) by Bobbé Christopherson.]

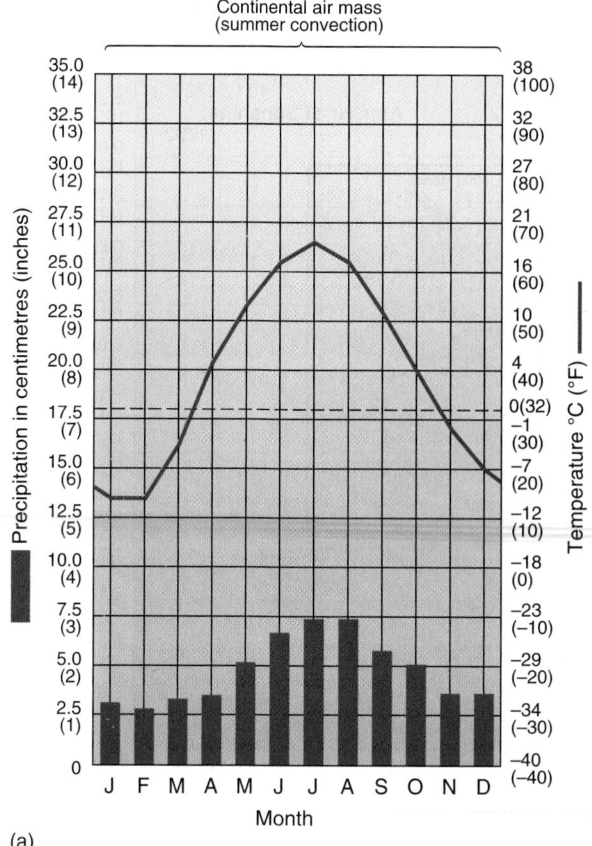

Station: Moscow, Russia
Lat/long: 55°45' N 37°34' E
Avg. Ann. Temp.: 4°C (39.2°F)
Total Ann. Precip.: 57.5 cm (22.6 in.)
Elevation: 156 m (511.8 ft)
Population: 11,460,000
Ann. Temp. Range: 29 C° (52.2 F°)
Ann. Hr of Sunshine: 1597

(b)

(c)

FIGURE 10.16 Humid continental cool-summer climate.
(a) Climograph for Moscow, Russia. (b) Springtime fields near Saratov, Russia, during the short summer season. (c) Winter scene of Sebago Lake and forests inland from Portland, Maine. [Photos by (b) Wolfgang Kaehler/Gamma, Inc.; (c) Bobbé Christopherson]

Characteristic cities are Duluth, Minnesota, and Saint Petersburg, Russia. Figure 10.16 presents a climograph for Moscow, which is at 55° N, or about the same latitude as the southern shore of Hudson Bay in Canada. The photos of landscapes near Moscow, Russia, and Sebago Lake (inland from Portland, Maine) show summer and late winter scenes, respectively.

The dry winter associated with the vast Asian landmass, specifically Siberia, is exclusively associated with the extremely dry and frigid winter high-pressure anticyclone that dominates. This system produces the dry monsoons of southern and eastern Asia in the winter months, as winds blow out of Siberia toward the Pacific and Indian Oceans (see Figure 6.21). The intruding dry cold of continental air is a significant winter feature. A representative *humid continental mild-summer* climate is Vladivostok, Russia, on the Sea of Japan, usually one of only two ice-free ports in that country.

Subarctic Climates

Farther poleward, seasonality becomes greater. The short growing season is more intense during long summer days. The cold *subarctic* climates include vast stretches of Alaska, Canada, northern Scandinavia with their cool summers, and Siberian Russia with its very cold winters. The subarctic regions transition into tundra to the north. Discoveries of minerals and petroleum reserves have led to new interest in portions of these regions.

Areas that receive 25 cm (10 in.) or more of precipitation a year on the northern continental margins are covered by the so-called snow forest of fir, spruce, larch, and birch—the *boreal* forests of Canada and the *taiga* of Russia. These forests are in transition to the more open northern woodlands and to the tundra region of the far north. Forests thin out to the north when the warmest summer month drops below an average temperature of 10°C (50°F).

Soils are thin in these lands once scoured by glaciers. Precipitation received and the demand for soil moisture both are low. Soils are generally moist and either partially or totally frozen beneath the surface, a phenomenon known as *permafrost* and discussed in Chapter 17.

The Churchill, Manitoba, climograph (Figure 10.17) shows average monthly temperatures below freezing for at least 7 months of the year, during which time light snow cover and frozen ground persist. High pressure dominates

Tundra Climate

In a *tundra* climate, land is under continuous snow cover for 8–10 months, with the warmest month above 0°C yet never warming above 10°C (50°F). However, when the snow melts and spring arrives, numerous plants appear—stunted sedges, mosses, flowering plants, and lichens. Much of the area experiences permafrost (frozen ground) conditions. The *tundra* also is the summer home of mosquitoes of legend and black gnats.

Approximately 410,500 km^2 (158,475 mi^2) of Greenland are ice free, an area of tundra and rock about the size of California. The rest of Greenland is ice sheet covering 1,756,00 km^2 (677,900 mi^2). Despite the severe climate a permanent population of 56,500 lives in this province of Denmark. There are only a couple of towns along Greenland's east coast. Ittoqqortoormiit, or Scoresby Sund, has 850 permanent residents. Figure 10.19b shows this village on the *tundra*.

Global climate change is bringing dramatic alterations to the tundra, its plants, animals, and permafrost. In 1998, parts of Canada registered temperatures 5 C° above average, 1.0 C° above normal for all of Canada—the warmest in the 51-year record. A 2002 study of 67 glaciers in Alaska discovered average thickness decreasing at more than a half metre a year, with 131 km^2 (430 mi^2) of land now uncovered and ice free. These conditions are having profound effects in the extent of the *tundra* regions.

Tundra climates are strictly a Northern Hemisphere occurrence, except for elevated mountain locations in the Southern Hemisphere and a portion of the Antarctic Peninsula, where plants are now growing for the first time. Because of elevation, the summit of Mount Washington in New Hampshire (1914 m, or 6280 ft) statistically qualifies as a highland *tundra* climate of small scale.

Ice Cap and Ice Sheet Climate

Most of Antarctica and Greenland fall within the *ice cap* and *ice sheet* climate, as does the North Pole, with all months averaging below freezing. These regions are dominated by dry, frigid air masses, with vast expanses that never warm above freezing. The area of the North Pole is actually a sea covered by ice, whereas Antarctica is a substantial continental landmass covered by Earth's greatest *ice sheet*. For comparison, winter minimums at the South Pole (July) can drop below the temperature of solid carbon dioxide or "dry ice" (that is, below −78°C, or −109°F). *Ice caps* are smaller in extent than an *ice sheet*, roughly less than 50,000 km^2 (19,300 mi^2), yet they completely bury the landscape like an ice sheet. An example in southeastern Iceland is the Vatnajökull Ice Cap.

Antarctica is constantly snow-covered but receives less than 8 cm (3 in.) of precipitation each year. Antarctic ice has accumulated to several kilometres thickness and is the largest repository of freshwater on Earth. Earth's two *ice sheets* cover the Antarctic continent and most of the island of Greenland. Figure 10.20 shows two scenes of these repositories of multiyear ice.

This ice is a vast historical record of Earth's atmosphere. Within it, evidence of thousands of past volcanic

(a)

(b)

FIGURE 10.19 Greenland tundra and a small town.
(a) *Tundra* is marked by an uneven, hummocky surface of mounds resulting from an active layer that freezes and thaws with the seasons, as it is here in east Greenland (see Chapter 17). Large trees are absent in the *tundra*; however, a relatively lush vegetation for the harsh conditions includes willow, dwarf birch and shrubs, sedges, moss, lichen, and cotton grass (white tufts). Some of the little (7.5 cm, 3 in. tall) willows can exceed 300 years in age. These September photos show the emerging fall colours of these small plants. (b) A town in the *tundra* is Ittoqqortoormiit (Scoresby Sund), Greenland, one of only a few settlements along the entire east coast. In the foreground sledge (sled) dogs rest to get ready for the winter's work ahead. [Photos by Bobbé Christopherson.]

(a)

(b)

FIGURE 10.20 Earth's ice sheets—Antarctica and Greenland.
These are Earth's frozen freshwater reservoirs. (a) Flowing glaciers carry ice off the Bruce Plateau, Antarctic Peninsula. (b) Three outlet glaciers drain the Greenland ice sheet into the North Atlantic from southeastern Greenland; winds swirl the water and some captive, drifting icebergs. [Photos by Bobbé Christopherson.]

eruptions from all over the world have deposited ash layers, and ancient combinations of atmospheric gases lie trapped in frozen bubbles. An analysis of ice cores taken from Greenland and Antarctica is in Chapter 17.

Polar Marine Climate

Polar marine areas are more moderate than other polar climates in winter, with no month averaging below −7°C (20°F), yet they are not as warm as *tundra* climates. Because of marine influences, annual temperature ranges are low. This climate exists along the Bering Sea, the tip of Greenland, northern Iceland, Norway, and in the Southern Hemisphere, generally over oceans between 50° S and 60° S. Precipitation, which frequently falls as sleet (ice pellets), is greater in these regions than in continental polar climates.

Arid and Semiarid Climates (permanent moisture deficits)

Dry climates are the world's arid deserts and semiarid regions, where we consider moisture efficiency along with temperature for understanding the climate. These regions have unique plants, animals, and physical features. Arid and semiarid regions occupy more than 35% of Earth's land area and clearly are the most extensive climate over land. The mountains, rock strata, long vistas, and the resilient struggle for life are magnified by the dryness. Sparse vegetation leaves the landscape bare; water demand exceeds the precipitation water supply throughout dry arid and semiarid climates, creating permanent water deficits (water balance is discussed in Chapter 9). The extent of these deficits distinguishes deserts from steppe climatic regions. (See specific annual and daily desert temperature regimes, including the highest record temperatures and surface energy budgets in Chapter 4; desert landscapes in Chapter 15; and desert environments in Chapter 20.) Important causal elements in these drylands include:

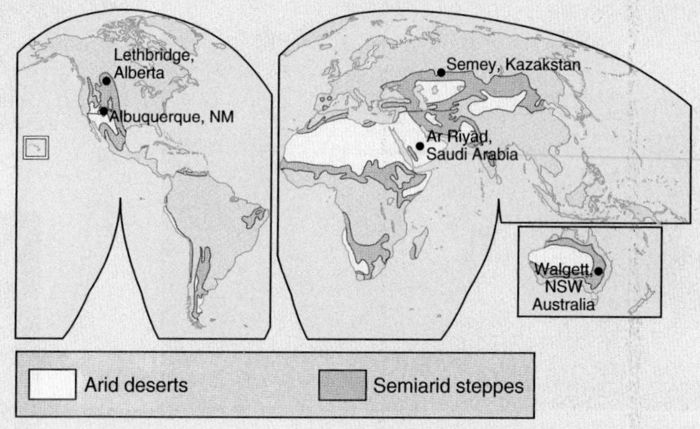

- Dry, subsiding air in subtropical high pressure systems dominates.
- Midlatitude deserts and steppes form in the rain shadow of mountains, those regions to the lee of precipitation-intercepting mountains.
- Continental interiors, particularly central Asia, are far from moisture-bearing air masses.
- Shifting subtropical high-pressure systems produce semiarid steppe lands around the periphery of arid deserts.

Dry climates are distributed by latitude and the amount of moisture deficits in four distinct regimes: *Arid deserts (low-latitude hot, midlatitude cold)* and *semiarid steppes (low-latitude hot, midlatitude cold)*.

Desert Characteristics

Desert vegetation is typically *xerophytic*: drought-resistant, waxy, hard-leafed, or otherwise adapted to aridity and low transpiration loss. Along stream channels, plants called *phreatophytes*, or "water-well plants," have roots that penetrate to great depths for the water they need (Figure 10.21).

The world climate map in Figure 10.5 reveals the pattern of Earth's dry climates, which cover broad regions between 15° and 30° N and S latitudes. In these areas, subtropical high-pressure cells predominate, with subsiding, stable air and low relative humidity. Under generally cloudless skies, these subtropical deserts extend to western continental margins, where cool, stabilizing ocean currents operate offshore and summer advection fog forms. The Atacama Desert of Chile, the Namib Desert of Namibia, the Western Sahara of Morocco, and the Australian Desert lie adjacent to a coastline.

Orographic lifting intercepts moisture-bearing weather systems to create rain shadows along mountain ranges that extend these dry regions into higher latitudes. Note these rain shadows in North and South America on the climate map. The isolated interior Asia, far distant from any moisture-bearing air masses, falls within the *dry arid* and *semiarid* climates as well.

Major subdivisions include *deserts* (precipitation supply roughly less than one-half of the natural moisture demand) and *semiarid steppes* (precipitation supply roughly more than one-half of natural moisture demand). Important is whether precipitation falls principally in the winter with a dry summer, falls in the summer with a dry winter, or is evenly distributed. Winter rains are most effective because they fall at a time of lower moisture demand. Relative to temperature, the lower latitude deserts and steppes tend to be hotter with less seasonal change than the midlatitude deserts and steppes where mean annual temperatures are below 18°C (64.4°F) and freezing winter temperatures are possible.

Low-Latitude Hot Desert Climates

Low-latitude hot desert climates are Earth's true tropical and subtropical deserts and feature annual average temperatures above 18°C (64.4°F). They generally are concentrated

(a)

(b)

(c)

FIGURE 10.21 Desert landscapes.
(a) Desert plants are particularly well adapted to the harsh environment of Joshua Tree National Park, part of the Mojave Desert in southeastern California. (b) Undependable water flows between the towering sandstone walls surrounding Chinle Wash in Canyon de Chelly, Arizona. (c) The silt-laden Colorado River flows just north of Moab, Utah, cutting through beautiful red sandstone. [Photos by (a) and (c) Bobbé Christopherson; (b) Robert W. Christopherson.]

on the western sides of continents, although Egypt, Somalia, and Saudi Arabia also fall within this climate regime. Rainfall is from local summer convectional showers. Some regions receive almost no rainfall, whereas others may receive up to 35 cm (14 in.) precipitation a year. A representative *low-latitude hot desert* station is Ar Riyāḑ (Riyadh), Saudi Arabia (Figure 10.22a and b).

Along the Sahara's southern margin is a drought-tortured region. Human populations suffered great hardship in the last several decades as desert conditions gradually expanded over their homelands. The sparse environment sets the stage for a rugged lifestyle and subsistence economies, pictured here near Timbuktu, Mali (Figure 10.22c). Chapter 15 presents the process of desertification (expanding desert conditions).

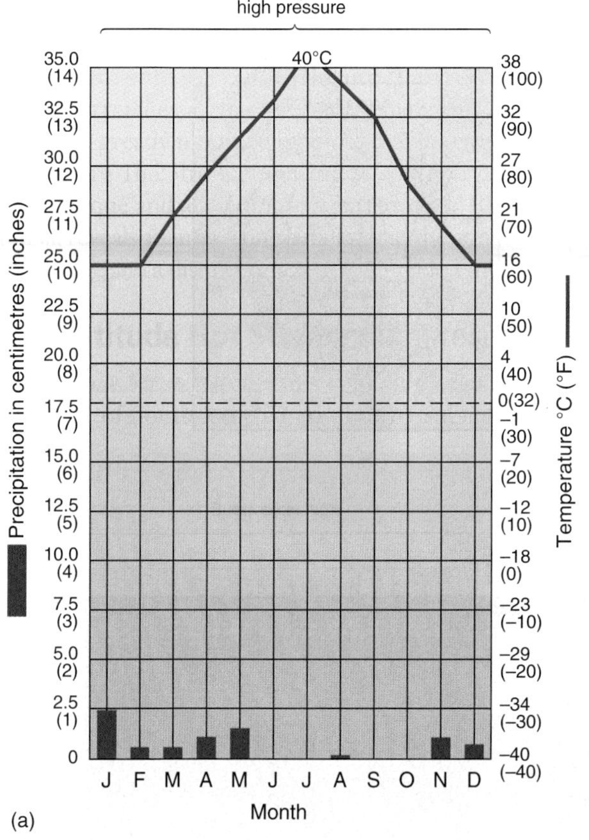

Station: Ar Riyāḑ (Riyadh), Saudi Arabia
Lat/long: 24°42'N 46°43' E
Avg. Ann. Temp.: 26°C (78.8°F)
Total Ann. Precip.: 8.2 cm (3.2 in.)
Elevation: 609 m (1998 ft)
Population: 5,024,000
Ann. Temp. Range: 24 C° (43.2 F°)

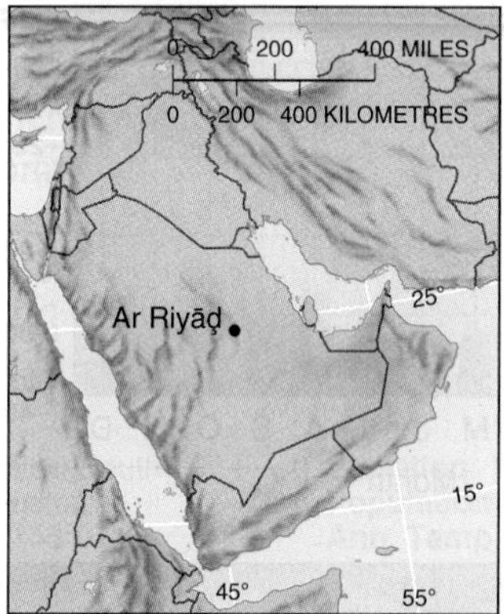

(b)

(c)

FIGURE 10.22 Low-latitude hot desert climate.
(a) Climograph for Ar Riyāḑ (Riyadh), Saudi Arabia (*low-latitude hot desert*). (b) The Arabian Desert sand dunes near Ar Riyāḑ. (c) Herders bring a few cattle to market near Timbuktu, Mali. Precipitation has been below normal in the region since 1966. [Photos by (b) Ray Ellis/Photo Researchers, Inc.; (c) by Betty Press/Woodfin Camp & Associates.]

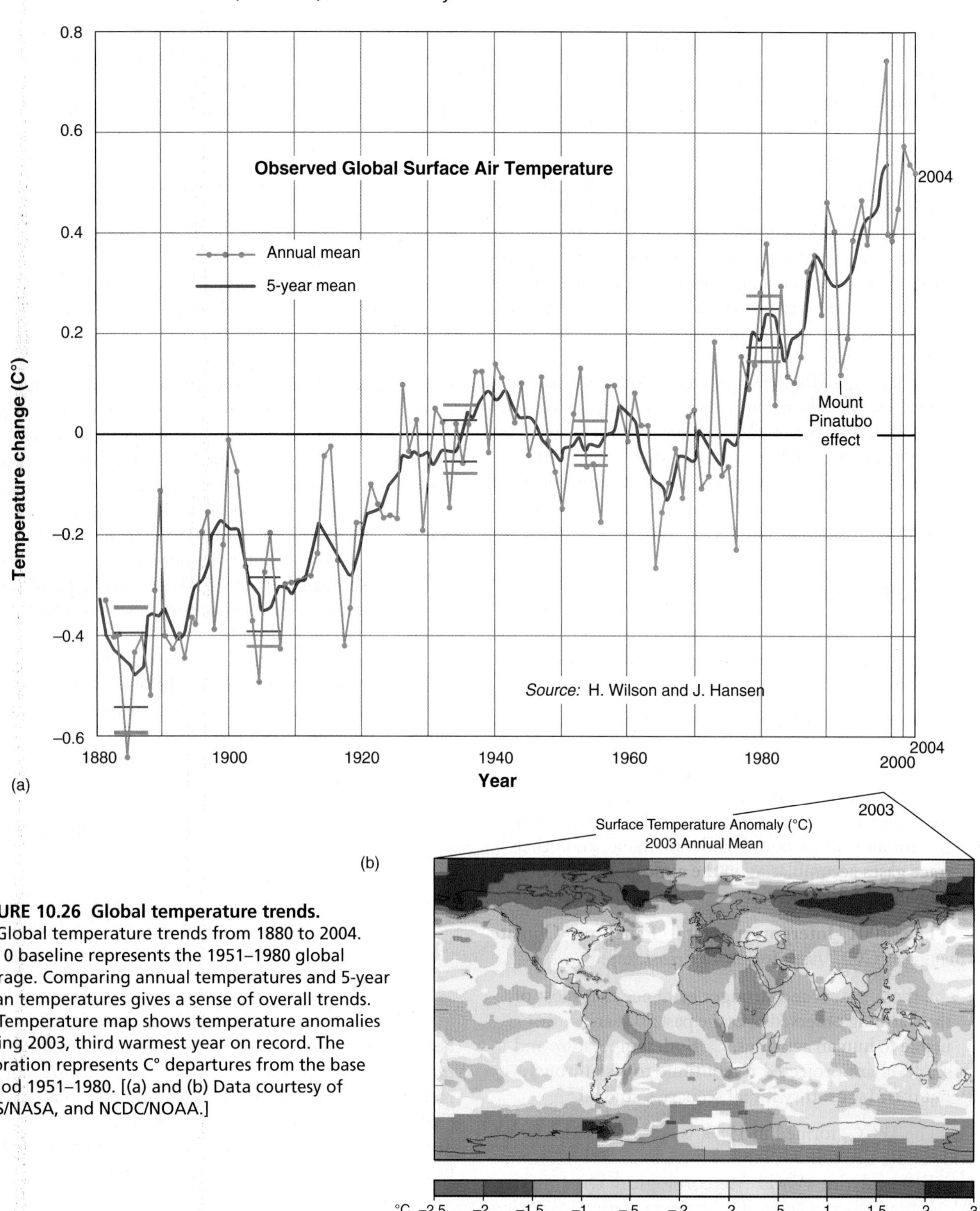

FIGURE 10.26 Global temperature trends. (a) Global temperature trends from 1880 to 2004. The 0 baseline represents the 1951–1980 global average. Comparing annual temperatures and 5-year mean temperatures gives a sense of overall trends. (b) Temperature map shows temperature anomalies during 2003, third warmest year on record. The coloration represents C° departures from the base period 1951–1980. [(a) and (b) Data courtesy of GISS/NASA, and NCDC/NOAA.]

methane, nitrous oxide, chlorofluorocarbons (CFCs), and water vapour, which absorb and radiate infrared wavelengths. They are transparent to light but opaque to the infrared wavelengths radiated by Earth. Thus, they transmit light from the Sun to Earth but delay heat-energy loss to space. While detained, this heat energy is absorbed and reradiated over and over, warming the lower atmosphere. As concentrations of these infrared-absorbing gases increase, more heat energy remains in the atmosphere and temperatures increase.

The Industrial Revolution, which began in the mid-1700s, initiated tremendous burning of fossil fuels. This, coupled with the destruction and inadequate replacement of harvested forests, continues to increase atmospheric carbon dioxide levels. Carbon dioxide alone is responsible for 64% of the global warming trend. Table 10.1 shows the increasing percentage of carbon dioxide in the lower atmosphere from pre-industrial 1750 to the present—a one-third increase—and gives estimates for the future. The current rate of increase is faster than at any time in the past 20,000 years, whereas the present concentration tops anything over the last 420,000 years.

Both Canada and the United States showed slight declines in total emissions from 1989–1991, followed in the 1990s by recoveries leading to all-time highs for Canada in 1997, and for the United States in 2000. The U.S. carbon emissions alone rose 13% between 1990 and 2000, to 24% of the global total. Canada has experienced a 9.5% decline in fossil-fuel CO_2 emissions since 1997, while the U.S. shows a 2.8% increase. Per capita emissions in Canada and the United States have been consistently high, and well above those for any other region. Coordination of climate change research is found in News Report 10.2 and information about energy efficiency, the tool that individuals can use to decrease our output of greenhouse gases, can be found at Natural Resources Canada (http://oee.nrcan.gc.ca/corporate/programs.cfm).

Figure 10.27 shows sources of excessive, non-natural, carbon dioxide by country or region in 1995 and forecast for 2025. Developing countries are clearly identified as the sector with the greatest probable growth in fossil fuel consumption and new carbon dioxide production. Emissions from North America have decreased from 46.4% of the global total in 1950 to 26.3% in 2000. This is largely the result of greater growth in the rest of the world rather than a decrease in emissions in North America. However, national and corporate policies could alter this forecast by actively steering developing countries toward alternative energy

Table 10.1 Carbon Dioxide Concentration in the Lower Atmosphere

Year	CO_2 Concentration*	
	Percent (%)	Parts per Million
1750	0.028	280
1888	0.029	290
1985	0.035	345.9
2003	0.038	375.6
2020 (estimate)	0.047	470
2050 (estimate)	0.053	530
2100 range (est.)	0.55–0.97	550–970

*See Chapter 3 and pp. 219–24 in IPCC Working Group I, *Climate Change 2001, The Scientific Basis* (Washington: Cambridge University Press, 2001). For update see data measured at Mauna Loa Climate Observatory, Hawai'i, at http://cdiac.esd.ornl.gov/ftp/maunaloa-co2/maunaloa.co2.

News Report 10.2

Coordinating Global Climate Change Research

A cooperative global network of all United Nations members participates in the United Nations Environment Programme (UNEP, http://www.unep.org) and the World Meteorological Organization (WMO, http://www.wmo.ch/index-en.html). The World Climate Research Programme (WCRP, http://www.wmo.ch/web/wcrp/wcrp-home.html) and its network under the supervision of the Global Climate Observing System (GCOS, http://www.wmo.ch/web/gcos/gcoshome.html) coordinate data gathering and research. The ongoing climate assessment process within the UNEP is conducted by the Intergovernmental Panel on Climate Change (IPCC, http://www.ipcc.ch/), with completed reports issued by three Working Groups in 1990, the 1992 supplementary report, 1995, and the latest *Third Assessment Report* in 2001.

In Canada, information about changing climate is found at the Environment Canada Climate Change Web sites (http://www.ec.gc.ca/climate/overview-e.html or http://climatechange.gc.ca/). These sites provide links to information about climate change and its impacts on Canada. The effect of global warming on permafrost, which involves half of Canadian land area, is found at http://www.socc.uwaterloo.ca.

In the United States coordination is found at the U.S. Global Change Research Program (http://www.usgcrp.gov/). An overall source for information is http://globalchange.gov/, which publishes an online monthly summary of all related developments. Also important are programs and services at NASA agencies such as Goddard Institute for Space Studies (GISS, http://www.giss.nasa.gov/), Global Hydrology and Climate Center (GHCC, http://www.ghcc.msfc.nasa.gov/), and at NOAA agencies at the National Climate Data Center (NCDC, http://www.ncdc.noaa.gov/oa/ncdc.html) and the National Environmental Satellite, Data, and Information Service (NESDIS, http://www.nesdis.noaa.gov/), among others. The Pew Center on Global Climate Change offers credible analysis and overview and has issued several policy reports at http://www.pewclimate.org/.

The Arctic Council initiated the Arctic Climate Impact Assessment (ACIA), see http://www.acia.uaf.edu/. Also, see the Arctic Monitoring and Assessment Program at http://www.amap.no/ and the International Arctic Science Committee at http://www.iasc.no/. The International Polar Year (March 2007 to March 2009) is coordinated at http://www.ipy.org/.

The multi-agency National Ice Center is at http://www.natice.noaa.gov/. Important research is done at the National Center for Atmospheric Research (http://www.ncar.ucar.edu/).

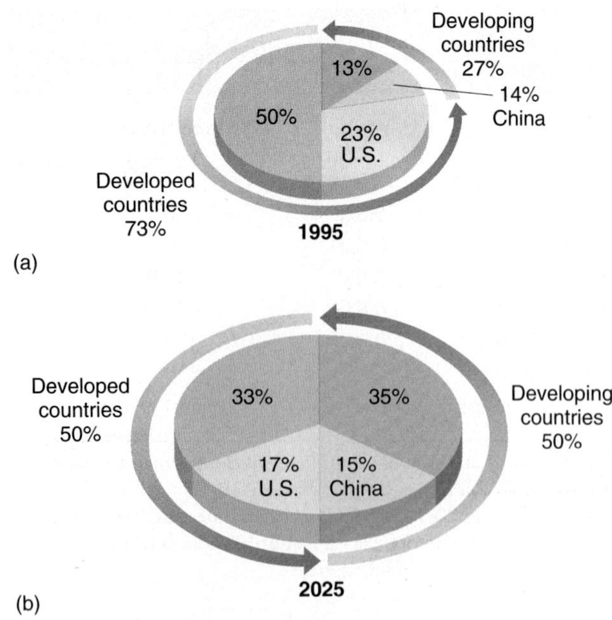

FIGURE 10.27 Origin of excessive carbon dioxide. Countries and regions of origin for excessive carbon dioxide (a) in 1995 and (b) forecast for 2025. [Data from United Nations Environment Programme.]

sources (renewable, low temperature matching end-use needs, and labour intensive as compared to capital intensive power plants) and redirecting industrial countries away from wasteful past practices and toward greater efficiencies.

Methane and Global Warming Another radiatively active gas contributing to the overall greenhouse effect is methane (CH_4), which, at more than 1% per year, is increasing in concentration even faster than carbon dioxide. Air bubbles in ice show that concentrations of methane in the past, between 500 and 27,000 years ago, were approximately 0.7 ppm (parts per million), whereas current atmospheric concentrations are 1.8 ppm, or more than double the preindustrial level. We are at an atmospheric concentration of methane that is higher than at any time in the past 420,000 years.

Methane is generated by such organic processes as digestion and rotting in the absence of oxygen (anaerobic processes). About 50% of the excess methane comes from bacterial action in the intestinal tracts of livestock and from organic activity in flooded rice fields. Burning of vegetation causes another 20% of the excess, and bacterial action inside the digestive systems of termite populations also is a significant source. Methane is thought responsible for at least 19% of the total atmospheric warming, complementing the warming caused by the buildup of carbon dioxide.

Other Greenhouse Gases Nitrous oxide (N_2O) is the third most important greenhouse gas that is forced by human activity—up 17% in atmospheric concentration since 1750, higher than at any time in the past 1000 years. Fertilizer use increases the processes in soil that emit nitrous oxide, although more research is needed to fully understand the relationships. Chlorofluorocarbons (CFCs) and other halocarbons also contribute to global warming. CFCs absorb infrared in wavelengths missed by carbon dioxide and water vapour in the lower troposphere. As radiatively active gases, CFCs enhance the greenhouse effect in the troposphere and are a cause of ozone depletion and slight cooling in the stratosphere.

Climate Models and Future Temperatures

The scientific challenge in understanding climate change is to sense climatic trends in what is essentially a nonlinear, chaotic natural climate system. Imagine the tremendous task of building a computer model of all climatic components and to program these linkages (shown in Figure 10.1) over different time frames and at various scales!

Using mathematical models originally established for forecasting weather, scientists developed a complex computer climate model known as a **general circulation model (GCM)**. There are at least a dozen established GCMs now operating around the world. Submodel programs for the atmosphere, ocean, land surface, cryosphere, and biosphere operate within the GCM. The most sophisticated models couple atmosphere and ocean submodels and are known as *Atmosphere-Ocean General Circulation Models (AOGCMs)*.

The first step in describing a climate is to define a manageable portion of Earth's climatic system for study. Climatologists create dimensional "grid boxes" that extend from beneath the ocean to the tropopause, in multiple layers (Figure 10.28). Resolution of these boxes in the atmosphere is about 250 km (155 mi) in the horizontal and 1 km (0.6 mi) in the vertical; in the ocean the boxes use the same horizontal resolution and a vertical resolution of about 200 to 400 m (650–1300 ft). Analysts deal not only with the climatic components within each grid layer but also with the interaction among the layers on all sides.

A comparative benchmark among the operational GCMs is *climatic sensitivity* to doubling of carbon dioxide levels in the atmosphere. GCMs do not predict specific temperatures, but they do offer various scenarios of global warming. In Canada, there is a history of climate modelling at Canada's Climate Centre for Climate Modelling and Analysis (CCCma, see the Web site for more information **http://www.cccma.bc.ec.gc.ca/eng_index.shtml**). The Centre developed a coupled atmosphere ocean general circulation model (CGCM1), refined to a second generation (CGCM2), that predicts a distinct warming by 2041 (Figure 10.29). Consistent with other computer studies, unambiguous warming appears over some continental regions, with the greatest warming predicted to occur over high latitudes. Note regions of forecast cooling on the map. Remarkably, as forecast, Canada had its warmest summer and year, and second warmest winter, in history in 1998—average temperatures in some areas were 2.5 C° (4.5 F°) above normal. GCM-generated maps correlate well with the observed global warming patterns experienced in the 1990s.

The 2001 IPCC *Third Assessment Report*, using a variety of GCM forecasts, predicted a range of average warming from 1990 to 2100 from a "low forecast" to a "high forecast." The "middle forecast," sometimes called the "B" scenario, alone represents a significant increase in global land and ocean temperatures and will produce consequences. IPCC temperature forecasts for the 21st century are:

- High forecast: 5.8 C° (10.4 F°),
- Middle forecast: 3.6 C° (6.5 F°),
- Low forecast: 1.4 C° (2.5 F°).

News Report 10.3 offers a summary overview of the IPCC process and a sample of findings.

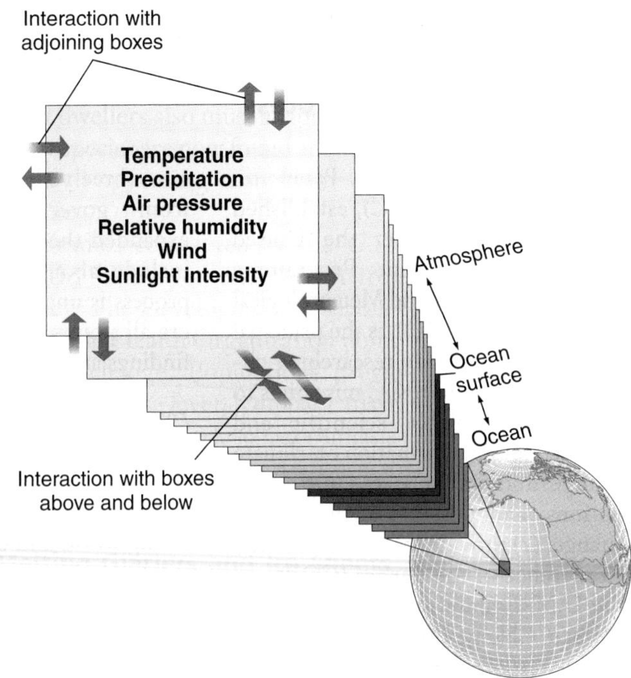

FIGURE 10.28 A general circulation model scheme. Temperature, precipitation, air pressure, relative humidity, wind, and sunlight intensity are sampled in myriad grid boxes. In the ocean, sampling is limited, but temperature, salinity, and ocean current data are considered. The interactions within a grid layer, and between layers on all six sides, are modelled in a general circulation model program.

Consequences of Global Warming

The consequences of uncontrolled atmospheric warming are complex. Regional climate responses are expected as temperature, precipitation, soil moisture, and air mass characteristics change. Although the ability to accurately forecast such regional changes is still evolving, some consequences of warming are forecast and in several regions are already underway.

The greatest warming is forecast to occur in polar regions rather than near the equator. Continental interiors are also forecast to warm to a greater degree than coastal areas. The combined temperature increase from greenhouse gases and sulphate aerosols shows clearly the increase in polar areas of the Northern Hemisphere (Figure 10.30).

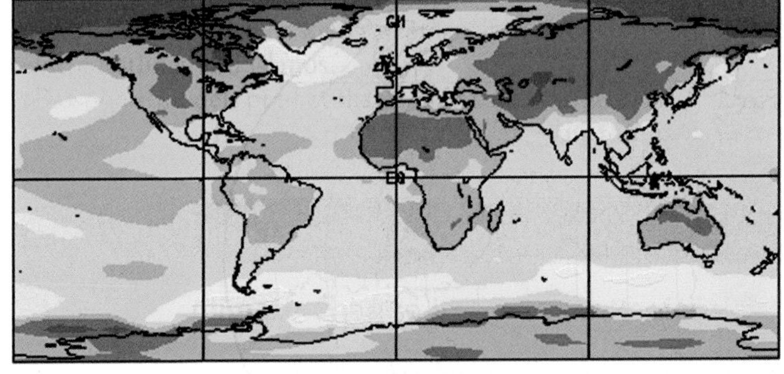

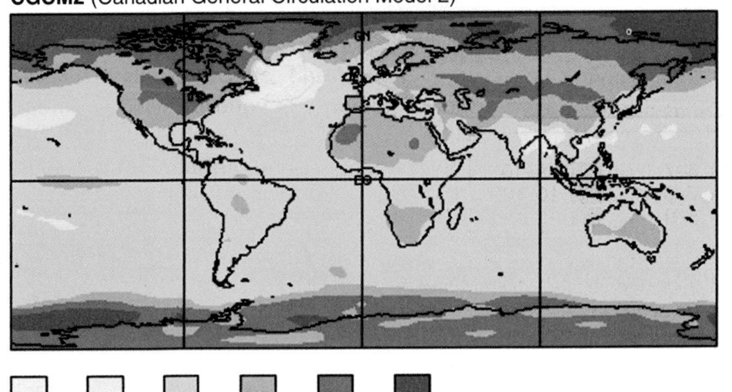

FIGURE 10.29 Annual mean surface air temperature change, 1971–1990 to 2041–2060. (a) The projection of the Canadian General Circulation Model 1 (CGCM1) and (b) from the refined, or second generation, Canadian General Circulation Model 2 (CGCM2). [Maps courtesy of © 2005, Her Majesty the Queen in Right of Canada, with permission of Natural Resources Canada.]

retreats beyond a critical limit, it may collapse rapidly as a result of disturbed mass balance.*

In response to the increasing warmth, the Antarctic Peninsula is sporting new vegetation growth, previously not seen there, reduced sea ice, and disruption of penguin feeding, nesting, and fledging activities.

A loss of polar ice mass, augmented by melting of alpine and mountain glaciers (which experienced more than 30% decrease in overall ice mass during the last century), will affect sea-level rise. The IPCC assessment states, "between one-third to one-half of the existing mountain glacier mass could disappear over the next hundred years." Also, "there is conclusive evidence for a worldwide recession of mountain glaciers. . . . This is among the clearest and best evidence for a change in energy balance at the Earth's surface since the end of the nineteenth century."

Changes in Sea Level Sea-level rise must be expressed as a range of values that are under constant reassessment. During the last century, sea level rose 10–20 cm (4–8 in.), a rate 10 times higher than the average rate during the last 3000 years. The 2001 IPCC forecast for global mean sea-level rise this century, given regional variations, are:

- Low forecast: 0.09 m (3.5 in.)
- Middle forecast: 0.48 m (18.9 in.)
- High forecast: 0.88 m (34.7 in.).

Remember that a 0.3 m rise in sea level would produce a shoreline retreat of 30 m (98 ft) on average. These increases would continue beyond 2100 even if greenhouse gas concentrations were stabilized.

The Scripps Institution of Oceanography in La Jolla, California, has kept ocean temperature records since 1916. Significant temperature increases are being recorded to depths of more than 1000 m (3000 ft), as ocean temperature records are set. Warming is now detected in bottom currents as well. Even the warming of the ocean itself will contribute about 25% of sea-level rise, simply because of *thermal expansion* of the water. In addition, any change in ocean temperature has a profound effect on weather and, indirectly, on agriculture and soil moisture. In fact the ocean system appears to have delayed some surface global warming during the past century through absorption of excess atmospheric heat.

A quick survey of world coastlines shows that even a moderate rise could bring change of unparalleled proportions. At stake are the river deltas, lowland coastal farming valleys, and low-lying mainland areas, all contending with high water, high tides, and higher storm surges. Particularly tragic social and economic consequences will affect small island states, which are unable to adjust within their present country boundaries—disruption of biological systems, loss of biodiversity, reduction in water resources, evacuation of residents. The increase in mean sea level no doubt worsened the impact along coastlines from the December 2004 tsunami that struck across the Indian Ocean—more than 150,000 people lost their lives in this catastrophe.

There could be both internal and international migration of affected human populations, spread over decades, as people move away from coastal flooding from the sea level rise. Clearly, physical geography is in an important position to synthesize all the spatial variables needed in planning to cope with these changes, whatever their mildness or severity.

*H. Rott, P. Skvarca, and T. Nagler, "Rapid collapse of northern Larsen Ice Shelf, Antarctica," *Science* 271 (February 9, 1996): 788.

Political Action to Slow Global Warming

A product of the 1992 Earth Summit in Rio de Janeiro was the United Nations Framework Convention on Climate Change (FCCC). The leading body of the Convention is the *Conference of the Parties* (*COP*) operated by the countries that ratified the FCCC, 186 countries by 2000. Meetings were held in Berlin (*COP-1*, 1995) and Geneva (*COP-2*, 1996). These meetings set the stage for *COP-3* in Kyoto, Japan, in December 1997, where 10,000 participants adopted the *Kyoto Protocol* by consensus. The latest gatherings were *COP-6* held in The Hague in late 2000 and *COP-7* in Marrakech, Morocco, in 2001 followed by *COP-8* held in New Delhi, 2002, *COP-9* in Milan, Italy, in 2003, and *COP-10* in Buenos Aires, December 2004. Seventeen national academies of science endorsed the Kyoto Protocol. (For updates on the status of the Kyoto Protocol, see **http://www.unfccc.int/2860.php**.)

The Kyoto Protocol binds more-developed countries to a collective 5.2% reduction in greenhouse gas emissions as measured at 1990 levels for the period 2008 to 2012. Within this group goal, various countries promised cuts: Canada is to cut 6% and moved quickly to ratify the Protocol, the European Union 8%, and Australia 8%, among many others. The *Group of* 77 countries plus China favour a 15% reduction by 2010. With Russian ratification in November 2004, the Kyoto Protocol is now international law with nearly 140 country signatories. The United States has not signed.

Relative to the United States and its goal of a 7% cut below 1990 levels, the administration withdrew in 2001 from the climate treaty process and abandoned emission control goals, alone in its dissent. The U.S. president asked the National Research Council to assess the level of IPCC science. The NRC quickly responded in a report affirming conclusions about human-induced climate change, saying that the IPCC *Third Assessment Report* ". . . accurately reflects the current thinking of the scientific community on this issue" (NRC, *Climate Change Science, An Analysis of Some Key Questions*, Washington: National Academy Press, May 2001).

As international law, the Kyoto Protocol is far-reaching in scope, including calling for international cooperation in meeting goals, technology development and emission transfers, leniency for less-developed countries, "clean development" initiatives, and "emissions trading" schemes between industrialized countries and individual industries. The goal, simply and boldly stated, is to "prevent dangerous anthropogenic interference with the climate system."

As the largest source of greenhouse-gas emissions the United States needs to join the Kyoto process.

Mitigation Actions with "No Regrets" The Intergovernmental Panel on Climate Change (IPCC) declared that "no regrets" opportunities to reduce carbon dioxide emissions are available in most countries. The IPCC Working Group III defines this as follows:

> No regrets options are by definition greenhouse gas emissions reduction options that have negative net costs, because they generate direct and indirect benefits that are large enough to offset the costs of implementing the options.

Benefits that equal or exceed their cost to society include reduced energy cost, improved air quality and health, reduction in tanker spills and oil imports, and deployment of renewable and sustainable energy sources, among others. This holds true without even considering the benefits of slowing the rate of climate change.

One key to "no regrets" is the untapped energy-efficiency potential. For Europe, scientists determined that carbon emissions could be reduced to less than half the 1990 level by 2030, at a negative cost (reported by the International Project for Sustainable Energy Paths, http://www.ipsep.org/). In the United States, five Department of Energy national laboratories (Oak Ridge, Lawrence Berkeley, Pacific Northwest, National Renewable Energy, and Argonne) reported that the United States can meet the Kyoto carbon emission reduction targets with negative overall costs (cash benefit savings) ranging from –$7 to –$34 billion. (For more, see Working Group III, *Climate Change 2001, Mitigation*, London: Cambridge University Press, 2001, pp. 21, 474–76, and 506–07.)

Summary and Review—Global Climate Systems

Define climate and climatology and *explain* the difference between climate and weather.

Climate is dynamic, not static. **Climate** is a synthesis of weather phenomena at many scales, from planetary to local, in contrast to weather, which is the condition of the atmosphere at any given time and place. Earth experiences a wide variety of climatic conditions that can be grouped by general similarities into climatic regions. **Climatology** is the study of climate and attempts to discern similar weather statistics and identify **climatic regions.**

climate (p. 283)
climatology (p. 284)
climatic regions (p. 284)

1. Define climate and compare it with weather. What is climatology?
2. Explain how a climatic region synthesizes climate statistics.
3. How does the El Niño phenomenon produce the largest interannual variability in climate? What are some of the changes and effects that occur worldwide?

Review the role of temperature, precipitation, air pressure, and air mass patterns used to establish climatic regions.

Climatic inputs include insolation (pattern of solar energy in the Earth–atmosphere environment), temperature (sensible heat energy content of the air), precipitation (rain, sleet, snow, and hail; the supply of moisture), air pressure (varying patterns of atmospheric density), and air masses (regional-sized homogeneous units of air). Climate is the basic element in ecosystems, the natural, self-regulating communities of plants and animals that thrive in specific environments.

4. How do radiation receipts, temperature, air pressure inputs, and precipitation patterns interact to produce climate types? Give an example from a humid environment and one from an arid environment.
5. Evaluate the relationships among a climatic region, ecosystem, and biome.

Review the development of climate classification systems and *compare* genetic and empirical systems as ways of classifying climate.

Classification is the process of ordering or grouping data in related categories. A **genetic classification** is based on causative factors, such as the interaction of air masses. An **empirical classification** is one based on statistical data, such as temperature or precipitation. This text analyzes climate using aspects of both approaches, with a map based on climatological elements.

classification (p. 289)
genetic classification (p. 289)
empirical classification (p. 289)

6. What are the differences between a genetic and an empirical classification system?
7. What are some of the climatological elements used in classifying climates?

Describe the principal climate classification categories other than deserts and *locate* these regions on a world map.

Here we focus on temperature and precipitation measures. Keep in mind these are measurable results produced by interacting elements of weather and climate. These data are plotted on a **climograph** to display the characteristics of the climate.

There are six basic climate categories. Temperature and precipitation considerations form the basis of five climate categories and their regional types:

- Tropical (equatorial and tropical latitudes)
  rain forest (rainy all year)
  monsoon (6 to 12 months rainy)
  savanna (less than 6 months rainy)

- Mesothermal (midlatitudes, mild winters)
  humid subtropical (hot summers)
  marine west coast (warm to cool summers)
  Mediterranean (dry summers)
- Microthermal (mid- and high latitudes, cold winters)
  humid continental (hot to warm summers)
  subarctic (cool summers to very cold winters)
- Polar (high latitudes and polar regions)
  tundra (high latitude or high altitude)
  ice caps and ice sheets (perpetually frozen)
  polar marine
- Highland (compared to lowlands at the same latitude, highlands have lower temperatures—recall the normal lapse rate)

Only one climate category is based on moisture efficiency as well as temperature:

- Deserts (permanent moisture deficits)
  arid deserts (tropical and midlatitudes)
  semiarid steppes (tropical and midlatitudes)

climograph (p. 290)

8. List and discuss each of the principal climate categories. In which one of these general types do you live? Which category is the only type associated with the annual distribution and amount of precipitation?
9. What is a climograph, and how is it used to display climatic information?
10. Which of the major climate types occupies the most land and ocean area on Earth?
11. Characterize the tropical climates in terms of temperature, moisture, and location.
12. Using Africa's tropical climates as an example, characterize the climates produced by the seasonal shifting of the ITCZ with the high Sun.
13. Mesothermal (subtropical and midlatitude, mild winter) climates occupy the second largest portion of Earth's entire surface. Describe their temperature, moisture, and precipitation characteristics.
14. Explain the distribution of the *humid subtropical hot-summer* and *Mediterranean dry-summer* climates at similar latitudes and the difference in precipitation patterns between the two types. Describe the difference in vegetation associated with these two climate types.
15. Which climates are characteristic of the Asian monsoon region?
16. Explain how a *marine west coast* climate type can occur in the Appalachian region of the eastern United States.
17. What role do offshore ocean currents play in the distribution of the *marine west coast* climates? What type of fog is formed in these regions?
18. Discuss the climatic conditions for the coldest places on Earth outside the poles.

Explain the precipitation and moisture efficiency criteria used to determine the arid and semiarid desert climates and *locate* them on a world map.

The dry and semiarid climates are described by precipitation rather than temperature. Dry climates are the world's arid deserts and semiarid regions, with their unique plants, animals, and physical features. The arid and semiarid climates occupy more than 35% of Earth's land area, clearly the most extensive climate over land.

Major subdivisions are *arid deserts* in tropical and midlatitude areas (precipitation—natural water supply—less than one-half of natural water demand) and *semiarid steppes* in tropical and midlatitude areas (precipitation more than one-half of natural water demand).

19. In general terms, what are the differences among the four desert classifications? How are moisture and temperature distributions used to differentiate these subtypes?
20. Relative to the distribution of arid and semiarid climates, describe at least three locations where they occur across the globe and the reasons for their presence in these locations.

Outline future climate patterns from forecasts presented and *explain* the causes and potential consequences.

Various activities of present-day society are producing climatic changes, particularly a global warming trend. The 1980s and 1990s were dominated by the highest average annual temperatures experienced since the advent of instrumental measurements. There is a scientific consensus building that global warming is related to the greenhouse effect.

These conditions were further supported by the 2001 *Third Assessment Report* from the Intergovernmental Panel on Climate Change. IPCC predicted surface-temperature response to a doubling of carbon dioxide with a range of increase from 1.4 C° (2.5 F°) to 5.8 C° (10.4 F°) between the present and 2100. Natural climatic variability over the span of Earth's history is the subject of **paleoclimatology**. A **general circulation model (GCM)** is used to forecast climate patterns and is evolving to greater capability and accuracy than in the past. People and their political institutions can use GCM forecasts to form policies aimed at reducing unwanted climate change.

paleoclimatology (p. 315)
general circulation model (GCM) (p. 318)

21. Explain climate forecasts. How do general circulation models (GCMs) produce such forecasts?
22. Describe the potential climatic effects of global warming on polar and high-latitude regions. What are the implications of these climatic changes for persons living at lower latitudes?
23. How is climatic change affecting agricultural and food production? Natural environments? Forests? The possible spread of disease?
24. What are the present actions being taken to delay the effects of global climate change? What is the Kyoto Protocol? The operation of the Conference of the Parties? What is the current status of Canadian and U.S. government action on the Protocol?

Critical Thinking

A. The text asked that you find the climate conditions for your campus and your birthplace and locate these two places on Figures 10.3, 10.4, and 10.5. Briefly describe the information sources you used: library, Internet, teacher, and phone calls to provincial or state climatologists. Now refer to Appendix C to refine your assessment of climate conditions for the two locations. Briefly show how you worked through the Köppen climate criteria given in the appendix that established the climate classification for your two cities.

B. El Niño conditions are forecast to return to the Pacific during the life of this edition of *Geosystems*. On the *Geosystems* Companion Website and in Focus Study 10.1 there are URL references for El Niño and La Niña. Sample three or four sources to determine the status of the El Niño phenomena at the present time. How are current conditions different from the record El Niño event in 1997–1998? Or La Niña in 1998–2000? What Internet links were most helpful to you in completing this status report?

C. Many external factors force climate. The chart "Global and annual mean radiative forcing for the year 2000, relative to 1750" is presented below (from *Climate Change 2001, The Scientific Basis*, Washington: Cambridge University Press, 2001, Figure 3, p. 8, and Figure 6.6, p. 392).

The estimates of radiative forcing in Watts per square metre units are given on the y-axis (vertical axis). The level of scientific understanding is noted along the x-axis (horizontal axis), arranged from "high" to "very low." Those columns above the "0" value (in red) indicate *positive forcing*, such as the greenhouse gases grouped in the far-left column. Columns that fall below the "0" value (in blue) indicate *negative forcing*, such as the haze from sulphate aerosols, fourth column from left. The vertical line between the markers on each column is an estimate of the uncertainty range. Where no column appears but there is instead a line denoting a range, there is no central estimate given present uncertainties, such as for mineral dust.

Assume you are a policy maker with a goal of reducing the rate of global warming, that is, reducing positive radiative forcing of the climate system. What strategies do you suggest to alter the height of the columns and adjust the mix of elements that cause warming? Assign priorities to each suggested strategy to denote most-to-least effective in moderating climate change. Brainstorm and discuss your strategies with others.

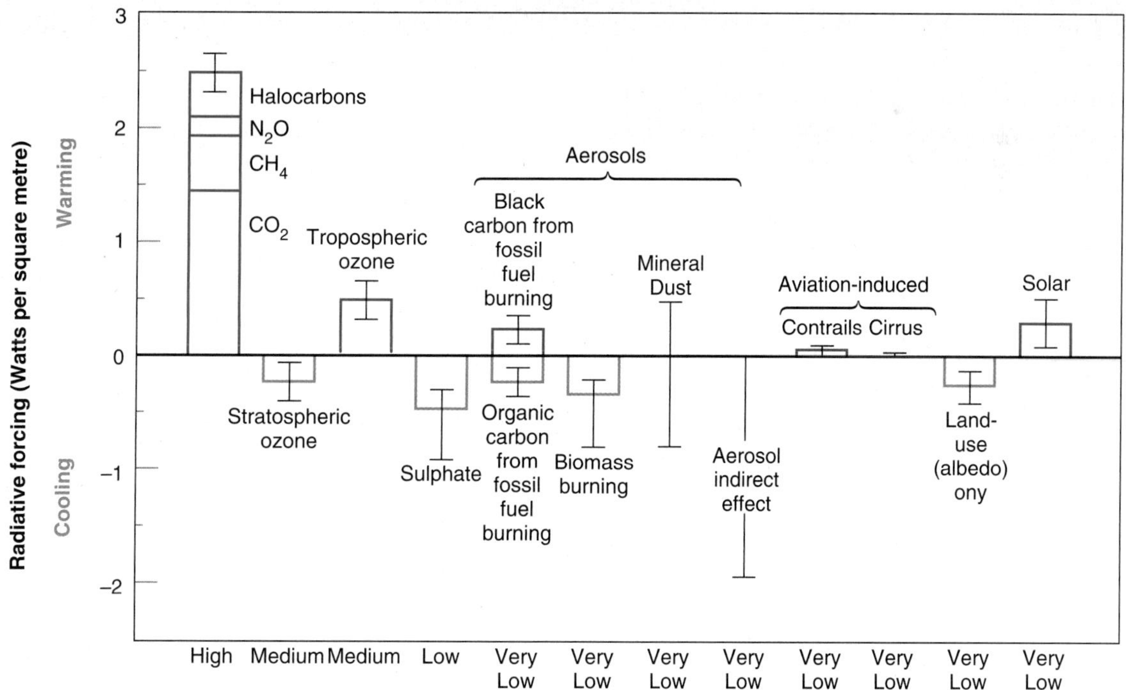

PART THREE

The Earth–Atmosphere Interface

Dramatic Hawaiian landscape where active lava flows form the Kamoamoa bench and represent some of the newest land surface on Earth. The glowing lava is 1200°C (2192°F) as it sluggishly makes its way to the sea, setting the surf to boil. The Kilauea eruptions are now the longest continuous period of active eruptions in history. The present episode has been active since January 1983. [Photo by Bobbé Christopherson.]

Earth is a dynamic planet whose surface is shaped by active physical and chemical agents of change. Two broad systems organize these agents in Part 3—endogenic and exogenic. The **endogenic system** (Chapters 11 and 12) encompasses internal processes that produce flows of heat and material from deep below Earth's crust. Radioactive decay principally powers these processes. The materials involved constitute the *solid realm* of Earth. Earth's surface responds by moving, warping, and breaking, sometimes in dramatic episodes of earthquakes and volcanic eruptions, constructing the crust.

At the same time, the **exogenic system** (Chapters 13 through 17) involves external processes that set into motion air, water, and ice, all powered by solar energy—this is the *fluid realm* of Earth's environment. These media carve, shape, and reduce the landscape. Weathering breaks up and dissolves the crust. Erosion picks up these materials; transports them in rivers, winds, coastal waves, and flowing glaciers; and deposits them along the way. Thus, variations in the topographic relief of the Earth's surface reflect the constant interaction between two vast open systems: the endogenic system that builds the landscape and topographic relief, and the exogenic system that tears it down, redistributing the weathered and eroded material to form sedimentary plains.

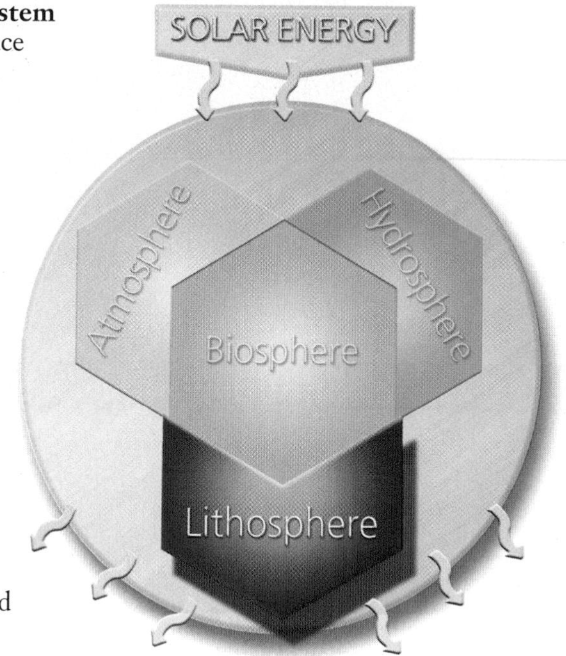

of crust, represent a much broader time scale of events, beyond the severe limitations of catastrophism.

Within the principle of uniformitarianism, catastrophic events such as massive landslides, earthquakes, volcanic eruptions, and sometimes cyclic episodes of mountain building punctuate geologic time. These episodes occur as interruptions in the generally uniform processes that shape the slowly evolving landscape. Here, the *punctuated equilibrium* concept studied in the life sciences and paleontology might apply to aspects of Earth's long developmental history.

To understand the phenomena seen at Earth's surface, we must have knowledge of our planet's internal structure and energy. Let us now journey deep within Earth to see its inner workings.

Earth's Structure and Internal Energy

Along with the other planets and the Sun, Earth is thought to have condensed and congealed from a nebula of dust, gas, and icy comets about 4.6 billion years ago (Chapter 2). Scientists are observing this same formation process underway elsewhere in our Milky Way Galaxy and the Universe. Previously, the oldest surface rock discovered on Earth (known as the Acasta Gneiss) was found in northwestern Canada; it was radiometrically dated to an age of 3.96 billion years. Scientists from Missouri's Saint Louis University, the Geological Survey of Canada, and Australian National University confirmed the age.

Recent research found detrital zircons (particles of pre-existing zirconium silica oxides transported and deposited, forming rock) in Western Australia dating between 4.2 and 4.4 billion years old; these are possibly the oldest materials in Earth's crust. These discoveries tell us something significant: Earth was forming continental crust at least 4 billion years ago, during the Archean Eon.

As Earth solidified, gravity sorted materials by density. Heavier substances such as iron gravitated slowly to its centre, and lighter elements such as silica slowly welled upward to the surface and became concentrated in the crust. Consequently, Earth's interior is sorted into roughly concentric layers, each one distinct in either chemical composition or temperature. Heat energy migrates outward from the centre by conduction and by physical convection in the more fluid or plastic layers in the mantle and nearer the surface.

Our knowledge of Earth's *internal differentiation* into these layers is acquired entirely through indirect evidence, because we are unable to drill more than a few kilometres into Earth's crust. There are several physical properties of Earth materials that enable us to approximate the nature of the interior. For example, when an earthquake or underground nuclear test sends shock waves through the planet, the cooler areas, which generally are more rigid, transmit these **seismic waves** at a higher velocity than do the hotter areas, where seismic waves are slowed to lower velocity. This is the science of *seismic tomography*, as if Earth is subjected to a kind of CAT scan with every earthquake.

Density also affects seismic-wave velocities. Plastic zones simply do not transmit some seismic waves; they absorb them. Some seismic waves are reflected as densities change, whereas others are refracted, or bent, as they travel through Earth. Thus, the distinctive ways in which seismic waves pass through Earth and the time they take to travel between two surface points help seismologists deduce the structure of Earth's interior (Figure 11.2).

Figure 11.3 illustrates the dimensions of Earth's interior compared with surface distances in North America to give you a sense of size and scale. An airplane flying from St. John's, Newfoundland and Labrador, to Prince Rupert, British Columbia, would travel the same distance as that from Earth's centre to its surface.

Earth's Core

A third of Earth's entire mass, but only a sixth of its volume, lies in its dense core. The **core** is differentiated into two regions—*inner core* and *outer core*—divided by a transition zone several hundred kilometres wide (see Figure 11.2b). The inner core is thought to be solid iron and well above the melting temperature of iron at the surface, but it remains solid because of tremendous pressure. The iron in the core is impure, probably combined with silicon and possibly oxygen and sulphur. Recent research points to the conclusion that the inner core may be a single, enormous crystal of iron. The outer core is molten, metallic iron with a lighter density than the inner core.

Earth's Magnetism The fluid outer core generates at least 90% of Earth's magnetic field and the magnetosphere that surrounds and protects Earth from the solar wind. One hypothesis explains that circulation patterns in the outer core are influenced by Earth's rotation and the new discovery that Earth's solid inner core rotates slightly faster than the rest of the planet. This convective circulation generates electrical currents, which in turn induce the magnetic field. The north magnetic pole (NMP) is near 83° N by 114° W (in the year 2005) in the Canadian Arctic, and the south magnetic pole is off the coast of Wilkes Land, Antarctica. These surface expressions of Earth's magnetic field migrate; for example, the NMP has moved 1100 km (685 mi) just this past century.

An intriguing feature of Earth's magnetic field is that its polarity sometimes fades to zero and then returns to full strength, with north and south magnetic poles reversed! In the process, the field does not blink on and off but instead diminishes slowly to low intensity and then rapidly regains its full strength. This **geomagnetic reversal** has taken place nine times during the past 4 million years and hundreds of times over Earth's history (Figure 11.4). The last 4 million years of Earth history span four major geomagnetic polarity chrons; chrons are defined as time intervals during which the Earth's geomagnetic field was entirely or predominantly of one polarity. For example, the Brunhes

Normal Chron in Figure 11.4 is characterized by normal geomagnetic polarity, and the Matuyama Reversed Chron is characterized by the predominance of reversed geomagnetic polarity. The average period of a magnetic reversal is 500,000 years; several hundred documented occurrences varied from as short as 20,000–30,000 years to 50 million years. Transition periods of low intensity last from 1000 to 10,000 years. The last reversal was 790,000 years ago, preceded by a transition ranging 2000 years in length along the equator to 10,000 years in the midlatitudes. The obvious question for us is, Why does this happen?

The reasons for these magnetic reversals are unknown at present. However, the spatial patterns they create at Earth's surface are a key tool in understanding the evolution of landmasses and the movements of the continents. When new iron-bearing rocks solidify from molten material (lava) at Earth's surface, the small magnetic particles in the rocks align according to the orientation of the magnetic poles at that time. This alignment is then locked in place as the rocks cool and solidify.

All across Earth, rocks of the same age bear an identical record of magnetic reversals in the form of measurable magnetic "stripes" in any magnetic material they contain, such as iron particles. These stripes illustrate global patterns of changing magnetism. Matching segments allow scientists to reassemble past continental arrangements. Later in this chapter we see the importance of these magnetic reversals.

Earth's Mantle

Figure 11.2b shows a transition zone several hundred kilometres wide, at an average depth of about 2900 km (1800 mi), dividing Earth's outer core from its mantle. Scientists at the California Institute of Technology analyzed more than 25,000 earthquakes and determined that this transition area is uneven, with ragged peak-and-valley-like formations. New scientific discoveries determined that some of the motions in the mantle may be created by this rough texture and low-velocity zone (speed of seismic waves in hot material) at what is called the *Gutenberg discontinuity*. A *discontinuity* is a place where physical differences occur between adjoining regions in Earth's interior, such as between the outer core and lower mantle.

The **mantle** (lower and upper together) represents about 80% of Earth's total volume. The mantle is rich in oxides of iron and magnesium and silicates (FeO, MgO, and SiO_2). They are dense and tightly packed at depth, grading to lesser densities toward the surface. A broad transition zone of several hundred kilometres, centred about

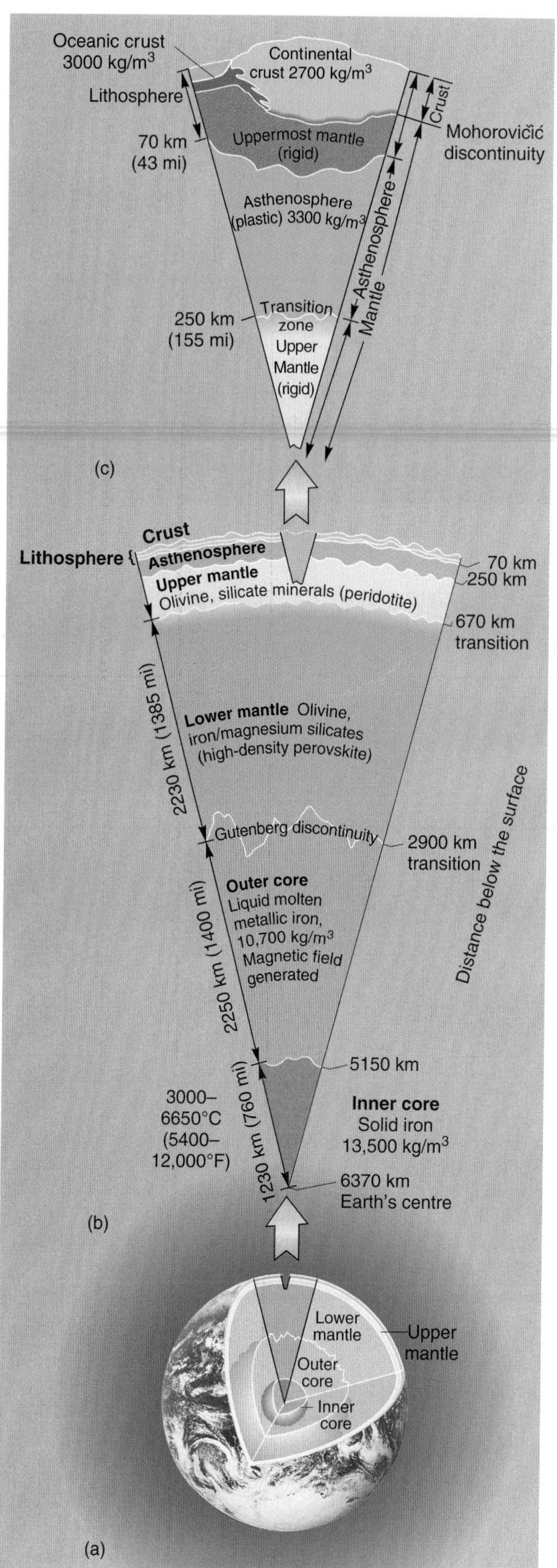

FIGURE 11.2 Earth in cross section.
(a) Cutaway showing Earth's interior. (b) Earth's interior in cross section, from the inner core to the crust. (c) Detail of the structure of the lithosphere and its relation to the asthenosphere. (For comparison to the densities noted, the density of water is 1000 kg/m³ and that of mercury, a liquid metal, is 13,000 kg/m³.) [Photo from NASA.]

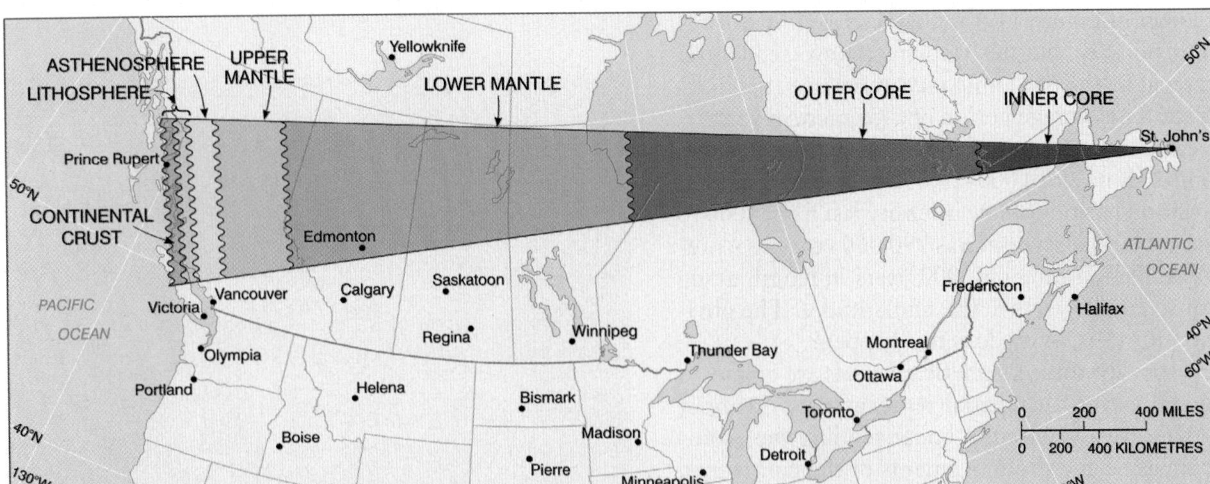

FIGURE 11.3 Distances from core to crust.
Surface map, using the distance from St. John's to Prince Rupert, to compare the distance from Earth's centre to the surface (6370 km, or 3963 mi). [Map by Robert W. Christopherson adapted by Keith Bigelow, University of Saskatchewan.]

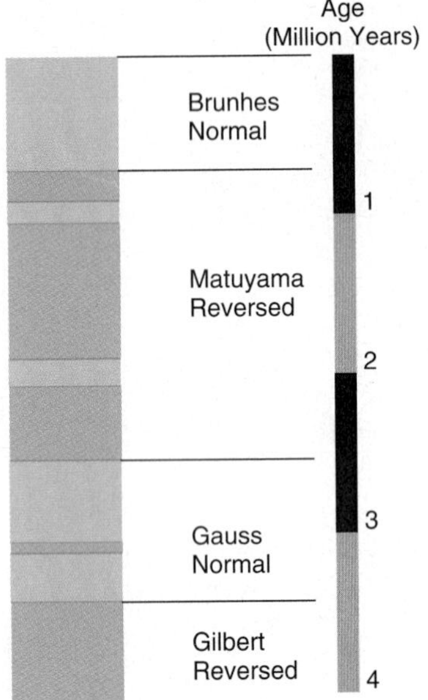

FIGURE 11.4 Geomagnetic reversals.
Periods of normal geomagnetic polarity (shown in blue) alternate with periods of reversed geomagnetic polarity (shown in orange). The radiometric ages of the rocks that preserve this record of paleomagnetism appear at the right of the figure. [Used by permission of the Minister of Public Works and Government Services Canada; Natural Resources Canada, Geological Survey of Canada.]

670 km (415 mi) below the surface, separates the upper mantle from the lower mantle. The entire mantle experiences a gradual temperature increase with depth and a stiffening due to increased pressures. The denser lower mantle is thought to contain a mixture of iron, magnesium, and silicates, with some calcium and aluminum.

The upper mantle divides into three fairly distinct layers: upper mantle, asthenosphere, and *uppermost mantle*, shown in Figure 11.2c. Next to the crust is the uppermost mantle, a high-velocity zone just below the crust, where seismic waves transmit through a rigid, cooler layer. This uppermost mantle, along with the crust, makes up the *lithosphere*, approximately 45–70 km thick.

Below the lithosphere, from about 70 km down to 250 km, is the **asthenosphere**, or plastic layer (from the Greek *asthenos*, meaning "weak"). It contains pockets of increased heat from radioactive decay and is susceptible to slow convective currents in these hotter (and therefore less dense) materials.

Because of its dynamic condition, the asthenosphere is the least rigid region of the mantle, with densities averaging 3300 kg/m^3. About 10% of the asthenosphere is molten in asymmetrical patterns and hot spots. The resulting slow movement in this zone disturbs the overlying crust and creates tectonic activity—the folding, faulting, and general deformation of surface rocks. In return, movement of the crust apparently influences currents throughout the mantle.

The depth affected by convection currents is the subject of much scientific research. One body of evidence states that mixing occurs throughout the entire mantle, upwelling from great depths at the core-mantle boundary, sometimes in small blobs of material, other times "megablobs" of mantle convect toward and away from the crust. Another view states that mixing in the mantle is layered, segregated above and below the 670-km boundary. Presently, evidence indicates some truth in both positions. As an example, there are hot spots on Earth, such as those under Hawai'i and Iceland, that appear to be at the top of tall plumes of rising mantle rock that are anchored deep in the lower mantle, where the rise of warmer, less dense material begins. In other surface regions, slabs of crust descend and penetrate to the lower mantle. For basics on Earth's interior and plate tectonics, see **http://www.solarviews.com/eng/earthint.htm**.

Earth's Lithosphere and Crust

The lithosphere includes the **crust** and uppermost mantle to about 70 km (43 mi) depth (Figure 11.2c). An important internal boundary between the crust and the high-velocity portion of the uppermost mantle is another discontinuity, called the **Mohorovičić discontinuity**, or **Moho** for short. It is named for the Yugoslavian seismologist who determined that seismic waves change at this depth owing to sharp contrasts of materials and densities.

Figure 11.2c illustrates the relation of the crust to the rest of the lithosphere and the asthenosphere below. Crustal areas beneath mountain masses extend deep, perhaps to 50–60 km (31–37 mi), whereas the crust beneath continental interiors averages about 30 km (19 mi) in thickness. Oceanic crust averages only 5 km (3 mi). The crust is only a fraction of Earth's overall mass. Drilling through the crust into the uppermost mantle remains an elusive scientific goal (see News Report 11.2).

The composition and texture of continental and oceanic crusts are quite different, and this difference is a key to the concept of drifting continents. The oceanic crust is denser than continental crust. In collisions, the denser oceanic material plunges beneath the lighter, more buoyant continental crust.

- *Continental crust* is essentially **granite**; it is crystalline and high in silica, aluminum, potassium, calcium, and sodium. (Sometimes continental crust is called *sial*, shorthand for *si*lica and *al*uminum.) Most important, continental crust is relatively low in density, averaging 2700 kg/m^3. Compare this with other densities given in Figure 11.2.
- *Oceanic crust* is **basalt**; it is granular and high in silica, magnesium, and iron. (Sometimes oceanic crust is called *sima*, shorthand for *si*lica and *ma*gnesium.) It is denser than continental crust, averaging 3000 kg/m^3.

Buoyancy is the principle that something less dense, such as wood, floats in something denser, such as water. The principles of buoyancy and balance were combined in the 1800s into the important principle of **isostasy**. Isostasy explains certain vertical movements of Earth's crust.

News Report 11.2

Drilling the Crust to Record Depths

Scientists wanting to sample mantle material directly have unsuccessfully tried for decades to penetrate Earth's crust to the Moho discontinuity (the crust-mantle boundary). The longest-lasting deep-drilling attempt is on the northern Kola Peninsula near Zapolyarny, Russia, 250 km (155 mi) north of the Arctic Circle—the *Kola Borehole (KSDB)*. Twenty years of high-technology drilling (1970–1989) produced a hole 12.262 km deep (7.6 mi, or 40,230 ft), purely for exploration and science. Crystalline rock 1.4 billion years old at 180°C (356°F) was reached. The site has other active boreholes, and the fifth is underway. (See an analysis log at **http://www.icdp-online.de/**.) A record holder for depth for a gas well is in Oklahoma; it was stopped at 9750 m (32,000 ft) when the drill bit ran into molten sulphur.

Oceanic crust is thinner than continental crust and is the object of several drilling attempts. The Integrated Ocean Drilling Program (IODP), a cooperative effort between the governments of Japan and the United States, replaced the former ODP effort directed by Texas A & M University in 2003. However, the university program is still the Science Operator of the research ship *JOIDES Resolution* and lead coordinator.

FIGURE 1 Ocean drilling ship. A modern ocean-floor drilling ship, the *JOIDES Resolution*. The International Ocean Drilling Program operates the research ship. Since it began operations in 1984, through 2001, *JOIDES* has spent more than 5000 days at sea, travelled more than half a million kilometres, drilled 1555 holes into the seafloor, and recovered hundreds of kilometres of core for analysis. [Photo by ODP/Texas A & M University.]

Previously, ODP drilled a 2.5-km-deep hole in an oceanic rift near the Galápagos Islands from 1975 to 1993, still the record. The new IODP plans further drilling at the site (Figure 1). An ocean floor of distinct layers of lava and deeper magma chambers was found. But the Moho and Earth's mantle remain untapped.

Over the past 40 years, about 1700 bore holes were completed, yielding 160 km of sediment and rock cores and more than 35,000 samples for researchers. Much of this science windfall helped put together the puzzle of geologic time and plate tectonics. See **http://www-odp.tamu.edu/** for background or **http://www.oceandrilling.org/** for the IODP home page information.

Construction of the largest deep-ocean drilling ship is ongoing in Okayama, Japan, with completion scheduled for 2006. Japan's *Chikyu* will be the largest research ship for this purpose and the first capable of high-latitude drilling in the Arctic. The new IODP ship will be able to drill to 7 km, more than three times the *JOIDES Resolution* limits. This *JOIDES*, workhorse of the ODP, is being refurbished for the new IODP program.

Think of Earth's crust as floating on the denser layers beneath, much as a boat floats on water. Where the load is greater, owing to glaciers, sediment, or mountains, the crust tends to sink, or ride lower in the asthenosphere. Without that load (for example, when a glacier melts), the crust rides higher, in a recovery uplift known as *isostatic rebound*. Thus, the entire crust is in a constant state of compensating adjustment, or isostasy, slowly rising and sinking in response to its own burdens, as it is pushed and dragged about by currents in the asthenosphere (Figure 11.5). An interesting development in Alaska relates this concept of isostatic rebound and climate change, as described in High Latitude Connection 11.1.

Earth's crust is the outermost shell: an irregular, brittle layer that resides restlessly on a dynamic and diverse interior. Let us examine the processes at work on this crust and the variety of rock types that compose the landscape.

The Geologic Cycle

Earth's crust is in an ongoing state of change, being formed, deformed, moved, and broken down by physical, chemical, and biological processes. While the endogenic (internal) system is at work building landforms, the exogenic (external) system is busily wearing them down. This vast give-and-take at the Earth–atmosphere–ocean interface is called the **geologic cycle**. It is fuelled from two sources—Earth's internal heat and solar energy from space—influenced by the ever-present levelling force of Earth's gravity.

Figure 11.6 (p. 340) illustrates the geologic cycle, combining many of the elements presented in this text. The geologic cycle is composed of three subsystems:

- The *hydrologic cycle* is the vast system that circulates water, water vapour, ice, and energy throughout the Earth–atmosphere–ocean environment. This cycle rearranges Earth materials through erosion, transportation, and deposition, and it circulates water as the critical medium that sustains life. (The hydrologic cycle and the discussion of water's properties were presented in Chapters 7 and 9.)
- The *rock cycle*, through processes in the atmosphere, crust, and mantle, produces three basic rock types—igneous, sedimentary, and metamorphic. We examine this next.
- The *tectonic cycle* brings heat energy and new materials to the surface and recycles old materials to mantle depths, creating movement and deformation of the crust. We discuss the tectonic cycle later in this chapter.

The Rock Cycle

To begin our look at the rock cycle, we see that only eight natural elements compose 99% of Earth's crust. Just two of these—oxygen and silicon—account for 74.3% of the crust (Table 11.1, p. 341). Oxygen, the most reactive gas in the lower atmosphere, readily combines with other elements. For this reason, the percentage of oxygen is greater in the crust (about 47%) than in the atmosphere (about 21%). The internal differentiation process explains the relatively large percentages of lightweight elements such as silicon and aluminum in the crust. These less-dense elements migrate toward the surface, as discussed earlier.

Minerals and Rocks Earth's elements combine to form minerals. A **mineral** is an inorganic (nonliving) natural compound having a specific chemical formula and possessing a crystalline structure. The combination of elements and the crystal structure give each mineral its characteristic hardness, colour, density, and other properties. For example, the common mineral *quartz* is silicon dioxide, SiO_2, and has a distinctive six-sided crystal.

High Latitude Connection 11.1

Isostatic Rebound in Alaska

The retreat of glacial ice following the last ice-age cycle unloaded much weight off the crust in Alaska, among those regions affected. Researchers from the Geophysical Institute at the University of Alaska-Fairbanks, using an array of global positioning systems (GPS) receivers, measured isostatic rebound of the crust following glacial ice losses. They expected to find a slowed rate of crustal rebound in southeastern Alaska as compared to the more rapid response in the distant past when the ice first retreated.

Instead, they detected some of the most rapid vertical motion on Earth, averaging about 36 mm (1.42 in.) per year. Scientists attribute this isostatic rebound to the loss of glaciers in the region, especially the areas from Yakutat Bay and the Saint Elias Mountains in the north, through Glacier Bay, Juneau, and on south through the inland passage. Only about 1 mm of this uplift is from post-ice-age response. This rapid rebound is attributable to glacial melt and retreat over the past 150 years and correlates with accelerating ice losses and record warmth across Alaska (see News Report 17.1).

For instance, Glacier Bay experienced a retreat of ice of more than 97 km (60 mi) since 1794. The land that was beneath this ice has isostatically rebounded 5.5 m (18 ft). The vertical action appears to be affecting some of the fault systems in the region, although the extent of this and its consequences are unknown at this writing.

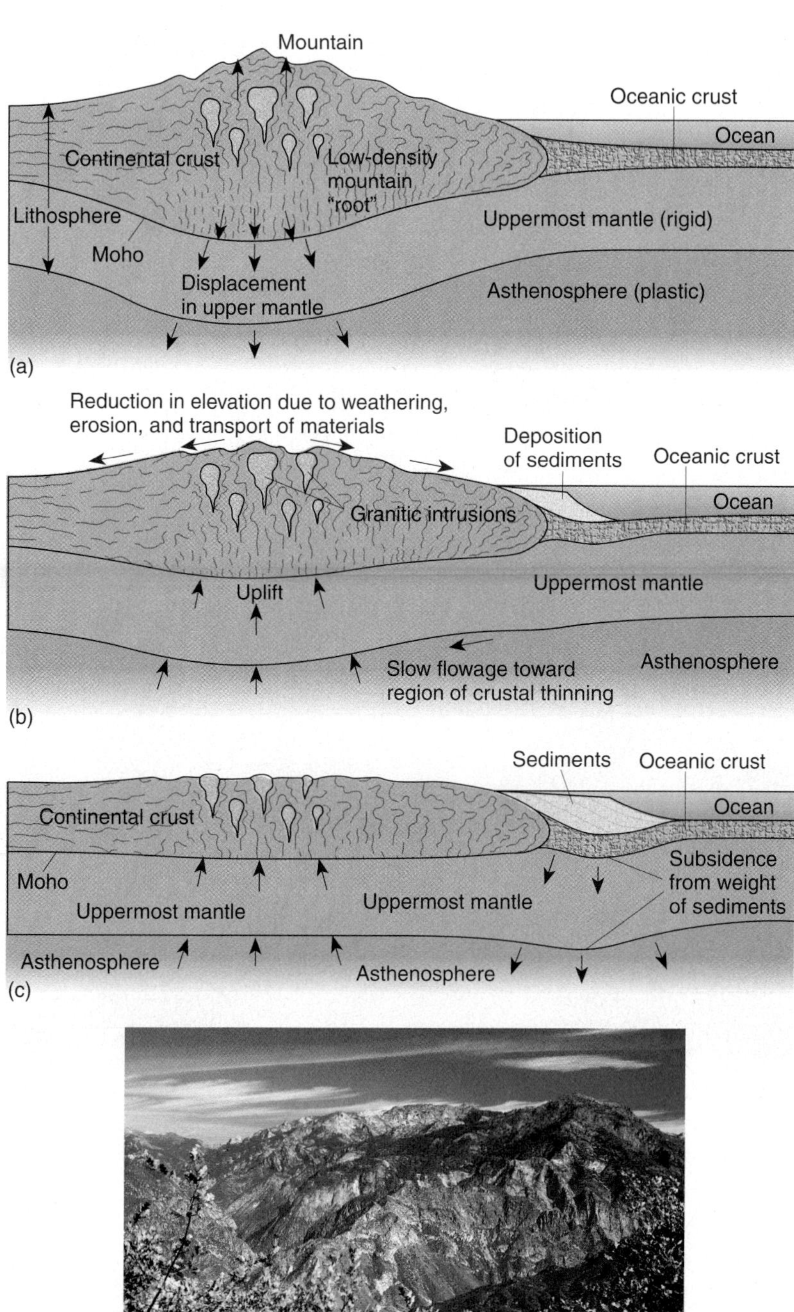

FIGURE 11.5 Isostatic adjustment of the crust.
Earth's entire crust is in a constant state of compensating adjustment, as suggested by these three sequential stages. In (a), the mountain mass slowly sinks, displacing mantle material. In (b), because of the loss of mass through erosion and transportation, the crust isostatically adjusts upward and sediments accumulate in the ocean. As the continental crust thins (c), the heavy sediment load offshore begins to deform the lithosphere beneath the ocean. (d) The melting of ice from the last ice age and losses of overlying sediments are thought to produce an ongoing isostatic uplift of portions of the Sierra Nevada batholith of the western United States. [Photo by Robert W. Christopherson.]

Of the more than 4200 minerals, about 30 minerals comprise the *rock-forming minerals* most commonly encountered. *Mineralogy* is the study of the composition, properties, and classification of minerals. (Note that mercury, a liquid metal, is an exception to this definition for it has no crystalline structure. Also, water is not a mineral but ice does fit the definition of a mineral.) For more on minerals see **http://webmineral.com/** or **http://www.minsocam.org/MSA/Research_Links.html**.

One of the most widespread mineral families on Earth is the *silicates*, because silicon and oxygen are so common and because they readily combine with each other and with other elements. This mineral family includes quartz, feldspar, clay minerals, and numerous gemstones. *Oxides* are a group of minerals in which oxygen combines with metallic elements, such as iron, to form hematite, Fe_2O_3. And, there are the *sulphides* and *sulphates* groups in which sulphur compounds combine with metallic elements, to form pyrite (FeS_2) and anhydrite ($CaSO_4$), respectively.

Another important mineral family is the *carbonate* group, which features carbon in combination with oxygen and other elements such as calcium, magnesium, and potassium. An example is the mineral calcite ($CaCO_3$), a form of calcium carbonate.

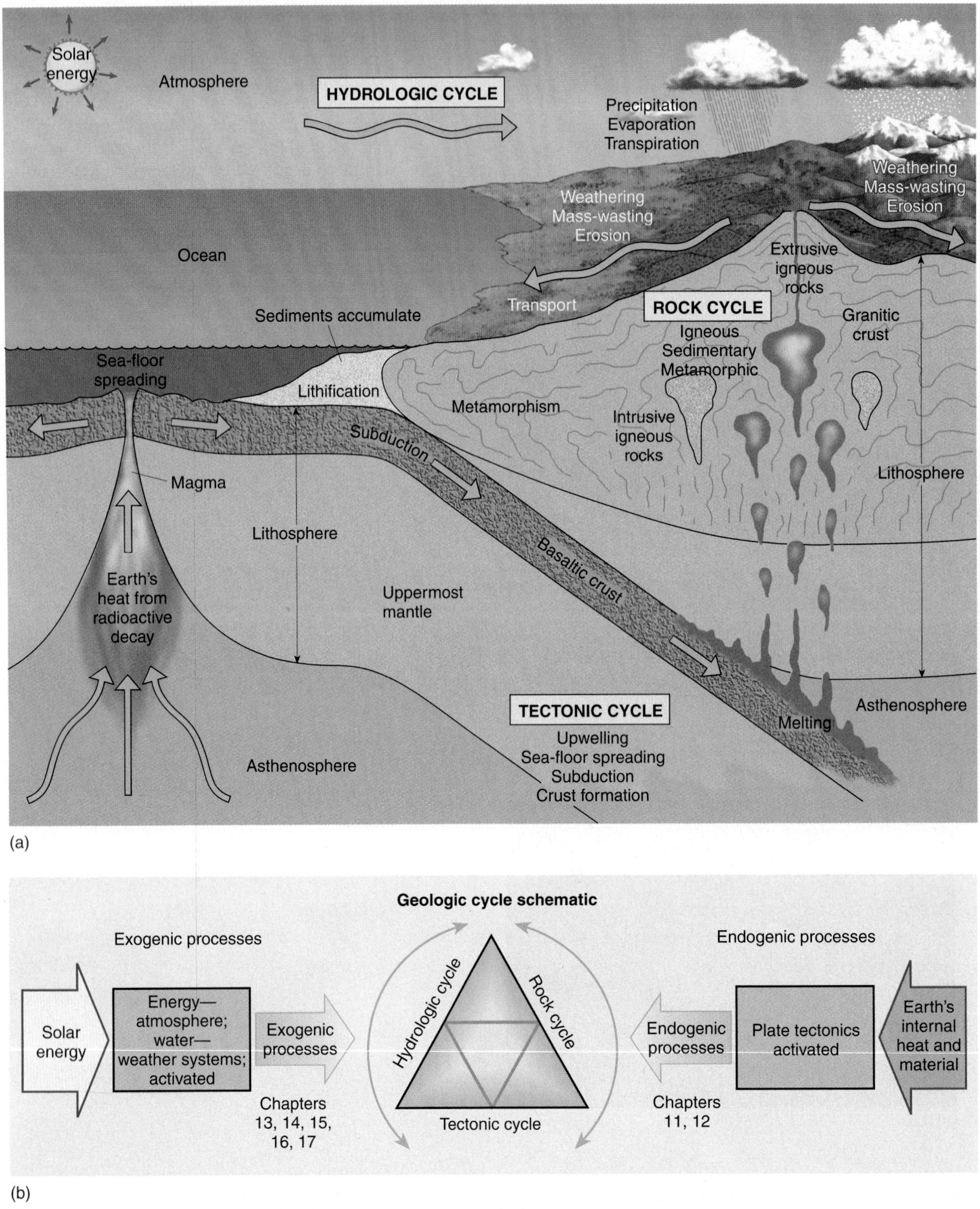

(a)

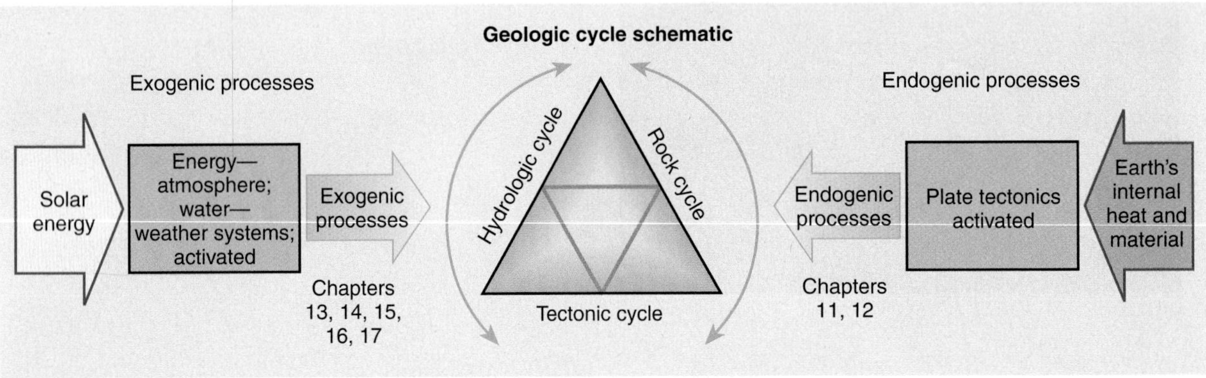

(b)

FIGURE 11.6 The geologic cycle.
(a) The geologic cycle is a model showing the interactive relation among the hydrologic cycle, rock cycle, and tectonic cycle. (b) Earth's surface is where two dynamic systems interact—the endogenic (internal) and exogenic (external).

A **rock** is an assemblage of minerals bound together (such as granite, a rock containing three minerals), or a mass of a single mineral (such as rock salt), or undifferentiated material (such as the noncrystalline glassy obsidian, volcanic glass), or even solid organic material (such as coal). All are rocks. Thousands of different rocks have been identified. All can be identified as one of three kinds, depending on the processes that formed them: *igneous* (melted), *sedimentary* (from settling out), and *metamorphic* (altered). Figure 11.7 illustrates these three processes and the interrelations

Table 11.1 Common Elements in Earth's Crust

Element	Percentage of Earth's Crust by Weight
Oxygen (O)	46.6
Silicon (Si)	27.7
Aluminum (Al)	8.1
Iron (Fe)	5.0
Calcium (Ca)	3.6
Sodium (Na)	2.8
Potassium (K)	2.6
Magnesium (Mg)	2.1
All others	1.5
Total	100.00

Note: A quartz crystal (SiO_2) consists of Earth's two most abundant elements, silicon (Si) and oxygen (O). Inset photo from *Laboratory Manual in Physical Geology*, 3rd ed., R. M. Busch, ed. © 1993 by Macmillan Publishing Co.

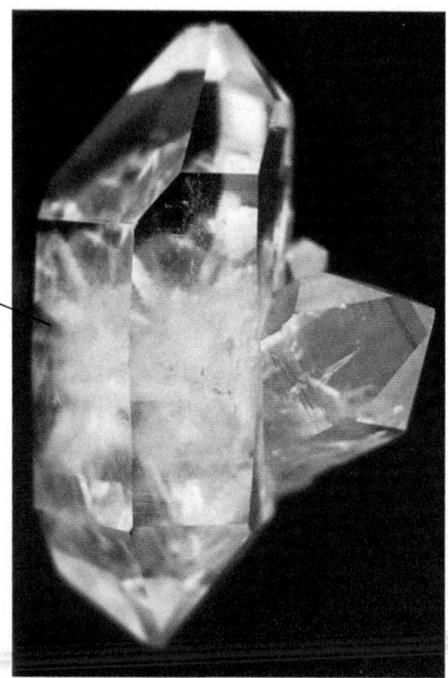

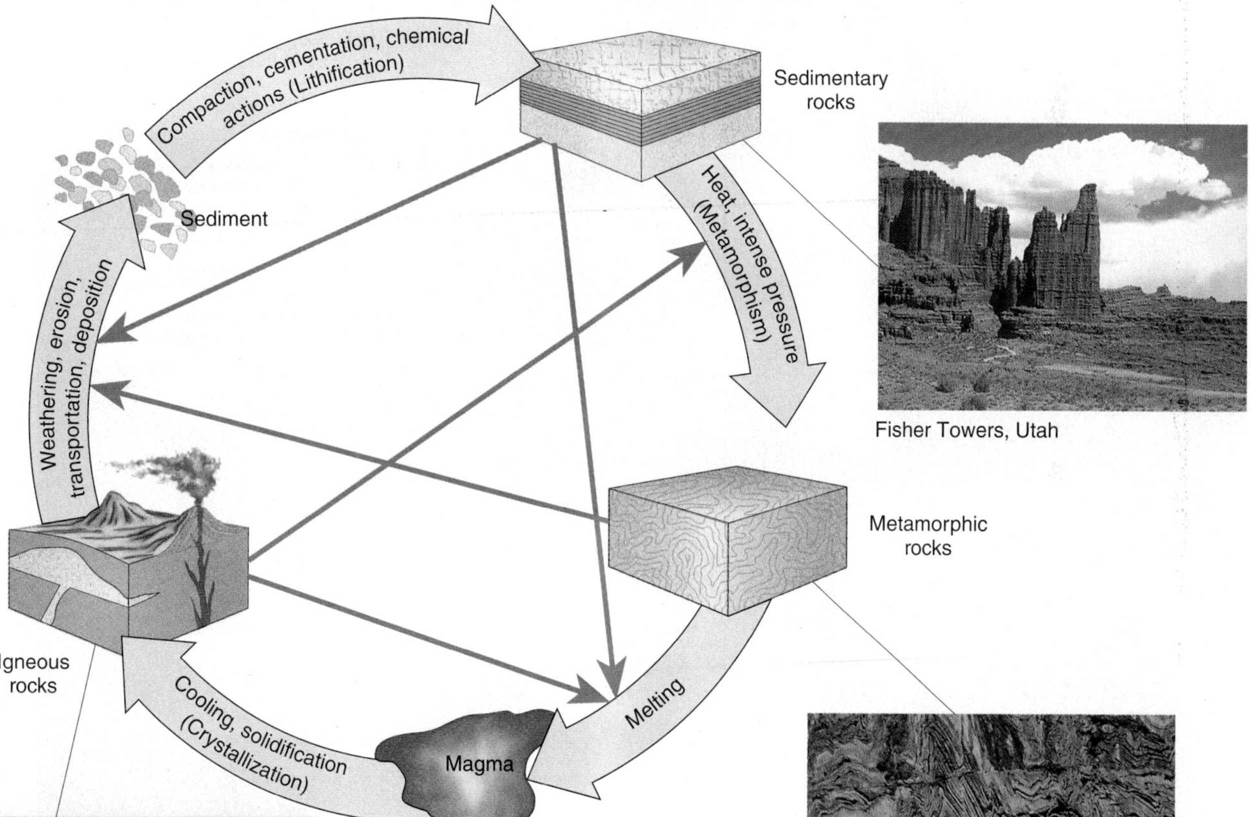

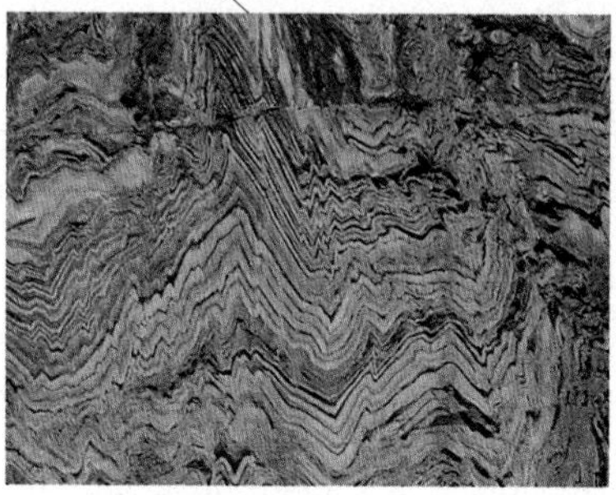

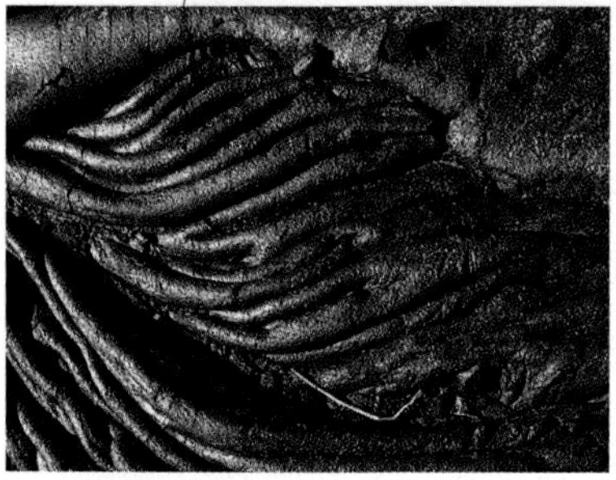

FIGURE 11.7 The rock cycle.
A rock-cycle schematic demonstrating the relation among igneous, sedimentary, and metamorphic processes. The arrows indicate that each rock type can enter the cycle at various points and be transformed into other rock types. [Adapted by permission from R. M. Busch, ed., *Laboratory Manual in Physical Geology*, 3rd ed., © 1993 by Macmillan Publishing Co.; photos by Bobbé Christopherson.]

NOTEBOOK The Rock Cycle

among them that constitute the **rock cycle**. Figure 11.8 maps the distribution of these rock types across Canada. Let us examine each rock-forming process.

Igneous Processes

An **igneous rock** is one that solidifies and crystallizes from a molten state. Familiar examples are granite, basalt, and rhyolite. Igneous rocks form from **magma**, which is molten rock beneath the surface (hence the name *igneous*, which means "fire-formed" in Latin). Magma is fluid, highly gaseous, and under tremendous pressure. It either *intrudes* into crustal rocks, cools, and hardens, or it *extrudes* onto the surface as **lava**.

The cooling history of an igneous rock—how fast it cooled and how steadily its temperature dropped—determines its crystalline physical characteristics, or crystallization. Igneous rocks range from coarse-grained (slower cooling, with more time for larger crystals to form) to fine-grained or glassy (faster cooling).

Igneous rocks comprise approximately 90% of Earth's crust, although they are frequently covered by sedimentary rocks (sandstone, shale, limestone), soil, or oceans.

Intrusive and Extrusive Igneous Rocks Intrusive igneous rock that cools slowly in the crust forms a **pluton**, a general term for any intrusive igneous rock body, regardless of size or shape that invaded layers of crustal rocks. The Roman god of the Underworld, Pluto, is the namesake. The largest pluton form is a **batholith**, defined as an irregular-shaped mass with a surface greater than 100 km^2 (40 mi^2) (Figure 11.10a). Batholiths form the mass of many large mountain ranges—for example, the Sierra Nevada batholith in California, the Idaho batholith, and the Coast Range batholith of British Columbia and Washington State.

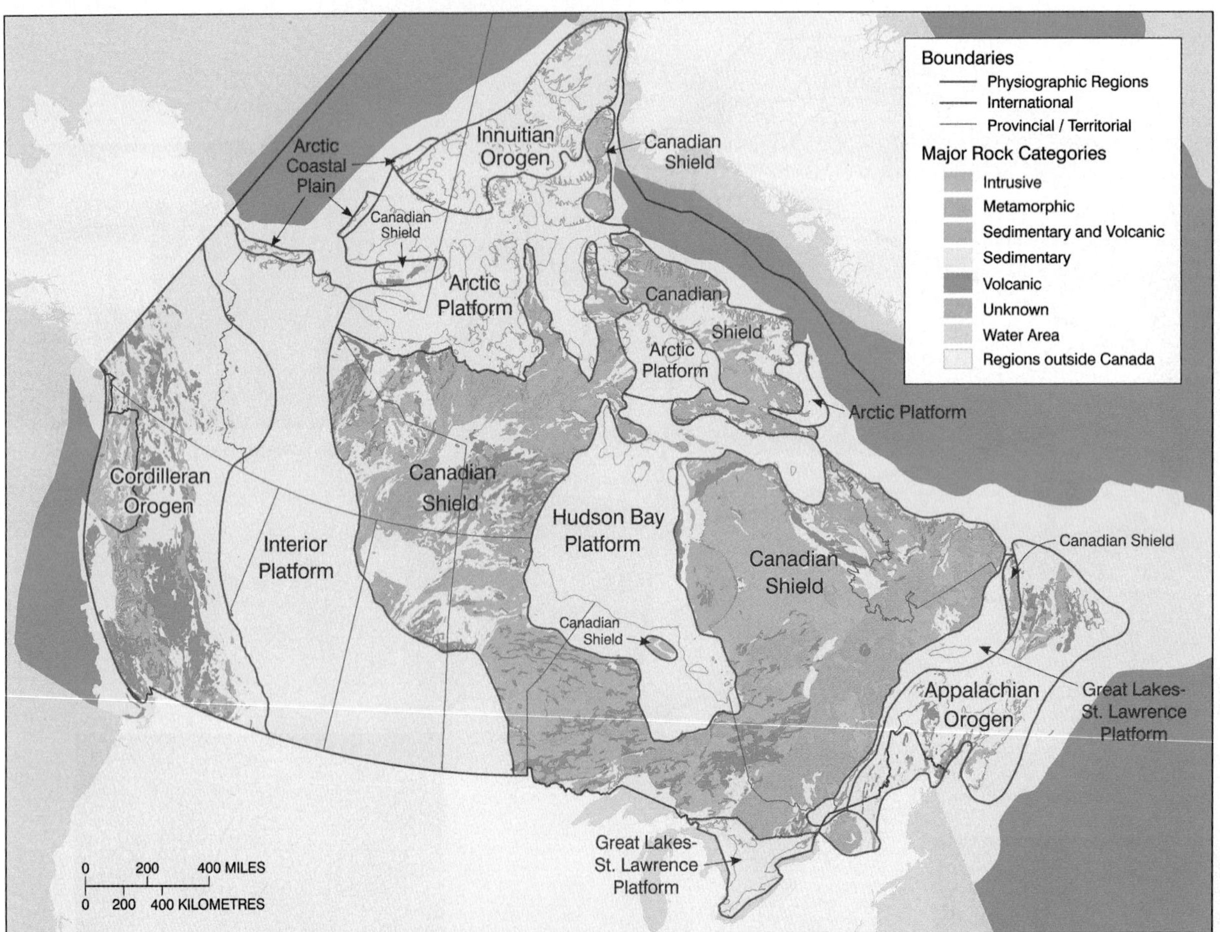

FIGURE 11.8 Bedrock geology and physiography of Canada.
Distribution of igneous, sedimentary, and metamorphic rocks within the various physiographic regions of Canada. Intrusive igneous rocks, volcanic rocks, and metamorphic rocks dominate the geology of the Canadian Shield. The geology of the Appalachian Orogen and Cordilleran Orogen represents a mixture of intrusive igneous rocks, volcanic rocks, metamorphic rocks, and deformed sedimentary rocks. The geology of the Innuitian Orogen is dominated by deformed sedimentary rocks with minor intrusive igneous rocks and volcanic rocks. The geology of the various sedimentary platforms (Great Lakes–St. Lawrence, Hudson Bay, Arctic, Interior) is dominated by clastic and chemical sedimentary rocks. The geology of the Arctic Coastal Plain consists largely of unlithified clastic sediments. [Map by Keith Bigelow, University of Saskatchewan. Data used by permission of the Minister of Public Works and Government Services Canada; Natural Resources Canada, Geological Survey of Canada.]

Smaller plutons include the magma conduits of ancient volcanoes that have cooled and hardened. Those that form parallel to layers of sedimentary rock are *sills*; those that cross layers of the rock they invade are *dikes* (see Figure 11.9). Magma also can bulge between rock strata and produce a lens-shaped body, called a *laccolith*, a type of sill. In addition, magma conduits themselves may solidify in roughly cylindrical forms that stand starkly above the landscape when finally exposed by weathering and erosion. Shiprock *volcanic neck* in New Mexico is such a feature, as suggested by the art in Figure 11.9 and shown in the photo. Weathering action of air, water, and ice can expose all of these intrusive forms.

Volcanic eruptions and flows produce extrusive igneous rock, such as lava that cools and forms basalt (Figure 11.10b). Chapter 12 presents volcanism.

Classifying Igneous Rocks Mineral composition and texture usually classify igneous rocks (Table 11.2). The two broad categories are

1. *Felsic* igneous rocks—derived both in composition and name from *fel*dspar and *silic*a. Felsic minerals are generally high in silica, aluminum, potassium, and sodium and have low melting points. Rocks formed

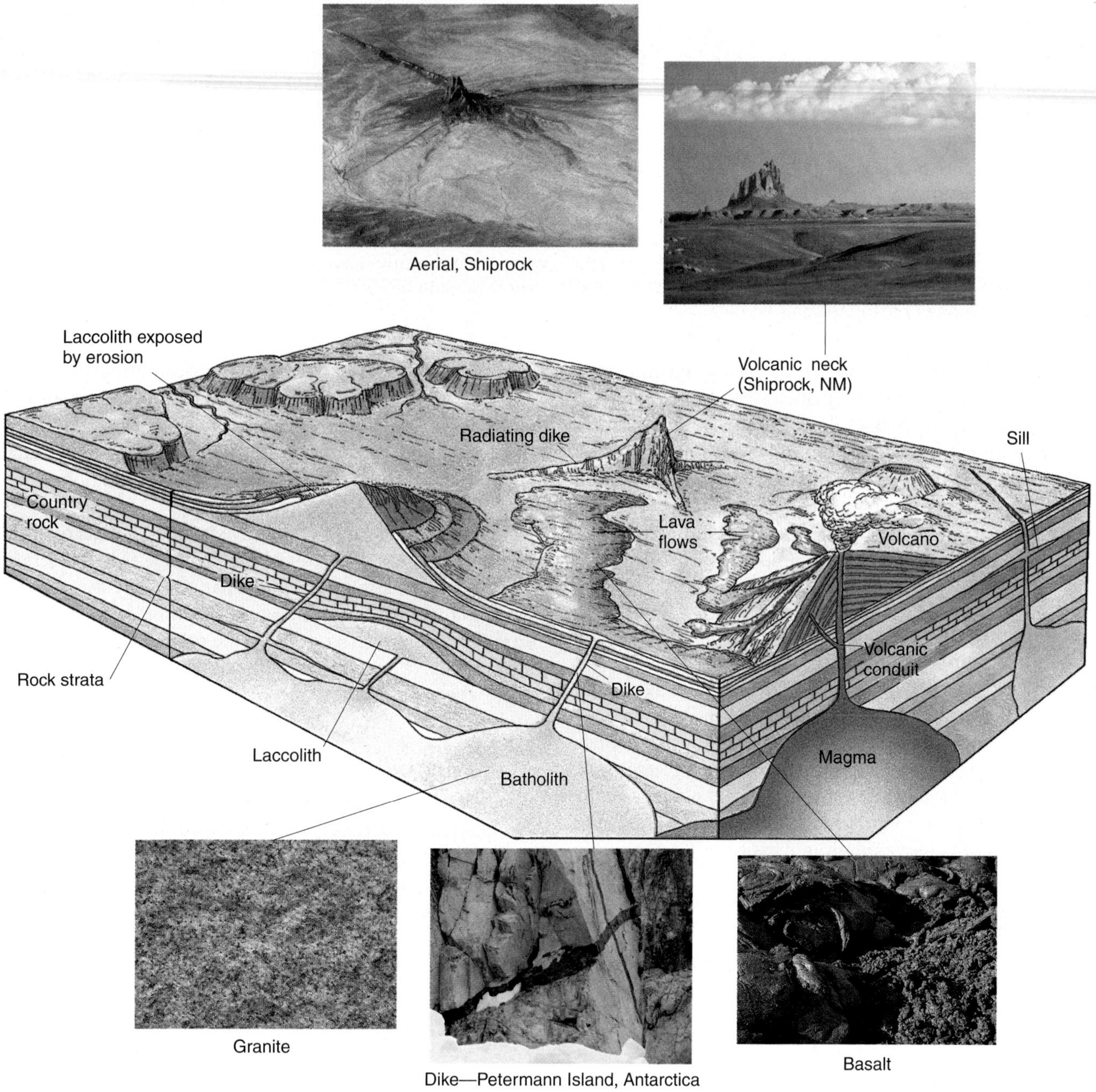

Aerial, Shiprock

Laccolith exposed by erosion
Volcanic neck (Shiprock, NM)
Radiating dike
Sill
Country rock
Lava flows
Volcano
Dike
Volcanic conduit
Rock strata
Dike
Laccolith
Magma
Batholith

Granite

Dike—Petermann Island, Antarctica

Basalt

FIGURE 11.9 Igneous rock types.
The variety of occurrences of igneous rocks, both intrusive (below the surface) and extrusive (on the surface). Photographs show samples of granite (intrusive) and basalt (extrusive). [Photos of rock samples by Bobbé Christopherson; photos of Shiprock volcanic neck by Robert W. Christopherson.]

Formation of Intrusive Igneous Features

(a)

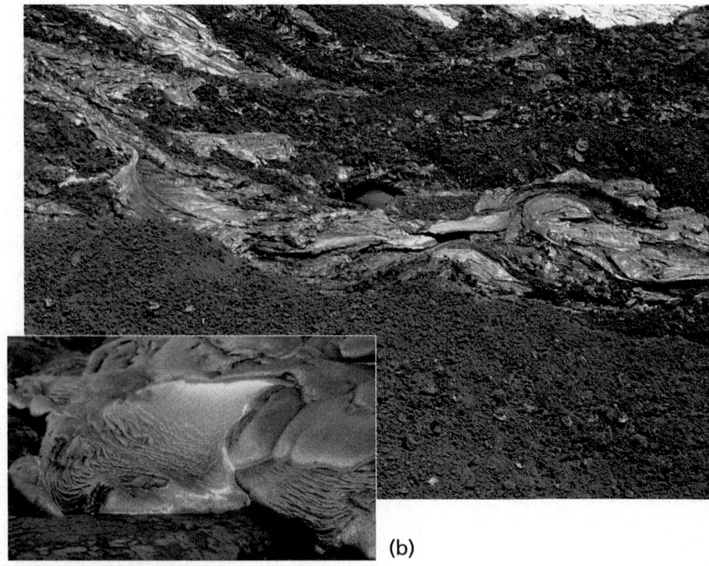
(b)

FIGURE 11.10 Intrusive and extrusive rocks.
(a) Exposed granite bedrock of the Canadian Shield, Nunavut (67° N 112° W). Glacial erosion has created a hummocky landscape characterized by ice-molded hills and water-filled rock basins. The boulders resting on the surface are erratics deposited by glacial ice that melted thousands of years ago. (b) Basaltic lava flows on Hawai'i; the glow is from a skylight into an active lava tube where molten lava is visible; the shiny surface is where lava recently flowed out of the skylight. [(a) Photo by Earth Sciences Sector, Natural Resources Canada GSC 2001-235; (b) photos by Bobbé Christopherson.]

from felsic minerals generally are lighter in colour and are less dense than mafic mineral rocks.

2. *Mafic* igneous rocks—derived both in composition and name from *ma*gnesium and *ferric* (Latin for iron). Mafic minerals are low in silica, high in magnesium and iron, and have high melting points. Rocks formed from mafic minerals are darker in colour and of greater density than felsic mineral rocks.

Table 11.2 shows that the same magma that produces coarse-grained granite, when it slowly cools beneath the surface, can form fine-grained *rhyolite* when it cools above the surface (see inset photo). If it cools quickly, magma having a silica content comparable to granite and rhyolite may form the dark, smoky, glassy-textured rock called *obsidian*, or volcanic glass (see inset photo). Another glassy rock, called *pumice*, forms when escaping gases bubble a frothy texture into the lava. Pumice is full of small holes, is light in weight, and is low enough in density to float in water (see inset photo).

On the mafic side, basalt is the most common fine-grained extrusive igneous rock. It makes up the bulk of the ocean floor, accounting for 71% of Earth's surface. It appears in lava flows such as those on the big island of Hawai'i (Figure 11.10b). An intrusive counterpart to basalt, formed by slow cooling of the parent magma, is *gabbro*.

Sedimentary Processes

Solar energy and gravity drive the process of *sedimentation*, with water as the principal transporting medium. Existing rock is disintegrated and dissolved by weathering, picked up and moved by erosion and transportation and deposited along river, beach, and ocean sites, where burial initiates the rock-forming process. The formation of **sedimentary rock** involves **lithification** processes of cementation, compaction, and a hardening of sediments.

Most sedimentary rocks derive from fragments of existing rock or organic materials. Bits and pieces of former rocks—principally quartz, feldspar, and clay minerals—erode and then are mechanically transported by water (lake, stream, ocean, overland flow), ice (glacial action), wind, and gravity. They are transported from "higher-energy" sites, where the carrying medium has the energy to pick up and move them, to "lower-energy" sites, where the material is dumped.

The common sedimentary rocks are *sandstone* (sand that became cemented together), *shale* (mud that became compacted into rock), *limestone* (bones and shells that became cemented or calcium carbonate that precipitated in ocean and lake waters), and *coal* (ancient plant remains that became compacted into rock). Some minerals, such as calcium carbonate, dissolve into solution and form sedimentary deposits by precipitating from those solutions to form rock. This is an important process in oceanic and karst (cave) environments.

Characteristically, sedimentary rocks are laid down by wind, water, or ice in horizontally layered beds. Different environmental conditions produce a variety of sedimentary forms. Various cements, depending on availability, fuse rock particles together. Lime, or calcium carbonate ($CaCO_3$), is the most common, followed by iron oxides (Fe_2O_3) and

Table 11.2 Igneous Rock Minerals

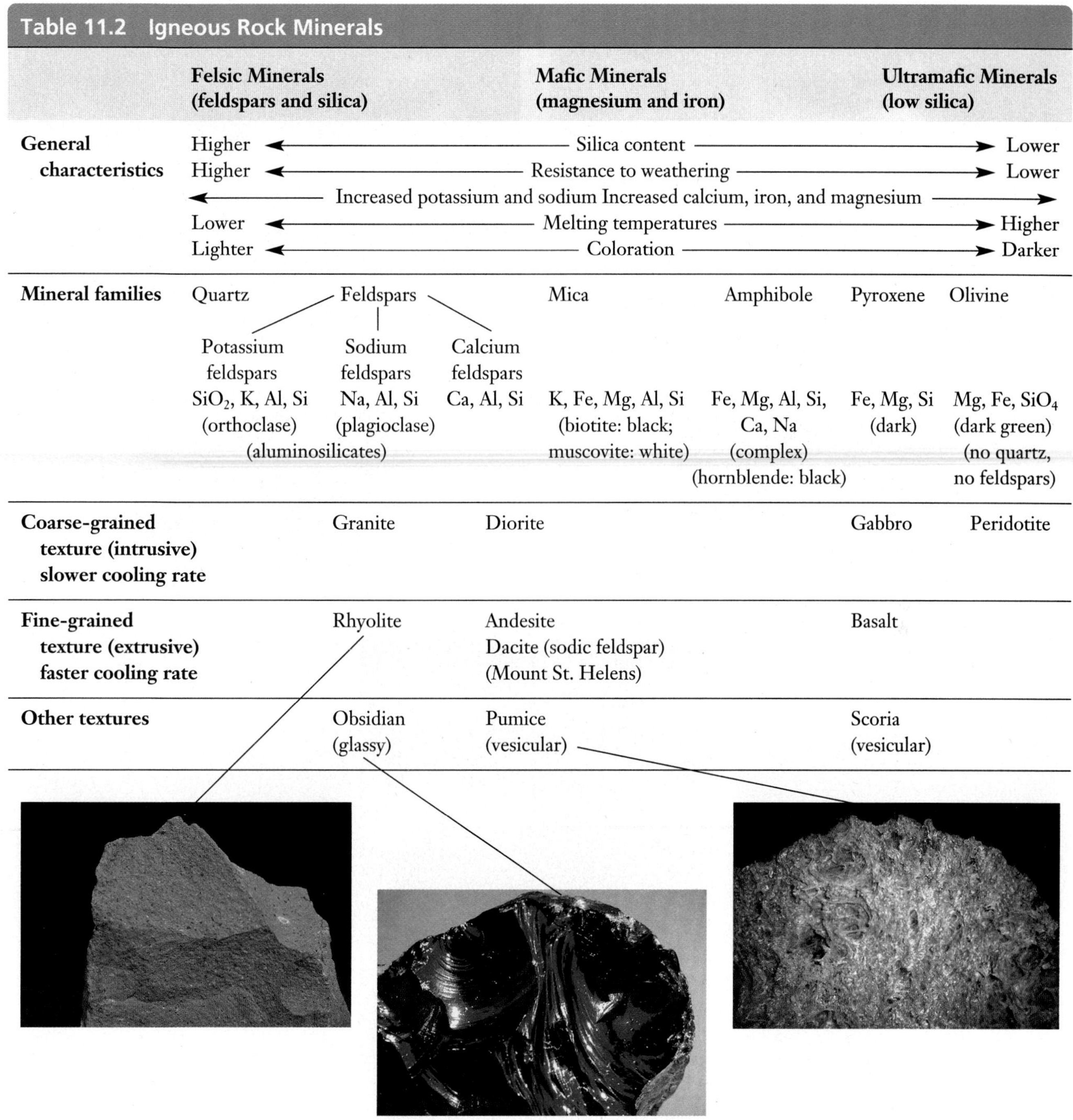

	Felsic Minerals (feldspars and silica)				Mafic Minerals (magnesium and iron)		Ultramafic Minerals (low silica)	
General characteristics	Higher ← Silica content → Lower Higher ← Resistance to weathering → Lower ← Increased potassium and sodium Increased calcium, iron, and magnesium → Lower ← Melting temperatures → Higher Lighter ← Coloration → Darker							
Mineral families	Quartz	Feldspars: Potassium feldspars SiO_2, K, Al, Si (orthoclase)	Sodium feldspars Na, Al, Si (plagioclase) (aluminosilicates)	Calcium feldspars Ca, Al, Si	Mica K, Fe, Mg, Al, Si (biotite: black; muscovite: white)	Amphibole Fe, Mg, Al, Si, Ca, Na (complex) (hornblende: black)	Pyroxene Fe, Mg, Si (dark)	Olivine Mg, Fe, SiO_4 (dark green) (no quartz, no feldspars)
Coarse-grained texture (intrusive) slower cooling rate			Granite	Diorite			Gabbro	Peridotite
Fine-grained texture (extrusive) faster cooling rate			Rhyolite	Andesite Dacite (sodic feldspar) (Mount St. Helens)			Basalt	
Other textures			Obsidian (glassy)	Pumice (vesicular)			Scoria (vesicular)	

Source: Photos from R. M. Busch, ed., *Laboratory Manual in Physical Geology*, 3rd ed., © 1993 by Macmillan Publishing Co.

silica (SiO_2). Drying (dehydration), heating, or chemical reactions can also unite particles.

The layered strata of sedimentary rocks form an important record of past ages. **Stratigraphy** is the study of the sequence (superposition), thickness, and spatial distribution of strata. These sequences yield clues to the age and origin of the rocks. The horizontal strata preserved in the sandstone illustrated in Figure 11.11a record the successive deposition of clastic sediments by rivers along an ancient coastline.

The two primary sources of sedimentary rocks are the mechanically transported fragments of former rock, called clastic sediments, and the dissolved minerals in solution, termed chemical sediments.

Clastic Sedimentary Rocks Weathered and fragmented rocks that are further worn in transport provide *clastic sediments*. Table 11.3 lists the range of *clast* sizes—everything from boulders to microscopic clay particles—and the form they take as *lithified rock*. Common sedimentary rocks from

(a)

(b)

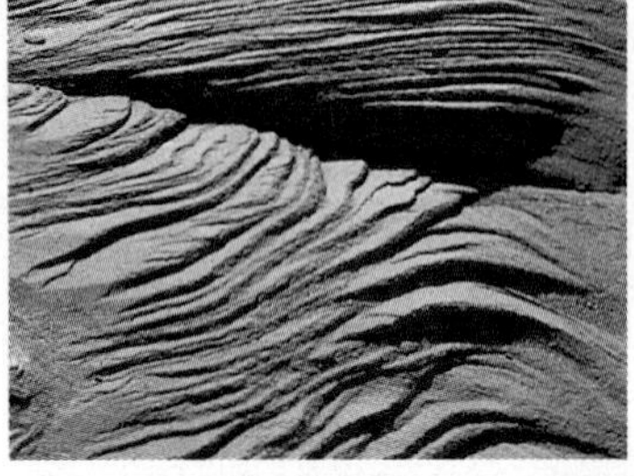

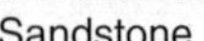

Sandstone

Limestone

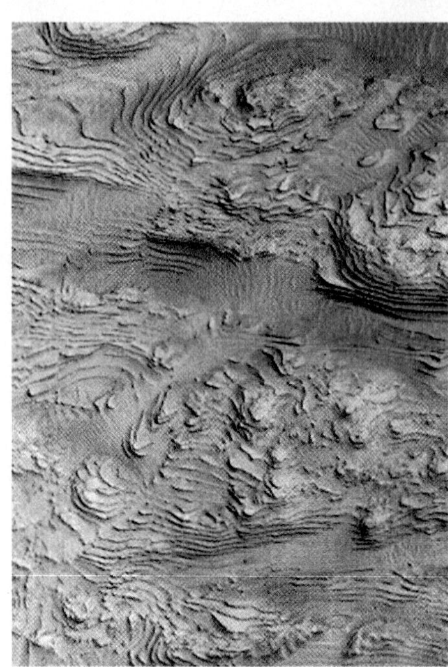

(c) Martian sedimentary formations

FIGURE 11.11 Sedimentary rock types.
(a) Hoodoos developed in weakly cemented Cretaceous sandstone, near Drumheller, Alberta. Physical weathering by frost action, associated with the repeated freezing (expansion) and thawing (contraction) of water, acts to break up the rocks to create these landforms. (b) Ball's Falls, Jordan Harbour, Ontario (43° N 79° W), along the length of the Niagara Escarpment in southern Ontario. The exposed cliff face is maintained by the action of running water that erodes the softer shale at the base of the cliff, progressively undermining the Paleozoic limestone until it collapses. (c) Ancient sediment deposition through repeated cycles or erosion and deposition is evident in the Martian western Arabia Terra (8° N and 7° W). [(a) Photo by J.A. Kraulis/Masterfile; inset photo by Robert W. Christopherson; (b) photo by Victor Last/Geographical Visual Aids; inset photo by Bobbé Christopherson; (c) image from Mars Global Surveyor courtesy of NASA/JPL/Malin Space Science Systems.]

Table 11.3 Clastic Sediment Sizes and Related Rock Form

Unconsolidated Sediment	Grain Size	Rock Form
Boulders, cobbles	>80 mm	Conglomerate (breccia, if pieces are angular)
Pebbles, gravel	>2 mm	
Coarse sand	0.5–2.0 mm	Sandstone
Medium-to-fine sand	0.062–0.5 mm	Sandstone
Silt	0.002–0.062 mm	Siltstone (mudstone)
Clay	<0.002 mm	Shale

clastic sediments include siltstone (silt) or mudstone (mud), shale (up to 0.06-mm-diameter particles), and sandstone (sand particles that range from 0.06 to 2 mm in diameter).

Chemical Sedimentary Rocks *Chemical sedimentary* rocks are not formed from physical pieces of broken rock but instead from dissolved minerals, transported in solution and chemically precipitated from solution (they are essentially nonclastic). The most common chemical sedimentary rock is **limestone**, which is lithified calcium carbonate, derived from inorganic and organic sources. A similar form is *dolomite*, which is lithified calcium-magnesium carbonate, $CaMg(CO_3)_2$. Limestone from marine organic origins is most common; it is biochemical—derived from shells produced by biological activity. Once formed, these rocks are vulnerable to chemical weathering, which produces unique landforms, as discussed in the weathering section of Chapter 13 and as shown in Figure 11.11b.

Chemical sediments from inorganic sources are deposited when water evaporates and leaves behind a residue of salts. These *evaporites* may exist as common salts, such as gypsum or sodium chloride (table salt). They often appear as flat, layered deposits across a dry landscape. The pair of photographs in Figure 11.12 dramatically demonstrates this process; one was made in Death Valley National Park one day after a record 2.57-cm (1.01-in.) rainfall, and the other photo was made one month later.

Chemical deposition also occurs in the water of natural hot springs from chemical reactions between minerals and oxygen. This is a sedimentary process related to *hydrothermal activity*. An example is the massive deposit of travertine, a form of calcium carbonate, at Mammoth Hot Springs in Yellowstone National Park (Figure 11.13a).

Hydrothermal activity also occurs on the ocean floor along the rift valleys formed by sea-floor spreading. These "black smokers" belch dark clouds of hydrogen sulphides, minerals, and metals that hot water (in excess of 380°C; 716°F) leached from the basalt. In contact with seawater, metals and minerals precipitate into deposits (Figure 11.13b). Along the Mid-Atlantic Ridge, one region of hydrothermal activity has 30- to 60-m tall vents of calcium carbonate that are at least 30,000 years old, and still active. Here, the interaction of the mineral-laden spring water reacts with seawater to produce rock. This area is nicknamed "The Lost City" because of the way the towering chimneys look from the observation submersibles.

Metamorphic Processes

Any rock, either igneous or sedimentary, may be transformed into a **metamorphic rock** by going through profound physical or chemical changes under pressure and increased

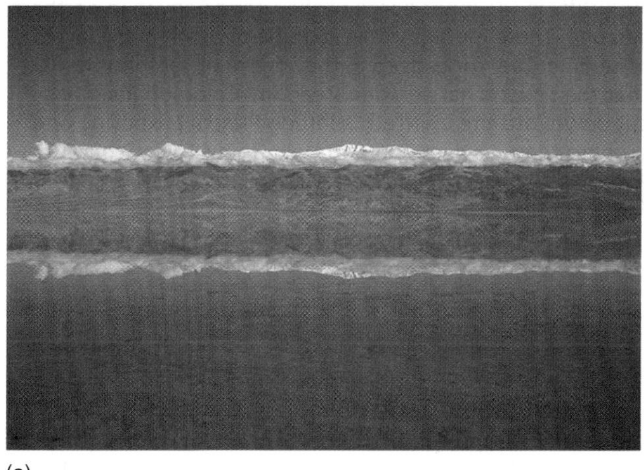

(a)

(b)

FIGURE 11.12 Death Valley, wet and dry.
A Death Valley landscape (a) one day after a record rainfall when the valley was covered by several square kilometres of water only a few centimetres deep. (b) One month later the water had evaporated, and the same valley was coated with evaporites (borated salts) shown in the close-up inset photo. [Photos by Robert W. Christopherson.]

his proposal included an incorrect driving mechanism for the moving continents, Wegener's arrangement of Pangaea and its breakup was correct, Pangaea being only the latest of earlier supercontinent arrangements over the span of Earth history.

To come up with his Pangaea fit, he studied the geologic record (rock strata), the fossil record, and the climatic record for the continents. He concluded that South America and Africa correlated in many complex ways. He decided that the large midlatitude coal deposits, which date to the Permian and Carboniferous Periods (245–360 million years ago), exist because these regions once were nearer the equator and therefore covered by lush vegetation that became coal.

As modern scientific capabilities built the case for continental drift, the 1950s and 1960s saw a revival of interest in Wegener's concepts and, finally, confirmation. Aided by an avalanche of discoveries, the plate tectonics theory today is universally accepted as an accurate model of the way Earth's surface evolves. *Tectonic*, from the Greek *tektonikùs*, meaning "building" or "construction," refers to changes in the configuration of Earth's crust as a result of internal forces. **Plate tectonic** processes include upwelling of magma, lithospheric plate movements, sea-floor spreading and subduction of lithosphere, earthquakes, volcanic activity, warping, folding, and faulting of the lithosphere.

Sea-Floor Spreading and Production of New Crust

The key to establishing the theory of continental drift was a better understanding of the seafloor. The seafloor has a remarkable feature: an interconnected worldwide mountain chain (ridge) some 64,000 km (40,000 mi) in extent and averaging more than 1000 km (600 mi) in width. A striking view of this great undersea mountain chain opens Chapter 12. How did this global mountain chain get there?

In the early 1960s, geophysicists Harry H. Hess and Robert S. Dietz proposed **sea-floor spreading** as the mechanism that builds this mountain chain and drives continental movement. Hess said that these submarine mountain ranges, called the **mid-ocean ridges**, were the direct result of upwelling flows of magma from hot areas in the upper mantle and asthenosphere and perhaps from the deeper lower mantle.

When mantle convection brings magma up to the crust, the crust fractures, and the magma extrudes onto the seafloor and cools to form new seafloor. This process builds the mid-ocean ridges and spreads the seafloor laterally. The concept is illustrated in Figure 11.15, which shows how the ocean floor is rifted (moves apart) and displaced along mid-ocean ridges. Figure 11.15b is a remote-sensing image of the mid-ocean ridge and 11.15c, a map of the system in the Atlantic. Figure 11.14d shows a portion of the mid-ocean ridge system that surfaces at Thingvellir, Iceland, forming these rifts—the North American plate along one side and the European plate on the other. Iceland's first Althing (parliament) met here in A.D. 930; leaders used the acoustics of the rift walls to be heard by the gathering.

As new crust generates and the seafloor spreads, magnetic particles in the lava orient with the magnetic field in force at the time the lava cools and hardens. The particles become locked in this alignment as new seafloor forms. This alignment creates a kind of magnetic tape recording in the seafloor. The continually forming oceanic crust records each magnetic reversal and reorientation of Earth's polarity.

Figure 11.16 illustrates just such a recording from the Mid-Atlantic Ridge south of Iceland. The colours denote the alternating magnetic polarization preserved in the minerals of the oceanic crust. Note the mirror images that develop on either side of the sea-floor rift as a result of the nearly symmetrical spreading of the sea floor. Each colour corresponds to a suite of rocks of similar geologic age: The relative age of these rocks increases with distance away from the ridge axis (Figure 11.17). These periodic reversals of Earth's magnetic field are a valuable clue to understanding sea-floor spreading, helping scientists fit together pieces of Earth's crust.

These sea-floor recordings of Earth's magnetic-field reversals and other measurements permitted the determination of the age of the seafloor. The complex harmony of the two concepts of plate tectonics and sea-floor spreading became clearer. The youngest crust anywhere on Earth is at the spreading centres of the mid-ocean ridges, and, with increasing distance from these centres, the crust gets steadily older (Figure 11.17). The oldest seafloor is in the western Pacific near Japan, dating to the Jurassic Period. Note on the map in the figure the distance between this basin and its spreading centre in the South Pacific west of South America.

Overall, the seafloor is relatively young—nowhere does it exceed 208 million years in age, remarkable when you remember that Earth's age is 4.6 billion years. The reason is that oceanic crust is short-lived—the oldest sections, farthest from the mid-ocean ridges, are slowly plunging beneath continental crust along Earth's deep oceanic trenches. The discovery that the seafloor is young demolished earlier thinking that the oldest rocks would be found there.

Subduction of Lithosphere

In contrast to the upwelling zones along the mid-ocean ridges are the areas of descending lithosphere elsewhere. On the left side of Figure 11.15a, note how one plate of the lithosphere is diving beneath another, into the mantle. Recall that the basaltic ocean crust has a density of 3000 kg/m^3, whereas continental crust averages a lighter 2700 kg/m^3. As a result, when continental crust and oceanic crust slowly collide, the denser ocean floor will grind beneath the lighter continental crust, thus forming a **subduction zone**, as shown in the figure.

The world's deep ocean trenches coincide with these subduction zones and are the lowest features on Earth's surface. Deepest is the Mariana Trench near Guam, which

(continued p. 353)

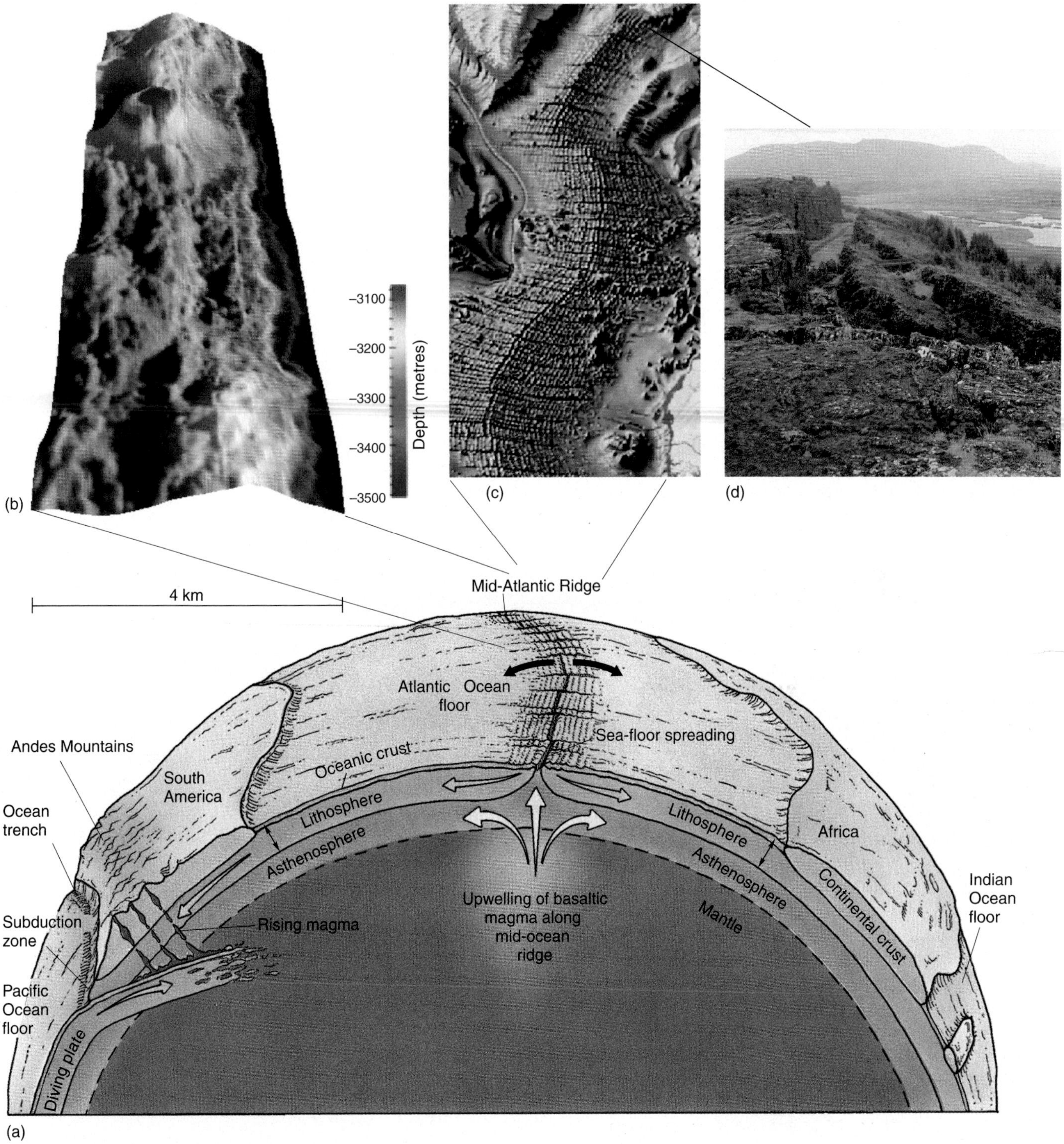

FIGURE 11.15 Crustal movements.
(a) Sea-floor spreading, upwelling currents, subduction, and plate movements, shown in cross section. Arrows indicate the direction of the spreading. (b) A 4-km-wide image of the Mid-Atlantic Ridge showing linear faults, a volcanic crater, a rift valley, and ridges. The image was taken by the TOBI (towed ocean-bottom instrument) at approximately 29° N latitude. The scale represents depth (metres) below sea level. (c) Detail from Tharp's ocean-floor map. (d) The mid-Atlantic rift surfaces through Iceland. This scene is at Thingvellir in southeastern Iceland, where the North American and European plates of Earth's crust meet. [(a) After P. J. Wyllie, *The Way the Earth Works*, © 1976, by John Wiley & Sons, adapted by permission; (b) image courtesy of D. K. Smith, Woods Hole Oceanographic Institute, Woods Hole, Massachusetts. All rights reserved; (c) Bruce C. Heezen and Marie Tharp, courtesy Marie Tharp; (d) photo by Bobbé Christopherson.]

Sea-floor Spreading, Subduction

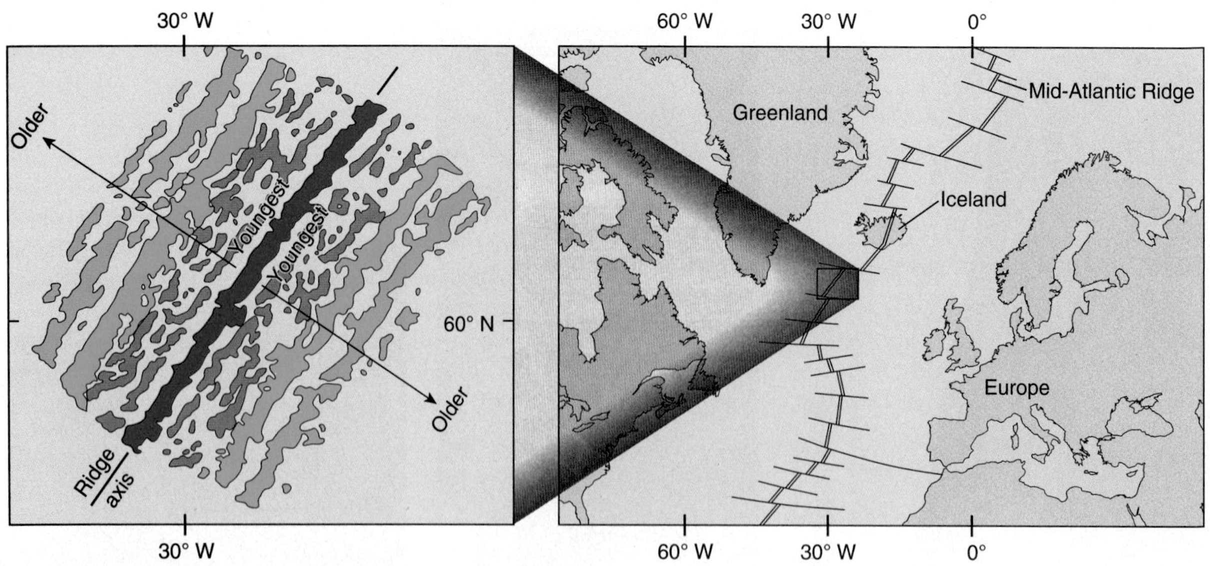

FIGURE 11.16 Magnetic reversals recorded in the seafloor.
Magnetic reversals recorded in the seafloor south of Iceland along the Mid-Atlantic Ridge. Note rocks with similar magnetic orientation are roughly the same distance from the spreading centre. [Magnetic reversals reprinted from J. R. Heirtzler, S. Le Pichon, and J. G. Baron, *Deep-Sea Research* 13, © 1966, Pergamon Press, p. 247.]

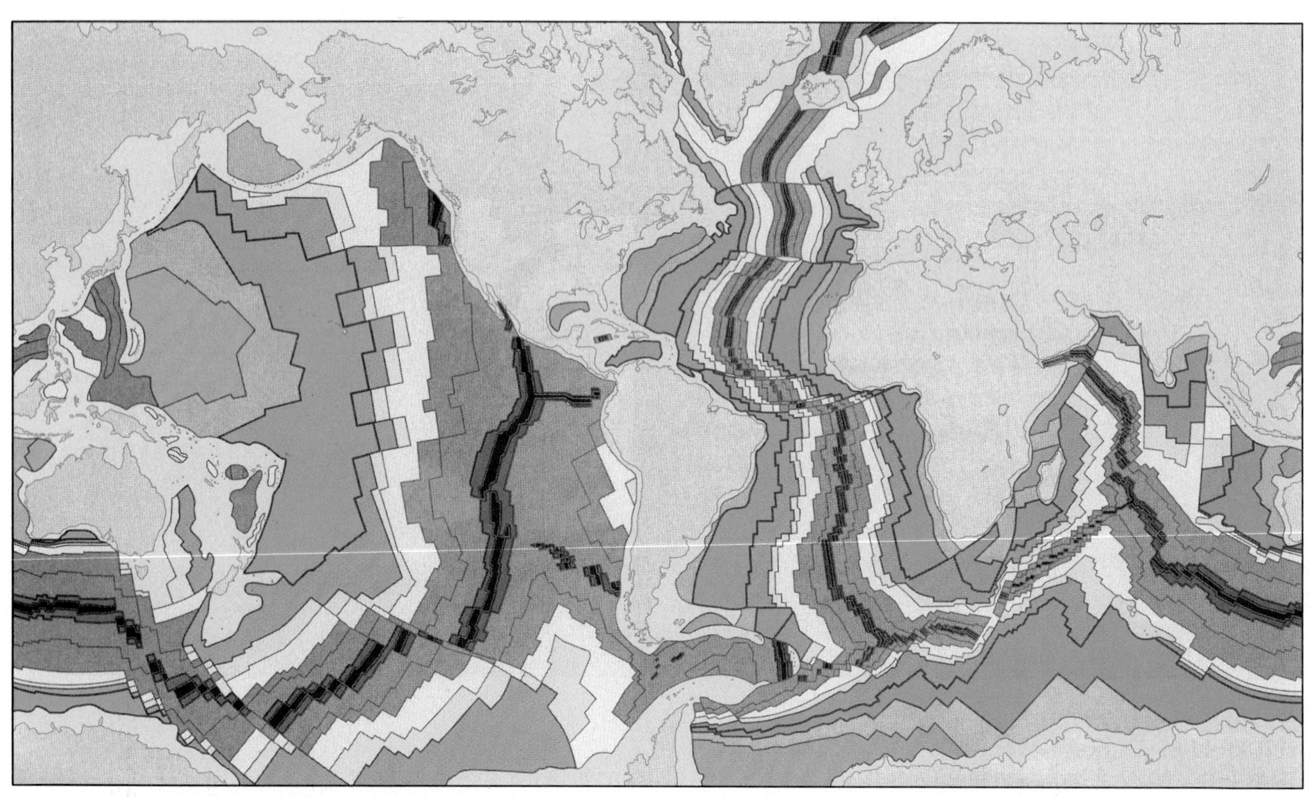

FIGURE 11.17 Relative age of the oceanic crust.
Compare the light tan colour near the East Pacific Rise in the eastern Pacific Ocean with the same light tan colour along the Mid-Atlantic ridge. What does the difference in width tell you about the rates of plate motion in the two locations? [Adapted with the permission of W. H. Freeman and Company from *The Bedrock Geology of the World* by R. L. Larson and others, © 1985.]

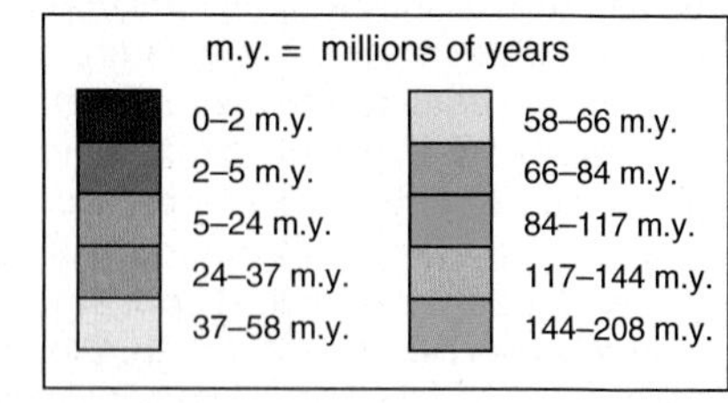

descends below sea level to –11,030 m (–36,198 ft); next in depth are the Puerto Rico Trench at –8605 m (–28,224 ft) and, in the Indian Ocean, the Java Trench at –7125 m (–23,376 ft).

The subducted portion of lithosphere travels down into the asthenosphere, where it remelts and eventually is recycled as magma, rising again toward the surface through deep fissures and cracks in crustal rock. Volcanic mountains such as the Andes in South America and the Cascade Range from northern California to southern British Columbia form inland of these subduction zones as a result of rising plumes of magma, as suggested in Figure 11.15a. Sometimes the diving plate remains intact for hundreds of kilometres, whereas at other times it can break into large pieces, thought to be the case under the Cascade Range with its distribution of volcanoes. The fact that spreading ridges and subduction zones are areas of earthquake and volcanic activity provides important proof of plate tectonics. Now, using current scientific findings, let us go back and reconstruct the past, and Pangaea.

The Formation and Breakup of Pangaea

The supercontinent of Pangaea and its subsequent breakup into today's continents represent only the last 225 million years of Earth's 4.6 billion years, or only the most recent 1/23 of Earth's existence. During the other 22/23 of geologic time, other things were happening. The landmasses as we know them were unrecognizable.

Figure 11.18a begins with the pre-Pangaea arrangement of 465 million years ago (during the middle Ordovician Period). Figure 11.18b illustrates an updated version of Wegener's Pangaea, 225–200 million years ago (Triassic–Jurassic Periods). The movement of plates that occurred by 135 million years ago (the beginning of the Cretaceous Period) is in Figure 11.18c. Figure 11.18d presents the arrangement 65 million years ago (beginning of the Tertiary Period). Finally, the present arrangement in modern geologic time (the late Cenozoic Era) is in Figure 11.18e.

Earth's present crust is divided into at least 14 plates, of which about half are major and half are minor, in terms of area (Figure 11.19). Literally hundreds of smaller pieces and perhaps dozens of microplates that migrated together comprise these broad plates. The arrows in the figure indicate the direction in which each plate is presently moving, and the length of the arrows suggests the rate of movement during the past 20 million years.

Compare Figure 11.19 with the image of the ocean floor in Figure 11.20 (p. 356). In the image, satellite radar-altimeter measurements determined the sea-surface height to a remarkable accuracy of 0.03 m, or 1 in. The sea-surface elevation is far from uniform; it is higher or lower in direct response to the mountains, plains, and trenches of the ocean floor beneath it. This sea-floor topography causes slight differences in Earth's gravity.

For example, a massive mountain on the ocean floor exerts a high gravitational field and attracts water to it, producing higher sea level above the mountain; over a trench there is less gravity, resulting in a drop in sea level. A mountain 2000 m (6500 ft) high that is 20 km (12 mi) across its base creates a 2-m rise in the sea surface. Until the Scripps Institution of Oceanography and NOAA developed this use of satellite technology, these tiny changes in height were not visible. Now we have a comprehensive map of the ocean *floor*, derived from remote sensing of the ocean *surface*!

The illustration of the seafloor that begins Chapter 12 also may be helpful in identifying the plate boundaries in the following discussion. It is interesting to correlate the features illustrated in Figures 11.19 and 11.20 and Chapter 12's opening map. For more on the science of plate tectonics, see **http://www.ig.utexas.edu/research/projects/plates/plates.htm**.

Plate Boundaries

The boundaries where plates meet clearly are dynamic places, although slow-moving within human time frames. The block diagram insets in Figure 11.18e show the three general types of motion and interaction that occur along the boundary areas:

- *Divergent boundaries* (lower left in figure) are characteristic of sea-floor spreading centres, where upwelling material from the mantle forms new seafloor ("constructional"), and lithospheric plates spread apart. The spreading makes these zones of tension. An example noted in the figure is the divergent boundary along the East Pacific rise, which gives birth to the Nazca plate (moving eastward) and the Pacific plate (moving northwestward). Whereas most divergent boundaries occur at mid-ocean ridges, there are a few within continents themselves. An example is the Great Rift Valley of East Africa, where crust is rifting apart.
- *Convergent boundaries* (upper left) are characteristic of collision zones, where areas of continental and oceanic lithosphere collide. These are zones of compression and crustal loss ("destructional"). Examples include the subduction zone off the west coast of South and Central America and the area along the Japan and Aleutian Trenches. Along the western edge of South America, the Nazca plate collides with and is subducted beneath the South American plate. This convergence creates the Andes Mountains chain and related volcanoes. The collision of India and Asia mentioned earlier is another example of a convergent boundary.
- *Transform boundaries* (lower right) occur where plates slide laterally past one another at right angles to a sea-floor spreading centre, neither diverging nor converging, and usually with no volcanic eruptions. These are the right-angle fractures stretching across the mid-ocean ridge system worldwide (visible in Figures 11.19 and 11.20 and the Chapter 12 opening illustration).

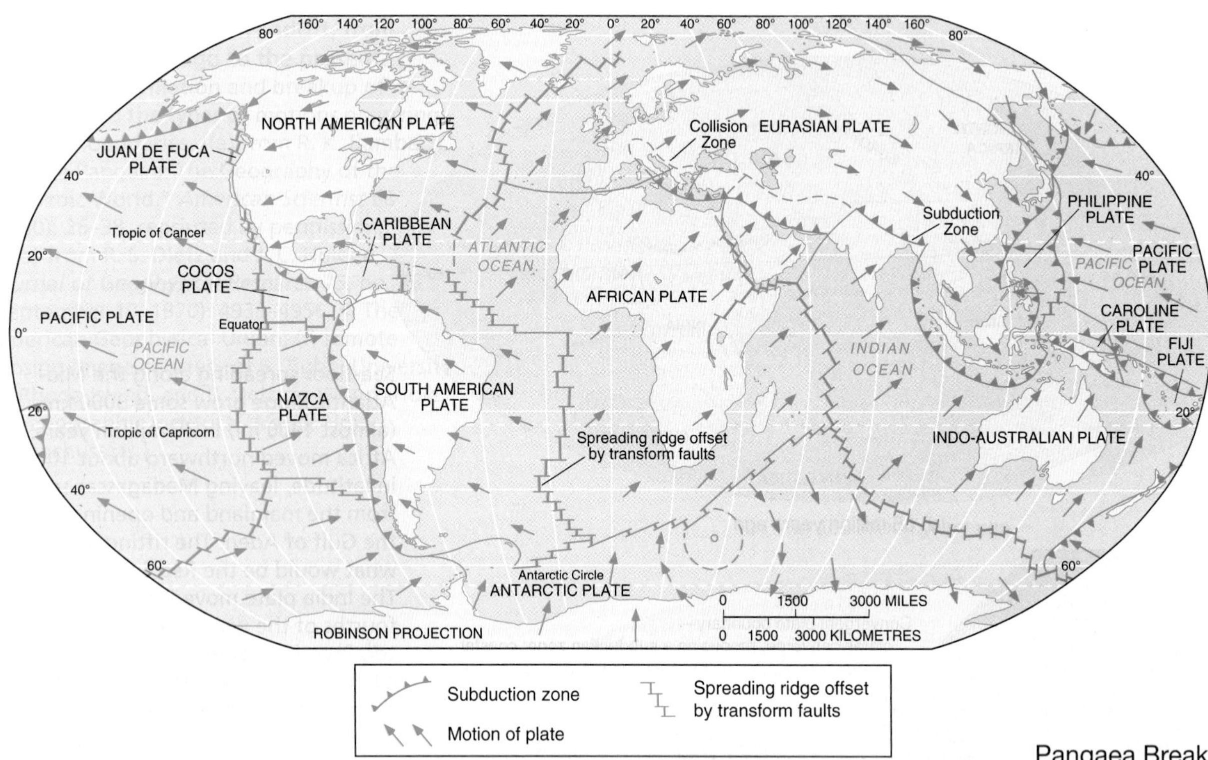

FIGURE 11.19 Earth's major lithospheric plates and their movements.
Each arrow represents 20 million years of movement. The longer arrows indicate that the Pacific and Nazca plates are moving more rapidly than the Atlantic plates. Compare the length of these arrows with those light-tan areas in Figure 11.17. [Adapted from U.S. Geodynamics Committee.]

Pangaea Breakup, Plate Movements, India Collision with Asia

NOTEBOOK

Plate Boundaries

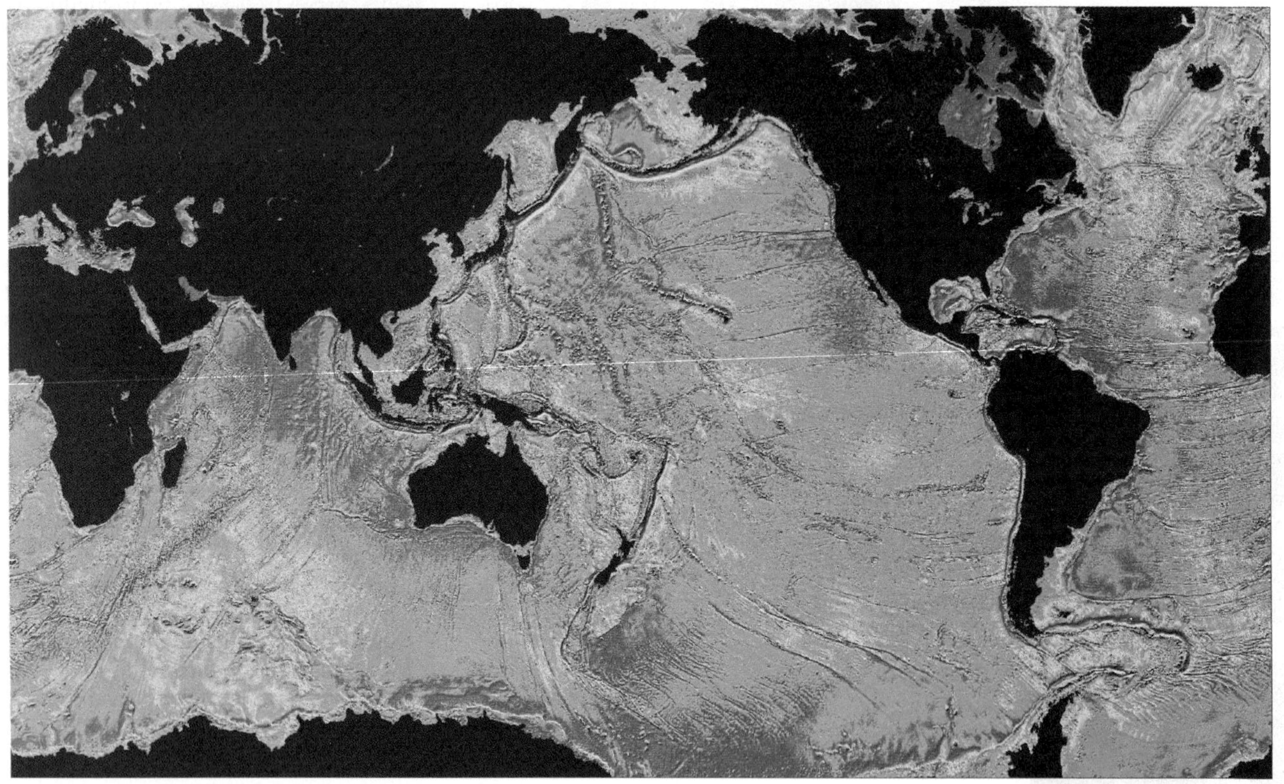

FIGURE 11.20 The ocean floor revealed.
A global gravity anomaly map derived from *Geosat* and *ERS-1* altimeter data. The radar altimeters measured sea-surface heights. Variation in sea-surface elevation is a direct indication of the topography of the ocean floor. [Global gravity anomaly map image courtesy of D. T. Sandwell, Scripps Institution of Oceanography. All rights reserved, 1995.]

Related to plate boundaries, another piece of the tectonic puzzle fell into place in 1965 when University of Toronto geophysicist J. Tuzo Wilson first described the nature of transform boundaries and their relation to earthquake activity (News Report 11.3). All the spreading centres on Earth's crust feature these perpendicular scars (Figure 11.21). Some transform faults are a few hundred kilometres long; others, such as those along the East Pacific rise, stretch out 1000 km or more (over 600 mi). Across the entire ocean floor, spreading-centre mid-ocean ridges are the location of **transform faults**. The faults generally are parallel to the direction in which the plate is moving. How do they occur?

You can see in Figure 11.21 that mid-ocean ridges are not simple straight lines. When a mid-ocean rift begins, it opens at points of weakness in the crust. The fractures you see in the figure began as a series of offset breaks in the crust in each portion of the spreading centre. As new material rises to the surface, building the mid-ocean ridges and spreading the plates, these offset areas slide past each other, in horizontal faulting motions. The resulting fracture zone, which follows these breaks in Earth's crust, is active only

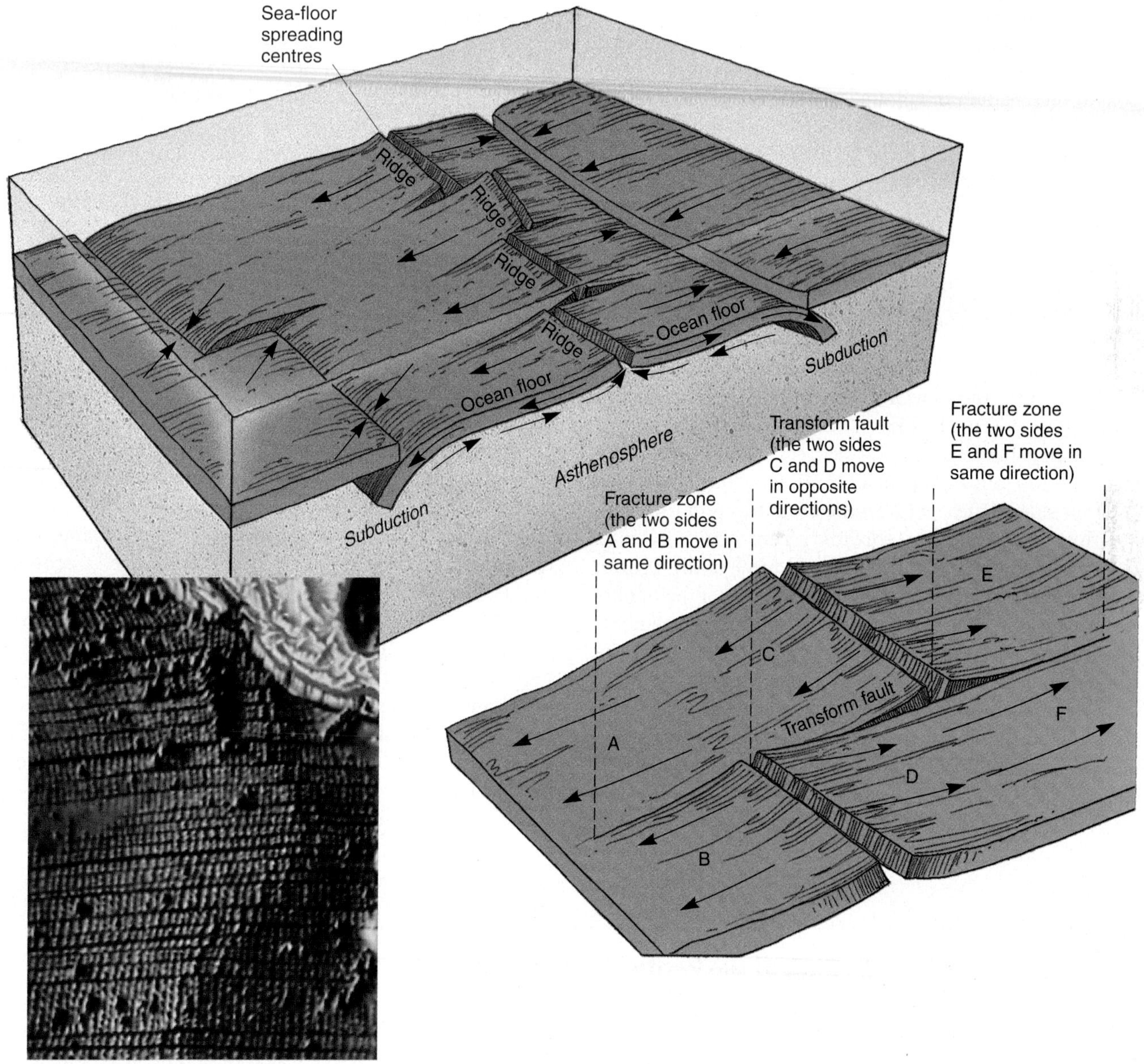

FIGURE 11.21 Transform faults.
Appearing along fracture zones, a transform fault is only that section between spreading centres where adjacent plates move in opposite directions—between C and D. [Adapted from B. Isacks, J. Oliver, and L. R. Sykes, *Journal of Geophysical Research* 73, (1968): 5855–5899, © The American Geophysical Union. Detail insert from Tharp's ocean-floor map, Bruce C. Heezen and Marie Tharp, courtesy Marie Tharp.]

Transform Faults, Plate Margins

News Report 11.3

J. Tuzo Wilson and the Theory of Plate Tectonics

J. Tuzo Wilson (1908–1993), a professor of geophysics at the University of Toronto from 1946 to 1974, was a leading proponent of the theory of plate tectonics. Dr. Wilson was the first-ever graduate in geophysical studies from a Canadian university. He introduced several concepts throughout the 1960s and 1970s that were crucial to the development of plate tectonics theory. His contributions include the recognition of hotspots in the mantle and their role in the creation of volcanic island chains (see Figures 11.22 and 11.23), the identification of a new class of faults, *transform faults*, that occur with displacement of oceanic ridges and result in the horizontal displacement of crust, and the demonstration that the continents exhibit a cyclic history of rifting, movement, and collision, followed by rifting again, with a period of about 100 million years (i.e., the Wilson Cycle).

In recognition of Wilson's important contributions to knowledge in the Earth sciences, a mountain range in Antarctica and an extinct volcano on the floor of the Pacific Ocean, off Canada's west coast, were named in his honour. He was inducted as a Fellow of the Royal Society of Canada in 1968 and as a Companion of the Order of Canada in 1984.

FIGURE 1 J. Tuzo Wilson. J. Tuzo Wilson was a Canadian pioneer in the theory of plate tectonics. [Photo courtesy the Ontario Science Centre.]

along the fault section between ridges of spreading centres, as shown in Figure 11.21.

Along transform faults (the fault section between C and D in the figure) the motion is one of horizontal displacement—no new crust is formed or old crust subducted. In contrast, beyond the spreading centres, the two sides of the fracture zones join and are inactive. In fact, the plate pieces on either side of the fracture zone are moving in the same direction, away from the spreading centre (the fracture zones between A and B and between E and F in the figure).

The name *transform* was assigned because of this apparent transformation in the direction of the fault movement. The famous San Andreas fault system in California, where continental crust has overridden a transform system, relates to this type of motion. The fault that triggered the 1995 Kobe earthquake in Japan also has this type of horizontal motion—as does the North Anatolian fault in Turkey and its latest 1999 quake.

Earthquake and Volcanic Activity

Plate boundaries are the primary location of earthquake and volcanic activity, and the correlation of these phenomena is an important aspect of plate tectonics. The next chapter discusses earthquakes and volcanic activity in more detail; however, their general relationship to tectonic plates is important to mention.

Figure 11.22 maps earthquake zones, volcanic sites, hot spots, and plate motion. The "ring of fire" surrounding the Pacific Basin, named for the frequent incidence of volcanoes, is evident. The subducting edge of the Pacific plate thrusts deep into the crust and mantle, producing molten material that makes its way back toward the surface, causing active volcanoes along the Pacific Rim. Such processes occur similarly at plate boundaries throughout the world, including the Pacific Coast of Canada (Focus Study 11.1).

Focus Study 11.1

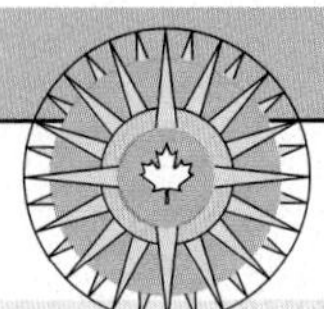

Tectonic Setting of the Pacific Coast of Canada

The Pacific Coast is the most seismically active region of Canada. This region is one of the few areas in the world where divergent, convergent, and transform plate boundaries occur in proximity to one another (Figure 1), resulting in significant earthquake activity. More than 100 earthquakes of magnitude 5 or greater (capable of causing damage) were recorded offshore in the past 70 years.

The oceanic Juan de Fuca plate, which extends from the northern tip of Vancouver Island to northern California (Figure 1), is moving toward North America. The Juan de Fuca plate is sliding beneath the North American plate within the Cascadia subduction zone at a convergence rate of about 4 cm (1.7 in.) per year. Earthquake activity in this region is

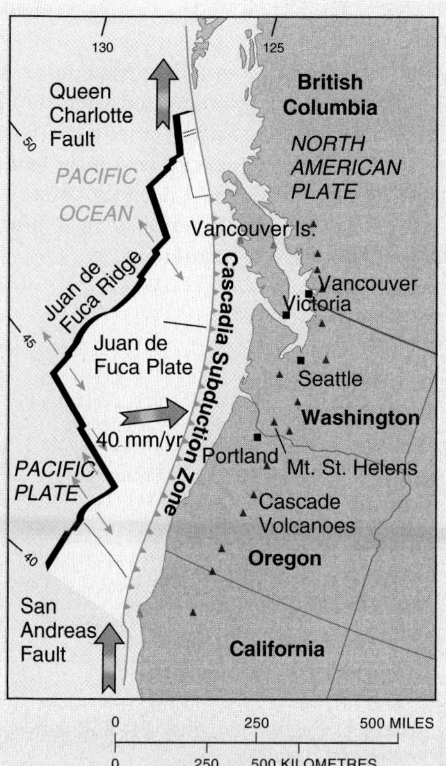

FIGURE 1 Plate tectonic setting of western North America. The Juan de Fuca plate is currently being subducted beneath the North American continent; the convergent plate boundary is indicated by the Cascadia subduction zone along the eastern margin of the Juan de Fuca plate. The blue arrow indicates the movement of this plate. A divergent plate boundary (indicated by green arrows) marks the western margin of the Juan de Fuca plate. This region is characterized by active volcanism and seismic activity. The San Andreas Fault–Queen Charlotte fault lies adjacent to the coastline of western North America. Blue arrows indicate movement along this fault. Seismic activity along this fault produces infrequent, large-magnitude (megathrust) earthquakes. [Used by permission of the Minister of Public Works and Government Services Canada; Natural Resources Canada, Geological Survey of Canada.]

unusual in that instruments record few small (low magnitude) earthquakes, and infrequent large magnitude events (Figure 2). A magnitude 7.3 earthquake that occurred in June 1946 on central Vancouver Island is the most powerful earthquake recorded in this region of Canada (Figure 3a). The earthquake caused considerable structural damage in communities on Vancouver Island and resulted in two deaths.

Farther north, in a region extending from northern Vancouver Island to Haida Gwaii (Queen Charlotte Islands), the oceanic Pacific plate is sliding northwestward relative to North America at a rate of 6 cm (2.4 in.) per year (Figure 1). The transform boundary separating the Pacific and North American plates is known as the Queen Charlotte fault, the Canadian equivalent of the San Andreas fault. A magnitude 8.1 earthquake, Canada's largest historical earthquake, occurred on this fault in August 1949 (Figure 3b). Limited structural damage in mainland communities such as Prince Rupert resulted.

The Canadian and American governments have established a network of Global Positioning System (GPS) receivers to monitor the motion of the

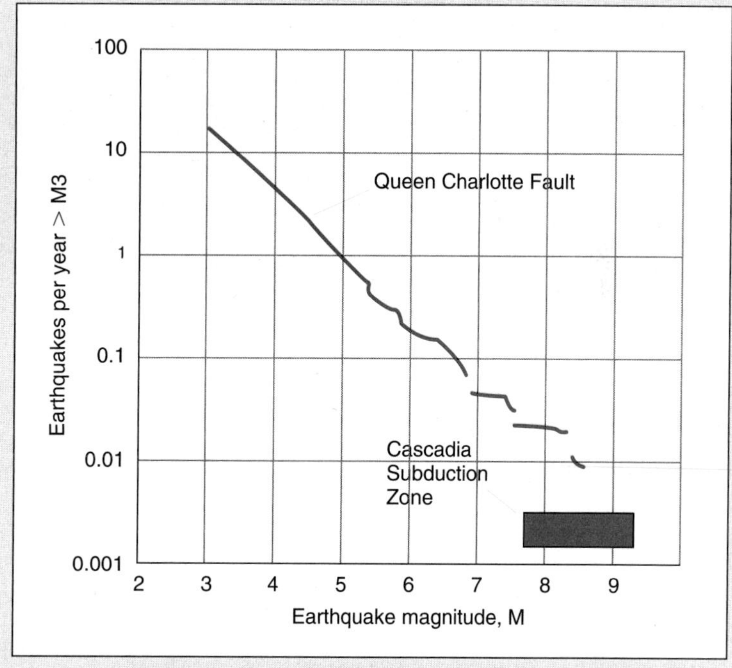

FIGURE 2 Seismic activity in western North America. The nature of seismic activity along the Cascadia subduction zone and the Queen Charlotte fault. Note that seismic activity along the Queen Charlotte fault is characterized by a wide range of intensities—low-magnitude events (M = 3) occur frequently while large-magnitude events (M > 8) rarely occur. In contrast, the Cascadia subduction zone exhibits a distinctly different level of seismic activity characterized by infrequent large-magnitude (M > 8) events. The box (red colour) in the bottom-right corner of the graph indicates that earthquakes in the Cascadia subduction zone exhibit magnitudes in the 8 to 9 range. [Used with permission of the Minister of Public Works and Government Services Canada; Natural Resources Canada, Geological Survey of Canada.]

(continued)

Focus Study 11.1 *(continued)*

Earth's surface in response to compression and shearing occurring along convergent plate boundaries (Cascadia subduction zone) and transform plate boundaries (San Andreas fault–Queen Charlotte fault, which separates the Pacific and North American plates), respectively. The Western Canada Deformation Array (WCDA), a network of eight GPS stations in southwestern British Columbia, is linked to Pacific Northwest Geodetic Array (PANGA), which operates in the northwestern United States. Data from these networks indicate that the Cascadia subduction zone is currently locked (**http://www.pgc.nrcan.gc.ca/geodyn/docs/slip/slip_info_1.html**) and that Vancouver Island is being compressed at a rate of 10 mm per year. Earth scientists believe that the energy currently being stored along the Cascadia subduction zone will be released in a future megathrust earthquake.

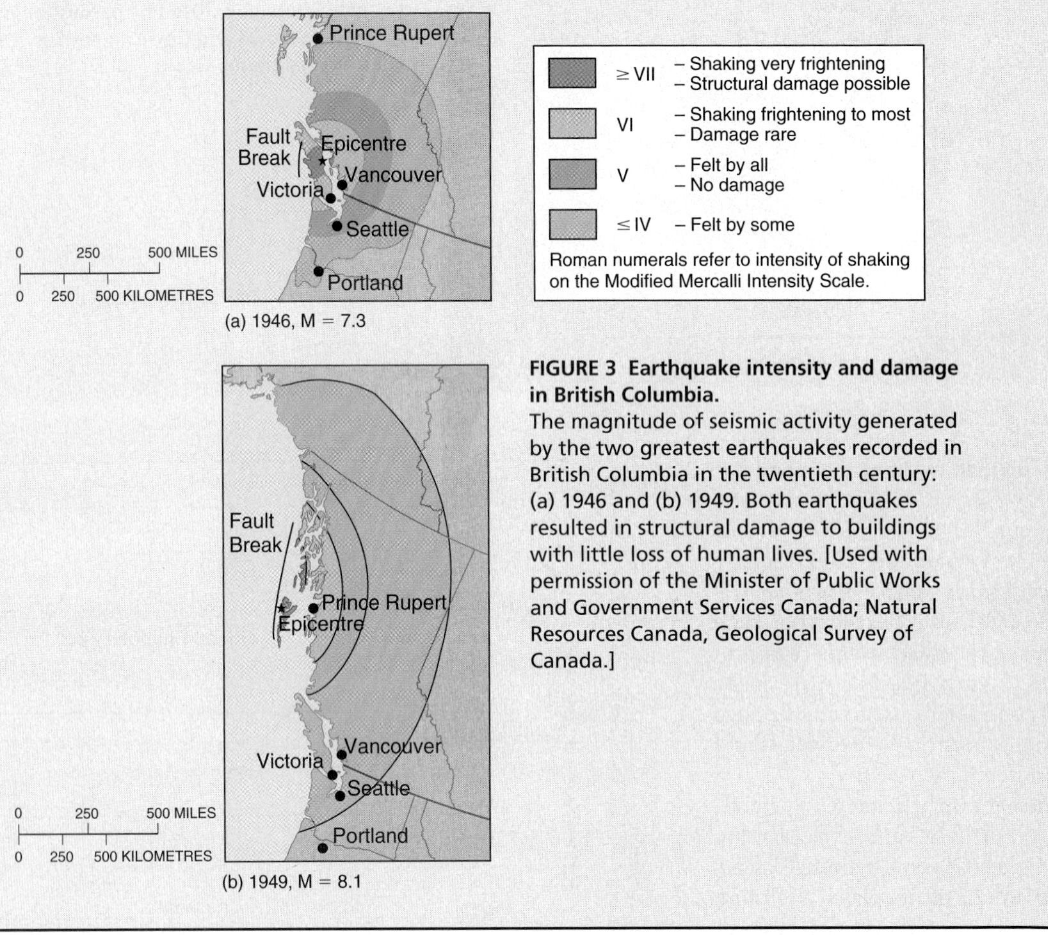

FIGURE 3 Earthquake intensity and damage in British Columbia.
The magnitude of seismic activity generated by the two greatest earthquakes recorded in British Columbia in the twentieth century: (a) 1946 and (b) 1949. Both earthquakes resulted in structural damage to buildings with little loss of human lives. [Used with permission of the Minister of Public Works and Government Services Canada; Natural Resources Canada, Geological Survey of Canada.]

Hot Spots

A dramatic aspect of Earth's internal dynamics is the estimated 50 to 100 **hot spots** across Earth's surface (also shown in Figure 11.22). These are individual sites of upwelling material arriving at the surface in tall plumes from the mantle or rising near the surface producing thermal effects in groundwater and the crust. Some of these sites can be developed for geothermal power (Focus Study 11.2). Hot spots occur beneath both oceanic and continental crust and are anchored deep in the stiff lower mantle, tending to remain fixed relative to migrating plates. Thus, the area of a plate that is above a hot spot is locally heated for the brief geologic time it is there (a few hundred thousand or million years).

The Pacific plate moved across a hot, upward-erupting plume for the last 80 million years, creating a string of volcanic islands stretching northwestward away from the hot spot. This hot spot produced, and continues to form, the Hawaiian-Emperor islands chain (Figure 11.23). Thus, the ages of the islands or seamounts in the chain increase northwestward from the island of Hawai'i, as you can see from the ages marked in the figure. The oldest island in the Hawaiian part of the chain is Kaua'i, approximately 5 million years old; it is weathered, eroded, and deeply etched with canyons and valleys.

To the northwest of this active hot spot in Hawai'i, the island of Midway rises as a part of the same system. From there, the Emperor Seamounts follow northwestward until they reach about 40 million years of age. At that

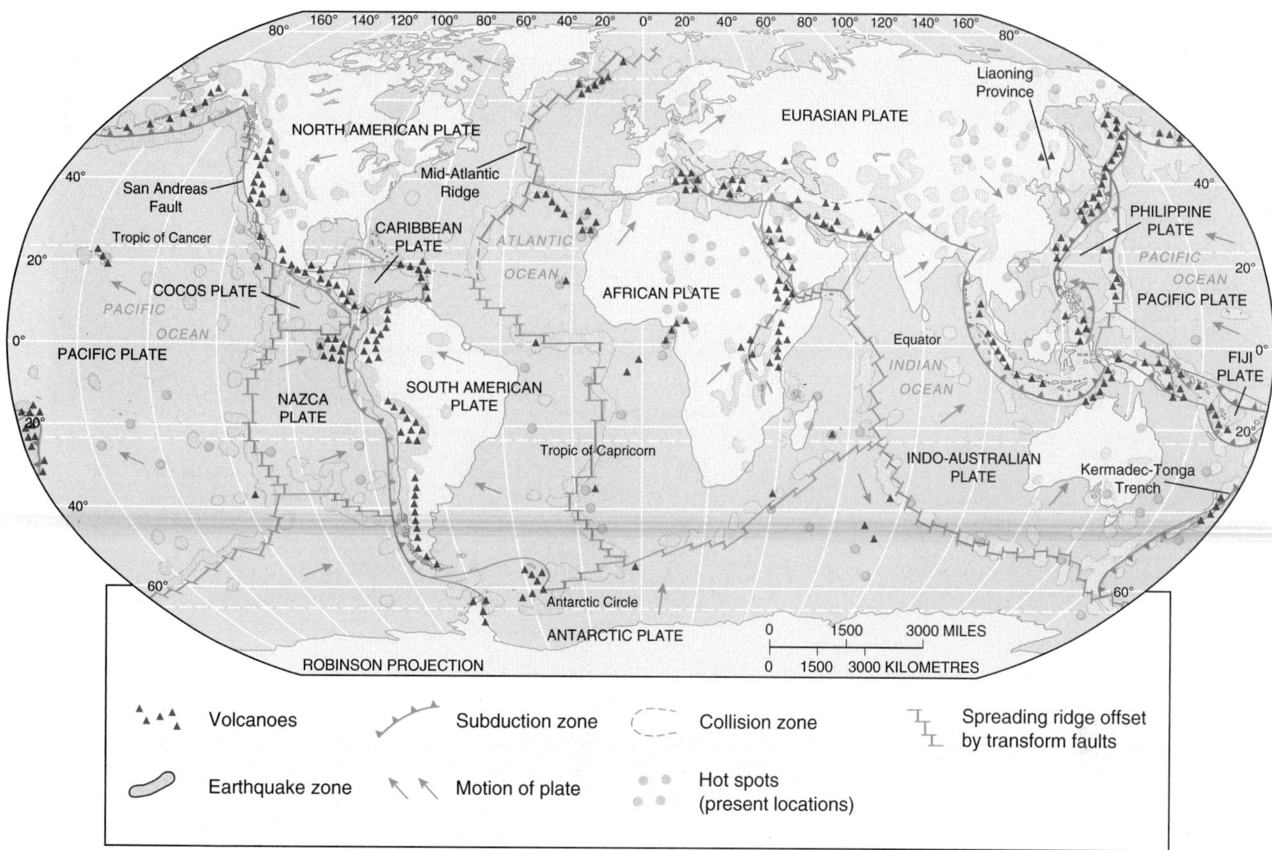

FIGURE 11.22 Earthquake and volcanic activity locations.
Earthquake and volcanic activity in relation to major tectonic plate boundaries and principal hot spots. [Earthquake and volcano data from *Earthquakes*, B. A. Bolt, © 1988 W. H. Freeman and Company; reprinted with permission. Hot spots adapted from USGA data.]

point, this linear island chain shifts direction northward. At the northernmost extreme, the seamounts that formed about 80 million years ago are now approaching the Aleutian Trench, where they eventually will be subducted beneath the Eurasian plate. Perhaps some 80 million years hence, the Hawaiian Islands too will slowly disappear into the trench. Aloha!

The big island of Hawai'i, the newest, actually took less than 1 million years to build to its present stature. The island is a huge mound of lava, melded from several seafloor fissures through five volcanoes, rising from the seafloor 5800 m (19,000 ft) to the ocean surface. From sea level, its highest peak, Mauna Kea, rises to 4205 m (13,796 ft) elevation. This total height of almost 10,000 m (32,800 ft) represents the highest mountain on Earth, if measured from the seafloor. In all, the island of Hawai'i contains about 40,000 km^3 of basalt, enough to cover the states of Massachusetts, Connecticut, and Rhode Island to a depth of 1 km!

The youngest island in the Hawaiian chain is still a seamount, a submarine mountain that does not reach the surface. It rises 3350 m (11,000 ft) from its base but is still 975 m (3200 ft) beneath the ocean surface. Even though this new island will not experience the tropical Sun for about 10,000 years, it is already named Lö'ihi (noted on the map).

Iceland is an example of an active hot spot sitting astride a mid-ocean ridge—visible on the different maps and images of the seafloor (see the chapter-opening photo and Figure 11.15d). It is an excellent example of a segment of mid-ocean ridge rising above sea level. This hot spot has generated enough material to form Iceland and eruptions continue from deep in the mantle. As a result, Iceland is still growing in area and volume. The youngest rocks are near the centre of the island, with rock age increasing toward the eastern and western coasts. This is further evidence that, indeed, Earth is a dynamic planet!

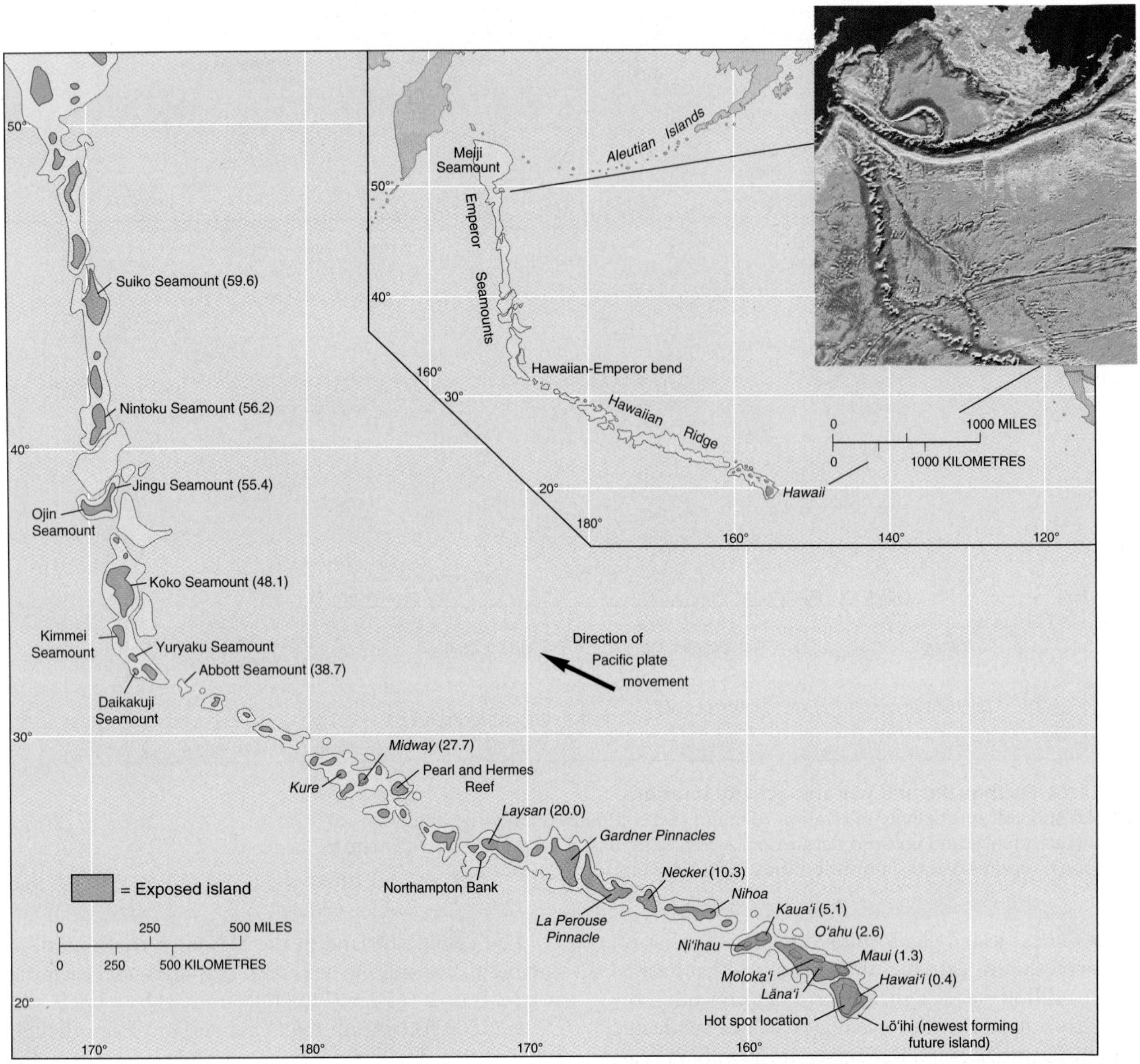

(a)

(b)

FIGURE 11.23 Hot spot tracks across the North Pacific. Hawai'i and the linear volcanic chain of islands known as the Emperor Seamounts. (a) The islands and seamounts in the chain are progressively younger toward the southeast. Ages, in millions of years, are shown in parentheses. Note that Midway Island is 27.7 million years old, meaning that the site was over the plume 27.7 million years ago. (b) Lō'ihi is forming 975 m (3200 ft) beneath the Pacific Ocean; presently an undersea volcano (seamount), it will continue to grow into the next Hawaiian island. This view is from South Point, Hawai'i; Lō'ihi is east of this headland. [(a) After D. A. Clague, "Petrology and K-Ar (Potassium-Argon) Ages of dredged volcanic rocks from the western Hawaiian Ridge and the southern Emperor Seamount chain," *Geological Society of America Bulletin* 86 (1975): 991; inset from global gravity anomaly map image, Scripps Institution of Oceanography. All rights reserved; (b) photo by Bobbé Christopherson.]

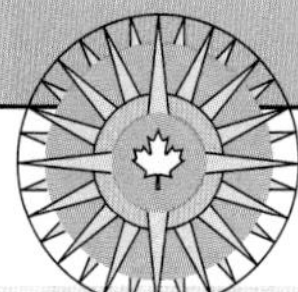

Focus Study 11.2

Heat from Earth—Geothermal Energy and Power

A tremendous amount of endogenic energy flows from Earth's interior toward the surface. Temperatures at the base of Earth's crust range from 200° – 1000°C (392° – 1800°F). Convection and conduction transports this geothermal energy in enormous quantities from the mantle to the crust; yet, geothermal power development is limited in extent to certain locations (Figure 1). Despite such site-specific limitations, applications of geothermal energy for power production are a viable energy source for the present and future.

Geothermal energy is produced when pockets of magma and hot portions of the crust heat groundwater. This energy is transmitted to the surface by heated water or steam accessed through the drilling of wells. For an effective *underground thermal reservoir* to form, an aquifer strata must have high porosity, and high permeability that allows heated water to move freely through connecting pore spaces. (See Figure 9.16 and the accompanying text for illustration and definition of these terms.)

Ideally, this aquifer should heat groundwater to 180° – 350°C (355° – 600°F) and be accessible to drilling within 3 km of the surface, although 6–7 km depths are workable (1.9 mi; 3.7–4.3 mi). Lower temperatures will still produce steam. With drilling costs as a major overhead expense, the shallower the well needed, the better. An impermeable rock strata above the thermal reservoir aquifer helps preserve the resource and describes a *hydrothermal reservoir*, the most common form of thermal repository.

Geothermal energy literally refers to heat from Earth's interior, whereas *geothermal power* relates to specific applied strategies of geothermal electric or geothermal direct applications. *Geothermal electric* uses steam, or hot water that flashes to steam, to drive a turbine-generator. In *geothermal direct*, hot water is used to heat buildings, to cool buildings using a heat exchange system, to heat greenhouses, to heat soil, for manufacturing processes, for aquaculture, and to heat swimming pools, among many uses.

For either electrical production or direct use, the end-use facilities must be fairly near the well head because of heat losses in piping the hot water or steam over distance. Of course, once electricity is generated, it can feed into the regional power grid for transmission to distant markets.

The first geothermal electrical generating station was built in Larderello, Italy, in 1904, and it has been in continuous operation since 1913 with an installed capacity of 360 MWe (megawatts electric). Today, geothermal applications are in use in 30 countries, through some 200 plants, producing an output of 8000 MWe and direct heat of 12,000 MWt (megawatts thermal). In Reykjavík, Iceland, 87% of space heating and 18% of electrical production is geothermal. The Svartsengi power plant (40 MWe) on the Reykjavík

(a)

(b)

FIGURE 1 Surface geothermal activity in Yellowstone and Iceland. (a) Yellowstone is the most famous national park that contains thermal features. Approximately 10,000 geysers, mudpots, and hot springs are evidence of molten pockets of heat in an unstable crust. This geothermal resource area crosses park boundaries to the north into Montana. A controversy involving development of those thermal aquifers and the possible changes that development might produce inside the national park is being debated. (b) This is the original Geysir, in Haukadalur, Iceland, from which we derive the name for all other geysers on Earth; historical accounts of Geysir's activity date back to A.D. 1294. [Photos by (a) Robert W. Christopherson; (b) Bobbé Christopherson.]

(continued)

Focus Study 11.2 *(continued)*

Peninsula is an example of such a modern facility (Figure 2). In the same area, a large array of wells collects heat from hot water that pumps to the city for geothermal direct applications.

In the Paris Basin, France, some 25,000 residences are heated using geothermal direct 70°C (158°F) water. In the Philippines almost 30% of total electrical production is generated with geothermal energy. The top six countries for installed geothermal electrical generation are the United States (2850 MWe), Philippines (1848 MWe), Italy (769 MWe), Mexico (743 MWe), Indonesia (590 MWe), and Japan (530 MWe). Worldwide potential is estimated to be in excess of 80,000 MWe and hundreds of thousands of MWt.

Other than the limiting factors of site-specific production and the locational aspect of having the power plant or end use near the well, there are several other considerations with which to deal: (1) Although fuel costs are low, equipment costs and maintenance are high due to mineral deposition on piping and equipment. (2) Corrosion of metal alloys, principally by sulphide and chloride compounds, is an ongoing problem. (3) Depending on how the resource is maintained, loss of aquifer pressure and lowering groundwater levels can reduce production after a decade or so, requiring new wells to be sunk into the thermal reservoir. And (4), local pollution from water discharges, localized fog formation, and some winter icing may pose some difficulties.

An important mitigation that can extend thermal reservoir potential is re-injection of water into the heat-bearing aquifer. This process can help dispose of surface wastewaters. In some locations reclaimed water (grey water) is used for re-injection. The Geysers in northern California, presently the world's largest-capacity geothermal electrical generation installation, uses this re-injection of wastewater.

The Geysers Geothermal Field (the name despite the lack of any geysers in the area) began production in 1960, increased to a peak in 1989 at 1967 MWe, and lowered to a present capacity of 1070 MWe (Figure 3). By the mid-1990s some 600 wells had been drilled. The average well depth is 2500 m (8200 ft). Declining production relates to the expected problems of decreased yields. The Geysers are operating below the capacity of the field potential at the time of this writing.

Some 2800 MWe of geothermal power capacity is operating in California, Hawai'i, Nevada, and Utah. Figure 4 maps low-, medium-, and high-temperature known geothermal resource areas (KGRA) in the United States. About 300 cities are within 8 km (5 mi) of a KGRA. The U.S.

FIGURE 2 Svartsengi geothermal power plant. On the Reykjavík Peninsula, southwest of Iceland's capital, the Svartsengi power plant produces electricity and provides hot water for homes and businesses. The plant's name means "Black Meadow," referring to the extensive lava beds throughout this region of Iceland. Pipelines carry the hot water into towns for radiant space heating and to the nearby Blue Lagoon spa. [Photo by Bobbé Christopherson.]

FIGURE 3 The Geysers Geothermal Field, California. The Geysers is the largest geothermal electric installation in the world. One of the 21 generating stations is Eagle Rock, Unit 11, with a 73-MWe capacity, in commercial operation since 1975. [Photo courtesy of Calpine, San Jose, California, http://www.geysers.com.]

Department of Energy has identified about 9000 potential development sites. In Canada, a proposed project at Mount Meager, B.C., will produce electricity; geothermal direct heats buildings at Carleton University, Ottawa; and some direct operations are in process in Nova Scotia.

As with other non–fossil fuel, potentially renewable energy resources, energy industry politics plays a role in the slow implementation of geothermal power. In times past, the price of geothermal steam was coupled with fossil fuel prices, so events completely unrelated to geothermal power could dictate its competitive stance. Apparently the potential of heat from Earth will have to wait a little longer to become a more significant player. (For more information see **http://www.eere.energy.gov/geothermal/**, or **http://geothermal.marin.org/**, or **http://www.geothermal.org/**, or **http://www.smu.edu/geothermal/**.)

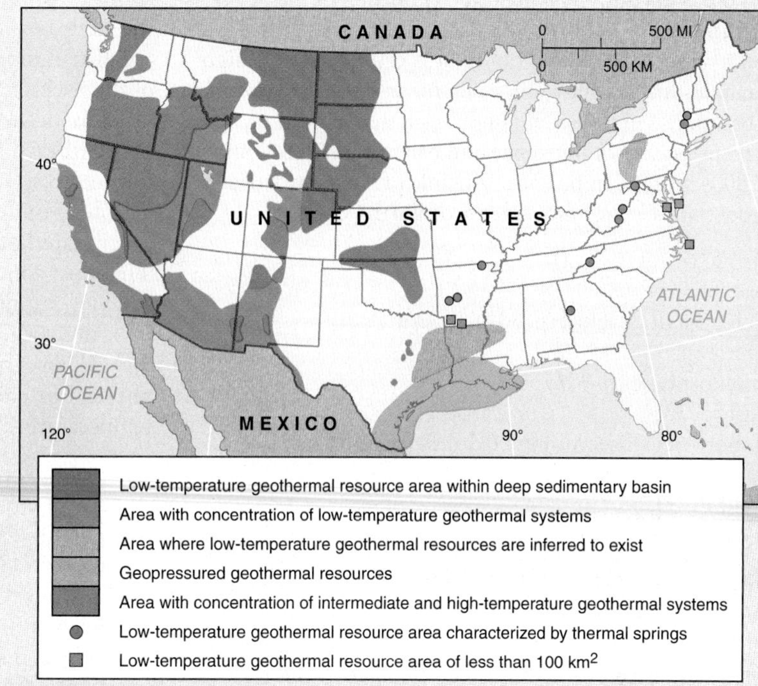

FIGURE 4 Geothermal resources.
Geothermal resources in the conterminous United States. [Map courtesy of USGS, from W. A. Duffield, J. H. Sass, and M. L. Sorey, *Tapping the Earth's Natural Heat*, USGS Circular 1125, 1994, p. 35.]

Summary and Review—The Dynamic Planet

● ***Distinguish*** **between the endogenic and exogenic systems,** ***determine*** **the driving force for each, and** ***explain*** **the pace at which these systems operate.**

The Earth–atmosphere interface is where the **endogenic system** (internal), powered by heat energy from within the planet, interacts with the **exogenic system** (external), powered by insolation and influenced by gravity. These systems work together to produce Earth's diverse landscape. The **geologic time scale** is an effective device for organizing the vast span of geologic time. It depicts the sequence of Earth's events (relative time) and the approximate actual dates (absolute time).

The most fundamental principle of Earth science is **uniformitarianism**. Uniformitarianism assumes that the *same physical processes active in the environment today have been operating throughout geologic time.*

endogenic system (p. 329)
exogenic system (p. 329)
geologic time scale (p. 332)
uniformitarianism (p. 332)

1. To what extent is Earth's crust active at this time in its history?
2. Define the endogenic and the exogenic systems. Describe the driving forces that energize these systems.
3. How is the geologic time scale organized? What is the basis for the time scale in relative and absolute terms?
4. Contrast uniformitarianism and catastrophism as models for Earth's development.

● ***Diagram*** **Earth's interior in cross section and** ***describe*** **each distinct layer.**

We have learned about Earth's interior from indirect evidence—the way its various layers transmit **seismic waves**. The **core** is differentiated into an inner core and an outer core—divided by a transition zone. Earth's magnetic field is generated almost entirely within the outer core. Polarity reversals in Earth's magnetism are recorded in cooling magma that contains iron minerals. The patterns of **geomagnetic reversal** frozen in rock help scientists piece together the story of Earth's mobile crust.

Beyond Earth's core lies the **mantle**, differentiated into lower mantle and upper mantle. It experiences a gradual temperature increase with depth and a stiffening due to increased pressures. The upper mantle is divided into three fairly distinct layers. The uppermost mantle, along with the crust, makes up the *lithosphere*. Below the lithosphere is the **asthenosphere**, or *plastic layer*. It contains pockets of increased heat from radioactive decay and is susceptible to slow convective currents in these hotter materials. An important internal boundary between the **crust** and the high-velocity portion of the uppermost mantle is the **Mohorovičić discontinuity**, or Moho. *Continental crust* is basically granite; it is crystalline and high in silica, aluminum, potassium, calcium, and sodium. *Oceanic crust* is basalt; it is granular and high in silica, magnesium, and iron. The principles of buoyancy and balance were combined in the 1800s into the important principle of **isostasy**. Isostasy explains certain vertical movements of Earth's crust.

seismic waves (p. 334)
core (p. 334)
geomagnetic reversal (p. 334)
mantle (p. 335)
asthenosphere (p. 336)
crust (p. 336)
Mohorovičić discontinuity (Moho) (p. 337)
granite (p. 337)
basalt (p. 337)
isostasy (p. 337)

5. Make a simple sketch of Earth's interior, label each layer, and list the physical characteristics, temperature, composition, and range of size of each on your drawing.
6. Briefly describe the evidence for changes in the Earth's magnetic field.
7. Describe the asthenosphere. Why is it also known as the plastic layer? What are the consequences of its convection currents?
8. What is a discontinuity? Describe the principal discontinuities within Earth.
9. Define isostasy and isostatic rebound, and explain the crustal equilibrium concept.
10. Diagram the uppermost mantle and crust. Label the density of the layers in kilograms per cubic metre. What two types of crust were described in the text in terms of rock composition?

● *Illustrate* the geologic cycle and *relate* the rock cycle and rock types to endogenic and exogenic processes.

The **geologic cycle** is a model of the internal and external interactions that shape the crust. A **mineral** is an inorganic natural compound having a specific chemical formula and possessing a crystalline structure. A **rock** is an assemblage of minerals bound together (such as granite, a rock containing three minerals), or it may be a mass of a single mineral (such as rock salt). Thousands of different rocks have been identified.

The geologic cycle comprises three cycles: the *hydrologic cycle*, the *tectonic cycle*, and the **rock cycle**. The rock cycle describes the three principal rock-forming processes and the rocks they produce. **Igneous rocks** form from **magma**, which is molten rock beneath the surface. Magma is fluid, highly gaseous, and under tremendous pressure. It either *intrudes* into crustal rocks, cools, and hardens, or it *extrudes* onto the surface as **lava**. Intrusive igneous rock that cools slowly in the crust forms a **pluton**. The largest pluton form is a **batholith**.

The cementation, compaction, and hardening of sediments into **sedimentary rocks** is called **lithification**. These layered strata form important records of past ages. **Stratigraphy** is the study of the sequence (superposition), thickness, and spatial distribution of strata that yield clues to the age and origin of the rocks.

Clastic sedimentary rocks are derived from the fragments of weathered rocks. Chemical sedimentary rocks are not formed from physical pieces of broken rock, but instead are dissolved minerals, transported in solution, and chemically precipitated out of solution (they are essentially nonclastic). The most common chemical sedimentary rock is **limestone**, which is lithified calcium carbonate, $CaCO_3$.

Any rock, either igneous or sedimentary, may be transformed into a **metamorphic rock**, by going through profound physical or chemical changes under pressure and increased temperature.

geologic cycle (p. 338)
mineral (p. 338)
rock (p. 340)
rock cycle (p. 342)
igneous rock (p. 342)
magma (p. 342)
lava (p. 342)
pluton (p. 342)
batholith (p. 342)
sedimentary rock (p. 344)
lithification (p. 344)
stratigraphy (p. 345)
limestone (p. 347)
metamorphic rock (p. 347)

11. Illustrate the geologic cycle and define each component: rock cycle, tectonic cycle, and hydrologic cycle.
12. What is a mineral? A mineral family? Name the most common minerals on Earth. What is a rock?
13. Describe igneous processes. What is the difference between intrusive and extrusive types of igneous rocks?
14. Characterize felsic and mafic minerals. Give examples of both coarse- and fine-grained textures.
15. Briefly describe sedimentary processes and lithification. Describe the sources and particle sizes of sedimentary rocks.
16. What is metamorphism, and how are metamorphic rocks produced? Name some original parent rocks and their metamorphic equivalents.

● *Describe* Pangaea and its breakup and *relate* several physical proofs that crustal drifting is continuing today.

The present configuration of the ocean basins and continents are the result of *tectonic processes* involving Earth's interior dynamics and crust. Alfred Wegener coined the phrase **continental drift** to describe his idea that the crust is moved by vast forces within the planet. **Pangaea** was the name he gave to a single assemblage of continental crust some 225 million years ago that subsequently broke apart. Earth's lithosphere is fractured into huge slabs or plates, each moving in response to flowing currents in the mantle. The all-encompassing theory of **plate tectonics** includes **sea-floor spreading** along **mid-ocean ridges** and denser oceanic crust diving beneath lighter continental crust along **subduction zones**.

continental drift (p. 349)
Pangaea (p. 349)
plate tectonics (p. 350)
sea-floor spreading (p. 350)
mid-ocean ridge (p. 350)
subduction zone (p. 350)

17. Briefly review the history of the theory of continental drift, sea-floor spreading, and the all-inclusive plate tectonics theory. What was Alfred Wegener's role?
18. Define upwelling, and describe related features on the ocean floor. Define subduction and explain the process.
19. What was Pangaea? What happened to it during the past 225 million years?
20. Characterize the three types of plate boundaries and the actions associated with each type.

- ***Portray* the pattern of Earth's major plates and *relate* this pattern to the occurrence of earthquakes, volcanic activity, and hot spots.**

Occurrences of often-damaging earthquakes and volcanoes are correlated with plate boundaries. Three types of plate boundaries form: divergent, convergent, and transform. Along the offset portions of mid-ocean ridges, horizontal motions produce **transform faults**.

As many as 50 to 100 **hot spots** exist across Earth's surface, where tall plumes of magma, anchored in the lower mantle, remain fixed as drifting plates are penetrated by eruptions. **Geothermal energy** literally refers to heat from Earth's interior, whereas *geothermal power* relates to specific applied strategies of geothermal electric or geothermal direct applications.

transform faults (p. 357)
hot spots (p. 360)
geothermal energy (p. 363)

21. What is the relation between plate boundaries and volcanic and earthquake activity? How is this activity manifested along the Pacific Coast of Canada?
22. What is the nature of motion along a transform fault? Name a famous example of such a fault.

Critical Thinking

A. Using the maps in this chapter, determine your present location relative to Earth's crustal plates. Now, using Figure 11.18b, approximately identify where your present location was 225 million years ago; express it in a rough estimate using the equator and the longitudes noted on the map.

B. Relative to the motion of the Pacific plate shown in Figure 11.23 (note the scale in lower-left corner), the island of Midway formed 27.7 million years ago over the hot spot that is active under the southeast coast of the big island of Hawai'i today. Given the scale of the map, roughly determine the average annual speed of the Pacific plate in cm per year for Midway to have travelled this distance.

In December 2004, the diving India plate megathrusted beneath the Burma plate off the island of Sumatra in Indonesia with such force that Earth tilt and rotation rate were slightly affected. The resulting magnitude 9.3 quake triggered a devastating tsunami (seismic sea wave) that hit Southeast Asia and travelled across the Indian Ocean striking India, Sri Lanka, and the coast of East Africa. The human death toll exceeded 150,000, with many thousands more at risk from post-event disease. Check this subduction plate boundary on Figure 11.19 and locate it on the chapter-opening map. Such is the drama covered in physical geography.

Volcanic eruptions pose threats to life and property to those who live in proximity to the hazard. Earth systems science is providing analysis and warnings to affected populations as never before. For instance, scientists are closely monitoring the growing bulge on the western flanks of the South Sister volcano in central Oregon. And, now in its third decade of eruption, the outpouring of lava from Kīlauea volcano, Hawai'i, continues to amaze both scientists and tourists. Note the Internet links in this chapter and the wealth of information that is readily available so that the public is kept up to date on these and other hazards.

Such tectonic activity has repeatedly deformed, recycled, and reshaped Earth's crust during its 4.6-billion-year existence, sometimes in dramatic episodes. The principal tectonic and volcanic zones lie along plate boundaries. The arrangement of continents and oceans, the origin of mountain ranges, topography, and the locations of earthquake and volcanic activity are all the result of dynamic Earth processes.

In this chapter: We examine processes that construct Earth's surface and create world structural regions. Tectonic processes deform, recycle, and reshape Earth's crust. These processes occur sometimes in dramatic episodes but most often in slow, deliberate

(a)

(b)

(c)

FIGURE 12.1 Earthquakes strike Iran, Alaska, and Taiwan. (a) Captured in 1-m resolution, the mud-brick and straw buildings in a section of Bam, Iran, lay in ruins, levelled by a magnitude 6.9 quake. The buildings look as if they were smudged and blurred by some giant thumb. (b) A magnitude 7.9 earthquake struck central Alaska, 66 km (41 mi) southeast of Denali National Park. A portion of the Trans-Alaska oil pipeline was knocked off its supports. (c) A 1999 earthquake caused damage in Chi-Chi, Nantou County, Taiwan, and killed over 2000 people, leaving 100,000 homeless. Because of extensive instrumentation in the region, a wealth of data on this quake was acquired for analysis. Damage to this dam and Shihkang reservoir and other building failures were severe. [Image by (a) *IKONOS* satellite, used by permission Space Imaging, Inc.; photos (b) and (c) Earthquake Engineering Research Institute.]

motions that build the landscape. Continental crust has been forming throughout most of Earth's 4.6-billion-year existence. The arrangement of continents and oceans, the origin of mountain ranges, the topography of the land and the seafloor, and the locations of earthquake and volcanic activity are all evidence of our dynamic Earth. Principal seismic and volcanic zones occur along plate boundaries and hot spot locations, thus linking plate tectonics to the devastation of major earthquakes and local threats of major volcanic eruptions and their attendant potential global climatic impact.

We begin our look at tectonics and volcanism on the ocean floor, hidden from direct view. The illustration that opens this chapter is a striking representation of Earth with its blanket of water and ice removed, as revealed to us through decades of direct and indirect observation. Careful examination of this portrait gives us a helpful review of the concepts learned in the previous chapter, laying the foundation for this and subsequent chapters. Be sure to take the quick tour presented with this chapter-opening map. Try to correlate this sea-floor illustration with the maps of crustal plates and plate boundaries shown in Figure 11.19 and the gravity anomaly image in Figure 11.20.

Earth's Surface Relief Features

Relief refers to vertical elevation differences in the landscape. Examples include the low relief of Nebraska and Saskatchewan, medium relief in foothills along mountain ranges, and high relief in the Rockies and Himalayas. The undulating form of Earth's surface, including its relief, is called **topography**, portrayed so effectively on topographic maps—the lay of the land.

The relief and topography of Earth's landforms played a vital role in human history: High mountain passes both protected and isolated societies, ridges and valleys dictated transportation routes, and vast plains necessitated developing faster methods of communication and travel. Earth's topography has stimulated human invention and spurred adaptation.

Crustal Orders of Relief

Today's computer capabilities and tools such as the global positioning system (GPS) for determining location and elevation have enhanced our understanding of Earth's relief and topography. Scientists put elevation data in digital form; the data then are available for computer manipulation and display. The resulting *digital elevation models* (*DEMs*) aid in the scientific analysis of topography, area-altitude distributions, slopes, and local stream-drainage characteristics.

For convenience of description, geographers group the landscape's topography into three *orders of relief*. These orders classify landscapes by scale, from vast ocean basins and continents down to local hills and valleys.

First Order of Relief The first order of relief is the coarsest level of landforms, including huge continental platforms and ocean basins. **Continental landmasses** are the masses of crust that reside above or near sea level, including the undersea continental shelves along the coastlines. The **ocean basins** are entirely below sea level and are portrayed in the chapter-opening illustration. Approximately 71% of Earth is covered by water.

Second Order of Relief The second order of relief is the intermediate level of landforms, for both continental and ocean-basin features. Continental features in the second order of relief include mountain masses, plains, and lowlands. A few examples are the Alps, Canadian and American Rockies, west Siberian lowland, and Tibetan Plateau. The great rock cores ("shields") that form the heart of each continental mass are of this second order. In the ocean basins, second order of relief includes continental rises, slopes, abyssal plains, mid-ocean ridges, submarine canyons, and oceanic trenches (subduction zones)—all visible in the sea-floor illustration that opens this chapter.

Third Order of Relief The third and most-detailed order of relief includes individual mountains, cliffs, valleys, hills, and other landforms of smaller scale. These features are identifiable as local landscapes.

Hypsometry Figure 12.2 is a *hypsographic curve* (from the Greek *hypsos* meaning "height") that shows the distribution of Earth's surface by area and elevation in relation to sea level. Relative to Earth's diameter of 12,756 km (7926 mi), the surface is of low relief, only about 20 km (12.5 mi) from highest peak to lowest oceanic trench. For perspective, Mount Everest is 8.8 km (5.5 mi) above sea level and the Mariana Trench is 11 km (6.8 mi) below sea level. Note the new GPS measurement for the summit of Mount Everest announced in November 1999—8850 m (29,035 ft). See News Report 12.1 for more on this geographic milestone.

The average elevation of Earth's solid surface is actually under water: –2070 m (–6790 ft) below mean sea level. The average elevation for exposed land is only +875 m (+2870 ft). For the ocean depths, average elevation is –3800 m (−12,470 ft). From this description you can see that, on the average, the oceans are much deeper than continental regions are high. Overall, the underwater ocean basins, ocean floor, and submarine mountain ranges form Earth's largest "landscape."

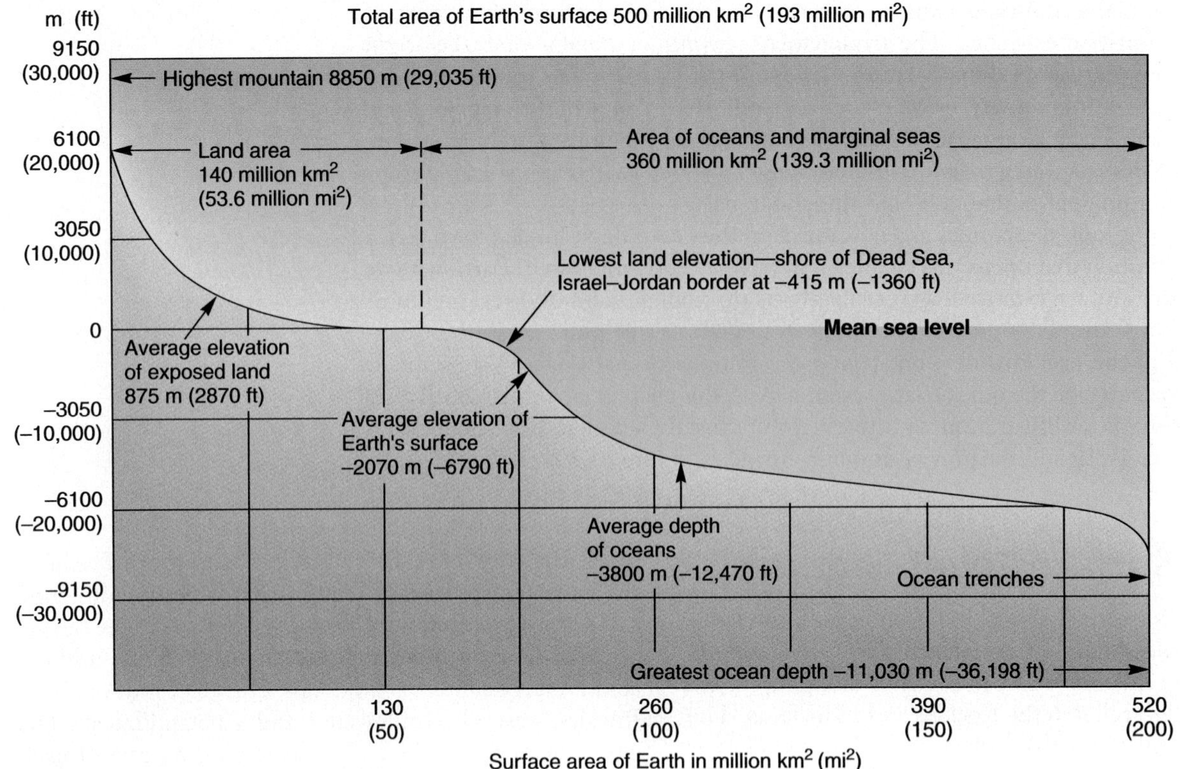

FIGURE 12.2 Earth's hypsometry.
Hypsographic curve of Earth's surface, charting area and elevation as related to mean sea level. From the highest point above sea level (Mount Everest) to the deepest oceanic trench (Mariana Trench), Earth's overall relief is almost 20 km (12.5 mi). The new height given for Mount Everest was announced in November 1999.

News Report 12.1

Mount Everest at New Heights

The announcement came November 11, 1999, in Washington, DC, at the opening reception of the 87th annual meeting of the American Alpine Club. Mount Everest had a new revised elevation, determined by direct Global Positioning System (GPS) placement on the mountain's icy summit!

In May 1999, mountaineers Pete Athans and Bill Crouse reached the summit with five Sherpas. The climbers operated Global Positioning System satellite equipment on the top of Mount Everest and determined the precise height of the world's tallest mountain. In Chapter 1, the photograph in News Report 1.3 shows a GPS unit placed by climber Wally Berg 18 m below the summit in 1998. This site is still Earth's highest benchmark, with a permanent metal marker installed in rock. Other GPS instruments in the region permit differential calibration for exact measurement (Figure 1). This is a continuation of a measurement effort begun in 1995 by Bradford Washburn, renowned mountain photographer/explorer and honorary director of Boston's Museum of Science.

Astronaut Thomas D. Jones made the photo of Mount Everest in Figure 2 during Space Shuttle flight STS-80 in 1996 aboard Space Shuttle *Columbia*. This startling view caught the mountain's triangular East Face bathed in morning light (east is to the lower left, north is to the lower right, south at the upper left; see locator map direction arrow). The North Face is in shadow. Several glaciers are visible flowing outward from the mountains, darkened by rock and debris.

Washburn announced the new measurement of 8850 m (29,035 ft). Everest's new elevation is close to the previous official measure of 8848 m (29,028 ft) set in 1954 by the Survey of India after picking the average measurements from 12 different survey points around the mountain. Washburn stated, "The reading of 29,035 feet (8850 metres) showed no measurable change in the height of Everest calculated since GPS observations began four years ago. But from these GPS readings it appears that the horizontal position of Everest seems to be moving steadily and slightly northeastward; between 3 and 6 mm a year (up to 0.25 in. a year)." The mountain range is being driven farther into Asia by plate tectonics—the continuing collision of Indian and Asian landmasses.

FIGURE 1 GPS installation measures Mount Everest.
A global positioning system (GPS) installation near Namche Bazar in the Khumbu (Everest) region of Nepal. The station is at latitude 27.8° N, longitude 86.7° E, at 3523 m (11,558 ft). The summit of Mount Everest is 30 km (18.6 mi) distant—visible above the right side of the weather dome. A network of such GPS installations correlated with the unit the climbers took to Everest's summit. [Photo by Charles Corfield, science manager to the 1998 and 1999 expeditions.]

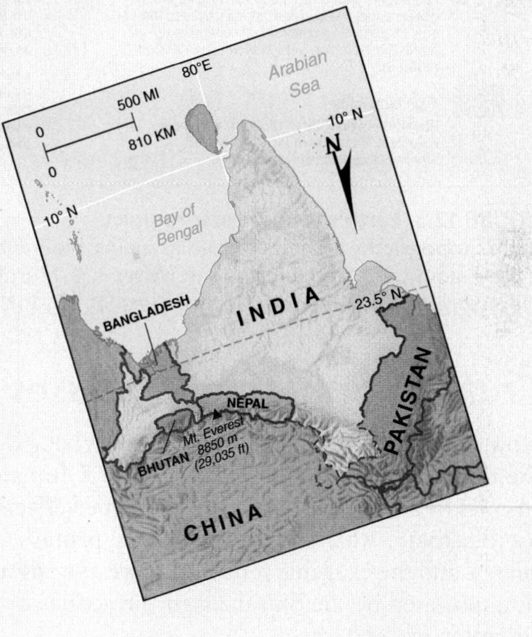

FIGURE 2 Mount Everest in morning light from orbit aboard Space Shuttle *Columbia*. [Photo courtesy of NASA, made by Dr. Thomas Jones, astronaut, 1996 (see Career Link 1.1).]

Earth's Topographic Regions

The three orders of relief can be further generalized into six topographic regions: plains, high tablelands, hills and low tablelands, mountains, widely spaced mountains, and depressions (Figure 12.3). An arbitrary elevation or descriptive limit that is in common use defines each type of topography (see the figure's legend).

Four of the continents possess extensive *plains*, areas with local relief of less than 100 m (325 ft) and slope angles of 5° or less. Some plains have high elevations of more than 600 m (2000 ft); in the United States, the high plains attain elevations above 1220 m (4000 ft). The Colorado Plateau, Greenland, and Antarctica are notable *high tablelands*, with elevations exceeding 1520 m (5000 ft). *Hills* and *low tablelands* dominate Africa.

Mountain ranges, characterized by local relief exceeding 600 m (2000 ft), occur on each continent. Earth's relief and topography are undergoing constant change as a result of processes that form crust.

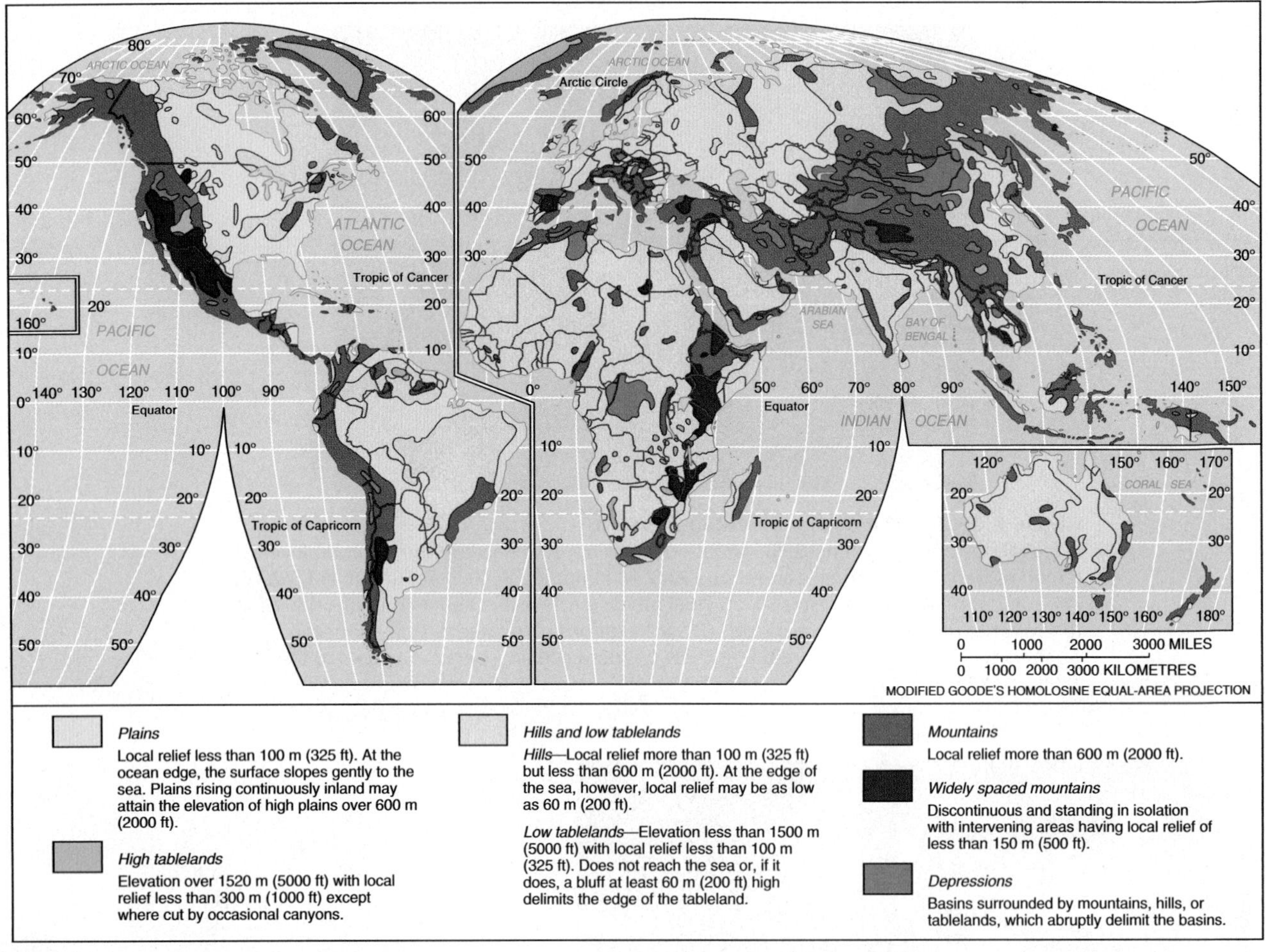

FIGURE 12.3 Earth's topographic regions.
Earth's topography is characterized as plains, high and low tablelands, mountains, widely spaced mountains, and depressions. [After R. E. Murphy, "Landforms of the world," *Annals of the Association of American Geographers* 58, no. 1 (March 1968). Adapted by permission.]

Crustal Formation Processes

How did Earth's continental crust form? What gave rise to the three orders of relief just discussed? Ultimately, the answers to both questions are the combined effects of tectonic activity, which is driven by our planet's internal energy, and the exogenic processes of weathering and erosion, powered by the Sun through the actions of gravity, air, water, ice, and waves.

Tectonic activity generally is slow, requiring millions of years. Endogenic (internal) processes result in gradual uplift and new landforms, with major mountain-building occurring along plate boundaries. These uplifted crustal regions are quite varied, but we think of them in three general categories, all discussed in this chapter:

- Residual mountains and stable continental cratons, formed from inactive remnants of ancient tectonic activity;
- Tectonic mountains and landforms, produced by active folding, faulting, and crustal movements;
- Volcanic features, formed by the surface accumulation of molten rock from eruptions of subsurface materials.

Thus, several distinct processes operate in concert to produce the continental crust we see around us.

Continental Shields

All continents have a nucleus of ancient crystalline rock on which the continent "grows" with the addition of crustal fragments and sediments. This nucleus is the *craton* of the continental crust. Cratons generally have been eroded to a low elevation and relief. Most exceed 2 billion years of age. The lack of basaltic components in these cratons offers a clue to their stability. The lithosphere in cratonic regions (crust and lithospheric uppermost mantle) is thicker than the lithosphere beneath younger portions of continents and oceanic crust.

A **continental shield** is a region where a craton is exposed at the surface. Figure 12.4 shows the principal areas of exposed shields and a photo of the Canadian shield. Layers of sedimentary rock surround these shields (see Figure 11.7) and appear quite stable over time. An example of such a stable *platform* is the region that stretches from east of the Rockies to the Appalachians and northward into central and eastern Canada.

(b)

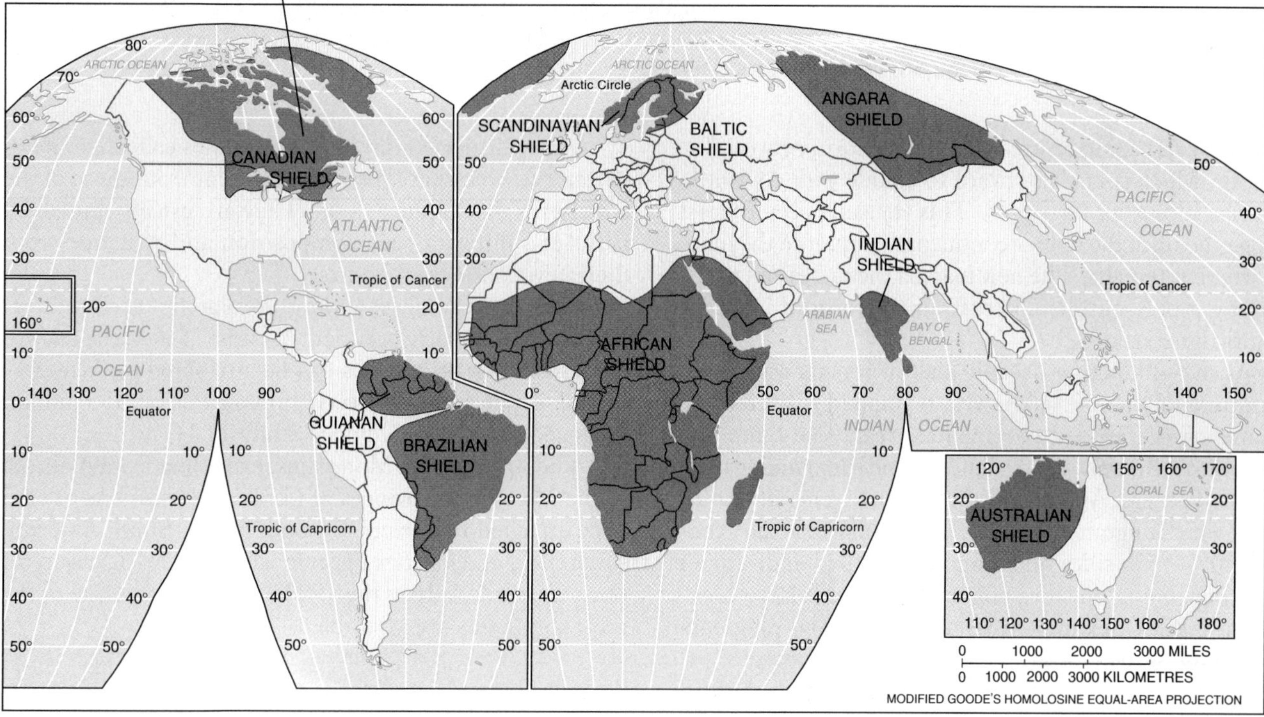

(a)

FIGURE 12.4 Continental shields.
(a) Portions of the major continental shields that have been exposed by erosion. Adjacent portions of these shields remain covered. (b) Canadian shield landscape in central Labrador interior, stable for hundreds of millions of years, stripped by past glaciations, and marked by intrusive igneous dikes (magmatic intrusions). [(a) After R. E. Murphy, "Landforms of the world," *Annals of the Association of American Geographers* 58, no. 1 (March 1968), adapted by permission; (b) photo by John Eastcott/Yva Momatiuk/The Image Works.]

Building Continental Crust and Terranes

The formation of continental crust is complex and takes hundreds of millions of years. It involves the entire sequence of sea-floor spreading and formation of oceanic crust, its later subduction and remelting, and its subsequent rise as new magma, all summarized in Figure 12.5.

To understand this process, study Figure 12.5 (and Figure 11.15). Begin with the magma that originates in the asthenosphere and wells up along the mid-ocean ridges. Basaltic magma is formed from minerals in the upper mantle that are rich in iron and magnesium. Such magma has less than 50% silica and has a low-viscosity (thin) texture—it tends to flow. This mafic material rises

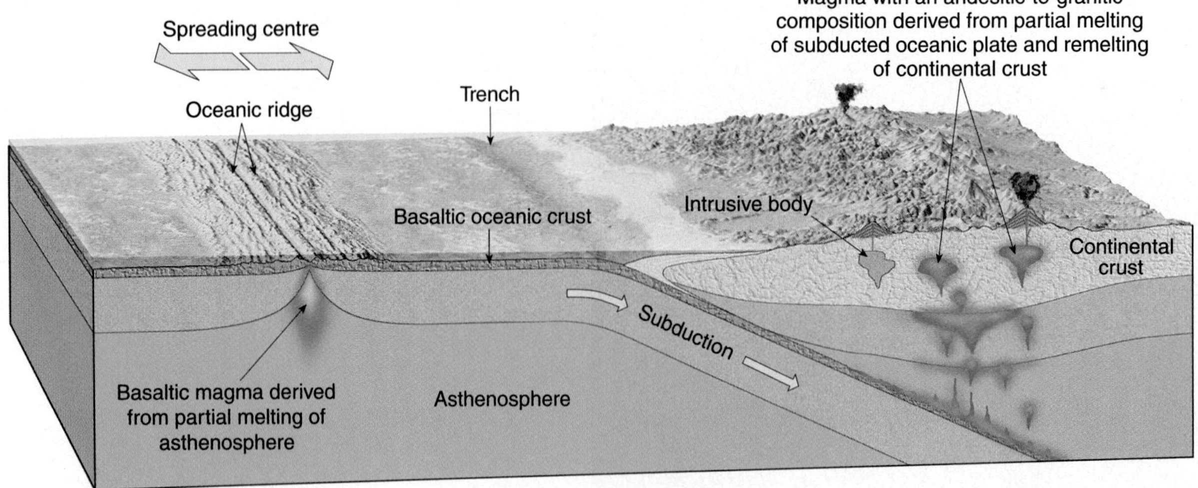

FIGURE 12.5 Crustal formation.
Material from the asthenosphere upwells along sea-floor spreading centres. Basaltic ocean floor is subducted beneath lighter continental crust, where it melts, along with its cargo of sediments, water, and minerals. This melting generates magma, which makes its way up through the crust to form igneous intrusions and extrusive eruptions. [After E. J. Tarbuck and F. K. Lutgens, *Earth, An Introduction to Physical Geology,* 5th ed. (© Prentice Hall, 1996) Figure 20.20, p. 502.]

to erupt at spreading centres and cools to form new basaltic seafloor, which spreads outward to collide with continental crust along its far edges. This denser oceanic crust plunges beneath the lighter continental crust, into the mantle, where it remelts. The new magma then rises and cools, forming more continental crust, in the form of intrusive granitic igneous rock.

As the subducting oceanic plate works its way under a continental plate, it takes with it trapped seawater and sediment from eroded continental crust. The remelting incorporates the seawater, sediments, and surrounding crust into the mixture. As a result, the magma, generally called a *melt,* which migrates upward from a subducted plate, contains 50%–75% silica and aluminum (called andesitic or silicic depending on silica content). The melt has a high-viscosity (thick) texture—it tends to block and plug conduits to the surface.

Bodies of such silica-rich magma may reach the surface in explosive volcanic eruptions, or they may stop short and become subsurface intrusive bodies in the crust, cooling slowly to form granitic crystalline plutons such as batholiths (see Figures 11.9 and 11.10a). Note that this composition is quite different from the magma that rises directly from the asthenosphere at spreading centres. In these processes of crustal formation, you can literally follow the cycling of materials in the tectonic cycle.

Each of Earth's major lithospheric plates actually is a collage of many crustal pieces acquired from a variety of sources. Crustal fragments of ocean floor, curving chains (or arcs) of volcanic islands, and other pieces of continental crust all have been forced against the edges of continental shields and platforms. These slowly migrating crustal pieces, which have become attached or accreted to the plates, are called **terranes** (not to be confused with "terrain," which refers to the topography of a tract of land).

These displaced terranes, sometimes called *microplate* or *exotic terranes,* have histories different from those of the continents that capture them. They are usually framed by faults and differ in rock composition and structure from their new continental homes.

In the region surrounding the Pacific, accreted terranes are particularly prevalent. At least 25% of the growth of western North America can be attributed to the accretion of terranes since the early Jurassic Period, 185 million years ago (Figure 12.6, Focus Study 12.1).

The Appalachian Mountains, extending from Alabama to the Maritime Provinces of Canada, possess bits of land once attached to ancient Europe, Africa, South America, Antarctica, and various oceanic islands. The discovery of terranes, made only in the 1980s, demonstrates one of the ways continents are assembled.

Crustal Deformation Processes

Rocks, whether igneous, sedimentary, or metamorphic, are subjected to powerful stress by tectonic forces, gravity, and the weight of overlying rocks. There are three types of stress: *tension* (stretching), *compression* (shortening), and *shear* (twisting or tearing), as shown in Figure 12.7.

Strain is how rocks respond to stress. Strain is expressed in rocks by *folding* (bending) or *faulting* (breaking). Think of stress as a force and resulting strain as the deformation in the rock. Whether a rock bends or breaks depends on several factors, including composition and how much pressure is on the rock. An important quality is whether the rock is *brittle* or *ductile.* The patterns created by these processes are clearly visible in the landforms we see today, especially in mountain areas. Figure 12.7 illustrates each type of stress and its resulting strain and the surface expressions that develop.

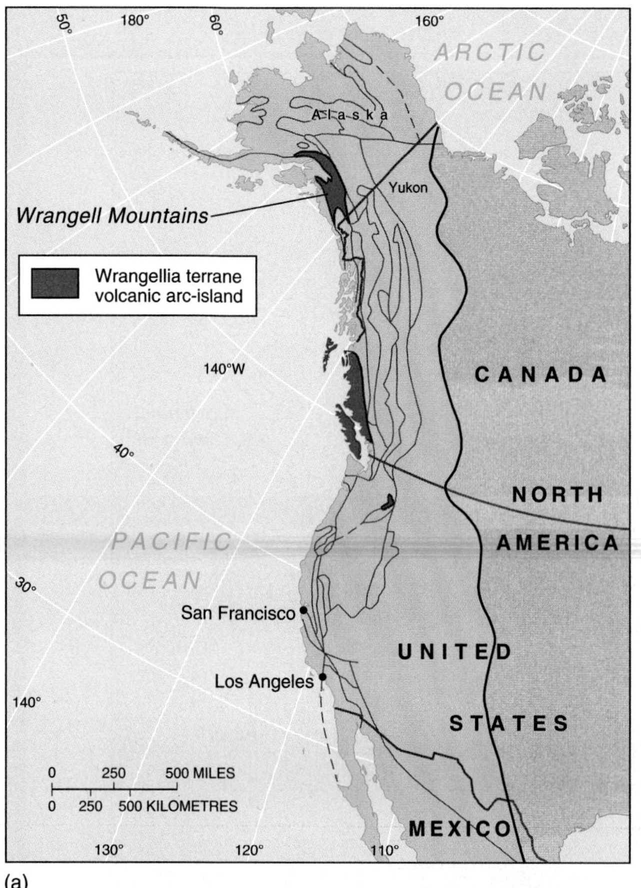

(a)

(b) Wrangell Mountains, Alaska

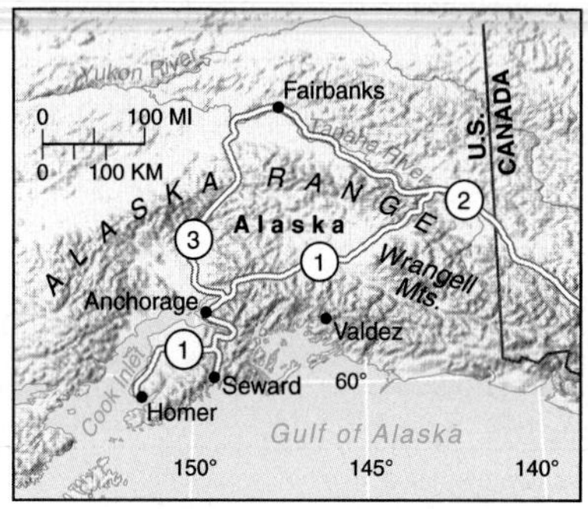

FIGURE 12.6 North American terranes.
The region highlighted in grey indicates the extent of exotic terranes in western North America. (a) Wrangellia terranes, highlighted among the other terranes, occur in four segments. (b) Snow-covered Wrangell Mountains north of the Chugach Mountains in this November 7, 2001, image in east-central Alaska and across the Canadian border. Note Mount McKinley (Denali) at 6194 m (20,322 ft), in upper-left part of the image, north of Cook Inlet, highest elevation in North America. [(a) Based on data from U.S. Geological Survey; (b) *Terra* image from MODIS sensor, courtesy of MODIS Land Rapid Response Team, NASA/GSFC.].

ANIMATION Terrane Formation

Focus Study 12.1

Exotic Terranes in Western Canada

The Western Cordillera is subdivided into five belts that are aligned parallel to the northwest–southeast trend of the Cordillera. Distinctive combinations of bedrock geology and landforms characterize each belt. See Natural Resources Canada Web site http://gsc.nrcan.gc.ca/org/vancouver/index_e.php for more information. These landscapes are dominated by features created during mountain-building events between the early Jurassic (185 m.y.a.) and early Tertiary (50 m.y.a.) periods. Moving from east to west the belts are called the Foreland, Omineca, Intermontane, Coast, and Insular belts (Figure 1).

The Rocky Mountains represent the Foreland Belt. The belt is underlain by an immense thickness of Precambrian and Phanerozoic sedimentary rocks. The rocks were deposited offshore of the old North American craton and, during mountain building between 100 and 55 million years ago, were folded and thrust eastward for at least 150 km onto the edge of the old continent.

The Omineca Belt derives its name from the Omineca Mountains of central British Columbia. This belt also includes the Purcell, Selkirk, Columbia, Monashee, and Cariboo mountain ranges of southern British Columbia. Metamorphic rocks with lesser amounts of granitic rocks dominate the bedrock geology of the Omineca Belt. The metamorphic rocks are complexly folded and faulted, and represent the roots of an ancient mountain chain that formed between 180 and 60 million years ago.

High plateaux and deep river valleys characterize the landscapes of the Intermontane Belt. This belt is under-

(continued)

Focus Study 12.1 *(continued)*

lain by a variety of Paleozoic and Mesozoic volcanic, granitic, and sedimentary rocks.

The presence of volcanic and granitic rocks in the Intermontane Belt, the intense metamorphism of these same rocks represented in the Omineca Belt, and the folding and thrust faulting of sedimentary rocks in the Foreland Belt, together record the initial phase of mountain building (180 to 100 m.y.a.) associated with the accretion of exotic terranes along the western margin of the old North American craton.

The Coast Belt includes the Coast and Cascade Mountains and the Fraser Lowland near the city of Vancouver. Long, deep fjords that were created by glacial erosion during Pleistocene glaciations dissect the mountain ranges. The bedrock consists largely of granite in the form of plutons and batholiths that intrude folded, faulted, and metamorphosed volcanic and sedimentary rocks. The granitic rocks represent the roots of deeply eroded volcanoes that formed at various times throughout the Mesozoic and early Cenozoic eras (170 to 45 m.y.a.).

The Insular Belt includes the mountain ranges on Vancouver Island and Haida Gwaii (Queen Charlotte Islands), as well as the rocks that underlie the continental shelf (Figure 2). This belt is composed of Paleozoic and Mesozoic volcanic and sedimentary rocks that have been intruded by Mesozoic and Cenozoic granitic rocks.

The presence of youthful mountain ranges in both the Insular and Coast Belts underlain by metamorphosed Paleozoic rocks and Mesozoic and Cenozoic granitic intrusions records a second phase of mountain building

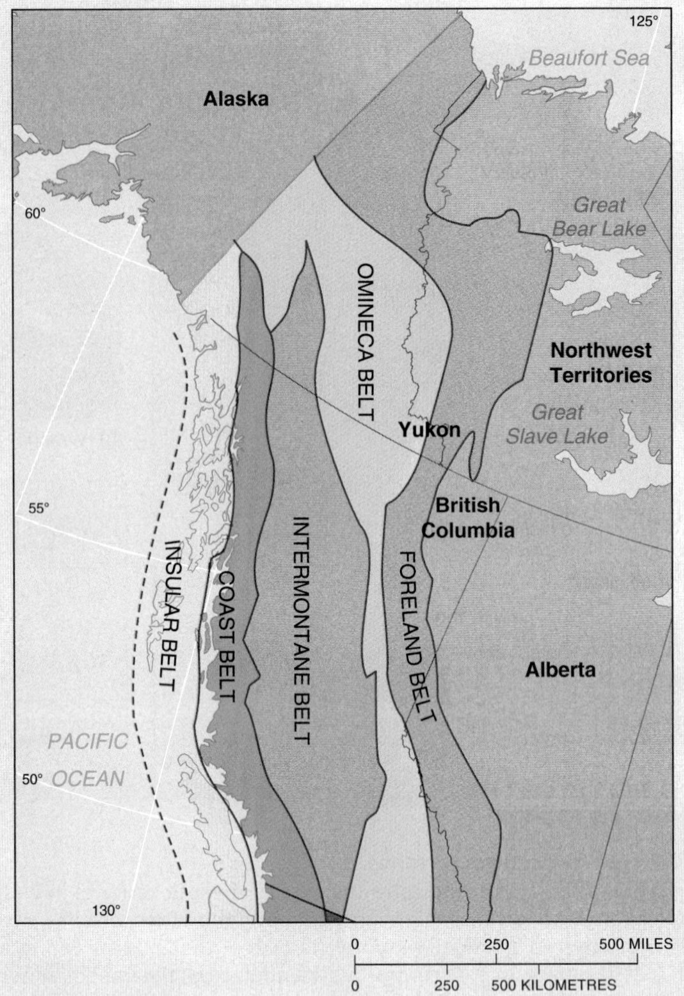

FIGURE 1 Exotic terranes of western Canada, including the five principal geomorphic belts. [Map adapted courtesy of LITHOPROBE Secretariat, The University of British Columbia.]

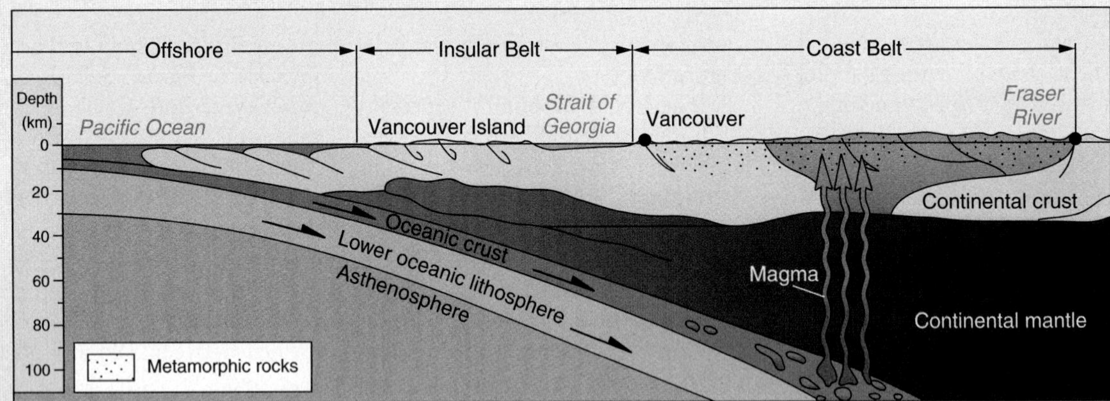

FIGURE 2 Plate tectonic setting of the Cascadia subduction zone. [Map adapted courtesy of LITHOPROBE Secretariat, The University of British Columbia, http://www.lithoprobe.ca.]

(84 to 40 m.y.a.). This phase is associated with the accretion of exotic terranes along the western margin of North America.

The Pacific Ocean floor started to move strongly northward along the margin of the advancing North American plate about 85 million years ago. Portions of the North American plate became coupled with the underlying oceanic plate and started to move northward with it. This movement caused widespread faulting within the Western Cordillera and the displacement of accreted terranes several hundreds of kilometres northward.

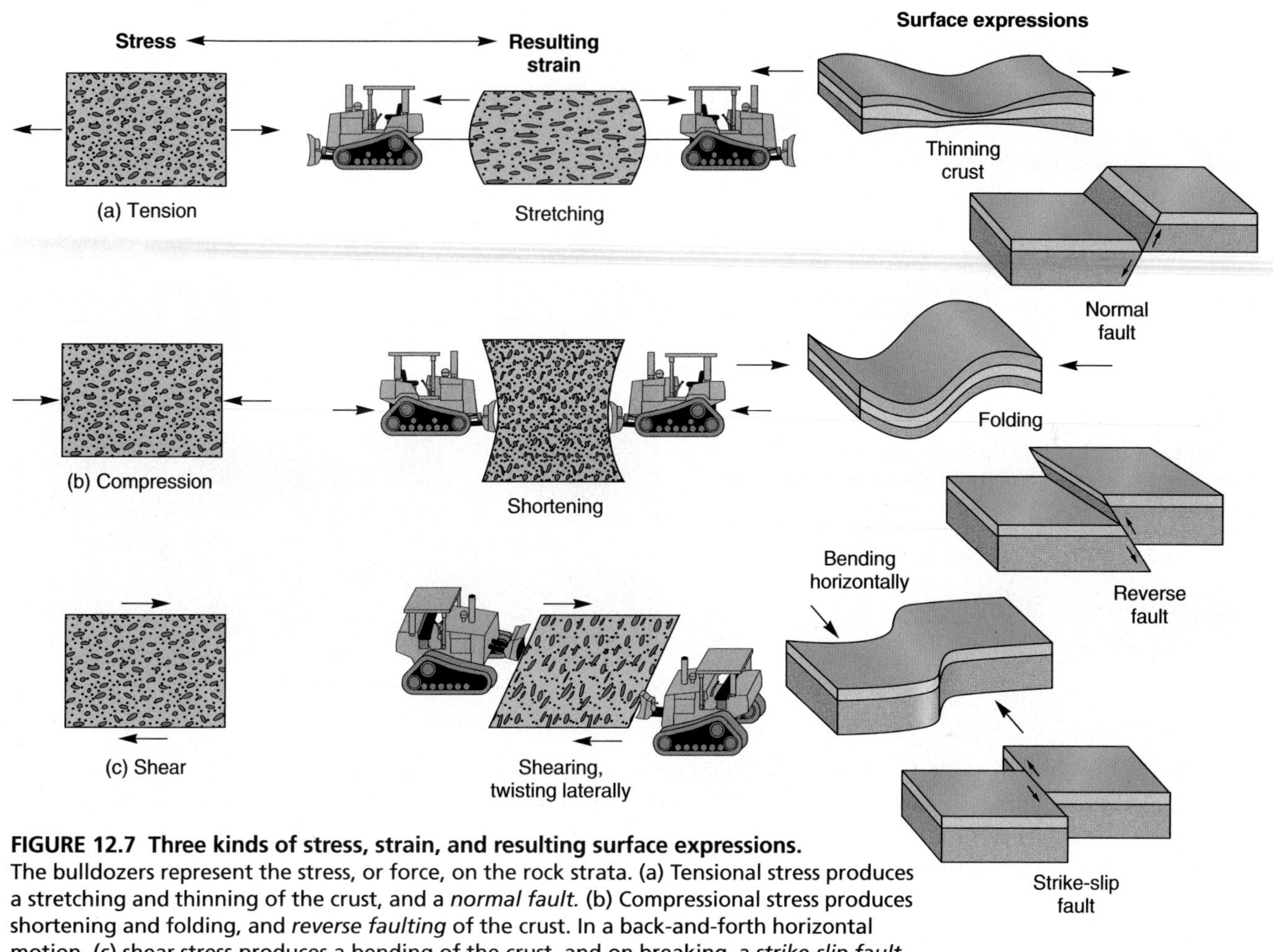

FIGURE 12.7 Three kinds of stress, strain, and resulting surface expressions. The bulldozers represent the stress, or force, on the rock strata. (a) Tensional stress produces a stretching and thinning of the crust, and a *normal fault.* (b) Compressional stress produces shortening and folding, and *reverse faulting* of the crust. In a back-and-forth horizontal motion, (c) shear stress produces a bending of the crust, and on breaking, a *strike-slip fault.*

Folding and Broad Warping

When rock strata that are layered and flat are subjected to compressional forces, they become deformed (Figure 12.8). Convergent plate boundaries intensely compress rocks, deforming them in a process known as **folding**. As an analogy, if we take sections of thick fabric, stack them flat on a table, and then slowly push on opposite ends of the stack, the cloth layers will bend and rumple into folds similar to those shown in Figure 12.8a.

If we then draw a line down the centre axis of a resulting ridge, and a line down the centre of a resulting trough, we are able to see how the names of the folds are assigned. Along the *ridge* of a fold, layers *slope downward away from the axis*, which is called an **anticline**. In the *trough* of a fold, however, layers *slope downward toward the axis*, called a **syncline**.

If the axis of either type of fold is not "level" (horizontal, or parallel to Earth's surface), the fold axis then *plunges* (inclined) at an angle. Knowledge of how folds are angled to Earth's surface and where they are located is important for the petroleum industry. For example, petroleum geologists know that oil and natural gas collect in the upper portions of anticlinal folds in permeable rock layers such as sandstone.

Figure 12.8a further illustrates various folds that have been weathered and reduced by exogenic processes:

- A residual "synclinal ridge" may form within a syncline, because different rock strata offer greater resistance to weathering processes.
- Compressional forces often push folds far enough that they actually overturn upon their own strata ("overturned anticline").

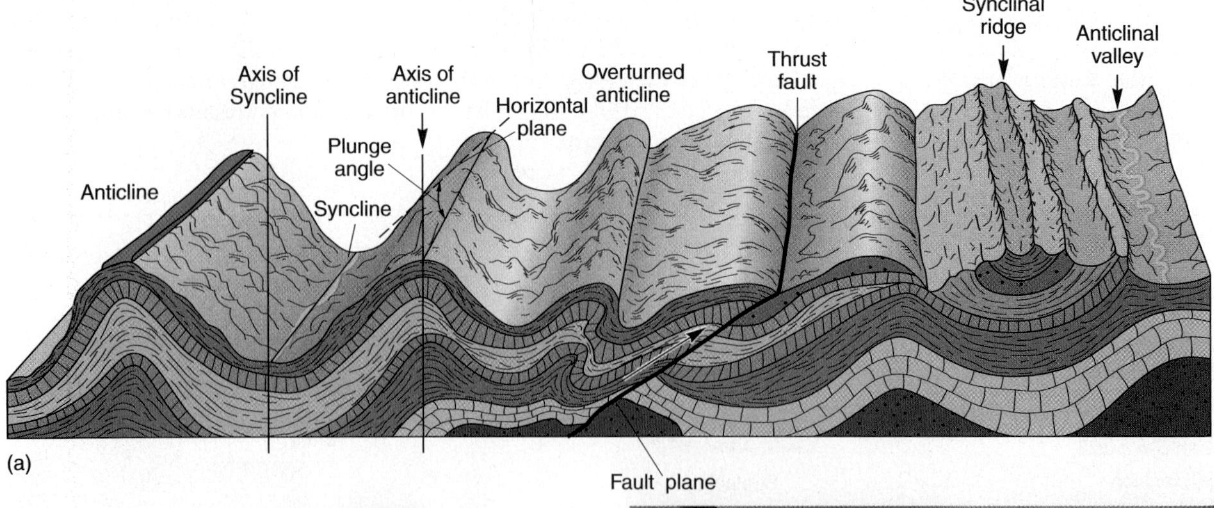

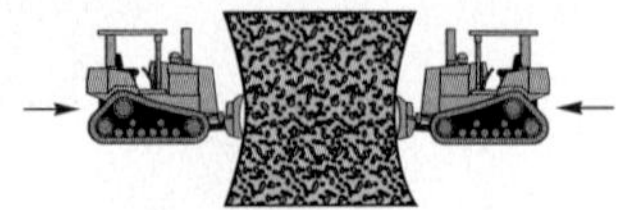

FIGURE 12.8 Folded landscapes.
(a) Folded landscape and the basic types of fold structures. (b) Interbedded limestone and shale strata in the Canadian Rocky Mountains that have been intensely folded in response to compression of the crust. [Photo by Gunter Marx Photography/CORBIS/MAGMA.]

Folds, Anticlines, and Synclines

- Further stress eventually fractures the rock strata along distinct lines, and some overturned folds are thrust upward, causing a considerable shortening of the original strata ("thrust fault").

The Canadian Rocky Mountains, the Appalachian Mountains, and areas of the Middle East illustrate well the complexity of folded landscapes. Satellites allow us to view many of these structures from an orbital perspective, as in Figure 12.9. Just north of the Persian Gulf are the Zagros Mountains of Iran. This area was a dispersed terrane that separated from the Eurasian plate. However, the collision produced by the northward push of the Arabian block is now shoving this terrane back into Eurasia and forming an active margin known as the Zagros crush zone, a zone of continuing collision more than 400 km (250 mi) wide. In the satellite image, anticlines form the parallel ridges; active weathering and erosion processes are exposing the underlying strata.

In addition to the rumpling of rock strata just discussed, broad warping actions also affect Earth's continental crust. These actions produce similar up-and-down bending of strata, but the bends are far greater in extent than those produced by folding. Warping forces include mantle convection, isostatic adjustment such as the weight of previous ice loads across northern Canada, and crustal swelling above an underlying hot spot. Warping features can be small, individual, foldlike structures called basins and domes (Figure 12.10a, b).

In the Queen Elizabeth Islands of Arctic Canada (Figure 12.10e), upwarped domes composed of the evaporite minerals gypsum ($CaSO_4 \cdot 2H_2O$) and anhydrite ($CaSO_4$)—known as *piercement domes*—represent distinctive landforms. The thick evaporite deposits (approximately 400 m) accumulated within a large sedimentary basin during the Carboniferous and Permian periods (approximately 290 m.y.a.). In the middle of the Cenozoic Era, a mountain-building event (Eurekan orogeny) resulted in folding and thrust faulting of the sedimentary rocks. The evaporite rocks were driven upward through the overlying Mesozoic sedimentary rocks (mostly sandstone and shale) to produce the piercement domes. The piercement domes attain heights of several hundreds of metres and diameters up to 10 km.

Faulting

A freshly poured concrete sidewalk is smooth and strong. But stress the sidewalk by driving heavy equipment over it, and the resulting strain might cause a fracture. Pieces on either side of the fracture may move up, down, or hori-

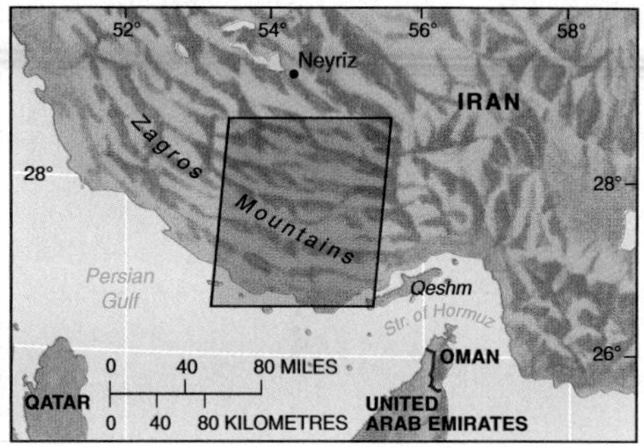

FIGURE 12.9 Folding in the Zagros crush zone, Iran.
The Zagros Mountains are a product of the Zagros crush zone between the Arabian and Eurasian plates. This area was a dispersed terrane (migrating crustal piece) that separated from the Eurasian plate. However, the collision produced by the northward push of the Arabian block is now shoving this terrane back into Eurasia and forming the folded mountains shown. [NASA image.]

zontally, depending on the direction of stress. Similarly, when rock strata are stressed beyond their ability to remain a solid unit, they express the strain as a fracture. Rocks on either side of the fracture are displaced relative to the other side in a process known as **faulting**. Thus, *fault zones* are areas where fractures in the rock demonstrate crustal movement. At the moment of fracture, a sharp release of energy occurs, called an **earthquake** or *quake*.

The fracture surface along which the two sides of a fault move is the *fault plane*. The names of the three basic types of faults, illustrated in Figure 12.11, are based on the tilt and orientation of the fault plane. A normal fault forms when rocks are pulled apart by tensional stress. A thrust or reverse fault results when rocks are forced together by compressional stress. And, a strike-slip fault forms when rocks are torn by lateral-shearing stress.

Normal Fault When forces pull rocks apart, the tension causes a **normal fault**, or tension fault. When the break occurs, rock on one side moves vertically along an inclined fault plane (Figure 12.11a). The downward-shifting side is the *hanging wall*; it drops relative to the *footwall block*. The exposed fault plane sometimes is visible along the base of faulted mountains, where individual ridges are truncated by the movements of the fault and appear as triangular facets at the ends of the ridges. A cliff formed by faulting is commonly called a *fault scarp*, or *escarpment*.

Reverse (Thrust) Fault Compressional forces associated with converging plates force rocks to move *upward* along the fault plane. This is a **reverse fault**, or compression fault (Figure 12.11b). On the surface, it appears similar to a normal fault, although more collapse and landslides may occur from the hanging wall component. In England, when miners worked along a reverse fault, they would stand on the lower side (footwall) and hang their lanterns on the upper side (hanging wall), giving rise to these terms.

If the fault plane forms a low angle relative to the horizontal, the fault is termed a **thrust fault**, or *overthrust fault*, indicating that the overlying block has shifted far over the underlying block (see Figure 12.8, "thrust fault"). Place your hands palms-down on your desk, with fingertips together, and slide one hand up over the other—this is the motion of a low-angle thrust fault, with one side pushing over the other.

In the Alps, several such overthrusts result from compressional forces of the ongoing collision between the African and Eurasian plates. Beneath the Los Angeles Basin, overthrust faults produce a high risk of earthquakes and caused many quakes in the 20th century, including the $30 billion 1994 Northridge earthquake. These blind (unknown until they rupture) thrust faults beneath the Los Angeles region are a major earthquake threat in the future.

Strike-Slip Fault If movement along a fault plane is horizontal, such as produced along a transform fault, it forms a **strike-slip fault** (Figure 12.11c; refer to Figure 11.21 for review). The movement is *right-lateral* or *left-lateral*, depending on the motion perceived when you observe movement on one side of the fault relative to the other side.

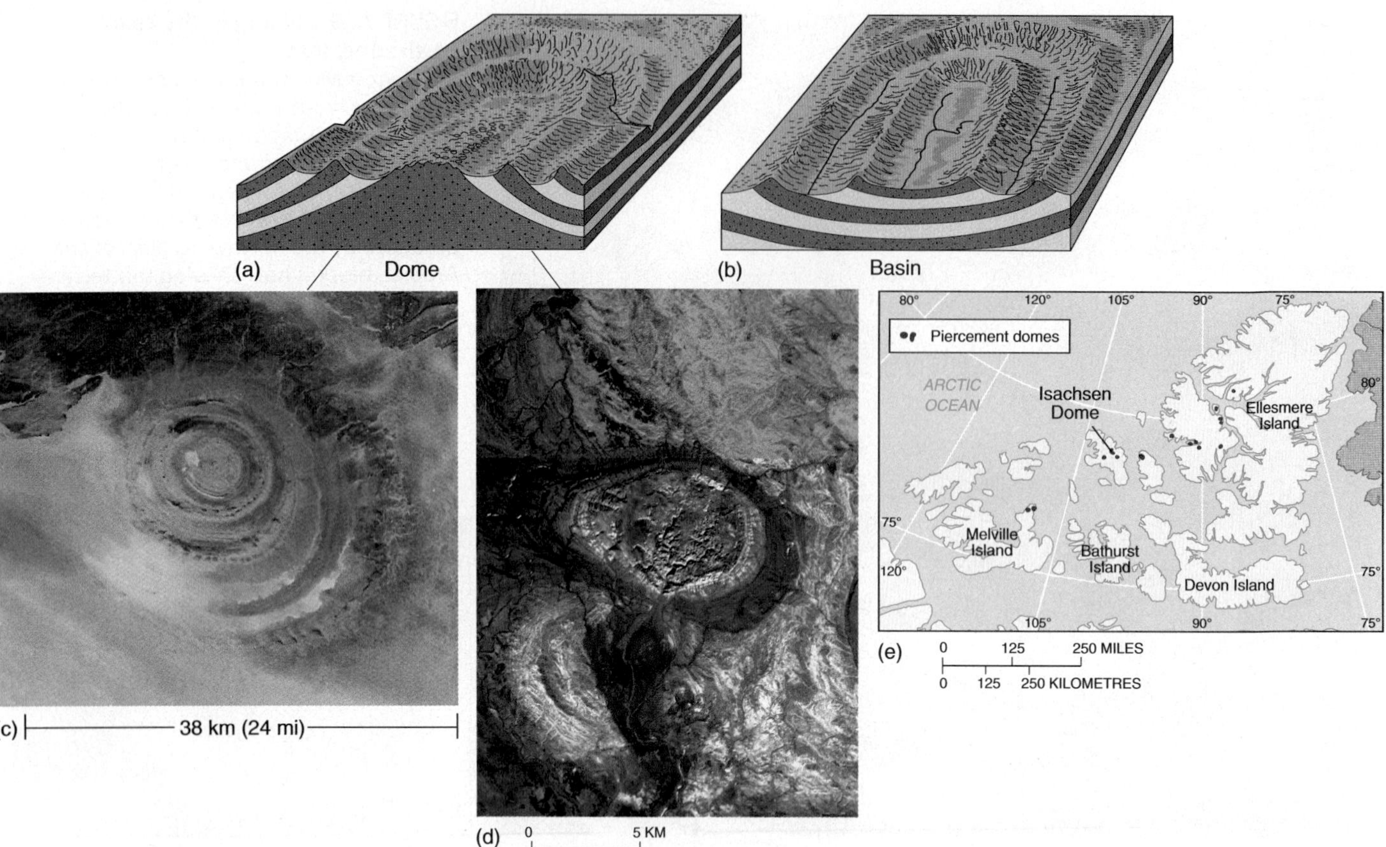

FIGURE 12.10 Domes and basins.
(a) An upwarped dome. (b) A structural basin. Denudation of weak (soft) rock strata has produced valleys and depressions in these landscapes. In contrast, strong (hard) rock strata stand in positive topographic relief forming ridges. (c) The Richat dome structure of Mauritania. (d) Isachsen dome, Ellef Ringnes Island, Nunavut, Canada. The piercement dome consists of Carboniferous evaporite rocks (represented by bright tones in the photograph) flanked by steeply dipping beds of Cretaceous shale (represented by dark tones in the photograph). (e) The distribution of piercement domes within the Queen Elizabeth Islands, Arctic Canada. [(c) Image from *Terra*, October 7, 2000, courtesy NASA/GSFC/MITI, and U.S./Japan ASTER team; (d) ASTER image from NASA and the Earth Remote Sensing Data Analysis Center, http://www.ersdac.or.jp/eng/index.E.html; (e) "Geology and economic minerals of Canada," *Economic Geology Report No. 1*, Geological Survey of Canada, Ottawa, p. 570, Figure X-8, in Thorsteinsson and E.T. Tozer. 1970. *Geology of the Arctic Archipelago*, in R.J.W. Douglas (editor).]

Although strike-slip faults do not produce cliffs (scarps), as do the other types of faults, they can create linear rift valleys. This is the case with the San Andreas fault system of California. The rift valley is clearly visible in Figure 12.11c, where the edges of the North American and Pacific plates are grinding past one another as a result of transform-fault movement. The evolution of this fault system is shown in Figure 12.12.

Note in the figure how the East Pacific rise developed as a spreading centre with associated transform faults (1), while the North American plate was progressing westward after the breakup of Pangaea. Forces then shifted the transform faults toward a northwest-southeast alignment along a weaving axis (2). Finally, the western margin of North America overrode those shifting transform faults (3). Note the convergence rate is a rapid 4 cm (1.6 in.) per year!

In *relative* terms, the motion along this series of transform faults is right-lateral, whereas in *absolute* terms the North American plate is still moving westward. Consequently, the San Andreas system is a series of faults that are *transform* (associated with a former spreading centre), *strike-slip* (horizontal in motion), and *right-lateral* (one side is moving to the right relative to the other side).

The North Anatolian fault system in Turkey is a strike-slip fault and has a right-lateral motion similar to the San Andreas system (Figure 12.13). A progression of earthquakes have hit along the entire extent of the fault system in Turkey since 1939; the latest devastation was in August and November 1999, and again in February 2002.

Faults in Concert Combinations of faults can produce distinctive landscapes. In the U.S. western interior, the *Basin and Range Province* (featuring a parallel series of mountains and valleys) experienced tensional forces caused by uplifting and thinning of the crust (illustrated later in Chapter 15, Figure 15.23). This movement cracked the

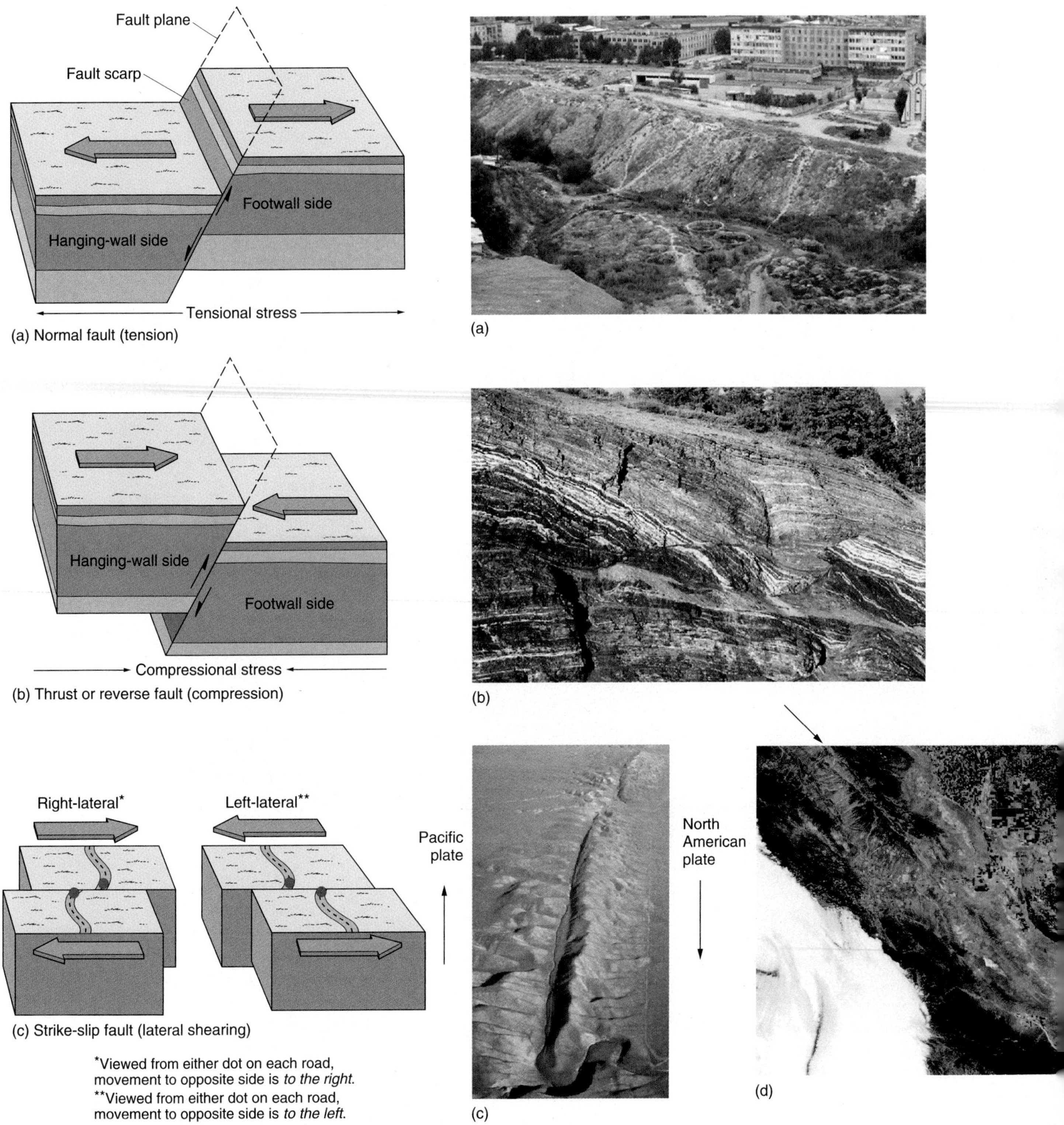

Fault plane
Fault scarp
Footwall side
Hanging-wall side
Tensional stress

(a) Normal fault (tension)

(a)

Hanging-wall side
Footwall side
Compressional stress

(b) Thrust or reverse fault (compression)

(b)

Right-lateral*
Left-lateral**

(c) Strike-slip fault (lateral shearing)

*Viewed from either dot on each road, movement to opposite side is *to the right.*
**Viewed from either dot on each road, movement to opposite side is *to the left.*

Pacific plate
North American plate

(c)

(d)

FIGURE 12.11 Types of faults.
(a) A normal fault produced by tension in the crust, visible along the edge in Tashkent, Uzbekistan. (b) A thrust, or reverse fault, produced by compression in the crust, visible in these offset strata in coal seams and volcanic ash in British Columbia. (c) A strike-slip fault produced by lateral shearing, clearly seen looking north along the San Andreas fault rift zone on the eastern edge of the Coast Ranges in California—Pacific plate to the left, North American plate to the right. (d) Can you find the San Andreas fault on the satellite image? Look for a linear rift stretching from southeast to northwest, at the edge of the coastal mountains and San Joaquin Valley. [(a) Photo by Fred McConnaughey/Photo Researchers, Inc.; (b) photo by Fletcher and Baylis/Photo Researchers, Inc.; (c) Kevin Schafer/Peter Arnold, Inc. (d) *Terra* MISR image courtesy of MISR Team, NASA/GSFC/JPL.]

Fault Types, Transform Faults, Plate Margins

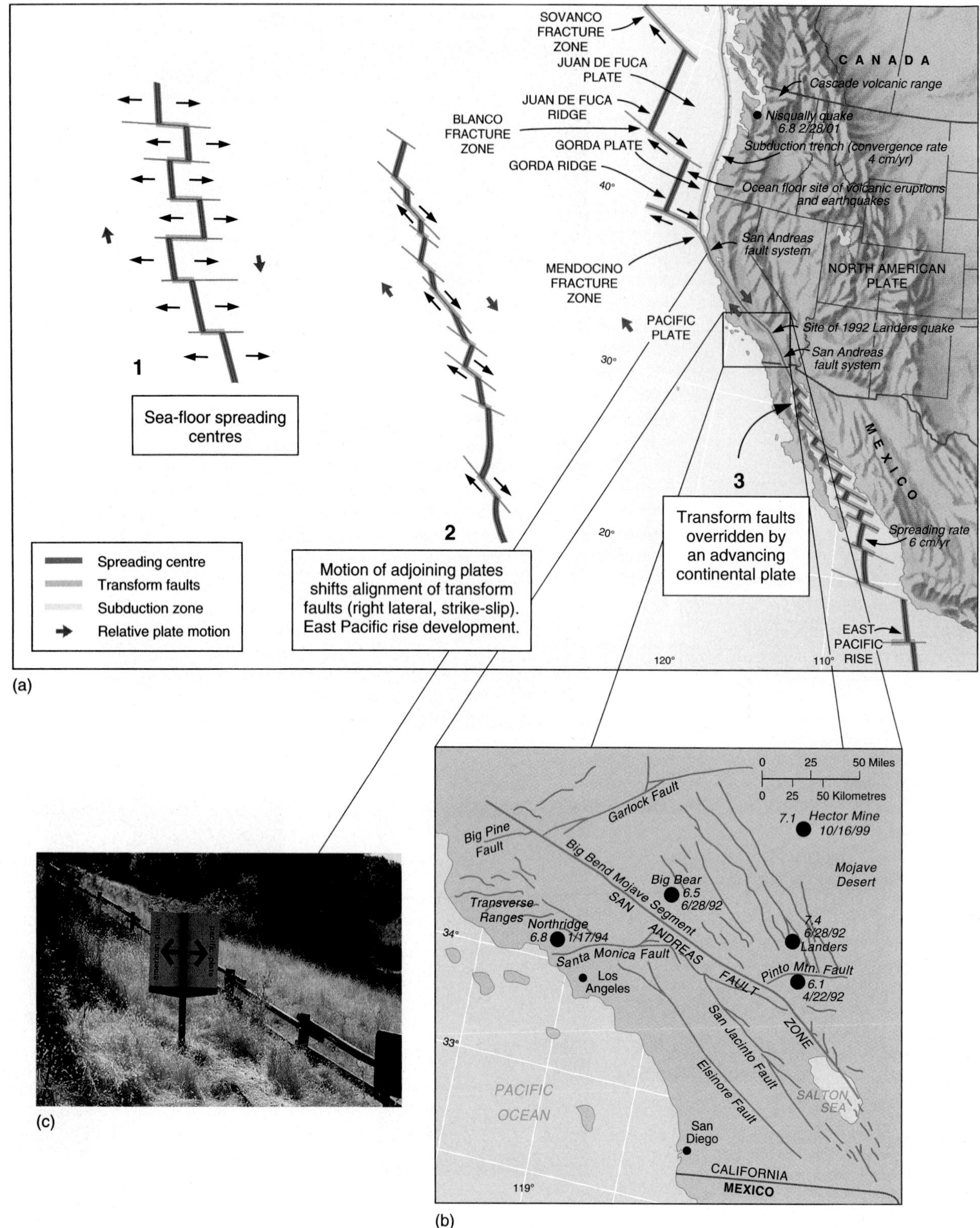

FIGURE 12.12 San Andreas fault formation.
(a) Formation of the San Andreas fault system as a series of transform faults in three successive stages. (b) Enlargement shows the portion of southern California where the 1992 Landers, the 1994 Northridge (Reseda), and 1999 Hector Mine earthquakes occurred. Magnitude ratings are shown for five quakes; a sixth quake is shown on the map in (a), the epicentre location of the January 2001 magnitude 6.8 Nisqually quake, Washington state, related to the subduction zone offshore. (c) Trail sign near the epicentre of the 1906 San Francisco earthquake roughly marks the Pacific–North American plate boundary, Marin County, Point Reyes National Seashore, California. [(c) Photo by Robert W. Christopherson.]

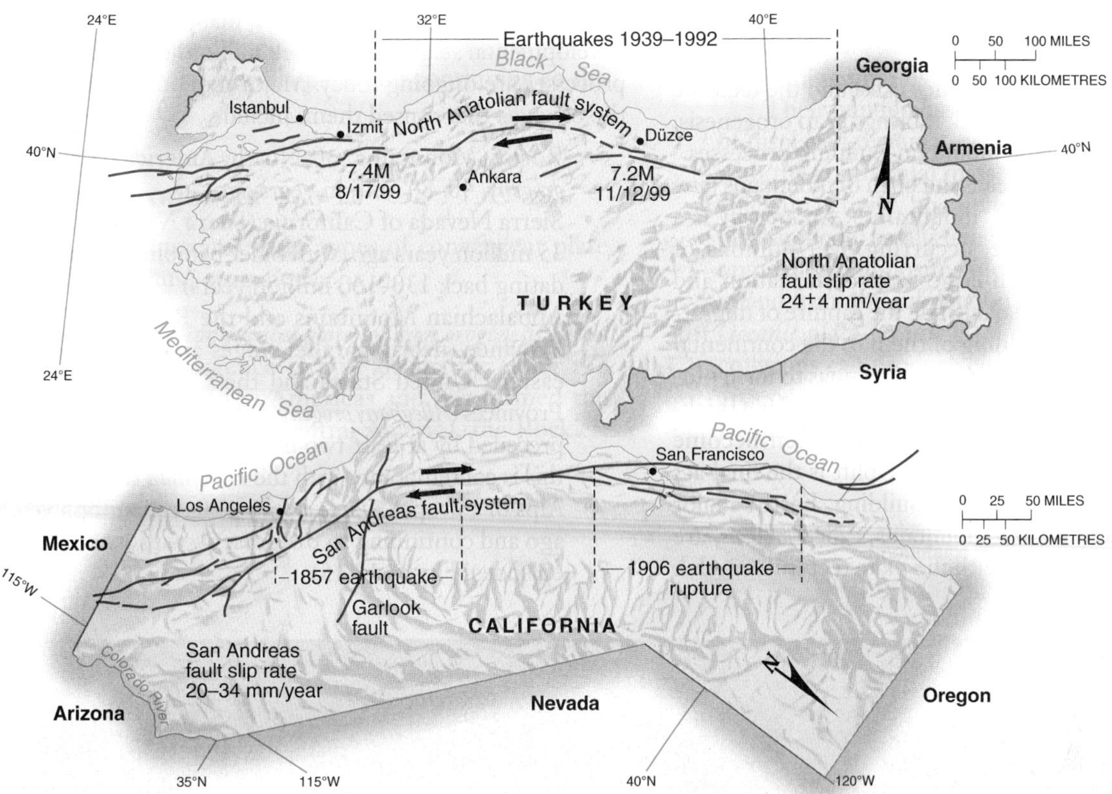

FIGURE 12.13 Strike-slip faults in Turkey and California.
Note these two strike-slip, right-lateral faults and the dates of activity along each—the North Anatolian (Turkey) and San Andreas (California). California is oriented with north to the right for comparison purposes. The San Andreas system is more complex than the North Anatolian because it is a dense network of active faults. [After USGS map by Ross S. Stein.]

surface to form aligned pairs of normal faults and a distinctive landscape (Figure 12.14a).

The term **horst** applies to upward-faulted blocks; **graben** refers to downward-faulted blocks. One example of a horst and graben landscape is the Great Rift Valley of East Africa (associated with crustal spreading); it extends northward to the Red Sea, which fills the rift formed by parallel normal faults (Figure 12.14b). Another example is the Rhine graben, through which the Rhine River flows in Europe.

FIGURE 12.14 Faulted landscapes.
(a) Pairs of faults produce a horst and graben landscape characteristic of the Basin and Range Province in the western United States. (b) The Red Sea occupies a down-dropped block that is part of the rift system that extends through East Africa. [(b) NASA photo from *Gemini*.]

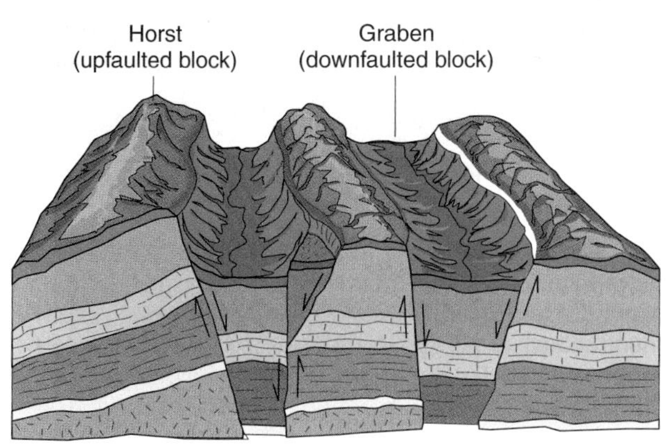

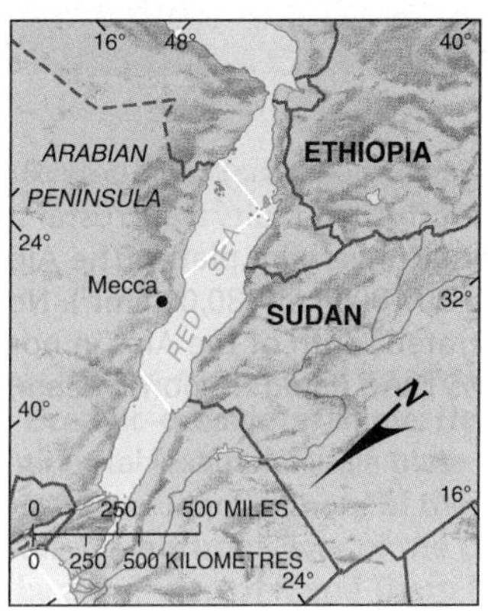

(a)

(b)

of rocks, and granitic intrusions. These processes formed the chains of island arcs and volcanoes that continue from the southwestern Pacific to the western Pacific, the Philippines, the Kurils, and on through portions of the Aleutians.

Both collision types, (a) oceanic–continental and (b) oceanic–oceanic, are active around the Pacific Rim. Both are thermal in nature, because the diving plate melts and migrates back toward the surface as molten rock. Subduction of oceanic lithosphere beneath continental lithosphere is facilitated by the differences in rock density. The lighter continental lithosphere, consisting largely of felsic rocks with an average density of 2700 kg/m^3, overrides the heavier oceanic lithosphere that consists largely of mafic rocks with an average density of 3000 kg/m^3. The region of active volcanoes and earthquakes around the Pacific is known as the **circum-Pacific belt** or, more popularly, the **ring of fire**.

(c) *Continental plate–continental plate collision orogenesis.* Here the orogenesis is mechanical; large masses of continental crust are subjected to intense folding, overthrusting, faulting, and uplifting. The converging plates crush and deform both marine sediments and basaltic oceanic crust. The formation of the European Alps is a result of such compression forces and includes considerable crustal shortening, forming great overturned folds, called *nappes* (see Figure 12.15).

As mentioned earlier, the collision of India with the Eurasian landmass produced the Himalayan Mountains. That collision is estimated to have shortened the overall continental crust by as much as 1000 km (about 600 mi) and to have produced telescoping sequences of thrust faults at depths of 40 km (25 mi). The Himalayas feature the tallest above-sea-level mountains on Earth, including Mount Everest at 8850 m elevation (29,035 ft; a 1999 GPS-based measurement) and all 10 of Earth's highest peaks.

The disruption created by this plate collision has reached far under China, and frequent earthquakes there signal the continuation of this rapid-paced collision. As evidence of this ongoing strain, the January 2001 quake in Gujarat, India, was along a shallow, east-west tending thrust fault that gave way under the pressure of the northward-pushing India plate. More than 1 million buildings were destroyed or damaged!

The Appalachian Mountains

The old, eroded, fold-and-thrust belt of the eastern United States and southeastern Canada (250–300 million years old) contrasts with the younger, higher mountains of western North America (35–80 million years old). As noted, the *Alleghany orogeny* followed at least two earlier orogenic cycles of uplift and the accretion of several captured terranes.

Each orogenic event was separated by long periods of time during which rock weathering and erosion gradually stripped material from the mountain summits. The end result of these processes was the production of upland plateaux with elevations equal to or greater than 700 m above sea level throughout much of Atlantic Canada, excluding Prince Edward Island.* Fluvial and glacial erosion has created steep-sided valleys that dissect the edge of the upland plateau (Figure 12.17).

The original material for the Appalachian Mountains resulted from the collisions that produced Pangaea. In fact, the Atlas Mountains of northwestern Africa were connected to the Appalachians at some time in the past, but the Atlas

*A. S. Trenhaile, *Geomorphology: A Canadian Perspective* (Oxford University Press, 2003).

(a)

(b)

FIGURE 12.17 Appalachian landscapes.
(a) The upland plateau of Cape Breton Island. (b) The Long Range Mountains in Newfoundland. The upland plateaux surfaces represent ancient erosion created by intense weathering and fluvial erosion, most likely under the warmer and moister climates of the late Cretaceous and early Tertiary periods. River valleys dissect the margins of the plateaux. The valleys were initiated as the plateaux were uplifted in preglacial time and progressively deepened by fluvial and glacial erosion. [Photos by (a) Irwin Barrett/firstlight.ca; (b) Len Wagg/CP Photo Archive.]

Mountains, embedded in the African plate, rafted apart from the Appalachians.

The Western Cordillera

The rugged topography that characterizes much of this region developed in response to volcanism and tectonism accompanying the accretion of exotic terranes throughout the Mesozoic and early Tertiary periods (180 to 45 m.y.a.). Mountain peaks commonly exceed elevations of 3000 m above sea level (Figure 12.18). The terrain in this region is composed of a variety of intrusive and extrusive igneous rocks, metamorphic rocks, and sedimentary rocks that have experienced folding and faulting.

Mount Logan, the highest point in Canada at an elevation of 5959 m above sea level, occurs within the Coast mountain ranges (Figure 12.19). Pleistocene alpine glaciation widened and deepened river valleys creating mountain passes and deep fjords. These important breaks in the mountain ridges greatly influenced European exploration of the region in the 18th and 19th centuries. The routes selected for several transcontinental railways in the latter part of the 19th century were guided by this topography.

FIGURE 12.18 Moraine Lake and the Bow Range Mountains in the vicinity of Banff, Alberta.
The rugged topography that characterizes the physiography of the Canadian Rocky Mountains is the product of orogenesis during the Paleozoic and Mesozoic Eras and subsequent erosion by Tertiary rivers and Quaternary glaciers. [Photo by Parks Canada, no. 09.93.03.08.]

The Innuitian Mountains

This region occupies the northeastern margin of the Queen Elizabeth Islands in Arctic Canada. Folding and thrust faulting of sedimentary rocks during the *Ellesmerian orogeny* in the late Paleozoic period (Devonian-Pennsylvanian) initiated mountain building, according to a report by Thorsteinsson and Tozer. This orogeny also involved the eruption of basaltic lava and the intrusion of granite plutons. The same authors state that late Cretaceous volcanism and folding and thrust faulting of sedimentary rocks during the mid-Cenozoic period *Eurekan orogeny* characterized a later phase of mountain building. Mountains in this region may attain elevations up to 2400 m (7874 ft) above sea level (Figure 12.20).

World Structural Regions

Examine the first two maps in this chapter (the chapter opener and Figure 12.3) and you will note two vast alpine systems on the continents. In the Western Hemisphere, the *Cordilleran system* stretches from Tierra del Fuego at the southern tip of South America to the massive peaks of Alaska, including the relatively young Rocky and Andes Mountains along the western margins of the North and South American plates. In the Eastern Hemisphere, the *Eurasian-Himalayan system* stretches from the European Alps across Asia to the Pacific Ocean and contains younger and older components.

These mountain systems also are shown on the structural region map as the *Alpine system* (Figure 12.21). The map defines seven fundamental structural regions that possess distinctive types of landscapes, grouped because of their shared physical characteristics. Looking at the distribution

FIGURE 12.19 Mount Logan.
Mount Logan, the highest point in Canada, is located in the St. Elias Range, Yukon Territory (60° N, 140° W). A team of six climbers made the first ascent in 1925. The crack in the ice in the background is a bergschrund; see Chapter 17 for a definition. [Photo by Parks Canada, no. 11.110.07.08.]

FIGURE 12.20 Mountains of the Princess Margaret Range, Axel Heiberg Island, Nunavut, Canada. The rugged topography that characterizes the physiography of the Innuitian orogeny is the product of orogenesis during the Paleozoic and Mesozoic Eras and subsequent erosion by Tertiary rivers and Quaternary glaciers. [Photo by Jerry Kobalenko/firstlight.ca.]

of these regions helps summarize the three rock-forming processes (igneous, sedimentary, and metamorphic), plate tectonics, landform origins and construction, and overall orogenesis.

As you examine the map, identify the continental shields at the heart of each landmass. Continental platforms composed of sedimentary deposits surround these areas. Various mountain chains, rifted regions, and isolated volcanic areas are noted on the map. On the continent of Australia, you see older mountain sequences to the east, sedimentary layers covering basement rocks west of these ranges, and portions of the original Gondwana, an ancient landscape in the central and western regions. (Remember that Gondwana was a landmass that included Antarctica, Australia, South America, Africa, and the southern portion of India; it broke away from Pangaea some 200 million years ago.)

Earthquakes

Crustal plates do not glide smoothly past one another. Instead, tremendous friction exists along plate boundaries. The *stress* (a force) of plate motion builds *strain* (a deformation) in the rocks until friction is overcome and the sides along plate boundaries suddenly break loose. The two sides of the fault plane then lurch into new positions, moving from centimetres to several metres, and release enormous amounts of seismic energy into the surrounding crust. This energy radiates throughout the planet, diminishing with distance, but sufficient enough to register on instruments worldwide. Earthquakes that devastated San Francisco in 1906, India in 2001, Bam, Iran, in 2003, and Indonesia in 2004 remind us of the danger and unpredictability of these tectonic forces of nature.

Expected Quakes and Those of Deadly Surprise

In the Liaoning Province of northeastern China, ominous indications of tectonic activity began in 1970. Troubling symptoms included land uplift and tilting, increasing minor tremors, and changes in the region's magnetic field—after almost 120 years of quiet. These precursors of tectonic events continued for almost 5 years before Chinese scientists took the bold step of forecasting an earthquake. In February 1975, some 3 million people evacuated in what turned out to be a timely manner; the quake struck 6 hours later, within the predicted time frame. Ninety percent of the buildings in the city of Haicheng fell. Thousands of lives were claimed saved—an earthquake had been forecast and preparatory action taken for the first time in history.

In contrast, only 17 months later, at Tangshan in the northeastern province of Hebei (Hopei), 145 km (90 mi) southeast of Beijing, China's capital city, a severe earthquake occurred without warning. No precursors (warning signs) were sensed for scientists to build a forecast. Consequently, this magnitude 7.4 quake killed about 250,000 people! (This is the official death toll; other estimates range as high as 650,000 fatalities.) The earthquake also destroyed 95% of the buildings and 80% of the industrial structures, and it severely damaged more than half the bridges and highways in the area. The jolt and ground acceleration threw people against the ceilings of their homes. An old, previously undetected fault ruptured, and the rocks shifted 1.5 m (5 ft) along 8 km (5 mi) in the heart of Tangshan. What are the mechanisms that produce such different tectonic events? Why are some expected, whereas most strike in total surprise?

Students and faculty at California State University-Northridge, in the San Fernando Valley of southern California, need no reminder of the power of earthquakes. Their campus was near the epicentre of the most devastating earthquake in U.S. history in terms of property damage—$30 billion in destruction across the region. The quake was caused by one of the many low-angle thrust faults that underlie the Los Angeles region. The January 17, 1994, Northridge (Reseda) earthquake, a magnitude 6.8, and more than 10,000 aftershocks caused approximately $350 million damage to campus buildings two weeks before the beginning of spring classes. The semester began just three weeks late in 450 temporary trailers. Geography professors taught some class sessions outdoors for a brief time. Amazingly, graduation was still held in May!

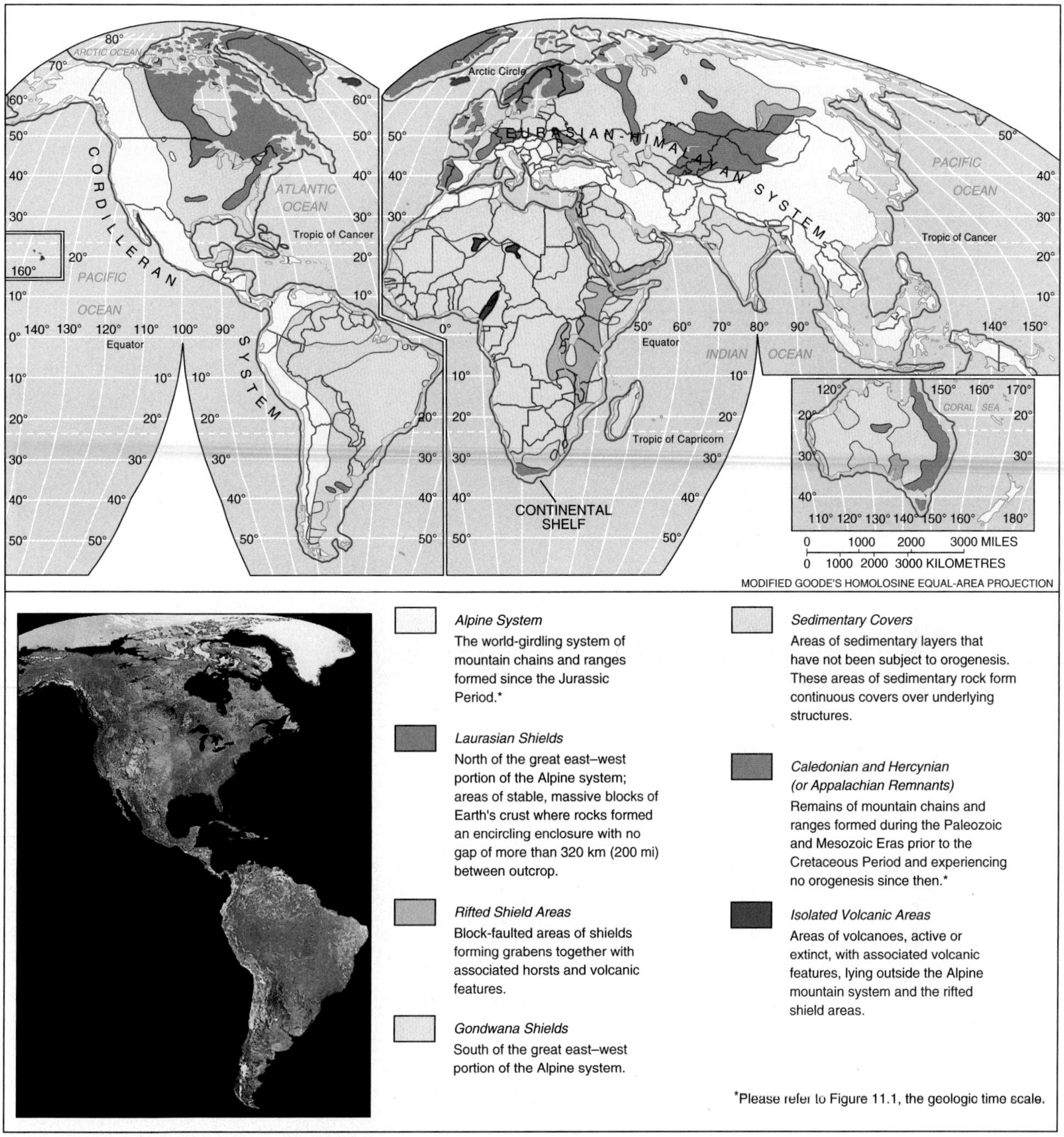

Alpine System
The world-girdling system of mountain chains and ranges formed since the Jurassic Period.*

Laurasian Shields
North of the great east–west portion of the Alpine system; areas of stable, massive blocks of Earth's crust where rocks formed an encircling enclosure with no gap of more than 320 km (200 mi) between outcrop.

Rifted Shield Areas
Block-faulted areas of shields forming grabens together with associated horsts and volcanic features.

Gondwana Shields
South of the great east–west portion of the Alpine system.

Sedimentary Covers
Areas of sedimentary layers that have not been subject to orogenesis. These areas of sedimentary rock form continuous covers over underlying structures.

Caledonian and Hercynian (or Appalachian Remnants)
Remains of mountain chains and ranges formed during the Paleozoic and Mesozoic Eras prior to the Cretaceous Period and experiencing no orogenesis since then.*

Isolated Volcanic Areas
Areas of volcanoes, active or extinct, with associated volcanic features, lying outside the Alpine mountain system and the rifted shield areas.

*Please refer to Figure 11.1, the geologic time scale.

FIGURE 12.21 World structural regions and major mountain systems. Some of the regions appear larger than the structures themselves because each region includes related landforms adjacent to the central feature. (Correlate aspects of this map with Figures 12.3 and 12.4.) Structural regions in the Western Hemisphere are visible on the composite false-colour *Landsat* image inset (vegetation is portrayed in red). [After R. E. Murphy, "Landforms of the world," *Annals of the Association of American Geographers* 58, no. 1 (March 1968). Adapted by permission. Inset image courtesy of EROS Data Center and the National Geographic Society.]

Focus, Epicentre, Foreshock, and Aftershock

P- and S-Waves, Seismology

The subsurface area along a fault plane, where the motion of seismic waves is initiated, is the *focus*, or hypocentre, of an earthquake (see labels in Figure 12.22). The area at the surface directly above the focus is the *epicentre*. Shock waves produced by an earthquake radiate outward through the crust from the focus and epicentre. Some of the seismic waves are conducted throughout the planet to distant instruments. From these seismic wave patterns and the nature of their transmission through the layers of the planet, Earth's interior is explored by scientists.

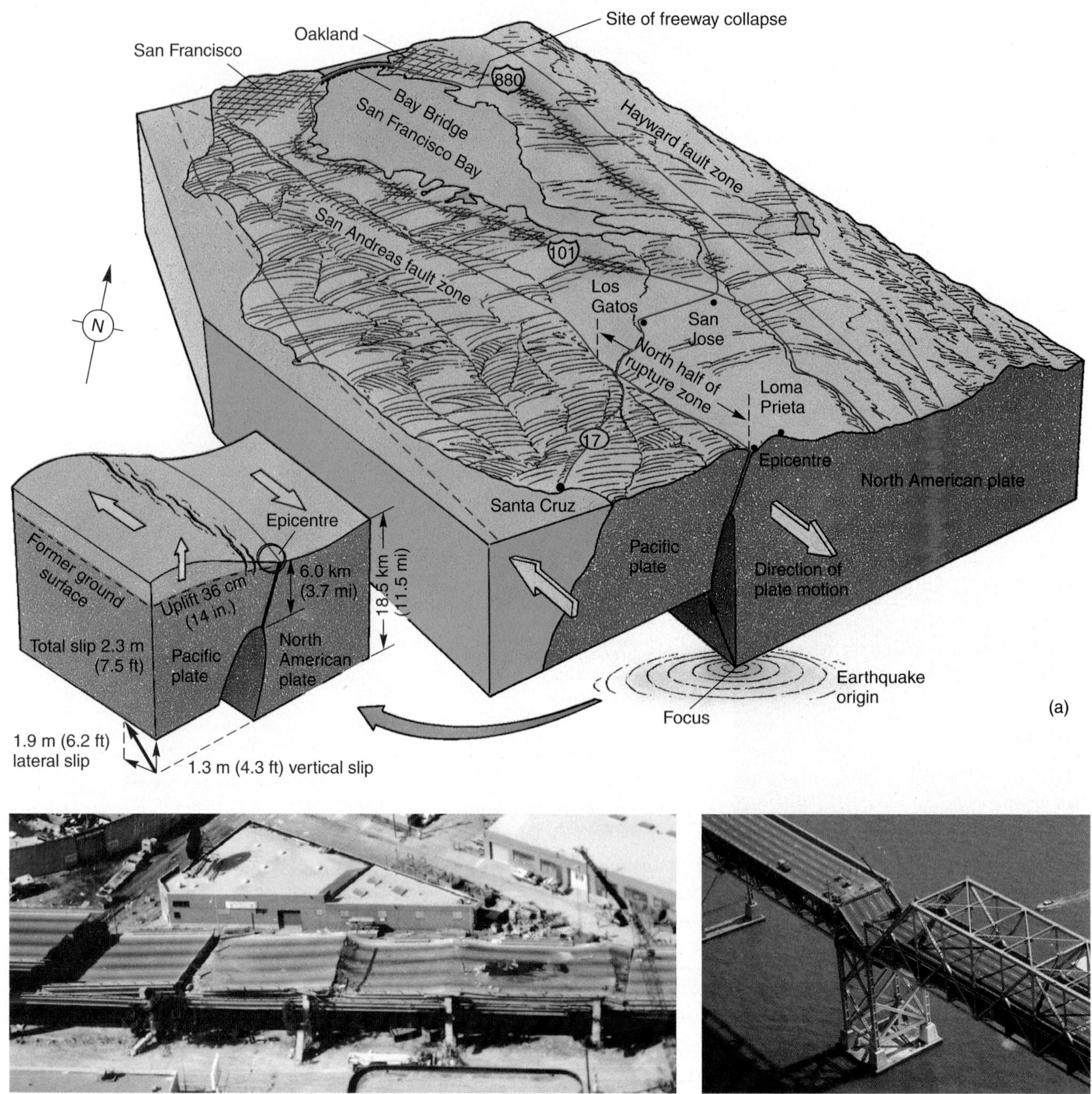

FIGURE 12.22 Anatomy of an earthquake.
(a) The fault-plane solution for the 1989 Loma Prieta, California, earthquake shows the lateral and vertical (thrust) movements occurring at depth. There was no surface expression of this fault plane. Damage totalled $8 billion, 14,000 people were displaced from their homes, 4000 were injured, and 67 killed. (b) In only 15 seconds, more than 2 km (1.2 mi) of the Route 880 Cypress Freeway collapsed. (c) Section failure in the San Francisco–Oakland Bay Bridge actually is the way the bridge handles strain without completely failing. [(a) After P. J. Ward and R. A. Page, *The Loma Prieta Earthquake of October 17, 1989* (Washington, DC: U.S. Geological Survey, November 1989), p. 1; (b) and (c) courtesy of California Department of Transportation.]

An *aftershock* may occur after the main shock, sharing the same general area of the epicentre; some aftershocks rival the main tremor in magnitude. A *foreshock* also is possible, preceding the main shock. The pattern of foreshocks is now regarded as an important consideration in the forecast effort. (Before the 1992 Landers earthquake in southern California, at least two dozen foreshocks occurred along the soon-to-fail portion of the fault.)

Earthquake Intensity and Magnitude

Tectonic earthquakes are those quakes associated with faulting. A worldwide network of more than 4000 **seismograph** instruments record vibrations transmitted as waves of energy throughout Earth's interior and in the crust. Using this device and actual observations, scientists rate earthquakes on two kinds of scales: a *qualitative* damage intensity scale and a *quantitative* magnitude-of-energy-released scale.

A damage *intensity scale* is useful in classifying and describing damage to terrain and structures after an earthquake. Earthquake intensity is rated on the arbitrary *Mercalli scale*, a Roman numeral scale from I to XII, representing "barely felt" to "catastrophic total destruction." It was designed in 1902 and modified in 1931. Table 12.1 shows this scale and the number of quakes in each category that are expected each year.

Moment Magnitude Scale Revises the Richter Scale

In 1935 Charles Richter designed a system to estimate earthquake magnitude. In this method, a seismograph located at least 100 km (62 mi) from the epicentre of the quake records the amplitude of seismic waves (**http://earthquake.usgs.gov/faq/meas.html**). That measurement is then charted on the **Richter scale**. The relation of magnitude to energy released is still a useful feature of his scale.

The Richter scale is logarithmic: Each whole number on it represents a 10-fold increase in the measured wave amplitude. Translated into energy, each whole number signifies a 31.5-fold increase in energy released. Thus, a magnitude of 3.0 on the Richter scale represents 31.5 times more energy than a 2.0, and 992 times more energy than a 1.0. It is difficult to imagine the power released by the Tangshan quake, which was rated a 7.6 on the Richter scale.

Today, the Richter scale is improved and made more quantitative. Revision was needed because the scale did not properly measure or differentiate between quakes of high intensity. Seismologists wanted to know more about what they call the *seismic moment* to understand a broader range of possible motions during an earthquake.

The **moment magnitude scale**, in use since 1993, is more accurate for large earthquakes than Richter's *amplitude magnitude* scale. Moment magnitude considers the amount of fault slippage produced by the earthquake, the size of the surface (or subsurface) area that ruptured, and the nature of the materials that faulted, including how resistant they were to failure. The new scale rates the 1994 Northridge quake, mentioned earlier, at magnitude 6.8 and considers extreme ground acceleration (movement upward), which the Richter amplitude magnitude method underestimated. Richter was familiar in everyday usage, although moment magnitude is the correct scale and is the scale used in this book unless stated otherwise.

A reassessment of past quakes has increased the rating of some and decreased that of others. As an example, the 1964 earthquake at Prince William Sound in Alaska had an amplitude magnitude of 8.6, but on the moment magnitude scale it increases to a magnitude 9.2. Please note that Table 12.2 includes more earthquakes for the period following 1960 than for the years before 1960. This is not because earthquake frequency has increased; rather, it reflects an effort to include recent events that affected increased population densities in vulnerable areas.

Seismologists locate an average of 1500 earthquakes in Canada each year. Figure 12.23 illustrates the intensity of seismic activity within Canada and the location of 15 significant twentieth-century Canadian earthquakes. The magnitude of these 15 seismic events is presented in Table 12.3. The regions that experience large magnitude earthquakes ($M > 5$) include the Ottawa River and St. Lawrence River valleys in eastern Canada, the Western Cordillera, the Mackenzie River valley, and the continental shelf of northwestern Baffin Bay.

The Nature of Faulting

We earlier described types of faults and faulting motions. The specific mechanics of how a fault breaks remain under study, but **elastic-rebound theory** describes the basic process. Generally, two sides along a fault appear to be

Table 12.1 Magnitude, Intensity, and Frequency of Earthquakes

Description	Effects in Populated Areas	Moment Magnitude Scale	Mercalli Intensity Scale (approximate)	Number per Year
Great	Damage nearly total	8 and higher	XII	1
Major	Great damage	7–7.9	X–XI	17*
Strong	Considerable-to-serious damage to buildings; railroad tracks bent	6–6.9	VIII–IX	134*
Moderate	Felt-by-all, with slight building damage	5–5.9	V–VII	1,319*
Light	Felt-by-some, to felt-by-many	4–4.9	III–IV	13,000 (estimated)
Minor	Slight, some feel it	3–3.9	I–II	130,000 (estimated)
Very minor	Not felt, but recorded	2–2.9	None to I	1,300,000 (estimated)

Source: USGS, Earthquake Information Center.
*Based on observations since 1990.

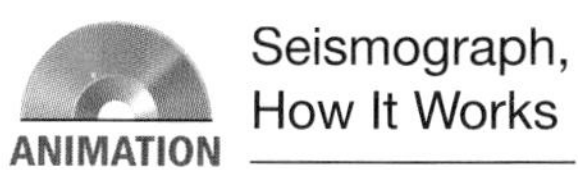

Table 12.2 A Sampling of Significant Earthquakes**

Year	Date	Location	Number of Deaths	Mercalli Intensity	Moment Magnitude (Richter)
1556	Jan. 23	Shaanxi Province, China	830,000	*	*
1737	Oct. 11	Calcutta, India	300,000	*	*
1812	Feb. 7	New Madrid, Missouri	Several	XI–XII	*
1857	Jan. 9	Fort Tejon, California	*	X–XI	*
1870	Oct. 21	Montréal to Québec, Canada	*	IX	*
1886	Aug. 31	Charleston, South Carolina	*	IX	6.7
1906	Apr. 18	San Francisco, California	3,000	XI	7.7 (8.25)
1923	Sept. 1	Kwanto, Japan	143,000	XII	7.9 (8.2)
1939	Dec. 27	Erzincan, Turkey	40,000	XII	7.6 (8.0)
1960	May 22	Southern Chile	5,700	XII	9.6 (8.6)
1964	Mar. 28	Southern Alaska	131	X–XII	9.2 (8.6)
1970	May 31	Northern Peru	66,000	*	7.9 (7.8)
1971	Feb. 9	San Fernando, California	65	VII–IX	6.7 (6.5)
1972	Dec. 23	Managua, Nicaragua	5,000	X–XII	6.2 (6.2)
1976	Jul. 28	Tangshan, China	250,000	XI–XII	7.4 (7.6)
1978	Sept. 16	Iran	25,000	X–XII	7.8 (7.7)
1985	Sept. 19	Mexico City, Mexico	7,000	IX–XII	8.1 (8.1)
1988	Dec. 7	Armenia–Turkey border	30,000	XII	6.8 (6.9)
1989	Oct. 17	Loma Prieta (near Santa Cruz, California)	66	VII–IX	7.0 (7.1)
1991	Oct. 20	Uttar Pradesh, India	1,700	IX–XI	6.2 (6.1)
1994	Jan. 17	Northridge (Reseda), California	66	VII–IX	6.8
1995	Jan. 17	Kobe, Japan	5,500	XII	6.9
1996	Feb. 17	Indonesia	110	X	8.1
1997	Feb. 28	Armenia–Azerbaijan	1,100	XII	6.1
1997	May 10	Northern Iran	1,600	XII	7.3
1998	May 30	Afghanistan–Tajikistan	4,000	XII	6.9
1998	Jul. 17	Papua New Guinea	2,200	X	7.1
1999	Jan. 26	Armenia, Colombia	1,000	VIII–IX	6.0
1999	Aug. 17	Izmit, Turkey	17,100	VIII–XI	7.4
1999	Sept. 7	Athens, Greece	150	VI–VIII	5.9
1999	Sept. 20	Chi-Chi, Taiwan	2,500	VI–X	7.6
1999	Sept. 30	Oaxaca, Mexico	33	VI	7.5
1999	Oct. 16	Hector Mine, California	0	*	7.1
1999	Nov. 12	Düzce, Turkey	700	VI–X	7.2
2001	Jan. 26	Gujarat state, India	19,998	X–XII	7.7
2002	Nov. 3	Near Denali National Park, Alaska	1	X	7.9
2003	Dec. 26	Bam, Iran	30,000	X–XII	6.9
2004	Dec. 26	Northern Sumatra (west coast)	150,000***	X–XII	9.3

*Data not available.
**There is not a recent increase in earthquakes; this table merely reflects more detail on the recent record.
***Estimated deaths from quake and resulting tsunami that travelled across the Indian Ocean.

Seismograph, How It Works

locked by friction, resisting any movement despite the powerful forces acting on the adjoining pieces of crust. Stress continues to build strain along the *fault plane* surfaces, storing elastic energy like a wound-up spring. When the strain buildup finally exceeds the frictional lock, both sides of the fault abruptly move to a condition of less strain, releasing a burst of mechanical energy. This type of sudden movement rocked the region around Kobe, Japan, in 1995, with a magnitude 6.9 quake. See News Report 12.2 for an account of this significant event.

Think of the fault plane as a surface with irregularities that act as sticking points, preventing movement, similar to two pieces of wood held together by drops of glue of different sizes rather than an even coating of glue. Research scientists at the USGS and the University of California identify these small areas of high strain as *asperities.* They are the points that break and release the sides of the fault.

If the fracture along the fault line is isolated to a small asperity break, the quake will be small in magnitude. Clearly, as some asperities break (perhaps recorded as small

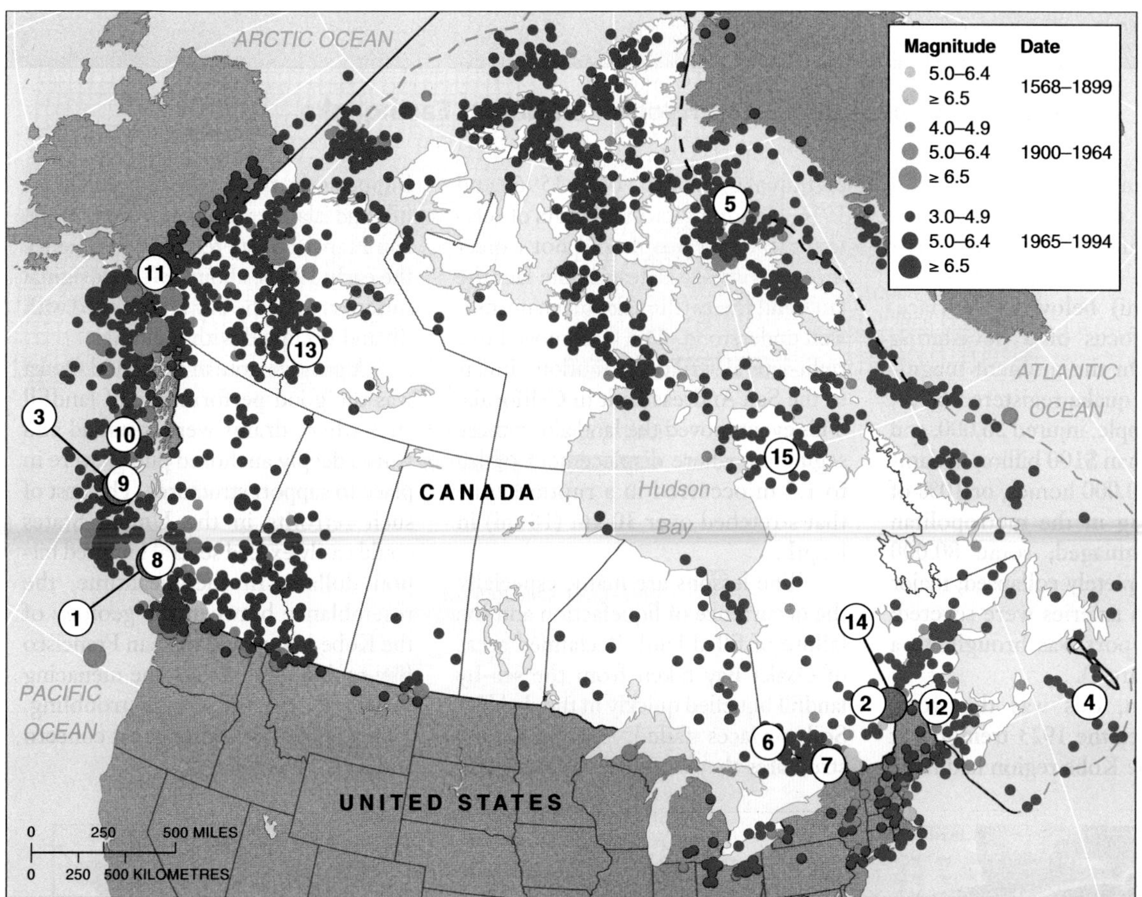

FIGURE 12.23 Seismic activity in Canada.
Damaging earthquakes (M > 5) are strongly associated with the Western Cordillera and the valleys of the Ottawa and St. Lawrence Rivers. [Used by permission of the Minister of Public Works and Government Services Canada; Natural Resources Canada, Geological Survey of Canada.]

Table 12.3 Significant Canadian Earthquakes of the 20th Century

Year	Date	Location	Moment Magnitude (Richter)
1. 1918	Dec. 6	Vancouver Island, British Columbia	7.0
2. 1925	Mar. 1	Charlevoix–Kamouraska region, Québec	6.2
3. 1929	May 6	Queen Charlotte Islands, British Columbia	7.0
4. 1929	Nov. 8	Atlantic Ocean, south of Newfoundland	7.2
5. 1933	Nov. 20	Baffin Bay, northeast of Baffin Island, Nunavut	7.3
6. 1935	Nov. 1	Temiscamingue region, Ontario–Québec border	6.2
7. 1944	Sept. 5	Cornwall region, Ontario–New York border	5.6
8. 1946	June 23	Vancouver Island, British Columbia	7.3
9. 1949	Aug. 22	Queen Charlotte Islands, British Columbia	8.1
10. 1970	June 24	Queen Charlotte Islands, British Columbia	7.4
11. 1979	Feb. 28	Yukon–Alaska border	7.2
12. 1982	Mar. 31	Miramichi region, New Brunswick	5.7
13. 1985	Dec. 23	Nahanni region, Northwest Territories	6.9
14. 1988	Nov. 12	Saguenay region, Québec	5.9
15. 1989	Dec. 25	Ungava region, Québec	6.3

Source: Used by permission of the Minister of Public Works and Government Services Canada; Natural Resources Canada, Geological Survey of Canada.

Los Angeles Region

Since the mid-1980s, an area east of Los Angeles has experienced seven earthquakes greater than 6.0 magnitude. After a magnitude 6.1 quake in 1992, a magnitude 7.4 tremor rocked the lightly populated area near Landers, California (see the enlargement map of southern California in Figure 12.12). Although it was the single largest quake in California in 30 years, the remote location kept injuries and damage slight. Involved in this series were four different faults and some unknown segments. The main faulting caused a displacement of 6.1 m (20 ft).

For yet unexplained reasons, related earthquakes over the next few weeks struck in Mammoth Lakes, about 645 km (400 mi) to the north; at Mount Shasta in northern California; in southern Nevada and Utah; and 1810 km (1125 mi) distant in Yellowstone National Park, Wyoming.

The 1971 San Fernando, 1987 Whittier, 1988 Pasadena, 1991 Sierra Madre, and 1994 Northridge (Reseda) earthquakes are a few of the many quakes associated with deeply buried thrust faults. Earthquakes roughly originate at foci 18 km (11 mi) deep in the crust. Although not directly aligned with the San Andreas, scientists think that southern California will be affected by more of these thrust-fault actions as strain continues to build along the nearby San Andreas system of faults. The fault line that marks the contact between the Pacific and the North American plates is indeed restless.

Earthquake Forecasting and Planning

The map in Figure 12.23 plots the epicentres of 20th century earthquakes in Canada. These occurrences give some indication of relative risk by region. The challenge is to discover how to predict the *specific time and place* for a quake in the short term. See News Report 12.3 for more on forecasting.

Actual implementation of an action plan to reduce death, injury, and property damage from earthquakes is difficult. The political environment adds complexity; sadly, an accurate earthquake prediction would be viewed as a threat to a region's economy (Figure 12.25). If we examine the potential socioeconomic impact of earthquake prediction on an urban community, we find surprising negative economic impacts in the period before the quake hits. Imagine a chamber of commerce, bank, real estate agent, tax assessor, or politician who would privately welcome an earthquake prediction and such negative publicity for their city.

News Report 12.3

Seismic Gaps, Nervous Animals, Dilitancy, and Radon Gas

How do you forecast an earthquake? One approach is to examine the history of each plate boundary and determine the frequency of past earthquakes, a study called *paleoseismology*. Paleoseismologists construct maps that provide an estimate of expected earthquake activity based on past performance. An area that is quiet and overdue for an earthquake is a *seismic gap*; such an area forms a gap in the earthquake occurrence record and is therefore a place that possesses accumulated strain. The area along the Aleutian Trench subduction zone had three such gaps until the great 1964 Alaskan earthquake filled one of them.

The areas around San Francisco and northeast of Los Angeles represent other such gaps where the fault system appears to be locked by friction, and stress is producing accumulating strain. The U.S. Geological Survey in 1988 made a prediction that there was a 30% chance of an earthquake occurring with a magnitude 6.5 within 30 years in the Loma Prieta portion of the fault system. The actual 1989 quake dramatically filled a portion of the seismic gap in that region. The Nojima fault in the area of Kobe occurred in another gap.

One potentially positive discovery from the Loma Prieta disaster was that Stanford University scientists found unusually great changes in Earth's magnetic field—about 30 times more than normal—three hours before the main shock. These measurements were made 7 km (4.3 mi) from the epicentre, raising hopes that short-term warnings might be possible in the future. A valid research question is whether animals have the ability to detect these minute changes in magnetic fields, an ability that was perhaps lost in humans. If so, strange prequake animal behaviour, often reported, might provide forecasting clues.

Dilitancy refers to the slight increase in volume of rock produced by small cracks that form under stress and accumulated strain. The affected region may tilt and swell in response to strain. Tiltmeters measure these changes in suspect areas. Another indicator of dilitancy is an increase in radon dissolved in groundwater, a naturally occurring, slightly radioactive gas. Presently, earthquake hazard zones have thousands of radon monitors taking samples in test wells.

A seismic network in operation in Mexico City is providing 70-second warnings of arriving seismic-wave energy from distant epicentres. Following the Loma Prieta earthquake, freeway-repair workers were linked to a broadcast system that gave them 20-second alerts of aftershocks from distant epicentres. In southern California the USGS is coordinating a Southern California Seismographic Network (SCSN at **http://www.trinet.org/scsn/scsn.html**) to correlate 350 instruments for immediate earthquake location analysis and disaster coordination.

Someday accurate earthquake forecasting may be a reality, but several questions remain. How will humans respond to a forecast? Can a major metropolitan region be evacuated for short periods of time? Can cities relocate after a disaster to areas of lesser risk?

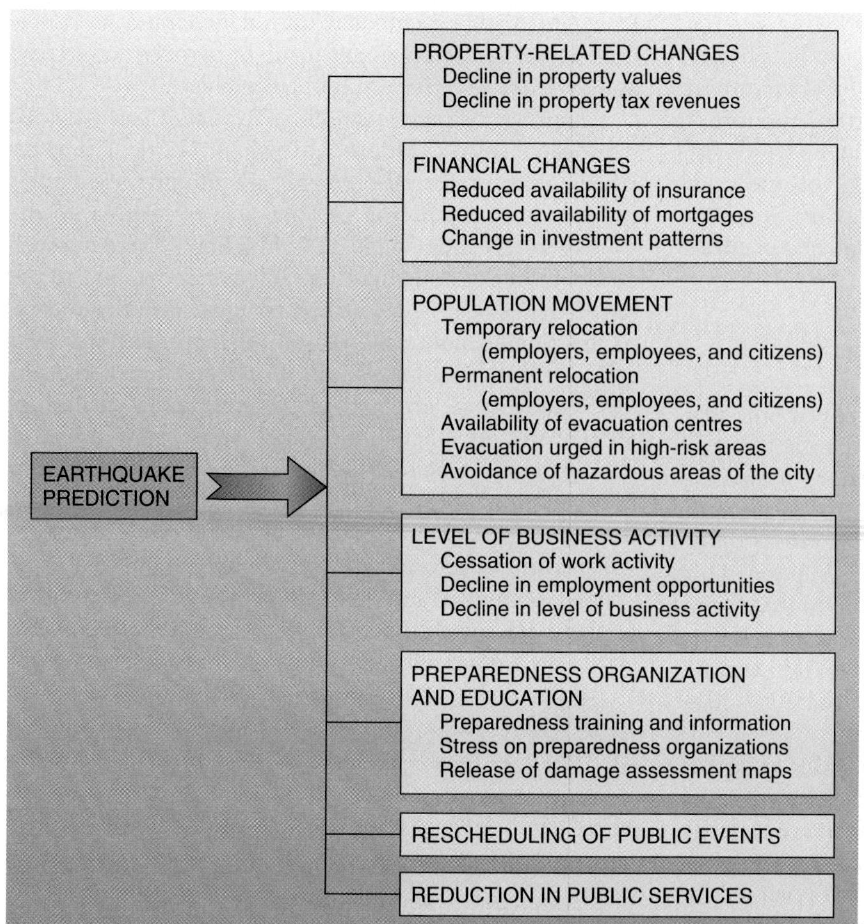

FIGURE 12.25 Socioeconomic impacts of an earthquake prediction. Business, political, and monetary interests are at stake as scientists get closer to being able to predict earthquakes. [After J. E. Haas and D. S. Mileti, *Socioeconomic Impact of Earthquake Prediction on Government, Business, and Community*. (Boulder: University of Colorado, Institute of Behavioral Sciences). Used by permission.]

Long-range planning is a complex subject. After the Loma Prieta earthquake in 1989, a committee report by the National Research Council concluded that

> One of the most jarring lessons from these quakes may be that earthquake professionals have long known many of the things that could have been done to reduce devastation. . . . The cost-effectiveness of mitigation and the importance of closing the knowledge gap among researchers, building professionals, government officials, and the public are only two of the many lessons from the Loma Prieta that need immediate action.

A valid and applicable generalization is that *humans and their institutions are unable or unwilling to perceive hazards in a familiar environment*. In other words, we tend to feel secure in our homes and communities, even if they are sitting on a quiet fault zone. Such an axiom of human behaviour certainly helps explain why large populations continue to live and work in earthquake-prone settings. Similar questions also can be raised about populations in areas vulnerable to floods, droughts, hurricanes and coastal storm surge, and settlements on barrier islands. (See "Coping with Natural Hazards in Canada: Scientific, Government and Insurance Industry Perspectives" at http://www.utoronto.ca/env/nh/toc.htm).

Volcanism

More than 1300 identifiable volcanic cones and mountains exist on Earth, although fewer than 600 are active—having at least one eruption in recorded history. An average of 60 volcanic eruptions a year occurs as reminders of Earth's internal energy, plate tectonics, and hot-spot activity. Eruptions in remote locations and at depths on the seafloor go largely unnoticed, but the occasional eruption of great magnitude near a population centre makes headlines.

North America has about 70 volcanoes (mostly inactive) along the western margin of the continent. Mount St. Helens in Washington State is a famous active example, and more than 1 million visitors a year travel to Mount St. Helens Volcanic National Monument to see volcanism for themselves. The map in Figure 11.22 located a sampling of volcanoes across the planet. Some of the many volcanoes that are currently active include the Soufrière Hills on Montserrat (Lesser Antilles/Caribbean Sea), Mount Etna (Italy), Mount Ruapehu (New Zealand), Popocatépetl, (Mexico), Axial Summit (sea-floor spreading centre off the coast of Oregon), Villarrica (Chile), Nyiragongo (Congo, Africa), Piton de la Fournaise (Island of Reunion), and Mayon (Philippines), and the ongoing Kīlauea eruptions in Hawai'i. For a listing of currently active volcanoes, with links, see http://volcano.und.nodak.edu/vwdocs/current_volcs/current.html.

Other useful Internet resources include an index to the world's volcanoes at http://vulcan.wr.usgs.gov/Volcanoes/framework.html and the Smithsonian's Global Volcanism Program at http://www.volcano.si.edu/gvp/. A source of information about volcanoes on the Web is at the University of North Dakota's "Volcano World" http://volcano.und.nodak.edu/, or check http://www.geo.mtu.edu/volcanoes/links/observatories.html for links to volcano observatories across the globe.

Volcanic Features

A **volcano** forms at the end of a central vent or pipe that rises from the asthenosphere and upper mantle through the crust into a volcanic mountain. A **crater**, or circular surface depression, usually forms at or near the summit. Magma rises and collects in a magma chamber deep below the volcano until conditions are right for an eruption. This subsurface magma emits tremendous heat, and in some areas it boils groundwater, producing *geothermal energy*, as seen in the thermal springs and geysers of Yellowstone National Park, or elsewhere in the world where it is harnessed for geothermal power production.

Lava (molten rock), gases, and **pyroclastics**, or *tephra* (pulverized rock and clastic materials of various sizes ejected violently during an eruption) pass through the vent to the surface and build a volcanic landform. There are two principal forms of flowing basaltic lava, both named in Hawaiian terms (Figure 12.26). **Aa** is a basaltic lava that is rough and jagged with sharp edges. This texture happens because the lava loses trapped gases, flows slowly, and develops a thick skin that cracks into the jagged surface. Another principal lava texture that is more fluid than aa is **pahoehoe**. As this lava flows it forms a thin crust that develops folds and appears "ropy," like coiled, twisted rope. Both forms can come from the same eruption, and sometimes pahoehoe will become aa as the flow progresses. Other types of basaltic magma are described later in this section.

A **cinder cone** is a small cone-shaped hill usually less than 450 m (1500 ft) high, with a truncated top formed from cinders that accumulate during moderately explosive eruptions. Cinder cones are made of pyroclastic material and *scoria* (cindery rock, full of air bubbles).

Another distinctive landform is a large basin-shaped depression called a **caldera** (Spanish for "kettle"). It forms when summit material on a volcanic mountain collapses inward after an eruption or other loss of magma. In the Cape Verde Islands (15° N 24.5° W), Fogo Island has such a caldera in the midst of a volcanic cone, opening to the sea on the eastern side. The best farmland is in the caldera, so the people choose to live and work on the floor of an active volcano. Unfortunately, eruptions began in April 1995, destroying farmland and forcing the evacuation of 5000 people. A cinder cone 600 m (1800 ft) high formed in the former farmlands. The area experienced eruptions between A.D. 1500 and 1750, followed by six more in the next century, each destroying houses and crops. The previous eruption before the 1995 activity was in 1951.

An example of a caldera in North America is beautiful Crater Lake in southern Oregon. News Report 12.4 discusses the Long Valley Caldera in California.

Formation of Crater Lake

Location and Types of Volcanic Activity

The location of volcanic mountains on Earth is a function of plate tectonics and hot-spot activity. Volcanic activity occurs in three settings:

1. Along subduction boundaries at continental plate–oceanic plate convergence (such as Mount St. Helens and Kliuchevskoi, Siberia) or oceanic plate–oceanic plate convergence (Philippines and Japan);
2. Along sea-floor spreading centres on the ocean floor (Iceland on the Mid-Atlantic Ridge, or off the coast of Oregon and Washington) and areas of rifting on continental plates (the rift zone in east Africa);
3. At hot spots, where individual plumes of magma rise to the crust (such as Hawai'i and Yellowstone National Park).

(a) Aa

(b) Pahoehoe

FIGURE 12.26 Two types of basaltic lava—Hawaiian examples.
(a) Aa is a rough, sharp-edged lava that is said to get its name from the sounds people make when they take off their shoes and attempt to walk on it. The gold-coloured strands are clumps of natural spun glass formed by the lava as it blew out into the air, and are called Pele's hair. (b) Pahoehoe forms ropy cords in twisted folds. [Photos by Bobbé Christopherson.]

Tectonic Settings and Volcanic Activity

News Report 12.4

Is the Long Valley Caldera Next?

Trees are dying in the forests on Mammoth Mountain, in a portion of the Long Valley Caldera, near the California–Nevada border. The oval caldera is about 15 by 30 km (9 by 19 mi) long in a north-south direction and sits at 2000 m (6500 ft) elevation, rising to 2600 m (8500 ft) along the western side.

About 1080 metric tons (1200 tons) of carbon dioxide is coming up through the soil in the old caldera each day. Carbon dioxide levels reach 30% to 96% of gases in some soil samples. The source: active and moving magma at some 3 km depth. Elsewhere in the world, this and other gas emissions assist forecasts of potential volcanic activity. At Mammoth Mountain, these gases signify magmatic activity and may be a portent of things to come (Figure 1).

A powerful volcanic eruption 730,000 years ago formed the Long Valley Caldera. This ancient eruption exceeded the volume output of the 1980 Mount St. Helens event by more than 500 times! Volcanic activity of a lesser extent has occurred in the area over the past several hundred thousand years, most recently between A.D. 1720 and 1850 in the Mono Lake area north of Long Valley.

In the late 1970s and again in 1996, continuing through 1998, swarms of earthquakes shook Long Valley—thousands of quakes overall, some three dozen greater than magnitude 3.0. The subsurface foci for these quakes is at about 11 km beneath the region. As of this writing, the surface has not been lifted or deformed by this activity. The combination of volcanic gas production and earthquakes is drawing scientific and public attention to this area because of the potential for a future massive eruption somewhere along the Mono-Inyo Craters stretching north of Long Valley. The region is a popular tourist mecca and recreational centre, with second-home residential development and a growing year-round population. For updates, see **http://lvo.wr.usgs.gov/**.

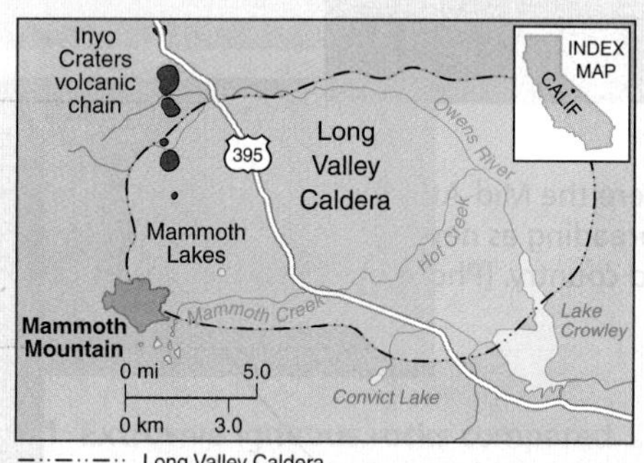

FIGURE 1 Trees are dying. Forest killed by carbon dioxide and a warning sign about the danger. The hazard has killed one person to date. The CO_2 is gassing up through soils from subsurface magma and related volcanic activity. [Photo by Bobbé Christopherson.]

Figure 12.27 illustrates the three types of volcanic activity, which you can compare with the active volcano sites and plate boundaries shown in Figure 11.22. Figures 12.28 to 12.33 illustrate the various aspects of volcanism presented in Figure 12.27.

The variety of forms among volcanoes makes them difficult to classify; most fall in transition between one type and another. Even during a single eruption, a volcano may behave in several different ways. The primary factors in determining an eruption type are (1) the magma's chemistry, which is related to its source, and (2) the magma's viscosity. Viscosity is the magma's resistance to flow ("thickness"), ranging from low viscosity (very fluid) to high viscosity (thick and flowing slowly). We consider two types of eruptions—effusive and explosive—and the characteristic landforms they build.

Effusive Eruptions

Effusive eruptions are the relatively gentle ones that produce enormous volumes of lava annually on the seafloor and in places such as Hawai'i and Iceland. These direct eruptions from the asthenosphere and upper mantle produce a low-viscosity magma that is very fluid and cools to form a dark, basaltic rock (less than 50% silica and rich in iron and magnesium). Gases readily escape from this magma because of its low viscosity, causing a relatively gentle **effusive eruption** that pours out on the surface, with relatively small explosions and little pyroclastics. However, dramatic fountains of basaltic lava sometimes shoot upward, powered by jets of rapidly expanding gases.

An effusive eruption may come from a single vent or from the flank of a volcano, through a side vent. If such vents form a linear opening, they are called *fissures*; these sometimes erupt in a dramatic *curtain of fire* (sheets of molten rock spraying into the air). In Iceland, active fissures are spread throughout the plateau landscape. Rift zones capable of erupting tend to converge on the central crater, or vent, as they do in Hawai'i. The interior of such a crater, often a sunken caldera, may fill with low-viscosity magma during an eruption, forming a molten lake, which then may overflow lava downslope in dramatic rivers and falls of molten rock.

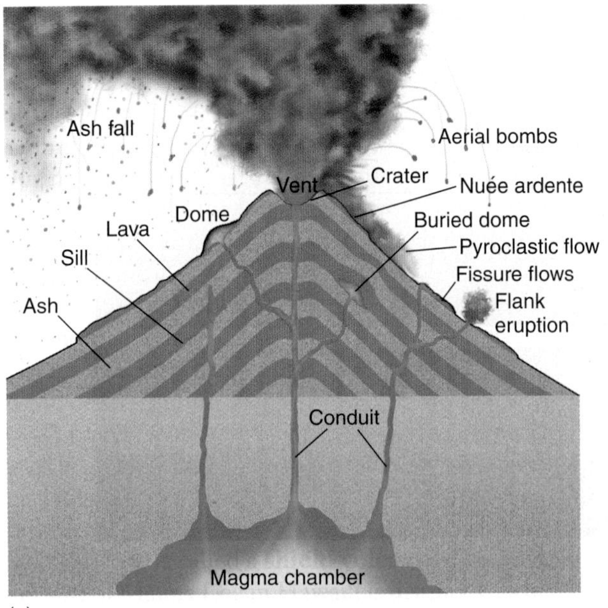

FIGURE 12.37 A composite volcano.
(a) A typical composite volcano with its cone-shaped form. (b) An eruption of Mount Shishaldin, Alaska, a composite volcano, during a 1995 eruption; it was active through 2001. [(b) Photo courtesy of AeroMap U.S., Inc., Anchorage, Alaska.]

reported eruption in 1500 B.C. The current cycle began with huge amounts of magma moving upward and inflating the summit in 1994. Dramatic Strombolian-type eruptions of spraying and jetting fountains of lava were visible from a 30-km distance. Summit and flank eruptions have marked the ensuing years, such as the latest in the sequence during October 2002 (Figure 12.38). The summit crater emitted ash during the spring of 2004, suggesting that magma was again on the move in the volcano's upper conduit. Rather than being perceived as an immediate danger, such activity is stimulating tourism.

Mount Pinatubo Eruption In June 1991, after 600 years of dormancy, Mount Pinatubo in the Philippines erupted. The summit of the 1460-m (4795-ft) volcano exploded, devastating many surrounding villages and permanently

(continued p. 408)

FIGURE 12.38 Ageless Mount Etna, on the isle of Sicily.
Mount Etna erupts in view of the International Space Station (ISS). Visible is the ash and steam from a vigorous eruption. Gas emissions are along the north slope (lower left) through a series of vents. Smoke on the lower slope is from wildfires set by lava-flows. View is to the southeast across the island of Sicily. Ashfall from this episode reached North Africa. [October 30, 2002, ISS photo courtesy of Earth Science and Image Analysis Laboratory, JSC, NASA.]

Table 12.4 Notable Composite Volcano Eruptions

Date	Location	Number of Deaths	Amount Extruded (mostly pyroclastics) in km^3 (mi^3)
Prehistoric	Yellowstone, Wyoming	Unknown	2400 (576)
4600 B.C.	Mount Mazama (Crater Lake, Oregon)	Unknown	50–70 (12–17)
1900 B.C.	Mount St. Helens	Unknown	4 (0.95)
A.D. 79	Mount Vesuvius, Italy	20,000	3 (0.7)
1500	Mount St. Helens	Unknown	1 (0.24)
1815	Tambora, Indonesia	66,000	80–100 (19–24)
1883	Krakatau, Indonesia	36,000	18 (4.3)
1902	Mont Pelée, Martinique	29,000	Unknown
1912	Mount Katmai, Alaska	Unknown	12 (2.9)
1943–1952	Paricutín, Mexico	0	1.3 (0.30)
1980	Mount St. Helens	54	4 (0.95)
1985	Nevado del Ruiz, Colombia	23,000	1 (0.24)
1991	Mount Unzen, Japan	10	2 (0.5)
1991	Mount Pinatubo, Philippines	800	12 (3.0)
1992	Mount Spurr/Mount Shishaldin, Alaska	0	1 (0.24)
1993	Galeras Volcano, Colombia	5	1 (0.24)
1993, 2003, 2004	Mount Mayon, Philippines	0	1 (0.24)
1994, 2004	Kliuchevskoi, Russia	0	1 (0.24)
1995–2004	Soufrière Hills, Montserrat, West Indies	0	Ash, steam, pyroclastic flows
2002	Nyiragongo, Congo	70	1 (0.24)

Focus Study 12.2

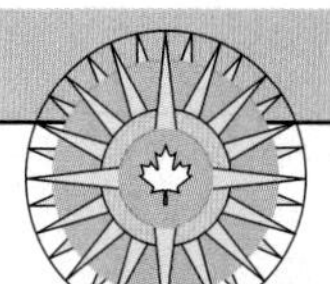

The 1980 Eruption of Mount St. Helens

Probably the most studied and photographed composite (explosive) volcano on Earth is Mount St. Helens, located 70 km (45 mi) northeast of Portland, Oregon, and 130 km (80 mi) south of the Tacoma–Seattle area of Washington. Mount St. Helens is the youngest and most active of the Cascade Range of volcanoes, which form a line from Mount Lassen in California to Mount Meager in British Columbia (Figure 1). The Cascade Range is the product of the Juan de Fuca sea-floor spreading centre off the coast of northern California, Oregon, Washington, and British Columbia and the plate subduction that occurs offshore, as identified in the upper right of Figure 12.12.

The mountain had been quiet since 1857. New activity began in March 1980, with a sharp earthquake registering a magnitude 4.1. The first eruptive outburst occurred one week later, beginning with a magnitude 4.5 quake and continuing with a thick black plume of ash and the development of a small summit crater. Ten days later, the first volcanic earthquake, called a *harmonic tremor*, registered on the many instruments that had been hurriedly placed around the volcano. Harmonic tremors are slow, steady vibrations, unlike the sharp releases of energy associated with tectonic earthquakes and faulting. Harmonic tremors told scientists that magma was on the move within the mountain.

Also developing was a massive bulge on the north side of the mountain. This bulge indicated the direction of the magma flow within the volcano. A bulge represents the greatest risk from a composite volcano, for it could signal a potential lateral burst through the bulge and across the landscape.

Early on Sunday, May 18, the area north of the mountain was rocked by a magnitude 5.0 quake, the strongest to date. The mountain, with its distended 245-m (800-ft) bulge, was shaken, but nothing happened. Then a second quake (magnitude 5.1) hit at 8:32 A.M., loosening the bulge and launching the eruption. David Johnston, a volcanologist with the U.S. Geological Survey, was only 8 km (5 mi) from the mountain, servicing instruments, when he saw the eruption begin. He radioed headquarters in Vancouver, Washington, saying, "Vancouver, Vancouver, this is it!" He perished in the eruption. For a continuously updated live picture of Mount St. Helens from Johnston's approximate observation point and other specifics, go to http://www.fs.fed.us/gpnf/volcanocams/msh/. The camera is mounted below the roof line at the Johnston Ridge Observatory 8 km from the mountain. The observatory is open to the public and is named for this brave scientist.

(continued)

Focus Study 12.2 *(continued)*

(a)

(b)

(c)

FIGURE 1 Mount St. Helens before and after the eruption—days and years later. (a) Mount St. Helens prior to the 1980 eruption. (b) The devastated and scorched land shortly after the eruption in 1980. The scorched earth and tree blowdown area covered some 38,950 hectares (95,000 acres). (c) A landscape in recovery as life moves back in and takes hold to establish new ecosystems in 1999 along the Toutle River and debris flow. [(a) Photo by Pat and Tom Lesson/Photo Researchers; (b) photo by Krafft-Explorer/Photo Researchers, Inc.; (c) photo by Bobbé Christopherson.]

As the contents of the mountain exploded, a surge of hot gas (about 300°C, or 570°F), steam-filled ash, pyroclastics, and a *nuée ardente* (rapidly moving, very hot, explosive ash and incandescent gases) moved northward, hugging the ground and travelling at speeds up to 400 kmph (250 mph) for a distance of 28 km (17 mi).

The slumping north face of the mountain produced the greatest landslide witnessed in recorded history; about 2.75 km^3 (0.67 mi^3) of rock, ice, and trapped air, all fluidized with steam, surged at speeds approaching 250 kmph (155 mph). Landslide materials travelled for 21 km (13 mi) into the valley, blanketing the forest, covering a lake, and filling the rivers below. A series of photographs, taken at 10-second intervals from the east looking west, records this sequence (Figure 2). The eruption continued with intensity for nine hours, first clearing out old rock from the throat of the volcano and then blasting new material.

As destructive as such eruptions are, they also are constructive, for this is the way in which a volcano eventually builds its height. Before the eruption, Mount St. Helens was 2950 m (9677 ft) tall; the eruption blew away 418 m (1370 ft). Today, Mount St. Helens is building a lava dome within its crater. The thick lava rapidly and repeatedly plugs and breaks in a series of lesser dome eruptions that may continue for several decades. The dome already is more than 300 m (1000 ft) high, so a new mountain is being born from the eruption of the old. The dome is covered with a dozen survey benchmarks and several tiltmeters to monitor the status of the volcano. Swarms of minor earthquakes along the north flank of the mountain began in November 2001, marking this mountain as still unstable. Dome eruptions of varying intensities occurred during 2004 and 2005. Intensive scientific research and monitoring has paid off, as every eruption since 1980 was successfully forecasted from days to as long as three weeks in advance, with the exception of one small eruption in 1984.

An ever-resilient ecology is recovering as plants and animals reclaim the devastated landscape. Please refer to the dramatic comparison photos from 1983 and 1999 in Figure 19.27. More than two decades have passed, yet strong interest in the area continues; scientists and more than 1 million tourists visit the Mount St. Helens Volcanic National Monument each year. For more information, see the Cascades Volcano Observatory at **http://vulcan.wr.usgs.gov/** and specifically Mount St. Helens at **http://vulcan.wr.usgs.gov/Volcanoes/MSH/framework.html.**

closing Clark Air Force Base operated by the United States. Fortunately, scientists from the U.S. Geological Survey and local scientists accurately predicted the eruption. A resulting timely evacuation of the surrounding countryside saved thousands of lives, but 800 people were killed.

Although volcanoes are regional events, their spatial implications can be worldwide. The single volcanic eruption of Mount Pinatubo was significant to the global environment and energy budget, as discussed in Chapters 1, 3, 4, 5, and 10:

- 13.6–18.1 million metric tons (15–20 million tons) of ash and sulphuric acid mist were blasted into the atmosphere, concentrating at 16–25 km (10–15.5 mi) altitude

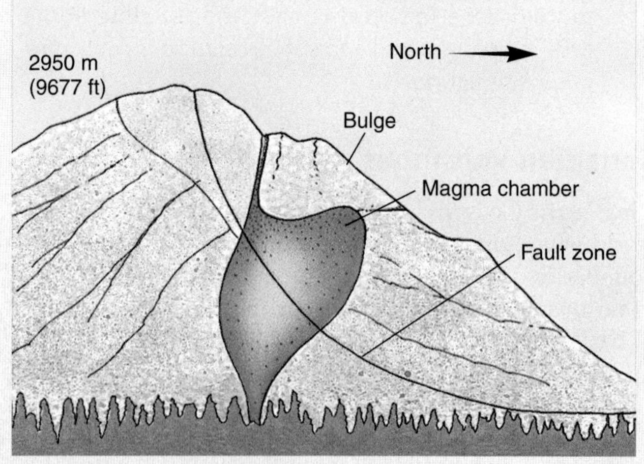

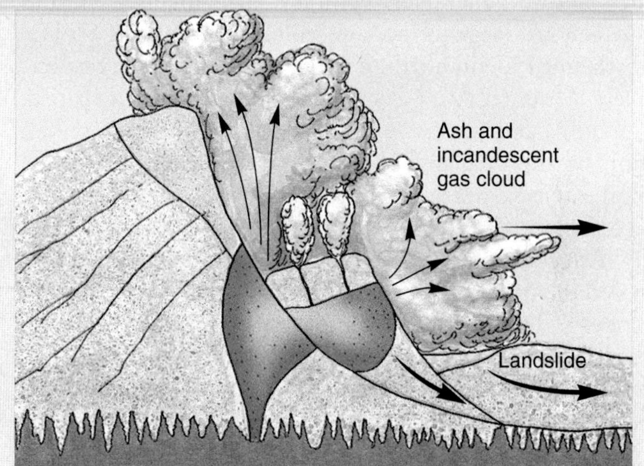

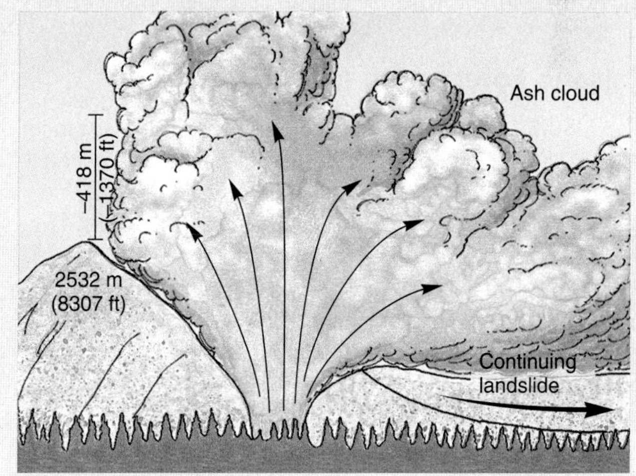

FIGURE 2 The Mount St. Helens eruption sequence and corresponding schematics.
[Photo sequence by Keith Ronnholm.]

- 12 km^3 (3.0 mi^3) of material was ejected and extruded by the eruption (12 times the volume from Mount St. Helens)
- 60 days after the eruption, about 42% of the globe was affected (from 20° S to 30° N) by the thin, spreading aerosol cloud in the atmosphere
- Colourful twilight and dawn skies were observed worldwide
- An increase in atmospheric albedo of 1.5% (4.3 W/m^2) occurred
- An increase in the atmospheric absorption of insolation followed (2.5 W/m^2)
- A decrease in net radiation at the surface and a lowering of Northern Hemisphere average temperatures of 0.5 C° (0.9 F°) were measured

- Atmospheric scientists and volcanologists were able to study the eruption aftermath using satellite-borne orbiting sensors and general circulation model computer simulations.

Canadian Volcanoes

The Pacific Coast of Canada is one of the few areas in the world where divergent, convergent, and transform plate boundaries occur in proximity to one another, giving rise to various types of volcanic activity (Figure 12.39). Mount Baker, Mount Garibaldi, Mount Meager, and Mount Edziza are among the most prominent volcanic landforms in western Canada. Mount Baker is a large, active, composite volcano situated in the Cascade Mountain Range of Washington State, approximately 100 km southeast of the city of Vancouver. Mount Garibaldi and Mount Meager are large composite volcanoes situated 80 km north and 150 km north of the city of Vancouver, respectively. Mount Edziza is situated in northwestern British Columbia and consists of four large composite volcanoes built on top of plateau basalts: It represents one of the most extensive volcanic regions in Canada covering an area of 1300 km^2 (502 mi^2).

Ash clouds, lava flows, and pyroclastic flows have dominated the post-glacial volcanic activity of all of these volcanoes and represent a threat to large population centres in British Columbia and Washington State. Airborne ash can result in severe damage to aircraft and represents the most important short-term hazard risk for the Canadian public. Debris flows (*lahars*) and floods (*jökulhlaups*) produced by the rapid melting of ice and snow on mountain summits can flow rapidly downslope and be extremely destructive.

FIGURE 12.39 Volcanoes and their tectonic environment in Western Canada.
Volcanic activity occurs in three tectonic settings: (1) along convergent plate boundaries experiencing subduction (for example, Mount Garibaldi, Mount Meager); (2) in regions of rifting on continental plates (for example, Mount Edziza, Mount Iskut); and (3) at hot spots where plumes of magma break through the crust (for example, Mount Nazko). The green lines indicate transform faults, while the circled areas indicate the boundaries of different types of volcanism. [Map adapted courtesy of Geological Survey of Canada, Hickson & Edwards 2002; *Volcanic Hazards: Canadian Hazards Atlas*, GSC Bulletin 548.]

Volcano Forecasting and Planning

The USGS and the Office of Foreign Disaster Assistance of the U.S. Agency for International Development operate the Volcano Disaster Assistance Program (VDAP; see **http://vulcan.wr.usgs.gov/Vdap/framework.html**). The need for such a program is evident in that, over the past 15 years, volcanic activity has killed 29,000 people, forced more than 800,000 to evacuate their homes, and caused more than $3 billion in damage. The program was established after 23,000 people died in the eruption of Nevado del Ruiz, Colombia, in 1985.

The U.S. VDAP is in place to help local scientists with eruption forecasts by setting up mobile volcano-monitoring systems at the most-threatened sites. An effort such as this led to the life-saving evacuation of 60,000 people hours before Mount Pinatubo exploded. In addition, satellite remote sensing is helping VDAP to monitor eruption cloud dynamics, atmospheric emissions and climatic effects, and lava and thermal measurements; to make topographic measurements; to estimate volcanic hazard potential; and to enhance geologic mapping—all in an effort to better understand our dynamic planet. Integrated seismographic networks and monitoring are making early warning systems possible.

In this era of the Internet you can access "volcano cams" positioned around the world to give you 24-hour surveillance of many volcanoes. For an exciting visual adventure, go to the following URL and add it to your bookmarks (note whether it is day or night for the location you are checking): **http://vulcan.wr.usgs.gov/Photo/volcano_cams.html**.

Applied Physical Geography

Magnitude and Frequency

Landscape processes operate at a number of different scales in time, space, and magnitude. The most frequently occurring processes often operate on smaller orders of magnitude. So powerful episodes occur less frequently than more gentle processes that operate on a daily or nearly continuous basis. The magnitude of a process refers to its size or intensity. Frequency refers to how often a process happens.

In considering earthquakes, intensity and magnitude are terms used in conjunction with an event. Intensity describes the effect of an earthquake at a particular location. Magnitude quantifies the energy released by an earthquake. Several scales can be used to measure earthquakes. The magnitude (M) of an earthquake is calculated, in part, by multiplying the distance the ground moved along a fault by the area of the fault's rupture surface. A surface rupture is the displacement of the ground surface that results from the movement of the fault deep within Earth.

Our current state of knowledge does not allow us to predict precisely when an earthquake will occur, but we can state an earthquake recurrence rate. We can use the record of the frequency and magnitude of earthquakes in an area as the basis for calculating the probability that an earthquake of a given magnitude will occur. First, assuming that earthquakes will occur in the future at the same rate and magnitude that they occurred in the past, we must have a historical record of earthquakes and their magnitudes. These must then be categorized and ranked. Then the return rate can be calculated by:

$$T_r = (n + 1)/m$$

where T_r is the return time, or the length of time in which we would expect the event to happen again, n is the total number of events, and m is the rank of the event. This method works well for areas that have a good history of earthquake occurrence. In areas where no large earthquake has been recorded, this would not be a good predictive tool. Table 12.1 (p. 393) presents a summary of the frequency of occurrence of minor and major earthquakes and the magnitude of these events.

We can use the recurrence rate equation to calculate the likelihood of a major quake (magnitude greater than 7) in western Canada based on the historic record provided in Table 1.

$$T_r = (n + 1)/m$$

$$T(\text{less than } 8) = (68 + 1)/1 = 69$$

Therefore, based on the historical record for western Canada, we would expect a major earthquake of greater than magnitude 7 to occur once in 69 years.

The probability of this occurrence can be calculated using the inverse of the above relationship expressed as a percentage.

$$T(\text{less than } 8) = (m/(n + 1)) \times 100 = (1/(68 + 1)) \times 100 = 1.45\%$$

There is a 1.45% likelihood that an earthquake greater than magnitude 7 will occur in western Canada based on the historical record.

Table 1 Frequency and Magnitude of Earthquakes Greater than 3.9 in Western Canada, 1995 to 2004

Magnitude	Frequency
Less than 5	40
Less than 6	20
Less than 7	7
Less than 8	1

Source: Reproduced with the permission of the Minister of Public Works and Government Services Canada, and Natural Resources Canada, Geological Survey of Canada. (**http://www.pgc.nrcan.gc.ca/seismo/recent/eqmaps.html**).

Summary and Review—Tectonics, Earthquakes, and Volcanism

- ***Describe* first, second, and third orders of relief and *relate* examples of each from Earth's major topographic regions.**

Earth's surface is dramatically shaped by tectonic forces generated within the planet. **Relief** is the vertical elevation difference in a local landscape. The undulating physical surface of Earth, including relief, is called **topography**. Convenient descriptive categories are termed *orders of relief*. The coarsest level of landforms includes the **continental landmasses** and **ocean basins**; the finest comprises local hills and valleys.

relief (p. 371)
topography (p. 371)
continental landmasses (p. 371)
ocean basins (p. 371)

1. How does the map of the ocean floor (chapter-opening illustration) exhibit the principles of plate tectonics? Briefly analyze.
2. What is meant by an "order of relief"? Give an example from each order.
3. Explain the difference between relief and topography.

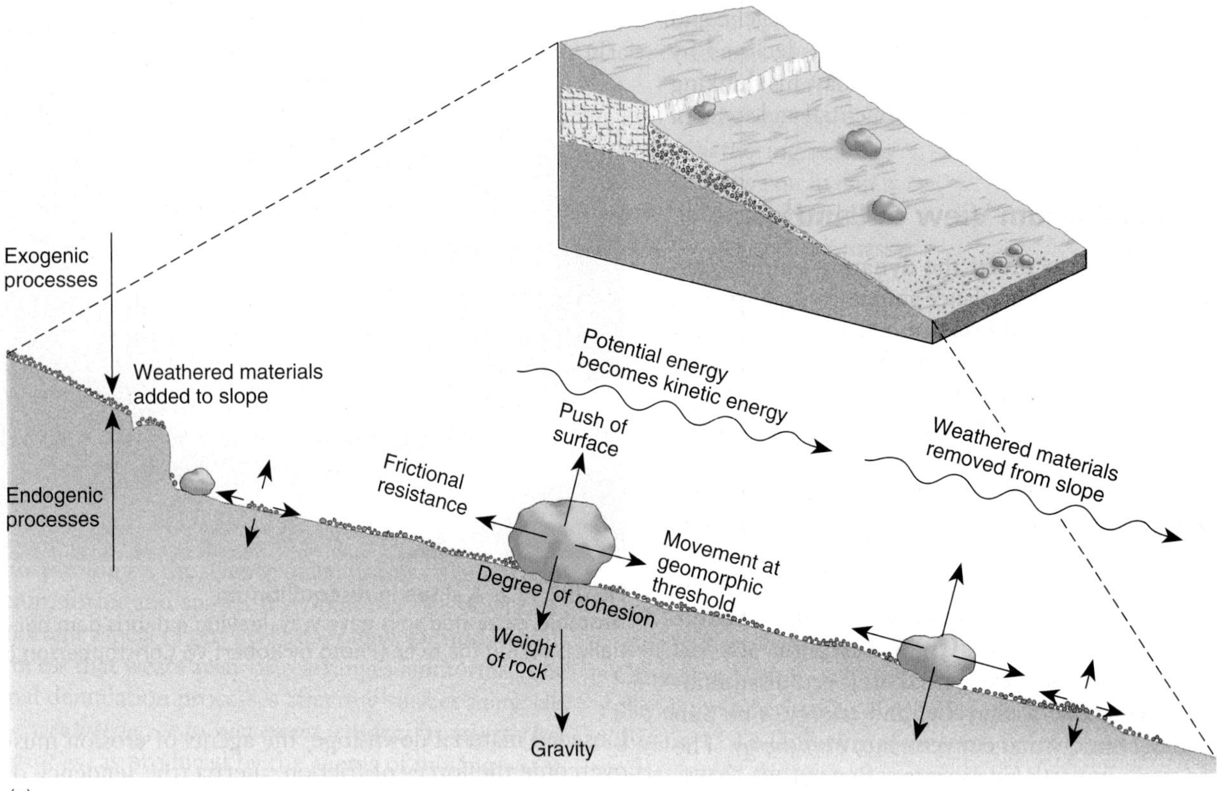

(a)

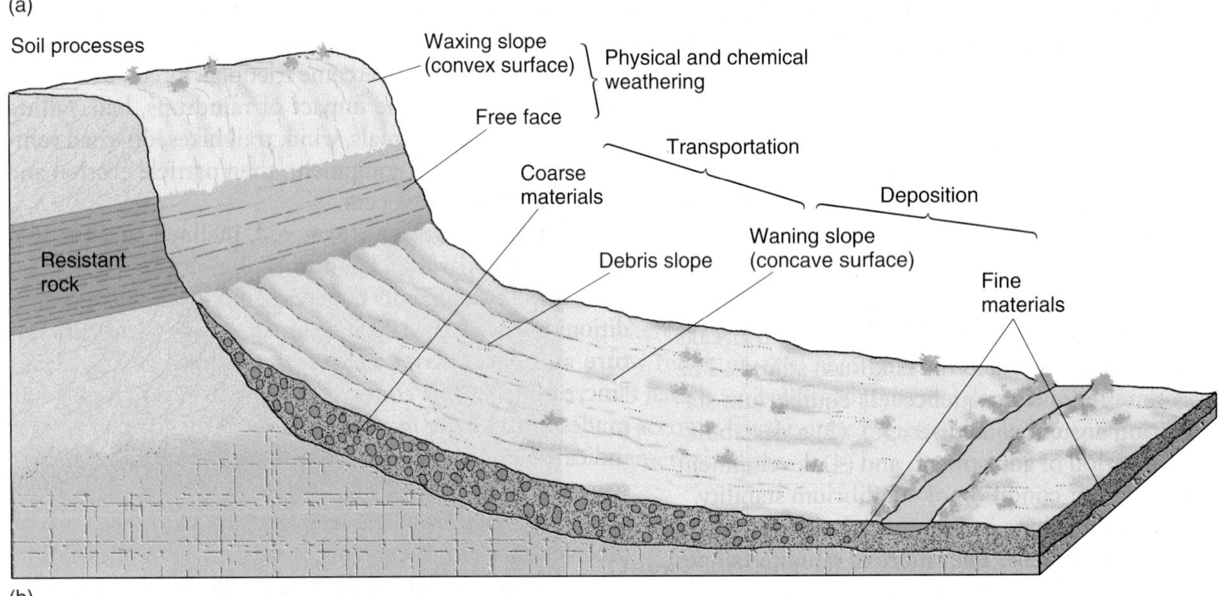

(b)

FIGURE 13.3 Slope mechanics and form.
(a) Directional forces (noted by arrows) act on materials along an inclined slope. (b) The principal elements of a slope.

The relation between rates of weathering and breakup of slope materials, coupled with the rates of mass movement and material erosion, shape slopes. A slope is *stable* if its strength exceeds these denudation processes and *unstable* if materials are weaker than these processes. Why are hillslopes shaped in certain ways? How do slope elements evolve? How do hillslopes behave during rapid, moderate, or slow uplift? These are topics of active scientific study and research.

Now, with the concepts of landmass denudation, dynamic equilibrium, and slope development in mind, let us examine specific processes that operate to wear away landforms.

Weathering Processes

Weathering processes attack rocks at Earth's surface and to some depth below the surface. **Weathering** processes

FIGURE 13.4 A hillslope example.
Compare this slope with the components mentioned in Figure 13.3. Note the role of the rock outcrop in interrupting the slope and the rock fragments that are loosened from the outcrop by frost action. [Photo by Robert W. Christopherson.]

either disintegrate rock into mineral particles or dissolve them in water. Weathering processes are both physical (mechanical) and chemical.

Weathering does not transport the materials; it simply generates them for erosion and transport by the agents of water, wind, waves, and ice—all influenced by gravity. In most areas, the upper surface of bedrock undergoes continual weathering, creating broken-up rock called **regolith**. Loose surface material comes from further weathering of regolith and from transported and deposited regolith (Figure 13.5a). In some areas, regolith may be missing or undeveloped, thus exposing an outcrop of unweathered bedrock. The thickness of the soil cover depends on a balance between soil production rates and erosion (removal of soil particles)—an equilibrium between competing processes.

Bedrock is the *parent rock* from which weathered regolith and soils develop. While a soil is relatively youthful, its parent rock is traceable through similarities in composition. For example, the sand in Figure 13.5c derives its colour and character from the parent rock in the cliff, just as the sediments on Mars derive their characteristics from the weathered parent material present (Figure 13.5d). This sandy unconsolidated fragmental material, known as **sediment**, combines with weathered rock to form the **parent material** from which soil evolves.

Factors Influencing Weathering Processes

Weathering is greatly influenced by the character of the bedrock: hard or soft, soluble or insoluble, broken or unbroken. *Jointing* in rock is important for weathering processes. **Joints** are fractures or separations in rock that occur without displacement of the sides (as would be the case in faulting). The presence of these usually plane (flat) surfaces increases the surface area of rock exposed to both physical and chemical weathering.

Important controls on weathering rates are climatic elements—precipitation, temperature, and freeze–thaw cycles. There is a relation among climate (annual precipitation and temperature), physical weathering, and chemical weathering processes. In general, physical weathering dominates in drier, cooler climates, whereas chemical weathering dominates in wetter, warmer climates. Extreme dryness reduces weathering rates, as is experienced in desert climates (*low- and midlatitude hot desert*). In the hot, wet, tropical and equatorial rain forest climates (*tropical rain forest*), most rocks weather rapidly, and the weathering extends deep below the surface. Also related to climate and significant weathering is the position of the water table and water movement on and within rock structures and the subsurface environment.

Another control over weathering rates is the *geographic orientation* of a slope—whether it faces north, south, east, or west. Orientation controls the slope's exposure to Sun, wind, and precipitation. Slopes facing away from the Sun's rays tend to be cooler, moister, and more vegetated than slopes in direct sunlight. This effect of orientation is especially noticeable in the middle and higher latitudes.

Vegetation is also a factor in weathering. Although vegetative cover can protect rock by shielding it from raindrop impact and providing roots to stabilize soil, it also produces organic acids from the partial decay of organic matter; these acids contribute to chemical weathering. Plant roots can enter crevices and break up a rock, exerting enough pressure to drive rock segments apart, thereby exposing greater surface area to other weathering processes (Figure 13.6). You may have observed how tree roots can heave the sections of a sidewalk or driveway sufficiently to raise and crack the concrete.

The scale at which we analyze weathering processes is important. Research at *microscale* levels reveals greater complexity in the relation of climate and weathering. At the small scale of actual reaction sites on the rock surface, both physical and chemical weathering processes can occur across varied climate types. Hygroscopic water (a molecule-thin water layer on soil particles) and capillary water (soil water) activates chemical weathering processes, even in the driest landscape. (Review sections in Chapter 9 for these water types.)

Imagine all the factors that influence weathering rates as operating in concert: climatic influence (precipitation and temperature), soil water and groundwater, rock composition and structure (jointing), slope orientation, vegetation, and microscopic boundary-layer conditions at reaction sites. We separate these processes here for convenience of study. Of course in all this, *time* is the crucial factor, for these processes require long periods of time to operate.

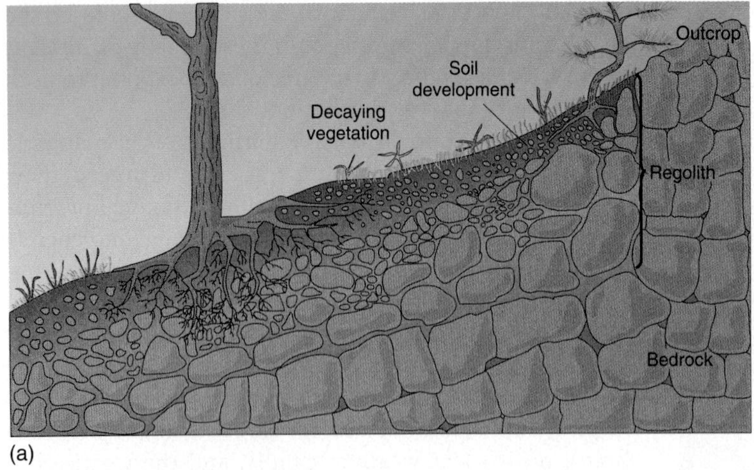

(a)

(b)

(c)

(d)

FIGURE 13.5 Regolith, soil, and parent materials.
(a) A cross section of a typical hillside. (b) A cliff exposes hillside components. (c) The red sand beaches of Prince Edward Island derive their colour from the red sandstone parent material of the cliff. (d) This image, from a larger panoramic scene, was made by the Mars Exploration Rover *Spirit* on March 12, 2004. Looking toward the Columbia Hills, you can see weathered rocks and windblown sand in approximate true colours. [Photos by (b) Robert W. Christopherson; (c) Mary-Louise Byrne; (d) Mars image courtesy of NASA/JPL and Cornell University.]

Physical Weathering Processes

When rock is broken and disintegrated without any chemical alteration, the process is called **physical weathering** or *mechanical weathering*. By breaking up rock, physical weathering produces more surface area on which chemical weathering may operate. A single rock that becomes broken into eight pieces has doubled its surface area susceptible to weathering processes. We look briefly at three physical weathering processes: frost action, crystallization, and pressure-release jointing.

Frost Action When water freezes, its volume expands as much as 9% (see Chapter 7). Such expansion creates a powerful mechanical force called **frost action**, or *freeze–thaw action*, which can exceed the tensional strength of rock. Repeated freezing (expanding) and thawing (contracting) of water breaks rocks apart (Figure 13.7). Freezing actions

(a)

(b)

FIGURE 13.6 Organic physical weathering.
(a) Can you find the tree root growing in and on the jointing fracture in the rock? (b) Roots exert a force on the sides of this joint in the rock. [Photos by Robert W. Christopherson.]

are important in the humid microthermal climates (*humid continental* and *subarctic*) and polar climates, and they occur at higher elevations in mountains worldwide in the highland climates. In arctic and subarctic climates, frost action dominates soil conditions (discussed in further detail in Chapter 17).

The work of ice begins in small openings, gradually expanding until rocks are cleaved (split). Figure 13.8a shows a block field in northwestern Manitoba. This rock surface was shattered and heaved by frost action. *Felsenmeer*, a result of a cold-climate process, usually forms in coarser grained rocks that contain few fines and results in a surface composed of coarse, angular blocks with soil absent from the upper layers. Frost action also causes *joint block separation* along existing joints and fractures (Figure 13.8c). This weathering action, called *frost-wedging*, pushes portions of rock apart. Cracking and breaking create varied shapes in the rocks depending on the rock structure.

In Figure 13.8b, frost wedging loosened rock from these cliffs. The angular pieces of rock fragments cascade down and form a **talus slope**, which is a poorly sorted, cone-shaped deposit of debris at the base of a steep slope. Several talus cones constitute such a talus slope in the photograph.

Frost action can have a dramatic effect on rock in areas of permafrost. In these areas where the ground temperature has remained below freezing for a considerable period of time, exposed bedrock surfaces can be covered with mounds of heaved rock called *rock blisters* that are 1–3 m high and 3–5 m in diameter. In the centre of Figure 13.9 is a rock blister in granite. The rock is broken along joint planes into equally sized blocks. In the background, the undisturbed bedrock is covered with glacially transported boulders. Rock blisters can occur on any type of rock. In western Nunavut, dolomite is a common sedimentary rock. *Frost-heaving* in jointed, horizontally bedded, competent bedrock

FIGURE 13.7 Climate and weathering.
A rock burst in a knob of Precambrian gneiss in permafrost terrain in northernmost Manitoba is evidence that the hydraulic pressures easily can exceed the strength of the rock. [Photo by Earth Sciences Sector, Natural Resources Canada GSC 2001-131.]

(a)

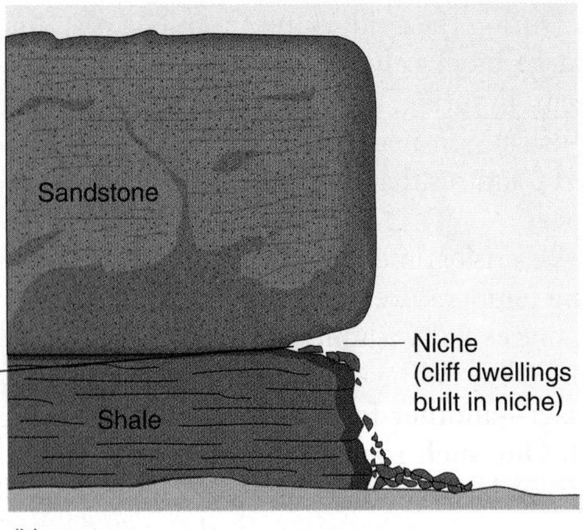

(b)

FIGURE 13.11 Physical weathering in sandstone. (a) Cliff dwelling site in Canyon de Chelly, Arizona, occupied by the Anasazi people until about 900 years ago. The niche in the rock was formed partially by crystallization, which forced apart mineral grains and broke up the rock. The dark streaks on the rock are thin coatings of desert varnish, composed of iron oxides with traces of manganese and silica. (b) Water and an impervious sandstone layer helped concentrate weathering processes in the niche. [Photo by Robert W. Christopherson.]

As an example of the way chemical weathering attacks rock, consider **spheroidal weathering**. The sharp edges and corners of rocks are rounded as the alteration of minerals progresses through the rock. Joints in the rock offer more surfaces of opportunity for more weathering. Water penetrates joints and fractures and dissolves the rock's weaker minerals or cementing materials. A boulder can be attacked from all sides, shedding spherical shells of decayed rock, like the layers of an onion. The resulting rounded edges are the basis for the name *spheroidal*.

Spheroidal weathering of rock resembles exfoliation, but it does not result from pressure-release jointing. Examples of spheroidal weathering include photos in Figure 13.13 from the Alabama Hills area of eastern California.

We now look at four chemical weathering processes: hydration, hydrolysis, oxidation, and carbonation and solution.

Hydration and Hydrolysis Two processes involving water, one of simple combination with a mineral and the other of chemical reaction with a mineral, work to decompose rock. In this book these are grouped under chemical weathering because both involve chemical actions. **Hydration**, meaning "combination with water," involves little chemical change. Water becomes part of the chemical composition of the mineral (e.g., gypsum or hydrous calcium sulphate: $CaSO_4 \cdot 2H_2O$). When some minerals hydrate, they expand, creating a strong mechanical effect that stresses the rock, forcing grains apart.

A cycle of hydration and dehydration can lead to granular disintegration and further susceptibility of the rock to chemical weathering. Hydration works together with carbonation and oxidation to convert feldspar, a common mineral in many rocks, to clay minerals and silica. The hydration process is also at work on the sandstone niches shown in Figure 13.11.

The process called **hydrolysis** occurs when minerals chemically combine with water. Hydrolysis is a decomposition process that breaks down silicate minerals in rocks. Compared with hydration, in which water attaches to minerals in the rock, hydrolysis involves active participation of water in chemical reactions to produce different compounds.

For example, the weathering of feldspar minerals in granite can be caused by a reaction to the normal mild acids dissolved in precipitation:

feldspar (K, Al, Si, O) + carbonic acid and water →
residual clays + dissolved minerals + silica

The by-products of chemical weathering of feldspar in granite include clay (such as kaolinite) and silica. As clay forms from some minerals in the granite, quartz (SiO_2) particles are left behind. The resistant quartz may wash downstream, eventually becoming sand on a distant beach. Clay minerals become a major component in soil and shale, a common sedimentary rock.

When weaker minerals in rock are changed by hydrolysis, the interlocking crystal network breaks down, the rock fails, and *granular disintegration* takes place. Such disintegration in granite may make the rock appear etched, corroded, and softened (Figure 13.13b).

In Table 11.2, the second line shows resistance to chemical weathering in igneous rocks. On the ultramafic end of the table (right side), the low-silica minerals olivine and periodotite are most susceptible to chemical weathering. Stability gradually increases toward the high-silica minerals such as feldspar. On the far left side of the table, quartz is resistant to chemical weathering. You can see that, because of the nature of the constituent minerals, basalt weathers faster chemically than granite.

Oxidation Another example of chemical weathering occurs when certain metallic elements combine with oxygen to form oxides. This is a chemical weathering process known as **oxidation**. Perhaps the most familiar oxidation form is the "rusting" of iron in rocks or soil that produces a reddish brown stain of iron oxide (Fe_2O_3). We have all left a tool or nails outside only to find them weeks later, coated with iron oxide. The rusty colour is visible on the surfaces of rock and in heavily oxidized soils such as those in Prince Edward Island, New Brunswick, the southeastern United States, southwestern deserts, or the tropics (Figure 13.14). Here is a simple oxidation reaction in iron:

$$\text{iron (Fe)} + \text{oxygen } (O_2) \rightarrow \text{iron oxide (hematite; } Fe_2O_3)$$

As iron is removed from the minerals in a rock, the disruption of the crystal structures in the rock's minerals makes the rock more susceptible to further chemical weathering and disintegration.

Carbonation and Solution The third form of chemical weathering occurs when a mineral dissolves into *solution*—for example, when sodium chloride (common table salt) dissolves in water. Water is the universal solvent because it

(a)

(b)

(c)

FIGURE 13.12 Exfoliation in granite.
Exfoliation processes loosen slabs of granite, freeing them for further weathering and downslope movement: (a) Great arches form in the White Mountains of New Hampshire. (b) Exfoliated layers of rock are visible in characteristic dome formations in granites. The loosened slabs of rock are susceptible to further weathering and downslope movement. This view is from the east side of Half Dome in Yosemite National Park, California. (c) Half Dome perspective from the west; relief is approximately 1500 m (5000 ft) from the top of the dome to the glaciated valley below. [Photos by (a) Bobbé Christopherson; (b) and (c) Robert W. Christopherson.]

(a)

(b)

(c)

FIGURE 13.13 Chemical weathering and spheroidal weathering.
(a) Chemical weathering processes act on the joints in granite to dissolve weaker minerals, leading to a rounding of the edges of the cracks. (b) Rounded granite outcrop demonstrates spheroidal weathering and the disintegration of rock. (c) The rugged, weathered Alabama Hills, Mount Whitney in the background, provides scenic backdrops for many commercials and movies. You can imagine a movie chase scene raising clouds of dust! [Photos by Bobbé Christopherson.]

is capable of dissolving at least 57 of the natural elements and many of their compounds.

Water vapour readily dissolves carbon dioxide, thereby yielding precipitation containing carbonic acid (H_2CO_3). This acid is strong enough to react with many minerals, especially limestone, in a process called **carbonation**. *Carbonation* simply means reactions whereby carbon combines with minerals.

Such carbonation chemical weathering transforms minerals that contain calcium, magnesium, potassium, and

(a)

(b)

FIGURE 13.14 Oxidation processes in rock and soil.
(a) Oxidation of iron minerals produces these brilliant red colours in the sandstone formations of the cliffs on the north shore of Prince Edward Island. (b) Soil on the island is coloured by the red Humo-Ferric Podzolic soil common to most of the province. [Photos by Mary-Louise Byrne.]

sodium. When rainwater attacks formations of limestone (which is calcium carbonate, $CaCO_3$), the constituent minerals dissolve and wash away with the mildly acidic rainwater:

calcium carbonate + carbonic acid and water →
calcium bicarbonate ($Ca_2^{2+}CO_2H_2O$)

Walk through an old cemetery and you can observe the carbonation of marble, a metamorphic form of limestone. Weathered limestone and marble, in tombstones or in rock formations, appear pitted and weathered wherever adequate water is available for carbonation. In this era of human-induced increases of acid precipitation, carbonation processes are greatly enhanced (see Focus Study 3.2, "Acid Deposition: A Continuing Blight on the Landscape").

The chemical weathering process of carbonation dominates entire landscapes composed of limestone. These are the regions of karst topography, which we examine next.

Karst Topography and Landscapes

Carbonate rocks, including limestone, are so abundant on Earth that many landscapes are composed of them (Figure 13.15). These areas are quite susceptible to chemical weathering and form the principal sites for *karst processes*, in operation on nearly 10% of the areas portrayed on the map. Such weathering creates a specific landscape of pitted, bumpy surface topography, poor surface drainage, and well-developed solution channels (dissolved openings and conduits) underground. Remarkable mazes of underworld caverns also may develop, owing to weathering and erosion caused by groundwater.

These are the hallmarks of **karst topography**, named for the Krš Plateau, Slovenia (formerly in Yugoslavia), where karst processes were first studied. Approximately 15% of Earth's land area has some karst features, with outstanding examples found in southern China, Japan, Puerto Rico, Cuba, the Yucatán of Mexico, Kentucky, Indiana, New Mexico, and Florida. As an example, approximately 38% of Kentucky has sinkholes and related karst features noted on topographic maps.

Formation of Karst

For a limestone landscape to develop into karst topography, there are several necessary conditions:

- The limestone formation must contain 80% or more calcium carbonate for solution processes to proceed effectively.
- Complex patterns of joints in the otherwise impermeable limestone are needed for water to form routes to subsurface drainage channels.
- There must be an aerated (containing air) zone between the ground surface and the water table.
- Vegetation cover supplies varying amounts of organic acids that enhance the solution process.

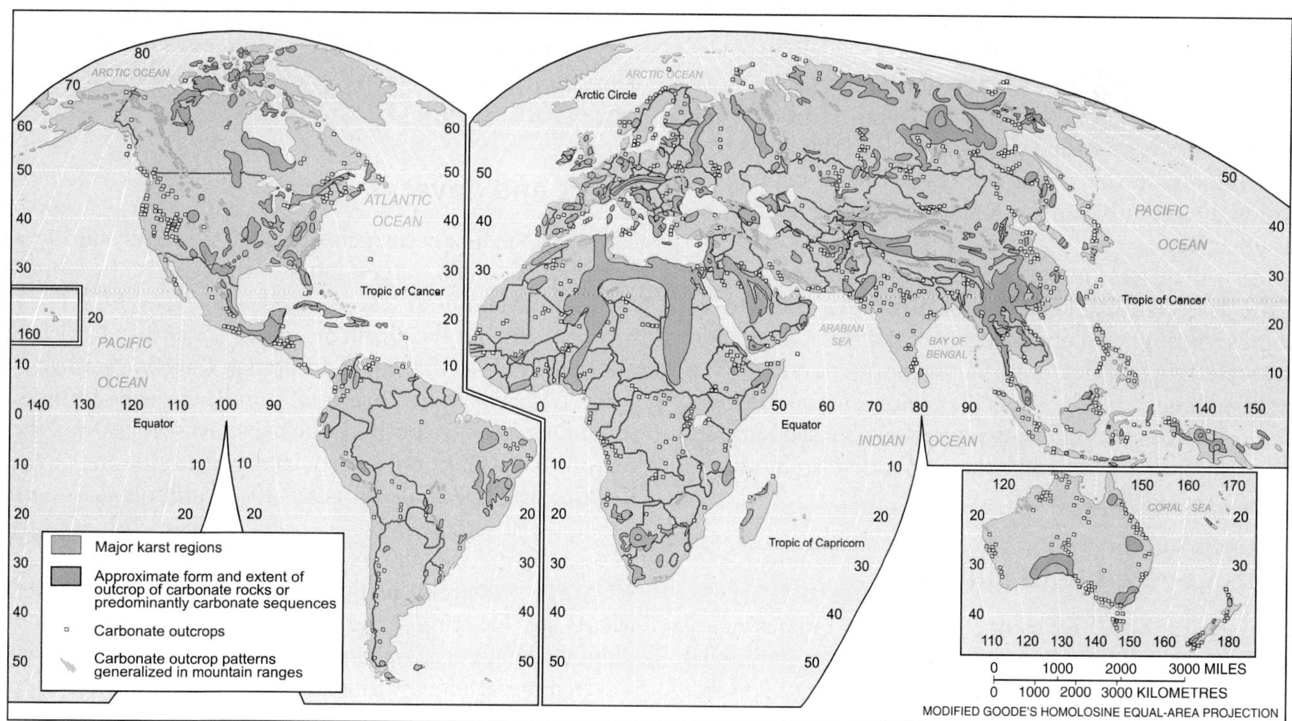

FIGURE 13.15 Global distribution of karst and carbonate rocks.
Major karst regions exist on every continent. The outcrops of carbonate rocks or predominantly carbonate sequences are dominated by limestone and dolostone, but may contain other carbonate rocks. [Map adapted by Pam Schaus, after R. E. Snead, *Atlas of the World Physical Features*, p. 76. © 1972 by John Wiley & Sons, and Ford, D. C. and P. Williams, *Karst Geomorphology and Hydrology*, p. 601. © 1989 by Kluwer Academic Publishers and Ford & Williams. Adapted by permission.]

Karst is a distinctive landscape and hydrology that is shaped, for the most part, by solution processes. The sculpting of the landscape may occur over thousands of years and results in unusual surface and subsurface features including *sinkholes*, vertical shafts, *disappearing streams* and springs, *karren*, *karst pavements*, and complex underground drainage systems and caves that affect up to 15% of Earth's surface (see Figure 13.15).

Many conditions have to exist for karst to develop. First, rock must have a suitable chemical composition and mechanical structure. Common rocks in karst areas worldwide are: limestone (calcium carbonate, $CaCO_3$); dolomite (calcium magnesium carbonate, $CaMg(CO_3)_2$); and gypsum ($CaSO_4 + H_2O$). Moderate to high temperatures coupled with large amounts of precipitation create a climate most conducive to karst development. The presence of vegetation increases the amount of carbon dioxide present, thus enhancing the dissolution process.

Vegetation is also important in the regulation of the water table in karst areas. Exposed, unmantled, uncovered, or *bare karst* is a landscape in which drainage into the underlying network of channels is efficient. If it is in a natural state, the karst can be forested, but once deforestation occurs, there is no means of maintaining a groundwater table, and a barren rocky landscape results. Mantled or *covered karst* develops where rock is overlain by the products of its own weathering and decomposition. Karstic processes then continue under the covering of humus and sediment. With sufficient rain, trees can grow and vegetation covers the rock.

This has two important effects on the geology. First, vegetation produces CO_2 in the regolith, which increases the rate of dissolution of limestone resulting in more rapid growth of caves than in bare karst. However, the second effect is that the vegetation covers the limestone from the air, so there is much less weather-dependent erosion. For example, in covered karst, frost action may be less effective.

As with all weathering processes, time is a factor. Early in the last century, karst landscapes were thought to progress through evolutionary stages of development, as if they were aging. Today, these landscapes are thought to be locally unique, a result of specific conditions, and there is little evidence that different regions evolve sequentially along similar lines. Nonetheless, mature karst landscapes do display certain characteristic forms.

Lands Covered with Sinkholes

The weathering of limestone landscapes creates many **sinkholes**, which form in circular depressions. (Traditional studies may call a sinkhole a *doline*.) A *collapse sinkhole* forms if a solution sinkhole collapses through the roof of an underground cavern. A gently rolling limestone plain might be pockmarked by slow subsidence of surface materials in *solution sinkholes* with depths of 2–100 m (7–330 ft) and diameters of 10–1000 m (33–3300 ft), as shown in Figure 13.16a. Through continuing solution and collapse, sinkholes may coalesce to form a *karst valley*—an elongated depression up to several kilometres long.

The area southwest of Orleans, Indiana, has more than 1000 sinkholes in just 2.6 km^2 (1 mi^2). In this area, the Lost River, a "disappearing stream," flows more than 13 km (8 mi) underground before it resurfaces at its Lost River rise (near the Orangeville rise shown in Figure 13.16e). The Lost River flow diverts from the surface through sinkholes and solution channels. Its dry bed can be seen on the lower left of the topographic map in Figure 13.16b.

In Florida, several sinkholes have made news because lowered water tables (lowered by pumping from municipal wells) caused their collapse into underground solution caves, taking with them homes, businesses, and even new cars from an auto dealership. One such sinkhole collapsed in a suburban area in 1981, and others in 1993 and 1998 (Figure 13.17).

A complex landscape in which sinkholes intersect is a cockpit karst. The sinkholes can be symmetrically shaped in certain circumstances; one at Arecibo, Puerto Rico, is shaped perfectly for a radio telescope installation (Figure 13.18).

Another type of karst topography forms in the wet tropics, where deeply jointed, thick limestone beds are weathered into gorges, leaving isolated resistant blocks standing. These resistant cones and towers are most remarkable in several areas of China where *tower karst* up to 200 m (660 ft) high interrupts an otherwise lower-level plain (Figure 13.19).

Also, gypsum is affected by solutional processes. Parts of the island of Newfoundland and Cape Breton Island are affected by the solution of gypsum layers, and the topography of the surface reflects a hummocky terrain with depressions and disorganized valleys that are typical of this type of karst (Figure 13.20, p. 431).

Caves and Caverns

Caves form in limestone rock, because it is so easily dissolved by carbonation. The largest limestone caverns in the United States are Mammoth Cave in Kentucky (also the longest surveyed cave in the world at 560 km, 350 mi), Carlsbad Caverns in New Mexico, and Lehman Cave in Nevada.

Carlsbad Caverns are in 200-million-year-old limestone formations deposited when shallow seas covered the region. Regional uplifts associated with building of the Rockies (the Laramide orogeny, 40–80 million years ago) elevated the region above sea level, subsequently leading to active cave formation (Figure 13.21, p. 432).

Caves generally form just beneath the water table, where later lowering of the water level exposes them to further development. *Dripstones* form as water containing dissolved minerals slowly drips from the cave ceiling. Calcium carbonate precipitates out of the evaporating solution, literally one molecular layer at a time, and accumulates at a point below on the cave floor. Forming depositional features, *stalactites* grow from the ceiling and *stalagmites* build from the floor; sometimes the two grow until they connect and form a continuous *column* (Figure 13.21b). A dramatic

(continued p. 431)

FIGURE 13.16 Features of karst topography in Indiana. (a) Idealized features of karst topography in southern Indiana. (b) Karst topography southwest of the town of Orleans, Indiana. On average, 1022 sinkholes occur per 2.6 km^2 in this area. On the map, note the contour lines: Depressions are indicated with small hachures (tick marks) on the downslope side of contour lines. (c) Gently rolling karst landscape and cornfields near Orleans, Indiana. (d) This pond is in a sinkhole depression near Palmyra, Indiana. (e) This is the Orangeville rise, near Orangeville, Indiana, just north of the Lost River rise. During periods of high rainfall, this rise is almost filled with water. [(a) Adapted from W. D. Thornbury, *Principles of Geomorphology*, illustration by W. J. Wayne, p. 326. © 1954 by John Wiley & Sons; (b) Mitchell, Indiana quadrangle, USGS; photos (c), (d), and (e) by Bobbé Christopherson.]

(c)

Karst Farm Park, Indiana

(a)

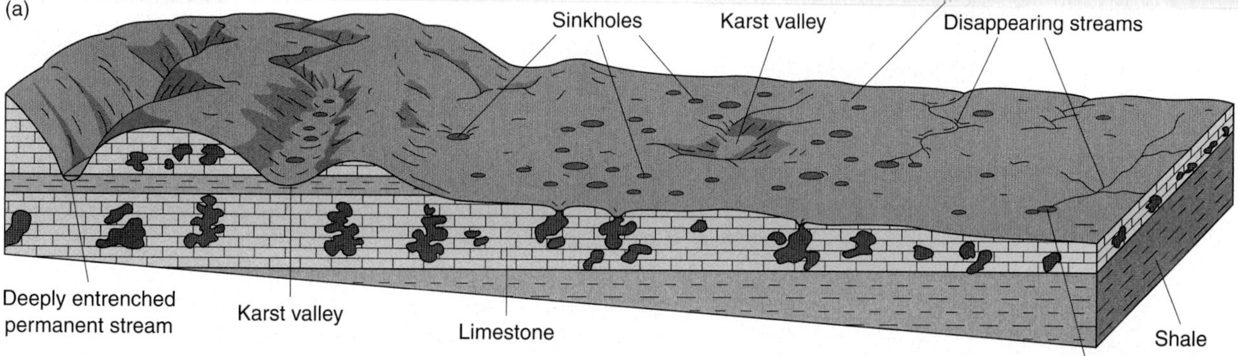

Sinkholes
Karst valley
Disappearing streams
Deeply entrenched permanent stream
Karst valley
Limestone
Shale

(b)

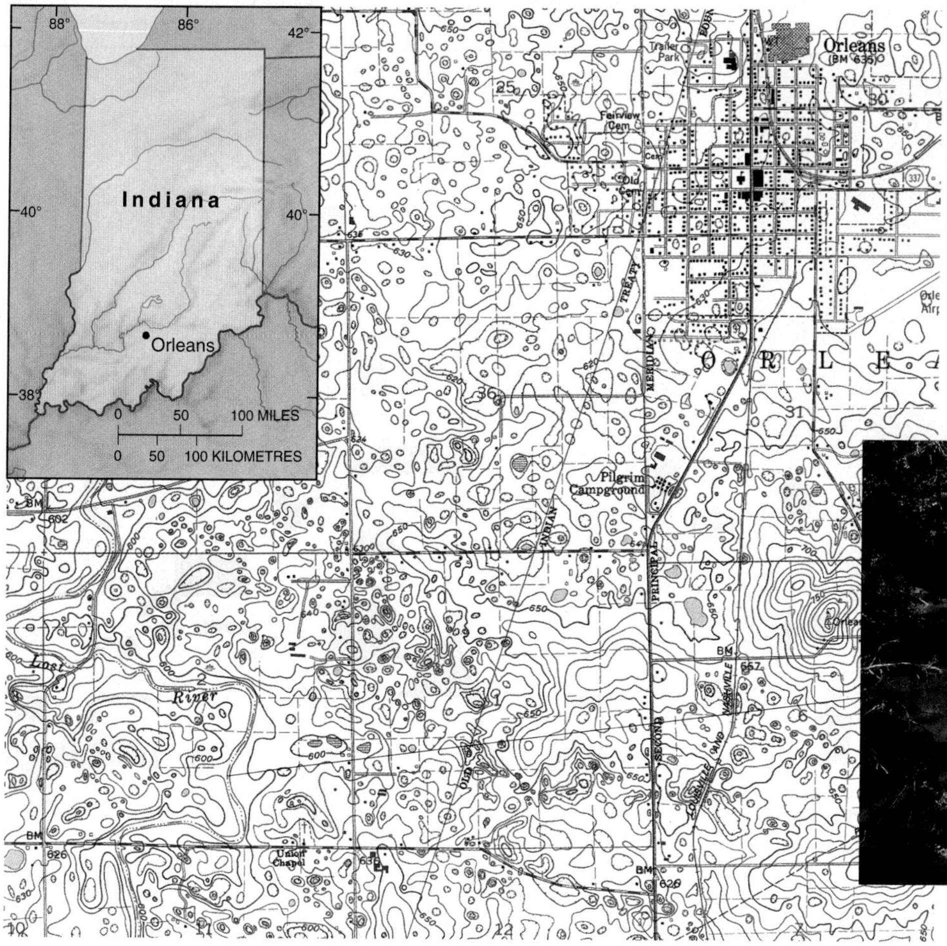

Indiana
Orleans
0 50 100 MILES
0 50 100 KILOMETRES
88°
86°
42°
40°
38°
Orleans
Fairview Cem
Old Cem
Trailer Park
Pilgrim Campground
Union Chapel
Lost River
MERIDIAN
TREATY
PRINCIPAL
SECOND
O R L E

(d)

(e) Orangeville rise

(a)

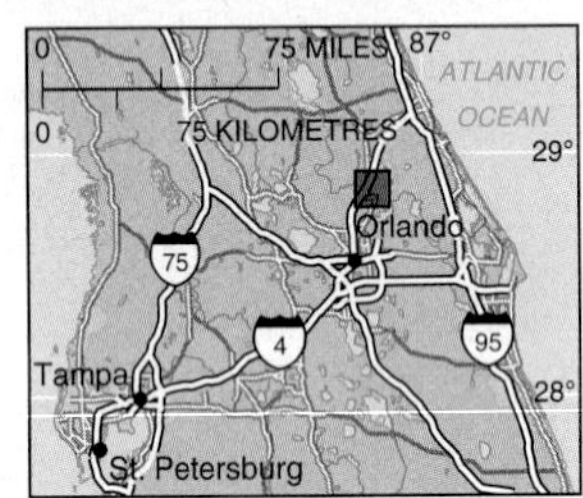

(b)

FIGURE 13.17 Sinkholes.
(a) Florida sinkhole, formed in 1981 in Winter Park, a suburb of Orlando. (b) Karst area 25 km (15.5 mi) north of Winter Park depicted on a topographic map. Note that the depressions are marked by small hachures (tick marks). [(a) Photo by Jim Tuten/Black Star; (b) Orange City quadrangle, USGS.]

FIGURE 13.18 Deep-space research from a sinkhole.
Cockpit karst topography near Arecibo, Puerto Rico, provides a natural depression for the dish antenna of a giant radio telescope. The Arecibo Observatory is part of the National Astronomy and Ionosphere Center, which is operated by Cornell University under contract with the National Science Foundation. [Photo courtesy of Cornell University.]

FIGURE 13.19 Tower karst of the Guangxi (Kwangsi) Province, China.
Resistant strata protect each tower as weathering removes the surrounding limestone. [Photo by Wolfgang Kaehler/Wolfgang Kaehler Photography.]

FIGURE 13.20 Cape Breton gypsum karst.
The lowland areas contain gypsum beds that were dissolved, producing an irregular hummocky terrain. Isolated flats are the remnants of the original, bevelled slope on the intervening sandstone and shale. Underlying the steeper, interior hills beyond is resistant volcanic rock. [Photo by © Raymond Gehman/CORBIS/MAGMA.]

subterranean world is thus created. This is an aspect of geomorphology where amateur cavers make important discoveries about these unique habitats (see News Report 13.1). (For more on caves and related formations, see the Canadian Cave and Karst Information Server **http://www.cancaver.ca/** or **http://www.goodearthgraphics.com/virtcave/virtcave.html**).

Mass Movement Processes

Nevado del Ruiz, northernmost of two dozen dormant (not extinct, sometimes active) volcanic peaks in the Cordilleran Central of Colombia, had erupted six times during the past 3000 years, killing 1000 people during its last eruption in 1845. On November 13, 1985, at 11 P.M. after a year of earthquakes and harmonic tremors, a growing bulge on its northeast flank, and months of small summit eruptions, Nevado del Ruiz violently erupted in a lateral explosion. The mountain was back in action.

On this night, the familiar pyroclastics, lava, and blast were not the worst problem. The hot eruption quickly melted ice on the mountain's snowy peak, liquefying mud and volcanic ash, sending a hot mudflow downslope. Such a flow is a *lahar*, an Indonesian word referring to mudflows of volcanic origin. This lahar moved rapidly down the Lagunilla River toward the villages below. The wall of mud was at least 40 m (130 ft) high as it approached Armero, a regional centre with a population of 25,000. The city slept as the lahar buried its homes: 23,000 people were killed there and in other afflicted river valleys; thousands were injured; 60,000 were left homeless. The volcanic debris flow is now a permanent grave for its victims. Not all mass movements are this destructive, but such processes play a major role in the denudation of the landscape.

For more on mass movement hazards, including landslides, see the Web site of the Natural Hazards Center at the University of Colorado, Boulder, at **http://www.Colorado.edu/hazards/** or the USGS Geologic Hazards page at **http://landslides.usgs.gov/index.html**.

Mass Movement Mechanics

Physical and chemical weathering processes create an overall weakening of surface rock, which makes it more susceptible to the pull of gravity. The term **mass movement** applies to any unit movement of a body of material, propelled and controlled by gravity, such as the lahar just described. Mass movements can be surface processes or they can be submarine landslides beneath the ocean. Mass movement content can range from dry to wet, slow to fast, or small to large, and from free-falling to gradual or intermittent (see Figure 13.23, p. 435).

The term *mass movement* is sometimes used interchangeably with **mass wasting**, which is the general process involved in mass movements and erosion of the landscape. To combine the concepts, we can say that the mass movement of material works to waste slopes and provide raw material for erosion, transportation, and deposition.

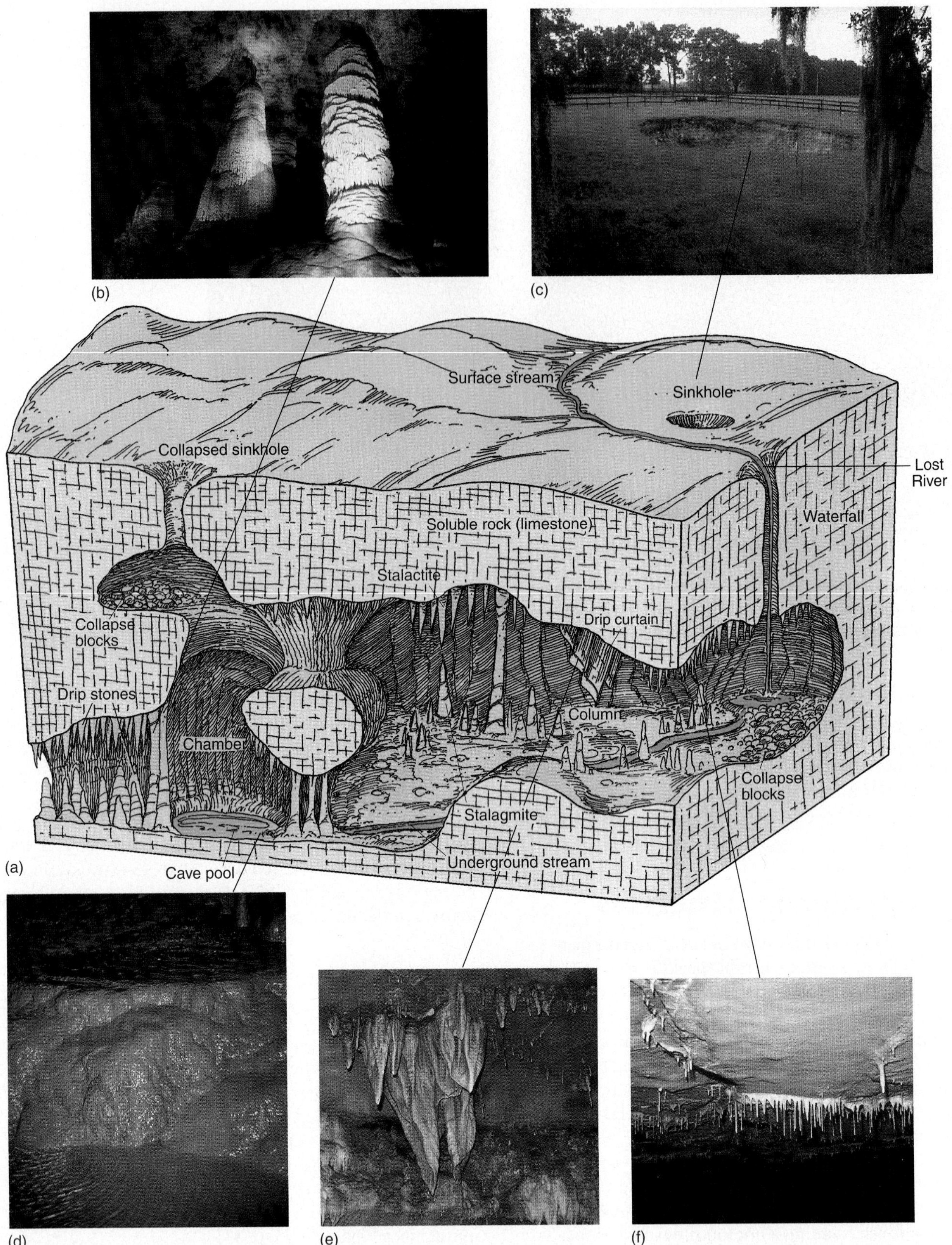

FIGURE 13.21 Cavern features.
(a) An underground cavern and related forms in limestone. (b) A column in Carlsbad Caverns, New Mexico, where a series of underground caverns includes rooms more than 1200 m (4000 ft) long and 190 m (625 ft) wide. Although a national park since 1930, unexplored portions remain. (c) A sinkhole in a Florida pasture. From Marengo Caves, Marengo, Indiana: (d) A flowstone and pool of water. (e) Dripstone drapery formations. (f) Soda straws hanging from ceiling cracks, forming one molecular layer at a time. [Photos by (b) Robert W. Christopherson; (c) Thomas M. Scott, Florida Geological Survey; (d), (e), and (f) Bobbé Christopherson.]

News Report 13.1

Amateurs Make Cave Discoveries

The exploration and scientific study of caves is *speleology*. Although professional physical and biological scientists carry on investigations, amateur cavers, or "spelunkers," have made many important discoveries. As an example, in the early 1940s George Colglazier, a farmer southwest of Bedford, Indiana, awoke to find his farm pond at the bottom of a deep collapsed sinkhole. This sinkhole is now the entrance to an extensive cave system that includes a subterranean navigable stream.

Cave habitats are unique. They are nearly closed, self-contained ecosystems with simple food chains and great stability. In total darkness, bacteria synthesize inorganic elements and produce organic compounds that sustain many types of cave life, including algae, small invertebrates, amphibians, and fish.

In a cave discovered in 1986, near Movile in southeastern Romania, cave-adapted invertebrates were discovered after millions of years of sunless isolation. Thirty-one of these organisms were previously unknown. Without sunlight, the ecosystem in Movile sustains on sulphur-metabolizing bacteria that synthesize organic matter using energy from oxidation processes. These chemosynthetic bacteria feed other bacteria and fungi that in turn support cave animals. The sulphur bacteria produce sulphuric acid compounds that may prove to be important in the chemical weathering of some caves.

The mystery, intrigue, and excitement of cave exploration lie in the variety of dark passageways, enormous chambers that narrow to tiny crawl spaces, strange formations, and underwater worlds that can be accessed only by cave diving. Private-property owners and amateur adventurers discovered many of the major caves, a fact that keeps this popular science/sport very much alive. (For nearly a thousand worldwide links and information, see the http://www.cbel.com/speleology/ Web site.)

The Role of Slopes All mass movements occur on slopes under the influence of gravitational stress. If we pile dry sand on a beach, the grains will flow downslope until an equilibrium is achieved. The steepness of the resulting slope depends on the size and texture of the grains; this steepness is called the **angle of repose**. This angle represents a balance of the driving force (gravity) and resisting force (friction and shear). The angle of repose for various materials commonly ranges between 33° and 37° (from horizontal), and 30° to 50° for snow avalanche slopes.

The *driving force* in mass movement is gravity. It works in conjunction with the weight, size, density, and shape of the surface material; the degree to which the slope is oversteepened (how far it exceeds the angle of repose); and the amount and form of moisture available (frozen or fluid). The greater the slope angle, the more susceptible the surface material is to mass wasting processes.

The *resisting force* is the shear strength of slope material, that is, its cohesiveness and internal friction, which work against gravity and mass wasting. To reduce shear strength is to increase shear stress, which eventually reaches the point at which gravity overcomes friction, initiating slope failure.

Clays, shales, and mudstones are highly susceptible to hydration (physical swelling in response to the presence of water). If such materials underlie rock strata in a slope, the strata will move with less driving force energy. When clay surfaces are wet, they deform slowly in the direction of movement, and when saturated they form a viscous fluid with little shear strength (resistance to movement) to hold back the slope. However, if the rock strata are such that material is held back from slipping, then more driving force energy may be required, such as that generated by an earthquake.

Madison River Canyon Landslide In the Madison River Canyon near West Yellowstone, Montana, a blockade of dolomite (a magnesium-rich carbonate rock) held back a deeply weathered and *oversteepened slope* (40° to 60° slope angle) for untold centuries (white area in Figure 13.22). Then, shortly after midnight on August 17, 1959, a magnitude 7.5 earthquake broke the dolomite structure along the foot of the slope. The break released 32 million cubic metres (1.13 billion cubic feet) of mountainside, which moved downslope at 95 kmph (60 mph), causing gale force winds through the canyon. Momentum carried the material more than 120 m (about 400 ft) up the opposite canyon slope, trapping several hundred campers with about 80 m (260 ft) of rock, killing 28 people.

The mass of material also effectively dammed the Madison River and thus created a new lake, dubbed Quake Lake. The landslide debris dam established a new temporary equilibrium for the river and canyon. A channel was quickly excavated by the U.S. Army Corps of Engineers to prevent a disaster below the dam, for if Quake Lake overflowed the landslide dam, the water would quickly erode a channel and thereby release the entire contents of the new lake onto farmland downstream. This event conveys a dramatic example of the role of slopes and tectonic forces in creating massive land movements.

Classes of Mass Movements

In any mass movement, gravity pulls on a mass until the critical shear-failure point is reached—a *geomorphic threshold*. The material then can *fall*, *slide*, *flow*, or *creep*—the four classes of mass movement. Figure 13.23 summarizes these classes. Note the temperature and moisture gradients in the margins of the illustration, which show the relation

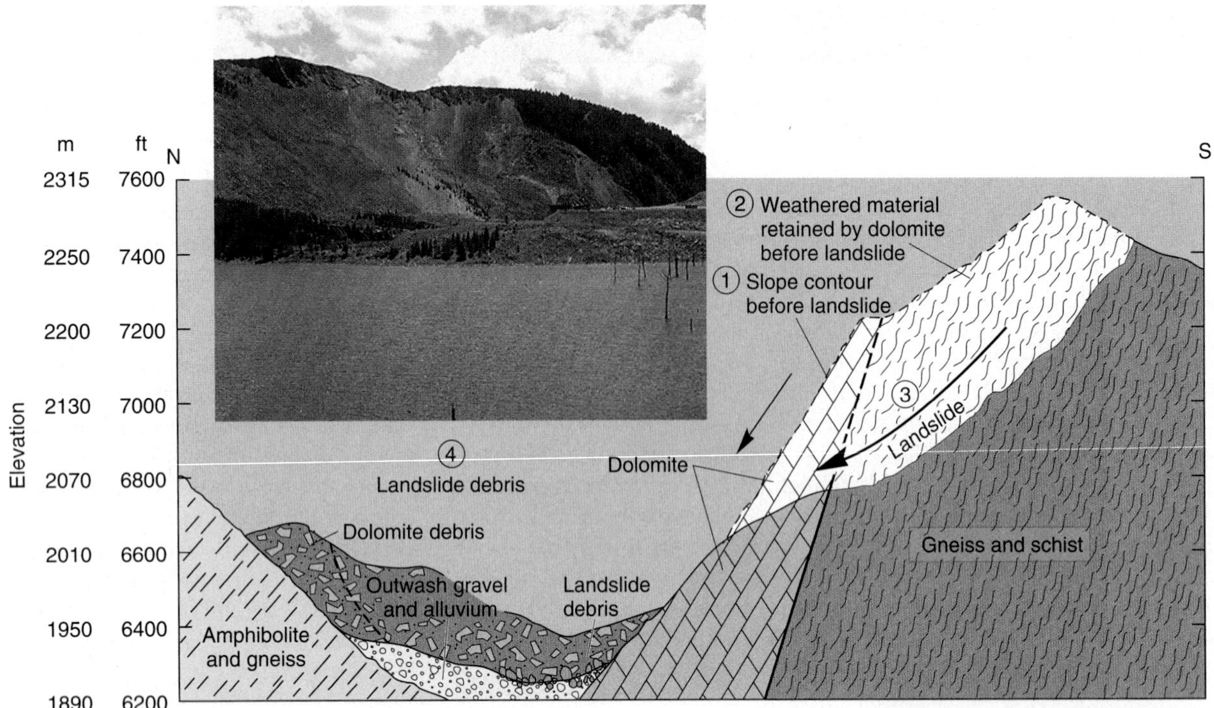

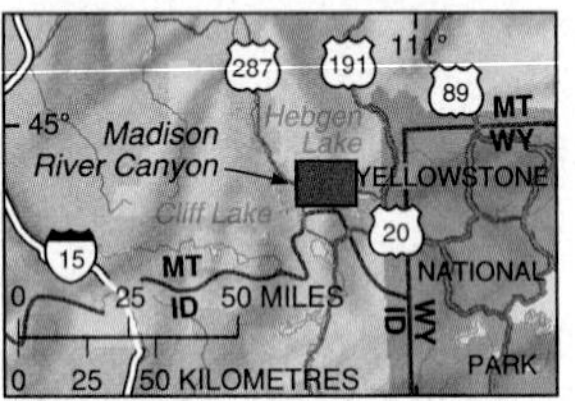

FIGURE 13.22 Madison River landslide.
Cross section showing geologic structure of the Madison River Canyon, in Montana, where an earthquake triggered a landslide in 1959. (1) Prequake slope contour. (2) Weathered rock that failed. (3) Direction of landslide. (4) Landslide debris blocking the canyon and damming the Madison River. [After J. B. Hadley, Landslides and Related Phenomena Accompanying the Hebgen Lake Earthquake of August 17, 1959, U.S. Geological Survey Professional Paper 435-K, p. 115. Inset photo by Bobbé Christopherson.]

between water content and movement rate. The Madison River Canyon event was a type of slide, whereas the Nevado del Ruiz lahar mentioned earlier was a flow. We now look at specific mass movement classes.

Falls and Avalanches This class of mass movement includes rockfalls and debris avalanches. A **rockfall** is simply a volume of rock that falls through the air and hits a surface. During a rockfall, individual pieces fall independently and characteristically form a cone-shaped pile of irregular broken rocks called a *talus slope* at the base of a steep incline (Figure 13.24).

A **debris avalanche** is a mass of falling and tumbling rock, debris, and soil. It is differentiated from a slower debris slide or landslide by the velocity of onrushing material. This speed often results from ice and water that fluidize the debris. The extreme danger of a debris avalanche results from its tremendous speed and consequent lack of warning.

In 1962 and again in 1970, debris avalanches roared down the west face of Nevado Huascarán, the highest peak in the Peruvian Andes. The 1962 debris avalanche contained an estimated 13 million cubic metres (460 million cubic feet) of material, burying the city of Ranrahirca and eight other towns, killing 4000 people.

An earthquake initiated the 1970 event. Upward of 100 million cubic metres (3.53 billion cubic feet) of debris buried the city of Yungay, where 18,000 people perished (Figure 13.25). This avalanche attained velocities of 300 kmph (185 mph), which is especially incredible when you consider the quantity of material involved and the fact that some boulders weighed thousands of metric tons. The avalanche covered a vertical drop of 4144 m (13,600 ft) and a horizontal distance of 16 km (10 mi) in just a few minutes.

A dramatic example of a debris flow that did not kill occurred in Banff National Park, Alberta, in August 1999. The failure was unexpected and resulted from an intense rainfall that was unrecorded because local weather stations were outside the focused area of precipitation. Debris blocked the highway for 24 hours, delaying thousands of travellers in Banff for a few days while cleanup occurred (Figure 13.26).

Landslides A sudden rapid movement of a cohesive mass of regolith or bedrock that is not saturated with moisture is a **landslide**—a large amount of material failing simultaneously. Surprise creates the danger, for the downward pull of gravity wins the struggle for equilibrium in an instant. Focus Study 13.1 describes one such surprise event that struck near Frank, Alberta, in 1903 (begins on p. 436).

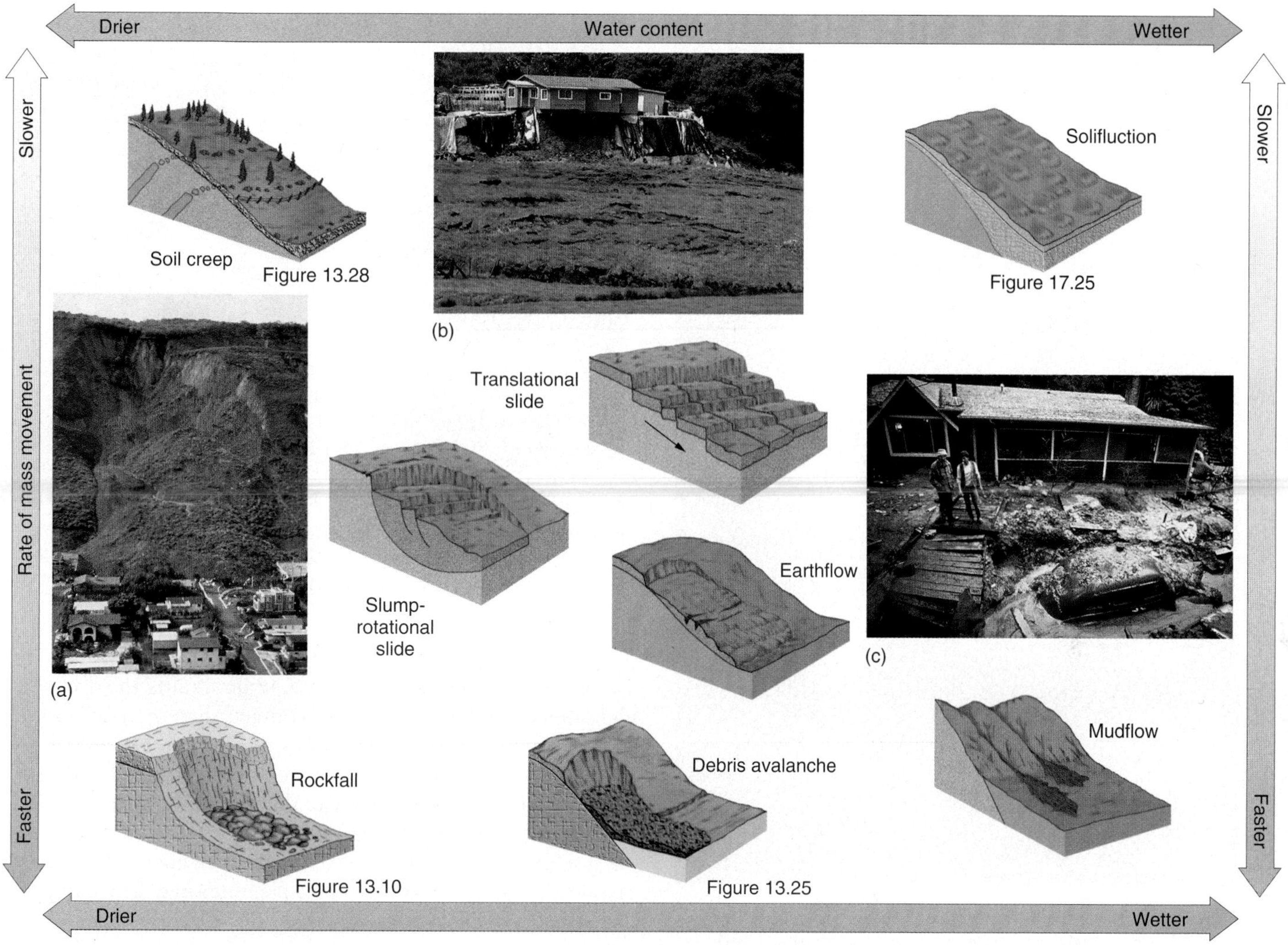

FIGURE 13.23 Mass movement classes.
Principal types of mass movement and mass wasting events. Variations in water content and rates of movement produce a variety of forms. (a) A 1995 slide in La Conchita, California, same site of the disastrous 2005 event that killed 10 people. (b) Saturated hillsides fail. (c) Mudflow 2 m deep in Santa Cruz County, California. [Photos by (a) Robert L. Schuster/USGS; (b) Alexander Lowry/Photo Researchers, Inc.; (c) James A. Sugar.]

To eliminate the surprise element, scientists are using the global positioning system (GPS) to monitor landslide movement. With GPS, scientists measure slight land shifts in suspect areas for clues to possible mass wasting. GPS was applied in two cases in Japan and effectively identified pre-landslide movements of 2–5 cm per year, providing information to expand the area of hazard concern and warning.

Slides occur in one of two basic forms: translational or rotational (see Figure 13.23 for an idealized view of each). *Translational slides* involve movement along a planar (flat) surface roughly parallel to the angle of the slope, with no rotation. The Madison Canyon landslide described earlier was a translational slide. Flow and creep patterns also are considered translational in nature.

Rotational slides occur when surface material moves along a concave surface. Frequently, underlying clay presents an impervious surface to percolating water. As a result,

FIGURE 13.24 Talus slope.
Rockfall and talus deposits at the base of a steep slope along Duve Fjord, Nordaustlandet Island. Can you see the lighter rock strata that are the source for the three talus cones? [Photo by Bobbé Christopherson.]

FIGURE 13.25 Debris avalanche, Peru.
A 1970 debris avalanche falls more than 4100 m (2.5 mi) down the west face of Nevado Huascarán, burying the city of Yungay, Peru. The same area was devastated by a similar avalanche in 1962 and by others in pre-Columbian times. A great danger remains for the cities and towns in the valley from possible future mass movements. [Photo by George Plafker.]

FIGURE 13.26 Five Mile Creek, Alberta, 1999.
In August 1999, an intense localized rainfall triggered this debris flow approximately 5 km west of Banff, in Banff National Park. [Photo by Earth Sciences Sector, Natural Resources Canada GSC 2002-584.]

water flows along the clay surface, undermining the overlying block and lubricating the contact, thereby reducing the friction force. The simplest form of rotational slide is a rotational slump, in which a small block of land shifts downward. The upper surface of the slide appears to rotate backward and often remains intact. The surface may rotate as a single unit, or it may present a stepped appearance. A landslide slide show and solution diagrams may be viewed at **http://www.kingston.ac.uk/~ku00323/slides.htm.**

Flows Flows include *earthflows* and more fluid **mudflows**. When the moisture content of moving material is high, the suffix *-flow* is used (see Figure 13.23). Heavy rains can saturate barren mountain slopes and set them moving.

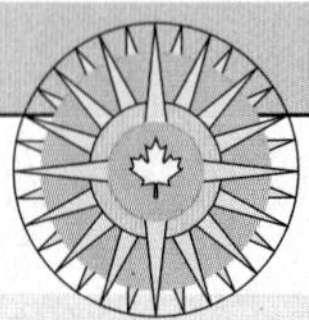

Focus Study 13.1

Frank Slide: Coal Mining and an Early Morning Disaster

On April 29, 1903, at 4:10 A.M., an estimated 82 million metric tons of rock and sediment slid down the east side of Turtle Mountain in southwestern Alberta at speeds nearing 140 kmph. The slide buried the wetland at the base of the mountain, roared through the southern edge of the town of Frank, continued across the valley, and came to a stop upslope on the opposite side of the valley. It took just 90 seconds for the mass of material to travel 1.5 km and to cover an area up to 3 km^2 an average depth of 14 m. One estimate counted 70 lives lost in Canada's deadliest landslide.

More than a century has passed since the Frank Slide, and scientists still do not agree about what caused the slide. The mountain is made of interbedded Paleozoic limestone and shale topping Mesozoic sandstone, with shale and coal at its base. A coal-mining shaft was sunk at the base of the mountain below the Turtle Mountain thrust fault (Figure 1). Mining at the base of the mountain was one of the final triggers that sent the rock downslope. The rockslide took place along the easterly dipping beds of the main geological structure—the Turtle Mountain anticline.

The actual mechanism of failure is complex and includes limestone creep over shales, siltstones, sandstones, and coal; adverse jointing and faulting of the rock mass; underground coal mining at the base of the mountain; ice wedging in cracks and discontinuities of the rock mass; excessive rainfall in the 4 years preceding the slide; and, seismic loading. All these factors contributed to the failure, but the greatest influence came from the geological instability.

The mechanism of movement of the material in the slide has also been the subject of considerable academic debate. One theory states that the debris in the slide remained in contact with the surface through most of its travel down the mountainside, across the valley bottom, and up the facing slope. A second theory proposes that the material had to be lubricated at the base by either compressed air or steam and that this compressed layer allowed the slide material to move freely downslope, across the valley, and up the other side.

The slide affected an entire face of the mountain (Figure 2), buried part of the town, the Canadian Pacific Railway, and the highway that passed through town, and dammed the Old Man River, forming a temporary lake. The continued threat from the geological instability of the mountain led to the relocation of much of the town—out of the potential path of future landslides. The road was rebuilt and the rail

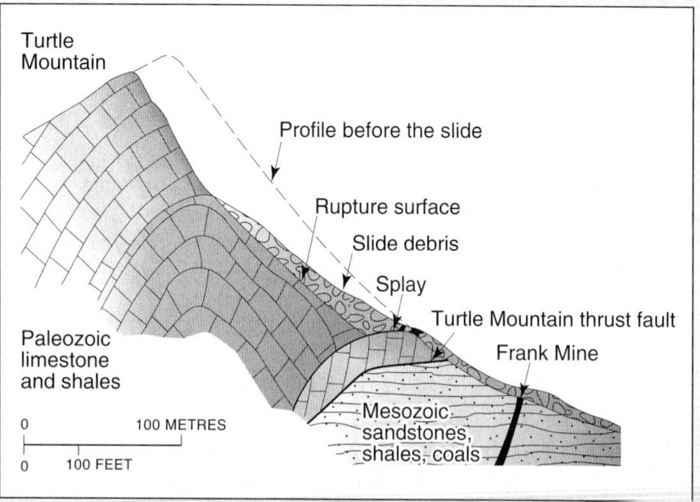

FIGURE 1 Cross section through the central part of the Frank Slide. Rock structure creates a natural instability in the rock of Turtle Mountain. Splay is a minor fault that branches off a major fault. [Illustration reprinted by permission of John Krahn.]

(a)

(b)

(c)

FIGURE 2 The Frank Slide in 1903 and 2003. (a) From a distance, you can see how the entire side of the mountain moved downslope. (b) The town was in the path of destruction: to the left the buried remains of the miner's houses, to the right the buildings left intact. (c) The slide scar in 2003 still clearly shows the path of movement of the slide. [Photos (a) from Glenbow Archives, NA 3011-7; (b) from Glenbow Archives, NA 411-9; (c) courtesy of Frank Slide Visitors' Centre.]

(continued)

Focus Study 13.1 *(continued)*

line reconstructed. The mine reopened, but closed again soon after.

In Canada, thousands of slides change the terrain every year in all parts of the country. From 1850 to the present, landslides have caused about 600 fatalities in Canada. From an economic perspective, slides have cost between $100 million and $200 million in property damage, blocked rail lines and roads, and caused pipeline explosions. Environmental damage, the costs of which are difficult to estimate, include damage to spawning grounds and localized deforestation and habitat destruction. Natural factors cause most slides—the geology, water, ice, wind, and temperature changes. However, human activities like urbanization, deforestation, and mining play a role as triggers to mass movement. The results remain a part of the landscape, such as Turtle Mountain—a reminder of times when mountains moved.

Figure 13.27 shows an earthflow in the Machiche River valley, in Trois-Rivières, Québec, known as the St. Boniface landslide. It occurred in late April 1996 causing approximately 7 million cubic metres of sediment to slide into the Machiche River valley, damming the river. This type of retrogressive earthflow can occur within sensitive glaciomarine sediments common to the St. Lawrence Lowlands and the Ottawa Valley regions. In these flows, the headwall erodes back into the valley side, and the landslide debris flows toward the river, away from the scarp. In January 2005, more than 300 mm (almost 12 in.) of rain in less than a week saturated the mountainside in North Vancouver, resulting in mudslides that caused millions of dollars of damage and claimed one life.

Creep A persistent, gradual mass movement of surface soil is called **soil creep**. In creep, individual soil particles are lifted and disturbed by the expansion of soil moisture as it freezes; by cycles of moistness and dryness; by diurnal temperature variations; or by grazing livestock or digging animals.

In the freeze–thaw cycle, particles lift at right angles to the slope by freezing soil moisture, as shown in Figure 13.28a. When the ice melts, however, the particles fall straight downward in response to gravity. As the process repeats, the surface soil gradually creeps its way downslope. The photograph in Figure 13.28b illustrates a **solifluction** rampart in Nunavut. Abundant soil water is available during spring snowmelt and causes the soil to liquefy and flow downslope. As water drains from the front of the flowing mass, movement ceases, leaving a "rampart" of soil. Because the process illustrated here is happening over permafrost, the specific type of solifluction occurring here is **gelifluction**.

The overall wasting of a slope may cover a wide area and may cause fence posts, utility poles, and even trees to lean downslope. Various strategies are used to arrest the

FIGURE 13.27 St. Boniface landslide, Québec, April 1996.
The St. Boniface landslide, a retrogressive earthflow, occurred in late April 1996. Here, the landslide debris forms a series of concentric ridges, visible in the centre of the photograph, effectively damming the river when it hit. [Photo by Earth Sciences Sector, Natural Resources Canada GSC 2002-703.]

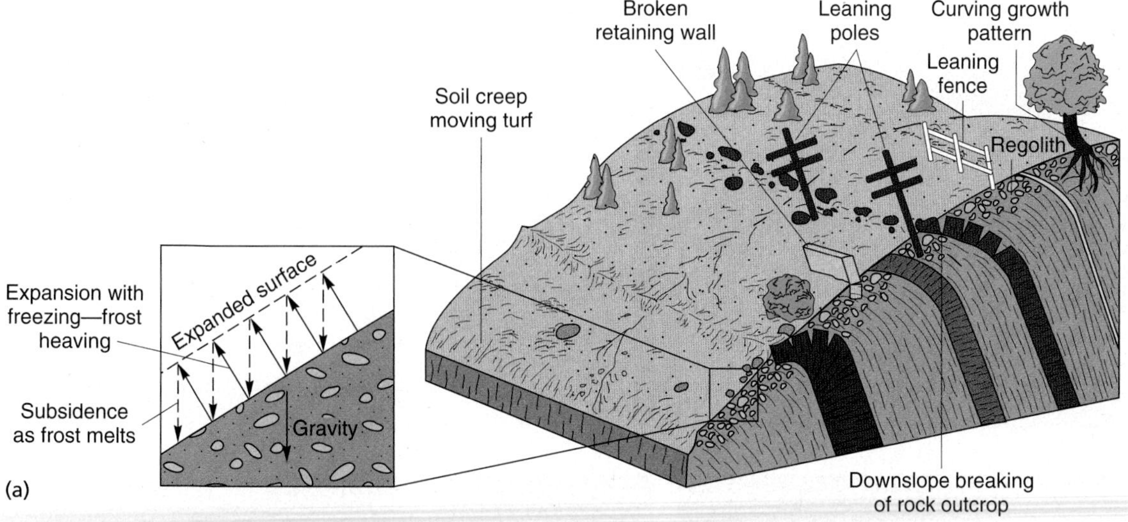

FIGURE 13.28 Soil creep.
(a) Soil creep and its effects. (b) Solifluction, rapid soil creep, in Nunavut. The rampart seen in the foreground is about 1 m high. [Photo by Earth Sciences Sector, Natural Resources Canada GSC 2002-452.]

mass movement of slope material—grading the terrain, building terraces and retaining walls, planting ground cover—but the persistence of creep nearly always wins.

Human-Induced Mass Movements (Scarification)

Every human disturbance of a slope—highway roadcut, surface-mining, or building of a shopping mall, housing development, or home—can hasten mass wasting. The newly destabilized and oversteepened surfaces are thrust into a search for a new equilibrium.

Large open-pit surface mines—such as the iron ore mine near Labrador City, the Bingham Copper Mine west of Salt Lake City, the Berkeley Pit in Butte, Montana, and numerous large coal surface mines in the U.S. East and West, such as Black Mesa (Figure 13.29a)—are examples of human-induced mass movements, generally called **scarification** (Figure 13.29).

At the Bingham Copper Mine, a mountain literally was removed, forming a pit 4-km wide and 1-km deep (Figure 13.29b). This is easily the largest human-made excavation on Earth, with ores containing copper, gold, silver, and molybdenum. The disposal of tailings (mined ore of little value) and waste material is a significant problem at any surface mine. Such large excavations produce tailing piles that are unstable and susceptible to further weathering, mass wasting, or wind dispersal. The leaching of toxic materials from tailings and waste piles poses an ever-increasing problem to streams, aquifers, and public health across the country.

In eastern Pennsylvania commercial slate deposits formed over millions of years. The Dally slate quarry in Pen Argyl is now working a second pit that is 55 m (180 ft) deep (Figure 13.29d). Removal of slate is guided by the grain of the metamorphic rock so as to produce the flattest pieces. Slate is mined for shingles and countertops. The local county turned the first quarry into a landfill—a practical use for the pit.

The Carol Project, Labrador City, mines about 38 million metric tons of crude iron ore per year and produces 21 million metric tons of tailings. Mine dewatering and flow from tailings and flotation plant effluent all discharge into Wabush Lake, producing significant pollution (Figure 13.29e).

Scientists can informally quantify the scale of human-induced scarification for comparison with natural denudation processes. R. L. Hooke, Department of Geology and Geophysics, University of Minnesota, used estimates of U.S. excavations for new housing, mineral production

(a) (b) (c) (d) (e)

FIGURE 13.29 Scarification.
(a) Black Mesa, Arizona, strip-mining for coal. (b) Bingham Canyon, Utah, west of Salt Lake City, strip-mining for copper and other minerals. (c) Spoil banks in a West Virginia coal-mining area. (d) The 55-m-deep Dally slate quarry in Pen Argyl, Pennsylvania. (e) The Carol Project, Labrador City, Newfoundland and Labrador. [Photos (a) and (c) by Robert W. Christopherson; (b) and (d) by Bobbé Christopherson; (e) courtesy of IOC.]

(including the three largest—stone, sand and gravel, and coal), and highway construction. He then prorated these quantities of moved earth for all countries, using their gross domestic product (GDP), energy consumption, and agriculture's effect on river sediment loads. From these he calculated a global estimate for human earth moving.

Hooke estimated that humans, as a geomorphic agent, annually move 36–41 billion metric tons (36–41 Gt/yr) of the planet's surface. Compare this quantity with natural river sediment transfer (13 Gt/yr), movement through stream meandering (35 Gt/yr), haulage by glaciers (3.9 Gt/yr), movement due to wave action and erosion (1.1 Gt/yr), wind transport (0.9 Gt/yr), sediment movement by continental and oceanic mountain building (31 Gt/yr), or deep-ocean sedimentation (6.4 Gt/yr). As Hooke stated,

> Homo sapiens has become an impressive geomorphic agent. Coupling our earth-moving prowess with our inadvertent adding of sediment load to rivers and the visual impact of our activities on the landscape, one is compelled to acknowledge that, for better or for worse, this biogeomorphic agent may be the premier geomorphic agent of our time.*

*R. L. Hooke, "On the efficacy of humans as geomorphic agents," *GSA Today* (The Geological Society of America) 4, no. 9 (September 1994): 217–226.

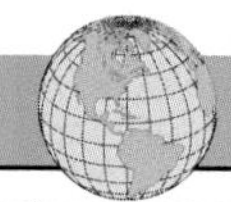

Applied Physical Geography

The Role of Gravity in Landform Development

Endogenic processes produce landforms through uplift and tectonism, while exogenic processes wear the forms away. Gravity has an important role to play in moving mineral matter and water downslope.

Gravity is the mutual force exerted by the masses of objects that are attracted to one another, and is produced in an amount proportional to each object's mass. It results in potential energy differences between the continents that have been uplifted and the ocean basins.

Mass movement is the downward movement of material under the influence of gravity. The rate and method of the movement depends upon the slope, the coherence of the material, and the moisture content (Figure 1).

When $W\sin\theta$ exceeds F, movement occurs. F is proportional to $W\cos\theta$ as:

$$F = f\,W\cos\theta$$

Decreasing f, or increasing θ, leads to movement.

Water adds weight and increases the cohesiveness of soils. This increases F and stabilizes the slope. Water also lubricates the potential slip faces, decreasing f and, in consequence F, leading to slope failure.

Soil saturated with water experiences increased water pressure that acts to decrease the contact pressure between soil grains, forcing the granular framework apart and decreasing stability.

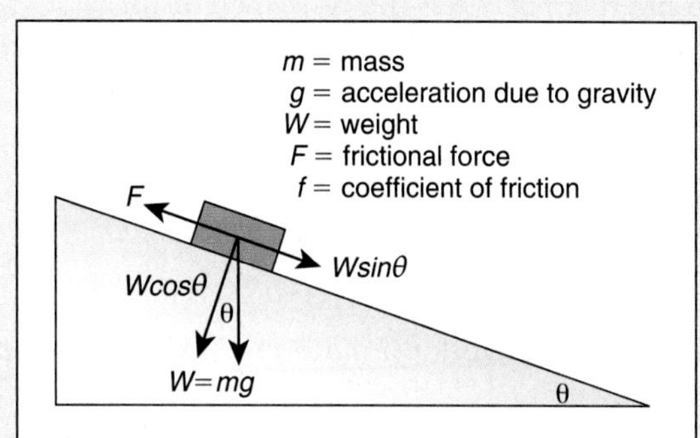

FIGURE 1 Mass movement.

In Focus Study 13.1, we learned that an estimated 82 million metric tons of rock and sediment failed, sliding down the side of Turtle Mountain at speeds nearing 140 kmph. The material moved through the valley bottom and up the opposite side. In 90 seconds, the mass of material travelled 1.5 km and covered an area up to 3 km^2 an average depth of 14 m.

The slide started as potential energy on the mountainside. When gravity overcame cohesion, the potential energy was converted to kinetic energy as the mass moved downslope. Kinetic energy dissipated as heat due to friction as the movement came to an end.

What force was applied by this moving mass?

$$F = m \times g$$

where F is the force, m is the mass of the object, and g is acceleration due to gravity. Filling in the numbers from the Turtle Mountain slide,

$$\begin{aligned} F &= m \times g \\ &= 8.2 \times 10^{10}\,\text{kg} \times 9.8\,\text{m/s}^2 \\ &= 8.036 \times 10^{11}\,\text{N} \end{aligned}$$

From this force, we can determine the *work* done.

$$W = F \times d$$

where W is work, F is force, and d is distance.

$$\begin{aligned} W &= F \times d \\ &= 8.036 \times 10^{11}\,\text{N} \times 1500\,\text{m} \\ &= 1.21 \times 10^{15}\,\text{J} \end{aligned}$$

We can now calculate power from this measure of work.

$$\begin{aligned} P &= W/T \\ &= 1.21 \times 10^{15}\,\text{J}/90\,\text{sec} \\ &= 1.34 \times 10^{13}\,\text{W} \end{aligned}$$

This is greater by far than the average rate of consumption of electric power in North America annually. The overwhelming power released by gravity in a slope failure is an illustration of the ability of nature to sculpt the landscape.

Summary and Review—Weathering, Karst Landscapes, and Mass Movement

● ***Define*** **the science of geomorphology.**

Geomorphology is the science that analyzes and describes the origin, evolution, form, and spatial distribution of landforms. The exogenic system, powered by solar energy and gravity, tears down the landscape through processes of landmass **denudation** involving weathering, mass movement, erosion, transportation, and deposition. Different rocks offer differing resistance to these weathering processes and produce a pattern on the landscape of **differential weathering**. Agents of change include moving air, water, waves, and ice. W. M. Davis's *geomorphic cycle model* characterized landscapes as evolving through stages from youth to old age. Since the 1960s, research and understanding of the processes of denudation have moved toward the **dynamic equilibrium model**, which considers slope and landform stability to be consequences of the resistance of rock materials to the attack of denudation processes.

geomorphology (p. 416)
denudation (p. 416)
differential weathering (p. 416)
dynamic equilibrium model (p. 417)

1. Define geomorphology, and describe its relationship to physical geography.

2. Define landmass denudation. What processes are included in the concept?
3. What is the interplay between the resistance of rock structures and weathering variabilities?
4. Give a brief overview of the geomorphic cycle model. What was W. M. Davis's principal contribution to the models of landmass denudation?
5. What are the principal considerations in the dynamic equilibrium model?

● *Illustrate* the forces at work on materials residing on a slope.

Slopes are shaped by the relation between rate of weathering and breakup of slope materials and the rate of mass movement and erosion of those materials. A slope is considered stable if it is stronger than these denudation processes; it is unstable if it is weaker. In this struggle against gravity, a slope may reach a **geomorphic threshold**—the point at which there is enough energy to overcome resistance against movement. **Slopes** that form the boundaries of landforms have several general components: *waxing slope*, *free face*, *debris slope*, and *waning slope*. Slopes seek an angle of equilibrium among the operating forces.

geomorphic threshold (p. 417)
slopes (p. 417)

6. Describe conditions on a hillslope that is right at the geomorphic threshold. What factors might push the slope beyond this point?
7. Given all the interacting variables, do you think a landscape ever reaches a stable, old-age condition? Explain.
8. What are the general components of an ideal slope?
9. Relative to slopes, what is meant by an "angle of equilibrium"? Can you apply this concept to the photograph in Figure 13.2?

● *Define* weathering and *explain* the importance of parent rock and joints and fractures in rock.

Weathering processes disintegrate both surface and subsurface rock into mineral particles or dissolve them in water. The upper layers of surface material undergo continual weathering and create broken-up rock called **regolith**. Weathered **bedrock** is the *parent rock* from which regolith forms. The unconsolidated, fragmented material that develops after weathering is **sediment**, which along with weathered rock forms the **parent material** from which soil evolves.

Important in weathering processes are **joints**, the fractures and separations in the rock. Jointing opens up rock surfaces on which weathering processes operate. Factors that influence weathering include character of the bedrock (hard or soft, soluble or insoluble, broken or unbroken), climatic elements (temperature, precipitation, freeze–thaw cycles), position of the water table, slope orientation, surface vegetation and its subsurface roots, and time.

weathering (p. 418)
regolith (p. 419)
bedrock (p. 419)
sediment (p. 419)
parent material (p. 419)
joints (p. 419)

10. Describe weathering processes operating on an open expanse of bedrock. How does regolith develop? How is sediment derived?
11. Describe the relationship between mesoscale climatic conditions and rates of weathering activities.
12. What is the relation among parent rock, parent material, regolith, and soil?
13. What role do joints play in the weathering process? Give an example from one of the illustrations in this chapter.

● *Describe* frost action, crystallization, pressure-release jointing, and the role of freezing water as physical weathering processes.

Physical weathering refers to the breakup of rock into smaller pieces with no alteration of mineral identity. The physical action of water when it freezes (expands) and thaws (contracts) is a powerful agent in shaping the landscape. This **frost action** may break apart any rock. Working in joints, expanded ice can produce *joint-block separation* through the process of *frost-wedging*. Frost action loosens rock that falls from a steep cliff, producing a **talus slope** of poorly sorted debris at the base of the slope.

Another process of physical weathering is *crystallization*; as crystals in rock grow and enlarge over time, they force apart mineral grains and break up rock.

As overburden is removed from a granitic batholith, the pressure of deep burial is relieved. The granite slowly responds with *pressure-release jointing*, with layer after layer of rock peeling off in curved slabs or plates. As these slabs weather, they slip off in a process called **sheeting**. This *exfoliation process* creates an arch-shaped or dome-shaped feature on the exposed landscape, forming an **exfoliation dome**.

physical weathering (p. 420)
frost action (p. 420)
talus slope (p. 421)
sheeting (p. 423)
exfoliation dome (p. 423)

14. What is physical weathering? Give an example.
15. Why is freezing water such an effective physical weathering agent?
16. What weathering processes produce a granite dome? Describe the sequence of events.

● *Describe* the susceptibility of different minerals to the chemical weathering processes called hydration, hydrolysis, oxidation, carbonation, and solution.

Chemical weathering is the chemical decomposition of minerals in rock. It can cause **spheroidal weathering**, in which chemical weathering occurs in cracks in the rock. As cementing and binding materials are removed, the rock begins to disintegrate, and sharp edges and corners become rounded.

Hydration occurs when a mineral absorbs water and expands, thus creating a strong mechanical force that stresses rocks. **Hydrolysis** breaks down silicate minerals in rock, as in the chemical weathering of feldspar into clays and silica. Water is not just absorbed, as in hydration, but actively participates in chemical reactions. **Oxidation** is the reaction of oxygen with certain metallic elements, the most familiar example being the rusting of iron, producing iron oxide. *Solution* is chemical weathering. For instance, a mild acid such as carbonic acid in rainwater will cause **carbonation**, wherein carbon combines with certain minerals, such as calcium, magnesium, potassium, and sodium.

chemical weathering (p. 423)
spheroidal weathering (p. 424)
hydration (p. 424)
hydrolysis (p. 424)
oxidation (p. 425)
carbonation (p. 426)

17. What is chemical weathering? Contrast this set of processes to physical weathering.

18. What is meant by the term spheroidal weathering? How is spheroidal weathering formed?

19. What is hydrolysis? How does it affect rocks?

20. Iron minerals in rock are susceptible to which form of chemical weathering? What characteristic colour is associated with this type of weathering?

21. With what kind of minerals do carbon compounds react, and under what circumstances does this reaction occur? What is this weathering process called?

● *Review* the processes and features associated with karst topography.

Karst topography refers to distinctively pitted and weathered limestone landscapes. Surface circular **sinkholes** form and may extend to form a *karst valley*. A sinkhole may collapse through the roof of an underground cavern, forming a *collapse sinkhole*. The formation of caverns is part of karst processes and groundwater erosion. Limestone caves feature many unique erosional and depositional features, producing a dramatic subterranean world.

karst topography (p. 427)
sinkholes (p. 428)

22. Describe the development of limestone topography. What is the name applied to such landscapes? From what area was this name derived?

23. Differentiate among sinkholes, karst valleys, and cockpit karst. Within which form is the radio telescope at Arecibo, Puerto Rico?

24. In general, how would you characterize the region southwest of Orleans, Indiana?

25. What are some of the unique erosional and depositional features you find in a limestone cavern?

26. What other types of rock experience karst?

● *Portray* the various types of mass movements and *identify* examples of each in relation to moisture content and speed of movement.

Any movement of a body of material, propelled and controlled by gravity, is **mass movement**, also called **mass wasting**. The **angle of repose** of loose sediment grains represents a balance of driving and resisting forces on a slope. Mass movement of Earth's surface produces some dramatic incidents, including **rockfalls** (a volume of rock that falls); **debris avalanches** (a mass of tumbling, falling rock, debris, and soil at high speed); **landslides** (a large amount of material failing simultaneously); **mudflows** (material in motion with a high moisture content); and **soil creep** (a persistent movement of individual soil particles that are lifted by the expansion of soil moisture as it freezes, by cycles of wetness and dryness, and temperature variations, or by the impact of grazing animals). **Solifluction** (a form of mass movement characterized by a slow movement of soil material downslope under the influence of gravity) creates lobe-shaped features in environments that experience cycles of freeze-thaw. **Gelifluction** (a class of solifluction that occurs in areas of permafrost), which is characterized by the movement of soil downslope under the influence of gravity over a permafrost layer, also produces lobe-shaped features. In addition, human mining and construction activities have created massive **scarification** of landscapes.

mass movement (p. 431)
mass wasting (p. 431)
angle of repose (p. 433)
rockfall (p. 434)
debris avalanche (p. 434)
landslide (p. 434)
mudflows (p. 436)
soil creep (p. 438)
solifluction (p. 438)
gelifluction (p. 438)
scarification (p. 439)

27. Define the role of slopes in mass movements, using the terms *angle of repose*, *driving force*, *resisting force*, and *geomorphic threshold*.

28. What events occurred in the Madison River Canyon in 1959?

29. What are the classes of mass movement? Describe each briefly and differentiate among these classes.

30. Name and describe the type of mudflow associated with a volcanic eruption.

31. Describe the difference between a landslide and what happened on the slopes of Nevado Huascarán.

32. What is scarification, and why is it considered a type of mass movement? Give several examples of scarification. Why are humans a significant geomorphic agent?

A series of meanders along the Red River. Gooseneck meander in the foreground will eventually erode away the narrow neck of land in a cutoff, allowing the river to take a shorter, more direct route. The massive agricultural development of this region stretches to the horizon in rectangular fields. The landscape of the Red River Valley is a flat topography, with a broad floodplain that contributed to the prevalence of spring flooding in 1966 and again in 1997. [Photo by G.R. Brooks, Earth Sciences Sector, Natural Resources Canada GSC 2002-686.]

14 River Systems and Landforms

Key Learning Concepts

After reading the chapter, you should be able to:

- *Define* the term fluvial and *outline* the fluvial processes: erosion, transportation, and deposition.
- *Construct* a basic drainage basin model and *identify* different types of drainage patterns and internal drainage, with examples.
- *Describe* the relation among velocity, depth, width, and discharge and *explain* the various ways that a stream erodes and transports its load.
- *Develop* a model of a meandering stream, including point bar, undercut bank, and cutoff, and *explain* the role of stream gradient in these flow characteristics.
- *Define* a floodplain and *analyze* the behaviour of a stream channel during a flood.
- *Differentiate* the several types of river deltas and *detail* each.
- *Explain* flood probability estimates and *review* strategies for mitigating flood hazards.

Earth's rivers and waterways form vast arterial networks that drain the continents. They also shape the landscape by removing the products of weathering, mass movement, and erosion and transporting them downstream. To call rivers "Earth's lifeblood" is no exaggeration, inasmuch as rivers redistribute mineral nutrients important for soil formation and plant growth and serve society in many ways.

Rivers not only provide essential water supplies, they also process waste (diluting and transporting it), provide critical cooling water for manufacturing and power generation, and form essential transportation networks. Rivers have been important in the geography of human history, influencing where settlements were built, where livelihoods were made, and where borders were drawn. This chapter discusses the dynamics of river systems and their landforms.

At any moment, approximately 1250 km^3 (300 mi^3) of water is flowing through Earth's waterways. Even though this volume is only 0.003% of all freshwater, the work performed by this energetic flow makes it a dominant agent of landmass denudation. Of the world's rivers, those with the greatest discharge (stream flow past a point in a given unit of time) are the Amazon of South America (Figure 14.1), the Congo (Zaire) of Africa, the Chang Jiang (Yangtze) of Asia, and the Orinoco of South America (Table 14.1). In North America, the greatest discharges are from the Missouri–Ohio–Mississippi, Saint Lawrence, and Mackenzie River systems.

Hydrology is the science of water and its global circulation, distribution, and properties, specifically water at and below Earth's surface. For hydrology links on the Web, see The Water Survey of Canada at **http://www.wsc.ec.gc.ca/index_e.cfm?cname=main_e.cfm**, The Hydrology Web at **http://hydrologyweb.pnl.gov/index.asp**, or the Global Hydrology and Climate Center at **http://www.ghcc.msfc.nasa.gov/**; also see the Amazon River at **http://boto.ocean.washington.edu/eos/index.html**.

In this chapter: We begin with a look at the largest rivers on Earth. Essential fluvial concepts of base level, drainage basin, drainage density and patterns follow. Factors that affect streamflow characteristics and the work performed by flowing water, including erosion, transport, and deposition, are discussed. Human response to floods and floodplain management are important aspects of river management that conclude the chapter.

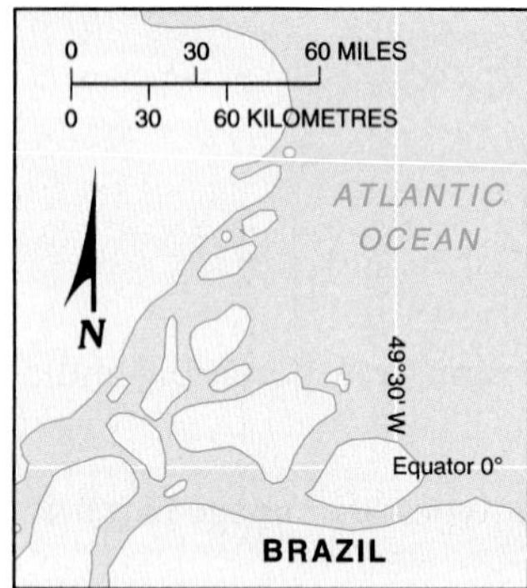

FIGURE 14.1 Mouth of the Amazon River.
The mouth of the Amazon River discharges a fifth of all the freshwater that enters the world's oceans. The mouth of the Amazon is 160 km (100 mi) wide. Millions of metric tons of sediments are derived from the Amazon's drainage basin, which is as large as the Australian continent. Large islands of sediment are left where the river's discharge leaves the mouth and flows into the Atlantic Ocean. [*Terra* MISR sensor image courtesy of NASA/GSFC/JPL and the MISR Team.]

Table 14.1 Largest Rivers on Earth Ranked by Discharge Volume and Length

Rank by Volume	Average Discharge at Mouth in Thousands of m³/s (cfs)	River (with Tributaries)	Outflow/Location	Length km (mi)	Rank by Length
1	180 (6350)	Amazon (Ucayali, Tambo, Ene, Apurimac)	Atlantic Ocean/Amapá-Pará, Brazil	6570 (4080)	2
2	41 (1460)	Congo, also known as the Zaire (Lualaba)	Atlantic Ocean/Angola, Congo	4630 (2880)	10
3	34 (1201)	Yangtze (Chàng Jiang)	East China Sea/Kiangsu, China	6300 (3915)	3
4	30 (1060)	Orinoco	Atlantic Ocean/Venezuela	2737 (1700)	27
5	21.8 (779)	La Plata estuary (Paraná)	Atlantic Ocean/Argentina	3945 (2450)	16
6	19.6 (699)	Ganges (Brahmaputra)	Bay of Bengal/India	2510 (1560)	23
7	19.4 (692)	Yenisey (Angara, Selenga or Selenge, Ider)	Gulf of Kara Sea/Siberia	5870 (3650)	5
8	18.2 (650)	Mississippi (Missouri, Ohio, Tennessee, Jefferson, Beaverhead, Red Rock)	Gulf of Mexico/Louisiana	6020 (3740)	4
9	16.0 (568)	Lena	Laptev Sea/Siberia	4400 (2730)	11
17	9.7 (348)	St. Lawrence	Gulf of St. Lawrence/Canada and United States	3060 (1900)	21
18	8.48 (300)	Mackenzie (Slave, Peace, Finlay)	Beaufort Sea/Canada	4241 (2635)	12
36	2.83 (100)	Nile (Kagera, Ruvuvu, Luvironza)	Mediterranean Sea/Egypt	6690 (4160)	1

Fluvial Processes and Landscapes

Stream-related processes are termed **fluvial** (from the Latin *fluvius*, meaning "river"). Geographers seek to describe stream patterns and the fluvial processes that created them. Fluvial systems, like all natural systems, have characteristic processes and produce predictable landforms. Yet a stream system can behave with randomness and disorder. The term *river* is applied to a trunk stream or an entire river system. *Stream* is a more general term not necessarily related to size. There is some overlap in usage between the two terms.

Insolation and gravity power the hydrologic cycle and are the driving forces of fluvial systems. Individual streams vary greatly, depending on the climate in which they operate, the composition of the surface, the topography over which they flow, the nature of vegetation and plant cover, and the length of time they have been operating in a specific setting.

Water dislodges, dissolves, or removes surface material in a process called **erosion**. Streams produce *fluvial erosion*, in which weathered sediment is picked up for transport to new locations. Thus, a stream is a mixture of water and solids; the solids are carried in solution, by suspension, and by mechanical **transport** (movement of material). Materials are laid down by another process, **deposition**. **Alluvium** is the general term for the clay, silt, and sand deposited by running water.

Base Level of Streams

American geologist and ethnologist John Wesley Powell (1834–1902) was a director of the U.S. Geological Survey, first director of the U.S. Bureau of Ethnology, explorer of the Colorado River, and a pioneer in understanding the landscape (Figure 14.2). In 1875 he put forward the idea of **base level**, or a level below which a stream cannot erode its valley. In general, the *ultimate base level* is sea level (the average level between high and low tides). As shown in Figure 14.3, you can imagine the base level as a surface extending inland from sea level, inclined gently upward under the continents. Ideally, this is the lowest practical level for all denudation processes.

Of course, Powell recognized that not every landscape has degraded all the way to sea level; clearly, other intermediate base levels are in operation. A *local base level*, or temporary one, may control the lower limit of local streams. The local base level may be a river, a lake, hard and resistant rock, or a human-made dam (see Figure 14.3). In arid landscapes, with their intermittent precipitation, valleys, plains, or other low points provide local control.

Over time, the work of streams modifies the landscape dramatically. Landforms are produced by two basic processes: (1) erosive action of flowing water, and (2) deposition of stream-transported materials. Let us begin our study by examining a basic fluvial unit—the drainage basin.

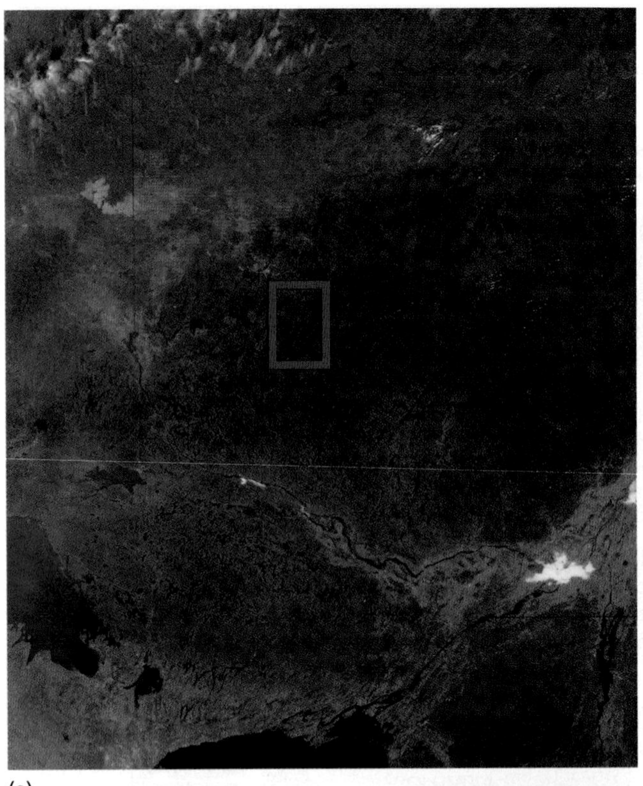

(a)

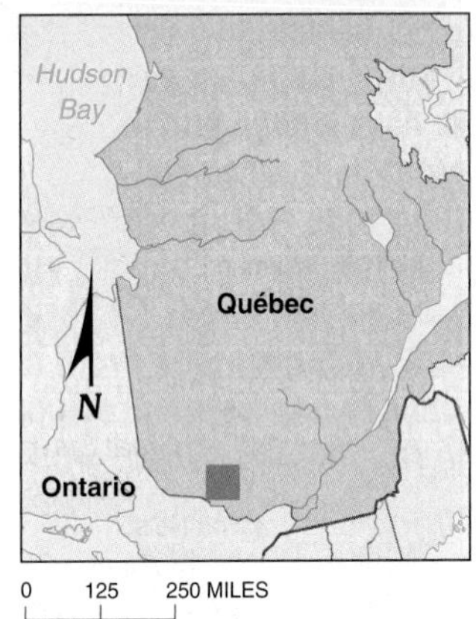

(b)

FIGURE 14.8 Deranged drainage in Québec.
(a) Deranged drainage on the Canadian Shield in Québec, north of the Ottawa River. The box indicates the area shown in the topographic map. (b) Topographic map covering a portion of the area in the satellite image. [Image (a) courtesy of NASA/GSFC; (b) map from the Canada Centre for Remote Sensing, Natural Resources Canada. Used by permission of the Minister of Public Works and Government Services.]

expended by this drainage system is efficient because the overall length of the branches is minimized.

The *trellis drainage* pattern (Figure 14.9b) is characteristic of dipping or folded topography. Such drainage exists in the nearly parallel mountain folds of the Ridge and Valley Province in the eastern United States. The inset sketch to Figure 14.9b suggests that a headward-eroding part of one stream (to the lower right of the inset) could break through a drainage divide and *capture* the headwaters of another stream in the next valley, and indeed this does happen. The dashed line is the abandoned former channel. The sharp bends in two of the streams in the illustration are called *elbows of capture* and are evidence that one stream has breached a drainage divide. This type of capture, or *stream piracy*, can also occur in other drainage patterns.

The remaining drainage patterns in Figure 14.9 are responses to other specific structural conditions:

- A *radial* drainage pattern (c) results when streams flow off a central peak or dome, such as occurs on a volcanic mountain.
- *Parallel* drainage (d) is associated with steep slopes.
- A *rectangular* pattern (e) is formed by a faulted and jointed landscape, which directs stream courses in patterns of right-angle turns.
- *Annular* patterns (f) are produced by structural domes, with concentric patterns of rock strata guiding stream courses. Figure 12.10c provides an example of annular drainage on a dome structure.
- In areas having disrupted surface patterns, such as the glaciated shield regions of Canada, northern Europe, and some parts of Michigan and other states, a *deranged* pattern (g) is in evidence, with no clear geometry in the drainage and no true stream valley pattern.

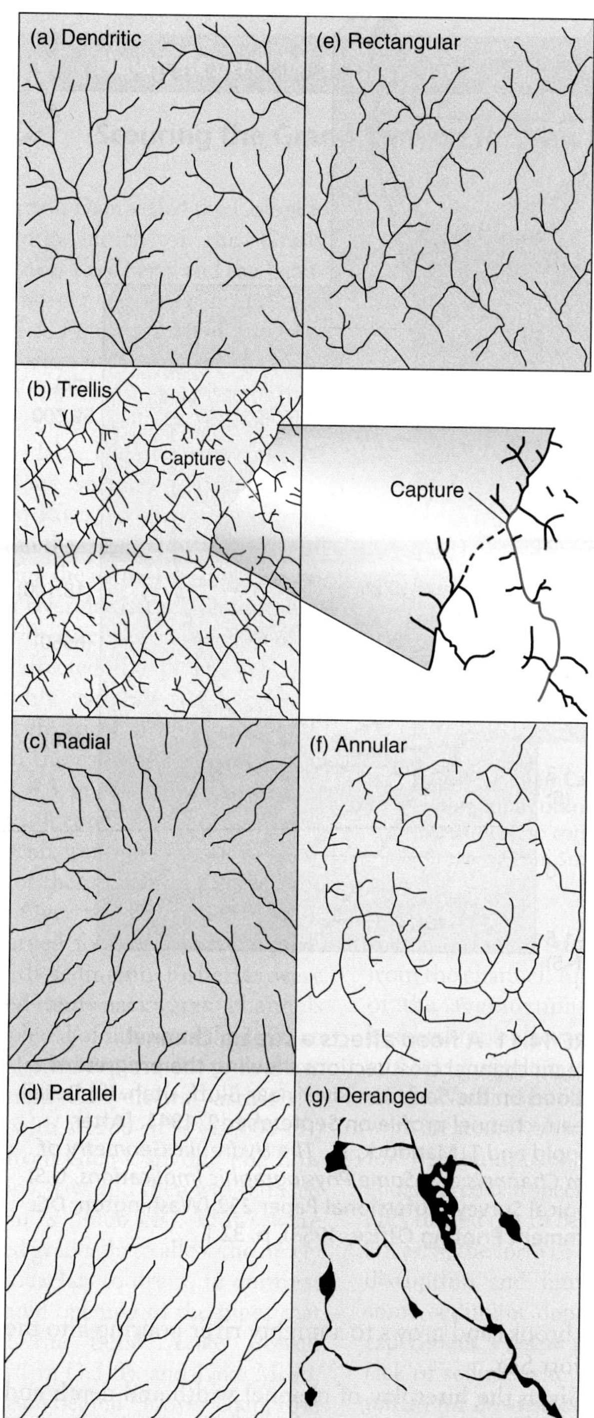

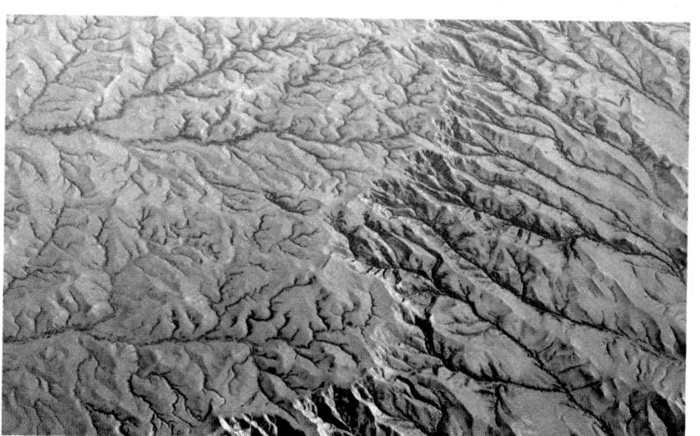
(h)

FIGURE 14.9 The seven most common drainage patterns. Each pattern is a visual summary of all the geologic and climatic conditions of its region. (h) Two of these drainage patterns dominate this scene from central Montana, in response to local relief and rock structure. [After A. D. Howard, "Drainage analysis in geological interpretation: A summation," *Bulletin of American Association of Petroleum Geologists* 51 (1967): 2248. Adapted by permission. (h) Photo by Bobbé Christopherson.]

The structure and relief of the land dictate these seven drainage patterns. In Figure 14.9h, you see two distinct drainage patterns. Of the seven types illustrated, which two patterns are most like those in the aerial photo, made in central Montana?

Drainage patterns also occur that are discordant with the landscape through which they flow. For example, a drainage system may flow in apparent conflict with older, buried structures that have been uncovered by erosion, so that the streams appear to be *superimposed*. Where an existing stream flows as rocks are uplifted, the stream keeps its original course, cutting into the rock in a pattern contrary to its structure. Such a stream is a *superposed stream* (the stream cuts across weak and resistant rocks alike). A few examples include Wills Creek, cutting a water gap through Haystack Mountain at Cumberland, Maryland; the Columbia River through the Cascade Mountains of Washington; and the River Arun that cuts across the Himalayas.

Streamflow Characteristics

A mass of water positioned above base level in a stream has potential energy. As the water flows downslope (downstream) under the influence of gravity, this energy becomes kinetic energy. The rate of this conversion from potential to kinetic energy depends on the steepness of the stream channel.

Stream channels vary in *width* and *depth*. The streams that flow in them vary in velocity and in the *sediment load* they carry. All of these factors increase with increasing discharge. **Discharge**, or a stream's flow rate per unit of time, is calculated by multiplying the velocity of the stream by its width and depth for a specific cross section of the channel, as stated in the simple expression:

$$Q = wdv$$

where, Q = discharge, w = channel width, d = channel depth, and v = stream velocity. As Q increases, some combination of channel width, depth, and stream velocity increases. Discharge is expressed either in cubic metres per second (m^3/s) or cubic feet per second (cfs).

Figure 14.10 illustrates the relation of discharge to width, depth, and velocity. The graphs show that mean velocity increases with greater discharge, despite the common misperception that downstream flow becomes more sluggish. (The increased velocity downstream often is

evapotranspiration (POTET) rates in the arid area. Such a stream is called an **exotic stream** (exotic means "of foreign origin").

The Nile River exemplifies exotic streams. This great river, Earth's longest, drains much of northeastern Africa. But as it courses through the deserts of Sudan and Egypt, it loses water instead of gaining it, because of evaporation and withdrawal for agriculture. By the time it empties into the Mediterranean Sea, the Nile's flow has dwindled so much that it ranks only 36th in discharge.

In the United States, the Colorado River is notable as an exotic stream. Its flow decreases with distance from its source; in fact, the river no longer produces enough discharge to reach its mouth in the Gulf of California! The exotic Colorado River is depleted not only by passage across dry, desert lands but also by upstream removal of water for agriculture and municipal uses—see Focus Study 15.1 for a satellite image of the river's former mouth.

Stream Erosion

A stream's erosional turbulence and abrasion carve and shape the landscape through which it flows. **Hydraulic action** is the work of flowing water alone. Running water causes hydraulic squeeze-and-release action that loosens and lifts rocks. As this debris moves along, it mechanically erodes the streambed further, through the process of **abrasion**, with rock particles grinding and carving the streambed like liquid sandpaper.

The upstream tributaries in a drainage basin usually have small and irregular discharges, and most of the stream's energy is expended in turbulent eddies. As a result, hydraulic action in these upstream sections is at maximum, whereas the coarse-textured load of such a stream is small. The downstream portions of a river, however, move much larger volumes of water past a given point and carry larger suspended loads of sediment (Figure 14.12). Stream velocity determines rates of erosion and deposition. Sediment particles are deposited onto the streambed at slower velocities, whereas they are eroded at higher velocities.

Stream Transport

You may have watched a river or creek after a rainfall, the water coloured brown by the heavy sediment load being transported. The amount of material available to a stream depends on topographic relief, the nature of rock and soil through which the stream flows, climate, vegetation, and human activity in a drainage basin. *Competence*, which is a stream's ability to move particles of a specific size, is a function of stream velocity. *Capacity* is the total possible load that a stream can transport. Four processes transport eroded materials: solution, suspension, saltation, and traction; each is shown in action in Figure 14.13.

Solution refers to the **dissolved load** of a stream, especially the chemical solution derived from minerals such as limestone or dolomite or from soluble salts. The main contributor of material in solution is chemical weathering. Sometimes the undesirable salt content that hinders human use of some rivers comes from dissolved rock formations and from springs in the stream channel; as an example, the San Juan and Little Colorado Rivers that flow into the Colorado River near the Utah–Arizona border add dissolved salts to the system.

The **suspended load** consists of fine-grained, clastic particles (bits and pieces of rock). They are held aloft in the stream, with the finest particles not deposited until the stream velocity slows nearly to zero. Turbulence in the water, with random upward motion, is an important mechanical factor in holding a load of sediment in suspension.

(a)

(b)

FIGURE 14.12 Stream velocity and discharge increase together.
(a) A low volume, low-velocity (but turbulent) mountain stream in Melville Peninsula, Nunavut. (b) High discharge, high-velocity (but laminar, or smooth water flow) portion of the Athabasca River, upstream of Whitecourt, Alberta. [Photos by (a) Earth Sciences Sector, Natural Resources Canada GSC 2002-449; (b) Earth Sciences Sector, Natural Resources Canada GSC 2002-619.]

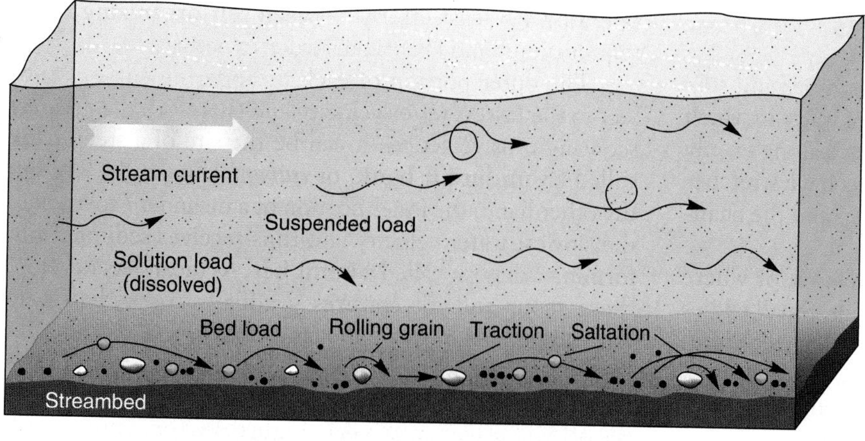

FIGURE 14.13 Fluvial transport.
Fluvial transportation of eroded materials through saltation, traction, suspension, and solution.

Bed load refers to coarser materials that are dragged along the streambed by **traction** or are rolled and bounced along by **saltation** (from the Latin *saltim*, which means "by leaps or jumps"). At times, it is difficult to distinguish traction from saltation and their effects on bed load. Particles transported by saltation are too large to remain in suspension, a distinction directly related to a stream's velocity and its ability to retain particles in suspension. With increased kinetic energy, parts of the bed load are rafted upward and become suspended load. Saltation is also a process in wind transport of materials (see Chapter 15).

The early explorers who visited the Grand Canyon reported in their journals that they were kept awake at night by the thundering sound of the river and rapids. Imagine the tremendous quantity of material being moved along by the natural Colorado River before any dams were built. Dams and reservoirs now trap sediments that formerly contributed to the river's bed load.

If the load (bed and suspended) exceeds a stream's capacity, sediments accumulate as **aggradation** (the opposite of degradation) and the stream channel builds up through deposition. With excess sediment, a stream becomes a maze of interconnected channels that form a **braided stream** pattern (Figure 14.14). Braiding often occurs when reduced discharge lowers a stream's transporting ability, such as after flooding, or when a landslide occurs upstream, or from increased load where weak banks of sand or gravel exist. Locally, braiding also may result from a new sediment load from glacial meltwaters, as in Alberta's Sunwapta River. Glacial materials also exceed stream capacity in the 15-km (9.3-mi) stretch of the Brahmaputra River about 35 km (22 mi) south of Lhasa, Tibet (Figure 14.14b).

(a)

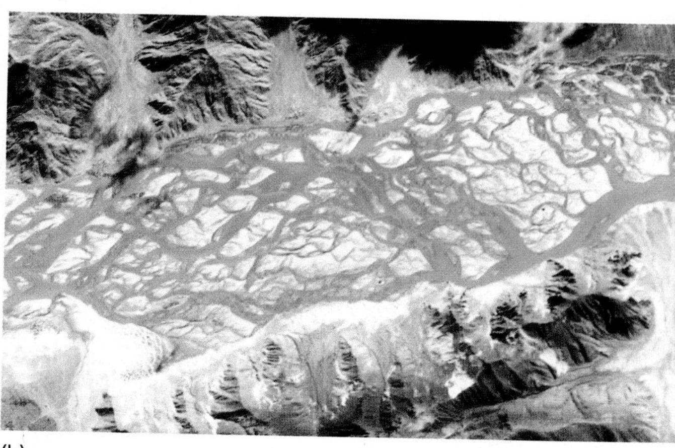
(b)

FIGURE 14.14 A braided stream.
(a) Sunwapta River, along the Icefields Parkway, southern Jasper National Park, Alberta.
(b) A 15-km stretch along the braided Brahmaputra River channel some 35 km (22 mi) south of Lhasa, Tibet, in a narrow valley south of the Tibetan Plateau. These streams reflect excessive sediment load associated with glacial meltwaters filled with fine sediments, or "glacial flour." [Photos by (a) Earth Sciences Sector, Natural Resources Canada GSC 2002-597; (b) October 13, 2001, International Space Station astronaut, courtesy of Earth Science and Image Analysis Lab, JSC/NASA.]

News Report 14.2

Rivers Make Poor Political Boundaries

There are several locations between Canada and the United States where rivers are used as the divide for the international boundary. The International Boundary Commission is responsible for maintaining the boundary between the two countries in a clearly marked fashion. It is also responsible for defining the location of the boundary for any legal situation involving the border. Nowhere is this more difficult than when the boundary is defined as a river. Borders and their demarcations, the boundary, do not change easily. However, rivers are constantly changing their locations and make poor political boundaries. In addition to the idea that the river changes its location through erosion and deposition, the level of the water in the stream affects the determination of the middle of the channel.

One of the most interesting cases of river boundaries involves the determination of the St. Croix River as the boundary between Maine in the United States and New Brunswick in Canada (Figure 1). In 1783 with the Treaty of Paris, the boundaries between the United States and what is now Canada were drawn up. It was agreed that the St. Croix River would be the boundary. However, there were several rivers that could be perceived as this particular stream and another treaty had to be passed to appoint three commissioners to identify the St. Croix River and its source. The boundary was identified in 1798.

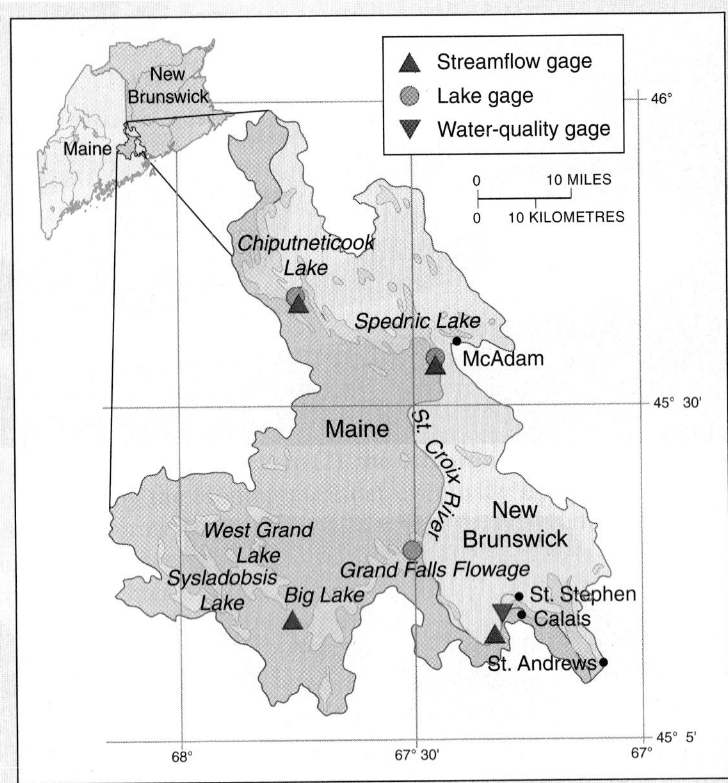

FIGURE 1 The St. Croix River.
The boundary between New Brunswick and Maine is determined by the function of the St. Croix River.

The problems of clear identification of the boundary were not yet resolved. Disputes arose over whether the channel margins, channel midline, or some other location was the actual boundary. The St. Croix River was the first to have an identification attached that was based on the function of the river. The boundary was determined to be the *thalweg* (zone of maximum flow of the stream) of the river. Recognizing that the thalweg changed over time with erosion and deposition along the riverbank, the commissioners relied on river soundings taken by the United States Coast Guard and the Geodetic Survey to determine the location of the thalweg. The thalweg was then mathematically calculated and plotted on a map. So, although the river was used as the boundary, potential disputes were resolved by measuring the fluvial geomorphology of the time and mapping the location.

The 1909 *Boundary Waters Treaty* established the International Joint Commission (IJC), an independent two-nation organization, to monitor potential border disputes and water issues. Signalling a new era for management of water quality, quantity, and border issues, the IJC adopted a complete watershed model for the St. Croix River in 2000. This ecosystem approach was facilitated by the merger of two important boards—the International St. Croix River Board of Control, established in 1915, and the International Advisory Board on Pollution Control–St. Croix River, in operation since 1962. The two boards had a history of cooperation. This combined effort manages the entire river watershed as a unit with a goal to improve the health of the St. Croix boundary-waters aquatic ecosystem.

characteristics, just the velocity required for transportation of the load supplied from the drainage basin.*

*J. H. Mackin, "Concept of the graded river," *Geological Society of America Bulletin* 59 (1948): 463.

In other words, a **graded stream** is one that attains a graded condition and does not mean that the stream is at its lowest gradient. Rather, graded represents a present balance (a dynamic equilibrium) among erosion, transportation, and deposition over time along a portion of the stream.

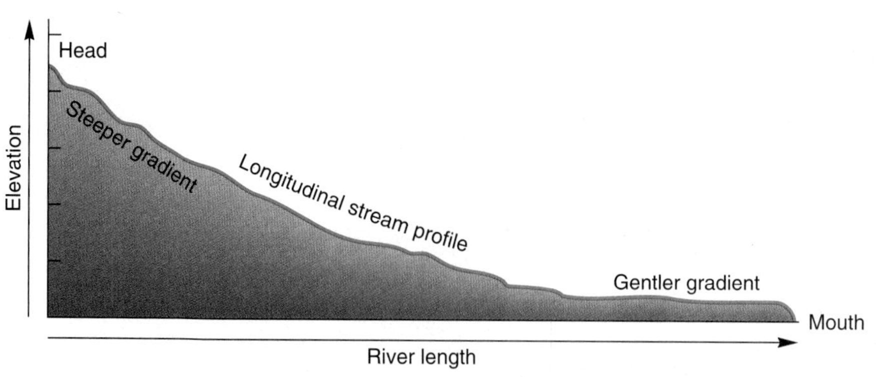

FIGURE 14.17 An ideal longitudinal profile.
Idealized cross section of the longitudinal profile of a stream, showing its gradient. Upstream segments have a steeper gradient; downstream, the gradient is gentler. The middle and lower portions in the illustration appear graded, or in dynamic equilibrium.

Both high-gradient and low-gradient streams can achieve a graded condition. The longitudinal profile of a graded stream is called a *profile of equilibrium*—a parabolic curve, gently flattening toward the mouth. Stream dynamics can then be compared against this ideal balance.

One problem with applying the graded stream concept is that an individual stream can have both graded and ungraded portions and may have graded sections without having an overall graded slope. Variations and interruptions are the rule rather than the exception. A profile of equilibrium may not be smooth throughout its course and cannot exist for long, for it represents a theoretical perfect balance. With streams, as in all of nature, change is the only constant.

Stream gradient may be affected by tectonic uplift of the landscape, which changes the base level. If tectonic forces slowly lift the landscape, the stream gradient will increase, stimulating renewed erosional activity. Imagine this occurring to the landscape in Figure 14.2. The meandering stream flowing through the uplifted landscape becomes rejuvenated; that is, the river actively returns to downcutting and eventually forms *entrenched meanders* in the landscape. Figure 14.18 depicts an actual rejuvenated landscape.

Nickpoints When the longitudinal profile of a stream shows an abrupt change in gradient, such as at a waterfall or an area of rapids, the point of interruption is termed a **nickpoint** (also spelled *knickpoint*). At a nickpoint, the conversion of potential energy to concentrated kinetic energy works to eliminate the nickpoint. Figure 14.19 shows a stream with two such interruptions.

Nickpoints can result when a stream flows across a zone of hard, resistant rock or from various tectonic uplift episodes, such as might occur along a fault line. Temporary blockage in a channel, caused by a landslide or a logjam, also could be considered a nickpoint; when the logjam breaks, the stream quickly readjusts its channel to its former grade.

Waterfalls are interesting and beautiful gradient breaks. At the edge of a fall, a stream is free-falling, moving at high velocity under the acceleration of gravity, causing increased abrasion on the channel below. The increased abrasion and hydraulic action generally undercut the waterfall. Eventually the excavation will cause the rock ledge at the lip of the fall to collapse, and the waterfall will shift a bit farther upstream. The height of the waterfall is gradually reduced as debris accumulates at its base. Thus, a nickpoint migrates upstream, sometimes for kilometres, until it becomes a series of rapids and is eventually eliminated.

At Niagara Falls on the Ontario–New York border, glaciers advanced and retreated over this region several times in the last million years. In doing so, they exposed resistant rock strata that are underlain by less-resistant shales. As this less-resistant material continues to weather and erode away, the overlying rock strata collapse, allowing

(a)

(b)

FIGURE 14.18 Entrenched meanders.
The San Juan River near Mexican Hat, Utah, cuts down into the uplifted Colorado Plateau landscape producing entrenched meanders, called the Goosenecks of the San Juan River. [Photos by (a) Betty Crowell; (b) Randall M. Christopherson.]

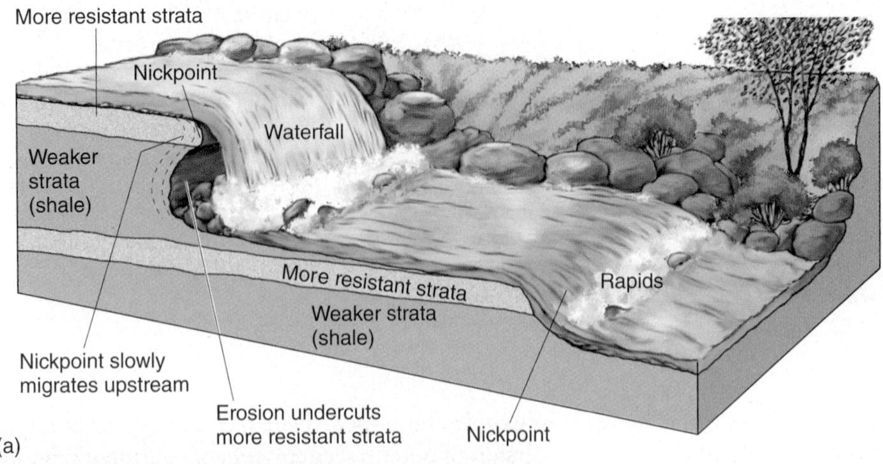

FIGURE 14.19 Nickpoints interrupt a stream profile.
(a) Longitudinal stream profile showing nickpoints produced by resistant rock strata. Potential energy is converted into kinetic energy and concentrated at the nickpoint, accelerating erosion, which will eventually eliminate the feature. (b) A nickpoint and granite pothole interrupts stream gradient on the Pemigewassey River, Franconia Notch Park, New Hampshire. [Photo by Bobbé Christopherson.]

the falls to erode farther upstream toward Lake Erie (Figure 14.20a).

Niagara Falls is a place where natural processes labour to eliminate a nickpoint, reducing this portion of the river to a series of mere rapids. In fact, the falls have retreated more than 11 km (6.8 mi) from the steep face of the Niagara Escarpment (cliff) during the last 12,000 years. In the past engineers have used control facilities upstream to reduce flows over the American Falls at Niagara for inspection of the cliff (Figure 14.20b). A

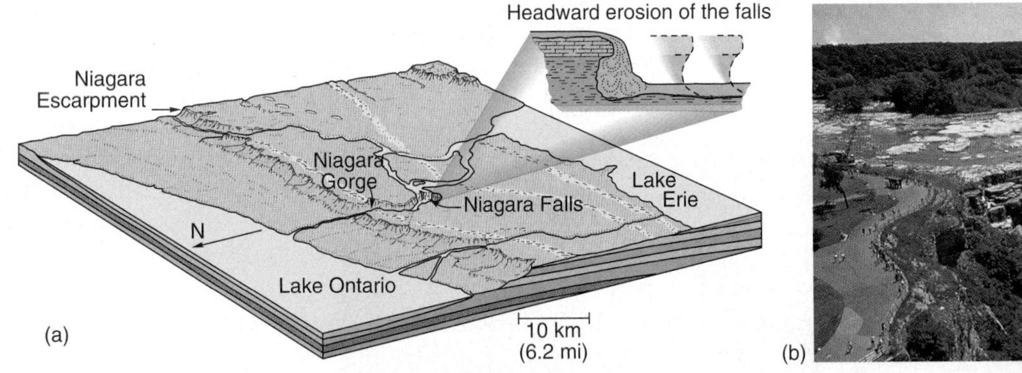

FIGURE 14.20 Retreat of Niagara Falls.
(a) Headward retreat of Niagara Falls from the Niagara escarpment. It has taken the falls about 12,000 years to reach this position at a pace of about 1.3 m (4.3 ft) per year. (b) Niagara Falls, with the American Falls portion almost completely shut off by upstream controls for inspection. Horseshoe Falls in the background is still flowing. Such inspections allow engineers to assess the progress of natural processes that are working to eliminate the Niagara Falls nickpoint. [(a) After W. K. Hamblin, *Earth's Dynamic Systems*, 6th ed. (Upper Saddle River, NJ: Macmillan Publishing, an imprint of Prentice Hall, Inc. © 1992), Figure 12.15, p. 246. Used by permission. (b) Photo courtesy of the New York Power Authority.]

nickpoint is a relatively temporary and mobile feature on the landscape.

Stream Gradient and Landscape Forms In Chapter 13, we introduced William Morris Davis, a geomorphologist who founded the Association of American Geographers in 1904. His evolutionary concepts of erosion also included fluvial processes. Drawing from G. K. Gilbert, an important geomorphologist and his contemporary, Davis incorporated the graded-stream concept into his model, identifying erosion stages in a cyclic model he called *youth*, *maturity*, and *old age*—old age is approached as the floodplain broadens and a low stream gradient produces a wide, meandering flow pattern.

Today, a *functional model of dynamic equilibrium* is supported by geomorphologists. The dynamic equilibrium model emphasizes the effects of individual processes interacting on streams and hillslope systems. Stream form and behaviour result from complex interactions of slope, discharge, and load, all of which are variable within different climates and with different rock types. Landscapes simply do not provide enough clear evidence to support a cyclic model of evolution. Regardless, Davis's work was a breakthrough in understanding landscapes, and many of his terms are still in use.

As suggested by S. A. Schumm and R. W. Lichty, two modern geomorphologists, the validity of cyclic or functional landscape models may depend on the *time frame*. Let us consider three time frames: geologic time, graded time, and steady time. Over the long span of *geologic time*, cyclic models of evolutionary development might explain the disappearance of entire mountain ranges through denudation, for example. At the other extreme of time, *steady time* applies to short-term adjustments ongoing in a drainage basin. *Graded time* is between the two time frames, and within it lies the realm of dynamic equilibrium conditions.

Stream Deposition

After weathering, mass movement, erosion, and transportation, deposition is the next logical event in a sequence. In *deposition*, a stream deposits alluvium, or unconsolidated sediments, thereby creating depositional landforms, such as floodplains, terraces, or deltas.

As discussed earlier, stream meanders tend to migrate downstream through the landscape. Over time, the landscape near a meandering river comes to bear meander scars of residual deposits from former, abandoned channels. Former point-bar deposits leave low-lying ridges, creating a *bar-and-swale relief* (a swale is a gentle low area). The *Landsat* image in Figure 14.21 exhibits characteristic meandering scars: meander bends, oxbow lakes, natural levees, point bars, and undercut banks.

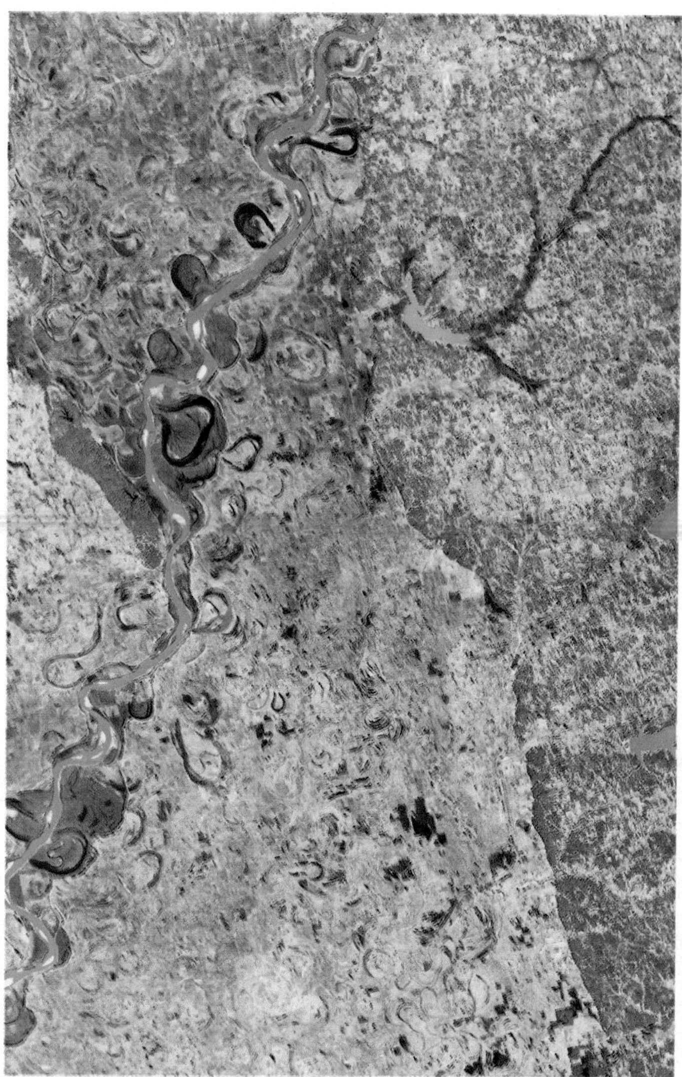

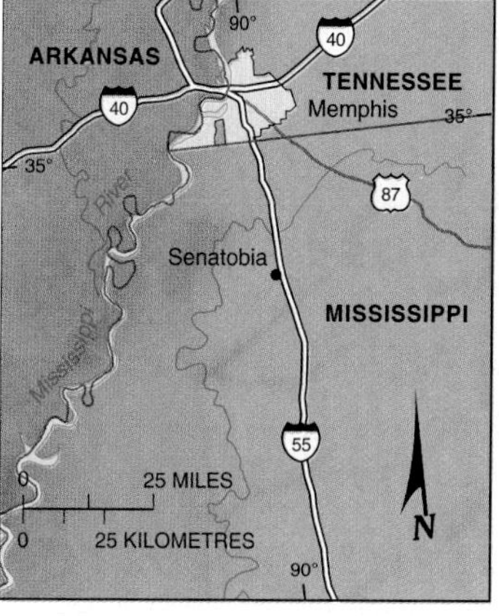

FIGURE 14.21 Meander scars.
The Mississippi River forms a portion of the Mississippi–Arkansas border near Senatobia, Mississippi. Characteristic meander patterns and scars of former channels are visible in the *Landsat* image. The map of northwestern Mississippi shows the portion of the Mississippi River that forms the Mississippi–Arkansas border. [Image by GEOPIC, Earth Satellite Corporation/ Photo Researchers, Inc.]

Floodplains The flat low-lying area flanking a stream channel that is subjected to recurrent flooding is a **floodplain**. It is formed when the river overflows its channel during times of high flow. Thus, when floods occur, the floodplain is inundated. When the water recedes, it leaves behind alluvial deposits that generally mask the underlying rock with their accumulating thickness. The present river channel is embedded in these alluvial deposits. Figure 14.22 illustrates a characteristic floodplain and a

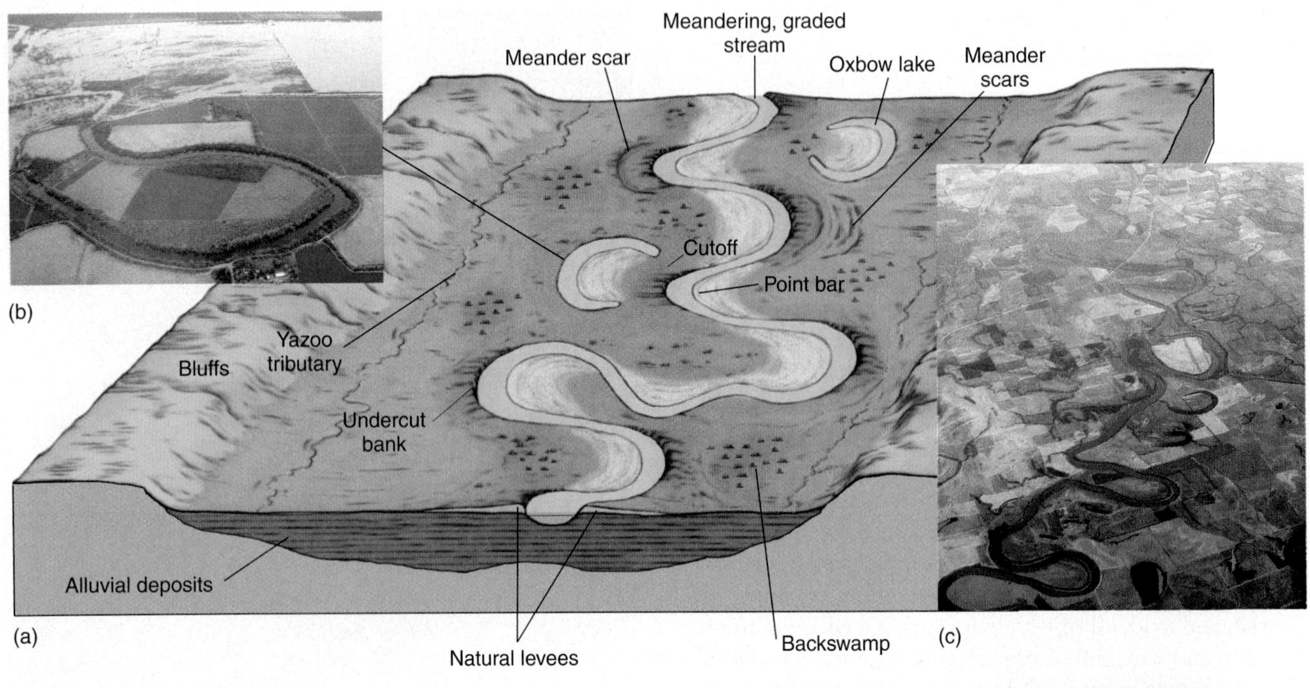

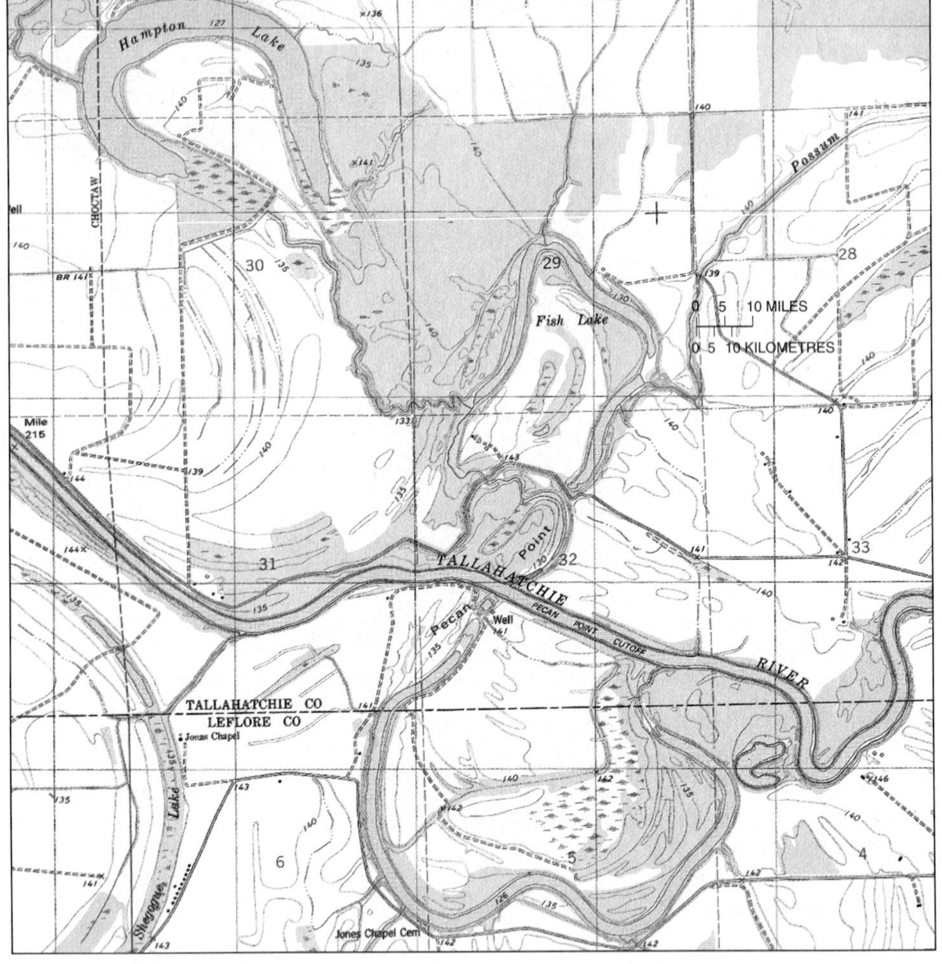

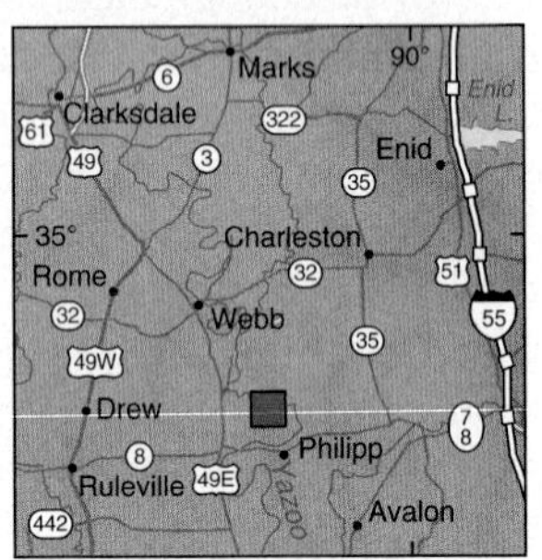

FIGURE 14.22 A floodplain.
(a) Typical floodplain landscape and related landscape features. (b) An oxbow lake. (c) Levees, oxbow lakes, farmland in a floodplain. (d) A portion of the Philipp, Mississippi, topographic map quadrangle. [Photos by (b) and (c) Bobbé Christopherson; (d) topographic map by USGS.]

Stream Processes, Floodplains, Oxbow Lake Formation

representative topographic map of an area near Philipp, Mississippi.

On either bank of most streams, **natural levees** develop as by-products of flooding. When floodwater arrives, the river overflows its banks, loses velocity as it spreads out, and drops a portion of its sediment load to form the levees. Larger sand-sized particles drop out first, forming the principal component of the levees, with finer silts and clays deposited farther from the river. Successive floods increase the height of the levees (*levée* is French for "raising"). The levees may grow in height until the river channel becomes elevated, or *perched* above the surrounding floodplain.

On the topographic map (Figure 14.22d), you can see the natural levees represented by several contour lines that occur immediately adjacent to the Tallahatchie River. These contour lines (5-ft interval) denote a height of 10–15 ft (3–4.5 m) above the river and the adjoining floodplain. Next time you have an opportunity to see a river and its floodplain, look for levees (they may be low and subtle).

Notice in Figure 14.22a an area labelled backswamp and a stream called a yazoo tributary. The natural levees and elevated channel of the river prevent this **yazoo tributary** from joining the main channel, so it flows parallel to the river and through the **backswamp** area. (The name comes from the Yazoo River in the southern part of the Mississippi floodplain.)

People build cities on floodplains despite the threat of flooding because floodplains are nearly level and they are next to water. People often are encouraged by government assurances of artificial protection from floods and disaster assistance if floods occur. Government assistance may provide the building of artificial levees on top of natural levees. Artificial levees do increase the capacity in the channel, but they also lead to even greater floods when they are overtopped by floodwaters or when they fail (Figure 14.23). Are there river floodplains where you live? If so, what is your impression of present land-use patterns, local planning and zoning, and people's hazard perception overall?

The catastrophic floods along the Red River and its tributaries in Manitoba in 1997 illustrate the risk of building settlements on floodplains. Damage estimates from those floods, detailed in News Report 14.3, exceeded $815 million. In the United States, the flooding in the Dakotas and Minnesota caused more than US$460 million in damage covered by state and federal assistance programs, and it is estimated that total damages were more than a billion dollars.

Stream Terraces As explained earlier, several factors may rejuvenate stream energy and stream-landscape relations so that a stream can scour downward with renewed vigour and increased erosion. The resulting entrenchment of the river deeper into its own floodplain produces **alluvial terraces**

(continued p. 470)

FIGURE 14.23 Flooding river and threatened dikes.
Ring dikes protected Morris, Manitoba, from the floodwaters of the Red River in 1997. A permanent ring dike surrounds the town, but the people of Morris topped it with sand bags to accommodate the increased flood level experienced that year. Wave action from 60 kmph winds tested the dike on April 28 as the crest approached. The dike held and the town was spared the ravages of the floodwaters. Check the map in News Report 14.3, Figure 2, to see the location of Morris and its relation to the regional flood. [Photo by G.R. Brooks. Used by permission of the Minister of Public Works and Government Services Canada; Natural Resources Canada, Geological Survey of Canada.]

Alluvial terraces (paired)

(a)

(b)

FIGURE 14.24 Alluvial stream terraces.
(a) Alluvial terraces are formed as a stream cuts into a valley. (b) Alluvial terraces along the Rakaia River, in New Zealand. [(a) After W. M. Davis, *Geographical Essays* (New York: Dover, 1964 [1909]), p. 515; (b) photo by Bill Bachman/Photo Researchers, Inc.]

on either side of the valley, which look like topographic steps above the river. Alluvial terraces generally appear paired at similar elevations on each side of the valley (Figure 14.24). If more than one set of paired terraces is present, the valley probably has undergone more than one episode of rejuvenation. The flat terrace areas, above the lowest section of floodplain along the river, have always been a location for settlement.

If the terraces on either side of the valley do not match in elevation, then entrenchment actions must have been continuous as the river meandered from side to side, with each meander cutting a terrace slightly lower in elevation—a condition of *unpaired terraces*. Thus, alluvial terraces represent what originally was a depositional feature (a floodplain) that subsequently has been eroded by its own stream because the stream experienced changes in stream load and capacity.

River Deltas The mouth of a river is where it reaches a base level. The river's forward velocity rapidly decelerates as it enters a larger body of water. The reduced velocity causes the transported load to quickly exceed the river's carrying capacity. Coarse sediments such as sand and gravel drop out first and are deposited closest to the river's mouth. Finer clays are carried farther and form the extreme end of the deposit. The depositional plain that forms at the mouth of a river is called a **delta** for its characteristic triangular shape, named after the Greek letter delta (Δ). The significance of the Nile River delta to food production was perceived by Herodotus in ancient times (see News Report 14.4).

Each flood stage deposits a new layer of alluvium over the surface of the delta so that it grows outward. At the same time, river channels divide into smaller courses known as *distributaries*, which appear as a reverse of the dendritic

News Report 14.4

The Nile Delta Is Disappearing

People along the Nile River have depended on its regular flow and annual floods for millennia. Herodotus noted in the 5th century B.C. how the people farmed the fields in the floodplain and delta regions. After harvesting their crops, they retreated from the area to their homes. They would await the annual floods that brought fresh silt and nutrients for next year's planting. This cycle of fertility continued until the completion of the Aswan High Dam in 1964. This structure caused a partial interruption in the supply of sediment to the delta, and as a result the delta coastline continues to actively recede. Herodotus stated in *The History*, Book Two, "in the part called the Delta, it seems to me that if the Nile no longer floods. . . for all time to come, the Egyptians will suffer."

J. Stanley, an oceanographer at the Smithsonian Institution, has proposed an intriguing explanation for what is happening in addition to the impact of the Aswan High Dam. Over the centuries, more than 9000 km (5500 mi) of canals were built in the delta to augment the natural distributary system. As the river discharge enters the network of canals, flow velocity is reduced, stream competence and capacity are lost, and sediment load is deposited far short of where the delta touches the Mediterranean Sea. River flows no longer effectively reach the sea.

The Nile delta is receding from the coast at an alarming 50 to 100 m (165 to 330 ft) per year. Seawater is intruding farther inland in both surface water and groundwater. Human action and reaction to this evolving situation will no doubt determine the delta's future. If Herodotus could only see the delta he described as it looks today!

drainage pattern of tributary streams discussed earlier. Here are a few examples:

- The Ganges River delta features an intricate pattern of distributaries in a *braided delta*. Bountiful alluvium carried from deforested slopes upstream provides excess sediment that is deposited to form many deltaic islands (Figure 14.25). The combined Ganges-Brahmaputra River delta complex is the largest in the world.
- The Nile River delta is an *arcuate* (arc-shaped) delta (Figure 14.26). Also arcuate are the Danube River delta in Romania where it enters the Black Sea and the Indus River delta. (See News Report 14.4 for an update on the condition of the disappearing Nile Delta.)
- The Tiber River in Italy has an *estuarine delta*, one that is in the process of filling an **estuary**, which is the seaward mouth of a river where the river's freshwater encounters seawater.

Mississippi River Delta The Mississippi River delta has an interesting history. Over the past 120 million years, the Mississippi has collected sediments throughout its vast basin and deposited them into the Gulf of Mexico. During the past 5000 years, the river has formed a succession of seven distinct deltaic complexes along the Louisiana coast (Figure 14.27).

Each generalized lobe in the illustration reflects distinct course changes in the Mississippi River, probably where the river broke through its natural levees during episodes of severe flooding, thus changing the configuration of the delta (Figure 14.27a). The seventh and current delta has been building for at least 500 years and is a classic example of a *bird-foot delta*—a long channel with many distributaries and sediments carried beyond the tip of the delta into the Gulf of Mexico.

The Mississippi River delta clearly is dynamic over time as sediments accumulate on the floor of the Gulf of Mexico and the distributaries shift (Figure 14.27b). The main channel persists because of much effort and expense directed at maintaining the artificial levee system. The 3.25-million-km^2 (1.25-million-mi^2) Mississippi drainage basin produces enough sediment to extend the Louisiana coast 90 m (295 ft) a year—550 million metric tons a year.

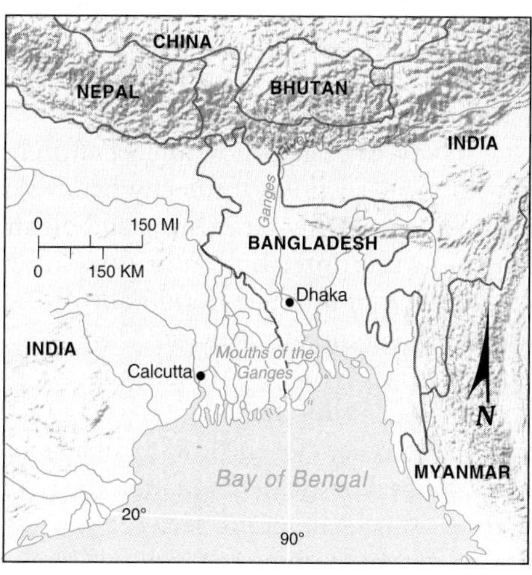

FIGURE 14.25 The Ganges River enters the Bay of Bengal.
The complex distributary pattern in the "many mouths" of the Ganges River delta in Bangladesh and extreme eastern India from the *Terra* satellite. [*Terra* MODIS sensor image courtesy of MODIS Land Team, NASA.]

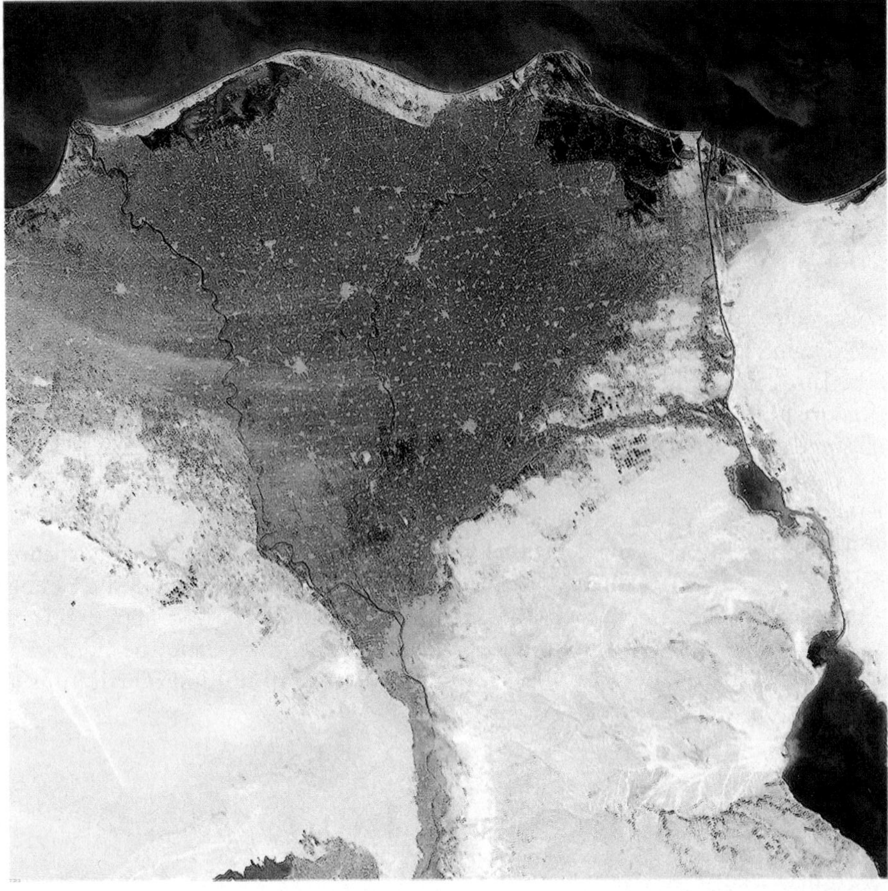

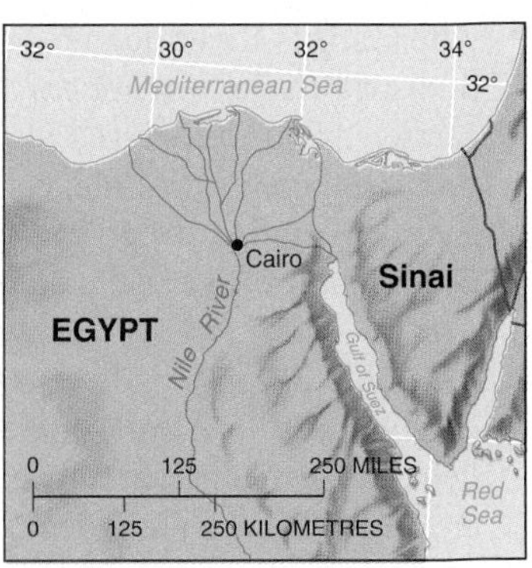

FIGURE 14.26 The Nile River delta.
The arcuate Nile River delta. Intensive agricultural activity and small settlements are visible on the delta and along the Nile River floodplain in this true colour image. Cairo is at the apex of the delta. You can see the two main distributaries: Damietta to the east and Rosetta to the west. [January 30, 2001, *Terra* MISR sensor image courtesy of MISR Team, NASA/GSFC/JPL.]

To further complicate this situation, compaction and the tremendous weight of the sediments in the Mississippi River and delta create isostatic adjustments in Earth's crust. These adjustments are causing the entire region of the delta to subside, thereby placing ever-increasing stress on natural and artificial levees and other structures along the lower Mississippi.

The city of New Orleans is now almost entirely below river level, with some sections of the city below sea level. Severe flooding is a certainty for existing and planned settlements unless further intervention or urban relocation occurs. The building of multiple flood-control structures and extensive reclamation efforts by the U.S. Army Corps of Engineers apparently have only delayed the peril, as demonstrated by recent flooding.

An additional problem for the lower Mississippi Valley is the possibility, in a worst-case flood, that the river could break from its existing channel and seek a new route to the Gulf of Mexico. If you examine the map in Figure 14.27c and look at the sediment plume to the west of the main delta in (b), an obvious alternative to the Mississippi's present channel is the Atchafalaya River (d).

The Atchafalaya would provide a much shorter route to the Gulf of Mexico, less than one-half the present distance, and it has a steeper gradient than the Mississippi. Presently this alternative-route distributary carries about 30% of the Mississippi's total discharge. For the Mississippi to bypass New Orleans entirely would be a blessing, for it would remove the flood threat. However, this shift would be a financial disaster, as a major U.S. port would silt in and seawater would intrude into freshwater resources.

At present, artificial barriers block the Atchafalaya from reaching the Mississippi at the point shown; without the floodgates the two rivers do connect. The Old River Control Project (1963) maintains three structures and a lock about 320 km (200 mi) from the Mississippi's mouth to keep these rivers in their channels (Figure 14.27e). A major flood is only a matter of time, and residents should prepare for the river-channel change.

Fraser River Delta The Fraser River delta was formed more recently than the Mississippi delta complex as sediment accumulated where the Fraser River now flows into the Strait of Georgia. Deglaciation of the region and the rapid development of the Fraser River floodplain westward down a glacially scoured, partially submerged trough preceded initial delta growth. As the floodplain extended

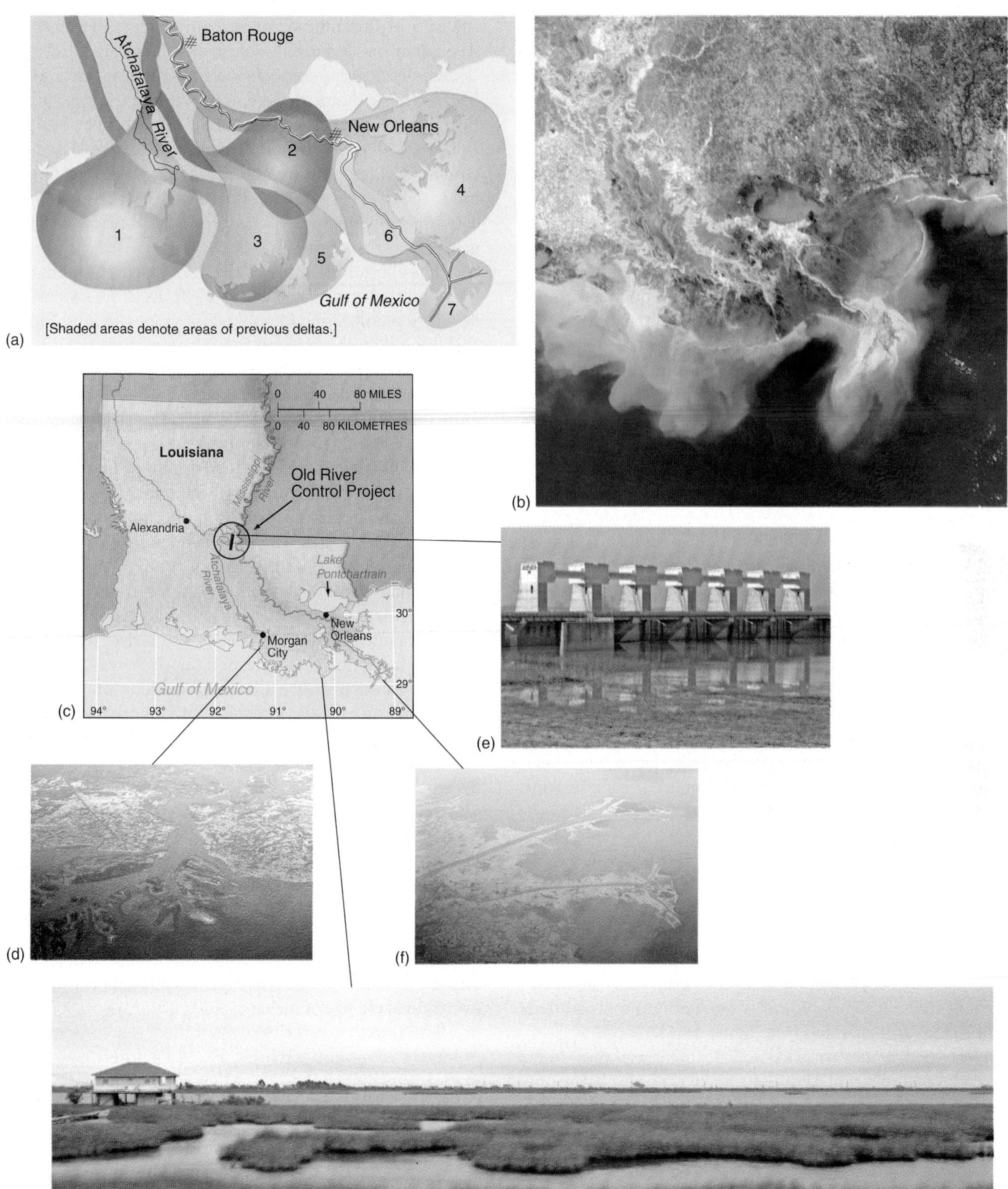

FIGURE 14.27 The Mississippi River delta.
(a) Evolution of the present delta, from 5000 years ago (1) to present (7). (b) The bird-foot delta of the Mississippi River receives a continuous supply of sediments, focused by controlling levees. The delta extends ever farther into the Gulf of Mexico, although subsidence of the delta and rising sea level have diminished the overall surface area. (c) Location map of the Old Control Structures and potential capture point (arrow) where the Atchafalaya River may one day divert the present channel. (d) Where the Atchafalaya River enters the Gulf. (e) Old River Control Auxillary Structure, one of the dams to keep the Mississippi in its channel. (f) The end of the bird-foot delta stretches far out in the Gulf. (g) Mississippi delta waterscape; note the house with the raised first floor on stilts. [(a) Adapted from C. R. Kolb and J. R. Van Lopik, "Depositional environments of the Mississippi River deltaic plain," in *Deltas in Their Geologic Framework* (Houston: Houston Geological Society, 1966); (b) *Terra* MODIS sensor image, March 5, 2001, courtesy of Liam Gumley, Space Science and Engineering Center, University of Wisconsin, and the MODIS Science Team, NASA; photos (d) through (g) by Bobbé Christopherson.]

westward, fluvial, deltaic, marine, and lacutrine sediments covered the floor of the trough.

About 10,000 years ago, the Fraser River began to empty directly into the Strait of Georgia through a gap in the Pleistocene uplands at New Westminster. Deposition advanced seaward 25 km over 10,000 years creating a landform that covers about 1000 km^2. Floods deposited silt and clay on the Fraser delta plain until the 1900s when dikes were constructed for protection of human development. The dikes stabilized the river channel, stifling natural processes. Dredging maintains shipping channels below New Westminster and dredged sand does not make its way to the delta front. The impact of human activity was to decrease the rate of sediment delivery to the edge of the delta, and erosion dominates in areas, increasing the delta slope and the risk of delta-slope failure. Prehistoric and historic failures are in evidence across the submarine slope of the Fraser delta. These occurred when there was little human habitation in the area.

The delta is an important agricultural area with deep fertile sediment and agriculturally favourable climate. It is also pressured by urban development and industrial growth in Richmond, Ladner, and Delta, and a coal port and ferry terminal at Tsawwassen and Point Roberts. Also, environmentalists value the area as habitat for migratory waterfowl and salmon fry. These competing uses of the delta are threatened by earthquake hazard. Liquefaction, the fluidization of water-saturated sediment when shaken, will cause subsidence of the delta plain and may cause buildings that are not properly anchored to tilt or collapse. Small earthquakes are common in the area, but a large-scale quake has not happened in the last hundred years. It is only a matter of time until the big one hits.

Rivers Without Deltas The Amazon River, Earth's highest-discharge stream, exceeds 175,000 m^3/s (6.2 million cfs) discharge and carries sediments far into the deep Atlantic offshore. Yet the Amazon lacks a true delta. Its mouth, 160 km (100 mi) wide, has formed an underwater deltaic plain deposited on a sloping continental shelf. As a result, the Amazon's mouth is braided into a broad maze of islands and channels (see Figure 14.1).

Other rivers also lack deltaic formations if they do not produce significant sediment or if they discharge into strong erosive currents. The Columbia River of the U.S. Northwest lacks a delta because offshore currents remove sediment before it can accumulate into a delta.

Floods and River Management

ANIMATION Stream Processes, Floodplains

Throughout history, civilizations have settled floodplains and deltas, especially since the agricultural revolution of 10,000 years ago, when the fertility of floodplain soils was discovered. Early villages generally were built away from the area of flooding, or on stream terraces, because the floodplain was dedicated exclusively to farming. However, as commerce grew, competition for sites near rivers grew, because these locations were important for transportation. Port and dock facilities were built, as were river bridges. Because water is a basic industrial raw material used for cooling and for diluting and removing wastes, waterside industrial sites became desirable. These competing human activities on vulnerable flood-prone lands place lives and property at risk during floods.

The abuse and misuse of river floodplains brought catastrophe to North Carolina in 1999. In short succession during September and October, Hurricanes Dennis, Floyd, and Irene delivered several metres of precipitation to the state, each storm falling on already saturated ground. About 50,000 people were left homeless and at least 50 died, while more than 4000 homes were lost and an equal amount were badly damaged (Figure 14.28a). The dollar estimate for the ongoing disaster now exceeds \$10 billion. However, the real tragedy will unfold for years to come.

Hogs, in factory farms, outnumber humans in North Carolina. More than 10 million hogs, each producing approximately two metric tons of waste per year, were located in about 3000 agricultural factories. These generally unregulated operations collect millions of metric tons of manure into open lagoons, many set on river floodplains. The hurricane downpour flushed out these waste lagoons, spewing hundreds of millions of gallons of untreated sewage into wetlands, streams, and eventually Pamlico Sound and the ocean—a spreading "dead zone." Add to this waste, hundreds of thousands of hog, poultry, and other livestock carcasses, industrial toxins, floodplain junkyard oil, and municipal waste, and you have an environmental catastrophe (Figure 14.28b). Final assessment of overall damage will take a decade, if not longer.

Catastrophic floods continue to be a threat, especially in poor nations. Bangladesh is perhaps the most persistent example. Bangladesh is one of the most densely populated countries on Earth, and more than three-fourths of its land area is a floodplain! The country's vast alluvial plain sprawls over an area the size of Alabama (130,000 km^2 or 50,000 mi^2).

The flooding severity is magnified as a consequence of human economic activities. Excessive forest harvesting in the upstream portions of the Ganges–Brahmaputra River watersheds increased runoff. Over time, the increased load carried by the river was deposited in the Bay of Bengal, creating new islands (see Figure 14.25). These islands, barely above sea level, became sites for new farming villages. As a result, about 150,000 people perished in the 1988 and 1991 floods. (For information on worldwide floods, see **http://www.dartmouth.edu/~floods/Resources.html** or a daily flood summary at **http://iwin.nws.noaa.gov/iwin/us/nationalflood.html**.)

Rating Floodplain Risk

A **flood** is a high water level that overflows the natural (or artificial) levees along any portion of a stream. Both floods and

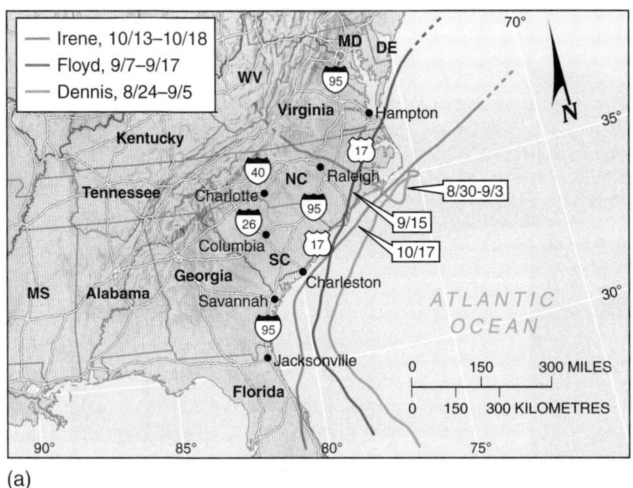

(a)

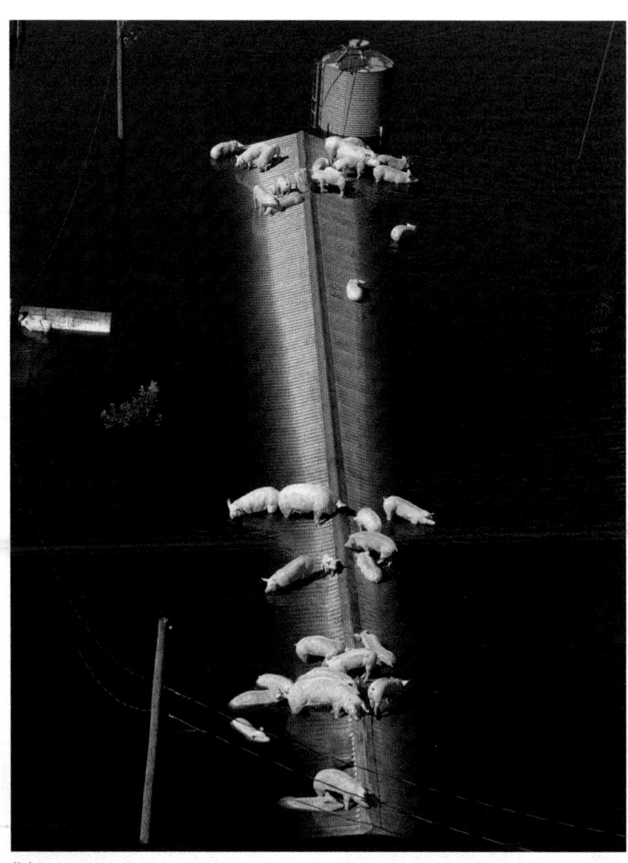

(b)

FIGURE 14.28 North Carolina 1999 floodplain disaster. (a) Three hurricanes deluged North Carolina with several feet of rain during September and October 1999, Hurricane Floyd being the worst. (b) Hundreds of thousands of livestock were killed in the floods, which also washed out hundreds of animal sewage lagoons into wetlands, streams, and the ocean. Many of these factory farms and lagoons were sited on floodplains. [Photo (b) by Mel Nathanson, *Raleigh News & Observer*.]

the floodplains they might occupy are rated statistically for the expected time intervals between floods. Thus, you hear about "10-year floods," "50-year floods," and so on. A *10-year flood* is the greatest level of flooding that is likely to occur once every 10 years. This also means that such flooding has only a 10% likelihood of occurring in any one year and is likely to occur about 10 times each century. For any given floodplain, such a frequency indicates a moderate threat.

A 50-year or 100-year flood is of greater and perhaps catastrophic consequence, but it is also less likely to occur in a given year. These probability ratings of flood levels are mapped for an area, and the defined floodplains that result are then labelled as a "50-year floodplain" or a "100-year floodplain."

These statistical estimates are probabilities that events will occur randomly during any single year of the specified period. Of course, two decades might pass without a 50-year flood, or a 50-year level of flooding could occur 3 years in a row. The record-breaking Mississippi River Valley floods in 1993 easily exceeded a 1000-year flood probability. See Focus Study 14.1 for more about floodplain hazards and management strategies.

Focus Study 14.1

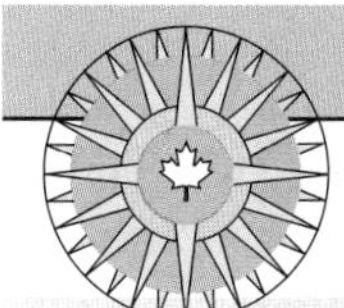

Floodplain Strategies

Detailed records of streamflows and flood records have been kept for only about the last 100 years in Canada. The coverage of stream gauging stations is concentrated in the southern part of the country, with stations on lakes, rivers, and streams of many sizes. Data from these recording stations are limited both spatially and temporally. However, hydrological engineers can use these data to model the flows of most rivers in the country. From these models, flooding hazards can be determined. Recurrence intervals of floods are calculated and the most commonly recognized standard is the 100-year flood. This standard is used for floodplain mapping to determine zones where development is limited. Floodplain delineation, assessment of flood risk, and flood forecasting are non-structural means of flood damage reduction.

In some cases, these do not limit development, and where development occurred prior to modern risk assessment, floods can cause catastrophic damage. A common scenario might go like this: (1) Minimal zoning precautions are not carefully supervised; (2) a flooding disaster occurs; (3) the public is outraged at being caught off guard; (4) businesses and homeowners are surprisingly resistant to stricter laws

(continued)

Focus Study 14.1 *(continued)*

Control,"* published more than 50 years ago, there are other ways to protect populations than with enormous, expensive, sometimes environmentally disruptive projects. Strictly zoning the floodplain is one approach. However, the flat, easily developed floodplains near pleasant rivers are desirable for housing, and thus weaken political resolve. A reasoned zoning strategy would set aside the floodplain for farming or passive recreation, such as a riverine park, golf course, or plant and wildlife sanctuary, or for other uses that are not hurt by natural floods. This study concludes that "urban and industrial losses would be largely obviated by set-back levees and zoning and thus cancel the biggest share of the assessed benefits which justify big dams."

*Walter Kollmorgen, *Economic Geography* 29, no. 3 (July 1953): 215.

Streamflow Measurement

Flood patterns in a drainage basin are as complex as the weather, for floods and weather are equally variable, and both include a level of unpredictability. Measuring and analyzing the behaviour of each large watershed and stream enables engineers and concerned parties to develop the best possible flood-management strategy. Unfortunately, reliable data often are not available for small basins or for the changing landscapes of urban areas.

The key to flood avoidance or management is to possess extensive measurements of *streamflow*, a stream's discharge and its flow pattern (Figure 14.29a). Once the cross section of a stream is fully measured, only the stream level is needed to determine discharge (using the calculation: discharge = width × depth × velocity). A *staff gauge* (a pole marked with water levels) is placed in a stream, as shown in the figure, to measure stream level. Another method involves a *stilling well* on the stream bank with a gauge mounted in it to measure stream level (Figure 14.29c). A

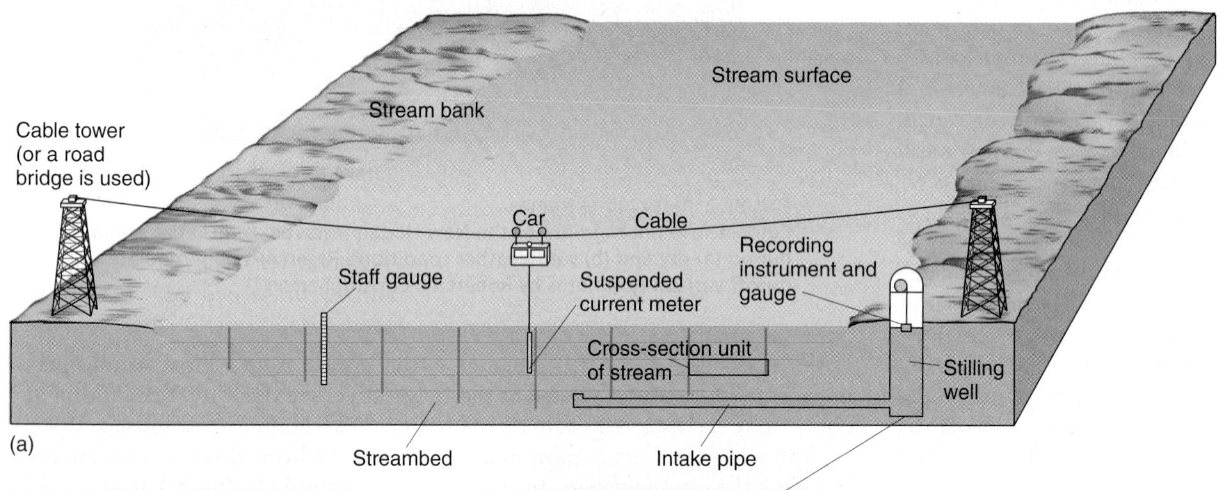

FIGURE 14.29 Streamflow measurement.
(a) A typical streamflow measurement installation may use a variety of devices: staff gauge, stilling well with recording instrument, and suspended current meter. An automated hydrographic station (b) and stilling well (c) send telemetry to a satellite for collection by the USGS. [Photos (b) courtesy of California Department of Water Resources; (c) by Bobbé Christopherson.]

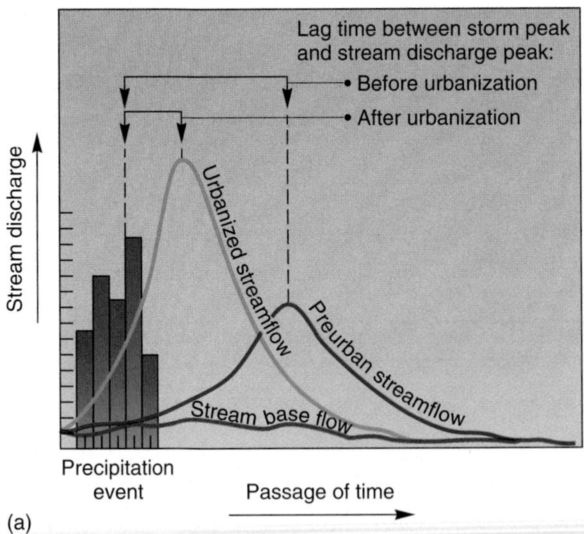

(b)

FIGURE 14.30 Urban flooding.
(a) Effect of urbanization on a typical stream hydrograph. Normal base flow is indicated with a dark blue line. The purple line indicates discharge after a storm, before urbanization. Following urbanization, stream discharge dramatically increases, as shown by the light blue line. (b) Severe flooding of an urban area in Linda, California, after a levee break on the Sacramento River in 1986. [(b) Photo from California Department of Water Resources.]

movable current meter can be used to sample stream velocity at various locations.

Environment Canada's Water Survey of Canada maintains more than 3000 gauging stations (see **http://www.wsc.ec.gc.ca/**). In the political climate surrounding hazards and planning, such hydrologic monitoring by the stream gauging network is under continual threats of budget cuts.

Hydrographs A graph of stream discharge over time for a specific place is a **hydrograph**. The hydrograph in Figure 14.30a shows the relation between precipitation input (the bar graph) and stream discharge (the curves). During dry periods, at low-water stages, the flow is described as base flow and is largely maintained by input from local groundwater (dark blue line).

When rainfall occurs in some portion of the watershed, the runoff collects and is concentrated in streams and tributaries. The amount, location, and duration of the rainfall episode determine the *peak flow*. Also important is the nature of the surface in a watershed; for example, a hydrograph for a specific portion of a stream changes after a forest fire or following urbanization of the watershed.

Human activities have enormous impact on water flow in a basin. The effects of urbanization are quite dramatic, both increasing and hastening peak flow, as you can see by comparing pre-urban stream flow (purple curve) and urbanized stream flow (light blue) in Figure 14.30a. In fact, urban areas produce runoff patterns quite similar to those of deserts. The sealed surfaces of the city drastically reduce infiltration and soil-moisture recharge; their effect is similar to that of the hard, nearly barren surfaces of the desert. A significant part of urban flooding occurs because of the alteration in surfaces. The flooded region in Figure 14.30b was hit in 1986 and again in 1997. These issues will intensify as urbanization of vulnerable areas continues.

Applied Physical Geography

Flood Frequency Analysis

The degree to which any phenomenon is a hazard depends on its magnitude and its frequency of occurrence. The frequency with which a flood of a certain magnitude can be expected to occur is called its recurrence interval. Recurrence intervals can be determined wherever long-term river gauging records are available, and are given by the formula:

$$Tr = n/m$$

where *Tr* is the recurrence interval, *n* is the number of years of record, and *m* is the number of floods of the given magnitude or larger during the years of record.

Table 1 shows peak discharges for a river gauging station for a period of record from 1970 to 1999.

(continued)

Applied Physical Geography *(continued)*

We calculate that in a recurrence interval of a flood with discharge of 425 m^3/s for 30 years of record, 425 is exceeded 4 times.

$$Tr\ (425) = 30/4 = 7.5$$

We then statistically expect a flood of magnitude 425 m^3/s to occur every 7.5 years.

This relationship can also be expressed as the chance or probability of the flood of given magnitude occurring in any given year. This is the reciprocal of the recurrence interval in percent:

$$P\ (425) = m/n \times 100 = 4/30 \times 100 = 13.3\%$$

There is a 13.3% chance of this magnitude of flood occurring.

Table 1 Peak Discharges 1970–1999

Year	Peak Discharge m^3/s	Year	Peak Discharge m^3/s	Year	Peak Discharge m^3/s
1970	113	1980	227	1990	113
1971	71	1981	2407	1991	241
1972	170	1982	411	1992	113
1973	212	1983	198	1993	311
1974	85	1984	255	1994	184
1975	42	1985	311	1995	198
1976	297	1986	113	1996	991
1977	57	1987	595	1997	71
1978	1770	1988	212	1998	28
1979	57	1989	227	1999	283

Summary and Review—River Systems and Landforms

● *Define* the term fluvial and *outline* the fluvial processes: erosion, transportation, and deposition.

River systems, fluvial processes and landscapes, floodplains, and river control strategies are important to human populations as demands for limited water resources increase. **Hydrology** is the science of water and its global circulation, distribution, and properties, specifically water at and below Earth's surface. Stream-related processes are called **fluvial**. Water dislodges, dissolves, or removes surface material in the process called **erosion**. Streams produce *fluvial erosion*, in which weathered sediment is picked up for **transport**, movement to new locations. Sediments are laid down by another process, **deposition**. **Alluvium** is the general term for the clay, silt, and sand deposited by running water.

Base level is the lowest elevation limit of stream erosion. A *local base level* occurs when something interrupts the stream's ability to achieve base level, such as is created by a dam or a landslide that blocks a stream channel.

hydrology (p. 449)
fluvial (p. 449)
erosion (p. 449)
transport (p. 449)
deposition (p. 449)
alluvium (p. 449)
base level (p. 449)

1. What role is played by rivers in the hydrologic cycle?
2. What are the five largest rivers on Earth in terms of discharge? Relate these to the weather patterns in each area and to regional POTET and PRECIP.
3. Define the term *fluvial*. What is a fluvial process?
4. What is the sequence of events that takes place as a stream dislodges material?
5. Explain the base-level concept. What happens to a local base level when a reservoir is constructed?

● *Construct* a basic drainage basin model and *identify* different types of drainage patterns and internal drainage, with examples.

The basic fluvial system is a **drainage basin**, which is an open system. *Drainage divides* define the **watershed** catchment (water receiving) area of the drainage basin. In any drainage basin, water initially moves downslope in a thin film called **sheetflow**, or *overland flow*. This surface runoff concentrates in *rills*, or small-scale downhill grooves, which may develop into deeper *gullies* and a stream course in a valley. High ground that separates one valley from another and directs sheetflow is termed an *interfluve*. Extensive mountain and highland regions act as **continental divides** that separate major drainage basins. Some regions, such as the Great Salt Lake Basin, have **internal drainage** that does not reach the ocean, the only outlets being evaporation and subsurface gravitational flow.

Drainage density is determined by the number and length of channels in a given area and is an expression of a landscape's topographic surface appearance. **Drainage pattern** refers to the arrangement of channels in an area as determined by the steepness, variable rock resistance, variable climate, hydrology, relief of the land, and structural controls imposed by the landscape. Seven basic drainage patterns are generally found in nature: dendritic, trellis, radial, parallel, rectangular, annular, and deranged.

drainage basin (p. 450)
watershed (p. 450)
sheetflow (p. 450)
continental divides (p. 450)
internal drainage (p. 452)
drainage density (p. 453)
drainage pattern (p. 453)

6. What is the spatial geomorphic unit of an individual river system? How is it determined on the landscape? Define the several relevant key terms used.
7. In Figure 14.5, follow the Saskatchewan–Nelson Rivers system to Hudson Bay. Analyze the pattern of tributaries and describe the channel. What role do continental divides and large lakes play in this drainage?
8. Describe drainage patterns. Define the various patterns that commonly appear in nature. What drainage patterns exist in your hometown? Where you attend school?

● *Describe* the relation among velocity, depth, width, and discharge and *explain* the various ways that a stream erodes and transports its load.

Stream channels vary in *width* and *depth*. The streams that flow in them vary in velocity and in the *sediment load* they carry. All of these factors may increase with increasing discharge. **Discharge** is calculated by multiplying the velocity of the stream by its width and depth for a specific cross section of the channel. Most streams increase discharge downstream. But, some streams originate in a humid region and flow through an arid region, such that discharge decreases with distance. Such an **exotic stream** is exemplified by the Nile River or the Colorado River.

Hydraulic action is the work of *turbulence* in the water. Running water causes hydraulic squeeze-and-release action to loosen and lift rocks and sediment. As this debris moves along, it mechanically erodes the streambed further, through a process of **abrasion**.

Solution refers to the **dissolved load** of a stream, especially the chemical solution derived from minerals such as limestone or dolomite or from soluble salts. The **suspended load** consists of fine-grained, clastic particles held aloft in the stream, with the finest particles not deposited until the stream velocity slows nearly to zero. **Bed load** refers to coarser materials that are dragged along the stream bed by **traction** or are rolled and bounced along by **saltation**. If the load in a stream exceeds its capacity, sediments accumulate as **aggradation** as the stream channel builds through deposition. With excess sediment, a stream becomes a maze of interconnected channels that form a **braided stream** pattern.

discharge (p. 455)
exotic stream (p. 458)
hydraulic action (p. 458)
abrasion (p. 458)
dissolved load (p. 458)
suspended load (p. 458)
bed load (p. 459)
traction (p. 459)
saltation (p. 459)
aggradation (p. 459)
braided stream (p. 459)

9. What was the impact of flood discharge on the channel of the San Juan River near Bluff, Utah? Why did these changes take place?
10. How does stream discharge do its erosive work? What are the processes at work in the channel?
11. Differentiate between stream competence and stream capacity.
12. How does a stream transport its sediment load? What processes are at work?

● *Develop* a model of a meandering stream, including point bar, undercut bank, and cutoff, and *explain* the role of stream gradient in these flow characteristics.

Where the slope is gradual, stream channels develop a sinuous form called a **meandering stream**. The outer portion of each meandering curve is subject to the fastest water velocity and can be the site of a steep **undercut bank**. On the other hand, the inner portion of a meander experiences the slowest water velocity and forms a **point bar** deposit. When a meander neck is cut off as two undercut banks merge, the meander becomes isolated and forms an **oxbow lake**.

Every stream develops its own **gradient** and establishes a longitudinal profile. A portion of the stream is designated a **graded stream** when the stream is adjusted among available discharge, channel characteristics, its velocity, and the load supplied from the drainage basin. An interruption in a stream's longitudinal profile is called a **nickpoint**. A nickpoint can occur as the stream flows across hard resistant rock or after tectonic uplift episodes.

meandering stream (p. 460)
undercut bank (p. 460)
point bar (p. 460)
oxbow lake (p. 460)
gradient (p. 461)
graded stream (p. 462)
nickpoint (p. 463)

13. Describe the flow characteristics of a meandering stream. What is the pattern of flow in the channel? What are the erosional and depositional features and the typical landforms created?
14. Explain these statements: (a) All streams have a gradient, but not all streams are graded. (b) Graded streams may have ungraded segments.
15. Why is Niagara Falls an example of a nickpoint? Without human intervention, what do you think would eventually take place at Niagara Falls?

16. What is meant by "the validity of cyclic or equilibrium models depends on which of three time frames is being considered"? Explain and discuss.

● *Define* a floodplain and *analyze* the behaviour of a stream channel during a flood.

Floodplains have been an important site of human activity throughout history. Rich soils, bathed in fresh nutrients by floodwaters, attract agricultural activity and urbanization. Despite our knowledge of historical devastation by floods, floodplains are settled, raising issues of human hazard perception. The flat low-lying area along a stream channel that is subjected to recurrent flooding is a **floodplain**. It is formed when the river overflows its channel during times of high flow. On either bank of most streams, **natural levees** develop as by-products of flooding. On the floodplain, backswamps and yazoo tributaries may develop. The natural levees and elevated channel of the river prevent a **yazoo tributary** from joining the main channel, so it flows parallel to the river and through the **backswamp** area. **Alluvial terraces** are formed by the entrenchment of a river into its own floodplain.

floodplain (p. 465)
natural levees (p. 467)
yazoo tributary (p. 467)
backswamp (p. 467)
alluvial terraces (p. 467)

17. Describe the formation of a floodplain. How are natural levees, oxbow lakes, backswamps, and yazoo tributaries produced?
18. Identify any of the features listed in question 17 on the Philipp, Mississippi, topographic quadrangle in Figure 14.22d.
19. Describe any floodplains near where you live or where you go to college. Have you seen any of the floodplain features discussed in this chapter? If so, which ones?

● *Differentiate* the several types of river deltas and *detail* each.

A depositional plain formed at the mouth of a river is called a **delta**. When the mouth of a river enters the sea and is inundated by the sea in a mix with freshwater, it is called an **estuary**.

delta (p. 470)
estuary (p. 471)

20. What is a river delta? What are the various deltaic forms? Give some examples.
21. How might life in New Orleans change in the next century? Explain.
22. Describe the Ganges River delta. What factors upstream explain its form and pattern? Assess the consequences of settlement on this delta.
23. What is meant by the statement "the Nile River delta is disappearing"?

● *Explain* flood probability estimates and *review* strategies for mitigating flood hazards.

A **flood** occurs when high water overflows the natural or artificial levees of a stream. Both floods and the floodplains they occupy are rated statistically for the expected time interval between floods. A 10-year flood is the greatest level of flooding that is likely once every 10 years. A graph of stream discharge over time for a specific place is called a **hydrograph**.

Collective efforts by government agencies undertake to reduce flood probability. Such management attempts include the construction of artificial levees, bypasses, straightened channels, diversions, dams, and reservoirs. Society is still learning how to live in a sustainable way with Earth's dynamic river systems.

flood (p. 474)
hydrograph (p. 479)

24. Specifically, what is a flood? How are such flows measured and tracked?
25. How important was the Red River flood of 1997 with respect to the record of flooding on the Canadian prairies? Speculate on what you think are the "lessons learned" by the public from such an event.
26. Differentiate between a hydrograph from a natural terrain and one from an urbanized area.
27. What do you see as the major consideration regarding floodplain management? How would you describe the general attitude of society toward natural hazards and disasters?
28. What do you think the author of the article "Settlement Control Beats Flood Control" meant by the title? Explain your answer, using information presented in the chapter.

Critical Thinking

A. Determine the name of the river drainage basin within which your campus is located. Where are its headwaters? Where is the river's mouth? If you are in Canada or the United States, use Figure 14.5 to locate the larger drainage basins and divides for your region. Is there any regulatory organization that oversees planning and coordination for this drainage basin?

B. Relative to the drainage basin you determined in (A), see if there is a topographic map on file in the library, geography department, or at a local outdoor recreation store that covers the portion of the basin near campus. After examining the map, can you discern a prominent drainage pattern for the area (Figure 14.9)?

C. Under "Destinations" in Chapter 14 of the *Geosystems* Companion Website, there are links to many flood sources. Relative to the discussion of the 1997 Red River flood in News Report 14.3 in this chapter, what related information do you find? Examine the sites and describe the available information.

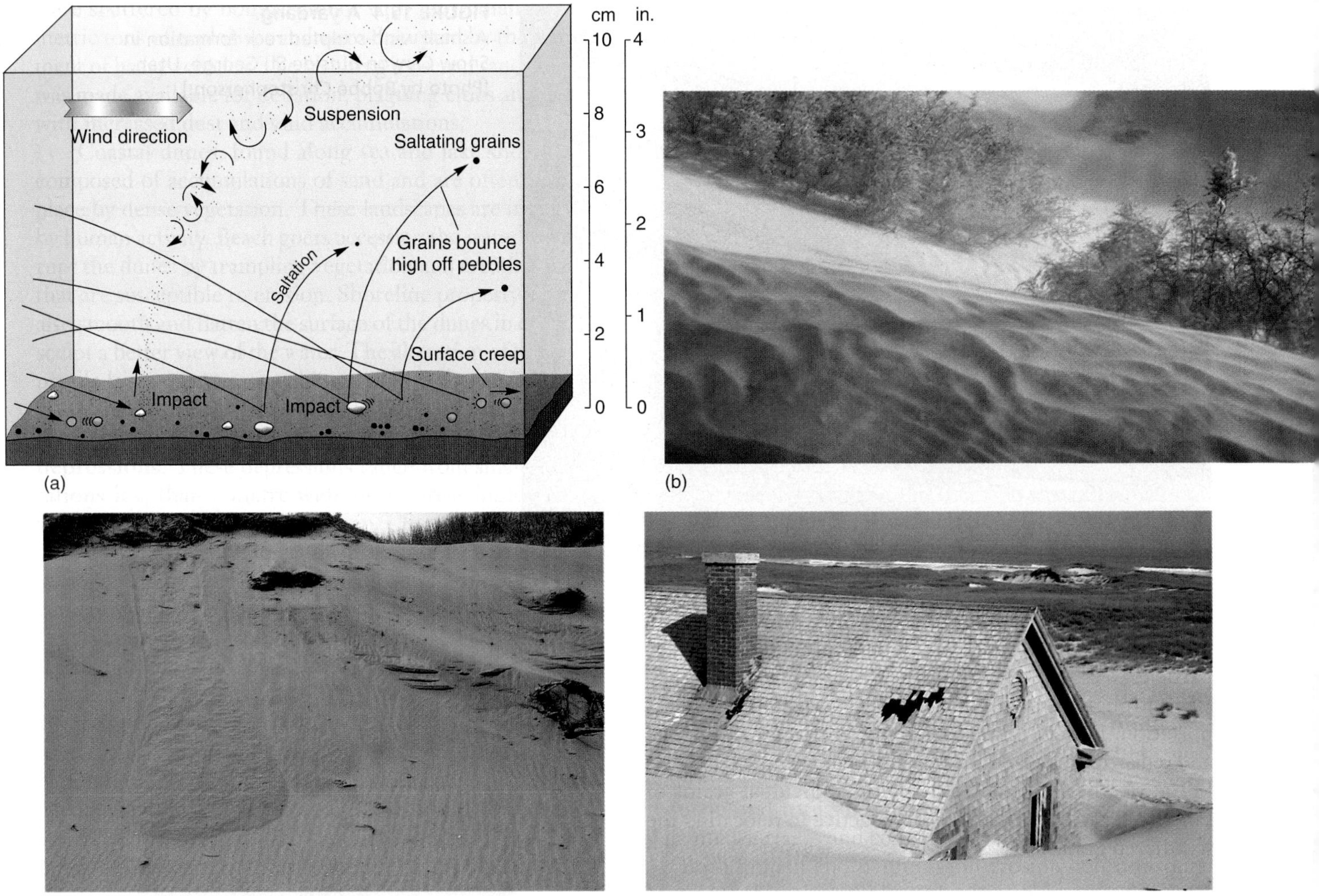

cm in.
10 4
8 3
6 2
4 1
2
0 0
Wind direction
Suspension
Saltating grains
Saltation
Grains bounce high off pebbles
Surface creep
Impact
Impact

(a)

(b)

(c)

(d)

FIGURE 15.6 How the wind moves sand.
(a) Eolian suspension, saltation, and surface creep are mechanisms of sediment transportation. Compare with the saltation and traction that occur in another fluid, water, in Figure 14.13. (b) Sand grains saltating along the surface in the Stovepipe Wells dune field, Death Valley. (c) Sand deposited by eolian processes oversteepens the slope, and failure results in sand flow. (d) Sand deposition buried this abandoned, two-storey life saving station on Sable Island, Nova Scotia. [Photos by (b) Robert W. Christopherson; (c) and (d) Mary-Louise Byrne.]

(a)

(b)

FIGURE 15.7 Sand ripples.
(a) Sand ripple patterns later may become lithified into fixed patterns in rock. (b) Planed-off ripples reveal the structures created by the migration of ripples on Cavendish Spit, Prince Edward Island. [Photos by Mary-Louise Byrne.]

FIGURE 15.8 A sand sea.
(a) The Sahara Marzūq, an erg desert that dominates southwestern Libya. Effective northwesterly winds shape the pattern and direction of the transverse and barchanoid (series of connected barchans) dunes. This sand sea exceeds 300 km across. (b) A similar pattern of dunes appears on the Martian surface in the southern area of Melas Chasma in Valles Marineris. Note the dust devil in the lower left. Area covered is about 2 km wide. [(a) *Terra* MODIS sensor image courtesy of MODIS Land Rapid Response Team, NASA/GSFC, November 9, 2001; (b) Mars Global Surveyor, Mars Orbiter Camera image courtesy of NASA/JPL/Malin Space Science Systems, July 11, 1999.]

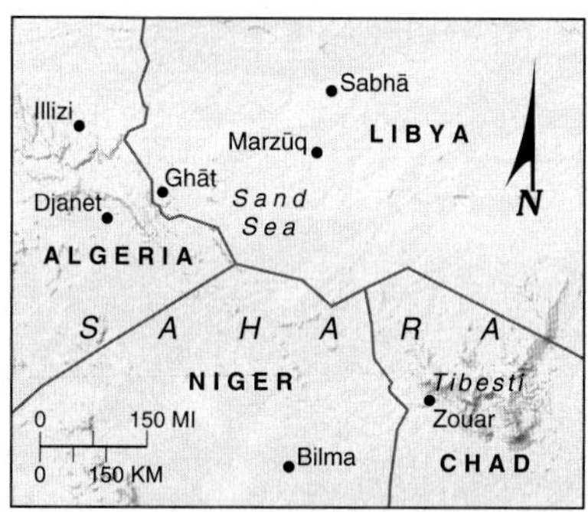

(a)

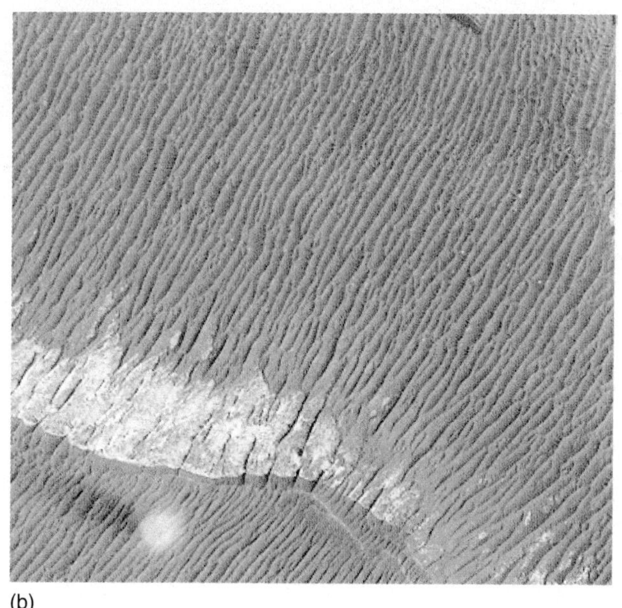
(b)

FIGURE 15.9 Dune cross section.
Successive slipfaces exhibit a distinctive pattern as the dune migrates in the direction of the effective wind.

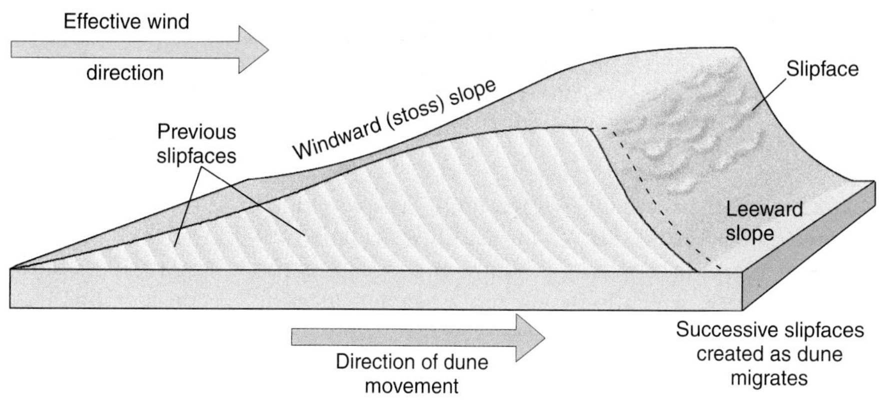

Class	Type	Description
Crescentic	Barchan	Crescent-shaped dune with horns pointed downwind. Winds are constant with little directional variability. Limited sand available. Only one slipface. Can be scattered over bare rock or desert pavement or commonly in dune fields.
	Transverse	Asymmetrical ridge, transverse to wind direction (right angle). Only one slipface. Results from relatively ineffective wind and abundant sand supply.
	Parabolic	Role of anchoring vegetation important. Open end faces upwind with U-shaped "blow-out" and arms anchored by vegetation. Multiple slipfaces, partially stabilized.
	Barchanoid ridge	A wavy, asymmetrical dune ridge aligned transverse to effective winds. Formed from coalesced barchans; look like connected crescents in rows with open areas between them.

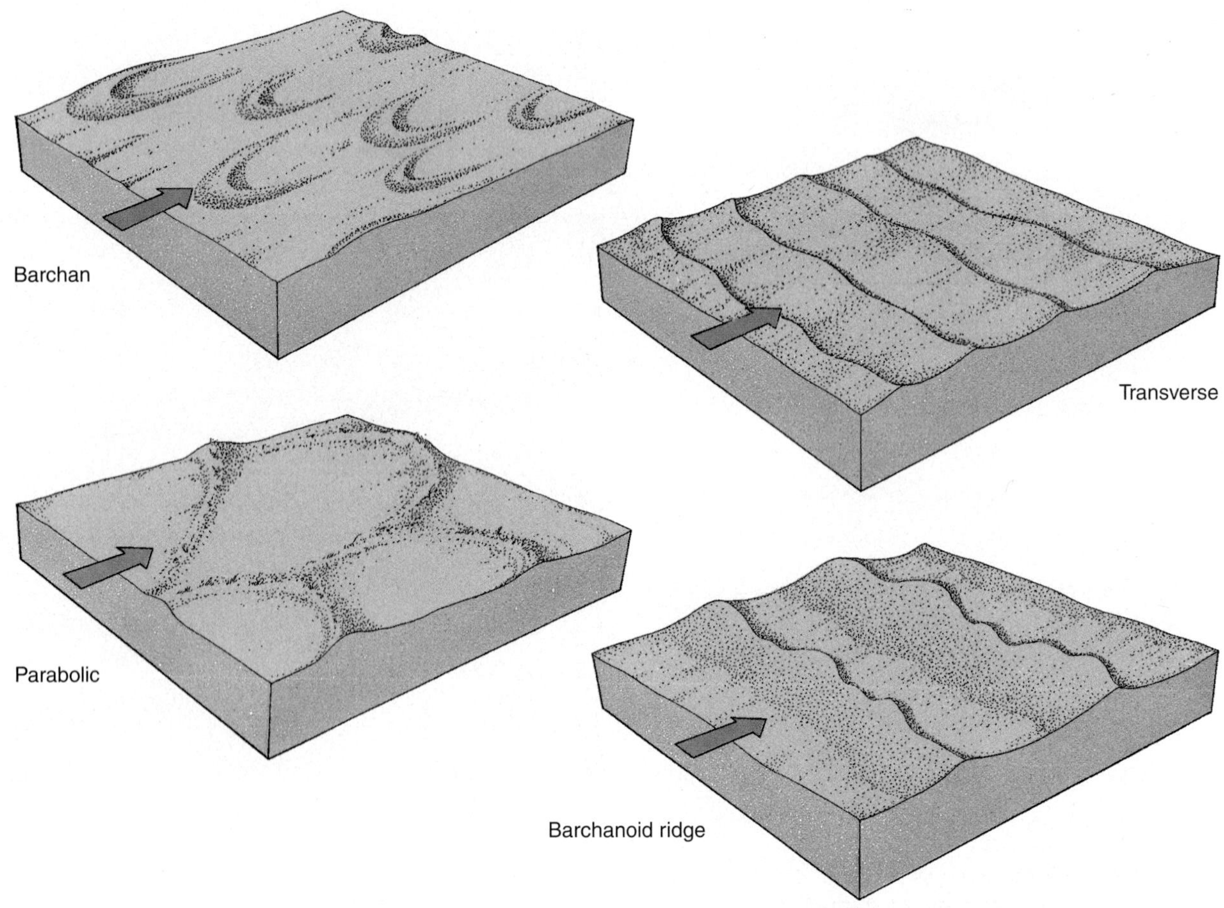

FIGURE 15.10 Major dune forms.
Arrows show wind direction. [Adapted from E. D. McKee, *A Study of Global Sand Seas*, U.S. Geological Survey Professional Paper 1052 (Washington, DC: U.S. Government Printing Office, 1979).]

windward side (stoss side), with a more steeply sloped **slipface** on the *leeward side*. A dune usually is asymmetrical in one or more directions. The angle of a slipface is the steepest angle at which loose material is stable—its *angle of repose*. Thus, the constant flow of new material makes a slipface a type of *avalanche slope*. Sand builds up as it moves over the crest of the dune to the brink; then it avalanches (falls and cascades) as the slipface continually adjusts, seeking its angle of repose (usually 30° to 34° in desert dunes, considerably higher in coastal and boreal dunes). In this way, a dune migrates downwind, as suggested by the successive dune profiles in Figure 15.9.

Class	Type	Description
Linear	Longitudinal	Long, slightly sinuous, ridge-shaped dune, aligned parallel with the wind direction; two slipfaces. Average 100 m high and 100 km long and can reach to 400 m high. Results from strong effective winds varying in one direction.
	Seif	After Arabic word for "sword"; a more sinuous crest and shorter than longitudinal dunes. Rounded toward upwind direction and pointed downwind. (Not illustrated.)
Star dune		The giant of dunes. Pyramidal or star-shaped with three or more sinuous radiating arms extending outward from a central peak. Slipfaces in multiple directions. Results from effective winds shifting in all directions. Tend to form isolated mounds in high effective winds and connected sinuous arms in low effective winds.
Other	Dome	Circular or elliptical mound with no slipface. Can be modified into barchanoid forms.
	Reversing	Asymmetrical ridge form intermediate between star dune and transverse dune. Wind variability can alter shape between forms.

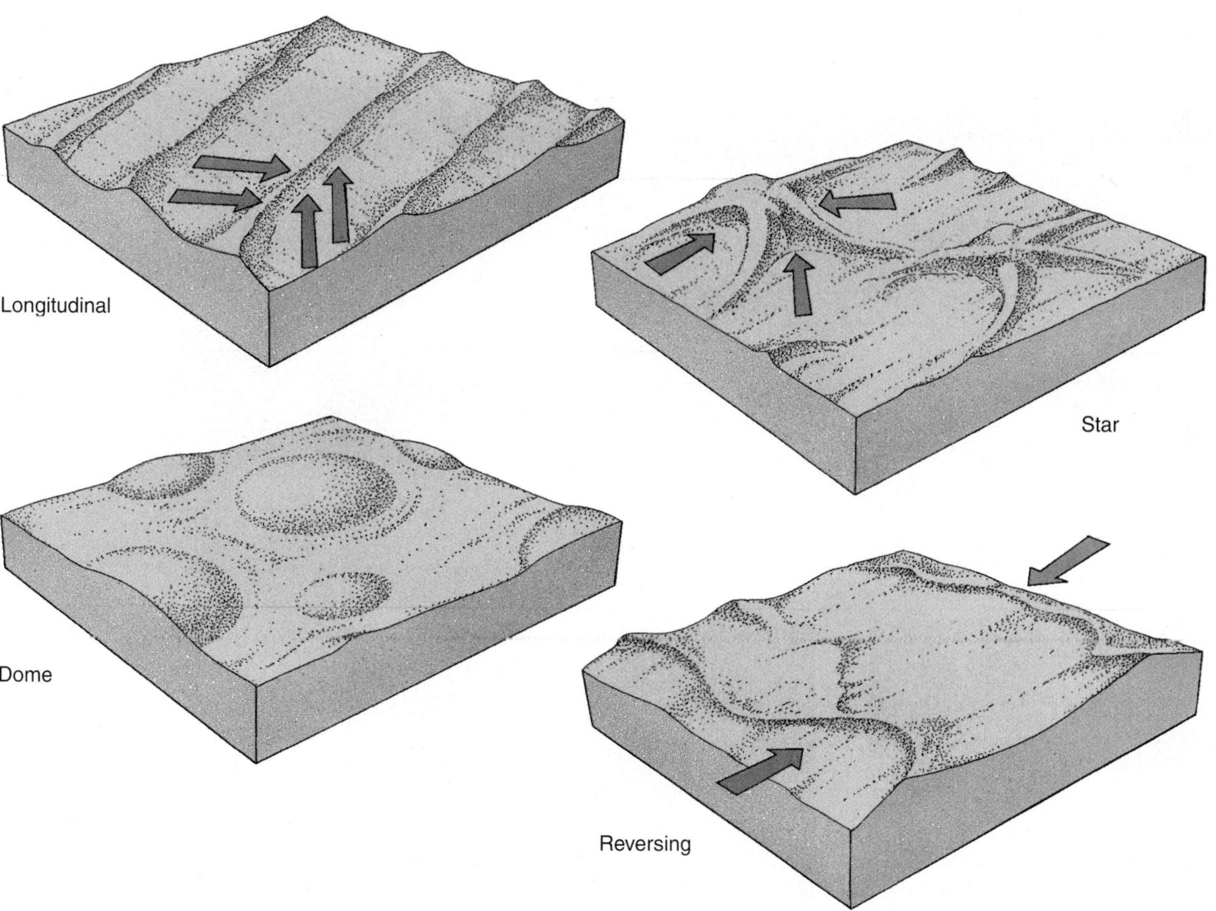

Dunes have many wind-shaped styles that make classification difficult. We can simplify dune forms into three classes—*crescentic* (crescent, curved shape), *linear* (straight forms), and *star dunes* (each is summarized in Figure 15.10). The ever-changing form of these eolian deposits is part of their beauty, eloquently described by one author: "I see hills and hollows of sand like rising and falling waves. Now at midmorning, they appear paper white. At dawn they were fog gray. This evening they will be eggshell brown."*

*J. E. Bowers, *Seasons of the Wind* (Flagstaff, AZ: Northland Press, 1985), p. 1.

FIGURE 15.11 Mountains of the desert.
Star dune in the Namib Desert in southwestern Africa. [Photo by Comstock.]

Star dunes are the mountainous giants of the sandy desert. They form in response to complicated, changing wind patterns and have multiple slipfaces. They are pinwheel-shaped, with several radiating arms rising and joining to form a common central peak. The best examples of star dunes are in the Sahara and the Namib Desert, where they approach 200 m (650 ft) in height (Figure 15.11).

The map in Figure 15.12 shows the correlation of active sand regions with deserts (tropical, continental interior, and coastal). Important is the limited extent of desert area covered by active sand dunes—only about 10% of all continental land between 30° N and 30° S. Also noted on the map are dune fields in humid climates such as along coastal Oregon, the shore of Lake Huron (Figure 15.12b), along the Gulf and Atlantic coastlines, in Europe, and else-

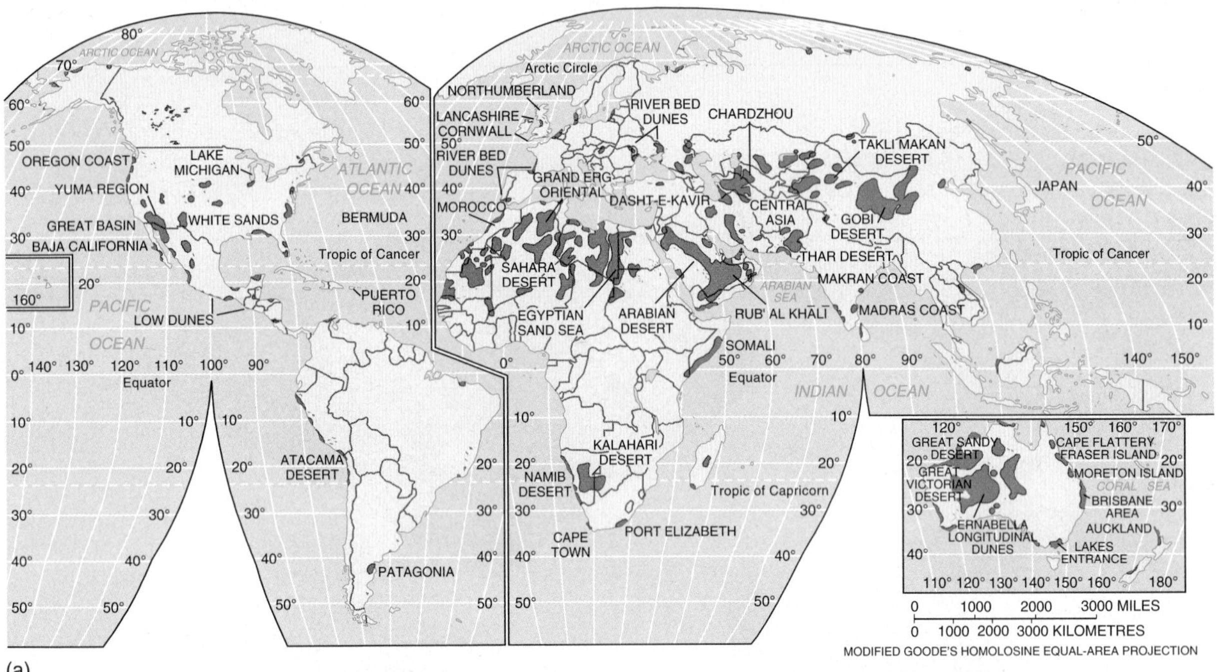

(a)

(b)

(c)

FIGURE 15.12 Sandy regions of the world.
(a) Worldwide distribution of active and stable sand regions. (b) Sand dunes along the shore of Lake Huron in Pinery Provincial Park, Ontario. (c) Sandy area in the Namib-Naukluft Park, Namib Desert, Namibia, Africa. (d) Coastal dunes can be large features as exemplified by "The Grand Canyon" at the east lighthouse on Sable Island, Nova Scotia. [(a) After R. E. Snead, *Atlas of World Physical Features*, p. 134, © 1972 by John Wiley & Sons. Adapted by permission of John Wiley & Sons, Inc.; photos by (b) and (d) Mary-Louise Byrne; (c) Nigel J. Dennis/Photo Researchers, Inc.]

(d)

where. The remarkable coastal desert sands of Namibia are pictured in Figure 15.12c.

These same dune-forming principles and terms (for example, dune and slipface) apply to snow-covered landscapes. *Snow drifts* are formed as wind deposits snow in drifts. In semiarid farming areas, capturing drifting snow with fences and tall stubble left in fields contributes significantly to soil moisture when the snow melts.

Loess Deposits

Approximately 15,000 years ago, in several episodes, Pleistocene glaciers retreated in many parts of the world, leaving behind large glacial outwash deposits of fine-grained clays and silts. These materials were blown great distances by the wind and redeposited in unstratified, homogeneous (evenly mixed) deposits. Peasants working along the Rhine River Valley in Germany gave these deposits the name **loess** (pronounced "luss"). No specific landforms were created; instead, loess covered existing landforms with a thick blanket of material that assumed the general topography of the existing landscape.

Because of its own binding strength, loess weathers and erodes into steep bluffs, or vertical faces. At Xi'an, Shaanxi Province, China, a loess wall has been excavated for dwelling space (Figure 15.13a). When a bank is cut into a loess deposit, it generally will stand vertically, although it can fail if saturated (Figure 15.13b).

Significant accumulations throughout the Mississippi and Missouri River valleys form continuous deposits 15–30 m (50–100 ft) thick. Loess deposits also occur in eastern Washington State and Idaho. This silt explains the fertility of the soils in these regions, for loess deposits are well drained and deep and have excellent moisture retention. The Loess Hills of western Iowa give evidence of the last ice age, as the finely ground sediments left by the glaciers were windblown to this setting (Figure 15.14). The loess layers in Iowa date from 159,000 to 12,500 years ago.

Loess deposits also cover much of Ukraine, central Europe, China, the Pampas-Patagonia regions of Argentina, and lowland New Zealand. The soils derived from loess are some of Earth's "breadbasket" farming regions. Figure 15.15 shows the worldwide distribution of loess deposits.

Deflation and wind transport of fine-grained soils produced a catastrophe in the Great Plains of North America in the 1930s, known as the Dust Bowl. Overgrazing and intensive agriculture left soil susceptible to drought and eolian processes. The deflation of many centimetres of soil occurred in the American southwest—southern Nebraska, Kansas, Oklahoma, Texas, and eastern Colorado where there are vast deposits of loess. In the northern Great Plains—Montana and the Dakotas in the United States and the southern prairies of Alberta, Saskatchewan, and southwestern Manitoba—silts and clays were blown out of the disturbed soils.

Fine sediments were lifted by winds to form severe dust storms. The transported sediment darkened the skies of cities and drifted over farmland. The drought that contributed to the Dust Bowl began in 1929, lasted until mid-summer in 1937, and affected over 7.3 million hectares of land in Canada alone. In Canada, the Prairie Farm Rehabilitation Administration (PFRA), a branch of Agriculture Canada, was established to combat the out-migration of prairie farmers as the drought caused them to abandon their land. Through soil and water conservation and the development of innovative farming practices, the PFRA assisted farmers through the Dust Bowl of the Dirty

(a)

(b)

FIGURE 15.13 Examples of loess deposits.
(a) Loess formation in Xi'an, Shaanxi Province, China, has sufficient structural strength to permit excavation for dwelling rooms. (b) A loess bluff in western Iowa. [Photos by (a) Betty Crowell; (b) Bobbé Christopherson.]

FIGURE 15.14 Loess Hills, western Iowa.
These windblown loess deposits reach heights of about 61 m (200 ft) above the nearby prairie farmlands and Missouri River. The Loess Hills stretch north and south more than 322 km (200 mi). [Photo by Bobbé Christopherson.]

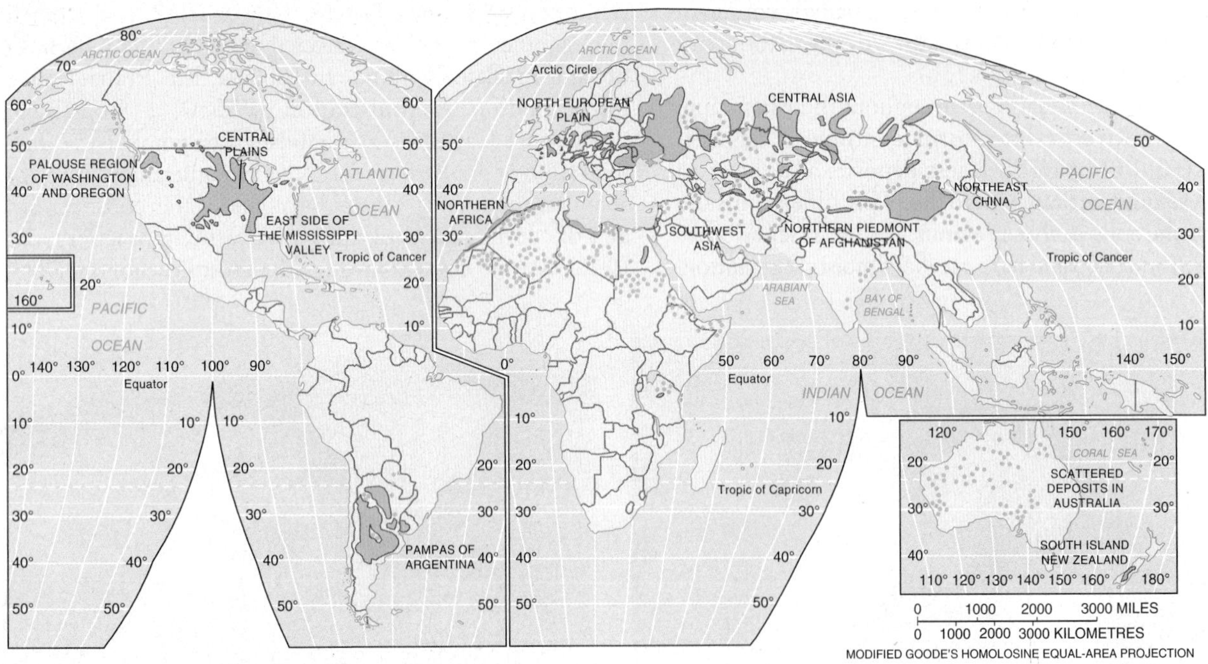

FIGURE 15.15 Worldwide loess deposits.
Dots represent small, scattered loess formations. [After R. E. Snead, *Atlas of World Physical Features*, p. 138, ©1972 by John Wiley & Sons. Adapted by permission of John Wiley & Sons, Inc.]

Thirties and allowed agriculture to continue in Canada's breadbasket. The PFRA today continues its role in soil and water conservation.

In Europe and North America, loess is thought to be derived mainly from glacial and periglacial sources. The vast deposits of loess in China, covering more than 300,000 km^2 (116,000 mi^2) are thought to be derived from windblown desert sediment rather than glacial sources. Accumulations in the Loess Plateau of China exceed 300 m (1000 ft) thickness, forming complex weathered badlands and some good agricultural land. These windblown deposits are interwoven with much of Chinese history and society.

Overview of Desert Landscapes

Dry climates occupy about 26% of Earth's land surface. If all semiarid climates are considered, they occupy perhaps as much as 35% of all land area, constituting the largest single climatic region on Earth (see Figures 10.4 and 10.5 for the location of these *arid deserts* and *semiarid steppe* climate regions and Figure 20.3 for the distribution of these desert environments).

Deserts occur worldwide as topographic plains, such as the Great Sandy and Simpson Deserts of Australia, the Arabian and Kalahari Deserts of Africa, and portions of the extensive Taklimakan Desert, which cover some 270,000 km^2 (105,000 mi^2) in the central Tarim Basin of China. Deserts also are found in mountainous regions: interior Asia, from Iran to Pakistan, and in China and Mongolia. In South America, lying between the ocean and the Andes, is the rugged Atacama Desert. And Earth's deserts are expanding, as we will discuss shortly. Now, let us look at the link between climate and Earth's deserts.

Desert Climates

The spatial distribution of dry lands is related to three climatological settings: to subtropical high-pressure cells between 15° and 35°, both N and S latitudes (see Figures 6.11 and 6.13), to the rain shadow on the lee side of mountain ranges (see Figure 8.9), and to areas at great distance from moisture-bearing air masses, such as central Asia. Figure 15.16 portrays this distribution according to the climate classification used in this text and presents photographs of four major desert regions.

Desert areas possess unique landscapes created by the interaction of intermittent precipitation events, weathering processes, and wind. Rugged, hard-edged desert landscapes of cliffs and scarps contrast sharply with the vegetation-covered, rounded and smoothed slopes characteristic of humid regions.

The daily surface energy balance for El Mirage, California, presented in Figure 4.22a and b, highlights the high sensible heat conditions and intense ground heating in the desert. Such areas receive a high input of insolation through generally clear skies, and they experience high radiative heat losses at night. A typical desert water balance experiences high potential evapotranspiration demand, low precipitation supply, and prolonged summer water deficits (see, for example, Figure 9.12e for Phoenix, Arizona). Fluvial processes in the desert generally are characterized by intermittent running water, with hard, poorly vegetated surfaces yielding high runoff during rainstorms (Figure 15.17).

Desert Fluvial Processes

Precipitation events in a desert may be rare indeed, a year or two apart, but when they do occur, a dry streambed can fill with a torrent called a **flash flood**. These channels may fill in a few minutes and surge briefly during and after a storm. Depending on the region, such a dry streambed is known as a **wash**, an *arroyo* (Spanish), or a *wadi* (Arabic). A desert highway that crosses a wash usually has signs posted to warn drivers not to proceed if rain is in the vicinity, for a flash flood can suddenly arise and sweep away anything in its path.

When washes fill with surging flash flood waters, a unique set of ecological relationships quickly develops. Crashing rocks and boulders break open seeds that respond to the timely moisture and germinate. Other plants and animals also spring into brief life cycles as the water irrigates their limited habitats.

At times of intense rainfall, remarkable scenes fill the desert. Figure 15.18 shows two photographs taken just one month apart in a sand dune field in Death Valley, California. A rainfall event produced 2.57 cm (1.01 in.) of precipitation in one day, in a place that receives only 4.6 cm (1.83 in.) in an average year. The stream in the photograph continued to run for hours and then collected in low spots on hard, underlying clay surfaces. The water was quickly consumed by the high evaporation demand so that, in just a month, these short-lived watercourses were dry and covered with accumulations of alluvial materials.

As runoff water evaporates, salt crusts may be left behind on the desert floor. This intermittently wet and dry low area in a region of closed drainage is called a **playa**, site of an *ephemeral lake* when water is present. Accompanying our earlier discussion of evaporites, Figure 11.12 shows such a playa in Death Valley, covered with salt precipitate just one month after this 1985 rainfall event.

The 1985 event just described was exceeded by one on August 15, 2004, when several thunderstorm cells stalled over the mountains along the east side of Death Valley. Rainfall totals reached 6.35 cm (2.5 in.) in little more than an hour. Cars were swept away from the Furnace Creek Inn parking lot; about 4.8 km (3 mi) of Highways 190 and 178 were washed out; and there were two fatalities in the Zabriskie Point area. One annex building had a 3-m- (10 ft-) high water mark on it. Again, water is sparse in the deserts, yet it is the major erosional force—sometimes dramatically so. For recent information and maps of Death Valley, see **http://www.nps.gov/deva/**.

Permanent lakes and continuously flowing rivers are uncommon features in the desert, although the Nile River and the Colorado River are notable exceptions. Both these rivers are *exotic streams*, having their headwaters in a wetter region and the bulk of their course through arid regions. Focus Study 15.1 discusses the Colorado River and its problem of overuse in an arid land (pp. 500–504).

In arid climates, a prominent landform is the **alluvial fan**, which occurs at the mouth of a canyon where it exits into a valley. The fan is produced by flowing water that abruptly loses velocity as it leaves the constricted channel of the canyon and therefore drops layer upon layer of sediment along the base of the mountain block. Water then flows over the surface of the fan and produces a braided

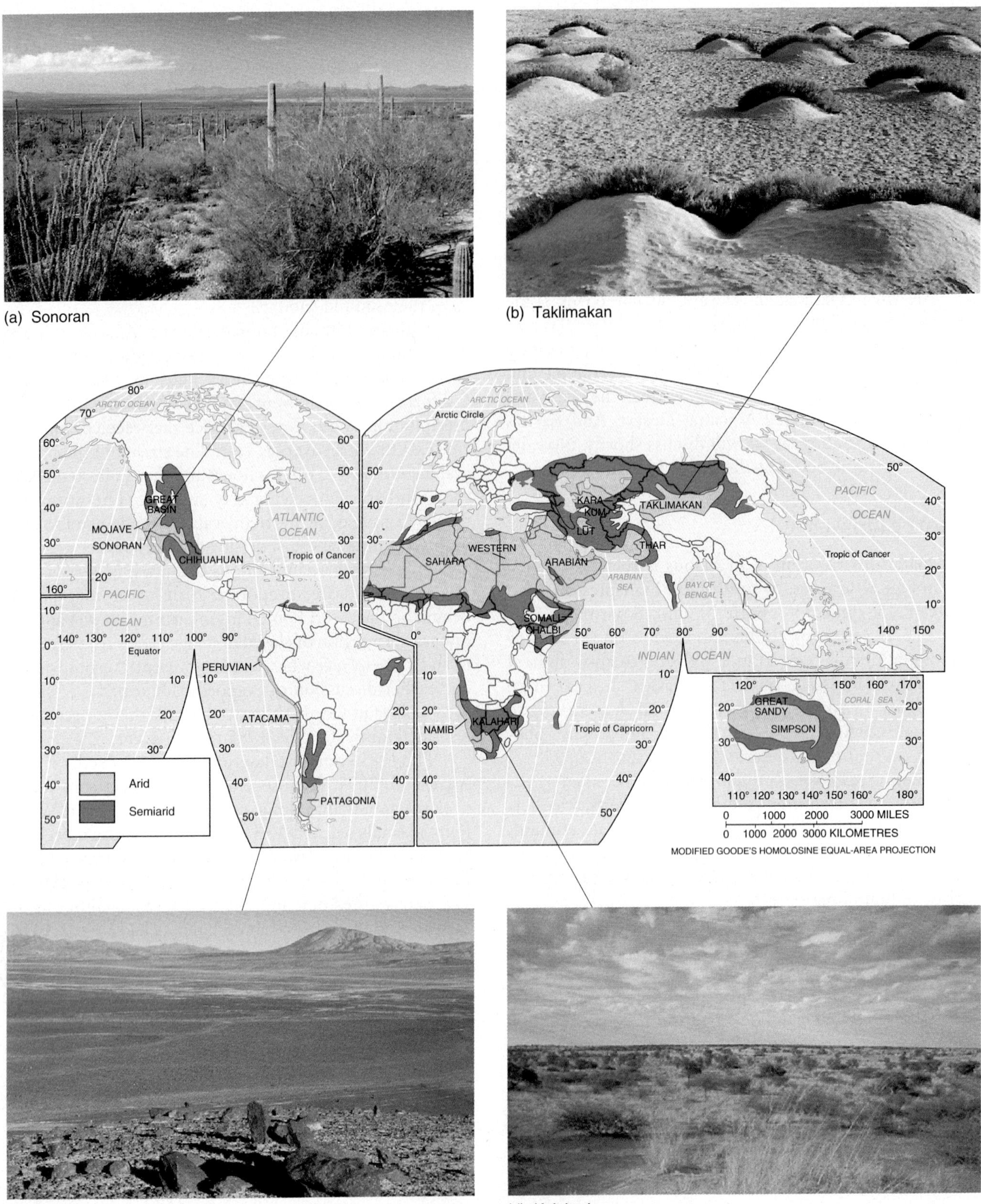

FIGURE 15.16 The world's dry regions.
Worldwide distribution of arid lands (*arid desert* climates) and semiarid lands (*semiarid steppe* climates). (a) Sonoran Desert in the American southwest. (b) Taklimakan Desert in central Asia. (c) Atacama Desert in subtropical Chile near Baquedano. (d) Kalahari Desert in south-central Africa. [Photos by (a) Robert W. Christopherson; (b) Wu Chunzhan/New China Pictures Co./East Photo; (c) Jacques Jangoux/Photo Researchers, Inc.; (d) Nigel J. Dennis/Photo Researchers, Inc.]

FIGURE 15.17 The land in Canyon de Chelly.
In this marginal land, undependable water flows between the towering sandstone walls surrounding Chinle Wash in Canyon de Chelly, Arizona. [Photo by Robert W. Christopherson.]

drainage pattern, shifting from channel to channel with each precipitation event (Figure 15.19, p. 504). A continuous apron, or **bajada** (Spanish for "slope"), may form if individual alluvial fans coalesce into one sloping surface (see Figure 15.24c). Fan formation is reduced in humid climates because perennial streams constantly carry away sediment, preventing its deposition.

An interesting aspect of an alluvial fan is the natural sorting of materials by size. Near the mouth of the canyon at the apex of the fan, coarse materials are deposited, grading slowly to pebbles and finer gravels with distance out from the mouth. Then sands and silts are deposited, with the finest clays and salts carried in suspension and solution all the way to the valley floor. Dissolved minerals accumulate as evaporite deposits on the valley floor are left after evaporation of the water from the playa.

Well-developed alluvial fans also can be a major source of groundwater. Some cities—San Bernardino, California, for example—are built on alluvial fans and extract their municipal water supplies from them. In other parts of the world, such water-bearing alluvial fans are known as *qanat* (Iran), *karez* (Pakistan), and *foggara* (western Sahara).

Desert Landscapes

Contrary to popular belief, deserts are not wastelands, for they abound in specially adapted plants and animals. Moreover, the limited vegetation, intermittent rainfall, intense insolation, and distant vistas produce starkly beautiful landscapes. And deserts are not all the same: For example, North American deserts have more vegetation cover than do the generally barren Asian desert expanses, as we saw in Figure 15.16.

The shimmering heat waves and related mirage effects in the desert are products of light refraction through layers of air that have developed a temperature gradient near the hot ground. The desert's enchantment is captured in the book *Desert Solitaire*:

> Around noon the heat waves begin flowing upward from the expanses of sand and bare rock. They shimmer like transparent, filmy veils between my sanctuary in the shade and all the sun-dazzled world beyond. Objects and forms viewed through this tremulous

(continued p. 504)

(a)

(b)

FIGURE 15.18 An improbable river in Death Valley.
The Stovepipe Wells dune field of Death Valley, California, shown (a) the day after a 2.57 cm (1.01 in.) rainfall and (b) one month later (identical location). [Photos by Robert W. Christopherson.]

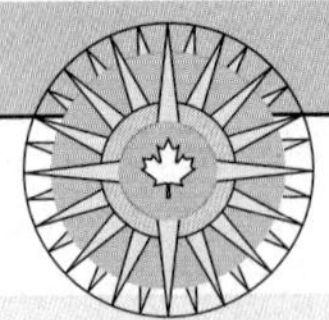

Focus Study 15.1

The Colorado River: A System Out of Balance

The headwaters of an exotic stream rise in a humid region of water surpluses but the stream flows mostly through arid lands for the rest of its journey to the sea. Exotic streams have few incoming tributaries. Consequently, an exotic stream has a discharge pattern that is opposite that of a typical stream: Instead of discharge increasing downstream, it decreases (see Chapter 14). The Nile and Colorado Rivers are prominent examples.

In the case of the Nile, the East African mountains and plateaus provide a humid source area. The Nile first rises as the remote headwaters of the Kagera River in the eastern portion of the Lake Plateau country of East Africa. On its way to Lake Victoria, it forms the partial boundary of Tanzania, Rwanda, and Uganda. The Nile itself then rises out of the lake and continues on its 6650 km (4132 mi) course to its mouth on the Mediterranean Sea near Cairo.

The Colorado River Basin

The Colorado rises on the high slopes of Mount Richthofen (3962 m, or 13,000 ft) in Rocky Mountain National Park, Colorado (Figure 1a) and flows almost 2317 km (1440 mi) to where a trickle of water disappears in the sand, kilometres short of its former mouth in the Gulf of California.

Orographic precipitation totalling 102 cm (40 in.) per year (mostly snow) falls in the Rockies, feeding the Colorado headwaters. But at Yuma, Arizona, near the river's end, annual precipitation is a scant 8.9 cm (3.5 in.), an extremely small amount when compared with the annual potential evapotranspiration demand in the Yuma region of 140 cm (55 in.).

From its source region, the Colorado River quickly leaves the humid Rockies and spills out into the arid desert of western Colorado and eastern Utah. At Grand Junction, Colorado, near the Utah border, annual precipitation is only 20 cm (8 in.) (Figure 1b). After carving its way through the intricate labyrinth of canyonlands in Utah, the river enters Lake Powell, 945 m (3100 ft) lower in elevation than the river's source area upstream in the Rockies some 982 km (610 mi) away (Figure 1c). The Colorado then flows through the Grand Canyon chasm, formed by its own erosive power.

West of the Grand Canyon, the river turns southward, tracing its final 644 km (400 mi) as the Arizona-California border. Along this stretch sits Hoover Dam, just east of Las Vegas (Figure 1d); Davis Dam, built to control the releases from Hoover (Figure 1e); Parker Dam for the water needs of Los Angeles; three more dams for irrigation water (Palo Verde, Figure 1f, Imperial, and Laguna) and finally, Morelos Dam at the Mexican border (Figure 1g). Mexico owns the end of the river and whatever water is left, although the river no longer reaches its mouth into the Gulf of California (Figure 1i).

Figure 1j shows the annual water discharge and suspended sediment load for the Colorado River at Yuma, Arizona, from 1905 to 1964. The completion of Hoover Dam in the 1930s dramatically reduced suspended sediment. Addition of Glen Canyon Dam upstream from Hoover Dam in 1963 further reduced streamflows. In fact, Lake Powell, which formed upstream behind the artificial base level of Glen Canyon Dam, is forecast to fill with sediment over the next 100 years, if it remains in operation.

Overall, the drainage basin encompasses 641,025 km^2 (247,000 mi^2) of mountain, basin-and-range, plateau, canyon, and desert landscapes, in parts of seven states and two countries. A discussion of the Colorado River is included in this chapter because of its crucial part in the history of the Southwest and its role in the future of this region and North America.

Dividing Up the Colorado's Dammed Water

John Wesley Powell (1834–1902), the first person of record to successfully navigate the Colorado River through the Grand Canyon, was the first director of the U.S. Bureau of Ethnology and later director of the U.S. Geological Survey (1881–1892). Powell perceived that the challenge of the West was too great for individual efforts and believed that solutions to problems such as water availability could be met only through private cooperative efforts. His 1878 study (reprinted 1962), *Report of the Lands of the Arid Region of the United States*, is a conservation landmark.

FIGURE 1 The Colorado River drainage basin. →
The Colorado River basin, showing division of the upper and lower basins near Lees Ferry in northern Arizona. (a) Headwaters of the Colorado River near Mount Richthofen in the Colorado Rockies. (b) The river near Moab, Utah. (c) Glen Canyon Dam, a regulatory, administrative facility near Lees Ferry, Arizona. (d) Hoover Dam spillways in rare operation during 1983 floods. (e) Davis Dam in full release during flood. (f) Irrigation canal and cropland irrigated with Colorado River water in the Palo Verde district. (g) Morelos Dam at the Mexican border is the final stop as the river dwindles to a mere canal. (h) Central Arizona Project aqueduct west of Phoenix. (i) The Colorado River (far upper left) stops short of its former delta. The bluish-purple water in the former channel is actually an inlet for Gulf of California water; the grey deposits are sediments in mud flats along this inlet. (j) Dam construction affects river discharge and sediment yields. [Photos by (a) Bobbé Christopherson; (b) through (g) Robert W. Christopherson; (h) Tom Bean/DRK Photo; (i) *Terra* ASTER (thermal emission and reflection) image courtesy of NASA/GSFC/MITI/ERSDAC/JAROS and the U.S./Japan ASTER Science Team, September 8, 2000; and, (j) data from USGS, 1985, *National Water Summary 1984*, Water Supply Paper 2275 (Washington, DC: Government Printing Office), p. 55).]

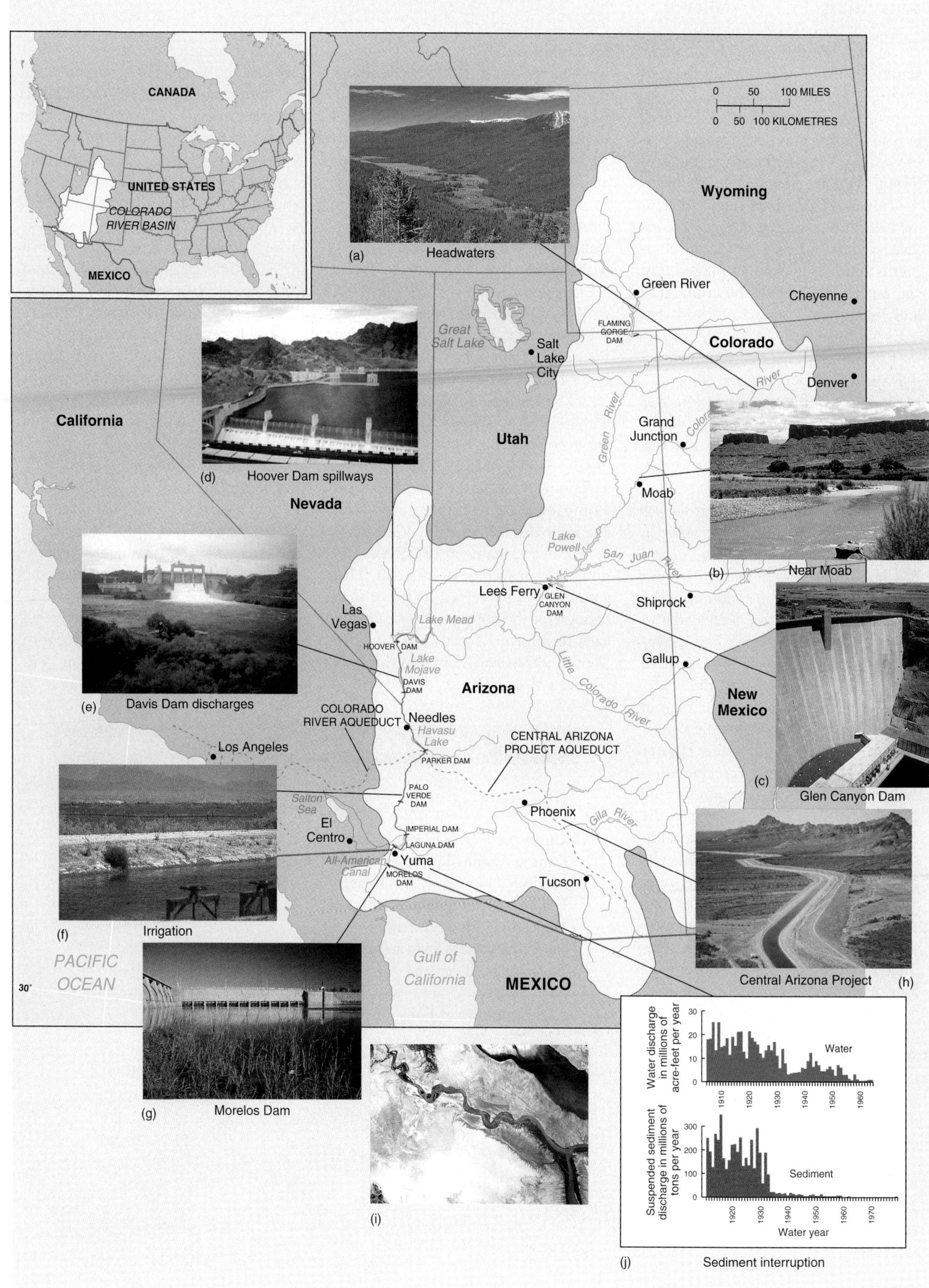

(a) Headwaters

(b) Near Moab

(c) Glen Canyon Dam

(d) Hoover Dam spillways

(e) Davis Dam discharges

(f) Irrigation

(g) Morelos Dam

(h) Central Arizona Project

(i)

(j) Sediment interruption

Focus Study 15.1 *(continued)*

Today, Powell probably would be skeptical of the intervention by government agencies in building large-scale reclamation projects. Lake Powell is named after him despite his probable opposition were he alive. An anecdote in Wallace Stegner's book *Beyond the Hundredth Meridian* relates that, at an 1893 international irrigation conference held in Los Angeles, development-minded delegates bragged that the entire West could be conquered and reclaimed from nature and that "rain will certainly follow the plow." Powell spoke against that sentiment: "I tell you, gentlemen, you are piling up a heritage of conflict and litigation over water rights, for there is not sufficient water to supply the land."* He was booed from the hall, but history has shown Powell to be correct.

The Colorado River Compact was signed by six of the seven basin states in 1923. (The seventh, Arizona, signed in 1944, the same year as the Mexican Water Treaty.) With this compact, the Colorado River basin was divided into an upper basin and a lower basin, arbitrarily separated for administrative purposes at Lees Ferry near the Utah–Arizona border (noted on the map in Figure 1). Congress adopted the *Boulder Canyon Act* in 1928, authorizing Hoover Dam as the first major reclamation project on the river. Also authorized was the All-American Canal into the Imperial Valley, which required an additional dam. Los Angeles then began its project to bring Colorado River water 390 km (240 mi) from still another dam and reservoir on the river to their city.

Shortly after Hoover Dam was finished and downstream enterprises were thus offered flood protection, the other projects were quickly completed. There are now eight major dams on the river and many irrigation works. The latest effort to redistribute Colorado River water is the Central Arizona Project, which carries water to the Phoenix area (Figure 1h).

Highly Variable River Flows

The flaw in all this planning and water distribution is that exotic streamflows are highly variable, and the Colorado is no exception. In 1917, the discharge measured at Lees Ferry totalled 24 million acre-feet (maf), whereas in 1934 it dropped by nearly 80%, to only 5.03 maf. In 1977, the discharge dropped again to 5.02 maf, but in 1984 it rose to an all-time high of 24.5 maf. Yet, in contrast, from 2000 to 2004, river discharge fell to exceptionally low levels, with 2002 dropping to a record low of 3.1 maf, and 2003 to 6.4 maf! The 2002 to 2004 water years marked the lowest 3-year average flow in the total record. Please see Table 1 for flow data and a water budget for the Colorado River.

The average flows between 1906 and 1930 were almost 18 maf a year, but averages dropped to 14.1 maf during the past 70 years (1930 to 2003). As a planning basis for the Colorado River Compact, the government used average river discharges from 1914 up to the Compact signing in 1923, an exceptionally high average of 18.8 maf. That amount was perceived as more than enough for the upper and lower basins, each to receive 7.5 maf, and, later, for Mexico to receive 1.5 maf in the 1944 Mexican Water Treaty.

We might question whether proper long-range planning should rely on the providence of high variability. Tree-ring analyses of past climates have disclosed that the only other time Colorado discharges were at the high 1914–1923 level was between A.D. 1606 and 1625! The dependable flows of the river have been consistently overestimated. This shortfall problem is shown in an estimated budget of 20 million acre-feet for the river (Table 1). Clearly the situation is out of balance, for there is not enough discharge to meet budgeted demands. A few wet years in the late 20th century sparked more confidence and triggered more disputes on how to divvy up the surpluses—only delaying the inevitable deficit crisis.

Presently, the seven states ideally want rights to a total as high as 25.0 maf. When added to the guarantee for Mexico, this comes up to 26.5 maf of wants. And six states share one common opinion: California's right to the water must be limited to a court-ordered 4.4 maf, which it exceeded every year until California's access to surplus Colorado River water was stopped in 2002. At present, there is no

Table 1 Estimated Colorado River Budget through 2003

Water Demand	Quantity Millions of litres (maf)[a]
Upper basin (7.5) Lower basin (7.5)[b]	18.60 (15.0)
Central Arizona Project (rising to 2.8 maf)	1.24 (1.0)
Mexican allotment (1944 Treaty)	1.86 (1.5)
Evaporation from reservoirs	1.86 (1.5)
Bank storage at Lake Powell	0.62 (0.5)
Phreatophytic losses (water-demanding plants)	0.62 (0.5)
Budgeted total demand	24.80 (20.0)
Average Flows at Lees Ferry	
1906–1930	21.95 (17.7)
1930–2003 average flow of the river	17.48 (14.1)
1990–2002	16.43 (13.25)
2000	13.71 (11.06)
2001	13.33 (10.75)
2002	3.84 (3.1)
2003	7.94 (6.4)

Source: Bureau of Reclamation states and states of Arizona, California, Nevada.
A water year runs from October 1 to September 30.
[a]1 million acre-feet = 325,872 gallons; 1.24 million litres; 43,560 ft^3.
[b]In-basin consumptive uses 75% agricultural.

*W. Stegner, *Beyond the Hundredth Meridian* (Boston: Houghton Mifflin, 1954), p. 343.

surplus during the ongoing western drought. And U.S. water planners continue to think that Canadian water resources could somehow be brought south.

Water Loss at Glen Canyon Dam and Lake Powell

Glen Canyon Dam was completed and began water impoundment (Lake Powell) in 1963, 27.4 km (17 mi) north of the basin division point at Lees Ferry. The advancing water slowly flooded the deep, fluted, inner gorges of many canyons, including the Glen, Navajo, Labyrinth, and Cathedral. Glen Canyon Dam's primary purpose, according to the Bureau of Reclamation, is to regulate flows between the upper and lower basins. An additional benefit is the production of hydroelectric power, which is sold wholesale at a low rate to utilities across the Southwest. Also, there is a growing recreation and tourism industry around Lake Powell, as previously inaccessible desert scenery now can be reached by boat.

Many thought that Lake Mead, behind Hoover Dam downstream, could have served the primary administrative function of flow regulation, especially considering the serious water-loss problems with the Glen Canyon Dam and the absorbent rocks that contain its reservoir. First, porous Navajo sandstone underlies most of the Lake Powell reservoir at Glen Canyon Dam. This sandstone absorbs an estimated 0.5 maf of the river's overall annual discharge as bank storage. The higher the lake level, the greater the loss into the sandstone. Second, Lake Powell is an open body of water in an arid desert, where hot, dry winds accelerate evaporative losses. Another 0.5 maf of the Colorado's overall discharge is lost annually from the reservoir in this manner, about a third of Colorado River reservoir evaporation losses. Third, now-permanent sand bars and banks have stabilized along the regulated river, allowing water-demanding plants called phreatophytes to establish and extract an additional 0.5 maf of the river flow.

Intense precipitation and heavy snowpack in the Rockies, attributable to the 1982–1983 El Niño (see Focus Study 10.1), led to record-high discharge rates on the Colorado, testing the controllability of one of the most regulated rivers in the world. Federal reservoir managers were not prepared for the high discharge, since they had set aside Lake Mead's primary purpose (flood control) in favour of competing water and power interests. What followed was a human-caused flood on the most engineered river in the world!

The only time the spillways at Hoover Dam had ever operated was more than 40 years earlier, when the reservoir capacity was artificially raised for a test; now they were opened to release the floodwaters (Figure 1d). Davis Dam, which regulates releases from Hoover Dam, was within 30 cm (1 ft) of overflow, a real problem for a structure made partially of earth fill (Figure 1e). In addition, Glen Canyon Dam was over capacity and at risk and was damaged by the volume of discharge tearing through its spillways. The decision to increase releases doomed towns and homeowners along the river, especially in subdivisions near Needles, California.

The Western Drought and Beyond

The severity of the western drought from 1999 to 2005, in its sixth year, surpasses anything in the historical record and is approaching the driest in the record according to tree-ring analyses. Satellites can spot the symptoms of this western drought: reduced snow pack in the Rockies, reduced soil moisture, the drought-stressed conditions of vegetation, the prevalence of wildfires, and lowered reservoir levels.

Since A.D. 1226, nine droughts lasting 10 to 20 years and four lasting more than 20 years occurred. Whether the current drought will be of this duration or be more like the three droughts of the 20th century that ran 4 to 11 years is unknown. However, this is the first drought to occur in the Colorado River system in the presence of a human demand for water that is increasing at such record levels.

Water inflow to Lake Powell in the summer of 2004 was 31% of the 30-year average (1961–1990)—2003 was 53% and 2002 was just 25%. By 2005, Lake Powell had dropped below levels not seen since it began filling more than 30 years ago—only 38% of capacity. Lake Mead dropped to 54% of capacity by the end of 2004. The maximum reservoir elevation of Lake Mead is 375 m (1229 ft), and by July 2004 Lake Mead dropped to 343 m (1126.7 ft). Forecasts place the level at 341 m (1118 ft) by December 2005. The production of hydroelectric power has fallen to just 31% of capacity from these dams.

An official "shortage" declaration has not been issued and managers think they can continue to meet lower basin needs from Lake Mead's storage. The official status in 2005 placed the system in a "drought condition," despite a wetter winter in 2004. There is speculation that Glen Canyon Dam might cease operations before the end of the decade because of these low-water conditions, leading some environmental groups to suggest decommissioning, possible removal, and restoration of the canyons to predevelopment status—an improbable outcome for political reasons.

The worst appears yet to come. As of 2005, the total system stands at 50% of capacity and engineers estimate that it will take *13 normal winters* of snowpack in the Rockies and basin-wide precipitation to "reset" the system. This recovery is much slower than previous drought recoveries because of the rapid increase in water demand across the Southwest. Arizona's population alone grew 36% between 1990 and 2000 (3.6 million to 5.55 million in 2004). Las Vegas went from 368,000 in 1985 to 2 million by the end of 2005 (540% increase!). Present probabilities for the period after 2016 place only a 20% chance of surplus occurring in any given year. Imagine the population after 2016 in the region if no steps are taken to control growth!

Government stopgap measures include, among others, buying water from farmers to meet contractual obligations for Colorado River water; reopening the desalination plant in Yuma, Arizona, to treat agricultural runoff water for its return to the river to meet international agreements with Mexico; and increasing storage, when possible, in upstream reservoirs in the system where evaporation rates are lower than at Lake Powell. Conservation

(continued)

Focus Study 15.1 *(continued)*

(using less water) and efficiency (using water more effectively) are not yet being stressed as ways to reduce the tremendous demand for water. However, southern Nevada has launched a campaign to replace lawns with drought-tolerant xeroscaping—desert landscaping. Limiting or halting further metropolitan construction and population growth in the Colorado River Basin is not part of the present strategy to lower demand. Despite the conditions along the river, we still seem to be "supply" focused in our approach—not focusing on "demand." Remember, it is the tremendous increase in the demand for this water that stands in the way of resetting the Colorado River system in the foreseeable future.

In a December 2003 speech in Las Vegas to the Colorado River Water Users Association, the director of the Bureau of Reclamation, in an obvious understatement about the water shortfall that could continue for a decade or more, stated:

> That's why the Colorado River must be carefully managed and used. That is why we'll keep encouraging all Colorado River water users to pay attention to their water use. And that is why Reclamation . . . will continue to manage the river more intensely than we ever had in the past.

We might wonder what John Wesley Powell would think if he were alive today to witness such errant attempts to control the mighty and variable Colorado. He foretold such a "heritage of conflict and litigation."

(continued from p. 499)

flow appear somewhat displaced or distorted. . . . The great Balanced Rock floats a few inches above its pedestal, supported by a layer of superheated air. The buttes, pinnacles, and fins in the windows area bend and undulate beyond the middle ground like a painted backdrop stirred by a draft of air.*

*E. Abbey, *Desert Solitaire* (New York: McGraw-Hill, 1968), p. 154. Copyright © 1968 by Edward Abbey.

FIGURE 15.19 An alluvial fan.
The photo shows an alluvial fan in a desert landscape. The topographic map shows the Cedar Creek alluvial fan. (Topographic map is the Ennis Quadrangle, 15-minute series, scale 1:62,500, contour interval = 40 ft; latitude/longitude coordinates for mouth of canyon are 45°2′ N 111°35′ W.) [Photo by Bobbé Christopherson; USGS map.]

The buttes, pinnacles, and mesas of arid landscapes are resistant horizontal rock strata that have eroded differentially. Removal of the less-resistant sandstone strata produces unusual desert sculptures—arches, windows, pedestals, and delicately balanced rocks (Figure 15.20). Specifically, the upper layers of sandstone along the top of an arch or butte are more resistant to weathering and protect the sandstone rock beneath.

The removal of all surrounding rock through differential weathering leaves enormous buttes as residuals on the landscape. If you imagine a line intersecting the tops of the Mitten Buttes shown in Figure 15.21, you can gain some idea of the quantity of material that has been removed. These buttes exceed 300 m (1000 ft) in height, similar to the Chrysler Building in New York City or First Canadian Place in Toronto.

Desert landscapes are places where stark erosional remnants can stand above the surrounding terrain as knobs or hills. Such a bare, exposed rock, called an *inselberg* (island mountain), is exemplified by Uluru (Ayers) Rock in Australia (Figure 15.22).

In a desert area, weak surface material may weather to a complex, rugged topography, usually of relatively low and varied relief. Such a landscape is called a *badland*, probably so named because in the American West it offered little economic value and was difficult to traverse in 19th-century wagons. The Badlands region of the Dakotas and north-central Arizona (the Painted Desert) are of this form.

Sand dunes that existed in some ancient deserts have lithified, forming sandstone structures that bear the imprint of *cross-stratification*. When such a dune was accumulating, sand cascaded down its slipface, and distinct bedding planes (layers) were established that remained after the dune lithified (Figure 15.23). Ripple marks, animal tracks, and fossils also are found preserved in these sandstones, which originally were eolian-deposited sand dunes.

FIGURE 15.20 A balanced rock—differential weathering. Balanced Rock in Arches National Park, Utah, where writer-naturalist Edward Abbey (quoted in text) worked as a ranger years before it became a park. The overall feature is 39 m (128 ft) tall and composed of Entrada sandstone. The balanced- rock portion is 17 m (55 ft) tall and weighs 3255 metric (3577 short) tons. [Photo by Robert W. Christopherson.]

Basin and Range Province

Geologically, a province is a large region that is characterized by several geologic or physiographic traits. Characterizing the **Basin and Range Province** of the

(a)

Resistent cap rock

Removed by weathering and erosion

(b)

FIGURE 15.21 Monument Valley landscape. (a) Mitten Buttes, Merrick Butte, and rainbow in Monument Valley, Navajo Tribal Park, along the Utah–Arizona border. (b) A schematic of the tremendous removal of material by weathering, erosion, and transport. [Photo by Robert W. Christopherson.]

FIGURE 15.22 Australian landmark.
Uluru (Ayers) Rock in Northern Territory, Australia, is an isolated mass of weathered rock. The formation is 348 m (1145 ft) high and is 2.5 km long by 1.6 km wide. Uluru Rock is sacred to Aboriginal peoples and has been protected in Uluru National Park since 1950. [Photo by Porterfield/Chickering.]

FIGURE 15.23 Cross-bedding in sedimentary rocks.
The bedding pattern, called cross-stratification, in these sandstone rocks tells us about patterns that were established in the dunes before lithification (hardening into rock). [Photo by Bobbé Christopherson.]

western United States are alternating basins (valleys) and mountain ranges that lie in the rain shadow of mountains to the west (Figure 15.24). The physiography and geography combine to give the province a dry climate, few permanent streams, and *internal drainage patterns*—drainage basins that lack any outlet to the ocean (see Figure 14.5, "Great Basin" and internal drainage).

The vast Basin and Range Province—almost 800,000 km^2 (300,000 mi^2)—was a major barrier to early settlers in their migration westward. The combination of desert climate and north–south trending mountain ranges presented harsh challenges. Today, when you traverse U.S. Highway 50 across Nevada, you cross five passes (horsts) of more than 1950 m (6400 ft) and numerous basins (grabens). Throughout the drive you are reminded where you are by prideful signs that plainly state, "The Loneliest Road in America." It is difficult to imagine crossing this topography with wagons and oxen (Figure 15.24e).

How the Basin and Range formed is interesting. As the North American plate lumbered westward, it overrode former oceanic crust and hot spots at such a rapid pace that slabs of subducted material literally were run over. The crust was stretched (tensional forces), creating a landscape fractured by many faults. The present landscape consists of nearly parallel sequences of *horsts* (upward-faulted blocks, which are the "ranges") and *grabens* (downward-faulted blocks, which are the "basins," or valleys). Figure 15.24c shows this pattern of normal faults.

John McPhee captured the feel of this desert province in his book *Basin and Range*:

> Supreme over all is silence. Discounting the cry of the occasional bird, the wailing of a pack of coyotes, silence—a great spatial silence—is pure in the Basin and Range. It is a soundless immensity with mountains in it. You stand . . . and look up at a high mountain front, and turn your head and look fifty miles down the valley, and there is utter silence.*

Basin-and-range relief is abrupt, and rock structures are angular and rugged. As the ranges erode, transported materials accumulate to great depths in the basins, gradually producing extensive desert plains. The basin's elevation averages roughly 1200–1500 m (4000–5000 ft) above sea level, with mountain crests rising higher by some 900–1500 m (3000–5000 ft). Death Valley, California, is the lowest of these basins, with an elevation of –86 m (–282 ft). However, to the west of the valley, the Panamint Range rises to 3368 m (11,050 ft) at Telescope Peak—almost 3.5 vertical kilometres (2.2 mi) of desert mountain relief!

In Figure 15.24c and d, note the **bolson**, a slope-and-basin area between the crests of two adjacent ridges in a dry region of internal drainage. Death Valley provides a dramatic example of these arid-land features. Figure 15.24c also identifies a *playa* (central salt pan), a *bajada* (coalesced alluvial fans), and a mountain front in retreat from weathering and erosional attack. A *pediment* is an area of bedrock that is layered with a thin veneer, or coating, of alluvium. It is an erosional surface, as opposed to the depositional surface of the bajada.

Vast arid and semiarid lands remain an enigma on the water planet. They challenge our technology, courage, and personal need for water. These lands hold a mysterious fascination, perhaps because they are so lacking in the moisture that infuses our lives.

Desertification

We are witnessing an unwanted expansion of the Earth's desert lands in a process known as **desertification**. This now is a worldwide phenomenon along the margins of semiarid and arid lands. Desertification is due principally to

*J. McPhee, *Basin and Range* (New York: Farrar, Straus, Giroux, 1981), p. 46.

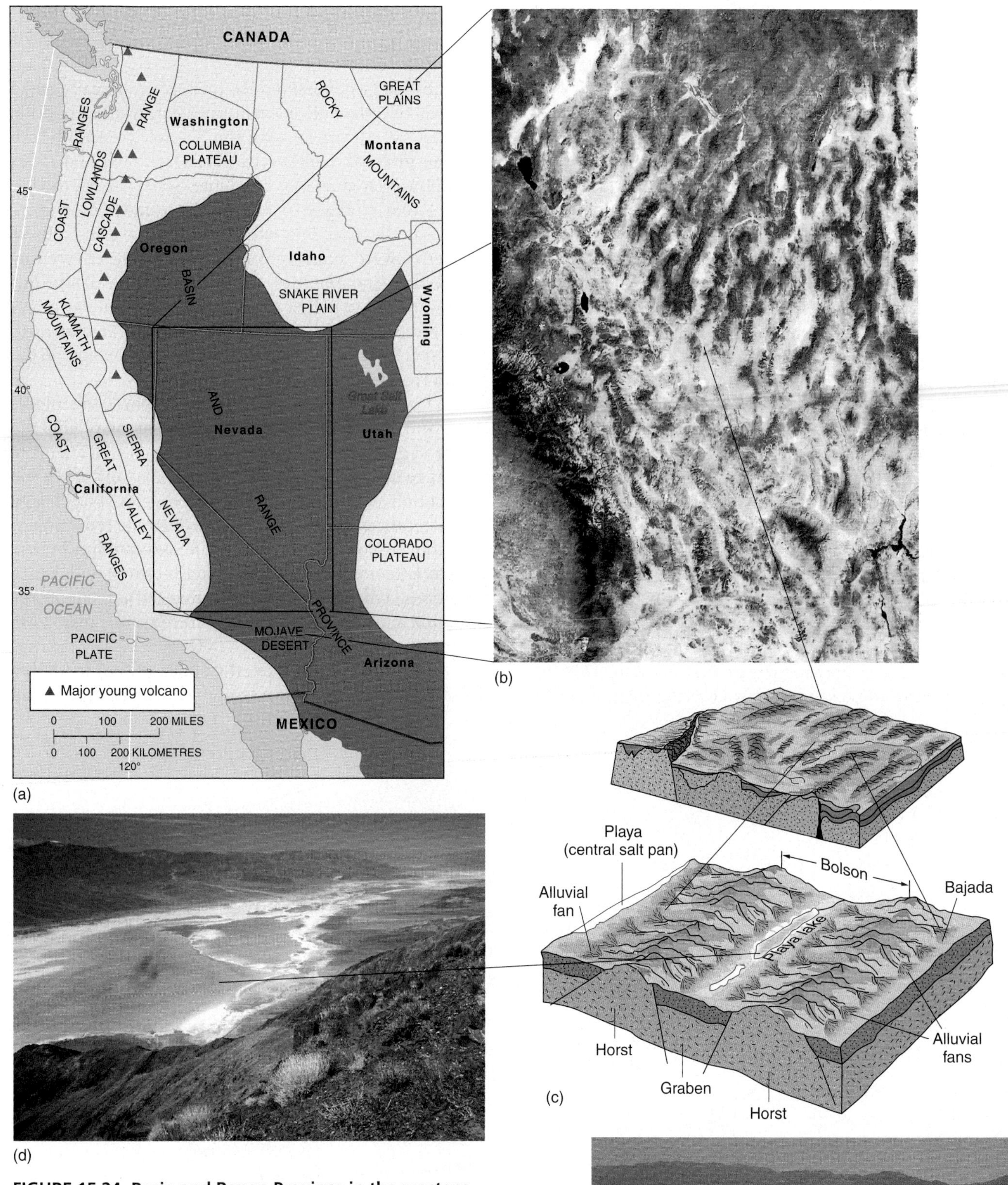

FIGURE 15.24 Basin and Range Province in the western United States.
(a) Map and (b) *Landsat* image of the area. Recent scientific discoveries demonstrate that this province extends south through northern and central Mexico. (c) A bolson in the mountainous desert landscape of the Basin and Range Province. Parallel normal faults produce a series of horsts (ranges) and grabens (basins). (d) Death Valley features a central playa, parallel mountain ranges, alluvial fans, and bajada along the base of the ranges. (e) "The Loneliest Road in America," Highway U.S. 50, slashes westward through the province. [(b) Image from NASA; photos by (d) by Robert W. Christopherson; (e) Bobbé Christopherson.]

poor agricultural practices (overgrazing and agricultural activities that abuse soil structure and fertility), improper soil-moisture management, erosion and salinization, deforestation, and the ongoing global climatic change, which is shifting temperature and precipitation patterns.

The southward expansion of Saharan conditions through portions of the *Sahel region* has left many African peoples on land that no longer experiences the rainfall of just two decades ago. Other regions at risk of desertification stretch from Asia and central Australia to portions of North and South America. The United Nations estimates that degraded lands have covered some 800 million hectares (2 billion acres) since 1930; many millions of additional hectares are added each year. An immediate need is to improve the database for a more accurate accounting of the problem and a better understanding of what is occurring.

Figure 15.25 is drawn from a map prepared for a U.N. conference on desertification. Desertification areas are ranked: A moderate hazard area has an average 10%–25% drop in agricultural productivity; a high hazard area has a 25%–50% drop; and a very high hazard area has more than a 50% decrease. Because human activities and economies, especially unwise grazing practices, appear to be the major cause of desertification, actions to slow the process are readily available. The severity of this problem is magnified by the poverty in many of the affected regions. For more on these global arid lands, see the U.N. site at **http://www.unccd.int/main.php**; and for the UNDP Dryland Development Centre work, see **http://www.undp.org/drylands/**.

Climate Change and Increased Aridity in Canada

Greenhouse gas emissions are increasing annually and a doubling of carbon dioxide emissions may take place within the next 50 years even with the Kyoto Protocol, which became international law in February 2005, and other greenhouse gas emissions restraints. Some climate models predict that changes in precipitation and temperature caused by this doubling will force existent grasslands to shift northward and to grow in regions now covered by boreal plant communities. As the existing grasslands shift northward and to higher elevations, the present day grasslands are predicted to become semi-desert. And in turn, the boreal forest is shifting northward, encroaching on the tundra regions.

When plant communities shift in response to temperature and precipitation changes, the intensity and the nature of geological processes that act in an area are likely to change as well, so increased aridity may influence the distribution and intensity of eolian processes. The change in eolian processes may result in the dramatic reduction of vegetation, exposing soil surfaces. The susceptibility of bare soils to eolian erosion is controlled by surface moisture conditions. Thus, changes in the timing and amount of precipitation and variations in temperature regime may cause changes in eolian erosion.

The Geological Survey of Canada (GSC) modelled the sensitivity of eolian processes to climate change on the

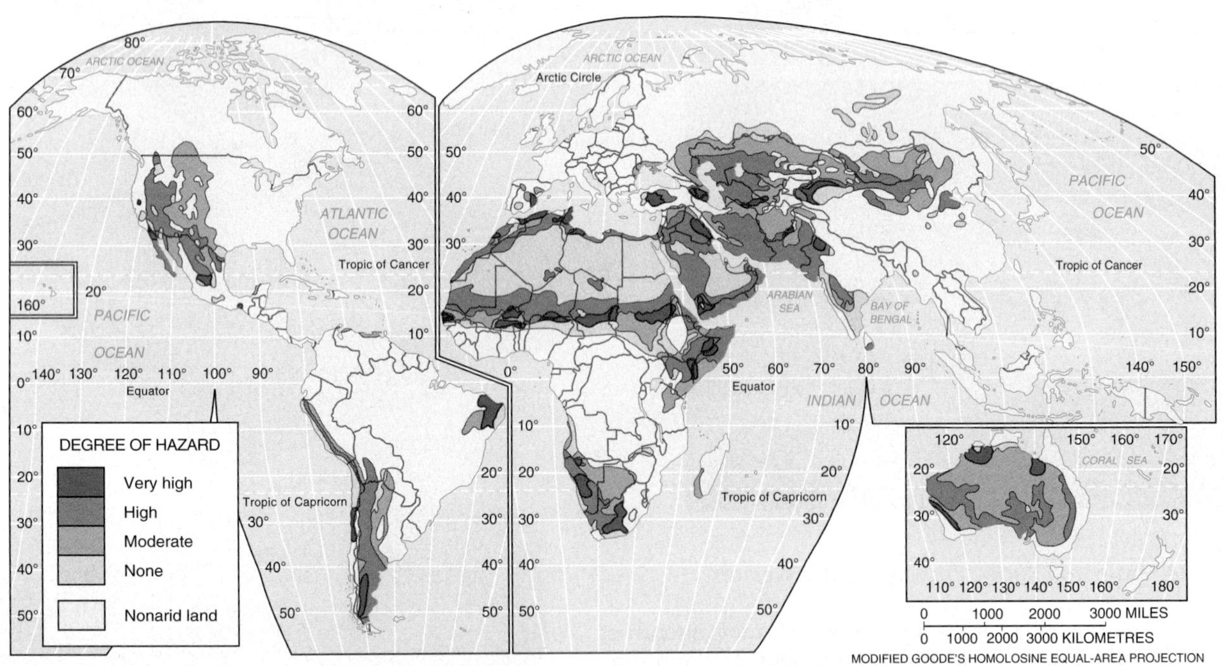

FIGURE 15.25 The desertification hazard.
Worldwide desertification estimates by the United Nations. [Data from U.N. Food and Agricultural Organization (FAO), World Meteorological Organization (WMO), United Nations Educational, Scientific, and Cultural Organization (UNESCO), Nairobi, Kenya; as printed in J. M. Rubenstein, *An Introduction to Human Geography*, Figure 14-16, p. 509. ©1999 Prentice Hall, Inc. Used by permission.]

basis of predicted shifts of vegetation communities. Climate model results indicate that reactivation and increased movement of sand dunes, and the increased erosion of unprotected, bare soils are likely to occur as climate changes. If predicted changes in vegetation cover and moisture conditions increase soil moisture deficits, sensitivity to eolian erosion increases (see chapter-opening photo process).

A survey of the sensitivity of dune areas in Canada that will be affected by climate change is illustrated in Figure 15.26. The least sensitive regions to potential increased eolian processes either have enough vegetation cover or enough surface soil moisture to suppress wind activity when carbon dioxide is doubled. The arctic, subarctic, boreal, cool temperate forest, and transitional grassland have a low sensitivity to changes in eolian processes.

Moderately sensitive areas include the existing boreal regions that may change to grassland and cool temperate regions that may change to moderate temperate regions. In these moderate regions—central Saskatchewan, some regions of Manitoba, Ontario, Québec, and the Maritimes—some reactivation of sand dunes and some soil erosion are likely. Areas that are currently grassland and moderate temperate regions are likely to become more arid. These regions of increased aridity are therefore predicted to be highly sensitive to climate change, and may experience significant increases in eolian and dune activity. These regions are predicted to change to semi-desert. The Palliser Triangle, including the Great Sand Hills of Saskatchewan and Alberta, has severe sensitivity to eolian activity. Figure 15.26 reflects wind erosion risk as well, throughout these low, moderate, and high sensitivity regions.

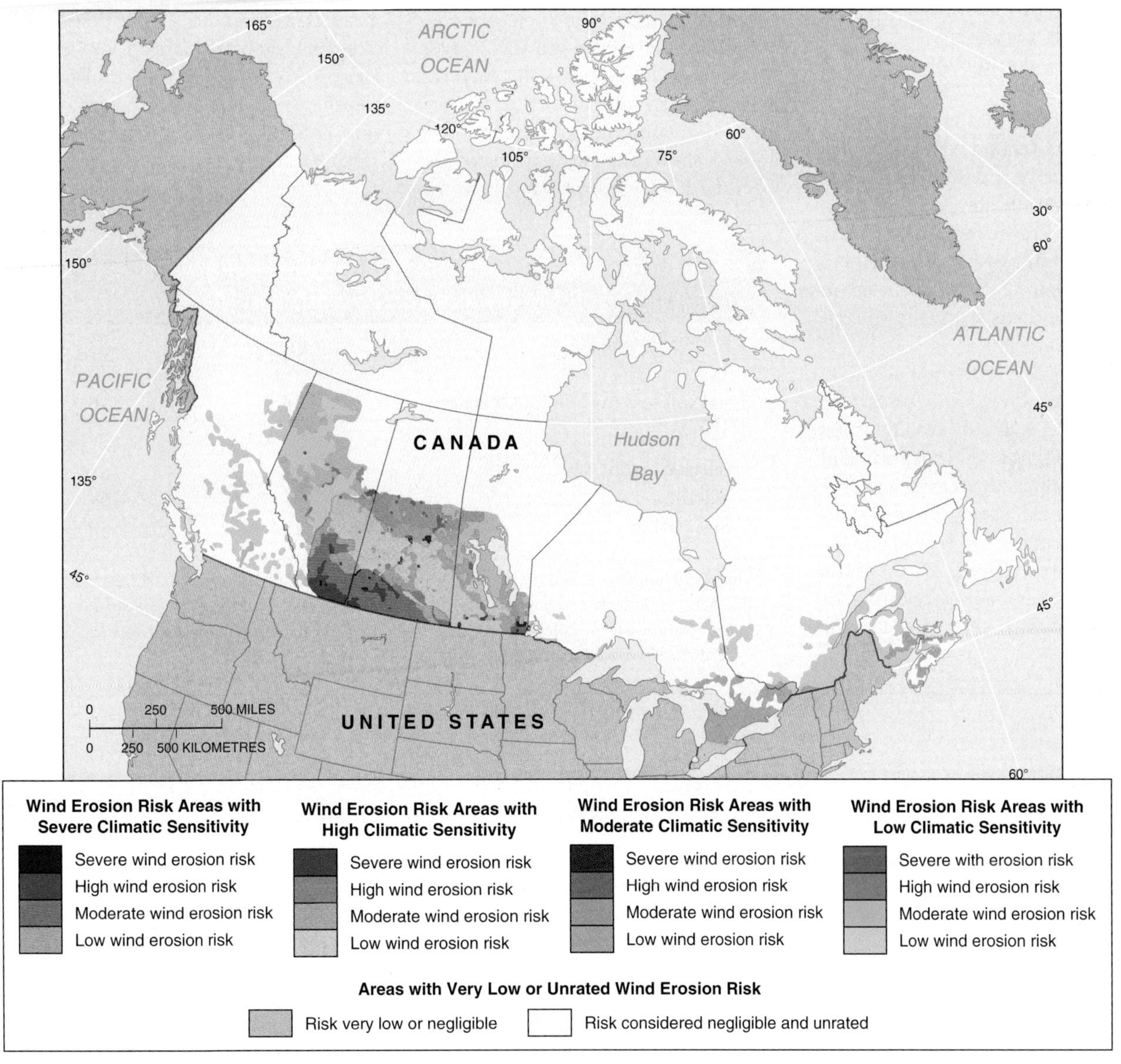

FIGURE 15.26 Sensitivity to wind erosion with climate change.
Risk for erosion of unprotected soils in areas sensitive to climate change is greatest in the southern and central Prairies and in southern-most Ontario. [Map adapted from *The Atlas of Canada*, with the permission of Natural Resources Canada.]

We now have the first circumarctic scientific analysis of the impact of global warming on the Arctic Region. The Arctic Council empowered the Arctic Monitoring and Assessment Programme (AMAP), Conservation of Arctic Flora and Fauna (CAFF), and the International Arctic Science Committee (IASC) to conduct this study and prepare a comprehensive report. The Arctic Climate Impact Assessment (**http://www.acia.uaf.edu**), released in November 2004 following four years of study by 300 scientists and indigenous peoples, stated in one section of the ACIA report regarding the impact of warming and potential desertification in the high latitudes:

> Because the rate of evaporation increases as temperatures climb, if precipitation does not rise enough to keep up with that increase, land areas would dry out . . . followed by desertification in some areas as warming continues.

Eolian processes and arid lands are dynamic systems.

Applied Physical Geography

Wind Erosion

The ability of wind to move objects is small when compared with other transporting agents (e.g., water, ice, gravity), but over time, the amount of material moved can be large. Figure 15.1 illustrates the exponential increase in the rate of sand movement with an increase in wind velocity. Erosion of surface material, especially soil, has long been a concern to Prairie farmers. The dry climate, the intensity of farming, and the open spaces of the Canadian Prairies make them especially susceptible to wind erosion.

Wind erosion of the soil occurs in three stages. First, soil must be detached. This is usually accomplished by frost action, mineral expansion and contraction, alternate wetting and drying, mechanical shear, or abrasion. Once detached, the soil is available for transport. Wind speed is lowest at the ground surface and increases exponentially upward until surface friction is overcome.

The most important factors to consider when calculating wind erosion are air velocity and turbulence; soil structure, density, and moisture content; and surface roughness, cover, obstructions, and topographic features. Mathematical models calculate soil losses by combining these factors. Table 1 shows the calculations of soil loss for a 1992 windstorm in Manitoba.

The loss of soil in metric tons/hectare is a volume measurement. What does this mean for depth of soil lost? If we assume a bulk density of 1mg/m^3, then 10 metric tons/hectare of soil loss is equal to 1 mm of soil depth. So, at Site 1, 1.625 mm of soil and, at Site 2, 1.845 mm of soil was lost during a single storm.

Table 1 Soil Loss from 1992 Windstorm and Breakdown of Soil Movement for Two Sites in Manitoba.*

	Site 1	Site 2
Total soil loss (metric tons/hectare)	16.25	18.45
% Soil loss from:		
Surface creep	1	1
Saltation	81	69
Suspension	18	30

*The field length was 400 m. Soil loss was calculated in kg on an area of 0.04 hectare (0.1 acre) (1-m wide and 400-m long). Wind speed for this event was 50–75 km/h).
Source: Manitoba Agriculture, Food and Rural Initiatives, **http://www.gov.mb.ca/agriculture/soilwater/soil/fbd01s01.html**.

Summary and Review—Eolian Processes and Arid Landscapes

● ***Characterize*** **the unique work accomplished by wind and eolian processes.**

Winds are produced by the movement of the atmosphere in response to pressure differences. Wind is a geomorphic agent of erosion, transportation, and deposition. **Eolian** processes modify and move sand accumulations along coastal beaches and deserts. Wind's ability to move materials is small compared with that of water and ice.

eolian (p. 486)

1. Who was Ralph Bagnold? What was his contribution to eolian studies?
2. Explain the term *eolian* and its application in this chapter. How would you characterize the ability of the wind to move material?

● ***Describe*** **eolian erosion, including deflation, abrasion, and the resultant landforms.**

Two principal wind-erosion processes are **deflation**, the removal and lifting of individual loose particles, and **abrasion**, the "sandblasting" of rock surfaces with particles captured in the air. Fine materials are eroded by wind deflation and moving water, leaving behind concentrations of pebbles and gravel called **desert pavement**. Wherever wind encounters loose sediment, deflation may remove enough material to form basins. Called **blowout depressions**, they range from small indentations less than a metre wide up to areas hundreds of metres wide and many metres deep. Rocks that bear evidence of eolian erosion are called **ventifacts**. On a larger scale, deflation and abrasion are capable of streamlining rock structures, leaving behind distinctive rock formations or elongated ridges called **yardangs**.

deflation (p. 486)
abrasion (p. 486)
desert pavement (p. 486)
blowout depressions (p. 488)
ventifacts (p. 488)
yardangs (p. 488)

3. Describe the erosional processes associated with moving air.
4. Explain deflation and the evolutionary sequence that produces desert pavement.
5. How are ventifacts and yardangs formed by the wind?

● ***Describe*** **eolian transportation and** ***explain*** **saltation and surface creep.**

Wind exerts a drag or frictional pull on surface particles until they become airborne. Only the finest dust particles travel significant distances, so the finer material suspended in a dust storm is lifted much higher than the coarser particles of a sandstorm. Saltating particles crash into other particles, knocking them both loose and forward. The motion called **surface creep** slides and rolls particles too large for saltation.

surface creep (p. 488)

6. Differentiate between a dust storm and a sandstorm.
7. What is the difference between eolian saltation and fluvial saltation?
8. Explain the concept of surface creep.

● ***Identify*** **the major classes of sand dunes and** ***present*** **examples within each class.**

In arid and semiarid climates and along some coastlines where sand is available, dunes accumulate. A **dune** is a wind-sculpted accumulation of sand. An extensive area of dunes, such as that found in North Africa, is characteristic of an **erg desert**, or **sand sea**. When saltating sand grains encounter small patches of sand, their kinetic energy (motion) is dissipated and they start to accumulate into a dune. As height increases above 30 cm (12 in.), a steeply sloping **slipface** on the lee side and characteristic dune features are formed. Dune forms are broadly classified as *crescentic*, *linear*, and *star*.

dune (p. 489)
erg desert (p. 489)
sand sea (p. 489)
slipface (p. 492)

9. What is the difference between an erg and a reg desert? Which type is a sand sea? Are all deserts covered by sand? Explain.
10. What are the three classes of dune forms? Describe the basic types of dunes within each class. What do you think is the major shaping force for sand dunes?
11. Which form of dune is the mountain giant of the desert? What are the characteristic wind patterns that produce such dunes?

● ***Define*** **loess deposits, their origins, locations, and landforms.**

Eolian-transported materials contribute to soil formation in distant places. Windblown **loess** deposits occur worldwide and can develop into good agricultural soils. These fine-grained clays and silts are moved by the wind many kilometres, where they are redeposited in unstratified, homogeneous deposits. The binding strength of loess causes it to weather and erode in steep bluffs, or vertical faces.

Significant accumulations throughout the Mississippi and Missouri River valleys form continuous deposits 15–30 m (50–100 ft) thick. Loess deposits also occur in eastern Washington State, Idaho, much of Ukraine, central Europe, China, the Pampas-Patagonia regions of Argentina, and lowland New Zealand.

loess (p. 495)

12. How are loess materials generated? What form do they assume when deposited?
13. Name a few examples of significant loess deposits on Earth.

● ***Portray*** **desert landscapes and** ***locate*** **these regions on a world map.**

Dry and semiarid climates occupy about 35% of Earth's land surface. The spatial distribution of these dry lands is related to subtropical high-pressure cells between 15° and 35° N and S, to rain shadows on the lee side of mountain ranges, or to areas at great distance from moisture-bearing air masses, such as central Asia.

Precipitation events are rare, yet running water is still the major erosional agent in deserts. Precipitation events may be rare, but when they do occur, a dry streambed fills with a torrent called a **flash flood**. Depending on the region, such a dry streambed is known as a **wash**, an *arroyo* (Spanish), or a *wadi* (Arabic). As runoff water evaporates, salt crusts may be left behind on the desert floor. This intermittently wet and dry low area in a region of closed drainage is called a **playa**, site of an *ephemeral lake* when water is present.

In arid climates, a prominent landform is the **alluvial fan** at the mouth of a canyon where it exits into a valley. The fan is produced by flowing water that abruptly loses velocity as it leaves the constricted channel of the canyon and deposits a layer of sediment along the mountain block. A continuous apron, or **bajada**, may form if individual alluvial fans coalesce. A *province* is a large region that is characterized by several geologic or physiographic traits. The **Basin and Range Province** of the western United States consists of alternating basins and mountain ranges. A slope-and-basin area between the crests of two adjacent ridges in a dry region of internal drainage is termed a **bolson**. **Desertification** is the process that leads to an unwanted expansion of the Earth's desert lands.

flash flood (p. 497)
wash (p. 497)
playa (p. 497)
alluvial fan (p. 497)
bajada (p. 499)
Basin and Range Province (p. 505)
bolson (p. 506)
desertification (p. 506)

14. Characterize desert energy and water balance regimes. What are the significant patterns of occurrence for arid landscapes in the world?
15. How would you describe the water budget of the Colorado River? What was the basis for agreements regarding distribution of the river's water? Why has thinking about the river's discharge been so optimistic?
16. Describe a desert bolson from crest to crest. Draw a simple sketch with the components of the landscape labelled.
17. Where is the Basin and Range Province? Briefly describe its appearance and character.
18. What is meant by desertification? Using the maps in Figures 15.16 and 15.25, and the text description, locate several of the affected regions of desert expansion.
19. With climate change, what changes are predicted for eolian processes in Canada? Which areas are most likely to experience change? Where will sand dunes most likely be active?

Critical Thinking

A. "Water is the major erosion and transport medium in the desert." Respond to this quotation. How is this possible? What factors have you learned from this chapter that prove this statement true?

B. Where are the nearest eolian features (coastal, lakeshore, or desert dunes, or loess deposits) to your present location? Which causative factors discussed in this chapter explain the features you identified?

C. Relative to the Colorado River system, define, compare, and contrast what you think is meant by a "supply strategy" and a "demand strategy" in dealing with the present Colorado River water budget (Table 1 in Focus Study 15.1). Which strategy seems focused on centralized or decentralized solutions? What political and economic forces do you think are at play in planning for the river? Who are the stakeholders? With your analysis, briefly speculate what strategies you think would be most effective in dealing with this situation. What are your thoughts about the possible role of Canadian water resources being moved south to augment further development in the western United States?

Career Link 15.1

Dr. Stephen Wolfe, Geomorphologist, Geological Survey of Canada, Ottawa

In his final year of high school, Stephen Wolfe took a senior course in geology, which counted as a first-year university credit. "I was captivated by rocks and landscape processes," he remembers. "Although I was not aware of it at the time, this was my first scholarly introduction to geomorphology."

Now a geomorphologist with the Geological Survey of Canada (GSC) in Ottawa, Stephen is project leader for Paleoenvironmental Records of Climate Change, which attempts to place the issue of climate change into context with past records from ice cores, tree rings, sediments, and geomorphology. He is an adjunct professor at several universities and conducts research into eolian processes and landforms in the Canadian Prairies, the Yukon, and the Queen Charlotte Islands.

"Both my parents had Ph.D.s in geography," says Stephen, describing the development of his interest in geomorphology. "My father had a background in karst geomorphology and taught in college and high school. My mother was a professor of geography and of rural planning and development at the University of Guelph. My earliest memories are filled with field trips to the Rocky Mountains, spelunking in the caves of West Virginia, and slide shows of cave formations. I grew up in the rural countryside of southern Ontario with its rolling moraines, kames, gravel pits, and limestone quarries. This was a great place for exploring."

As an undergraduate at Carleton University in Ottawa, Stephen volunteered to work in the physical geography laboratory in his spare time and later took on summer jobs in climatology

Figure 1 Stephen Wolfe, research scientist. Stephen's research deals with issues of environment impacts in sensitive terrain. His work has applications for land-use management of farmland, rangeland, and forests, particularly with respect to potential climate change. [Photo by Peter Beninger.]

and soils at Guelph and Carleton. "I became fascinated with the Arctic and took every course I could find related to the North. At the end of my third year, I travelled to the Tuktoyaktuk and Yukon coastlands on the Beaufort Sea as a summer student with the GSC."

Stephen went on to earn an M.Sc. in geology from Queen's University, in Kingston, Ontario. His thesis topic was an investigation of an aggrading coastal shoreline in permafrost. During this time he continued to work as a summer student for the GSC on investigations of permafrost and ground ice in the Beaufort Sea region.

At the University of Guelph in 1989, he redirected his studies toward eolian geomorphology and soon found himself with a research team studying wind erosion and dust storms in Mali, West Africa. For his Ph.D. thesis, "Sparse Vegetation as a Surface Control on Wind Erosion," he studied rangelands and abandoned farmlands of western Arizona.

Stephen re-entered the Geological Survey in 1993 as a post-doctoral fellow studying drought and wind erosion in southwestern Saskatchewan. He eventually accepted a job with the GSC as a permafrost geologist, stationed in Yellowknife, NWT. He was soon mapping permafrost terrain and investigating occurrences of massive ground ice in the Slave Geological Province.

Clearly, Stephen was caught by the "lure of the North." He explains, "it is still a comparatively remote part of Canada, where one still senses the feeling of exploration." He cherishes the time spent in the field "largely because of that sense of exploration and first discovery."

He enjoys interacting with students, occasionally giving university lectures on aspects of his research and co-supervising student research (at Ph.D., master's, or undergraduate levels). "This aspect of my work," says Stephen, "provides an opportunity to get other people enthused about aspects of geomorphology that I like very much. And it has been mutually beneficial, helping answer questions within my own area of research and developing topics of study for students."

Since 1999, when Stephen was transferred to the GSC in Ottawa, he has been investigating the links between past climate changes and sand-dune activity in the Prairie provinces. This research has applications for land-use management of farmland, rangeland, and forests, particularly with respect to potential climate change. "Because sand hills on the prairies are used for cattle grazing," he explains, "the issue of dune activity relates mostly to grazing capacity of rangeland. The Prairies also play host to military bases and considerable oil and gas development. Consequently, there are always issues of environmental impacts in sensitive terrain to consider, including conservation of rare or endangered flora and fauna found only in sand hills."

Stephen believes that the field of eolian geomorphology is one that will expand in the future. "The issue of climate change increased the concern about drought on the Prairies," he says. "Our observations in the Great Sand Hills of southern Saskatchewan tell us that severe droughts can trigger reactivation of the dunes, and that once activated such sand hills and dunes can take many decades, or even centuries, to restabilize." See Stephen's photo of this area in the chapter opener which shows how the sand dunes are reactivating.

Stephen Wolfe does not spend as much time in Canada's North these days, and with a young family he tries not to be away for long periods of time, but he still gets a great sense of satisfaction from his work, both in the field and in the office. "I have come to realize," he tells us, "that you do not have to travel to exotic places to explore new things—more often than not there are many unanswered questions in places that we have travelled over many times." He keeps asking those spatial questions.

The accumulation of sand that makes up Blooming Point Spit separates Tracadie Bay on the north shore of Prince Edward Island from the Gulf of St. Lawrence. [Photo by Mary-Louise Byrne.]

16

The Oceans, Coastal Processes, and Landforms

Key Learning Concepts

After reading the chapter, you should be able to:

- *Describe* the chemical composition of seawater and the physical structure of the ocean.
- *Identify* the components of the coastal environment and *list* the physical inputs to the coastal system, including tides and mean sea level.
- *Describe* wave motion at sea and near shore and *explain* coastal straightening as a product of wave refraction.
- *Identify* characteristic coastal erosional and depositional landforms.
- *Describe* barrier islands and their hazards as they relate to human settlement.
- *Assess* living coastal environments: corals, wetlands, salt marshes, and mangroves.
- *Construct* an environmentally sensitive model for settlement and land use along the coast.

Walk along a shoreline and you witness the dramatic interaction of Earth's vast oceanic, atmospheric, and lithospheric systems. At times, the ocean attacks the coast in a stormy rage of erosive power; at other times, the moist sea breeze, salty mist, and repetitive motion of the water are gentle and calming. Few have captured this confrontation between land and sea as well as biologist Rachel Carson:

> The edge of the sea is a strange and beautiful place. All through the long history of Earth it has been an area of unrest where waves have broken heavily against the land, where the tides have pressed forward over the continents, receded, and then returned. For no two successive days is the shoreline precisely the same. Not only do the tides advance and retreat in their eternal rhythms, but the level of the sea itself is never at rest. It rises or falls as the glaciers melt or grow, as the floors of the deep ocean basins shift under its increasing load of sediments, or as the earth's crust along the continental margins warps up or down in adjustment to strain and tension.

> Today a little more land may belong to the sea, tomorrow a little less. Always the edge of the sea remains an elusive and indefinable boundary.*

Despite such variability between sea and land, many people live and work near the ocean because of commerce, shipping, fishing, and tourism. A 1995 scientific assessment estimates that about 40% of Earth's population lives within 100 km (62 mi), and 49% within 200 km (145 mi), of coastlines. In Canada, more than 42% of the people live in areas designated as *coastal* (this includes the Great Lakes). Therefore, an understanding of coastal processes and landforms is important to humanity. And because these processes along coastlines often produce dramatic change, they are essential to consider in planning and development. A World Resources Institute study found as much as 50% of the world's coastlines at some risk of loss through such things as erosion, rising sea level, or disruption from pollution.

The ocean is a vast ecosystem, intricately linked to life on the planet and to life-sustaining systems in the atmosphere, the hydrosphere, and the lithosphere. In the recent *Atlas of the Oceans—The Deep Frontier*, Jean-Michel Cousteau on "The Future of the Ocean" states,

> Today, we are coming to better appreciate the extent to which our actions affect an ecosystem—and the people who depend on it—thousands of miles away. The reef fisherman in Fiji is not undone by the local poacher, but by global warming intensified by the driving of a car in downtown Toronto, Canada. Yet these connections are not all bad news. The web of interdependence is built with strands of responsibility and hope. Our ever-expanding ability to communicate across borders and oceans is helping to drive a truly global dialogue about the planet's most pressing environmental challenges.†

In this chapter: We begin the chapter with a brief look at our global oceans and seas—1998 was celebrated as The International Year of the Ocean by all United Nations countries (see **http://www.yoto98.noaa.gov/**). The physical and chemical properties of the sea distinguish it from the waters of the continent. The coastlines are areas of dynamic change and beauty, where oceans and seas confront the land. Coverage includes discussions about tides, waves, coastal erosional and depositional landforms, beaches, barrier islands, and organic processes, including corals, wetlands, salt marshes, and mangroves. A systems framework of specific inputs (components and driving forces), actions (movements and processes), and outputs (results and consequences) organize our discussion of coastal processes. We conclude with a look at the considerable human impact on coastal environments.

Global Oceans and Seas

The ocean is one of Earth's last great scientific frontiers and is of great interest to geographers. Remote sensing from orbit, aircraft, surface vessels, and submersibles is providing a wealth of data and a new capability to understand the oceanic system. The pattern of sea-surface temperatures is presented in Figure 5.11 and ocean currents in Figure 6.22. The world's oceans, their area, volume, and depth, are listed in a table in Figure 7.3. The locations of oceans and major seas are shown and listed alphabetically in Figure 16.1.

*"The Marginal World," in *The Edge of the Sea* by Rachel Carson. © 1955 by Rachel Carson, © renewed 1983 by R. Christie (Boston: Houghton Mifflin), p. 11.

†*Atlas of the Oceans—The Deep Frontier* by Sylvia Earle. © 2001 by National Geographic Society, text © 2001 by Sylvia Earle (Washington: National Geographic Society), p. 171.

Chemical Composition of Seawater

Water is called the "universal solvent," dissolving at least 57 of the 92 elements found in nature. In fact, most natural elements and the compounds they form are found in the seas as dissolved solids, or *solutes*. Thus, seawater is a solution, and the concentration of dissolved solids is called **salinity**.

The ocean remains a remarkably homogeneous mixture. The ratio of individual salts does not change, despite minor fluctuations in overall salinity. In 1874 the British HMS *Challenger* sailed around the world, taking surface and depth measurements and collecting samples of seawater. Analyses of those samples first demonstrated the uniform composition of seawater.

Although ocean chemistry was thought to be fairly constant during the Phanerozoic Eon (the past 542 million years), recent evidence suggests that seawater chemistry has varied over time within a narrow range. The variations are consistent with changes in sea-floor spreading rates, volcanism, and sea level. Evidence is gathered from fluid

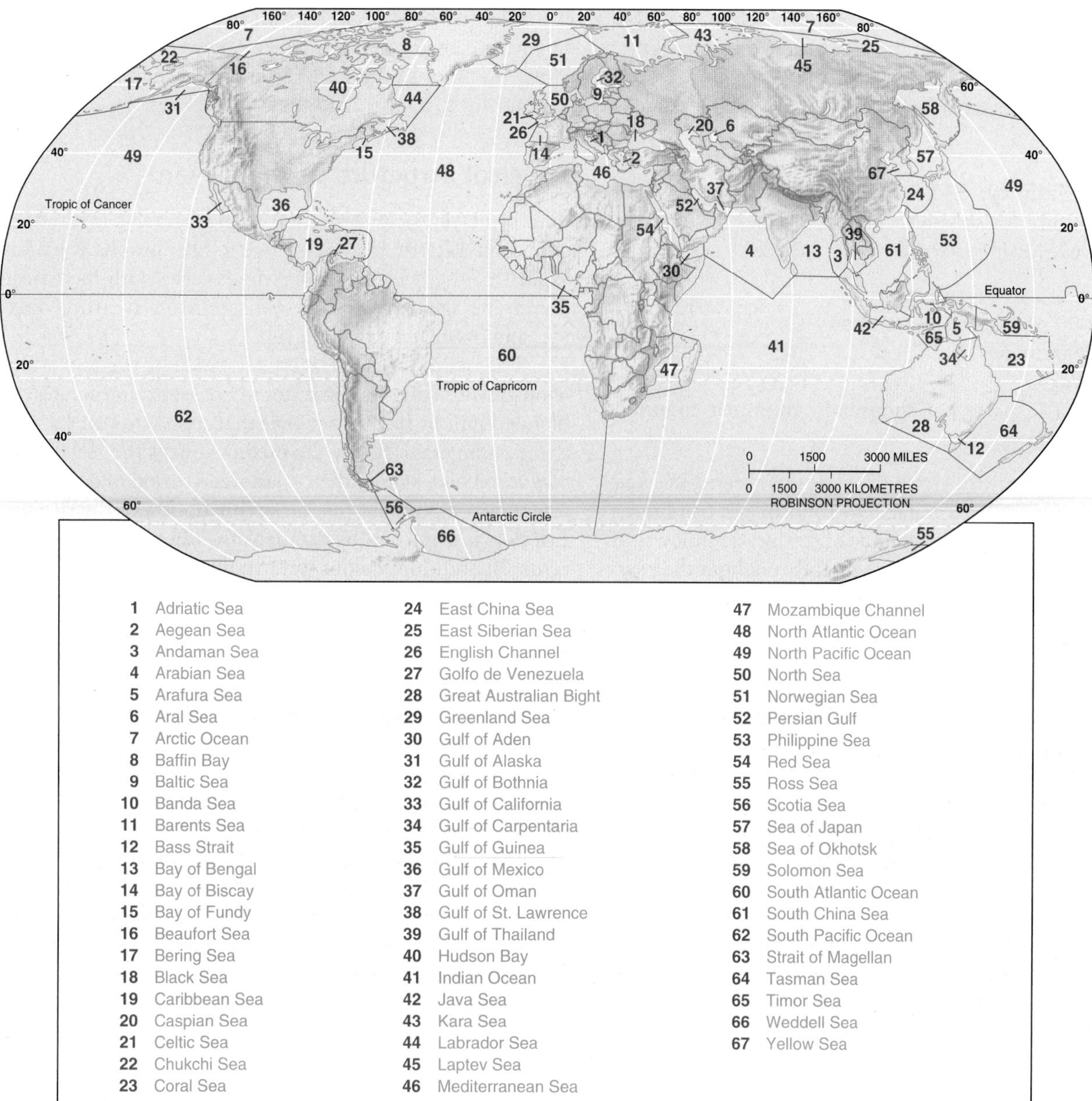

FIGURE 16.1 Principal oceans and seas of the world.
A sea is generally smaller than an ocean and is near a landmass; sometimes the term refers to a large, inland, salty body of water. Match the alphabetized name and number with its location on the map.

inclusions in marine formations such as in limestones and evaporites, which contain ancient seawaters. The ocean reflects conditions in Earth's environment. As an example, the high-latitude oceans are freshening over the past decade in response to the large volume of fresh water coming from glacial ice melt and increased precipitation in response to warmer temperatures, increasing discharge from the Russian rivers that drain into the Arctic Ocean.

Ocean Chemistry Ocean chemistry is a result of complex exchanges among land drainage, seawater, the atmosphere, minerals, bottom sediments, and living organisms. In addition, significant flows of mineral-rich water enter the ocean through hydrothermal (hot water) vents in the ocean floor. (These vents are called "black smokers" for the dense, black mineral-laden water that spews from them. See Figure 11.13b.) The uniformity of seawater results from complementary chemical reactions and continuous mixing—after all, the ocean basins interconnect, and water circulates among them.

Seven elements account for more than 99% of the dissolved solids in seawater. They are (with their ionic form) chlorine (as chloride Cl^-), sodium (as Na^+), magnesium (as Mg^{2+}), sulphur (as sulphate SO_4^{2-}), calcium (as Ca^{2+}), potassium (as K^+), and bromine (as bromide Br^-). Seawater also contains dissolved gases (such as carbon dioxide, nitrogen, and oxygen), suspended and dissolved organic matter, and a multitude of trace elements.

Commercially, only sodium chloride (common table salt), magnesium, and bromine are extracted in any significant amount from the ocean. Future mining of minerals from the seafloor is technically feasible, although it remains uneconomical.

Average Salinity: 35‰ There are several ways to express salinity (dissolved solids by volume) in seawater, using the worldwide average value:

- 3.5% (% parts per hundred)
- 35,000 ppm (parts per million)
- 35,000 mg per litre
- 35 g/kg
- 35‰ (‰ parts per thousand), the most common notation

Salinity worldwide normally varies between 34‰ and 37‰; variations are attributable to atmospheric conditions above the water and to the volume of freshwater inflows. In equatorial water, precipitation is great throughout the year, diluting salinity values to slightly lower than average (34.5‰). In subtropical oceans—where evaporation rates are greatest because of the influence of hot, dry subtropical high-pressure cells—salinity is more concentrated, increasing to 36‰. Figure 16.2 plots the difference between evaporation and precipitation and salinity by latitude to illustrate this slight spatial variability. Can you answer the question in the caption?

The term **brine** is applied to water that exceeds the average of 35‰ salinity. **Brackish** applies to water that is less than 35‰ dissolved salts. In general, oceans are lower in salinity near landmasses because of freshwater runoff and river discharges. Extreme examples include the Baltic Sea (north of Poland and Germany) and the Gulf of Bothnia (between Sweden and Finland), which average 10‰ or less salinity because of heavy freshwater runoff and low evaporation rates.

On the other hand, the Sargasso Sea, within the North Atlantic subtropical gyre, averages 38‰. The Persian Gulf has a salinity of 40‰ as a result of high evaporation rates in a nearly enclosed basin. Deep pockets, or "brine lakes," along the floor of the Red Sea and the Mediterranean Sea register up to a salty 225‰.

Physical Structure of the Ocean

The basic physical structure of the ocean is layered, as shown in Figure 16.3. The figure also graphs four key aspects of the ocean, each of which varies with increasing depth: average temperature, salinity, dissolved carbon dioxide, and dissolved oxygen level.

The ocean's surface layer is warmed by the Sun and is wind-driven. Variations in water temperature and solutes are blended rapidly in a *mixing zone* that represents only 2% of the oceanic mass. Below the mixing zone is the *thermocline transition* zone, a more than 1-km-deep region of decreasing temperature gradient that lacks the motion of the surface. Friction at these depths dampens the effect of surface currents. In addition, colder water temperatures at the lower margin tend to inhibit any convective movements.

From a depth of 1–1.5 km (0.6–0.9 mi) to the ocean floor, temperature and salinity values are quite uniform. Temperatures in this *deep cold zone* are near 0°C (32°F). Water in the deep cold zone does not freeze, however, because of its salinity and intense pressures at those depths; seawater freezes at about –2°C (28.4°F) at the surface. The coldest water is along the bottom, except near the poles, where the coldest water may be near or at the surface. Now let us shift to the edge of the sea and examine Earth's coastlines. (Many scientific activities related to the ocean are coordinated and conducted by the U.S. National Ocean Service. You can find information about these activities at **http://www.nos.noaa.gov/**.)

Coastal System Components

We know that the continents were formed over many millions of years. However, most of Earth's coastlines are

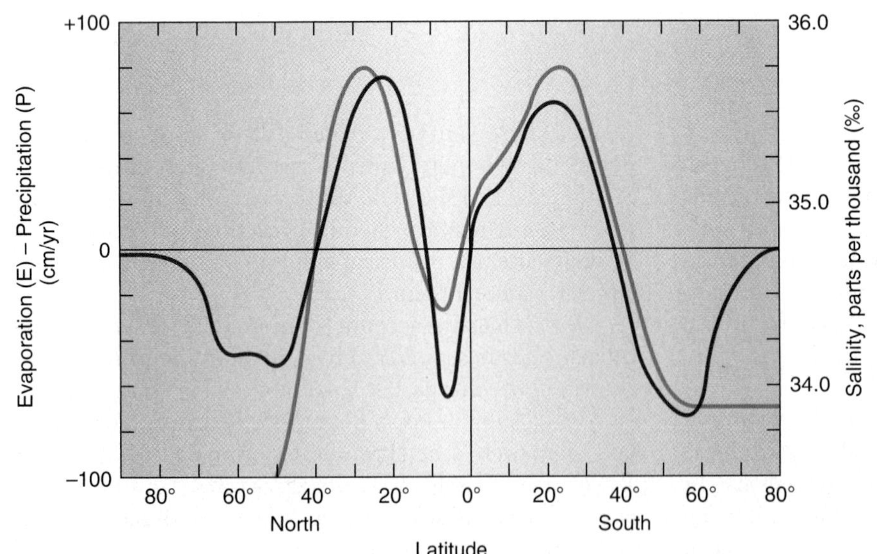

FIGURE 16.2 Variation in ocean salinity by latitude.
Salinity (green line) is principally a function of climatic conditions. Specifically important is the moisture relation expressed by the difference between evaporation and precipitation (E–P) (purple line). Why is salinity higher in the subtropics and lower along the equator? [G. Wüst, 1936.]

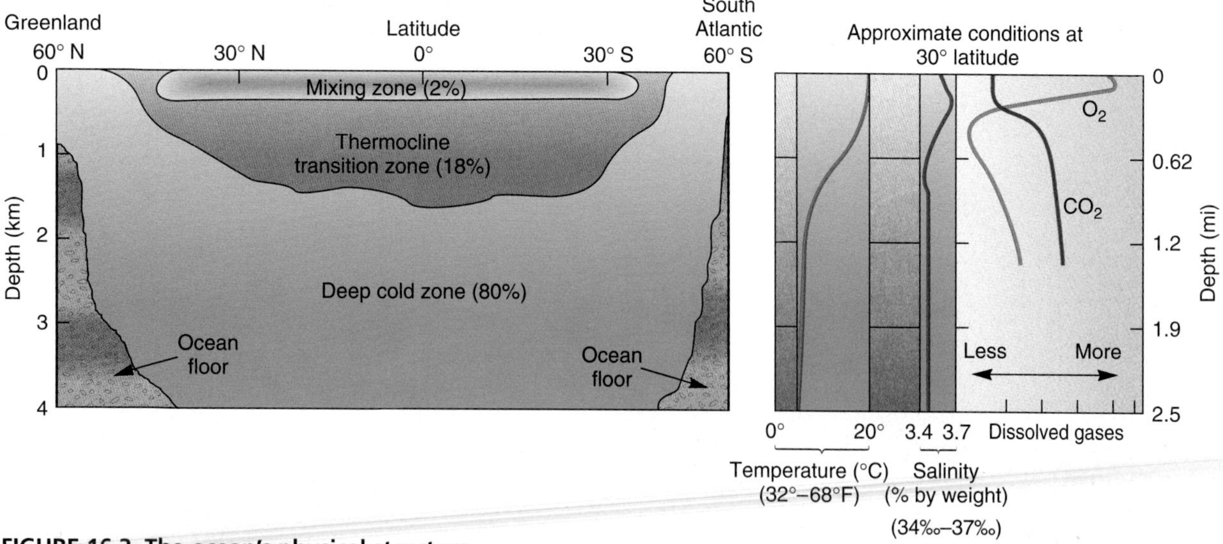

FIGURE 16.3 The ocean's physical structure.
Schematic of average physical structure observed throughout the ocean's vertical profile as sampled along a line from Greenland to the South Atlantic. Temperature, salinity, and dissolved gases are shown plotted by depth.

ANIMATION Midlatitude Productivity

relatively new, existing in their present state as the setting for continuous change. A dynamic equilibrium exists among the energy of waves, tides, wind, and currents, the supply of materials, the slope of the coastal terrain, and the fluctuation of relative sea level. These interactions produce an infinite variety of erosional and depositional features and coastlines of diverse beauty.

Inputs to the Coastal System

Inputs to the coastal environment include many elements we have already discussed:

- *Solar energy* input drives the atmosphere and the hydrosphere. The conversion of insolation to kinetic energy produces prevailing winds, weather systems, and climate.
- *Atmospheric winds*, in turn, generate ocean currents and waves, key inputs to the coastal environment.
- *Climatic regimes*, which result from insolation and moisture, strongly influence coastal geomorphic processes.
- The nature of *coastal rock* is important in determining rates of erosion and sediment production.
- *Human activities* are an increasingly significant input to coastal change.

All of these inputs occur within the ever-present influence of gravity's pull, not only from Earth but also from the Moon and Sun. Gravity provides the potential energy of position for materials in motion and generates the tides.

The Coastal Environment and Sea Level

The coastal environment is called the **littoral zone**, from the Latin word for "shore." Figure 16.4 illustrates the littoral zone and includes specific components discussed later in the chapter. The littoral zone spans some land as well as water. Landward, it extends to the highest water line that occurs on shore during a storm. Seaward, it extends to where water is too deep for storm waves to move sediments on the seafloor—usually around 60 m, or 200 ft, in depth. The specific contact line between the sea and the land is the *shoreline*, although this line shifts with tides, storms, and sea-level adjustments. The *coast* continues inland from high tide to the first major landform change and may include areas considered to be part of the coast in local usage.

Because the level of the ocean varies, the littoral zone naturally shifts position from time to time. A rise in sea level causes submergence of land, whereas a drop in sea level exposes new coastal areas. In addition, uplift and subsidence of the land itself initiates changes in the littoral zone.

Sea level is an important concept. Every elevation you see in an atlas or on a map is referenced to mean sea level. Yet this average sea level changes daily with the tides and over the long term with changes in climate, tectonic plate movements, and glaciation. Thus, *sea level* is a relative term. At present, there exists no international system to determine exact sea level over time. The Global Sea Level Observing System (GLOSS) is an international group actively working on sea level issues. (For copies of their newsletters and other scientific discussion, see **http://www.pol.ac.uk/psmsl/gb.html**. GLOSS is part of the larger Permanent Service for Mean Sea Level, which you can find at **http://www.pol.ac.uk/psmsl/programmes/**.)

Mean sea level (MSL) is a value based on average tidal levels recorded hourly at a given site over many years. MSL varies spatially because of ocean currents and waves, tidal variations, air temperature and pressure differences, ocean temperature variations, slight variations in Earth's gravity, and changes in oceanic volume. Presently sea level is rising at a historical rate related to global climate change. For more information, see News Report 16.1.

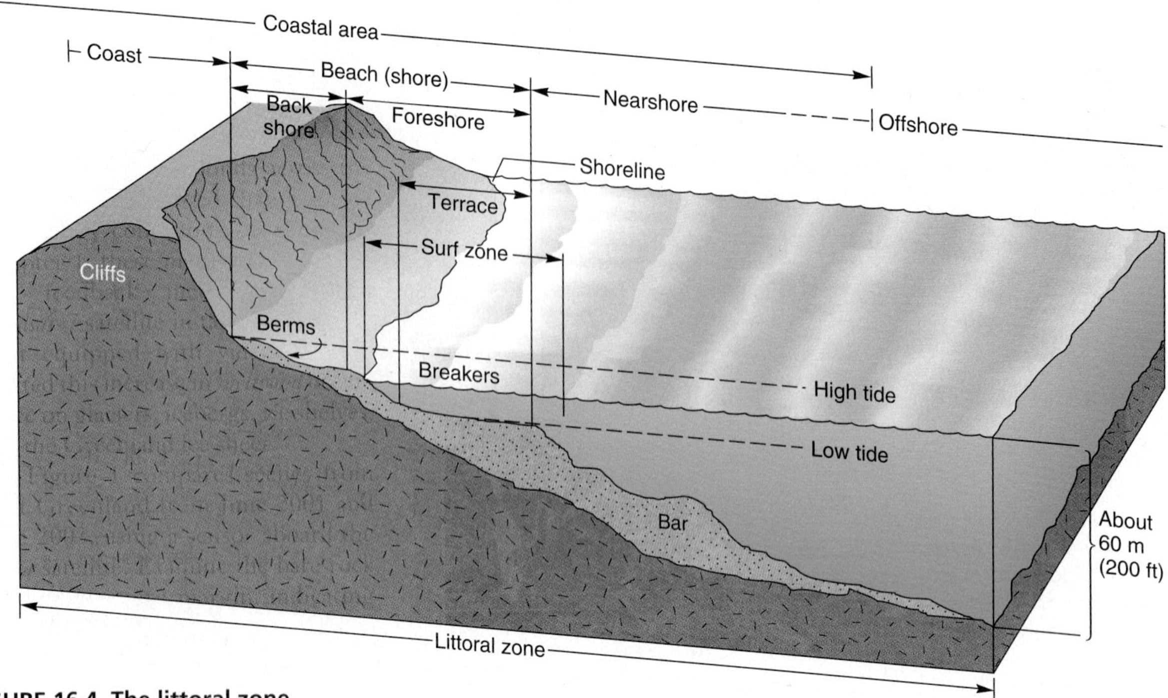

FIGURE 16.4 The littoral zone.
The littoral zone includes the coast, beach, and nearshore environments.

News Report 16.1

Sea Level Variations and the Present MSL Increase

Sea level varies along the full extent of North American shorelines. The mean sea level (MSL) of the U.S. Gulf Coast is about 25 cm (10 in.) higher than that of Florida's east coast, which is the lowest in North America. MSL rises northward along the eastern coast, to 38 cm (15 in.) higher in Maine than in Florida. Along the U.S. western coast, MSL is higher than Florida by about 58 cm (23 in.) in San Diego and by about 86 cm (34 in.) in Oregon.

Overall, North America's Pacific coast MSL averages about 66 cm (26 in.) higher than the Atlantic coast MSL. MSL is affected by differences in ocean currents, air pressure and wind patterns, water density, and water temperature.

Over the long term, sea-level fluctuations expose a range of coastal landforms to tidal and wave processes. As average global temperatures cycle through cold or warm climatic spells, the quantity of ice locked up in the ice sheets of Antarctica and Greenland and in hundreds of mountain glaciers can increase or decrease and result in sea level changes accordingly. At the peak of the most recent Pleistocene glaciation about 18,000 B.P. (years before the present), sea level was about 130 m (430 ft) lower than it is today. On the other hand, if Antarctica and Greenland ever became ice-free (ice sheets fully melted), sea level would rise at least 65 m (215 ft) worldwide.

Just 100 years ago sea level was 38 cm (15 in.) lower along the coast of southern Florida. Venice, Italy, has experienced a rise of 25 cm (10 in.) since 1890. During the last century, sea level rose 10–20 cm (4–8 in.), a rate ten times higher than the average rate during the last 3000 years. The present sea-level rise is spatially uneven; for instance, the rate along the coast of Argentina is nearly ten times the rate along the coast of France.

Given these trends and the predicted climatic change, sea level will continue to rise and be potentially devastating for many coastal locations. A rise of only 0.3 m (1 ft) would cause shorelines worldwide to move inland an average of 30 m (100 ft)! This elevated sea level would inundate some valuable real estate along coastlines worldwide. Some 20,000 km^2 (7800 mi^2) of land along North American shores alone would be drowned, at a staggering loss of $650 billion. A 95-cm (3.1-ft) sea-level rise could inundate 15% of Egypt's arable land, 17% of Bangladesh, and many island nations and communities. However, uncertainty exists in these forecasts, and the pace of the rise should be slow.

In 2001 the Intergovernmental Panel on Climate Change (IPCC, discussed in Chapter 10) forecast global mean sea-level rise for this century, given regional variations, as a range from 0.09 to 0.88 m (3.5 to 34.7 in.). Review the "Global Climate Change" section in Chapter 10 for specific forecasts. Despite any uncertainty, planning should start now along coastlines worldwide because preventive strategies are cheaper than recovery costs from possible destruction. Insurance underwriters have begun the process by refusing coverage for shoreline properties vulnerable to rising sea level.

A recent study completed by a team from Natural Resources Canada, Environment Canada, Dalhousie University, the Centre of Geographic Sciences of the Nova Scotia Community College, the City of Charlottetown, and other partners assessed the physical and socioeconomic impacts of climate change and the potential accelerated sea-level rise on the coast of Prince Edward Island. The study findings estimate the cost associated with flooding of property in Charlottetown at between $190 and $202 million dollars and the value of property lost to erosion on the north shore to be $22,000 per year for cottages to $1100 per year for non-cottage property. These losses result from increased frequency and extent of storm surge flooding in Charlottetown and increased erosion from a decrease in sea ice, an increase in wind energy with the resulting increase in wave energy on the north shore of the province.

The study suggests three levels of adaptation to these changes in the coastal zone that depend upon the type of coastal land use. The first adaptation is shore protection, but because protection is costly and has limited long-term effectiveness, it should only be used to armour structures that are in immediate risk of flooding or erosion. The second adaptation is accommodation through redesign of structures, zoning to prevent costly building in the coastal zone, and efforts to increase natural resilience in the coastal ecosystem. The final adaptation is retreat from the coastal zone through restrictive zoning laws.

At present, the overall North American MSL is calculated at approximately 45 locations along the coastal margins of the continent. These sites are being upgraded with new equipment in the Next Generation Water Level Measurement System, using next-generation tide gauges, specifically along the U.S. and Canadian Atlantic coasts, Bermuda, and the Hawaiian Islands. The *NAVSTAR* satellites that make up the Global Positioning System (GPS) make possible the correlation of data within a network of ground- and ocean-based measurements.

Remote-sensing technology, including the *TOPEX/Poseidon* satellite launched in 1992 and still in service, augments these measurements (see **http://topex-www.jpl.nasa.gov/**). This satellite has two radar altimeters that measure changes in mean sea level at any one location every 10 days between 66° N and 66° S latitudes. These measurements are made to an astonishing precision of 4.2 cm (1.7 in.) (Figure 16.5)! Spectacular *TOPEX/Poseidon* portraits of El Niño and La Niña in the Pacific are in Focus Study 10.1. Another ocean surface topography satellite launched in December 2001, named *Jason-1*, is extending the science of determining mean sea level, ocean topography, and ocean circulation. These satellites tracked the devastating 2004 tsunami (seismic sea wave) across the Indian Ocean.

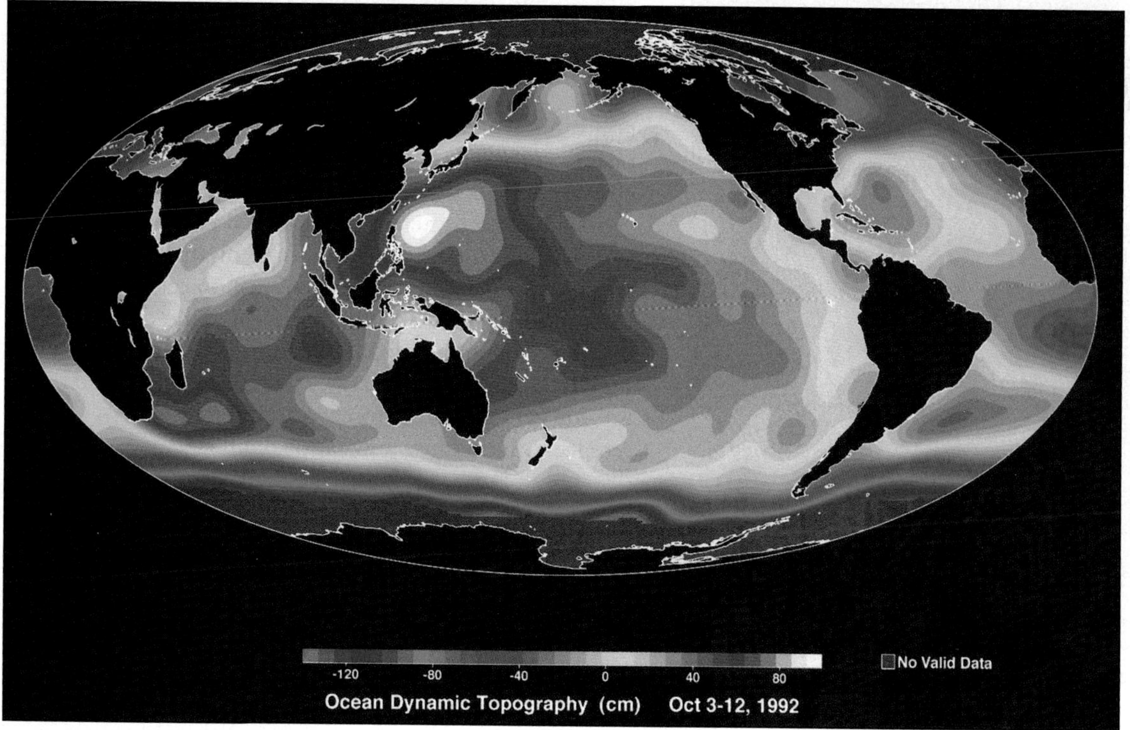

FIGURE 16.5 Ocean topography as revealed by satellite.
Sea-level data recorded by the radar altimeter aboard the *TOPEX/Poseidon* satellite, October 3–12, 1992. The colour scale is given in centimetres above or below Earth's geoid. The overall relief portrayed in the image is about 2 m (6.6 ft). The maximum sea level is in the western Pacific Ocean (white). The minimum is around Antarctica (blue and purple). [Image from JPL and NASA's Goddard Space Flight Center. *TOPEX/Poseidon* is a joint U.S.–French Mission.]

Coastal System Actions

The coastal system is the scene of complex tidal fluctuation, winds, waves, ocean currents, and the occasional impact of storms. These forces shape landforms ranging from gentle beaches to steep cliffs, and they sustain delicate ecosystems.

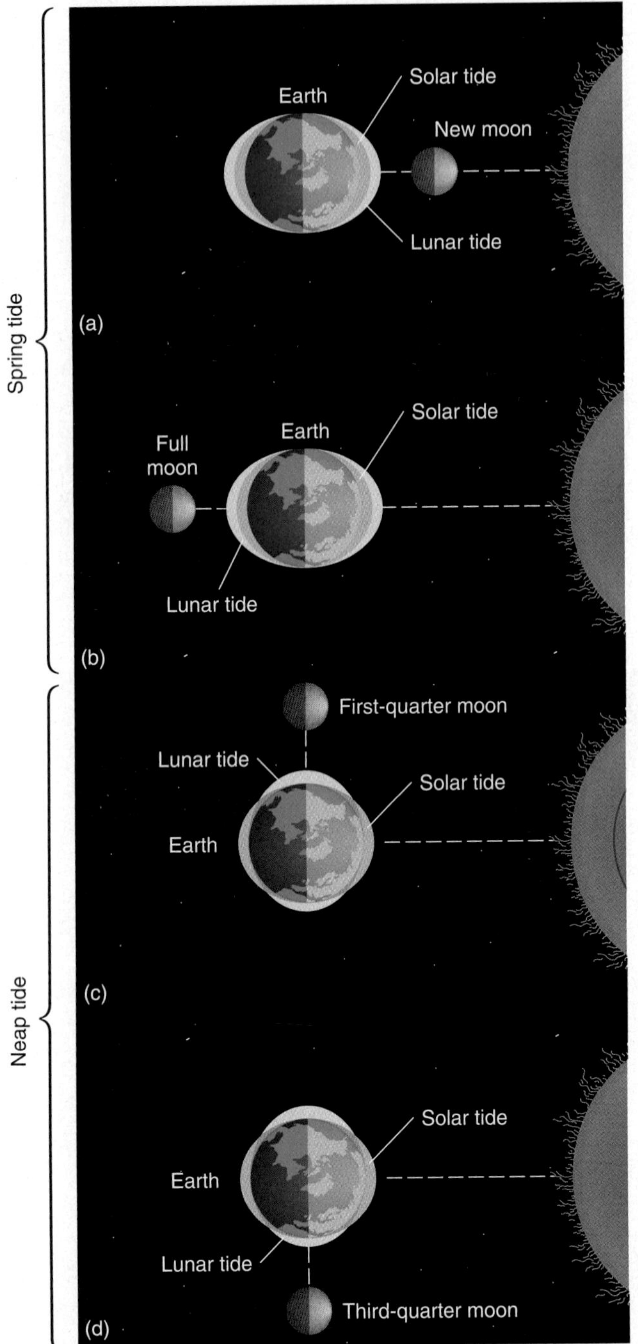

FIGURE 16.6 The cause of tides.
Gravitational relations of Sun, Moon, and Earth combine to produce spring tides (a), (b) and neap tides (c), (d). (Tides are greatly exaggerated for illustration.)

ANIMATION Monthly Tidal Cycles

Tides

Tides are complex daily oscillations in sea level, ranging worldwide from barely noticeable to several metres. They are experienced to varying degrees along every ocean shore around the world. Tidal action is a relentless energy agent for geomorphic change. As tides flood (rise) and ebb (fall), the daily migration of the shoreline landward and seaward causes significant changes that affect sediment erosion, transportation, and deposition.

Tides also are important in human activities, including navigation, fishing, and recreation. Tides are especially important to ships because the entrance to many ports is limited by shallow water, and thus high tide is required for passage. Tall-masted ships may need a low tide to clear overhead bridges. Tides also exist in large lakes, but because the tidal range is small, tides are difficult to distinguish from changes caused by wind. Lake Superior, for instance, has a tidal variation of only about 5 cm (2 in.).

Causes of Tides Tides are produced by the gravitational pull of both the Sun and the Moon. (Earth's astronomical relation to the Sun and the Moon is discussed in Chapter 2.) The Sun's influence is only about half that of the Moon's because of the Sun's greater distance from Earth, although it is a significant force. Figure 16.6 illustrates the relation among the Moon, the Sun, and Earth and the generation of variable tidal bulges on opposite sides of the planet.

The gravitational pull of the Moon tugs on Earth's atmosphere, oceans, and lithosphere. The same is true for the Sun, to a lesser extent. Earth's solid and fluid surfaces all experience some stretching as a result of this gravitational pull. The stretching raises large *tidal bulges* in the atmosphere (which we can't see), smaller tidal bulges in the ocean, and very slight bulges in Earth's rigid crust. Our concern here is the tidal bulges in the ocean.

Gravity and inertia are essential elements in understanding tides. *Gravity* is the force of attraction between two bodies. *Inertia* is the tendency of objects to stay still if motionless or to keep moving in the same direction if in motion. The gravitational effect on the side of Earth facing the Moon or Sun is greater than that experienced by the far side, where inertial forces are slightly greater. This difference exists because gravitational influences decrease with distance. It is this difference in the net force of gravitational attraction and inertia that generates the tides.

Figure 16.6a shows the Moon and the Sun in *conjunction* (lined up with Earth), a position in which the sum of their gravitational forces produces a large tidal bulge. The corresponding tidal bulge on Earth's opposite side is primarily the result of the farside water remaining in position (being left behind) because its inertia exceeds the gravitational pull of the Moon and Sun. In effect, from this inertial point of view, as the nearside water and Earth are drawn toward the Moon and Sun, the farside water is left behind because of the slightly weaker gravitational pull. This arrangement produces the two opposing tidal bulges on opposite sides of Earth.

Tides appear to move in and out along the shoreline, but they do not actually do so. Instead, Earth's surface rotates into and out of the relatively "fixed" tidal bulges as Earth changes its position in relation to the Moon and Sun. Every 24 hours and 50 minutes, any given point on Earth rotates through two bulges as a direct result of this rotational positioning. Thus, every day, most coastal locations experience two high (rising) tides, known as **flood tides**, and two low (falling) tides, known as **ebb tides**. The difference between consecutive high and low tides is considered the *tidal range*.

Spring and Neap Tides The combined gravitational effect of the Sun and Moon is strongest in the conjunction alignment and results in the greatest tidal range between high and low tides, known as **spring tides**. (*Spring* means to "spring forth"; it has no relation to the season of the year.) Figure 16.6b shows the other alignment that gives rise to spring tides, when the Moon and Sun are at *opposition*. In this arrangement, the Moon and Sun cause separate tidal bulges, affecting the water nearest to each of them. In addition, the left-behind water resulting from the pull of the body on the opposite side augments each bulge.

When the Moon and the Sun are neither in conjunction nor in opposition but are more or less in the positions shown in Figure 16.6c and d, their gravitational influences are offset and counteract each other, producing a lesser tidal range known as **neap tide**. (*Neap* means "without the power of advancing.")

Tides also are influenced by other factors, including ocean basin characteristics (size, depth, and topography), latitude, and shoreline shape. These factors cause a great variety of tidal ranges. For example, some locations may experience almost no difference between high and low tides. The highest tides occur when open water is forced into partially enclosed gulfs or bays. The Bay of Fundy in Nova Scotia records the greatest tidal range on Earth, a difference of 16 m (52.5 ft) (Figure 16.7a, b; News Report 16.2). (For more on tides and tide prediction, contact the Scripps Institution of Oceanography library at **http://scilib.ucsd.edu/sio/tide/**.)

Tidal Power The fact that sea level changes daily with the tides suggests an opportunity: Could these predictable flows be harnessed to generate electricity? The answer is yes, given the right conditions. Bays and estuaries tend to focus tidal energy, concentrating it in a smaller area than in the open ocean. This circumstance provides an opportunity to construct a dam with water gates, locks to let ships through, and turbines to generate power.

Only 30 locations in the world are suited for tidal power generation. At present, only three are producing electricity. Two are outside North America—a 4-megawatt-capacity station in Russia in operation since 1968 (at Kislaya-Guba Bay on the White Sea) and a facility in France operating since 1967 (on the Rance River estuary on the Brittany coast). The tides in the Rance estuary fluctuate up to 13 m (43 ft), and power production has been almost continuous there, providing an electrical generating capacity of a moderate 240 megawatts (about 20% of the capacity of Hoover Dam).

The third area is the Bay of Fundy in Nova Scotia, Canada. At one of several favourable sites on the Bay, the Annapolis Tidal Generating Station was built in 1984. Nova Scotia Power Incorporated operates this 20-megawatt plant (Figure 16.7c). According to the Canadian government, tidal power generation at ideal sites is economically competitive with fossil fuel plants.

However, the costs to the ecosystem can be great with the alteration of the tidal channels when dams are installed. *Siltation* of the channel often results. Producing less impact, another form of tidal power is taking form in Norway that involves sea-floor devices that harness the motion of coastal currents. Windmill-like turbines are set in motion by the tides and currents, as are paddle-driven turbines. Electrical production began in 2003.

Waves

Friction between moving air (wind) and the ocean surface generates undulations of water called **waves**. Waves travel in groups, called *wave trains*. Waves vary widely in scale; on a small scale, a moving boat creates a wake of small waves; at a larger scale, storms generate large groups of wave trains. At the extreme is the wind wake produced by the presence of the Hawaiian Islands, traceable westward across the Pacific Ocean surface for 3000 km (1865 mi). The islands disrupt the steady trade winds and produce related surface temperature and wind changes.

A stormy area at sea is called a *generating region* for large wave trains, which radiate outward in all directions. These waves are receiving energy from the wind and are called either *storm waves* or *sea waves*. The ocean is crisscrossed with intricate patterns of waves travelling in all directions. The waves seen along a coast may be the product of a storm centre thousands of kilometres away.

Regular patterns of smooth, rounded waves, called **swells**, are the mature undulations of the open ocean. As waves leave the generating region, wave energy continues to run in these swells, which can range from small ripples to very large flat-crested waves. A wave leaving a deep-water generating region tends to extend its wavelength horizontally for many metres. Tremendous energy occasionally accumulates to form unusually large waves. In April 2005, a 294-m-long ocean liner going to New York, carrying more than 2000 passengers, was struck by a 21-m surprise rogue wave some 400 km off the coast of Georgia; fortunately, all made it to port safely.

As you watch waves in open water, it appears that water is migrating in the direction of wave travel, but only a slight amount of water is actually advancing. It is the *wave energy* that is moving through the flexible medium of water. Water within a wave in the open ocean is simply transferring energy from molecule to molecule in simple cyclic undulations, called *waves of transition* (Figure 16.8, p. 526).

(a) (b) (c) (d)

FIGURE 16.7 Tidal range and tidal power.
Tidal range is great in some bays and estuaries, such as Halls Harbour near the Bay of Fundy at flood tide (a) and ebb tide (b). The flow of water between high and low tide is ideal for turning turbines and generating electricity, as is done at the Annapolis Tidal Generating Station (c), near the Bay of Fundy in Nova Scotia, in operation since 1984. (d) In areas like the north shore of Prince Edward Island, where tidal range is low (about 1 m), the area affected by the change in water level can still be large when the slope of the nearshore is low. The wetted area of sand was covered by water 4 hours before this photograph was taken. [Photos by (a), (b), and (c) Jeff Newbery; (d) Mary-Louise Byrne.]

Individual water particles move forward only slightly, forming a vertically circular pattern.

The diameter of the paths formed by the orbiting water particles decreases with depth. As a deep-ocean wave approaches the shoreline and enters shallower water (10–20 m or 30–65 ft), the orbiting water particles are vertically restricted. This restriction causes more-elliptical, flattened orbits to form near the bottom. This change from circular to elliptical orbits slows the entire wave, although more waves continue arriving. The resultant effects are closer-spaced waves, growing in height and steepness, slowing in forward velocity, with sharper wave crests. As the crest of each wave rises, a point is reached when its height exceeds its vertical stability and the wave falls into a characteristic **breaker**, crashing onto the beach (Figure 16.8b).

In a breaker, the orbital motion of transition gives way to elliptical *waves of translation* in which both energy and water move toward shore. The slope of the shore determines wave style. Generally, plunging breakers indicate a steep bottom profile, whereas spilling breakers indicate a gentle, shallow bottom profile. In some areas, unexpected high waves can arise suddenly. It is a good idea to learn to recognize severe wave conditions before you venture along the shore in these areas. When the backwash of water flows to the ocean from the beach in a concentrated column, usually at a right angle to the line of breakers, it is a *rip current*.

News Report 16.2

Size Matters When It Comes to Tides

On the open sea, the water levels change by about a metre between high and low tide. However, in some parts of the world, the difference between high and low tide can be remarkably larger. For many years, Burncoat Head in the Minas Basin in the Bay of Fundy, Nova Scotia (Figure 1), claimed to have the highest tidal range in the world and the *Guinness Book of World Records* supported the claim. In the late 1990s, the Arctic Québec community of Tasiujaq, Leaf Basin, challenged the claim (Figure 2). In response to the challenge, the Canadian Hydrographic Service (CHS), a government agency responsible for mapping waterways, contracted a company to measure the tide levels at both locations. After a year of monitoring and then modelling the tides in each location—the entire tidal cycle takes 18 years—CHS declared a tie. The difference between Leaf Basin in Ungava Bay (tidal range of 16.8 m) and Burncoat Head (tidal range of 17.0 m) was too small to declare a clear winner. Each community is now recorded on the CHS Web site as having the highest tidal range (**http://www.waterlevels-niveauxdeau.gc.ca/english/FrequentlyAskedQuestions.shtml#plusgrandes**).

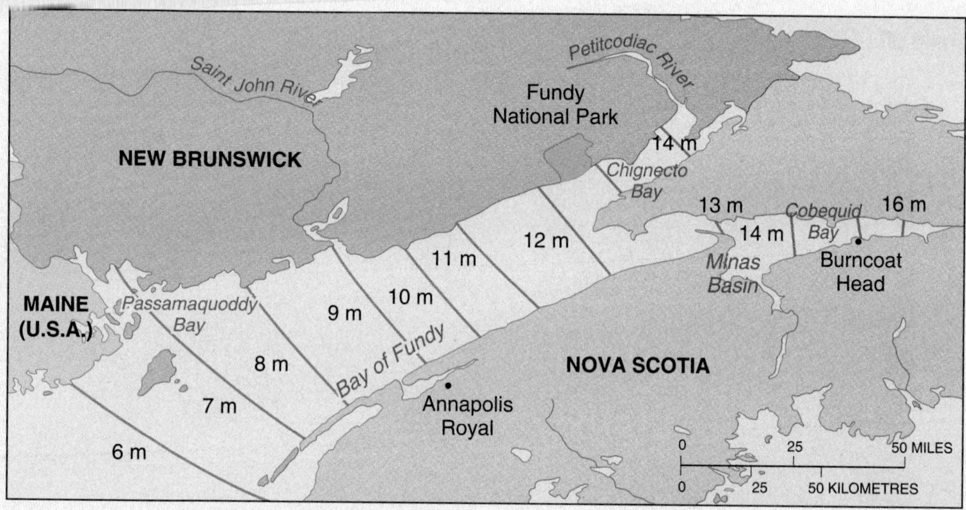

FIGURE 1 Tidal map of the Bay of Fundy.
Tidal waves resonate up the Bay of Fundy, increasing to their maximum at Burncoat Head. The nested funnel shapes of Cobequid Bay, Minas Basin, and the Bay of Fundy act to successively increase the size of the wave. [Map courtesy of The Hopewell Rocks.]

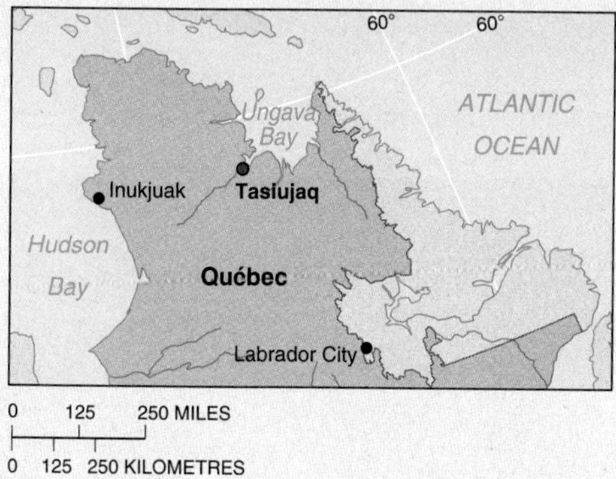

FIGURE 2 Tasiujaq, Leaf Basin, Ungava Bay.
The nested funnel shape of Leaf Basin on Ungava Bay is not as easily seen by the human eye, but the tidal wave resonates up to Tasiujaq to tie as one of the locations with the highest tidal range in the world. [Map adapted from *The Atlas of Canada* © 2004 with the permission of Natural Resources Canada.]

A person caught in one of these can be swept offshore, but usually only a short distance. These brief, short torrents of water can be dangerous (Figure 16.8c).

As various wave trains move along in the open sea, they interact by *interference*. These interfering waves sometimes align so that the wave crests and troughs from one wave train are in phase with those of another. When this in-phase condition occurs, the height of the waves is increased, sometimes dramatically. The resulting "killer waves," "rogue waves," or "sleeper waves" can sweep in unannounced and overtake unsuspecting victims. Signs at Peggy's Cove, Nova Scotia, on the Atlantic coast, and along portions of the California, Oregon, Washington, and British Columbia coastline warn beachcombers to watch for "killer waves." On the other hand, out-of-phase wave trains will dampen wave energy at the shore. When you observe the breakers along a beach, the changing beat of the surf actually is produced by the patterns of *wave interference* that occurred in far-distant areas of the ocean.

Wave Refraction In general, wave action tends to straighten a coastline. Where waves approach an irregular coast, they bend around headlands, which are protruding landforms generally composed of resistant rocks

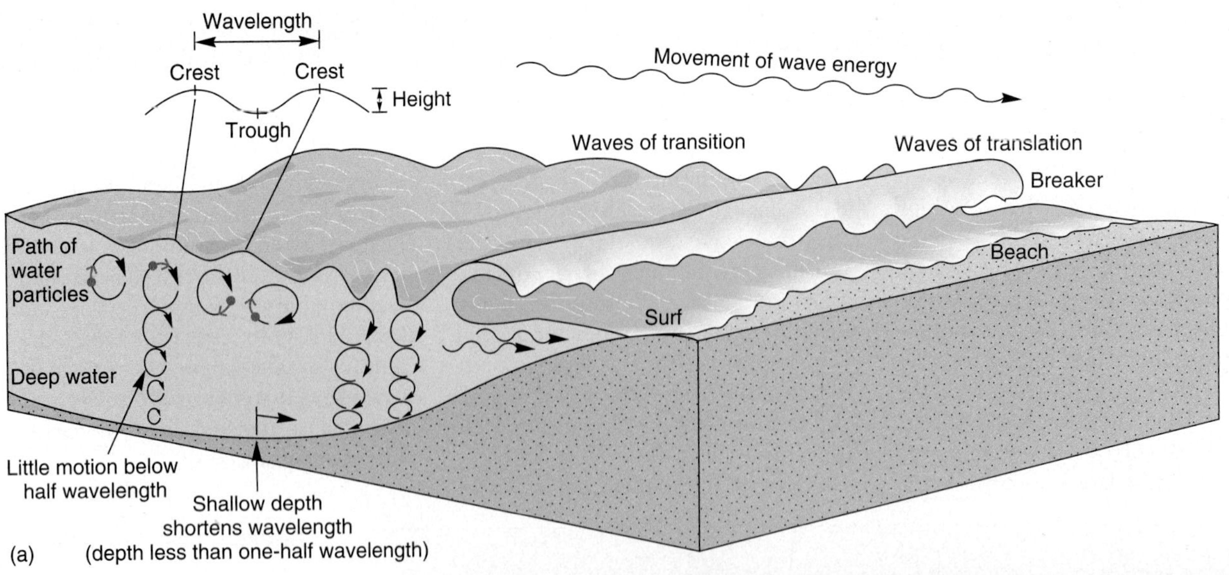

(b)

(c)

(d)

FIGURE 16.8 Wave formation and breakers.
(a) The orbiting tracks of water particles change from circular motions and swells in deep water (waves of transition) to more-elliptical orbits near the bottom in shallow water (waves of translation). (b) Cascades of waves attack the shore along Baja California, Mexico. (c) A dangerous rip current interrupts approaching breakers. Note the churned-up water where the rip current enters the surf. (d) Wave trains on the Gulf of St. Lawrence side of Blooming Point Spit in Prince Edward Island, break in the nearshore, expending energy before reaching the shoreline. [Photos by (b) and inset, and (c) Bobbé Christopherson; (d) Mary-Louise Byrne.]

Wave Motion/ Wave Refraction

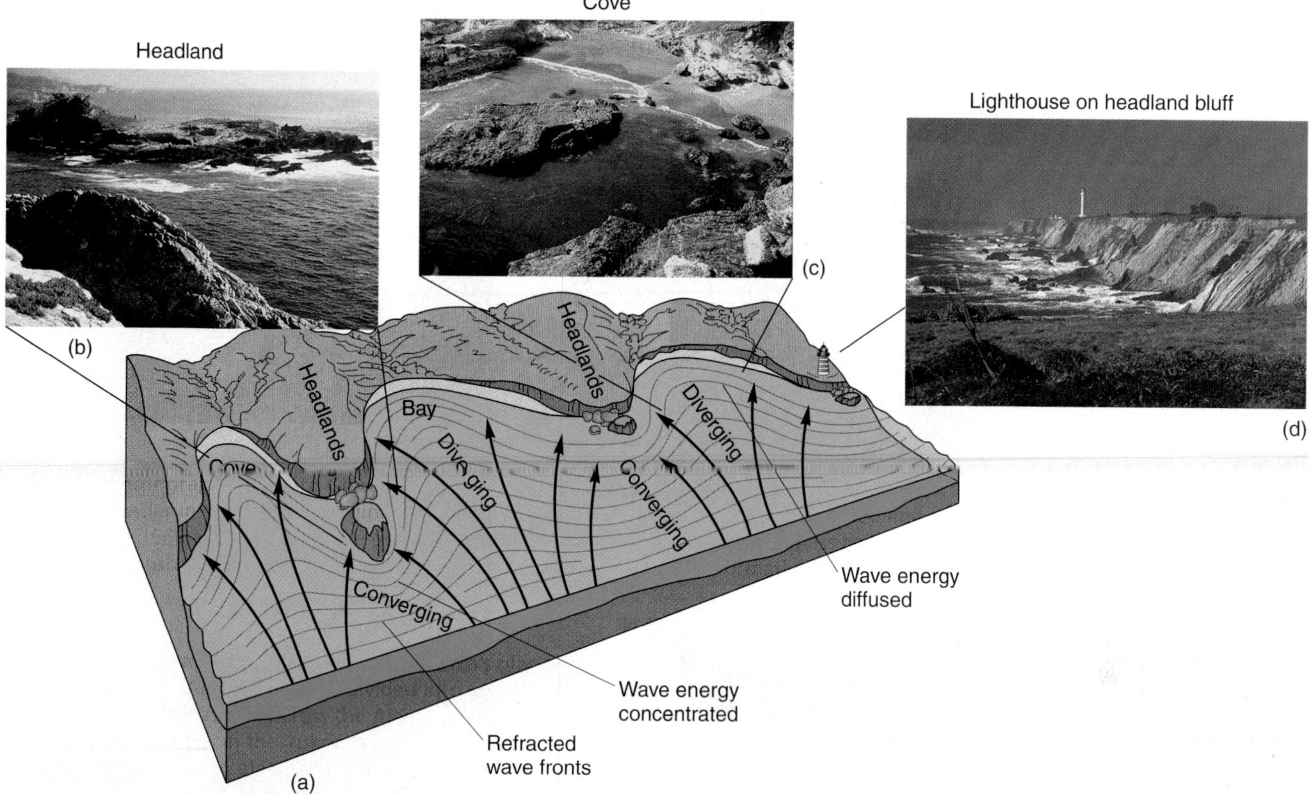

FIGURE 16.9 Coastal straightening.
(a) The process of coastal straightening is brought about by wave refraction. Wave energy is concentrated as it converges on headlands (b) and is diffused as it diverges in coves and bays (c). Headlands are frequent sites for lighthouses such as the light at Point Arena, California (d). [Photos by (b) and (c) Robert W. Christopherson; (d) Bobbé Christopherson.]

(Figure 16.9). The submarine topography refracts (bends) approaching waves. The refracted energy is focused around headlands and dissipates energy in coves, bays, and the submerged coastal valleys between headlands. Thus, headlands receive the brunt of wave attack along a coastline. This **wave refraction** redistributes wave energy so that different sections of the coastline vary in erosion potential, with the long-term effect of straightening the coast.

Figure 16.10 shows waves approaching the coast at an angle, for they usually arrive at some angle other than parallel. As the waves enter shallow water, they are refracted as the shoreline end of the wave slows. The wave portion in deeper water moves faster in comparison, thus producing a current parallel to the coast, zigzagging in the prevalent direction of the incoming waves. This **longshore current**, or *littoral current*, depends on wind direction and wave direction. A longshore current is generated only in the surf zone and works in combination with wave action to transport large amounts of sand, gravel, sediment, and debris along the shore as *longshore drift*, or to use the more comprehensive term, **littoral drift**.

Particles on the beach also are moved along as **beach drift**, shifting back and forth between water and land with each *swash* and *backwash* of surf. Individual sediment grains trace arched paths along the beach. You have perhaps stood on a beach and heard the sound of myriad sand grains and seawater in the backwash of surf. These dislodged materials are available for transport and eventual deposition in coves and inlets and can represent a significant volume.

Tsunami, or Seismic Sea Wave An occasional wave that momentarily but powerfully influences coastlines is the tsunami. **Tsunami** is Japanese for "harbour wave," named for its devastating effect where its energy is focused in harbours. Often tsunami are reported incorrectly as "tidal waves," but they have no relation to the tides. They are formed by sudden, sharp motions in the seafloor, caused by earthquakes, submarine landslides, or eruptions of undersea volcanoes. Thus, they properly are called *seismic sea waves*.

A tsunami typically begins when a large undersea disturbance generates a solitary wave of great wavelength, or sometimes a group of two or three long waves. These waves generally exceed 100 km (60 mi) in wavelength, but they are only a metre or so in height. Because of their great wavelength, tsunami are affected by the topography of the deep-ocean floor and are refracted by rises and ridges. They travel at great speeds in deep-ocean water—velocities of 600 to 800 kmph (375 to 500 mph) are not uncommon—but they often pass unnoticed on the open sea because their great length makes the slow rise and fall of water hard to observe.

As a tsunami approaches a coast, however, the shallow water forces the wavelength to shorten. As a result, the wave

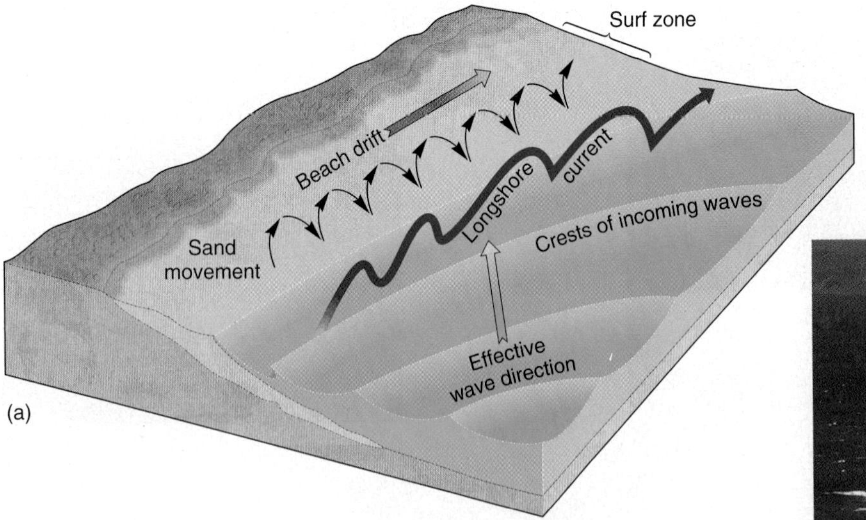

(a)

(b)

(c)

FIGURE 16.10 Longshore current and beach drift. (a) Longshore currents are produced as waves approach the surf zone and shallower water. Longshore and beach drift results as substantial volumes of material are moved along the shore. (b) Processes at work along Point Reyes Beach, Point Reyes National Seashore, California. (c) Shoals in the nearshore area in Prince Edward Island develop through an interaction of the tides and the longshore currents. Over time, with a great enough sediment supply, these may become subaerially exposed. [Photos by (b) Robert W. Christopherson; (c) Mary-Louise Byrne.]

ANIMATION Beach Drift, Coastal Erosion

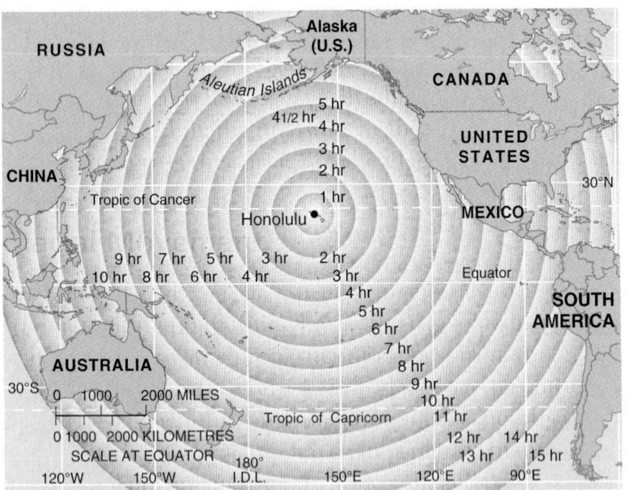

FIGURE 16.11 Tsunami travel times to Honolulu, Hawai'i. [After NOAA.]

height may increase up to 15 m (50 ft) or more. Such a wave has the potential to devastate a coastal area, causing property damage and death. For example, in 1992 the citizens of Casares, Nicaragua, were surprised by a 12-m (39-ft) tsunami that took 270 lives. A 1998 Papua New Guinea tsunami, launched by a massive undersea landslide some 4 km^3 (1 mi^3), killed 2000. During the 20th century, there were 141 damaging tsunami and perhaps 900 smaller ones, with a total death toll of about 70,000. On December 26, 2004, a 9.3 magnitude earthquake struck off the west coast of northern Sumatra, triggering a massive tsunami across the Indian Ocean. Total deaths from the quake and tsunami exceeded 150,000, and a final count may never be known (Figure 16.12).

Hawai'i is vulnerable to tsunami because of its position in the open central Pacific, surrounded by the ring of fire that outlines the Pacific Basin. The U.S. Army Corps of Engineers has reported 41 damaging tsunami in Hawai'i during the past 142 years—statistically, 1 every 3.5 years. Figure 16.11 illustrates tsunami travel times across the Pacific Ocean to Honolulu; for instance, it would take a tsunami 10 hours to reach Hawai'i from the Philippines.

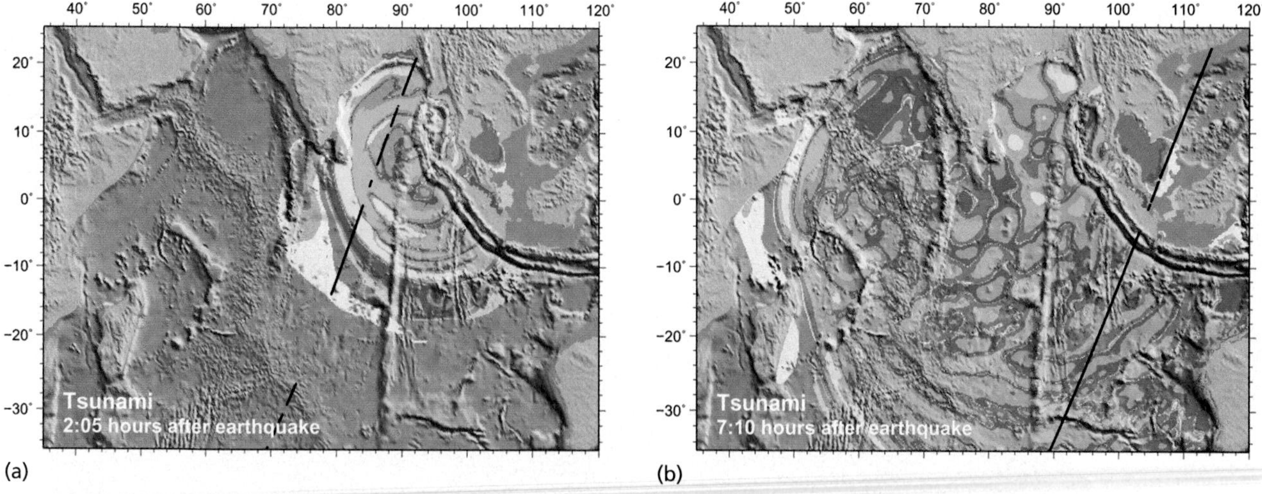

FIGURE 16.12 Satellites track tsunami waves across the Indian Ocean, 2004. (a) A *Jason-1* image 2 hours after the 9.3 earthquake showing wave heights of 60 cm (24 in.) radiating outward from the epicentre off Sumatra. (b) The *GFO*-satellite radar captured the wave patterns 7 hours and 10 minutes after the earthquake. [Images courtesy of NOAA, Laboratory for Satellite Altimetry.]

Because tsunami travel such great distances so quickly and are undetectable in open ocean, accurate forecasts are difficult and occurrences are often unexpected. A warning system now is in operation for nations surrounding the Pacific, where the majority of tsunami occur. A warning is issued whenever seismic stations detect a significant quake under water, where it might generate a tsunami. A new tsunami hazard mitigation network began operating in 2004 with the deployment of six pressure sensors on the ocean floor with accompanying surface buoys—this is the Deep-ocean Assessment and Reporting of Tsunamis (DART). Three instruments are along the Aleutian Islands, south of Alaska, two along the U.S. west coast, and one near the equator off South America.

No warning system was in place in the Indian Ocean as it is in the Pacific Ocean to detect the December 2004 tsunami disaster. NOAA provided images from four Earth-orbiting radar satellites, including *Jason-1*, *GFO* (Geosat Follow-On), *Envisat*, and *TOPEX/Poseidon* that clearly showed the tsunami wave energy travelling across the Indian Ocean (Figure 16.12). The challenge to the world community is to apply this technology so early warnings are possible in all vulnerable oceans, such as the Indian.

Coastal System Outputs

As you can see, coastlines are very active places, with energy and sediment being continuously delivered to a narrow environment. The action of tides, currents, wind, waves, and changing sea level produces a variety of erosional and depositional landforms. We look first at erosional coastlines, then at depositional coastlines.

Erosional Coastal Processes and Landforms

The active margin of the Pacific Ocean along North and South America is a typical erosional coastline. *Erosional coastlines* tend to be rugged, of high relief, and tectonically active, as expected from their association with the leading edge of colliding lithospheric plates (review the plate tectonics discussion in Chapter 11). Figure 16.13 presents features commonly observed along an erosional coast.

Sea cliffs are formed by the undercutting action of the sea. As indentations slowly grow at water level, a sea cliff becomes notched and eventually will collapse and retreat. Other erosional forms evolve along cliff-dominated coastlines, including *sea caves*, *sea arches*, and *sea stacks*. As erosion continues, arches may collapse, leaving isolated stacks in the water (Figure 16.13c; News Report 16.3). Parts of the east coast of Canada, parts of the Great Lakes coastline, and the coasts of southern England and Oregon are prime examples of such erosional landscapes.

The combined effect of wave action, weathering (especially frost action), and several other processes can cut a horizontal bench in the inter-tidal zone, extending from a sea cliff out into the sea. Such a structure is a **wave-cut platform**, or *shore platform* (Figure 16.13e). If the relation between the land and sea level has changed over time, multiple platforms or terraces may rise like stairsteps back from the coast. These marine terraces are remarkable indicators of a changing relation between the land and sea, with some terraces more than 370 m (1200 ft) above sea level. A tectonically active region, such as the California coast, has many examples of multiple shore platforms, which at times can be unstable and vulnerable to failure (Figure 16.13d).

Depositional Coastal Processes and Landforms

Depositional coasts generally are located along land of gentle relief, where sediments from many sources are available. Such is the case in parts of Atlantic Canada and the Atlantic and Gulf coastal plains of the United States, which lie along the relatively passive, trailing edge of the North

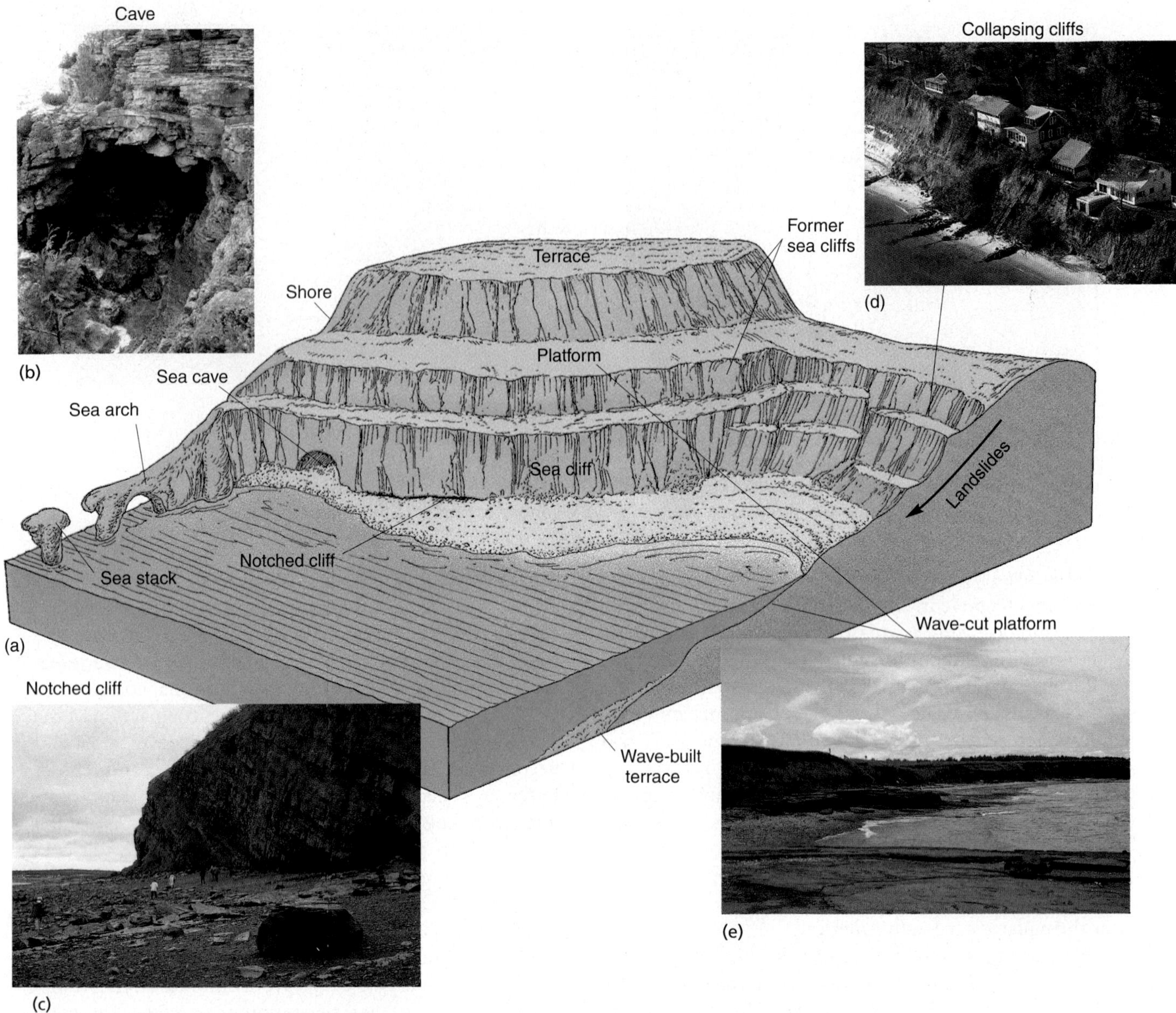

FIGURE 16.13 Erosional coastal features.
(a) Characteristic coastal erosional landforms: caves, arches. (b) Cave known as The Grotto, Bruce Peninsula National Park. (c) Notched cliffs at Joggins, Nova Scotia. (d) Collapsing cliffs. (e) Wave-cut platform, or shore platform, cut into soft sandstone of Les Îles de la Madeleine, Québec. [Photos by (b), (c), and (e) Mary-Louise Byrne; (d) Lowell Georgia/Photo Researchers, Inc.]

American lithospheric plate. Erosional processes and inundation, particularly during storm activity, influence depositional coasts.

Sediment budgets are important considerations for depositional coastlines. A sediment budget is a calculation of the flow of sediment within the coastal system. It accounts for sediment sources, sinks, and transport pathways. In locations where the sediment budget is positive, there is more sediment coming into the area than leaving. In areas where sediment budget is negative, more sediment leaves an area than comes in. Depositional coastlines have a positive sediment budget. Sediment budget is calculated for an area based on the *littoral cell*—a self-contained shoreline system that has no movement of sediment across its boundaries. The longshore limits of the cell are defined by natural formations or artificial barriers where net sediment movement changes direction or becomes zero. Littoral cells usually contain littoral drift that moves in a more or less continuous direction, with some variation due to local or temporal shifts in wind and current directions. The direction of sediment movement in a littoral cell determines the growth of depositional features.

Figure 16.14 illustrates characteristic landforms deposited by waves and currents. One notable deposition landform is the **barrier spit**, which consists of material deposited in a long ridge extending out from a coast. It partially crosses and blocks the mouth of a bay. Classic examples of a barrier spit include Cavendish Spit, Prince Edward

News Report 16.3

Elephant Rock Collapses

In the 1980s, coastal erosion of the soft sandstone of Prince Edward Island carved out the arch that created Elephant Rock. The coastal feature resembled an elephant with its trunk in the sea (Figure 1). A photograph of the landform appeared in a tourism guide and the stack and arch became one of the most visited and photographed natural features on Prince Edward Island. The forces that created the elephant also led to its demise. In December 1998, a particularly harsh storm knocked the trunk off this elephant sculpture (Figure 2). Promoters of the island's shoreline beauty search for a new rock to highlight the wonders of coastal dynamics; however, through physical geography we see this as still a place to visit and experience Earth's systems in action.

FIGURE 1 Elephant Rock, Prince Edward Island. Waves, tides, and currents have sculpted the red sandstone of Prince Edward Island and differential erosion created this elephant shaped rock, a coastal tourist attraction since the 1980s. [Photo by Aggie Gaudet.]

FIGURE 2 Elephant Rock collapsed. Processes that created the tourist attraction on the coast of the island eventually caused its demise when the trunk eroded through and collapsed into the surf. [Photo by Aggie Gaudet.]

Island, and Cape Cod, Massachusetts. The Little Sur River in California (Figure 16.14a) and North Rustico Harbour Inlet in Prince Edward Island (Figure 16.14b) have barrier spits forming partway across the mouths of a river and a bay.

If a spit grows to completely cut off the bay from the ocean and form an inland lagoon, it is called a **bay barrier**, or *baymouth bar*. Spits and barriers are made up of materials that have been eroded and transported by *littoral drift* (beach and longshore drift combined). For much sediment to accumulate, offshore currents must be weak; strong currents carry material away before it can be deposited. Tidal flats and salt marshes are characteristic low-relief features wherever tidal influence is greater than wave action. If these deposits completely cut off the bay from the ocean, an inland **lagoon** is formed.

A **tombolo** occurs when sediment deposits connect the shoreline with an offshore island or sea stack (Figure 16.13c). The tombolo forms when sediments accumulate on an underwater wave-built terrace. High Latitude Connection 16.1 examines isostatic rebound of the crust, causing such shoreline features to rise in relation to sea level.

Beaches Of all the features associated with a depositional coastline, beaches probably are the most familiar. Beaches vary in type and permanence, especially along coastlines dominated by wave action. Technically, a **beach** is that place along a coast where sediment is in motion, deposited by waves and currents. Material from the land temporarily resides on the beach while it is in active transit along the shore. You may have experienced a beach at some time, along a sea coast, a lake shore, or even a stream. Perhaps you have even built your own "landforms" in the sand, only to see them washed away by the waves: a lesson in erosion.

On average, the beach zone spans from about 5 m (16 ft) above high tide to 10 m (33 ft) below low tide (see Figure 16.4). However, the specific definition varies greatly along individual shorelines. Worldwide, quartz (SiO_2) dominates beach sands because it resists weathering and therefore remains after other minerals are removed. In volcanic areas, beaches are derived from weathered and eroded fragments of volcanic rock. Hawai'i and Iceland, for example, feature some black-sand beaches.

Many beaches, such as those in southern France and western Italy, lack sand and are composed of pebbles and cobbles—a type of *shingle beach*. Some shores have no beaches at all; scrambling across boulders and rocks may be the only way to move along the coast. The coasts of Maine and portions of Canada's Atlantic provinces are classic examples. These coasts, composed of resistant granite rock, are scenically rugged and have few beaches.

FIGURE 16.14 Depositional coastal features.
Characteristic coastal depositional landforms: beaches, spits, barriers, lagoons, and tombolos. (a) The Little Sur River enters the Pacific Ocean, a barrier spit nearly blocks its way. (b) Barrier spit forming across the North Rustico Harbour, north shore Prince Edward Island. (c) A tombolo at Point Sur along the central California coast, where sediment deposits connect the shore with an island. [Photos by (a) and (c) Bobbé Christopherson; (b) Mary-Louise Byrne.]

High Latitude Connection 16.1

A Rebounding Shoreline and Coastal Features

We learned in Chapter 11, Figure 11.5, that the lighter crust rests on denser materials beneath—the principle of buoyancy applies. Where the load is greater, owing to glaciers, sediment, or mountains, the crust tends to sink, or ride lower. When a glacier melts, for instance, the crust rides higher with the decreased load, in a recovery uplift known as *isostatic rebound*. Thus, the entire crust is in a constant state of compensating adjustment.

As Earth systems came out of the last ice age and the massive glaciers and continental ice retreated, the unburdened crust began its rebound, or *post-glacial uplift*. The last continental ice retreated about 6000 years ago. The floor of Hudson Bay, for example, is rising about 15 mm a year. Recently, as we see in Chapter 17, southeastern Alaska has been experiencing an accelerated rise beyond the post-glacial uplift associated with the last ice age—a rebound rate of 36 mm/year discussed in Chapter 11. This new uplift is thought to be a result of the substantial losses of glacial ice related to increasing temperatures across Alaska.

In the Svalbard Archipelago in the Arctic Ocean north of Norway, along Duve Fjord on Nordaustlandet Island, the land is rising at approximately 2.5 m (8.3 ft) per century. Figure 1 shows landscape features caused by this phenomenon. The former shoreline appears in successive terraces. Where a depositional tombolo had formed, the neck of land connecting to the offshore island is now stranded above sea level (Figure 1b), marked with raised shorelines where former beaches were active.

(a)

(b)

FIGURE 1 A rebounding coast.
Along Duve Fjord, Nordaustlandet Island, Arctic Ocean: (a) Each curved terrace of cobbles along this coast is a former shoreline, formed as the island isostatically rebounded following the retreat of the glaciers. (b) A raised tombolo on the uplifting coast. [Photos by Bobbé Christopherson.]

A beach acts to stabilize a shoreline by absorbing wave energy, as is evident by the amount of material that is in almost constant motion (see "sand movement" in Figure 16.10). Some beaches are stable. Others cycle seasonally: They accumulate during fair weather, are moved offshore by waves during stormy weather, form a submerged bar, and are redeposited onshore during the next fair weather period. Protected areas along a coastline tend to accumulate sediment, which can lead to large coastal sand dunes. Prevailing winds often drag such coastal dunes inland, sometimes burying trees and highways.

Maintaining Beaches Changes in coastal sediment transport can fight against human activities—beaches are lost, harbours are closed, and coastal highways and beach houses can be inundated with sediment. Thus, people use various strategies to interrupt longshore drift and beach drift. The goal is either to halt sand accumulation or to force accumulation in a desired way through construction of engineered structures, called "hard" shoreline protection.

Figure 16.15 illustrates common approaches: a *jetty* to block material from harbour entrances, a *groyne* to slow drift action along the coast, and a *breakwater* to create a zone of still water near the coastline. However, interrupting the littoral drift that is the natural replenishment for beaches may lead to unwanted changes in sediment distribution downcurrent. Careful planning and impact assessment should be part of any strategy for preserving or altering a beach.

Beach nourishment refers to the artificial replacement of sand along a beach. Through such efforts, a beach that normally experiences a net loss of sediment will instead show a net gain. Years of human effort and expense to build beaches can be erased by a single storm, as occurred when Hurricane Camille completely eliminated offshore islands along the Gulf Coast in 1969, or in 2004 when Hurricanes Charley, Frances, Ivan, and Jeanne devastated coastal Florida beaches and barrier islands.

Barrier Formations Barrier chains are long, narrow, depositional features, generally of sand, that form offshore roughly parallel to the coast. Common forms are **barrier beaches**, or the broader, more extensive landform, **barrier islands**. Tidal variation in the area usually is moderate to low, with adequate sediment supplies coming from nearby coastal plains. Figure 16.16 illustrates the many features of barrier chains, using North Carolina's famed Outer Banks as an example, including Cape Hatteras, across Pamlico Sound from the mainland. The area presently is designated as one of three national seashore reserves supervised by the National Park Service.

On the landward side of a barrier formation are tidal flats, marshes, swamps, lagoons, coastal dunes, and beaches, visible in Figure 16.16. Barrier beaches appear to adjust to sea level and may naturally shift position from time to time in response to wave action and longshore currents. A break in a barrier forms an inlet that connects a bay with the ocean. The name *barrier* is appropriate, for these formations take the brunt of storm energy and actually shield the mainland.

Because of the continuing loss to a barrier island, the famous Cape Hatteras lighthouse was moved inland in 1999 to safer ground (Figure 16.16c). Its new position is about 488 m (1600 ft) from the ocean, or approximately the distance it was in 1870 when it was built—that much sand was lost back to the sea. (See **http://www.ncsu.edu/coast/chl/** for details of the extraordinary effort to save this landmark.)

Vulnerable settlements fill the Outer Banks and Cape Hatteras and are repeatedly slammed by tropical storms (Hurricanes Emily, 1993, Dennis, Floyd, and Irene, 1999, and Isabel in 2003) causing damage and beach erosion. And

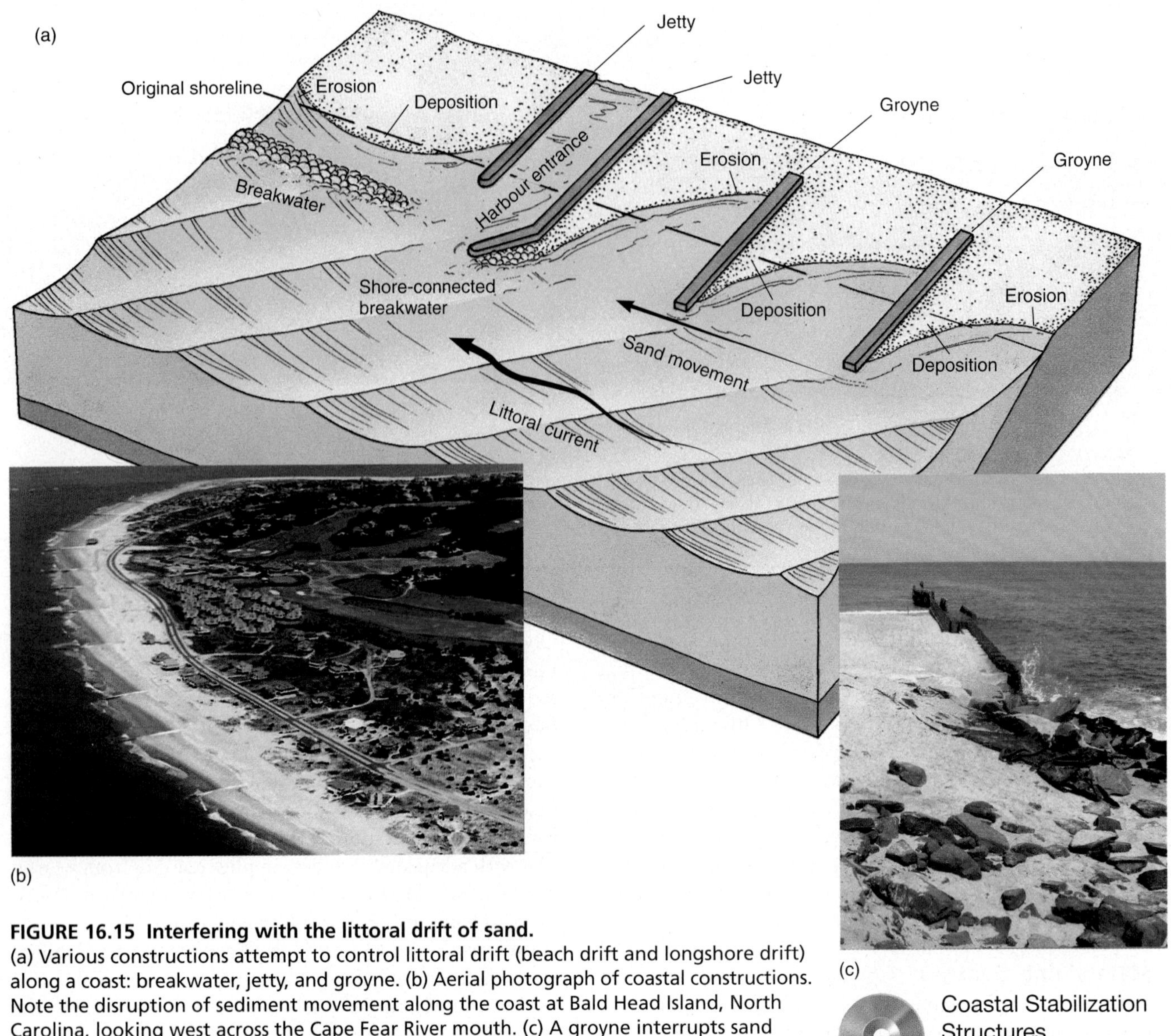

FIGURE 16.15 Interfering with the littoral drift of sand.
(a) Various constructions attempt to control littoral drift (beach drift and longshore drift) along a coast: breakwater, jetty, and groyne. (b) Aerial photograph of coastal constructions. Note the disruption of sediment movement along the coast at Bald Head Island, North Carolina, looking west across the Cape Fear River mouth. (c) A groyne interrupts sand transport along a coast. [Photos by (b) Robert H. Goslee; (c) Bobbé Christopherson.]

ANIMATION Coastal Stabilization Structures

previous damage is visible, such as the salt-spray burned vegetation from Hurricane Dennis (Figure 16.16e).

Barrier beaches and islands are quite common worldwide, lying offshore of nearly 10% of Earth's coastlines. Examples are found offshore of Africa, India's eastern coast, Sri Lanka, Australia, Alaska's northern slope, and the shores of the Baltic and Mediterranean Seas. Earth's most extensive chain of barrier islands is along the U.S. Atlantic and Gulf Coast, extending some 5000 km (3100 mi) from Long Island to Texas and Mexico.

Barrier Island Origin and Hazards Various hypotheses have been proposed to explain the formation of barrier islands. They may begin as offshore bars or low ridges of submerged sediment near shore and then gradually migrate toward shore as sea level rises.

Because many barrier islands seem to be migrating landward, they are an unwise choice for homesites or commercial buildings. Nonetheless, they are a common choice, even though they take the brunt of storm energy. The hazard represented by the settlement of barrier islands was made graphically clear when Hurricane Hugo assaulted South Carolina in 1989.

In the Charleston area, Hugo swept away beachfront houses, barrier-island developments, and millions of metric tons of sand; the hurricane destroyed up to 95% of the single-family homes in one community. The southern portion of one island was torn away. With increased development and continuing real estate appreciation, each future storm can be expected to cause ever-increasing capital losses.

The barrier islands off the Louisiana shore are disappearing at rates approaching 20 m (65 ft) per year. Hurricanes have taken their toll on these barrier islands. Also, they are affected by subsidence through compaction of Mississippi delta sediments and a changing sea level that

FIGURE 16.16 Barrier island chain.
(a) *Landsat* image of barrier island chain along the North Carolina coast. You can see key depositional forms: spit, island, beach, lagoon, and inlet. A sound is a large inlet of the ocean; Pamlico Sound forms an ideal example. (b) View of Cape Hatteras lighthouse at its old location illustrates the narrow strand of sand that stands between the ocean and the mainland. (c) The path, partially a parking lot, along which the Cape Hatteras lighthouse was moved inland in 1999 to safer ground. (d) Construction continues along Hatteras and the Outer Banks ocean front despite the great risk. (e) Salt spray from Hurricane Dennis "burned" these trees south of the lighthouse. [(a) *Terra* MODIS image courtesy of NASA/GSFC; all photos by Bobbé Christopherson.]

is rising at 1 cm (0.4 in.) per year in the region. Hurricane Andrew eroded much sand from these barrier islands in 1992. In 1998, Hurricane Georges destroyed large tracts of the Chandeleur Islands (30 to 40 km, 19 to 25 mi, from the Louisiana and Mississippi Gulf Coast), leaving the mainland with reduced protection (Figure 16.17). The regional office of the USGS predicts that in a few decades the barrier islands may be gone. Louisiana's increasingly exposed

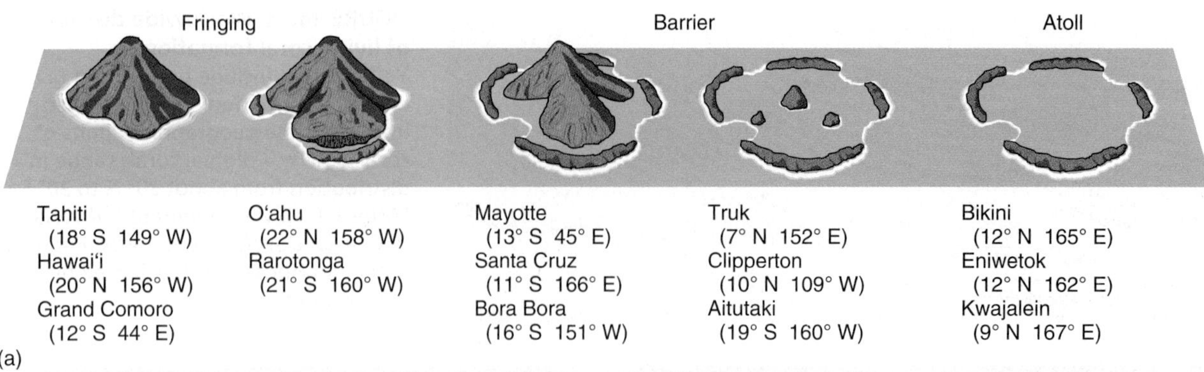

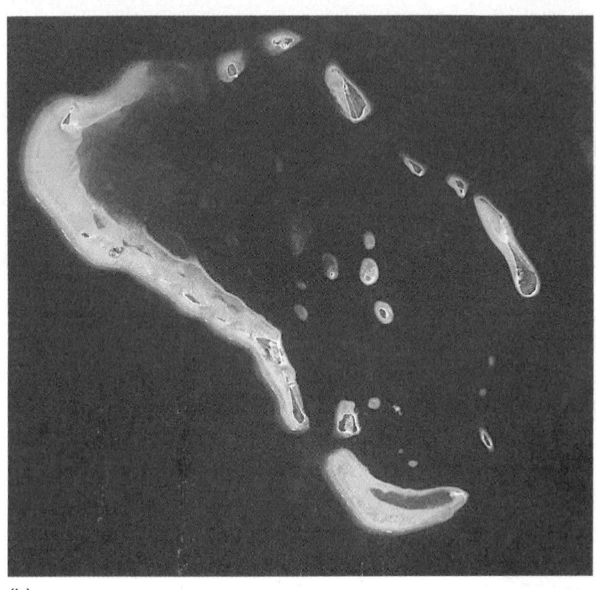

(b)

(c)

(d)

FIGURE 16.19 Coral forms.
(a) Common coral formations in a sequence of reef growth formed around a subsiding volcanic island: fringing reefs, barrier reefs, and an atoll. (b) Satellite image of a portion of the Maldive Islands, in the Indian Ocean (5° N 75° E). (c) Aerial photograph of the atolls in Bora Bora, Society Islands (16° S 152° W). (d) The Bahamas are the largest fringing reef in the world. The lighter areas feature ocean depths to 10 m (33 ft). The darker blues indicate depths dropping off to 4000 m (13,100 ft). The name Bahamas is from the Spanish *baja mar*, for "shallow sea." [(a) After D. R. Stoddart, *The Geographical Magazine* 63 (1971): 610; (b) *Landsat-7* image courtesy of NASA; (c) photo by Harvey Lloyd/Stock market; (d) *Terra* MODIS sensor image courtesy of NASA/GSFC and MODIS Land Response Team, April, 18, 2000.]

Wetlands, Salt Marshes, and Mangrove Swamps

Some coastal areas have great *biological productivity* (plant growth, spawning grounds for fish, shellfish, and other organisms) stemming from trapped organic matter and sediments. For instance, tidal salt marshes can greatly outproduce a wheat field in raw vegetation per hectare. Thus, coastal marshes can support rich wildlife habitats. Unfortunately, these wetland ecosystems are quite fragile and are threatened by human development.

Wetland soils are dominated by *hydrophytic vegetation* (plants that grow in water or tolerate very wet soil). Geographically, **wetlands** occur not only along coastlines, but as peatlands (bogs and mires) extending across large reaches of boreal Canada and the U.S., potholes in the prairie regions, treed swamps in river bottomlands and floodplains, and as permafrost marshes in arctic and subarctic environments.

Coastal Wetlands

Coastal wetlands are of two general types—salt marshes and mangrove swamps. In the Northern Hemisphere,

FIGURE 16.20 Coastal salt marsh.
Salt marshes are productive ecosystems commonly occurring poleward of 30° latitude in both hemispheres. This is Gearheart Marsh, part of the Arcata Marsh system on the Pacific Coast in northern California. [Photo by Bobbé Christopherson.]

salt marshes tend to form north of the 30th parallel, whereas **mangrove swamps** form equatorward of that line. This distribution is dictated by the occurrence of freezing conditions, which control the survival of mangrove seedlings. Roughly the same latitudinal limits apply in the Southern Hemisphere.

Salt marshes usually form in estuaries and behind barrier beaches and spits. An accumulation of mud produces a site for the growth of *halophytic* (salt-tolerant) plants. This vegetation then traps additional alluvial sediments and adds to the salt marsh area. Because salt marshes are in the inter-tidal zone (between the farthest reaches of high and low tides), sinuous, branching channels are produced as tidal waters flood into and ebb from the marsh (Figure 16.20).

(a)

(b)

(c)

FIGURE 16.21 Mangroves.
Mangroves tend to grow equatorward of 30° latitude. (a) Mangroves along the East Alligator River (12° S latitude) in Kakadu National Park, Northern Territory, Australia. (b) Mangroves retain sediments and can form anchors for island formations, such as Aldabra Island (9° S), Seychelles. (c) Mangroves in the Florida Keys. [Photos by (a) Belinda Wright/ DRK Photo; (b) Wolfgang Kaehler Photography; (c) Robert W. Christopherson.]

Applied Physical Geography *(continued)*

Table 1 Sediment Gains and Losses—High Hinterland Coast

Potential Gains	(10^3 m^3/yr)	Potential Losses	(10^3 m^3/yr)
Longshore in	140	Longshore out	240
Beach erosion	0	Beach accretion	5
Rivers	230	Dune accretion and overwash	135
Cliff erosion	45	Inlets	0
Total	415	Total	380
Offshore in	0	Offshore out	35

TABLE 1 Sediment gains and losses—high hinterland coast. There are greater potential gains than losses of sediment in this environment. Although there are large amounts of sediment moved out of this cell by longshore processes, cliff erosion and rivers carry more sediment in than is lost. [Table by Mary-Louise Byrne and Brian McCann.]

Table 2 Sediment Gains and Losses—Low Hinterland Coast

Potential Gains	(10^3 m^3/yr)	Potential Losses	(10^3 m^3/yr)
Longshore in	120	Longshore out	90
Beach erosion	195	Beach accretion	0
Rivers	0	Dune accretion and overwash	165
Cliff erosion	0	Inlets	215
Total	315	Total	470
Offshore in	155	Offshore out	0

TABLE 2 Sediment gains and losses—low hinterland coast. There are more potential losses than gains in this environment through coastal processes. Large amounts of sediment are brought into the system through the inlets. This volume of sediment is deposited in the lagoon and represents a loss. Over time, the barriers will maintain their shape, but be driven landward by wave action. [Table by Mary-Louise Byrne and Brian McCann.]

Summary and Review—The Oceans, Coastal Processes, and Landforms

● *Describe* the chemical composition of seawater and the physical structure of the ocean.

Water is called the "universal solvent," dissolving at least 57 of the 92 elements found in nature. Most natural elements and the compounds they form are found in the seas as dissolved solids. Seawater is a solution, and the concentration of dissolved solids is called **salinity**. **Brine** exceeds the average 35‰ (parts per thousand) salinity; **brackish** applies to water that is less than 35‰. The ocean is divided by depth into a narrow mixing zone at the surface, a thermocline transition zone, and the deep cold zone.

salinity (p. 516)
brine (p. 518)
brackish (p. 518)

1. Describe the salinity of seawater: its composition, amount, and distribution.
2. Analyze the latitudinal distribution of salinity as shown in Figure 16.2. Why is salinity less along the equator and greater in the subtropics?
3. What are the three general zones relative to physical structure within the ocean? Characterize each by temperature, salinity, dissolved oxygen, and dissolved carbon dioxide.

● *Identify* the components of the coastal environment and *list* the physical inputs to the coastal system, including tides and mean sea level.

The coastal environment is called the **littoral zone** and exists where the tide-driven, wave-driven sea confronts the land. Inputs to the coastal environment include solar energy, wind and weather, ocean currents and waves, climatic variation, and the nature of coastal rock. **Mean sea level (MSL)** is based on average tidal levels recorded hourly at a given site over many years. MSL varies spatially because of ocean currents and waves, tidal variations, air temperature and pressure differences, ocean temperature variations, slight variations in Earth's gravity, and changes in oceanic volume.

Tides are complex daily oscillations in sea level, ranging worldwide from barely noticeable to many metres. Tides are produced by the gravitational pull of both the Moon and the Sun. Most coastal locations experience two high (rising) **flood tides**, and two low (falling) **ebb tides** every day. The difference between consecutive high and low tides is the tidal range. **Spring tides** exhibit the greatest tidal range, when the Moon and Sun are either in conjunction or opposition. **Neap tides** produce a lesser tidal range.

littoral zone (p. 519)
mean sea level (MSL) (p. 519)
tides (p. 522)
flood tide (p. 523)
ebb tide (p. 523)
spring tide (p. 523)
neap tide (p. 523)

4. What are the key terms used to describe the coastal environment?

5. Define mean sea level. How is this value determined? Is it constant or variable around the world? Explain.
6. What interacting forces generate the pattern of tides?
7. What characteristic tides are expected during a new Moon or a full Moon? During the first-quarter and third-quarter phases of the Moon? What is meant by a flood tide? An ebb tide?
8. Is tidal power being used anywhere to generate electricity? Explain briefly how such a plant would utilize the tides to produce electricity. Are there any sites in North America? Where are they?

Describe wave motion at sea and near shore and *explain* coastal straightening as a product of wave refraction.

Friction between moving air (wind) and the ocean surface generates undulations of water that we call **waves**. Wave energy in the open sea travels through water, but the water itself stays in place. Regular patterns of smooth, rounded waves, called **swells**, are the mature undulations of the open ocean. Near shore, the restricted depth of water slows the wave, forming *waves of translation*, in which both energy and water actually move forward toward shore. As the crest of each wave rises, the wave falls into a characteristic **breaker**.

Wave refraction redistributes wave energy so that different sections of the coastline vary in erosion potential. Headlands are eroded, whereas coves and bays receive materials, with the long-term effect of straightening the coast. As waves approach a shore at an angle, refraction produces a **longshore current** of water moving parallel to the shore. This current produces the *longshore drift* of sand, sediment, and gravel and assorted materials moving along the beach as **beach drift**—together these materials make up the overall *littoral drift*. **Littoral drift** drift is the transport of materials along the shore; a more comprehensive term, it considers *beach drift* and *longshore drift* combined.

A **tsunami** is a seismic sea wave triggered by an undersea landslide or earthquake. It travels at great speeds in the open sea and gains height as it comes ashore, posing a coastal hazard.

wave (p. 523)
swell (p. 523)
breaker (p. 524)
wave refraction (p. 527)
longshore current (p. 527)
beach drift (p. 527)
littoral drift (p. 527)
tsunami (p. 527)

9. What is a wave? How are waves generated, and how do they travel across the ocean? Does the water travel with the wave? Discuss the process of wave formation and transmission.
10. Describe the refraction process that occurs when waves reach an irregular coastline. Why is the coastline straightened?
11. Define the components of beach drift and the longshore current and longshore drift.
12. Explain how a seismic sea wave attains such tremendous velocities. Why is it given a Japanese name?

Identify characteristic coastal erosional and depositional landforms.

An *erosional coast* features wave action that cuts a horizontal bench in the tidal zone, extending from a sea cliff out into the sea. Such a structure is a **wave-cut platform**, or *shore platform*, or *terrace*. In contrast, *depositional coasts* generally are located along land of gentle relief, where depositional sediments are available from many sources. Characteristic landforms deposited by waves and currents are a **barrier spit** (material deposited in a long ridge extending out from a coast); a **bay barrier**, or *baymouth bar* (a spit that cuts off the bay from the ocean and forms an inland **lagoon**); a **tombolo** (where sediment deposits connect the shoreline with an offshore island or sea stack); and a **beach** (land along the shore where sediment is in motion, deposited by waves and currents). A beach helps to stabilize the shoreline, although it may be unstable seasonally.

wave-cut platform (p. 529)
barrier spit (p. 530)
bay barrier (p. 531)
lagoon (p. 531)
tombolo (p. 531)
beach (p. 531)

13. What is meant by an erosional coast? What are the expected features of such a coast?
14. What is meant by a depositional coast? What are the expected features of such a coast?
15. How do people attempt to modify littoral drift? What strategies are used? What are the positive and negative impacts of these actions?
16. Describe a beach—its form, composition, function, and evolution.
17. How has erosion impacted the Prince Edward Island coast?

Describe barrier islands and their hazards as they relate to human settlement.

Barrier chains are long, narrow, depositional features, generally of sand, that form offshore roughly parallel to the coast. Common forms are **barrier beaches**, and the broader, more extensive **barrier islands**. Barrier formations are transient coastal features, constantly on the move, and they are a poor, but common, choice for development.

barrier beach (p. 533)
barrier island (p. 533)

18. On the basis of the information in the text and any other sources at your disposal, do you think barrier islands and beaches should be used for development? If so, under what conditions? If not, why not?
19. After the Grand Strand off South Carolina was destroyed by Hurricane Hazel in 1954, settlements were rebuilt, only to be hit by Hurricane Hugo 35 years later, in 1989. Why do these recurring events happen to human populations?

- ***Assess* living coastal environments: corals, wetlands, salt marshes, and mangroves.**

A **coral** is a simple marine invertebrate that forms a hard calcified external skeleton. Over generations, corals accumulate in large reef structures. Corals live in a *symbiotic* (mutually helpful) relationship with algae; each is dependent on the other for survival.

Wetlands are lands saturated with water that support specific plants adapted to wet conditions. They occur along coastlands and inland in bogs, swamps, and river bottomlands. Coastal wetlands form as **salt marshes** poleward of the 30th parallel in each hemisphere and **mangrove swamps** equatorward of these parallels.

coral (p. 536)
wetlands (p. 538)
salt marshes (p. 539)
mangrove swamps (p. 539)

20. How are corals able to construct reefs and islands?
21. Describe a trend in corals that is troubling scientists, and discuss some possible causes.
22. Why are the coastal wetlands poleward of 30° N and S latitude different from those that are equatorward? Describe the differences.

- ***Construct* an environmentally sensitive model for settlement and land use along the coast.**

Coastlines are zones of specific constraints. Poor understanding of this resource and a lack of environmental analysis often go hand in hand, producing frequent disasters to coastal ecosystems and real property losses. Society must reconcile ecology and economics if these coastal environments are to be sustained.

23. What type of environmental analysis is needed for rational development and growth in a region like the New Jersey shore? Evaluate South Carolina's approach to coastal hazards and protection.

Critical Thinking

A. This chapter includes the following statement: "The key to protective environmental planning and zoning is to *allocate responsibility and cost in the event of a disaster*. An ideal system places a hazard tax on land, based on assessed risk, and restricts the government's responsibility to fund reconstruction or an individual's right to reconstruct at frequently damaged sites." What do you think about this as a policy statement? How would you approach implementing such a strategy? In what way could you use geographic information systems (GIS), as described in Chapter 1, to survey, assess, list owners, and follow taxation status for a vulnerable stretch of coastline?

B. Under "Destinations" in Chapter 16 of the *Geosystems* Companion Website there is a link called "Coral Reefs." Sample some of the links on this page. Do you find any information about the damage to and bleaching of coral reefs reported in 1998? Which places in the world? Are there some suspect causes presented in "Bleaching Hot Spots" or any of the "Coral Reef Alliance" references?

Career Link 16.1

Kathryn Parlee, Research Network Coordinator, Halifax, Nova Scotia

Even if Kathryn Parlee didn't know at the time that she would have a career in geology and physical geography, her parents did. As a child, she remembers, "I was always dragging piles of rock and sand home." She was born in St. John's and, by the time she finished high school, had lived in several communities in Newfoundland and Labrador, Nova Scotia, and Prince Edward Island. Before settling in Halifax, where she now lives and works, she also spent time in Ontario, Nunavut, and other parts of Nova Scotia.

Planning to study astrophysics at Saint Mary's University in Halifax, Kathryn switched direction after discovering geology in a science elective. "My interest in sedimentary geology and Earth processes provided a natural progression into physical geography and geomorphology," she says. "Once I was exposed to coastal geomorphology, I was hooked and knew I had found my passion."

Armed with a Bachelor of Science in geography and geology, Kathryn went to Wilfrid Laurier University for a master's degree in Environmental Studies. For her thesis she studied beaches and dunes at a Georgian Bay provincial park. Kathryn then attended the College of Geographic Sciences in Lawrencetown, Nova Scotia, where she earned an advanced diploma in geographic information systems (GIS).

For the past three years Kathryn served as the coordinator for the Coastal Zone sector of the Canadian Climate Impacts and Adaptation Research Network (C-CIARN), a national network that facilitates the generation of new climate-change knowledge. She works out of the Bedford Institute of Oceanography for Natural Resources Canada, Geological Survey of Canada (Atlantic).

Kathryn began her career with Natural Resources Canada as a GIS/multimedia specialist at the Canada-Nunavut Geoscience Centre in Iqaluit. "While in this position, I had the opportunity to collaborate on a project to develop an educational poster on climate change impacts for Nunavut," she says. "I became very interested in climate change, particularly its current and potential impacts on the natural and human environment. When the C-CIARN Coastal Zone coordinator job became available, it seemed like an ideal combination of my interests, and I was able to use my background and experience to secure the position."

As coordinator, Kathryn spends much of her time facilitating research. As she explains, "This involves educating researchers and others on climate change and the implications for Canada's coastal zone, promoting the importance of effective coastal management and adaptation, identifying issues and research needs, and encouraging the development of projects or initiatives." She also provides a central source of information on coastal climate change impact and adaptation issues: she develops educational materials, maintains a Web site and bibliographic database, and produces newsletters, articles, and reports on various aspects of coastal climate change.

What makes her job especially enjoyable, Kathryn tells us, is "interacting with the various members of the coastal community from across Canada, whether researchers, government, aboriginal groups, non-government organizations, municipalities, or the private sector. Perhaps the most fulfilling aspect of the job is being involved in raising awareness and providing information about the coastal environment, coastal management and development, and climate change. And, I get a lot of satisfaction from helping the right people get together to deal with specific problems." This kind of synthesis of science, government and nongovernment organizations, the private sector, and indigenous peoples matches what is at the heart of the Arctic Council's Arctic Climate Impact Assessment (ACIA, see Chapters 10 and 21)—a bringing together of elements and interests to construct a complete picture.

Even though she is in a coordinating position and not doing research directly, Kathryn finds that geography is key to her work: "I use my knowledge and experience in geosciences daily to help identify and better understand current coastal impacts, the implications of climate change, and different approaches for managing or adapting to these problems."

Like many scientists with careers in physical geography, Kathryn is particularly attracted to outdoor activities, at least the sorts of things one can do with a toddler in tow. She finds that an understanding of geography and geoscience provides added value to many of her family's outdoor recreational pursuits. And, like others, she found that her career choice provided her with unique opportunities, "such as the chance to live and work in northern Canada and experience its amazing culture and climate."

We asked Kathryn what challenges she sees in her work for the immediate future. "Highlighting the need for people to take immediate action on climate change," she replies. "Many coastal areas have not looked at their current vulnerability, which will likely be exacerbated under climate change," as outlined in the ACIA report. As always, funding for research is a challenge. "Although climate change is quickly becoming a priority issue in Canada," Kathryn says, "much of the available money is for mitigation—reducing greenhouse gas emissions, for example. Encouraging study or action on climate-change impacts and adaptation can be difficult when there is little money available to researchers or practitioners."

On the personal side, Kathryn misses the research. "I have a strong research background and often find it difficult not to have the option to participate in projects that are of particular interest. For the future, I would like to be involved in research and the development of coastal management plans for the use and conservation of our coastal regions."

FIGURE 1 Kathyrn Parlee, Research Network Coordinator.
Kathryn's work is based in Halifax, Nova Scotia, where she advises on and promotes effective coastal management. She is seen here at Oakfield Park near Halifax. [Photo by Geoffrey Davis.]

Ellesmere Island, Nunavut, dominates this *Terra* satellite image made September 10, 2003. The northwest coast of Greenland is to the east and Nansen Sound and Greely Fjord to the west. The centre of the image is at 80° N. The Ward Hunt Ice Shelf, recently reported as breaking up, is near the centre on the north coast. (See News Report 17.2 for more on this event.) [*Terra* MODIS sensor image courtesy of MODIS Land Rapid Response Team, NASA/GSFC.]

17

Glacial and Periglacial Processes and Landforms

Key Learning Concepts

After reading the chapter, you should be able to:

- *Differentiate* between alpine and continental glaciers and *describe* their principal features.
- *Describe* the process of glacial ice formation and *portray* the mechanics of glacial movement.
- *Describe* characteristic erosional and depositional landforms created by alpine glaciation and continental glaciation.
- *Analyze* the spatial distribution of periglacial processes and *describe* several unique landforms and topographic features related to permafrost and frozen ground phenomena.
- *Explain* the Pleistocene ice age epoch and related glacials and interglacials and *describe* some of the methods used to study paleoclimatology.

About 77% of Earth's freshwater is frozen, with the bulk of that ice sitting restlessly in just two places—Greenland and Antarctica. The remaining ice covers various mountains and fills some alpine valleys. More than 29 million cubic kilometres (7 million cubic miles) of water is tied up as ice. These deposits provide an extensive frozen record of Earth's climatic history over the past several million years and perhaps some clues to its climatic future.

Worldwide glacial ice is in retreat, melting at rates exceeding anything in the ice record. In the European Alps alone some 75% of the glaciers have receded in the past 50 years, losing more than 50% of their ice mass since 1850. At this rate, the European Alps will have only 20% of their pre-industrial glacial ice left by 2050. Mount Kilimanjaro in Africa, the South American Andes, and the Himalayas of Asia could lose their glacial ice within the next several decades, affecting local water resources.

Significant to towns and cities is that many mountain cliffs and slopes are held together by permanently frozen conditions (permafrost). With the meltdown underway these slopes are thawing, making rockfalls and landslides an increasing hazard probability.

In this chapter: We focus on Earth's extensive ice deposits—their formation, movement, and the ways in which they produce various erosional and depositional landforms. Glaciers, transient landforms themselves, leave in their wake a variety of landscape features. The fate of glaciers is intricately tied to change in global temperature, which ultimately concerns us all. We discuss the methods used to decipher past climates—the science of *paleoclimatology*—and the clues for understanding future climate patterns. Exciting discoveries are arising from ice cores taken from Earth's two ice sheets, one dating back 740,000 years from the present.

We examine the cold world of permafrost and periglacial geomorphic processes. These periglacial environments may be separated from actual glacial ice across time (glaciers from past ages) and space (physical distance in the present). Approximately 25% of Earth's land area is subject to freezing conditions and frost action characteristic of periglacial regions, including areas that once were dominated by periglacial processes and have specific related features of relict, or past, permafrost. These areas near former and existing glaciers contain evidence of the last ice age.

Rivers of Ice

A **glacier** is a large mass of ice, resting on land or floating as an ice shelf in the sea adjacent to land. Glaciers are not frozen lakes or groundwater ice. Instead, they form by the continual accumulation of snow that recrystallizes under its own weight into an ice mass. Glaciers are not stationary; they move slowly under the pressure of their own great weight and the pull of gravity. In fact, they move slowly in streamlike patterns, merging as tributaries into large rivers of ice, as you can see in Figure 17.1a.

Today, about 11% of Earth's land area is dominated by these slowly flowing rivers of ice. But during colder episodes in the past, as much as 30% of continental land was covered by glacial ice. Through these "ice ages," below-freezing temperatures prevailed at lower latitudes than they do today, allowing snow to accumulate year after year.

Glaciers form in areas of permanent snow, both at high latitudes and at high elevations at any latitude. A **snowline** is the lowest elevation where snow can survive year-round; specifically, it is the lowest line where winter snow accumulation persists throughout the summer. Glaciers form on some high mountains along the equator, such as in the Andes Mountains of South America and on Mount Kilimanjaro in Tanzania, Africa. On equatorial mountains, the snowline is around 5000 m (16,400 ft); on midlatitude mountains, such as the European Alps, snowlines average 2700 m (8850 ft); and in southern Greenland, snowlines are as low as 600 m (1970 ft). CRYSYS (CRYosphere SYStem) is a Canadian program in the NASA Earth Observing System Program. The main goal is to monitor and analyze regional and larger-scale variations in sea ice, snow cover, freshwater ice, glaciers and ice caps, and frozen ground/permafrost in the periglacial realm. Also, CRYSYS gathers and maintains historical, operational, and research data sets for climate systems research. The CRYSYS Web site is a good entry point into the cryosphere, at **http://www.msc.ec.gc.ca/crysys/overview/crysys_whatis_e.cfm**. Additionally, see the Global Land Ice Measurements from Space at **http://www.flag.wr.usgs.gov/GLIMS/glimshome.html**, or the National Snow and Ice Data Center at **http://nsidc.org**. *Landsat*-7 images are listed at **http://www.emporia.edu/earthsci/gage/glacier7.htm**.

Glaciers are as varied as the landscape itself and exist all over the world. Antarctica has over 86% of the world's ice in the form of an ice sheet covering an area of 13.9 million km^2. This is followed by the Greenland ice sheet with 10.5% of all glacial ice (1.7 million km^2). Canada's ice, found in alpine glaciers and ice caps, makes up 1.24% of the world's perennial ice in an area totalling about 200,000 km^2. Canada's glaciers can be classified as Arctic, Coastal, and Rocky Mountain (Figure 17.1b). All glaciers fall into two general groups, based on their form, size, and flow characteristics: alpine glaciers and continental glaciers.

Alpine Glaciers

With few exceptions, a glacier in a mountain range is called an **alpine glacier**, or *mountain glacier*. The name comes from the Alps mountains of central Europe, where such glaciers abound. Alpine glaciers form in several subtypes. One prominent type is a *valley glacier*, literally a river of ice confined within a valley that originally was formed by stream action. Such glaciers range in length from only 100 m (325 ft) to more than 100 km (60 mi).

In Figure 17.2a, at least a half a dozen valley glaciers are identifiable. These are named on the map and include the Athabasca, Saskatchewan, and Dome glaciers that fill the valleys as they move downslope from the Snow Dome.

As a valley glacier flows slowly downhill, the mountains, canyons, and river valleys beneath its mass are profoundly altered by its erosive passage. Some of the debris created by the glacier's excavation is transported on the ice, visible as dark streaks and bands being transported for deposition elsewhere; other portions of its debris load are carried within or along its base (see Figures 17.1 and 17.7f).

Most alpine glaciers originate in a mountain *snowfield* that is confined in a bowl-shaped recess. This scooped-out erosional landform at the head of a valley is called a **cirque**. A glacier that forms in a cirque is called a *cirque glacier*. Several cirque glaciers may jointly feed a valley glacier, as

(a)

FIGURE 17.1 Rivers of ice.
(a) Alpine glaciers merge from adjoining glacial valleys in the northeast region of Ellesmere Island (80° N 75° W) in the Canadian Arctic. (b) Distribution of glacial ice in Canada can be described as Coastal, Arctic, and Rocky Mountain. [(a) *Terra* ASTER image courtesy of University of Alberta, NASA/GSFC/ERSDAC/JAROS and the U.S./Japan ASTER Science Team, July 31, 2000; (b) Map courtesy of *Canadian Geographic*.]

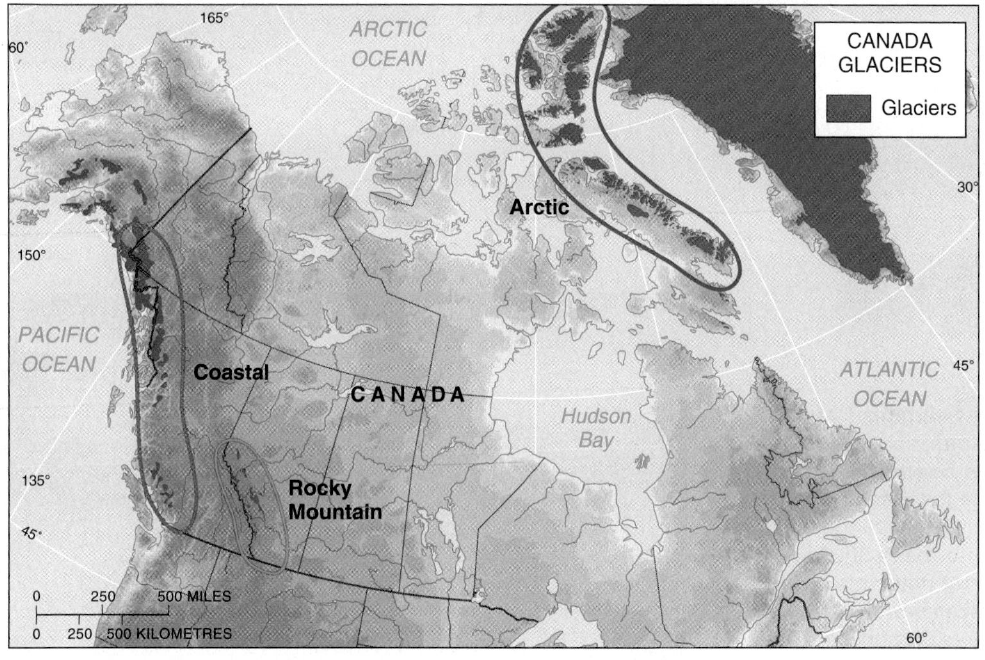

(b)

shown on the topographic map and photograph in Figure 17.3. The glaciers flowing north from Sugarloaf Mountain in the Battle Range are fed by many cirque glaciers that surround the mountain peak. In the satellite image in Figure 17.1 and the topographic map in Figure 17.3, how many valley glaciers can you identify?

Wherever several valley glaciers pour out of their confining valleys and coalesce at the base of a mountain range, a *piedmont glacier* is formed and spreads freely over the lowlands. Malaspina Glacier is an excellent example of a piedmont glacier (Figure 17.4, p. 554). The debris deposits on the surface of the ice form beautiful streaked patterns as the glacier fans out over the coastal plain and into Yakutat Bay. A *tidal glacier*, such as the Columbia Glacier on Prince William Sound in Alaska, ends in the sea, calving (breaking off) to form floating ice called **icebergs** (Figure 17.4b and c). Icebergs usually form wherever glaciers meet the ocean. (See Glaciers of Prince William Sound at **http://www.alaska.net/~sea/glacier.html**.)

Continental Glaciers

On a much larger scale than individual alpine glaciers, a continuous mass of ice is called a **continental glacier**. In its most extensive form, it is an **ice sheet**. Most of Earth's glacial ice exists in the ice sheets that blanket 80% of Greenland (1.8 million cubic kilometres, or 0.43 million cubic miles) and 90% of Antarctica (13.9 million cubic kilometres, or 3.3 million cubic miles).

The Antarctic and Greenland ice sheets have such enormous mass that large portions of each landmass beneath the ice are isostatically depressed (pressed down by weight) below sea level. Each ice sheet is more than 3000 m (10,000 ft) deep, burying all but the highest peaks.

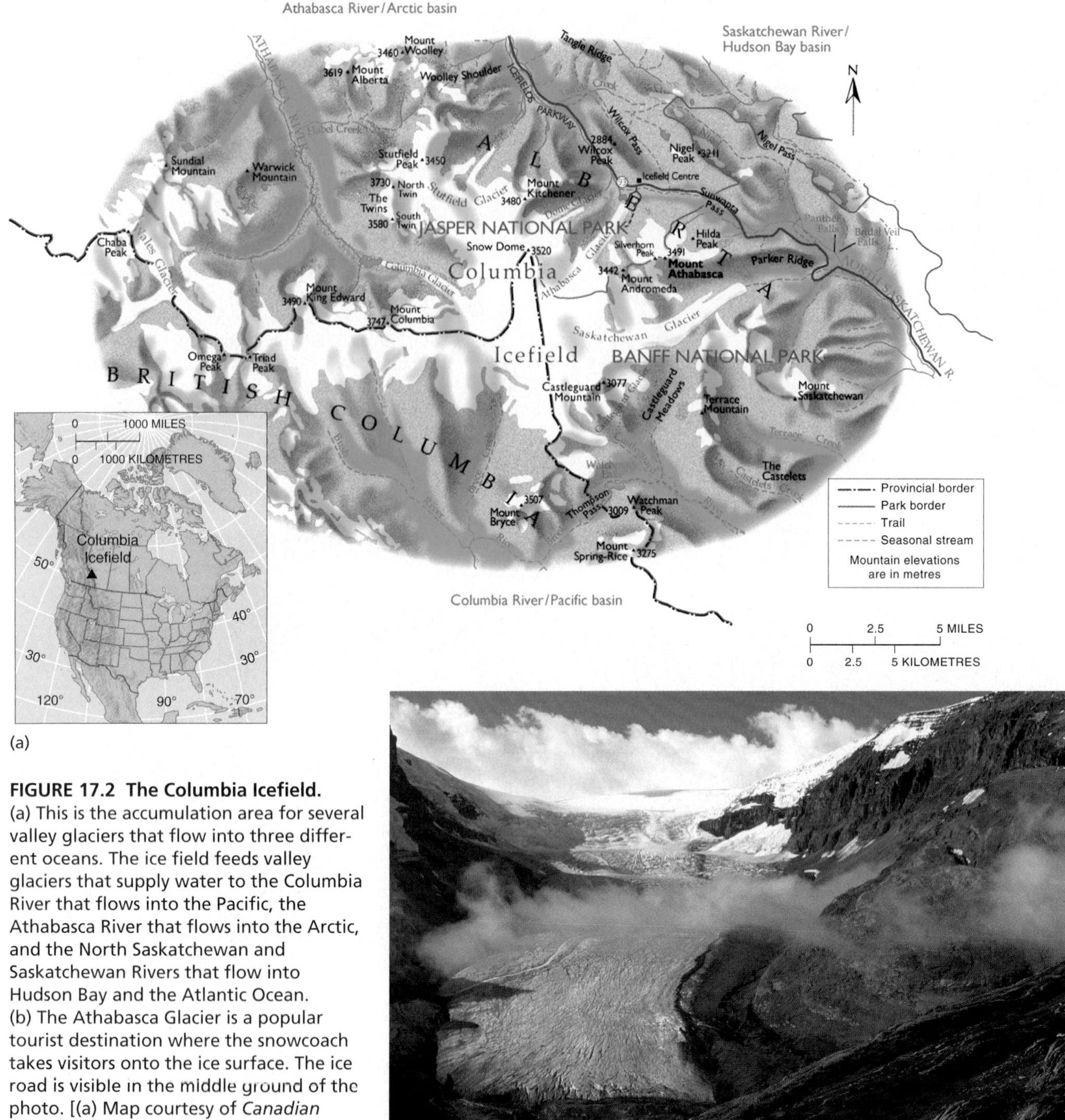

(a)

(b)

FIGURE 17.2 The Columbia Icefield. (a) This is the accumulation area for several valley glaciers that flow into three different oceans. The ice field feeds valley glaciers that supply water to the Columbia River that flows into the Pacific, the Athabasca River that flows into the Arctic, and the North Saskatchewan and Saskatchewan Rivers that flow into Hudson Bay and the Atlantic Ocean. (b) The Athabasca Glacier is a popular tourist destination where the snowcoach takes visitors onto the ice surface. The ice road is visible in the middle ground of the photo. [(a) Map courtesy of *Canadian Geographic*. (b) Photo by Gordon Peterson/firstlight.ca.]

Two additional types of continuous ice cover associated with mountain locations are *ice caps* and *ice fields*. An **ice cap** is a dome-shaped cover of perennial snow and ice, less than 50,000 km^2 in area. Ice caps are found in polar regions, and, like ice sheets, are not constrained by the existing relief. They exert a modifying effect on the climate, cooling the local area. In Canada, there are well-developed ice caps in the high Arctic (Agassiz Ice Cap, Northern Ellesmere Island; Melville Island South Ice Cap; Devon Ice Cap; Meighen Ice Cap, White Glacier on Axel Heiberg Island; Penny and Barnes Ice Caps on Baffin Island). The Barnes Ice Cap on Baffin Island is the last remnant of the Laurentide Ice Sheet that covered almost all of Canada and a portion of the northern United States at the peak of the Wisconsinan glaciation. The ice in the Barnes Ice Cap is over 100,000 years old, making it Canada's oldest.

The volcanic island of Iceland features several ice caps, such as the Vatnajökull Ice Cap in Figure 17.5a's *Landsat* image (p.555). Volcanoes lie beneath these icy surfaces. Iceland's Grímsvötn Volcano erupted in 1996, producing large quantities of melted glacial water and floods, a flow called *jökulhlaup* by Icelanders.

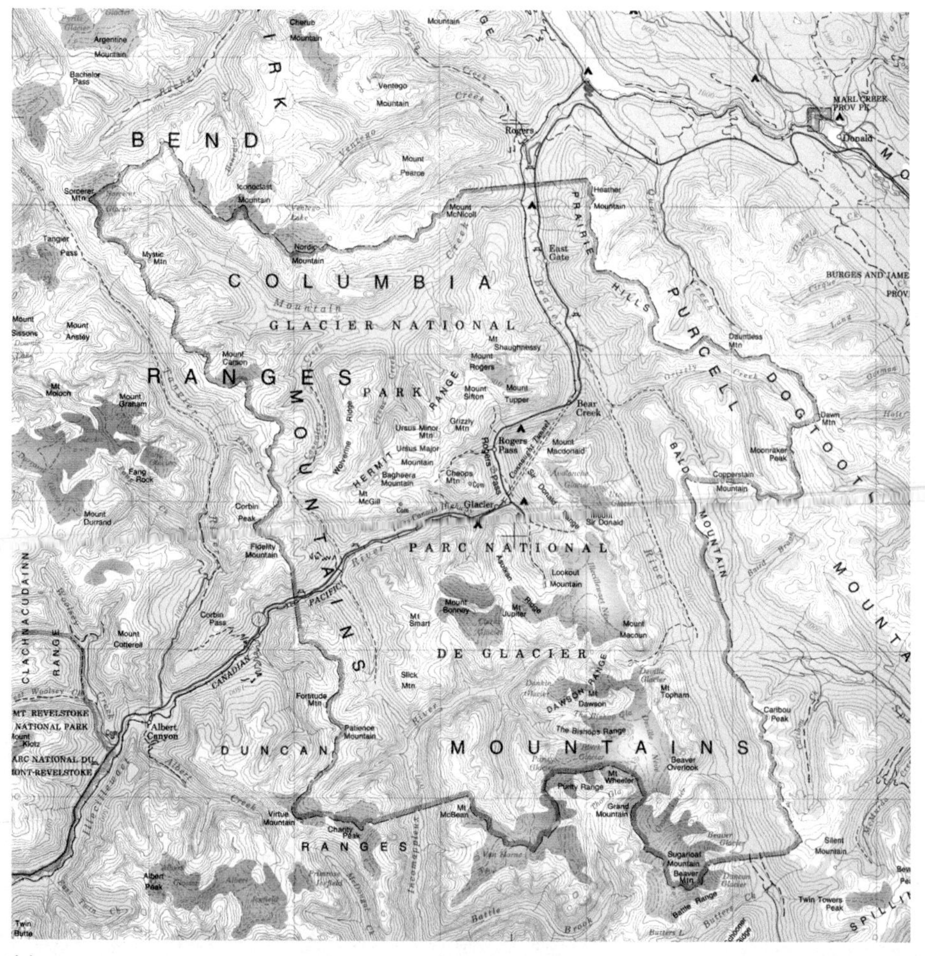

(a)

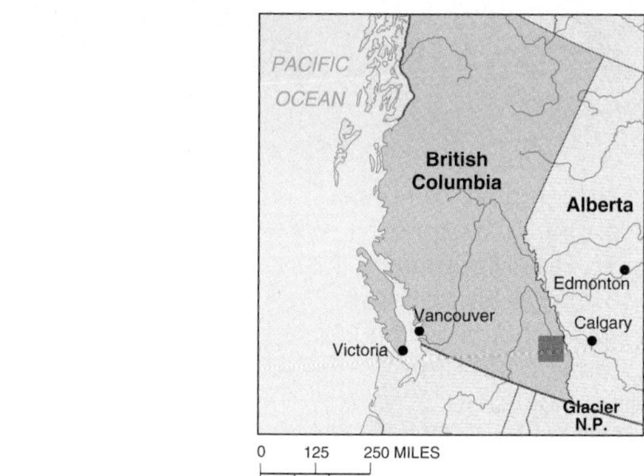

(b)

FIGURE 17.3 Topographic map from Glacier National Park. (a) Numerous cirque glaciers depicted on a topographic map of Glacier National Park, British Columbia. Blue areas represent active glaciers. (b) Dramatic landscape of ice and rock in Glacier National Park. Most glacial ice in the National Park will be melted away by 2030, owing to regional warming trends. [(a) Map used with permission of Natural Resources Canada; (b) photo by J. A. Kraulis/Masterfile.]

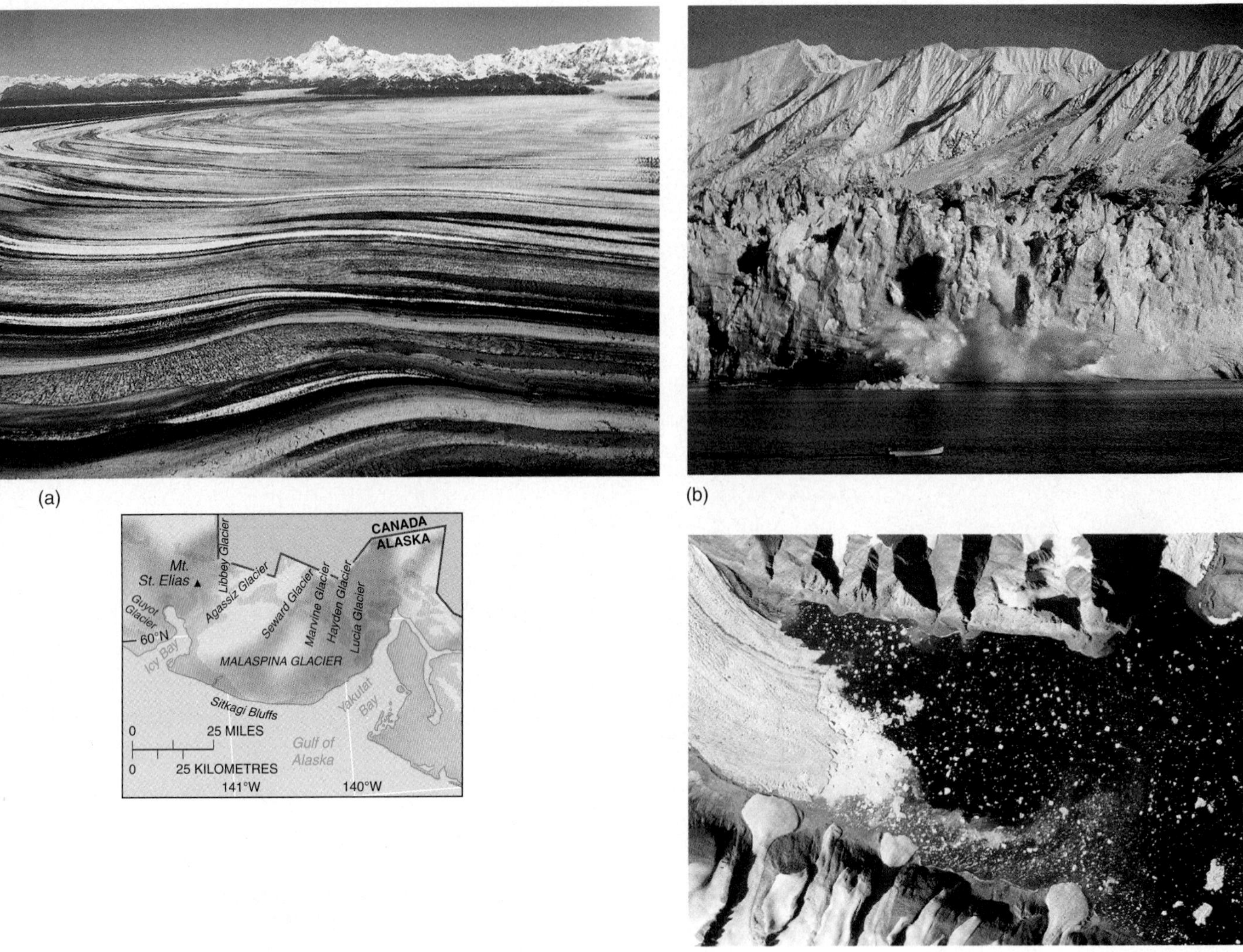

FIGURE 17.4 Piedmont glacier and ice calving into the sea.
(a) Malaspina Glacier in southeastern Alaska. This piedmont glacier is nearly the size of Prince Edward Island and covers some 5000 km^2 (1950 mi^2). About 70% of Malaspina's ice comes from the Seward Glacier (upper centre), which is fed by ice fields in the St. Elias Mountain Range. (b) When glaciers reach the sea, large blocks begin calving off, forming icebergs, such as from Hubbard Glacier into Disenchantment Bay, Alaska. (c) Eugenie Glacier floats out on the water and breaks up into icebergs in Dobbin Bay, Ellesmere Island, Canada. [(a) High-altitude photo courtesy of AeroMap U.S., Inc., Anchorage, Alaska; (b) photo by Steve McCutcheon/Visuals Unlimited. (c) *Terra* ASTER sensor image courtesy of University of Alberta, NASA/GSFC/MITI/ERSDAC/JAROS, and U.S./Japan ASTER Science Team.]

An **ice field** is not extensive enough to form the characteristic dome of an ice cap; instead, it extends in a characteristic elongated pattern in a mountainous region. In an ice field, ridges and peaks are visible above the buried terrain; the term *nunatak* refers to these peaks, visible in Figure 17.5b. A fine example is the Patagonian ice field of Argentina and Chile, one of Earth's largest. It attains only 90 km (56 mi) width, but stretches 360 km (224 mi), from 46° to 51° S latitude (equivalent in latitude from South Dakota to central Manitoba in the Northern Hemisphere). Scientists published the news in late 2003 that 63 Patagonian glaciers had significant ice loss since 1978, in amounts equalling 41 km^3 of ice per year.

In Canada, the Columbia Icefield (see Figure 17.2) straddles the continental divide between Banff and Jasper, Alberta. The highest elevation on the ice field, Snow Dome, reaches 3520 m (>11,000 ft) and represents the triple point in the drainage divide system of North America: Arctic, Atlantic, and Pacific. Eight glaciers flow out from the ice field including the Athabasca, Saskatchewan, Dome, Stutfield, Castleguard, and Columbia. Covering an area of about 325 km^2, the Columbia Icefield is one of the largest in the Rocky Mountains.

Continuous ice sheets or ice caps are drained by rapidly moving, solid *ice streams* that form around their periphery, moving to the sea or to lowlands. Such frozen ice streams

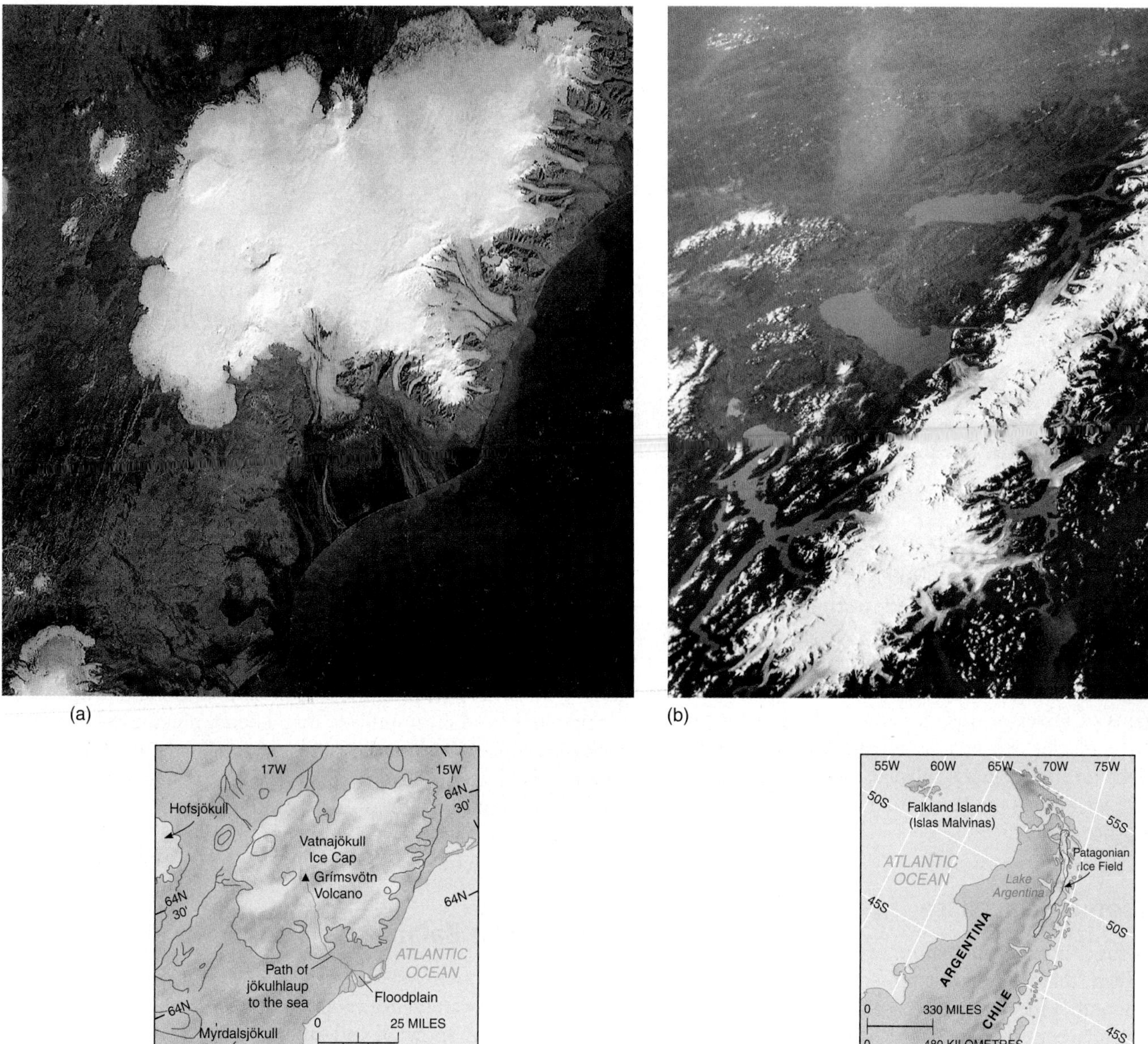

FIGURE 17.5 Ice cap and ice field.
(a) The Vatnajökull Ice Cap in southeastern Iceland (*jökull* means "ice cap" in Danish). Note the location of the Grímsvötn Volcano on the map and the path of the floods to the sea.
(b) The southern Patagonian ice field of Argentina. This ice field has experienced significant losses since this photo was taken in 1978. [(a) *Landsat* image from NASA; (b) photo by Cosmonauts G. M. Greshko and Yu V. Romanenko, *Salyut 6*.]

flow from the edges of Greenland and Antarctica, through stationary and slower moving ice. An *outlet glacier* flows out from an ice sheet or ice cap but is constrained by a mountain valley or pass (Figure 17.6).

An **ice shelf** is a very thick sheet of ice with a gently undulating to level surface that extends over the sea and floats on water. It is attached to the land along a coastal *grounding line* and also may be attached where ice flows around islands. On the seaward side, it is bounded by a steep cliff called the *ice front* that can be 2 to 50 m or more above sea level. Ice shelves are important climatic indicators because they respond much more rapidly to changes than glaciers or grounded ice sheets. Ice shelves have formed along polar coasts in Antarctica, in the Canadian Arctic Archipelago, and in Greenland. Ice shelves can be wide, with some extending several hundreds of kilometres from the coastline. Ice shelves increase in mass from annual snow accumulation and from the seaward extension of grounded ice sheets and glaciers. They decrease in size from warming, melting, and calving of icebergs at their seaward margin. (See News Report 17.2.)

FIGURE 17.6 Greenland's southeast coast. Ice streams from the ice sheet and outlet glaciers flowing to the sea dominate the southeast coast of Greenland. Centre of the image is near the Arctic Circle (66.5° N) [Photo by Bobbé Christopherson.]

Glacial Processes

A glacier is a dynamic body, moving relentlessly downslope at rates that vary within its mass, excavating the landscape through which it flows. The mass is dense ice that is formed from snow and water through a process of compaction, recrystallization, and growth. A glacier's *mass budget* consists of net gains or losses of this glacial ice, which determine whether the glacier expands or retreats. Let us now look at glacial ice formation, mass balance, movement, and erosion before we discuss the fascinating landforms produced by these processes.

Formation of Glacial Ice

Consider for a moment the nature of ice. You may be surprised to learn that ice is both a mineral (an inorganic natural compound of specific chemical makeup and crystalline structure) and a rock (a mass of one or more minerals). Ice is a frozen fluid, a trait that it shares with igneous rocks. The accumulation of snow in layered deposits is similar to sedimentary rock formations. To give birth to a glacier, snow and ice are transformed under pressure, recrystallizing into a type of metamorphic rock. Glacial ice is a remarkable material!

The essential input to a glacier is snow that accumulates in a snowfield, a glacier's accumulation zone (Figure 17.7a and 17.7c). Snowfields typically are at the highest elevation of an ice sheet, ice cap, or head of a valley glacier, usually in a cirque. Avalanches from surrounding mountain slopes can add to the snowfield.

As the snow accumulation deepens in sedimentary-like layers, the increasing thickness results in increased weight and pressure on underlying ice. Rain and summer snowmelt then contribute water, which stimulates further melting, and that meltwater seeps down into the snowfield and refreezes.

Snow that survives the summer and into the following winter begins a slow transformation into glacial ice. Air spaces among ice crystals are pressed out as snow packs to a greater density. The ice recrystallizes and consolidates under pressure. In a transition step to glacial ice, snow becomes **firn**, which has a compact, granular texture.

As this process continues, many years pass before dense glacial ice is produced. Formation of **glacial ice** is analogous to metamorphic processes: Sediments (snow and firn) are pressured and recrystallized into a dense metamorphic rock (glacial ice). In Antarctica, glacial ice formation may take 1000 years because of the dryness of the climate (minimal snow input), whereas in wet climates the time is reduced to just a few years because of rapid, constant snow input to the system.

Glacial Mass Balance

A glacier is an open system, with *inputs* of snow and *outputs* of ice, meltwater, and water vapour. At its upper end, a glacier is fed by snowfall and other moisture in the *accumulation zone* (Figure 17.7a). This area ends at the **firn line**, indicating where the winter snow and ice accumulation survived the summer melting season. Toward a glacier's lower end, it is wasted (reduced) through several processes: melting on the surface, internally, and at its base; ice removal by deflation (wind); the calving of ice blocks; and sublimation (recall from Chapter 7 that this is the direct evaporation of ice). Collectively, these losses are called **ablation**.

The zone where accumulation gain balances ablation loss is the *equilibrium line* (Figure 17.7b). This area of a glacier generally coincides with the firn line. A glacier achieves *positive net balance* of mass—grows larger—during cold periods with adequate precipitation. In warmer times, the equilibrium line migrates up-glacier, and the glacier retreats—grows smaller—because of its *negative net balance*. Internally, gravity continues to move a glacier forward even though its lower terminus might be in retreat owing to ablation. The mass-balance graph from the Peyto Glacier provides a case in point of glacial ice loss (News Report 17.1).

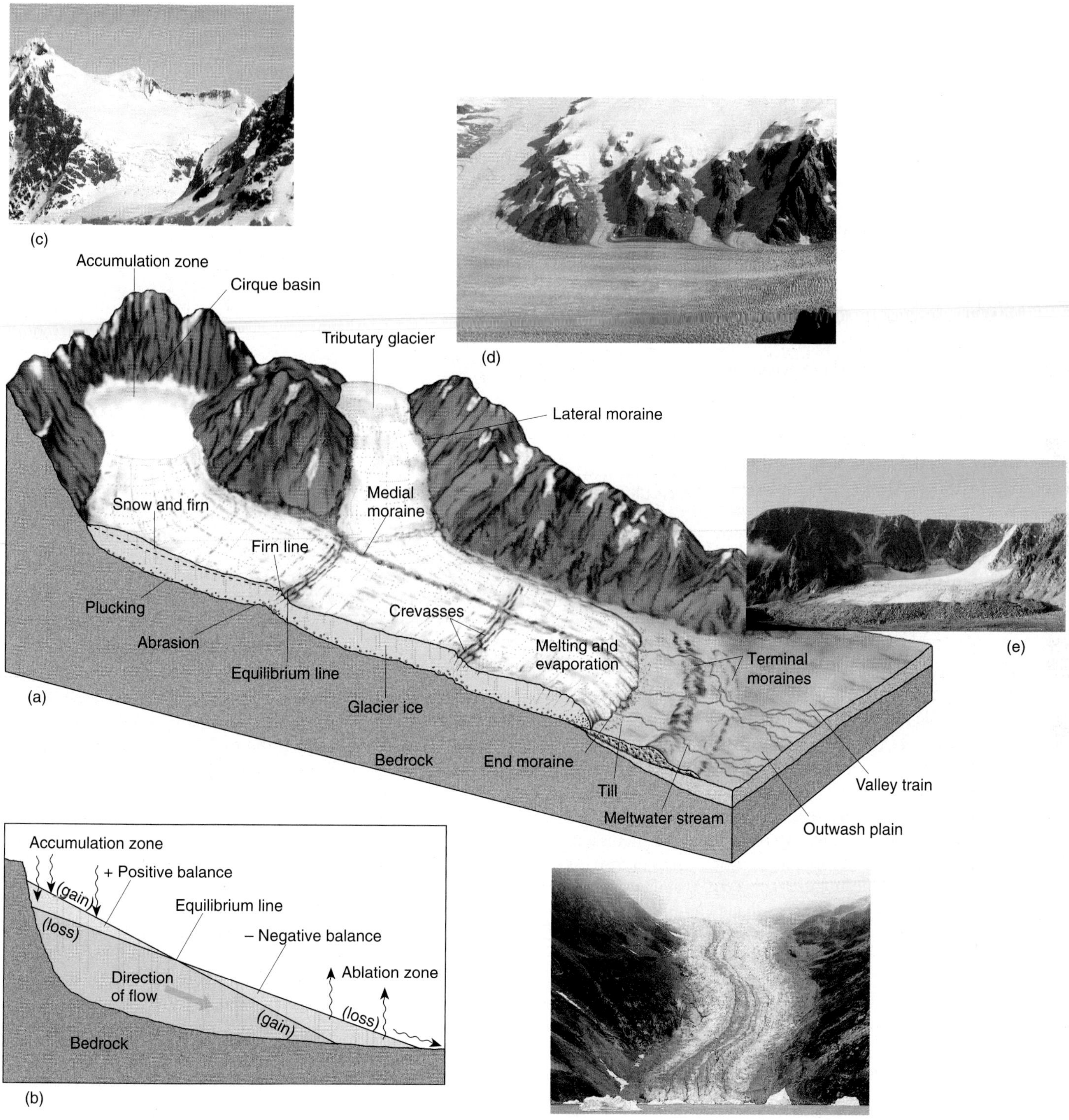

FIGURE 17.7 A retreating alpine glacier and mass balance.
(a) Cross section of a typical retreating alpine glacier. (b) Annual mass balance of a glacial system, showing how the relation between accumulation and ablation controls the location of the equilibrium line. (c) The accumulation zone for a glacier in Antarctica. (d) Four tributary glaciers flow into a compound valley glacier in Greenland. (e) A terminal moraine marks the farthest advance of this glacier on Nordaustlandet Island, Arctic Ocean. (f) Moraine rock and debris stain this glacier in Greenland as it advances to the sea. [All photos by Bobbé Christopherson.]

Budget of a Glacier, Mass Balance, Flow of Ice Within a Glacier.

News Report 17.1

Western Glaciers Lose Mass

Mass balance is a method used to monitor the behaviour of glaciers and can give an indication, if a long enough time series exists, of the regional warming or cooling of climate. A positive balance implies that the glacier accumulation is greater than the ablation in a particular year; a negative balance implies that there is more ablation than accumulation. A zero balance implies that accumulation and ablation are equal. Across the surface of the glacier, there is an elevation where accumulation and ablation are equal—this is marked by the equilibrium line.

Glacial mass budgets are declining along a global trend with significant ice losses in Alaska, the Andes, the European Alps, and the Himalayas. The Columbia Glacier in southern Alaska retreated 12 km (7.5 mi) and reduced its thickness by more than 400 m (1312 ft) between 1982 and 2000. In the same time period, its flow speed increased from 5 to 30 m (16.4 to 98.4 ft) per day. (See R. M. Krimmel, *Photogrammetric Data Set, 1957–2000, and Bathymetric Measurements for Columbia Glacier, Alaska*, USGS Water-Resources Report 01-4089, Tacoma, Washington, 2001.)

The net mass balance of Peyto Glacier, one of the most extensively studied glaciers in North America, demonstrates significant losses between 1966 and 1999. Peyto Glacier, in the Rocky Mountains of Alberta, ranges in elevation from 2140 to 3180 m above sea level and covers an area of about 12 km^2. The glacier terminus is retreating with the long-term negative mass balance and the surface is lowering along the west side of the glacier.

An analysis of the data for net mass balance reveals that the seasonal balance has been lower than average since 1976 (Figure 1). The Peyto Glacier mass balance analysis has been coupled with studies in other parts of the Rocky Mountains, the Coast Mountains, and the Cordilleran glaciers in Alaska, and the results show that some of the variability of the winter balance can be related to the El Niño–Southern Oscillation. The pattern of below average winter accumulation ended in the late 1980s, but the 1997 to 1998 budget year resulted in a record mass loss (210 cm/yr of loss). During that time, there was below average accumulation and increased losses through ablation (combined loss from melt, sublimation, and evaporation) that was both intense and prolonged. The balance for the next budget year (1998 to 1999) returned to nearly normal with 31 cm/yr of loss.

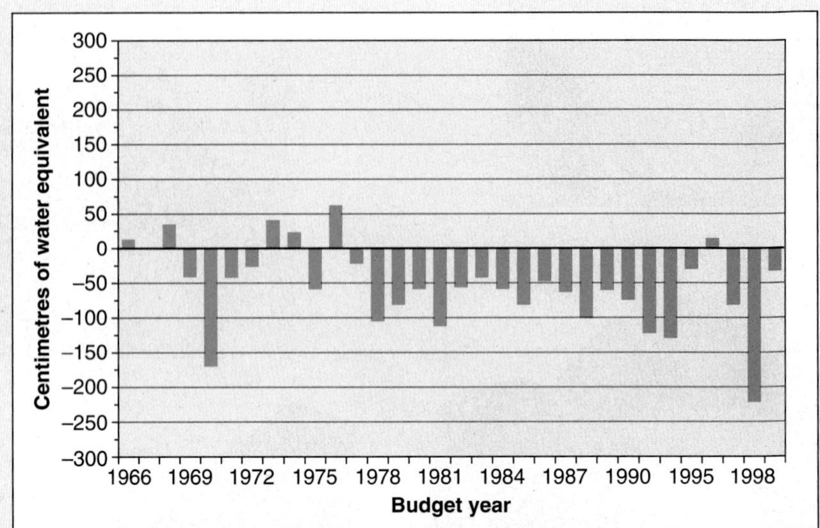

FIGURE 1 Peyto Glacier net mass balance, 1966 to 1999. A negative net mass balance has dominated this shrinking glacier since 1966. Data are in cm. [Graph by M. N. Demuth and R. Keler, 2004. "An Assessment of the Mass Balance of Peyto Glacier (1966–1995) and Its Relation to Recent and Past Century Climatic Variability." In Chapter 4, *Peyto Glacier: One Century of Science*, M. N. Demuth, D. S. Munro, and G. J. Young (editors). Environment Canada–National Hydrology Research Institute, 83–132.]

ANIMATION Budget of a Glacier, Mass Balance

The photographs in Figure 2 portray the magnitude of change in Peyto Glacier over the last half-century. Examination of the glacial deposits allows a determination of the greatest extent of the glacier, noted as the Neoglacial maximum (Figure 2b). The previous extent of the glacier's terminus in 1966 is drawn on the 2001 photo for comparison.

Research covering almost 50 years of 67 glaciers in Alaska was published in 2002. The study estimated volume changes in these glaciers. The glaciers were grouped into seven regions, shown in Figure 3a. The rate of glacier-wide thickness loss for 67 glaciers between the mid-1950s and 1995 and for 28 glaciers between 1995 and 2001 are in Figure 3b.

A total volume change was estimated to be -52 ± 15 km^3 per year (-12.5 ± 3.6 mi^3). These losses alone account for a rise in global sea level. Therefore, about 9% of global sea-level rise is coming from the Alaskan meltdown.

The reasons for these losses are complex. Thinning and wastage are not solely a result of climatic warming; however, these changes appear to be initiated by negative mass balances due to the warming. The individual dynamics of each glacier must be considered. Relative to the contribution of the Alaskan meltdown to sea-level rise, the scientists summarized:

> Compared with estimated inputs from the Greenland ice sheet and other sources, Alaskan glaciers have, over the past 50 years, made the largest single glacio-

(a) 1966

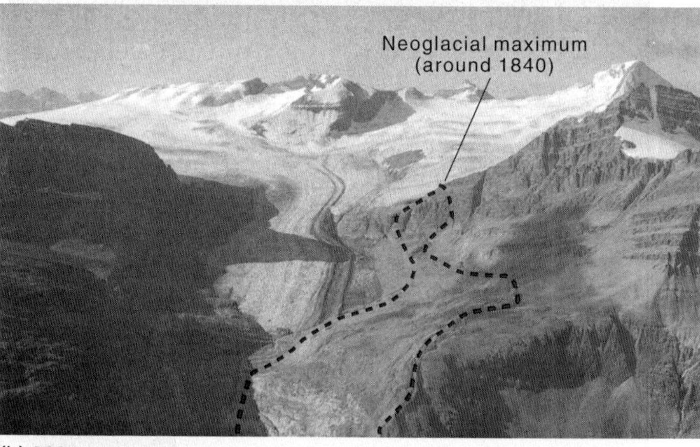

(b) 2001

FIGURE 2 Photographs of Peyto Glacier.
(a) Peyto Glacier in 1966 at the beginning of the mass balance record. (b) In 2001, dashed line represents the extent of glacial ice in 1966 and illustrates the quantity of ice that has retreated since the mass balance was recorded. [Photos by (a) Mike Demuth, National Water Research Institute, Canadian Glacier Information Centre; (b) Mike Demuth.]

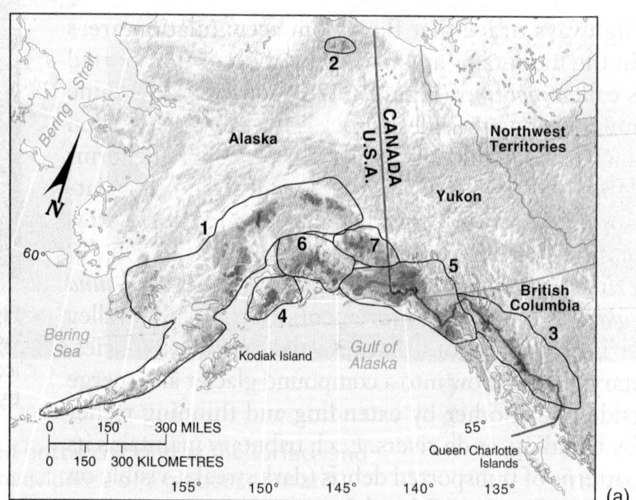

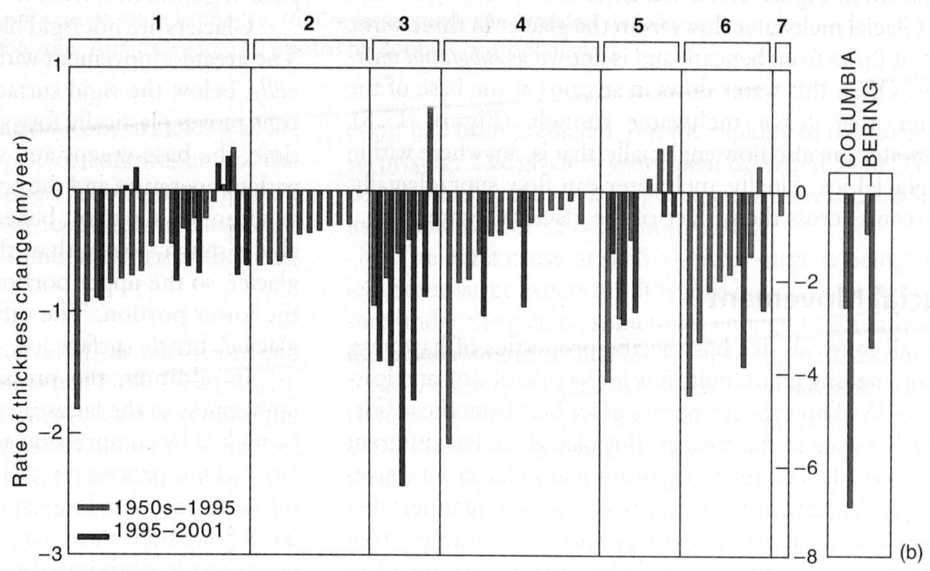

FIGURE 3 Negative mass balances for Alaska's glaciers. (a) Sixty-seven Alaskan glaciers divided into seven regions: 55 in Alaska, 11 cross the Alaskan–Canadian border, and one is in the Yukon. (b) Rate of change (metres per year) in glacierwide thickness for 67 glaciers in the earlier period (1950s to 1995, solid brown bars) and 28 glaciers in the recent period (1995 to 2001, red bars). Note the grouping of glaciers into seven regions indicated on the map in (a). [Adapted by permission of AAAS, from Anthony A. Arendt et al., Figures 1 and 3, "Rapid wastage of Alaska glaciers and their contribution to rising sea level," *Science 297* (July 19, 2002): 382–86.]

logical contribution to rising sea level yet measured. . . . the different rates of thinning observed in the various Alaskan regions may be important in characterizing patterns of climate change.*

*A. A. Arendt et al., "Rapid Wastage of Alaska Glaciers and Their Contribution to Rising Sea Level," *Science* 297 (July 19, 2002): 382–86.

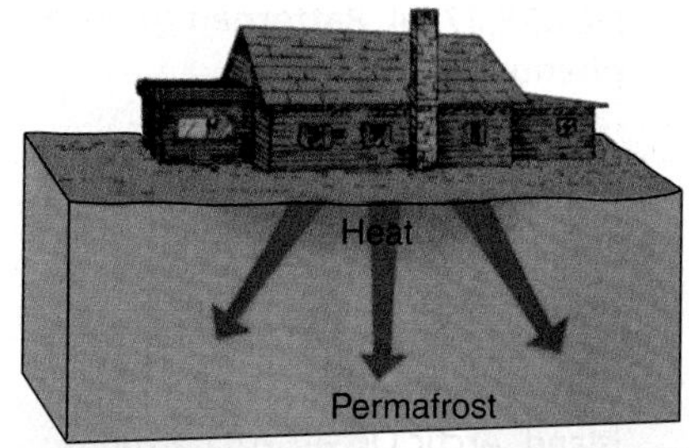

FIGURE 17.26 Permafrost thawing and structure collapse.
Building failure due to improper construction and the melting of permafrost, south of Fairbanks, Alaska. [Adapted from U.S. Geological Survey. Photo by Steve McCutcheon, illustration based on U.S. Geological Survey pamphlet "Permafrost" by L. L. Ray.]

rail lines become warped, twisted, and fail, and utility lines are disrupted. In addition, any building placed directly on frozen ground will "melt" into the defrosting soil, creating subsidence in structures (Figure 17.26).

Construction in periglacial regions dictates placing structures above the ground to allow air circulation beneath. This airflow allows the ground to cycle through its normal annual temperature pattern. Utilities such as water and sewer lines must be built above ground in "utilidors" to protect them from freezing and thawing ground (Figure 17.27). Likewise, the Trans-Alaska oil pipeline was constructed above ground on racks for 675 of its 1285-km (420 of its 800-mi) length to avoid melting the frozen ground, causing shifting that could rupture the line. The pipeline that is underground uses a cooling system to keep the permafrost around the pipeline stable.

The effects of global warming are already showing up in Siberia, where the active layer is now more than twice the depth it was in the past. Buildings constructed with shallow pilings for support will certainly fail if this trend continues. In an era of global change, the regions of permafrost may provide further climatic indicators.

(a)

(b)

FIGURE 17.27 Special structures for permafrost.
(a) Proper construction in periglacial environments requires raising of buildings aboveground and running water and sewage lines in elevated "utilidors," here in Barentsburg, a Russian settlement on Spitsbergen Island. (b) Supporting the Trans-Alaska oil pipeline on racks protects the permafrost from heat. [Photos by (a) Bobbé Christopherson; (b) Galen Rowell/Mountain Light Photography, Inc.]

The Pleistocene Ice Age Epoch

Imagine almost a third of Earth's land surface buried beneath ice sheets and glaciers—most of Canada, the northern Midwest, England, and northern Europe, and many mountain ranges, beneath thousands of metres of ice! This is how it was at the height of the Pleistocene Epoch of the late Cenozoic Era. In addition, periglacial regions along the margins of the ice during the last ice age covered about twice their present areal extent.

The Pleistocene is thought to have begun about 1.65 million years ago and is one of the more prolonged cold periods in Earth's history. It featured not just one glacial advance and retreat, but at least 18 expansions of ice over Europe and North America, each obliterating and confusing the evidence from the ones before. Apparently, glaciation can take about 90,000 years, whereas deglaciation is rapid, requiring less than about 10,000 years to melt away the accumulation.

The term *ice age* is applied to any extended period of cold (not a single brief cold spell). An **ice age** is an episode of generally cold climate that includes one or more *glacials*, interrupted by brief warm spells known as *interglacials*. Each glacial and interglacial is given a name that is usually based on the location where evidence of the episode is prominent—for example, "Wisconsinan glacial."

Modern research techniques to understand past climates include the examination of ancient ratios of oxygen isotopes, depths of coral growth in the tropics, analysis of ocean and lake sediments worldwide, and analysis of the latest ice cores from Greenland and Antarctica, including the Dome C ice core that plunges the record back 740,000 years (as of 2003). These techniques have opened the way for a new chronology and understanding of past climates and for putting perspective on the present warming trends. The record is clear and correlates across all proxy methods—present levels of CO_2 and methane (CH_4) are the highest in 440,000 years. Earth systems have no experience in dealing with levels this high during this time span, and these concentrations are increasing.

Glaciologists currently recognize the Illinoian glacial and Wisconsinan glacial, with the Sangamon interglacial between them. These events span the 300,000-year interval prior to our present Holocene Epoch (Figure 17.28).

The chart shows that the Illinoian glacial actually consisted of two glacials occurring during Marine (oxygen) Isotope Stages (MIS) 6 and 8, as did the Wisconsinan (MIS 2 and 4). The oxygen isotope glacial/interglacial stages on the chart are numbered back to MIS 23 at approximately 900,000 years ago. To overcome local bias in core records, investigators correlate oxygen isotope data with other indicators worldwide. (For web links on glaciers and the Pleistocene, see **http://research.umbc.edu/~miller/geog111/glacierlinks.htm**.)

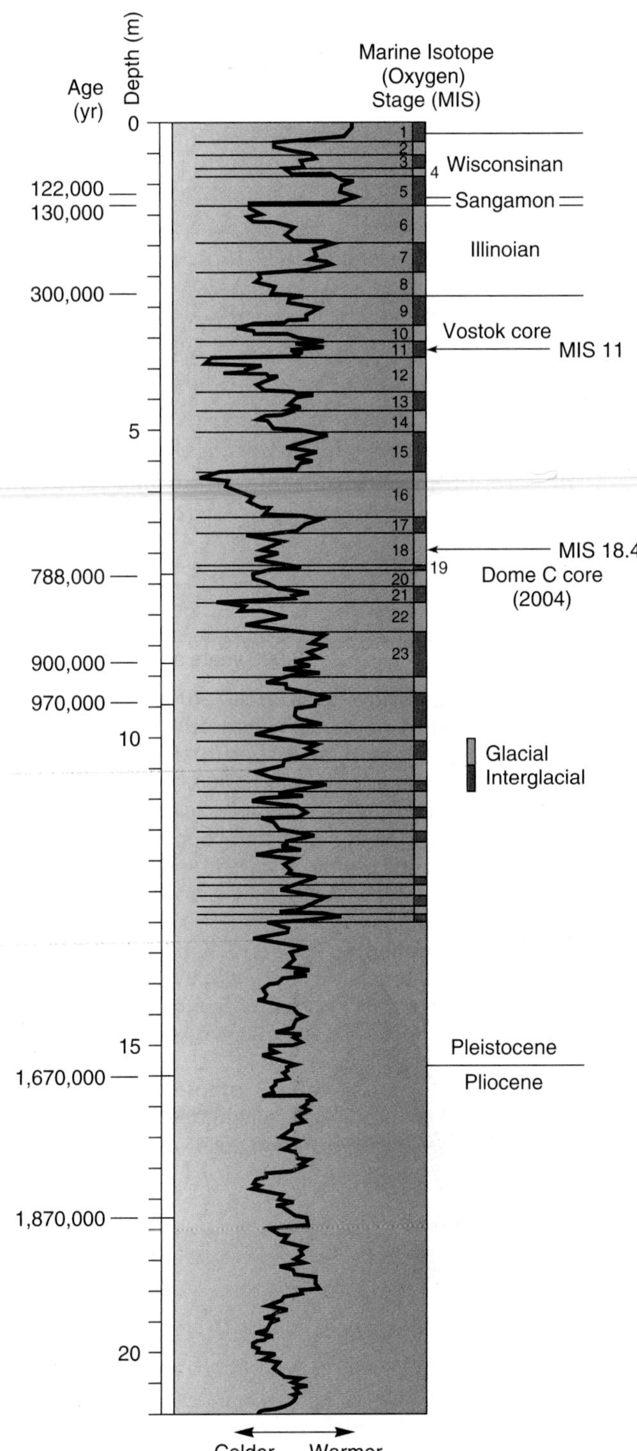

FIGURE 17.28 Temperature record of the past 2 million years.
Pleistocene temperatures, determined by oxygen isotope fluctuations in fossil planktonic foraminifera (tiny marine organisms having a calcareous shell) from deep-sea cores. Twenty-three Marine (oxygen) Isotope Stages (MIS) cover 900,000 years, with names assigned for the past 300,000 years. See Focus Study 17.1 for application of this scale to ice-core data. [After N. J. Shackelton and N. D. Opdyke, *Oxygen-Isotope and Paleomagnetic Stratigraphy of Pacific Core V28-239, Late Pliocene to Latest Pleistocene*. Geological Society of America Memoir 145. ©1976 by the GSA. Adapted by permission.]

Changes in the Landscape

The continental ice sheets covered portions of Canada, the United States, Europe, and Asia about 18,000 years ago, as

Summary and Review—Glacial and Periglacial Processes and Landforms

Differentiate between alpine and continental glaciers and *describe* their principal features.

More than 77% of Earth's freshwater is frozen. Ice covers about 11% of Earth's surface, and periglacial features occupy another 20% of ice-free but cold-dominated landscapes. A **glacier** is a mass of ice sitting on land or floating as an **ice shelf** in the ocean next to land. Glaciers form in areas of permanent snow. A **snowline** is the lowest elevation where snow occurs year-round and its altitude varies by latitude—higher near the equator, lower poleward.

A glacier in a mountain range is an **alpine glacier**. If confined within a valley, it is termed a *valley glacier*. The area of origin is a snowfield, usually in a bowl-shaped erosional landform called a **cirque**. Where alpine glaciers flow down to the sea, they calve and form **icebergs**. A **continental glacier** is a continuous mass of ice on land. Its most extensive form is an **ice sheet**; a smaller, roughly circular form is an **ice cap**; and the least extensive form, usually in mountains, is an **ice field**.

glacier (p. 550)
ice shelf (p. 555)
snowline (p. 550)
alpine glacier (p. 550)
cirque (p. 550)
iceberg (p. 551)
continental glacier (p. 551)
ice sheet (p. 551)
ice cap (p. 552)
ice field (p. 554)

1. Describe the location of most freshwater on Earth today.
2. What is a glacier? What is implied about existing climate patterns in a glacial region?
3. Differentiate between an alpine glacier and a continental glacier.
4. Name the three types of continental glaciers. What is the basis for dividing continental glaciers into types? Which type covers Antarctica?

Describe the process of glacial ice formation and *portray* the mechanics of glacial movement.

Snow becomes glacial ice through accumulation, increasing thickness, pressure on underlying layers, and recrystallization. Snow progresses through transitional steps from **firn** (compact, granular) to a denser **glacial ice** after many years.

A glacier is an open system with inputs and outputs that can be analyzed through observation of the growth and wasting of the glacier itself. A **firn line** is the lower extent of a fresh snow-covered area. A glacier is fed by snowfall and is wasted by **ablation** (losses from its upper and lower surfaces and along its margins). Accumulation and ablation achieve a mass balance in each glacier.

As a glacier moves downhill, vertical **crevasses** may develop. Sometimes a glacier will move rapidly in a **glacier surge**. The presence of water along the basal layer appears to be important in glacial movements. As a glacier moves, it plucks rock pieces and debris, incorporating them into the ice, and this debris scours and scrapes underlying rock through **abrasion**.

firn (p. 556)
glacial ice (p. 556)
firn line (p. 556)
ablation (p. 556)
crevasses (p. 560)
glacier surge (p. 561)
abrasion (p. 562)

5. Trace the evolution of glacial ice from fresh fallen snow.
6. What is meant by glacial mass balance? What are the basic inputs and outputs underlying that balance?
7. What is meant by a glacier surge? What do scientists think produces surging episodes?

Describe characteristic erosional and depositional landforms created by alpine glaciation and continental glaciation.

Extensive valley glaciers have profoundly reshaped mountains worldwide, carving V-shaped stream valleys into U-shaped glaciated valleys, producing many distinctive erosional and depositional landforms. As cirque walls erode away, sharp **arêtes** (sawtooth, serrated ridges) form, dividing adjacent cirque basins. Two eroding cirques may reduce an arête to a saddlelike **col**. A **horn** results when several cirque glaciers gouge an individual mountain summit from all sides, forming a pyramidal peak. An ice-carved rock basin left as a glacier retreats may fill with water to form a **tarn**; tarns in a string separated by moraines are called **paternoster lakes**. Where a glacial valley trough joins the ocean, and the glacier retreats, the sea extends inland to form a **fjord**.

All glacial deposits, whether ice-borne or meltwater-borne, constitute **glacial drift**. Glacial meltwater deposits are sorted and are called **stratified drift**. Direct deposits from ice, called **till**, are unstratified and unsorted. Specific landforms produced by the deposition of drift are **moraines**. A **lateral moraine** forms along each side of a glacier; merging glaciers with lateral moraines form a **medial moraine**; and eroded debris dropped at the glacier's terminus is a **terminal moraine**.

Continental glaciation leaves different features than does alpine glaciation. A **till plain** forms behind end moraines, featuring unstratified coarse till, low and rolling relief, and deranged drainage. Beyond the morainal deposits, **outwash plains** of stratified drift feature stream channels that are meltwater-fed, braided, and overloaded with debris that is sorted and deposited across the landscape. An **esker** is a sinuously curving, narrow ridge of coarse sand and gravel that forms along the channel of a meltwater stream beneath a glacier. An isolated block of ice left by a retreating glacier becomes surrounded with debris; when the block finally melts, it leaves a steep-sided **kettle**. A **kame** is a small hill, knob, or mound of poorly sorted sand and gravel that is deposited directly by water or by ice in crevasses.

Glacial action forms two types of streamlined hills: the erosional **roche moutonnée** is an asymmetrical hill of exposed bedrock, gently sloping upstream and abruptly sloping downstream; the depositional **drumlin** is deposited till, streamlined in the direction of continental ice movement (blunt end upstream and tapered end downstream).

arête (p. 562)
col (p. 562)
horn (p. 562)
tarn (p. 562)
paternoster lakes (p. 562)
fjord (p. 562)
glacial drift (p. 565)
stratified drift (p. 565)
till (p. 565)
moraine (p. 565)
lateral moraine (p. 565)
medial moraine (p. 565)
terminal moraine (p. 565)
till plain (p. 566)
outwash plain (p. 566)
esker (p. 566)
kettle (p. 566)
kame (p. 566)
roche moutonnée (p. 568)
drumlin (p. 568)

8. How does a glacier accomplish erosion?
9. Describe the evolution of a V-shaped stream valley to a U-shaped glaciated valley. What features are visible after the glacier retreats?
10. How is an iceberg generated?
11. Differentiate between two forms of glacial drift—till and outwash.
12. What is a morainal deposit? What specific moraines are created by alpine and continental glaciers?
13. What are some common depositional features encountered in a till plain?
14. Contrast a roche moutonnée and a drumlin regarding appearance, orientation, and the way each forms.

● *Analyze* the spatial distribution of periglacial processes and *describe* several unique landforms and topographic features related to permafrost and frozen ground phenomena.

The term **periglacial** describes cold-climate processes, landforms, and topographic features that exist along the margins of glaciers, past and present. Periglacial regions occupy more than 20% of Earth's land surface. These areas have either near-permanent ice or are at high elevation, and the ground is seasonally snow-free. When soil or rock temperatures remain below 0°C (32°F) for at least 2 years, **permafrost** ("permanent frost") develops. An area of permafrost that is not covered by glaciers is considered periglacial. Note that this criterion is based solely on temperature and has nothing to do with how much or how little water is present. The **active layer** is the zone of seasonally frozen ground that exists between the subsurface permafrost layer and the ground surface. **Patterned ground** forms in the periglacial environment where freezing and thawing of the ground create polygonal forms of arranged rocks at the surface; these forms can be circles, polygons, stripes, nets, and steps.

periglacial (p. 568)
permafrost (p. 568)
active layer (p. 570)
patterned ground (p. 572)

15. In terms of climatic types, describe the areas on Earth where periglacial landscapes occur. Include both higher latitude and higher altitude climate types.
16. Define two types of permafrost, and differentiate their occurrence on Earth. What are the characteristics of each?
17. Describe the active zone in permafrost regions, and relate the degree of development to specific latitudes.
18. What is a talik? Where might you expect to find taliks, and to what depth do they occur?
19. What is the difference between permafrost and ground ice?
20. Describe the role of frost action in the formation of various landform types in the periglacial region.
21. Relate some of the specific problems humans encounter in developing periglacial landscapes.

● *Explain* the Pleistocene ice age epoch and related glacials and interglacials and *describe* some of the methods used to study paleoclimatology.

An **ice age** is any extended period of cold. The late Cenozoic Era has featured pronounced ice-age conditions in an epoch called the Pleistocene. During this time, alpine and continental glaciers covered about 30% of Earth's land area in at least 18 glacials, punctuated by interglacials of milder weather. Evidence of ice-age conditions is gathered from ice cores drilled in Greenland and Antarctica, from ocean sediments, from coral growth in relation to past sea levels, and from rock. The study of past climates is *paleoclimatology*.

The apparent pattern followed by these low-temperature episodes indicates cyclic causes. A complicated mix of interacting variables appears to influence long-term climatic trends: celestial relations, solar variability, tectonic factors, atmospheric variables, and oceanic circulation.

ice age (p. 575)

22. What is paleoclimatology? Describe Earth's past climatic patterns. Are we experiencing a normal climate pattern in this era, or have scientists noticed any significant trends?
23. Define an ice age. When was the most recent? Explain "glacial" and "interglacial" in your answer.
24. Summarize what science has learned about the causes of ice ages by listing and explaining at least four possible factors in climate change.
25. Describe the role of ice cores in deciphering past climates. What record do they preserve? Where were they drilled?
26. Explain the relationship between the criteria defining the Arctic and Antarctic regions. Is there any coincidence in these criteria and the distribution of Northern Hemisphere forests on the continents?

Critical Thinking

A. After checking back issues of the *New South Polar Times*, 1993–1998, at **http://www.spotsylvania.k12.va.us/nspt/home.htm**, imagine duty there for yourself. Of the 28 people who winter over at the station, some serve as scientists, technicians, and support staff. The station commander for the 1998 season was Katy McNitt-Jensen, in her third tour at the pole. Remember, the last airplane leaves mid-February and the first airplane lands mid-October—such is the isolation. What do you see as the positives and negatives to such service? How would you combat the elements? The isolation? The cold and dark conditions?

B. Analyze and compare the initial results from ice-core drilling efforts in Greenland and Antarctica as described in this chapter (Focus Study 17.1 and text). What do they tell us about past climates? How far back do they go in time? Have they found any evidence of humans on Earth in the cores?

C. What is the relationship between knowing about paleoclimates and being able to forecast future climates? Is there a link? Have scientists discovered any cyclic behaviour to Earth's past climates that might repeat in the future? Explain.

Career Link 17.1

LeeAnn Fishback, Environmental Geochemist, Scientific Coordinator, Churchill Northern Studies Centre

LeeAnn Fishback grew up on the family dairy farm north of Tillsonburg, Ontario. Her parents always included her in the daily chores around the farm and answered her many questions about how the farm worked.

By the time she went to university she was still asking questions, and, to help better understand the natural world around her, she chose to study science and geography. With a scholarship to Wilfrid Laurier University, she earned a B.Sc. with high distinction, majoring in geography and minoring in chemistry. As an undergraduate, LeeAnn made her first visit to the Canadian Arctic to conduct field research, and she states, "I fell in love with the Canadian North." To date she has completed eight field research seasons in the High Arctic and two in the subarctic.

LeeAnn finished her Master of Science degree in Earth Sciences at the University of Waterloo. Her thesis topic, "Predicting Seasonal Active Layer Development: Colour Lake, Axel Heiberg Island," allowed her to specialize in geochemistry while making visits to the farthest northern reaches of the country.

At the University of Western Ontario, in London, Ontario, she focused on soil development and lake sediment geochemistry for her Ph.D. dissertation. After completing her Ph.D. in 2002, her goal was to find a job that would allow her to pursue a research career in the Canadian North.

LeeAnn now works at the Churchill Northern Studies Centre (CNSC), where she has held the position of scientific coordinator since September 2002. CNSC is a non-profit research and education facility located east of Churchill, Manitoba, on the west coast of Hudson Bay (**http://www.churchillmb.net/~cnsc**). She is enthusiastic about her job: "I usually spend four months in Churchill at different times of the year," she explains. "This way I get to experience all the seasons of the subarctic while doing field research at times of the year that are typically understudied."

LeeAnn is in Churchill in mid-February during winter, late April to early May during snowmelt, late June to early July, late August to early September, and October to November during freeze-up. She spends most of the October–November stint helping with the Centre's educational programs during polar bear tourism season. "Being on the lookout for polar bears is an added challenge when doing field work around Churchill." she says.

When not in Churchill, she telecommutes from her home office in Kenora, Ontario, where she lives with her husband. Off the job LeeAnn says, "I like to spend time outdoors. My favourite pursuits include kayaking, hiking, snowshoeing, and running my four dogs."

FIGURE 1 LeeAnn Fishback, environmental geochemist.
LeeAnn in Churchill, Manitoba. At the Churchill Northern Studies Centre, she often assists with educational programs during polar bear tourism season. An added challenge of doing field work includes being on the lookout for polar bears. [Photo by Jen Rausch.]

As scientific coordinator for CNSC, LeeAnn plans and does research, including CNSC long-term monitoring projects and her own research program. "My challenge is to raise the profile of the Centre domestically and internationally," she tells us. She also provides logistical and technical assistance for CNSC research clients and promotes collaborations between researchers where possible.

This theme of assistance to others runs through much of LeeAnn's work. "I am able to help out a number of researchers working in the Churchill area with their projects when they aren't able to be there—troubleshooting equipment or extra data collection, for example," she says. "I also enjoy the educational component of my job. I often work with school groups, university field credit courses, and general public learning vacations, including programs by Elderhostel International, EarthWatch Institute, and CNSC's own Learning Vacations. This job gives me the opportunity to transfer scientific knowledge and research to the general public and raise awareness of northern issues." LeeAnn also communicates current science issues via guest lectures, workshops, seminars, and conferences.

At the University of Winnipeg, where she is an adjunct professor in the Department of Geography, she participates in university-centred research projects as a co-investigator where needed. Her individual research at CNSC enhances the ongoing research carried out in the geography department at both universities.

There are special challenges to working in Canada's North. "It's sometimes difficult to get things done," says LeeAnn, "because of the weather, obtaining required gear, and shipping to the field location—and the bears, of course." But there seems little chance that she will soon abandon the North for a more forgiving climate. "I am continually learning new things and expanding my knowledge of the area, from atmospheric science to astrophysics and bear biology," she explains. "Having a multidisciplinary science degree with geography and its spatial analysis tools has provided me with a strong basis to learn and understand more about the northern environment."

PART FOUR

Soils, Ecosystems, and Biomes

Forests and farms sweep down to meet the long, narrow Vagavatnet Lake near the town of Vagamo in south-central Norway. The interaction of atmosphere, hydrosphere, lithosphere, and the passage of continental glaciation during the last ice age produce such a serene and productive biosphere at 62° N latitude. [Photo by Bobbé Christopherson.]

Earth is the home of the only known biosphere in the Solar System—a unique, complex, and interactive system of abiotic (nonliving) and biotic (living) components working together to sustain a tremendous diversity of life. Energy enters the biosphere through conversion of solar energy by photosynthesis in the leaves of plants. Soil is the essential link among the lithosphere, plants, and the rest of Earth's physical systems. Thus, soil helps sustain life.

Life is organized into a feeding hierarchy from producers to consumers, ending with decomposers. Taken together, the soils, plants, animals, and all abiotic components produce aquatic and terrestrial ecosystems, generally grouped together in various biomes. Today we face crucial issues, principally the preservation of the diversity of life in the biosphere and the survival of the biosphere itself. Patterns of land and ocean temperatures, precipitation, weather phenomena, stratospheric ozone, among many elements, are changing as global climate systems shift. The resilience of the biosphere, as we know it, is being tested in a real-time, one-time experiment. These important issues of biogeography are considered in Part 4.

Gray-Brown Luvisolic soils dominate the Waterloo Region just north of Cambridge, Ontario. The soil in this field consists of well-drained sandy loam of the Caledon Series, which developed on outwash plains. These soils are fertile and with management support a variety of crops in mixed-farming agriculture. They are used extensively for grains like corn and beans, as well as for livestock pasture. [Photo by Mary-Louise Byrne.]

18 The Geography of Soils

Key Learning Concepts

After reading the chapter, you should be able to:

- *Define* soil and soil science and *describe* a pedon, polypedon, and typical soil profile.
- *Describe* soil properties of colour, texture, structure, consistence, porosity, and soil moisture.
- *Explain* basic soil chemistry, including cation-exchange capacity, and *relate* these concepts to soil fertility.
- *Evaluate* principal soil formation factors, including the human element.
- *Describe* the 10 soil orders of the Canadian System of Soil Classification and *explain* their general occurrence.

Earth's landscape generally is covered with soil. **Soil** is a dynamic natural material composed of fine particles in which plants grow, and it contains both mineral fragments and organic matter. The soil system includes human interactions and supports all human, other animal, and plant life. If you have ever planted a garden, tended a houseplant, or been concerned about famine and soil loss, this chapter will interest you. A knowledge of soil is at the heart of agriculture and food production.

You kneel down and scoop a handful of prairie soil, compressing it and breaking it apart with your fingers. You are holding a historical object, one that bears the legacy of the last 15,000 years or more. This lump of soil contains information about the last ice age and intervening warm intervals, about distinct and distant source materials, about several physical processes. We are using and abusing this legacy at rates much faster than it formed. Soils do not reproduce, nor can they be re-created.

Soil science is interdisciplinary, involving physics, chemistry, biology, mineralogy, hydrology, taxonomy, climatology, and cartography. Physical geographers are interested in the spatial patterns formed by soil types and the environmental factors that interact to produce them. As an integrative science, physical geography is well suited to the study of soils.

Pedology concerns the origin, classification, distribution, and description of soil (*ped* from the Greek pedon, meaning "soil" or "earth"). Pedology is at the centre of learning about soil as a natural body, but it does not dwell on its practical uses. *Edaphology* (from the Greek *edaphos*, meaning "soil" or "ground") focuses on soil as a medium for sustaining higher plants. Edaphology emphasizes plant growth, fertility, and the differences in productivity among soils. Pedology gives us a general understanding of soils and their classification, whereas edaphology reflects society's concern for food and fibre production and the management of soils to increase fertility and reduce soil losses.

In many locales, an *agricultural extension service* can provide specific information and perform a detailed analysis of local soils. Soil surveys and local soil maps are available for most Canadian provinces and for counties in the United States. Agriculture Canada's soil information system is available on the Web (**http://sis.agr.gc.ca/cansis/intro.html**) and the soil landscape of Canada can be viewed online (**http://sis.agr.gc.ca/cansis/nsdb/slc/intro.html**). For the United States, the National Soil Survey Center's site is at **http://soils.usda.gov/** and for links related to world soils, see **http://soils.usda.gov/use/worldsoils/**.

In this chapter: The geography of soils deals spatially with a complex substance, the characteristics of which vary from kilometre to kilometre, and even centimetre to centimetre. We begin with soil characteristics and the basic soil sampling and soil-mapping units. The soil profile is a dynamic structure, mixing and exchanging materials and moisture across its horizons. Properties of soil include texture, structure, porosity, moisture, and chemistry—all integrating to form soil types. The chapter discusses both natural and human factors that affect soil formation. A global concern exists over the loss of soils to erosion, mistreatment, and conversion to other uses. The chapter concludes with a brief examination of the Canadian System of Soil Classification (CSSC) and a comparison with other systems that are widely used.

Soil Characteristics

Classifying soils is similar to classifying climates, because both involve interacting variables. Before we look at soil classification, let us examine the physical properties that distinguish soils as they develop through time, in response to climate, relief, and topography.

Soil Profiles

Just as a book cannot be judged by its cover, so soils cannot be evaluated at the surface only. Instead, a soil profile should be studied from the surface to the deepest extent of plant roots, or to where regolith or bedrock is encountered. Such a profile, called a **pedon**, is a hexagonal column measuring 1 to 10 m^2 in top surface area (Figure 18.1). At the sides of the pedon, the various layers of the soil profile are visible in cross section and are labelled with letters. *A pedon is the basic sampling unit used in soil surveys.*

Many pedons together in one area make up a **polypedon**, which has distinctive characteristics differentiating it from surrounding polypedons. A polypedon is an essential soil individual, comprising an identifiable series of soils in an area. It can have a minimum dimension of about 1 m^2 and no specified maximum size. *The polypedon is the basic mapping unit used in preparing local soil maps.*

Soil Horizons

Each distinct layer exposed in a pedon is a **soil horizon**. A horizon is roughly parallel to the pedon's surface and has characteristics distinctly different from horizons directly above or below. The boundary between horizons usually is distinguishable in the field, on the basis of the properties of colour, texture, structure, consistence (meaning soil consistency or cohesiveness), porosity, the presence or absence of certain minerals, moisture, and chemical processes (Figure 18.2). Soil horizons are the building blocks of soil classification. Following is a summary of a typical, idealized sequence of soil horizons.

At the top of the soil profile is the *O* (organic) *horizon*, named for its organic composition, derived from plant and animal litter that was deposited on the surface and transformed into humus. **Humus** is not just a single material; it is a mixture of decomposed and synthesized organic materials, usually dark in colour. Microorganisms work busily on this organic debris, performing a portion of the *humification* (humus-making) process. The O horizon is 20%–30% or more organic matter, which is important because of its ability to retain water and nutrients and for the way it acts in a complementary manner to clay minerals.

At the bottom of the soil profile is the *R* (rock) *horizon*, a layer too hard to break with the hands or to dig with a spade when moist. The lithic contact is the boundary between the rock layer and the overlying, unconsolidated material. When bedrock physically and chemically weathers into regolith, it may or may not contribute to overlying soil horizons. The A, Ae, B, and C horizons mark differing mineral strata between O and R. These middle layers are composed of sand, silt, clay, and other weathered by-products. (Table 11.3 presents a description of grain sizes for these weathered soil particles.)

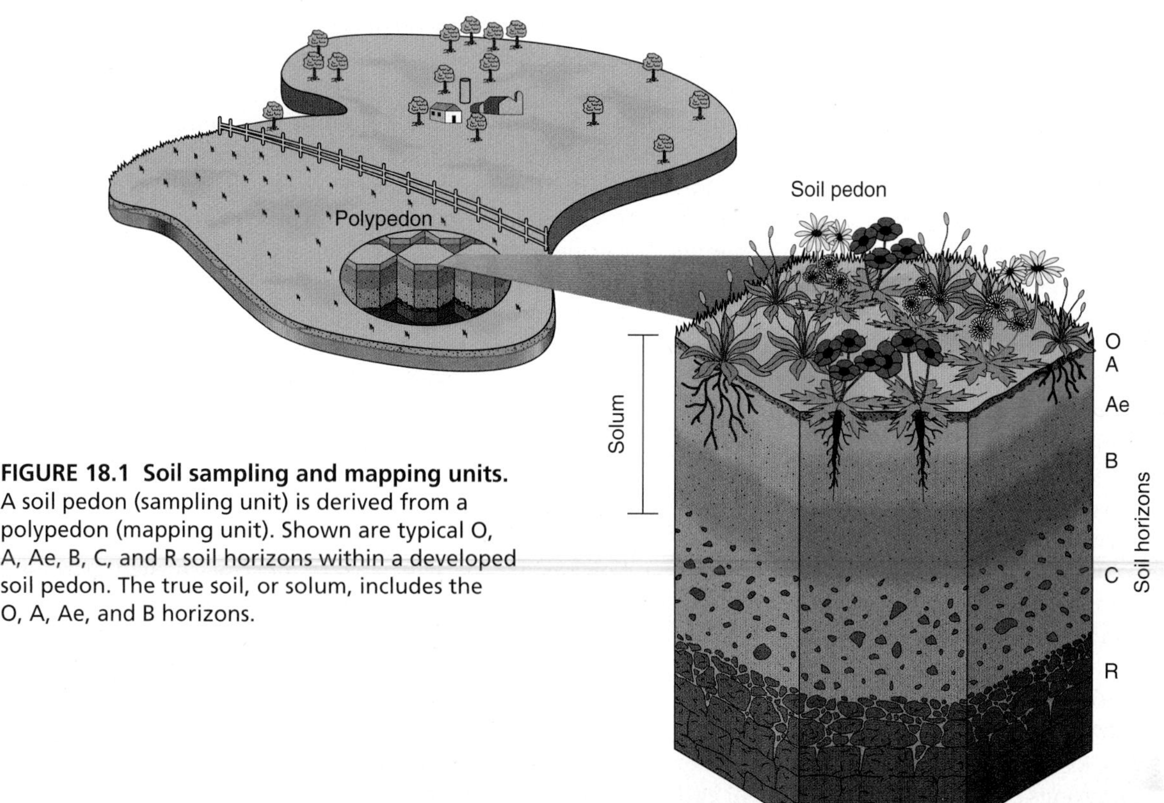

FIGURE 18.1 Soil sampling and mapping units. A soil pedon (sampling unit) is derived from a polypedon (mapping unit). Shown are typical O, A, Ae, B, C, and R soil horizons within a developed soil pedon. The true soil, or solum, includes the O, A, Ae, and B horizons.

The *A horizon* is a mineral layer that forms at or near the surface. It exists in the zone of maximum accumulation of organic matter, or in the zone of leaching of materials either in solution or suspension, or both. The accumulation of organic material usually results in a darkening of the surface soil. The A horizon can be enriched in organic matter (Ah) or depleted in mineral matter (Ae). The Ae horizon is lighter in colour, coarser in texture and is the transition from the A horizon to the B horizon.

The removal of fine particles and minerals by water, leaving behind sand and silt is termed **eluviation**—thus the "e" notation. Silicate clays and oxides of aluminum and iron are removed by water, or leached, and carried to lower horizons with the water as it percolates through the soil. More soluble material can be fully removed from the soil quickly, while iron and aluminum oxides are residual and may move more slowly.

The accumulation or enrichment of organic matter, oxides, or clay, dominates the B horizon. The deposition of these materials is known as **illuviation**. Accumulated organic material (Bh) results in a layer darker in colour relative to the *C horizon*. Finer soil texture or coatings of clay

FIGURE 18.2 A typical soil profile. This is a Gleysol from southern Ontario. The parent material is till and glaciolacustrine sediment and the soil is poorly drained. The dark O and A horizons are above the #7 and transition into the Ae horizon to the #13. Below the #13 is the mottled B horizon. [Photo courtesy of Agriculture and Agri-Food Canada.]

on the peds and in the pores results from clay accumulation (Bt). Soil structure may also develop in the B horizon with prismatic or columnar units and coating or stainings, significant amounts of exchangeable sodium, or other changes of structure from the parent material.

Some materials occurring in the B horizon may have formed in place from weathering processes rather than arriving there by *translocation*, or migration. In the humid tropics, these layers often develop to some depth. Likewise, clay losses in an A horizon may be caused by destructive processes and not eluviation. Research to better understand erosion and deposition of clays between soil horizons is one of the challenges in modern soil science.

The combination of the A and B horizons is designated the **solum**, considered the true definable soil of the pedon. The A and B horizons experience active soil processes (labelled on Figure 18.1).

Below the solum is the *C horizon* of weathered bedrock or weathered parent material. This zone is identified as *regolith* (although the term sometimes is used to include the solum as well). The C horizon is not much affected by soil operations in the solum and lies outside the biological influences experienced in the shallower horizons. Plant roots and soil microorganisms are rare in the C horizon. It lacks clay concentrations and generally is made up of carbonates, gypsum, or soluble salts, or of iron and silica, which form cemented soil structures. In dry climates, calcium carbonate commonly forms the cementing material of these hardened layers. In many glaciated parts of North America the C horizon consists of glacial deposits, commonly till.

Soil Properties

Soils are complex and varied, as this section reveals. Observing a real soil profile will help you identify colour, texture, structure, and other soil properties. A good opportunity to observe soil profiles is at a construction site or excavation, perhaps on your campus, or at a road cut along a highway. Manuals for describing, mapping, surveying, and analyzing soils can be found at the Agriculture and Agri-Food Web site (**http://sis.agr.gc.ca/cansis/publications/manuals/**).

Soil Colour

Colour is important, for it sometimes suggests composition and chemical makeup. If you look at exposed soil, colour may be the most obvious trait. Among the many possible hues are the reds and yellows found in soils of New Brunswick and Prince Edward Island and in soils of the southeastern United States (high in iron oxides), the blacks of the prairie soils in parts of southern Alberta and Saskatchewan and portions of the U.S. grain-growing regions and Ukraine (richly organic), and white-to-pale hues found in soils containing silicates and aluminum oxides. However, colour can be deceptive: Soils of high humus content are often dark, yet clays of warm-temperate and tropical regions with less than 3% organic content are some of the world's blackest soils.

To standardize colour descriptions, soil scientists describe a soil's colour by comparing it with a *Munsell Color Chart* (developed by artist and teacher Albert Munsell in 1913). These charts display 175 colours arranged by *hue* (the dominant spectral colour, such as red), *value* (degree of darkness or lightness), and *chroma* (purity and saturation of the colour, which increase with decreasing greyness). A Munsell notation identifies each colour by a name, so soil scientists can make worldwide comparisons of soil colour. Soil colour is checked against the chart at various depths within a pedon (Figure 18.3).

Soil Texture

Soil texture, perhaps a soil's most permanent attribute, refers to the mixture of sizes of its particles and the proportion of different sizes. Individual mineral particles are called *soil separates*. All particles smaller in diameter than 2 mm (0.08 in.), such as very coarse sand, are considered part of the soil. Larger particles such as granules, pebbles, gravel, or cobbles, are not part of the soil. (Sands are graded from coarse, to medium, to fine, down to 0.05 mm, silt to 0.002 mm, and clay to less than 0.002 mm.)

Figure 18.4 is a *soil texture triangle* showing the relation of sand, silt, and clay concentrations in soil. Each corner of the triangle represents a soil consisting solely of the particle size noted (although rarely are true soils composed of a single separate). Every soil on Earth is defined somewhere in this triangle.

Figure 18.4 includes the common designation **loam**, which is a balanced mixture of sand, silt, and clay that is beneficial to plant growth. A sandy loam with clay content below 30% (lower left) usually is considered ideal by farmers

FIGURE 18.3 A Munsell Soil Color Chart page. A soil sample is viewed through the hole to match it with a colour on the chart. Hue, value, and chroma are the characteristics of colour assessed by this system. [Photo courtesy of Gretag Macbeth, Munsell Color.]

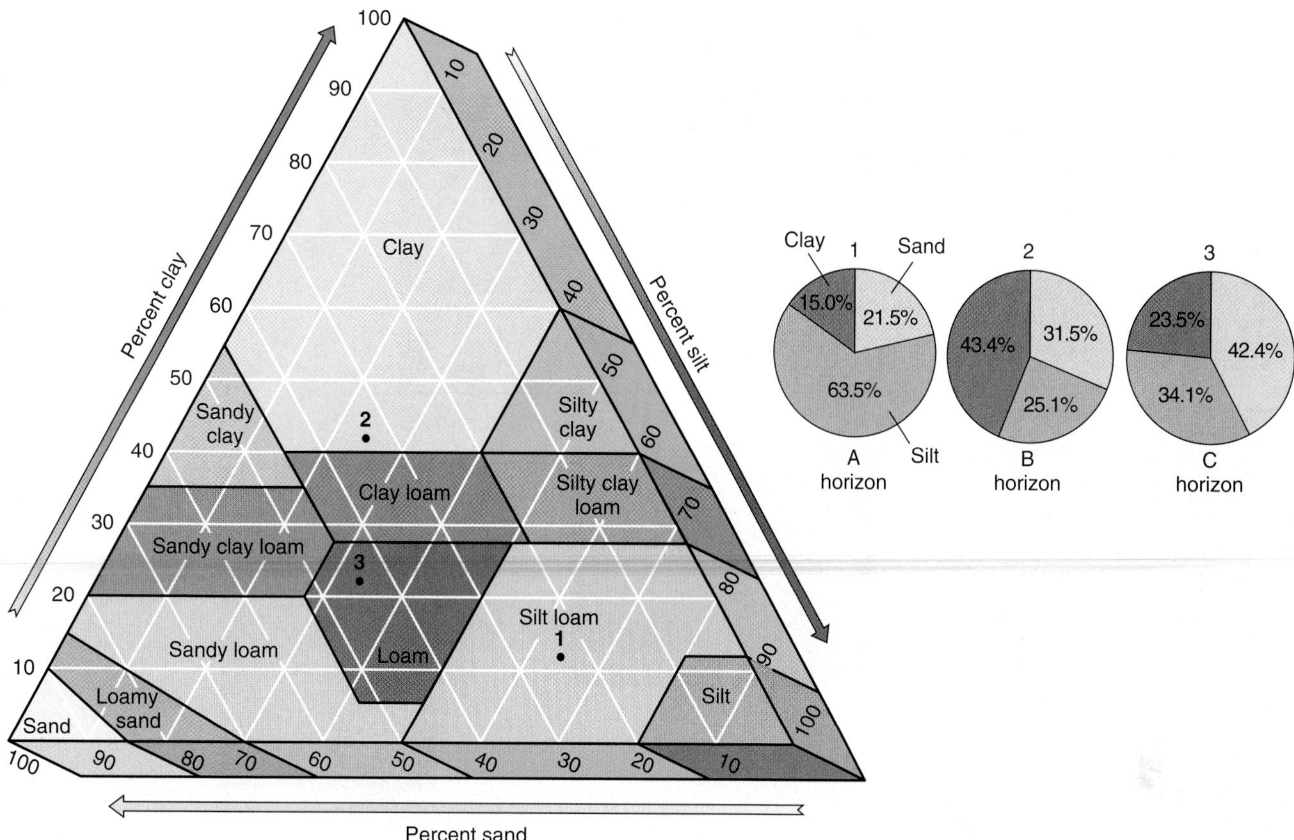

FIGURE 18.4 Soil texture triangle.
Measures of the ratio of clay, silt, and sand determine soil texture. As an example, points 1 (horizon A), 2 (horizon B), and 3 (horizon C) designate samples taken at three different horizons in the Miami silt loam in Indiana. Note the ratio of sand to silt to clay shown in the three pie diagrams. [After U.S. Department of Agriculture, Natural Resources Conservation Service, *Soil Survey Manual*, Agricultural Handbook No. 18, p. 138 (Washington, DC: U.S. Government Printing Office, 1993).]

because of its water-holding characteristics and ease of cultivation. Soil texture is important in determining water-retention and water-transmission traits.

To see how it works, consider a soil type in Indiana called the *Miami silt loam*. Samples from it are plotted on the soil texture triangle as points 1, 2, and 3. A sample taken near the surface in the A horizon is recorded at point 1, in the B horizon at point 2, and in the C horizon at point 3. Textural analyses of these samples are summarized in Table 18.1. Note that silt dominates the surface, clay the B horizon, and sand the C horizon. The *Soil Survey Manual* presents guidelines for estimating soil texture by feel, a relatively accurate method when used by an experienced person. However, laboratory methods using graduated sieves and separation by mechanical analysis in water allow more-precise measurements.

Table 18.1 Textural Analysis of Miami Silt Loam

Sample Points	% Sand	% Silt	% Clay
1 = A horizon	21.5	63.5	15.0
2 = B horizon	31.5	25.1	43.4
3 = C horizon	42.4	34.1	23.5

Soil Structure

Soil *texture* describes the size of soil particles, but soil *structure* refers to the *arrangement* of them. Structure can partially modify the effects of soil texture. The smallest natural lump or cluster of particles is a *ped*. The shape of soil peds determines which of the structural types the soil exhibits: crumb or granular, platy, blocky, prismatic, or columnar (Figure 18.5).

Peds separate from each other along zones of weakness, creating voids (pores) that are important for moisture storage and drainage. Rounded peds have more pore space between them and greater permeability than other shapes. They are therefore better for plant growth than are blocky, prismatic, or platy peds, despite comparable fertility. Terms used to describe soil structure include fine, medium, or coarse. Adhesion among peds ranges from weak to strong.

FIGURE 18.5 Types of soil structure.
Structure is important because it controls drainage, rooting of plants, and how well the soil delivers nutrients to plants. The shape of individual peds shown here controls a soil's structure. [Photos by National Soil Survey Center, Natural Resources Conservation Service, USDA, Soil Survey Staff.]

Soil Consistence

In soil science, the term *consistence* is used to describe the consistency of a soil or cohesion of its particles. Consistence is a product of texture (particle size) and structure (ped shape). Consistence reflects a soil's resistance to breaking and manipulation under varying moisture conditions:

- A *wet soil* is sticky between the thumb and forefinger, ranging from a little adherence to either finger, to sticking to both fingers, to stretching when the fingers are moved apart. *Plasticity*, the quality of being mouldable, is roughly measured by rolling a piece of soil between your fingers and thumb to see whether it rolls into a thin strand.
- A *moist soil* is filled to about half of field capacity (the usable water capacity of soil), and its consistence grades from loose (noncoherent), to *friable* (easily pulverized), to firm (not crushable between thumb and forefinger).
- A *dry soil* is typically brittle and rigid, with consistence ranging from loose, to soft, to hard, to extremely hard.

Soil particles are sometimes cemented together, to some degree. Soils are described as weakly cemented, strongly cemented, or *indurated* (hardened). Calcium carbonate, silica, and oxides or salts of iron and aluminum all can serve as cementing agents. The cementation of soil particles that occurs in various horizons is a function of consistence and may be continuous or discontinuous.

Soil Porosity

Soil porosity, permeability, and moisture storage are discussed in Chapter 9. Pores in the soil horizon control the movement of water—its intake, flow, and drainage—and air ventilation. Important porosity factors are pore *size*, pore *continuity* (whether they are interconnected), pore *shape* (whether they are spherical, irregular, or tubular), pore *orientation* (whether pore spaces are vertical, horizontal, or random), and pore *location* (whether they are within or between soil peds).

Porosity is improved by the biotic actions of plant roots, animal activity such as the tunnelling of gophers or worms, and human intervention through soil manipulation (plowing, adding humus or sand, or planting soil-building crops). Much of a farmer's soil preparation work before planting, and for the home gardener as well, is done to improve soil porosity.

Soil Moisture

Reviewing Figures 9.9 and 9.10 (soil moisture types and availability) will help you understand this section. Plants operate most efficiently when the soil is at *field capacity*, which is the maximum water availability for plant use after large pore spaces have drained of gravitational water. Field capacity is determined by soil type. The depth to which a plant sends its roots determines the amount of soil moisture to which the plant has access. If soil moisture is removed below field capacity, plants must exert increased energy to obtain available water. This moisture removal inefficiency worsens until the plant reaches its wilting. Beyond this point, plants are unable to extract the water they need, and they die. Soil moisture regimes and their associated climate types shape the biotic and abiotic properties of the soil more than any other factor.

Soil Chemistry

Recall that soil pores may be filled with air, water, or a mixture of the two. Consequently, soil chemistry involves both air and water. The atmosphere within soil pores is mostly nitrogen, oxygen, and carbon dioxide. Nitrogen concentrations are about the same as in the atmosphere, but oxygen is less and carbon dioxide is greater because of ongoing respiration processes.

Water present in soil pores is called the *soil solution*. It is the medium for chemical reactions in soil. This solution is critical to plants as their source of nutrients, and it is the foundation of *soil fertility*. Carbon dioxide combines with the water to produce carbonic acid, and various organic materials combine with the water to produce organic acids. These acids are then active participants in soil processes, as are dissolved alkalis and salts.

To understand how the soil solution behaves, let us go through a quick chemistry review. An *ion* is an atom, or group of atoms, that carries an electrical charge (examples: Na^+, Cl^-, HCO_3^-). An ion has either a positive charge or a negative charge. For example, when NaCl (sodium chloride) dissolves in solution, it separates into two ions: Na^+ a *cation* (positively charged ion), and Cl^- an *anion* (negatively charged ion). Some ions in soil carry single charges, whereas others carry double or even triple charges (e.g., sulphate, SO_4^{2-}; and aluminum, Al^{3+}).

Ions in soil are retained by **soil colloids**. These tiny particles of clay and organic material (humus) carry a negative electrical charge and consequently attract any positively charged ions in the soil (Figure 18.6). The positive ions, many metallic, are critical to plant growth. If it were not for the negatively charged soil colloids, the positive ions would be leached away by the soil solution and thus would be unavailable to plant roots.

Individual clay colloids are thin and plate-like, with parallel surfaces that are negatively charged (see Figure 18.6). They are more chemically active than silt and sand particles but less active than organic colloids. Metallic cations attach to the surfaces of the colloids by *adsorption* (not *ab*sorption, which means "to enter"). Colloids can exchange cations between their surfaces and the soil solution, an ability called **cation-exchange capacity (CEC)**, which is the measure of soil fertility. A high CEC means that the soil colloids can store or exchange more cations

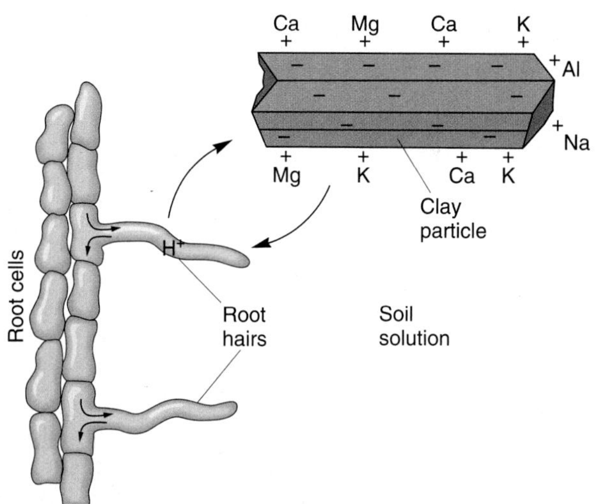

FIGURE 18.6 Soil colloids and cation-exchange capacity (CEC).
This typical soil colloid retains mineral ions by adsorption to its surface (opposite charges attract). This process holds the ions until they are absorbed by root hairs.

ANIMATION Soil Ion Exchange: Soil Particles and Soil Water

from the soil solution, an indication of good soil fertility (unless there is a complicating factor, such as a soil that is too acid).

Therefore, **soil fertility** is the ability of soil to sustain plants. Soil is fertile when it contains organic substances and clay minerals that absorb water and adsorb certain elements needed by plants. Billions of dollars are expended to create fertile soil conditions, yet the future of Earth's most fertile soils is threatened because soil erosion and other soil losses are on the increase worldwide.

Soil Acidity and Alkalinity

A soil solution may contain significant hydrogen ions (H^+), the cations that stimulate acid formation. The result is a soil rich in hydrogen ions, or an *acid soil*. On the other hand, a soil high in base cations (calcium, magnesium, potassium, sodium) is a *basic* or *alkaline soil*. Such acidity or alkalinity is expressed on the pH scale (Figure 18.7).

Pure water is nearly neutral, with a pH of 7.0. Readings below 7.0 represent increasing acidity. Readings above 7.0 indicate increasing alkalinity. Acidity usually is regarded as strong at 5.0 or lower on the pH scale, whereas 10.0 or above is considered strongly alkaline.

The major contributor to soil acidity in this modern era is acid precipitation (rain, snow, fog, or dry deposition). Acid rain actually has been measured below pH 2.0—an incredibly low value for natural precipitation, as acid as lemon juice. Because most crops are sensitive to specific pH levels, acid soils below pH 6.0 may require treatment to raise the pH. This soil treatment is accomplished by the addition of bases in the form of minerals that are rich in

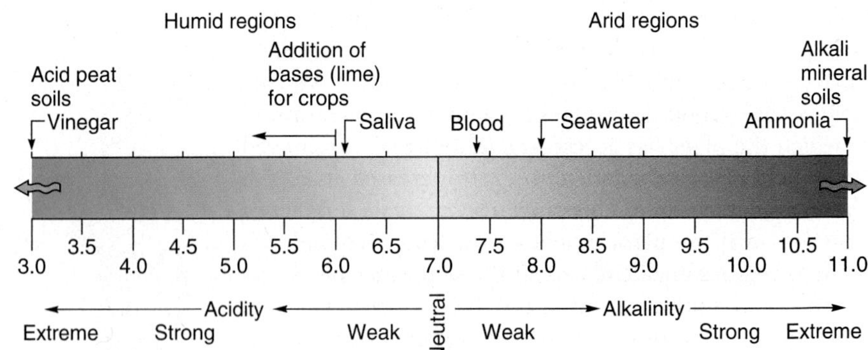

FIGURE 18.7 pH scale.
The pH scale measures acidity (lower pH) and alkalinity (higher pH). (The complete pH scale ranges between 0 and 14.)

base cations, usually lime (calcium carbonate, $CaCO_3$). Increased acidity in the soil solution accelerates the chemical weathering of mineral nutrients and increases their depletion rates.

Soil Formation Factors and Management

Soil is an open system involving physical inputs and outputs. Soil-forming factors are both *passive* (parent material, topography and relief, and time) and *dynamic* (climate, biology, and human activities). These factors work together as a system to form soils. The roles of these factors are considered here and in the soil order discussions that follow.

Natural Factors

Physical and chemical weathering of rocks in the upper lithosphere provides the raw mineral ingredients for soil formation. These are called *parent materials*, and their composition, texture, and chemical nature help determine the type of soil that forms. Clay minerals are the principal weathered by-products in soil. Also important in soil is the organic content present and all that is living in soil—bacteria, algae, fungi, worms, and insects.

Climate types correlate closely with soil types worldwide. The moisture, evaporation, and temperature regimes of climates determine the chemical reactions, organic activity, and eluviation rates of soils. Not only is the present climate important, but many soils exhibit the imprint of past climates, sometimes over thousands of years. Most notable is the effect of glaciation, particularly on the development of soils of Canada. Among other contributions, glaciation produced the loess soil materials that have been windblown thousands of kilometres to their present locations (Chapter 15).

Vegetation, animal, and bacterial activity determine the organic content of soil. The chemical makeup of the vegetation contributes to the acidity or alkalinity of the soil solution. For example, broadleaf trees tend to increase alkalinity, whereas needleleaf trees tend to produce higher acidity. Thus, when civilization moves into new areas and alters the natural vegetation by logging or ploughing, the affected soils are likewise altered, often permanently.

Topography also affects soil formation. Slopes that are too steep cannot have full soil development because gravity and erosional processes remove materials. Lands that are nearly level inhibit soil drainage and can become waterlogged. The compass orientation of slopes is important because it controls exposure to sunlight. In the Northern Hemisphere, a south-facing slope is warmer overall through the year because it receives direct sunlight. Water-balance relations are affected because north-facing slopes are colder, causing slower snowmelt and slower evaporation, providing more moisture for plants than is available on south-facing slopes, which tend to dry faster.

All of the identified factors in soil development (climate, biological activity, parent material, landforms and topography, and human activity) require *time* to operate. Over geologic time we learned that plate tectonics has redistributed landscapes, and thus subjected soil-forming processes to diverse conditions. Figure 18.8 illustrates how these factors combine to affect soil fertility.

Pedogenic Regimes Prior to the CSSC and the Soil Taxonomy systems, **pedogenic regimes** were used to describe soils. These regimes keyed specific soil-forming processes to climatic regions. Although each pedogenic process may be active in several soil orders and in different climates, not all are present in Canada, like the lateritic processes in the tropics. Such climate-based regimes are convenient for relating climate and soil processes. However, both the CSSC and the Soil Taxonomy system *recognize the great uncertainty and inconsistency in basing soil classification on such climatic variables*. Aspects of several pedogenic processes are discussed with appropriate soil orders:

- **laterization**: a leaching process active in humid and warm climates (in the tropics and subtropics and not in Canada)
- **salinization** (p. 615): a process that concentrates salts in soils in climates with excessive potential evapotranspiration (POTET) rates, discussed with the Solonetzic order
- **calcification** (Figure 18.12, p. 607): a process that produces an illuviated accumulation of calcium carbonates in continental climates, discussed with the Chernozemic order

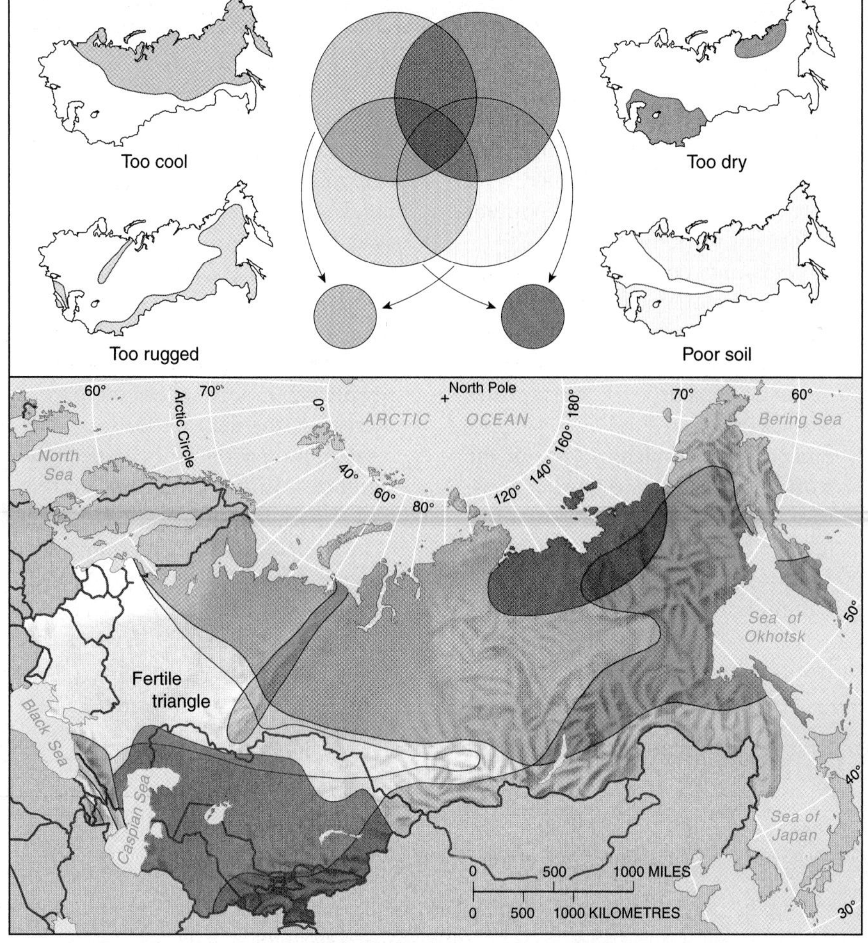

FIGURE 18.8 Soil fertility in Eurasia. Top: Four main factors influence soil fertility. Bottom: The fertile triangle of central Eurasia. The white area is highest in soil fertility (no negative factors). Areas shown with any colour or colour combination are limited for the reasons shown in the top illustration. The least-fertile area in Russia is northeastern Siberia. [After P. W. English and J. A. Miller, *World Regional Geography: A Question of Place*, p. 183, ©1989. Adapted by permission of John Wiley & Sons, Inc.]

- **podzolization** (Figure 18.20, p. 615): a process of soil acidification associated with forest soils in cool climates, discussed with the Podzolic order
- **gleysation** (p. 607): a process that includes an accumulation of humus and a thick, water-saturated grey layer of clay beneath, usually in cold, wet climates and poor drainage conditions, discussed with the Gleysolic order

The Human Factor

Human intervention has a major impact on soils. Millennia ago, farmers in most cultures learned to plant slopes "on the contour"—to make rows or mounds around a slope at the same elevation, not vertically up and down the slope. Planting on the contour prevents water from flowing straight down the slope and thus reduces soil erosion. It was common to plant and harvest a floodplain but to live on higher ground nearby. Floods were celebrated as blessings that brought water, nutrients, and more soil to the land. Society is drifting away from these commonsense strategies.

A few centimetres' thickness of prime farmland soil may require *500 years* to mature. Yet, this same thickness is being lost annually through soil erosion when the soil-holding vegetation is removed and the land is plowed regardless of topography. Over the same period, exposed soils may be completely leached of needed cations, thereby losing their fertility. Unlike living species, soils do not reproduce nor can they be recreated.

Some 35% of farmlands are losing soil faster than it can form—a loss exceeding 23 billion metric tons (25 billion tons) per year. Soil depletion and loss are at record levels from Iowa to China, Peru to Ethiopia, the Middle East to the Americas. The impact on society is potentially disastrous as population and food demands increase (see News Report 18.1).

Soil erosion can be compensated for in the short run by using more fertilizer, increasing irrigation, and by planting higher-yielding strains. But the potential yield from prime agricultural land will drop by as much as 20% over the next 20 years if only moderate erosion continues. One 1995 study tabulated the market value of lost nutrients and other variables in the most comprehensive soil-erosion study to date. The sum of direct damage (to agricultural land) and indirect damage (to streams, society's infrastructure, and human health) was estimated at more than $25 billion a year in the United States and hundreds of billions of dollars worldwide. (Of course, this is a controversial assessment in the agricultural industry.) The cost to bring erosion under control in the United States is estimated at approximately $8.5 billion, or about 30 cents on

News Report 18.1

Soil Is Slipping Through Our Fingers

- The U.S. General Accounting Office estimates that from 3 to 5 million acres of prime farmland are lost each year in the United States through mismanagement or conversion to nonagricultural uses. About half of all cropland in Canada and the United States is experiencing excessive rates of soil erosion—these countries are two of the few that monitor loss of topsoil.
- The Canadian Environmental Advisory Council estimated that the organic content of cultivated prairie soils has declined by as much as 40% compared with noncultivated native soils. In Ontario and Québec, losses of organic content are as high as 50%, and losses are even higher in the Atlantic Provinces, which were naturally low in organic content before cultivation.
- A 1995 study completed at Cornell University concluded that soil erosion is a major environmental threat to the sustainability and productive capacity of agriculture worldwide.
- Since 1950, as much as 38% of the world's farmable land has been lost to soil erosion, and the rate continues at 5 to 6 million hectares (about 12 to 15 million acres) per year—560 million hectares, 1380 million acres, to date (World Resources Institute and UNEP, 1997).
- The causes for degraded soils, in order of severity, include overgrazing, vegetation removal, agricultural activities, overexploitation, and industrial and bioindustrial use (UNEP, 1997).
- The world's human population is growing at the rate of 6.9 million people a month (net increase), increasing the demand for food and agricultural productivity. Especially significant is that proportion of the global population that are adopting a meat-centred diet as American tastes and food outlets spread worldwide—as we see in the next chapter, meat production is an inefficient use of the grain supply.

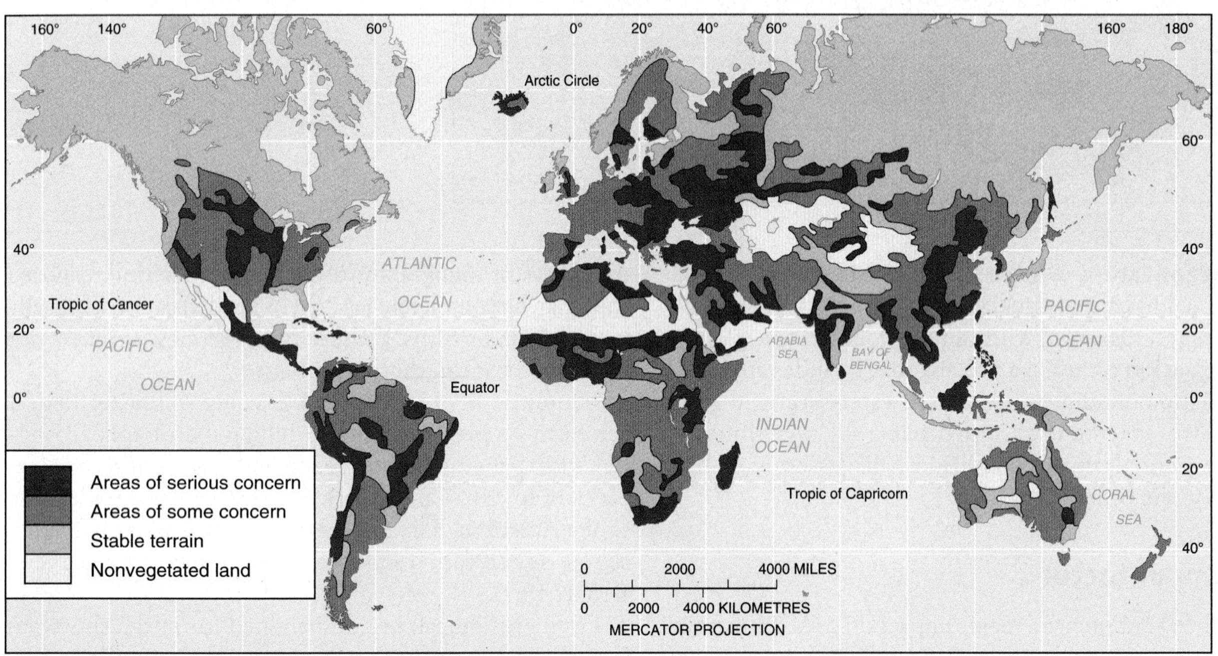

(a)

(b)

FIGURE 18.9 Soil degradation.
(a) Approximately 1.2 billion hectares (3.0 billion acres) of Earth's soils suffer degradation through erosion caused by human misuse and abuse. (b) Typical loss through soil sheet erosion on a northeastern Wisconsin farm. One millimetre of soil lost from an acre weighs about 4.5 metric tons (5 tons). [(a) *A Global Assessment of Soil Degradation*, adapted from United Nations Environment Programme, International Soil Reference and Information Centre, "Map of Status of Human-Induced Soil Degradation," Sheet 2, Nairobi, Kenya, 1990; (b) photo by D. P. Burnside/Photo Researchers, Inc.]

every dollar of damage and loss. In Canada as well, erosion prevention is cheaper than the cost of losses from soil erosion. Figure 18.9 maps regions of soil loss.

Our spatial impact on the precious soil resource must be recognized and protective measures taken. There is a need for cooperative international action. Critical is a long-term assessment of cost (continued behaviour) and benefits (mitigated damage and preservation of the market value of prime soils) of continued practices versus soil conservation actions—a cost–benefit analysis. In sustaining natural systems, the benefits of doing things right far outweigh the continued costs of doing things wrong, over the long term. Focus Study 18.1 (p. 619) examines where planning could have avoided huge losses to soil and wildlife.

Soil Classification

Classification of soils is complicated by the continuing interaction of physical properties and processes just discussed. This interaction creates thousands of distinct soils, with well over 15,000 soil series identified in Canada and the United States alone. Not surprisingly, different classification systems are in use worldwide. Canada, the United States, the United Kingdom, Germany, Australia, Russia, and the United Nations Food and Agricultural Organization each have their own soil classification system. Each system reflects the environment of its country. The remainder of this chapter will outline the Canadian System of Soil Classification (CSSC). Appendix B contains information about the U.S. Soil Taxonomy system for classifying soils. For information on tropical soils not in the CSSC, please refer to the Soil Taxonomy in Appendix B.

The Canadian System of Soil Classification (CSSC)

Canadian efforts at soil classification began in 1914 with the partial mapping of Ontario's soils by A. J. Galbraith. Efforts to develop a taxonomic system spread countrywide, anchored by universities in each province. Regional differences in soil classification emerged, further confused by a lack of specific soil details. By 1936, only 1.7% of Canadian soil had been surveyed (15 million hectares).

Canadian scientists needed a taxonomic system based on observable and measurable properties in soils specific to Canada. This meant a departure from Marbut's 1938 U.S. classification. Canada's first taxonomic system was introduced in 1955, splitting away from the soil classification effort in the United States and the Fourth Approximation stage. Classification work progressed through the Canada Soil Survey Committee after 1970 and was replaced by the Expert Committee on Soil Survey in 1978, all under Agriculture Canada. In 1978, the Expert Committee on Soil Survey was formed, replacing the Canada Soil Survey Committee. This committee worked on interpretation, mapping systems, soil degradation, and soil classification and produced the second edition of the *Canadian System of Soil Classification* in 1987. Work continued and with the classification of Vertisols and further development of the CSSC. The third edition of the *Canadian System of Soil Classification* was published in 1998.

The **Canadian System of Soil Classification (CSSC)** provides taxa for all soils presently recognized in Canada and is adapted to Canada's expanses of forest, tundra, prairie, frozen ground, and colder climates. As in the U.S. Soil Taxonomy system, the CSSC classifications are based on observable and measurable properties found in real soils rather than idealized soils that may result from the interactions of genetic processes. The system is flexible in that its framework can accept new findings and information in step with progressive developments in the soil sciences.

Categories of Classification in the CSSC

Categorical levels are at the heart of a taxonomic system. These categories are based on soil profile properties organized at five levels, nested in a hierarchical pattern to permit generalization at several levels of detail. Each level is referred to as a category of classification. The levels in the CSSC are briefly described here, as adapted from *The Canadian Soil Classification System*, Third Edition, Publication 1646 (Ottawa: Research Branch, Agriculture and Agri-Food Canada, 1998), p. 7.

- *Order*: Each of ten soil orders has pedon properties that reflect the soil environment and effects of active soil-forming processes.
- *Great group*: Subdivisions of each order reflect differences in the dominant processes or other major contributing processes. As an example, in Luvic Gleysols (great group name followed by order) the dominant process is gleying—reduction of iron and other minerals—resulting from poor drainage under either grass or forest cover with Aeg and Btg horizons (see Table 18.2).
- *Subgroup*: Subgroups are differentiated by the content and arrangement of horizons that indicate the relation of the soil to a great group or order or the subtle transition toward soils of another order.
- *Family*: This is a subdivision of a subgroup. Parent material characteristics such as texture and mineralogy, soil climatic factors, and soil reactions are important.
- *Series*: Detailed features of the pedon differentiate subdivisions of the family—the essential soil-sampling unit. Pedon horizons fall within a narrow range of colour, texture, structure, consistence, porosity, moisture, chemical reaction, thickness, and composition.

Soil Horizons in the CSSC

Soil horizons are named and standardized as diagnostic in the classification process. Several mineral and organic horizons and layers are used in the CSSC. Three mineral horizons are recognized by capital letter designation, followed by lowercase suffixes for further description. Principal soil-mineral horizons and suffixes are presented in Table 18.2.

Table 18.2 Three Mineral Horizons and Mineral Horizon Suffixes Used in the CSSC

Symbol	Mineral Horizon Description
A	Forms at or near the surface; experiences *eluviation*, or leaching, of finer particles or minerals. Several subdivisions are identified, with the surface usually darker and richer in organic content than lower horizons (***Ah***); or a paler, lighter zone below that reflects removal of organic matter with clays and oxides of aluminum and iron leached (removed) to lower horizons (***Ae***).
B	Experiences *illuviation*, a depositional process, as demonstrated by accumulations of clays (***Bt***), sesquioxides of aluminum or iron, and possibly an enrichment of organic debris (***Bh***), and the development of soil structure. Coloration is important in denoting whether hydrolysis, reduction, or oxidation processes are operational for the assignment of a descriptive suffix.
C	Exhibits little effect from pedogenic processes operating in the ***A*** and ***B*** horizons, except the process of gleysation associated with poor drainage and the reduction of iron, denoted (***Cg***), and the accumulation of calcium and magnesium carbonates (***Cca***) and more soluble salts (***Cs***) and (***Csa***).

Symbol	Horizon Suffix Description
b	A buried soil horizon.
c	Irreversible cementation of a pedogenic horizon; e.g., cemented by $CaCO_3$.
ca	Lime accumulation of at least 10 cm thickness that exceeds in concentration that of the unenriched parent material by at least 5%.
cc	Irreversible cemented concretions, typically in pellet form.
e	Used with ***A*** mineral horizons (***Ae***) to denote eluviation of clay, Fe, Al, or organic matter.
f	Enriched principally with illuvial iron and aluminum combined with organic matter, reddish in upper portions and yellowish at depth, determined through specific criteria. Used with ***B*** horizons alone.
g	Grey to blue colours, prominent mottling, or both, produced by intense chemical reduction. Various applications to ***A, B***, and ***C*** horizons.
h	Enriched with organic matter: accumulation in place or biological mixing (***Ah***) or subsurface enrichment through illuviation (***Bh***).
j	A modifier suffix for ***e, f, g, n***, and ***t*** to denote limited change or failure to meet specified criteria denoted by that letter.
k	Presence of carbonates as indicated by visible effervescence with dilute hydrochloric acid (HCl).
m	Used with ***B*** horizons slightly altered by hydrolysis, oxidation, or solution, or all three to denote a change in colour or structure.
n	Accumulation of exchangeable calcium (Ca) in ratio to exchangeable sodium (Na) that is 10 or less, with the following characteristics: prismatic or columnar structure, dark coatings on ped surfaces, and hard consistence when dry. Used with ***B*** horizons alone.
p	***A*** or ***O*** horizons disturbed by cultivation, logging, and habitation. May be used when ploughing intrudes on previous ***B*** horizons.
s	Presence of salts, including gypsum, visible as crystals or veins or surface crusts of salt crystals, and by lowered crop yields. Usually with ***C*** but may appear with any horizon and lowercase suffixes.
sa	A secondary enrichment of salts more soluble than Ca or Mg carbonates, exceeding unenriched parent material, in a horizon at least 10 cm thick.
t	Illuvial enrichment of the ***B*** horizon with silicate clay that must exceed in overlying ***Ae*** horizon by 3% to 20%, depending on the clay content of the ***Ae*** horizon.
u	Markedly disrupted by physical or faunal processes other than cryoturbation.
x	Fragipan formation—a loamy subsurface horizon of high bulk density and very low organic content. When dry, it has a hard consistence and seems to be cemented.
y	Affected by cryoturbation (frost action) with disrupted and broken horizons and incorporation of materials from other horizons. Application to ***A, B***, and ***C*** horizons and in combination with other suffixes.
z	A frozen layer.

Four organic horizons are identified in the Canadian classification system. O is further defined through subhorizon designations. Note that for organic soils, such layers are identified as *tiers*. These organic horizons are detailed in Table 18.3.

The Ten Soil Orders of the CSSC

The ten orders of the CSSC, and related great groups, are summarized below with a general description of properties, related great groups, an estimated percentage of land area

Table 18.3 Four Organic Horizons Used in the CSSC

Symbol	Description
O	Organic materials, mainly mosses, rushes, and woody materials
L	Mainly discernible leaves, twigs, and woody materials
F	Partially decomposed, somewhat recognizable **L** materials
H	Indiscernible organic materials
O is further defined through subhorizon designations:	
Of	Readily identifiable fibric materials
Om	Mesic materials of intermediate decomposition
Oh	Humic material at an advanced stage of decomposition—low fibre, high bulk density

for the soil order, a fertility assessment, and any applicable soil taxonomy equivalent. Figure 18.10 is a generalized map of the soil landscapes of Canada. This map illustrates the great variation of soils across the country.

The *Soil Landscapes of Canada* (SLC) site at **http://sis.agr.gc.ca/cansis/** is useful. Here you will find a wonderful assortment of landscape and soil profile photographs, arranged geographically across Canada from east to west. The site also has an interactive GIS online mapping application. Version 2.2 SLC Component Mapping (December 1996) is operational and involves the CSSC and the Canadian Land Resource Network (CLRN). The component mapping involves a GIS model consisting of layers that include the major characteristics of soil and land for all of Canada. You can select a spatial area and a variety of attributes to display on the map (drainage class, soil type, rooting depth, local surface form, slope, and vegetation cover, among others).

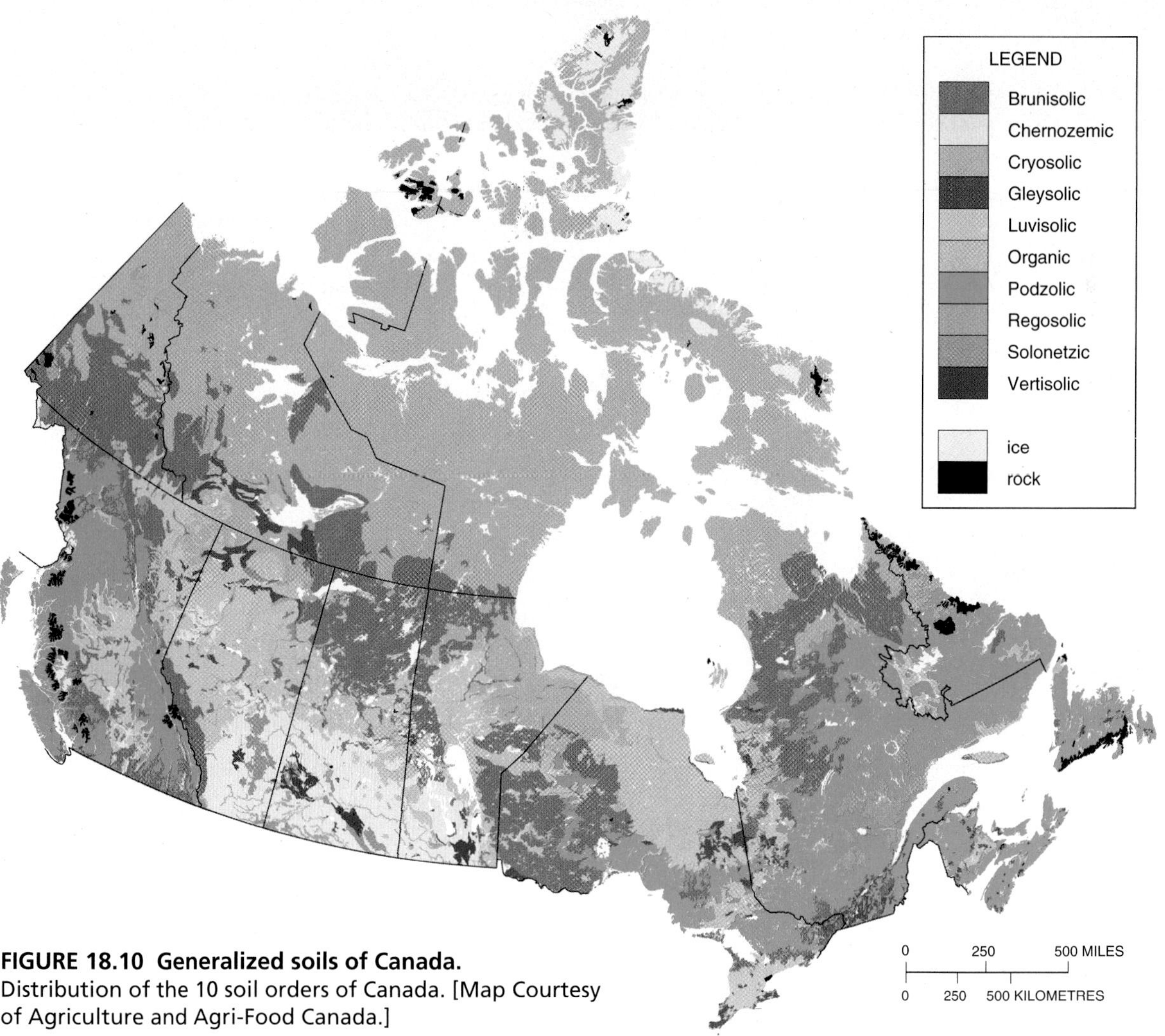

FIGURE 18.10 Generalized soils of Canada. Distribution of the 10 soil orders of Canada. [Map Courtesy of Agriculture and Agri-Food Canada.]

At the heart of the Canadian System of Soil Classification are 10 general orders. These orders were developed specifically for soils in Canada and are presented here with their associated great groups and subgroups. The following descriptions are summarized from the *Canadian System of Soil Classification*.

Brunisolic Order The **Brunisolic** order is the first order alphabetically. These soils are sufficiently developed to exclude them from the Regosolic order, but the degree of development of soil horizons is so low that they are different from other orders (Figure 18.11). These soils form under mixed forest and have brownish Bm horizons,

(a)

(b)

Brunisolic

0 500 Kilometres

(c)

FIGURE 18.11 Brunisolic order.
(a) Soil profile from southern Ontario. (b) Hay and pastureland that is typical of the Melanic Brunisolic landscape in southern Ontario. (c) Map of distribution of Brunisolic order in Canada. [Photos by (a) and (b) Agriculture and Agri-Food Canada; (c) map by Pam Schaus, data from Agriculture and Agri-Food Canada, Soil Landscapes of Canada.]

although various colours are possible. They can also develop under shrubs and grassland. Their B horizon is the most diagnostic feature with Bm, Bfj, thin Bf, or Btj horizons. Brunisols develop under well- to imperfectly drained conditions and lack the Podzolic B horizon of the Podzols, although they are surrounded by them in the St. Lawrence Lowlands. The soils of this order are rated as medium and variable in fertility and account for 14% of the surface area of Canada. The great groups of the Brunisolic order include Melanic Brunisol, Eutric Brunisol, Sombric Brunisol, and Dystric Brunisol. There are 18 subgroups within this order.

Calcification Process Some Brunisolic and Chernozemic soils and other soil orders are highly calcareous. *Calcification* (Figure 18.12) is the accumulation of calcium carbonate or magnesium carbonate in the B and C horizons. Calcification by calcium carbonate ($CaCO_3$), among others, forms a diagnostic subsurface horizon along the boundary between dry and humid climates. These deposits harden or cement to become *caliche*, which can form in the southern prairies.

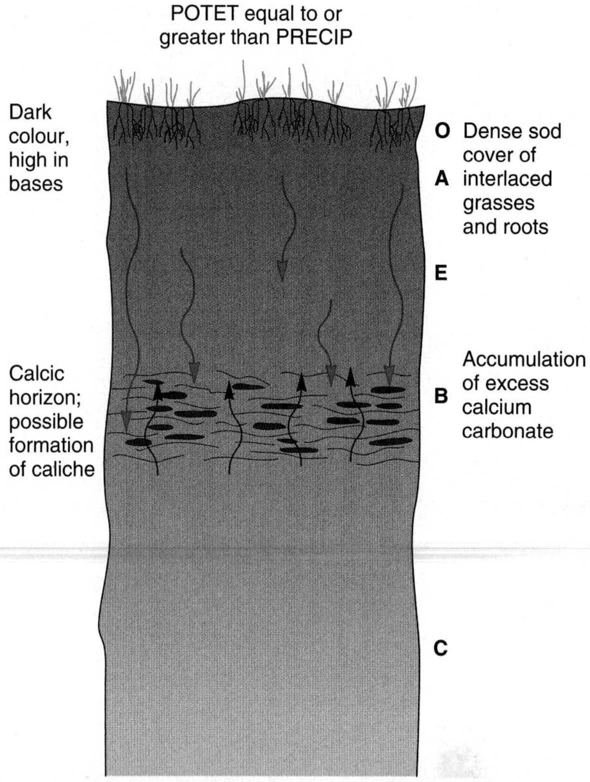

FIGURE 18.12 Calcification in soil.
The calcification process in drier Brunisolic soils (in the U.S. the Aridisol/Mollisol soils) occurs in climatic regimes that have potential evapotranspiration equal to or greater than precipitation.

Chernozemic Order The **Chernozemic** order includes well- to imperfectly drained soils of the steppe–grassland–forest transition in southern Alberta; Saskatchewan; Manitoba; Okanagan Valley, British Columbia; and Palouse Prairie, British Columbia and accounts for 4% of the solid surface of Canada. The surface horizons are darkened by organic matter accumulation that results from decomposition of grasses and forbs in the vegetation cover (Figure 18.13). Most soils are frozen in winter and dry in summer with a mean annual soil temperature greater than or equal to 0°C, but usually less than 5.5°C.

Chernozemic soils have high fertility, especially for growing wheat, but can be subject to salinization. Salinization results from excessive potential evapotranspiration rates in deserts and semiarid regions. Salts dissolved in soil water migrate to surface horizons and are deposited there as the water evaporates. These deposits appear as subsurface salty horizons, which will damage or kill plants when the horizons occur near the root zone. This process is especially of concern where soils are irrigated. Focus Study 18.1 outlines the problems associated with salinization and the buildup of toxic materials in the soil. The great groups of the Chernozemic order are Brown Chernozem, Dark Brown Chernozem, Black Chernozem, and Dark Grey Chernozem. There are 38 subgroups within this order. Figure 18.14 shows the transition between great groups within the Chernozem order, principally in response to climate differences.

Cryosolic Order The **Cryosolic** order dominates the northern third of Canada, with permafrost closer to the surface and composed of mineral and organic soil deposits. Generally, it is found north of the treeline, in fine-textured soils in the subarctic forest, or in some organic soils in Boreal forests (Figure 18.15, p. 610). The Ah horizon is lacking or thin. Cryoturbation (frost action) is common and is often denoted by patterned ground circles, polygons, and stripes. Cryosols have a mean annual temperature less than or equal to 0°C. The subgroups of this order are based on the degree of cryoturbation and the nature of the mineral or organic soil material. Fertility ratings are not applicable to these soils that cover 28% of Canada's land area. The great groups are Turbic Cryosol, Static Cryosol, and Organic Cryosol and there are 15 subgroups in this order.

Gleysolic Order *Gleysation* is a soil-forming process in poorly drained conditions where organic matter accumulates in the upper soil layers and mottling occurs in the lower layers resulting from reduction of iron and other elements. The **Gleysolic** order of soils is defined on the basis of colour and mottling that results from chronic reducing conditions inherent in poorly drained mineral soils under wet conditions. A high water table and long periods of water saturation are common to these soils. They are spotty in areal distribution, appearing within other soil orders, occasionally being the dominant soil of an area (Figure 18.16, p. 611) and account for 3% of the land surface. A diagnostic Bg horizon is present in these soils that are rated as high to medium in fertility. The great groups of this order are Luvic Gleysol, Humic Gleysol, and Gleysol. There are 13 subgroups.

Luvisolic Order *Eluviation-illuviation* processes produce a light-coloured Ae horizon and a diagnostic Bt horizon.

(a)

FIGURE 18.13 Chernozemic order.
(a) Soil profile from southern Prairies. Chernozemic landscape images associated with dry grasslands can be seen in Figure 18.14.
(b) Map showing distribution of the Chernozemic order in Canada. [(a) Photo by Agriculture and Agri-Food Canada; (b) map by Pam Schaus, data from Agriculture and Agri-Food Canada, Soil Landscapes of Canada.]

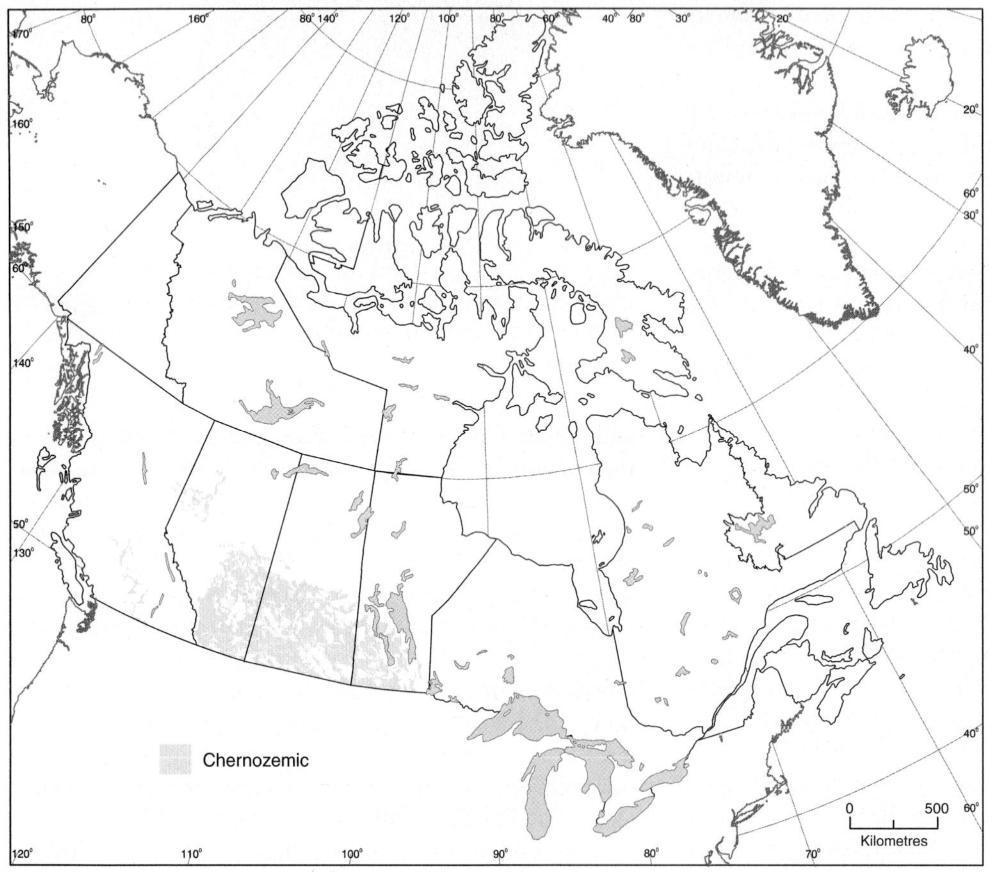

(b)

Soils of this order develop beneath the mixed deciduous–coniferous forests. There are major occurrences of **Luvisolic** soils in the St. Lawrence Lowlands. Luvisolic soils occur from the zone of permafrost to the southern extremity of Ontario and from Newfoundland to British Columbia. Their greatest areal extent is in the northern Interior Plains under deciduous, mixed, and coniferous forest (Figure 18.17, p. 612). The fertility rating is high for these soils that cover 7% of the land surface. The great groups of the Luvisolic order are Gray Brown Luvisol and Gray Luvisol and include 18 subgroups.

Organic Order Soils of the **Organic** order are composed largely of organic materials. They include peat, bog, and muck soils and are commonly saturated with water for prolonged periods of time (Figure 18.18, p. 613). They are widespread and are associated with poorly to very poorly drained depressions, but can be found under upland forest environments (Folisols) and account for 9% of the land surface. To qualify as organic, these soils must contain greater than 17% organic carbon and exceed 30% organic matter by weight overall. Organic soils are rated as high to medium in fertility depending upon drainage and the available nutri-

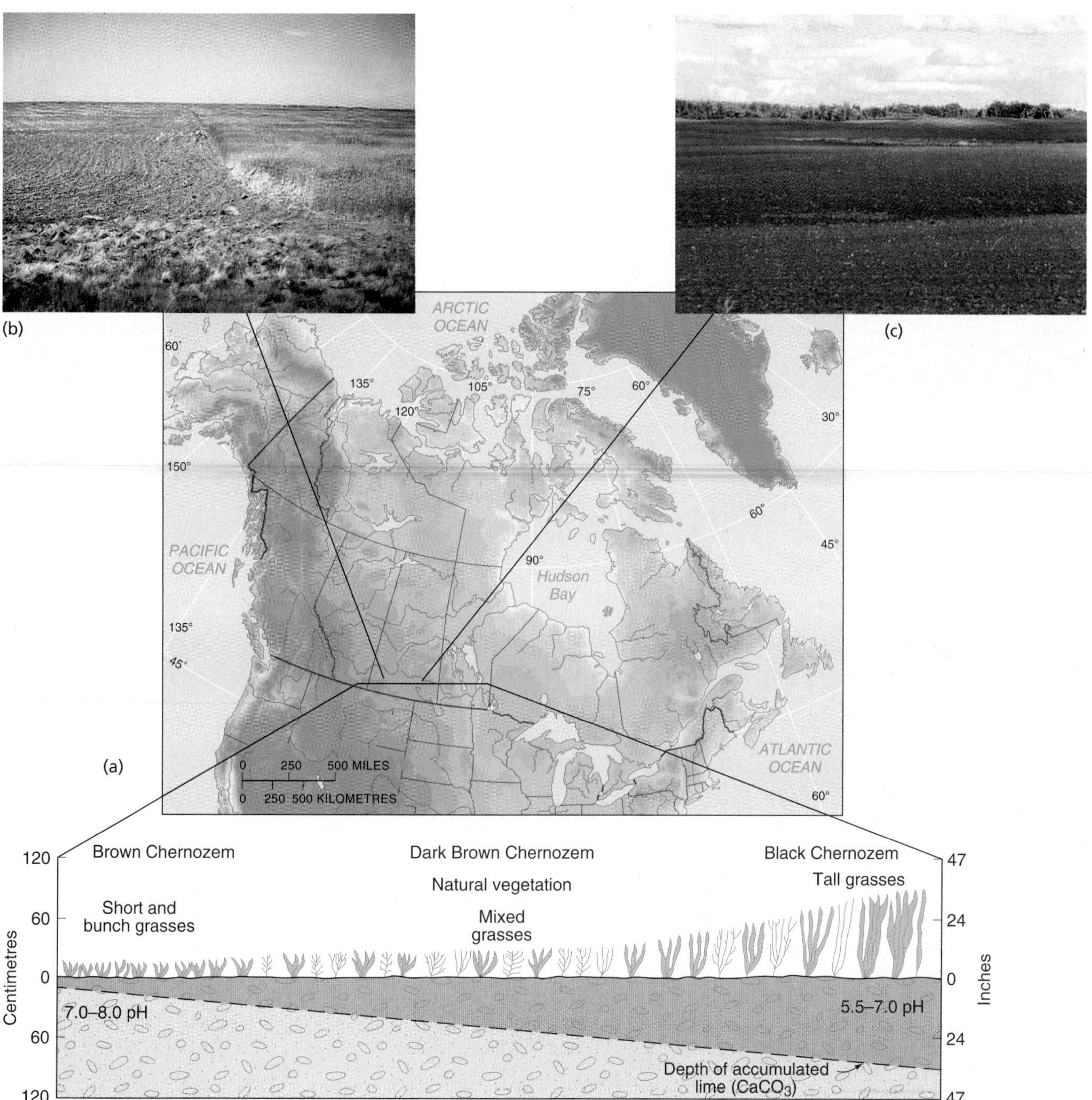

FIGURE 18.14 Soils of the southern Prairies.
(a) Brown Chernozemic soils in the west, Dark Brown Chernozemic in the central portions, and Black Chernozemic in the east—a soil continuum in the southern Canadian Prairies. (b) Brown Chernozemic soil landscape—soils developed in the short grass prairie of the southwestern Prairies in Alberta and Saskatchewan. Photo from south-central Saskatchewan shows typical crops. (c) Black Chernozem landscape—soils are typical of the mixed to tall grass prairie found in eastern Saskatchewan and southern Manitoba. [(a) Illustration adapted from N. C. Brady, *The Nature and Properties of Soils*, 10th ed., © 1990 by Macmillan Publishing Company, adapted by permission; photos (b) and (c) courtesy of Agriculture and Agri-Food Canada.]

ents. The great groups contained in this order are Fibrisol, Mesisol, Humisol, and Folisol and include 31 subgroups.

Podzolic Order **Podzolic** soils develop beneath coniferous forests and sometimes heath vegetation and result from leaching of the overlying horizons in moist, cool to cold climates (Figure 18.19, p. 614). They result from *podzolization*, a soil-forming process in which a highly leached soil with strong surface acidity develops in cool, moist climates (Figure 18.20, p. 615). The Boreal forest that encircles the globe in northern latitudes is largely underlain by Podzolic soils. Iron, aluminum, and organic

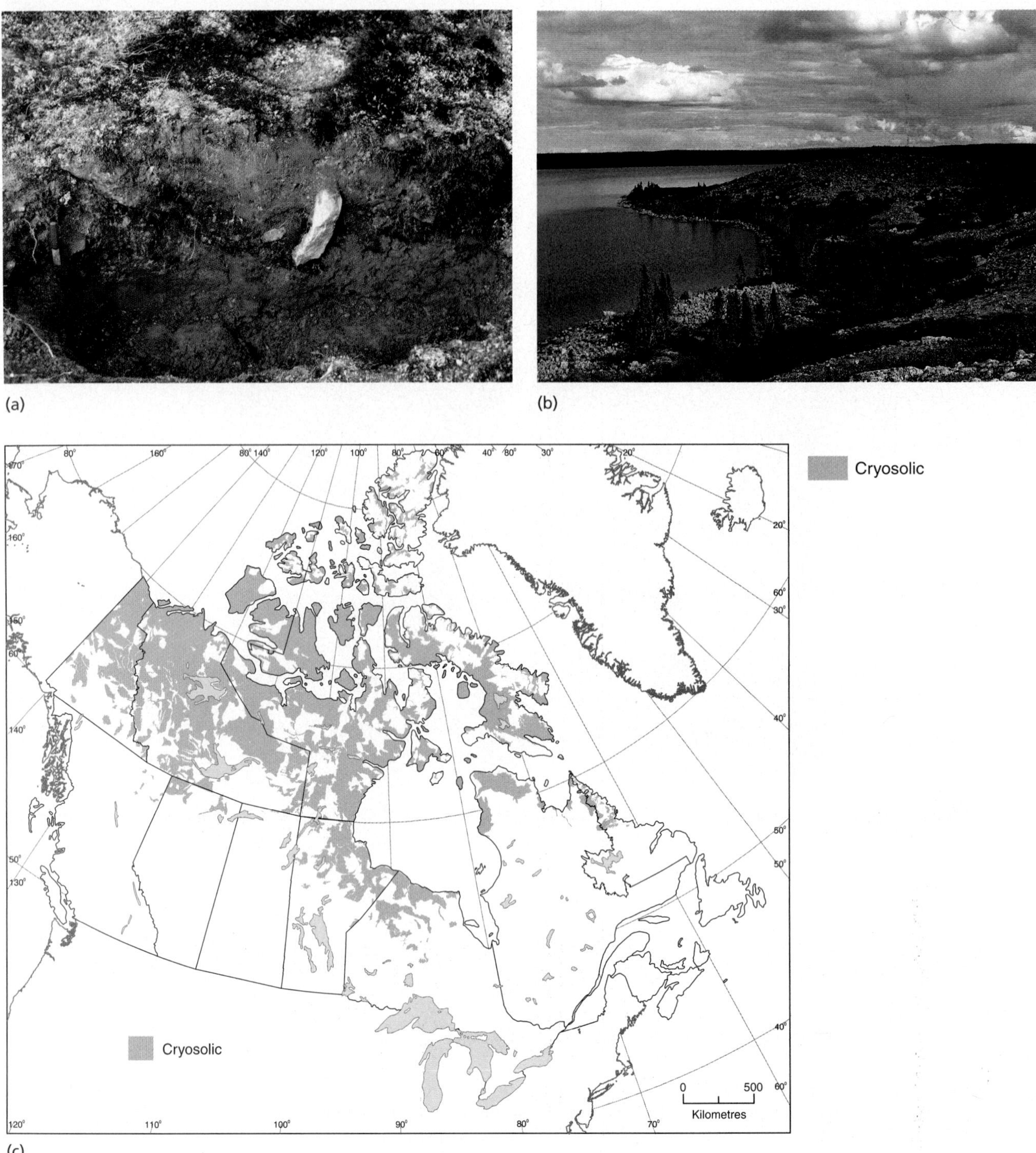

FIGURE 18.15 Cryosolic order.
Cryosols discussed on p. 607. (a) Soil profile of Turbic Cryosolic soil from Northwest Territories. (b) Turbic Cryosolic landscape in Northwest Territories in which patches of soil support vegetation growth. (c) Map of distribution of Cryosolic order in Canada. [Photos (a) and (b) courtesy of Agriculture and Agri-Food Canada; (c) map by Pam Schaus, data from Agriculture and Agri-Food Canada, Soil Landscapes of Canada.]

matter form the L, F, and H horizons and are redeposited in the Podzolic B horizon. A diagnostic Bh, Bhf, or Bf horizon is present depending upon the great group. Podzolic soils dominate in western British Columbia, Ontario, Québec, and Atlantic Canada and account for most of the agricultural surface cover in Canada, 14% of the total land area. The fertility rating for Podzolic soils is low to medium depending on acidity. The great groups in the Podzolic order are Humic, Ferro-humic Podzol, and Humo-ferric Podzol and include 25 subgroups.

(continued p. 615)

(a)

(b)

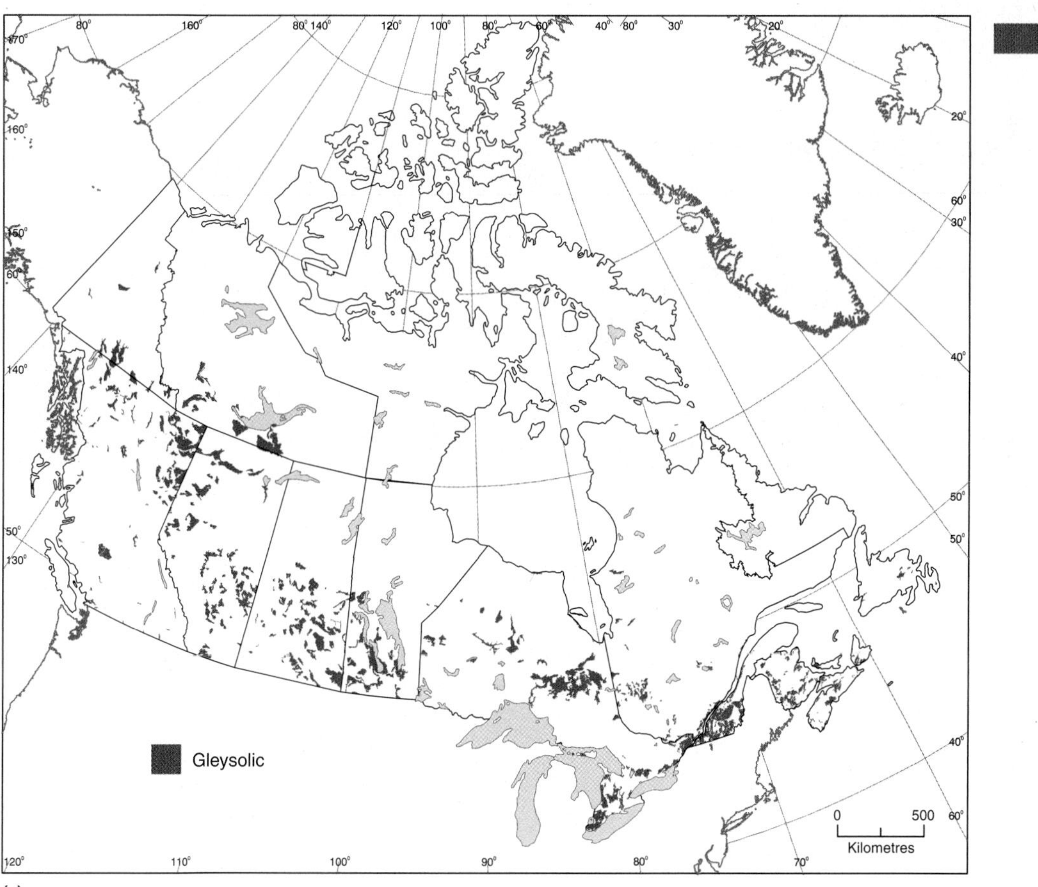

(c)

FIGURE 18.16 Gleysolic order.
Gleysols discussed on p. 607. (a) Soil profile of Gleysol from Atlantic Canada. (b) Poorly drained soils of the Gleysolic landscape in Atlantic Canada are often used for forage crops. These soils are highly fertile when drainage is improved. (c) Map of distribution of Gleysolic order in Canada. [Photos (a) and (b) courtesy of Agriculture and Agri-Food Canada; (c) map by Pam Schaus, data from Agriculture and Agri-Food Canada, Soil Landscapes of Canada.]

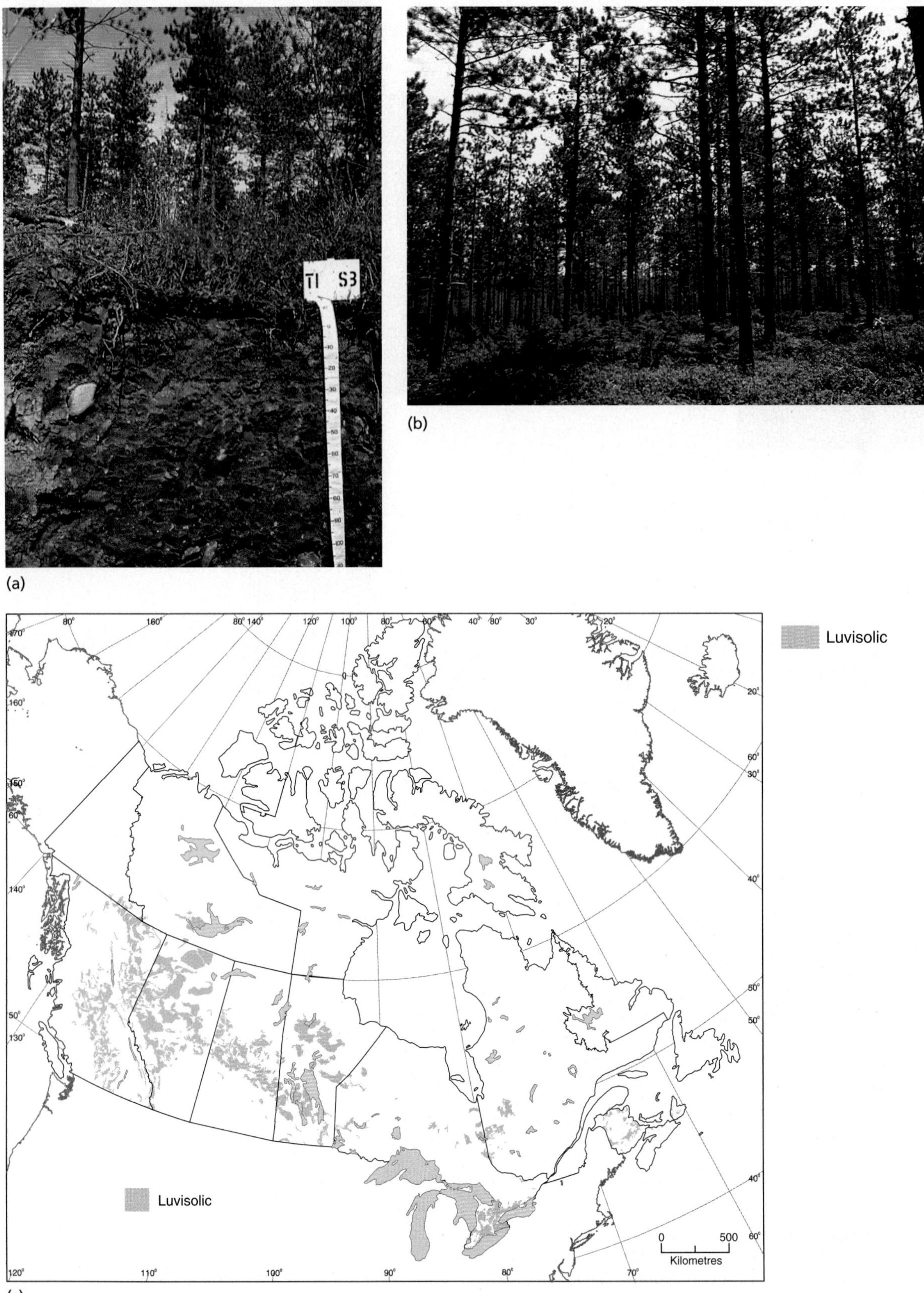

FIGURE 18.17 Luvisolic order.
Luvisols discussed on p. 607. (a) Soil profile of Gray Luvisol from Atlantic Canada. (b) Coniferous forests are typical of the Gray Luvisol landscape in Atlantic Canada. (c) Map of distribution of Luvisolic order in Canada. [Photos (a) and (b) courtesy of Agriculture and Agri-Food Canada; (c) map by Pam Schaus, data from Agriculture and Agri-Food Canada, Soil Landscapes of Canada.]

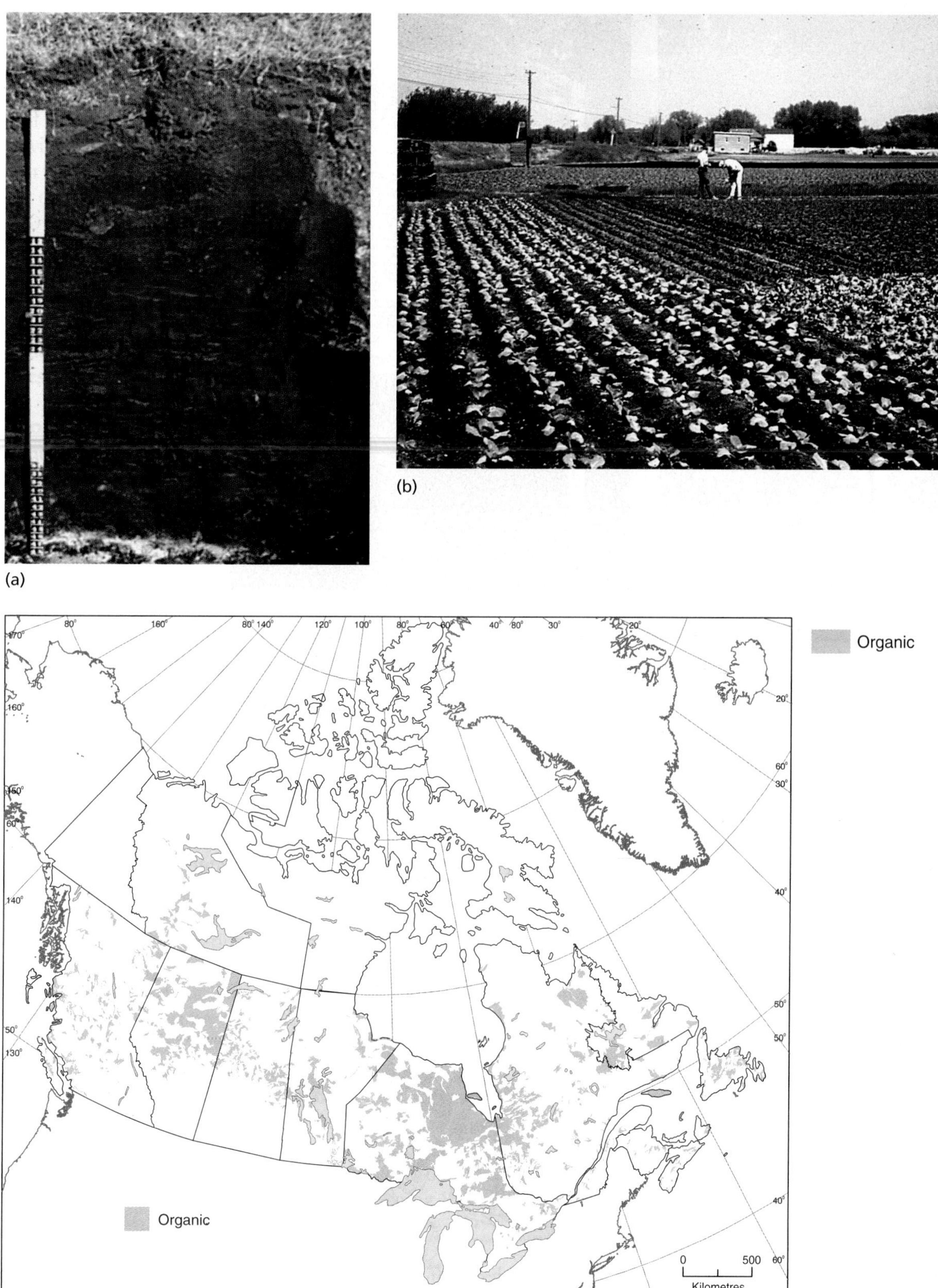

FIGURE 18.18 Organic order.
Organic soil order discussed on p. 608. (a) Organic soil profile from Southern Ontario. (b) Vegetable and market crops are often grown on drained organic soils in southern Ontario. (c) Map of distribution of Organic order in Canada. [Photos (a) and (b) courtesy of Agriculture and Agri-Food Canada; (c) map by Pam Schaus, data from Agriculture and Agri-Food Canada, Soil Landscapes of Canada.]

The biosphere, the sphere of life and organic activity, extends from the ocean floor to about 8 km (5 mi) altitude in the atmosphere. The biosphere includes myriad ecosystems from simple to complex, each operating within general spatial boundaries. An **ecosystem** is a self-sustaining association of living plants and animals and their nonliving physical environment. Earth's biosphere itself is a collection of ecosystems within the natural boundary of the atmosphere and Earth's crust.

Natural ecosystems are open systems for both solar energy and matter, with almost all ecosystem boundaries functioning as transition zones rather than as sharp demarcations. Distinct ecosystems—for example, forests, seas, mountaintops, deserts, beaches, islands, lakes, and ponds—make up the larger whole.

Ecology is the study of the relationships between organisms and their environment and among the various ecosystems in the biosphere. The word *ecology*, developed by German naturalist Ernst Haeckel in 1869, is derived from the Greek *oikos* ("household," or "place to live") and *logos* ("study of"). **Biogeography** is the study of the distribution of plants and animals, the diverse spatial patterns they create, and the physical and biological processes, past and present, that produce Earth's species richness.

The degree to which modern society understands Earth's biogeography and conserves Earth's living legacy will determine the extent of our success as a species and the long-term survival of a habitable Earth:

> The time is ripe to step up and expand current efforts to understand the great interlocking systems of air, water, and minerals nourishing the Earth. . . . Moreover, without vigorous action toward that goal, nations will be seriously handicapped in trying to cope with proven and suspected threats to ecosystems and to human health and welfare resulting from alterations in the cycles of carbon, nitrogen, phosphorus, sulfur, and related materials. . . . Society depends upon this life-support system of planet Earth.*

Earth's most influential biotic (living) agents are the humans. This is not arrogance; it is fact, because we powerfully influence every ecosystem on Earth. From the time humans first developed agriculture, the raising of animals, and the use of fire, we began a process that has led to our dominance over Earth's physical systems. The penguin colony in the chapter-opening photo has declined 24% in numbers since 1970 because of environmental changes we discuss in this chapter.

Since life arose on the planet, there have been six major extinctions. The fifth one was 65 million years ago, whereas the sixth is happening across the present decades. Of all these extinction episodes, this is the only one of biotic origin, caused for the most part by human activity. We are the greatest evolutionary force as we essentially dominate freshwater quantity and quality, croplands, ocean fishery production, nitrogen and other chemical budgets, the concentration of greenhouse gases, and the present extinction rate.

In this chapter: We explore ecosystems, and the community, habitat, and niche concepts. Plants are the essential living component in the biosphere, translating solar energy into usable forms to energize life. The role of nonliving systems, including biogeochemical cycles, is examined. We cover the organization of living ecosystems along complex food chains and webs. The biodiversity of living organisms is seen as a product of biological evolution over the past 3.6 billion years. Ecosystem stability and resilience, and how living landscapes change over space and time through the process of succession, is important. Included is coverage of the effects of global change on ecosystems and rates of succession.

Ecosystem Components and Cycles

An ecosystem is a complex of many variables, all functioning independently yet in concert, with complicated flows of energy and matter (Figure 19.1). An ecosystem includes both *biotic* (living) and *abiotic* (nonliving) components. Nearly all ecosystems depend on a direct input of solar energy; the few limited ones that exist in dark caves, in wells, or on the ocean floor depend on chemical reactions (chemosynthesis).

Ecosystems are divided into subsystems, with the biotic portion composed of producers (plants), consumers (animals), and detritus feeders (worms, mites, bacteria, fungi).

*G. F. White and M. K. Tolba, *Global Life Support Systems*, United Nations Environment Programme Information, No. 47 (Nairobi, Kenya: United Nations, 1979), p. 1.

FIGURE 19.1 The web of life.
"Life devours itself: everything that eats is itself eaten; everything that can be eaten is eaten; every chemical that is made by life can be broken down by life; all the sunlight that can be used is used. . . . The web of life has so many threads that a few can be broken without making it all unravel, and if this were not so, life could not have survived the normal accidents of weather and time, but still the snapping of each thread makes the whole web shudder, and weakens it. . . . You can never do just one thing: the effects of what you do in the world will always spread out like ripples in a pond." [Quotation from Friends of the Earth and Amory Lovins, The United Nations Stockholm Conference, *Only One Earth* (London: Earth Island Limited, 1972), p. 20. Photo by Robert W. Christopherson.]

The abiotic flows in an ecosystem include gaseous, hydrologic, and mineral cycles. Figure 19.2 illustrates these essential elements of an ecosystem.

Communities

A convenient biotic subdivision within an ecosystem is a community. A **community** is formed by interactions among populations of living animals and plants at a particular time in a prescribed area. An ecosystem is the interaction of many communities with the abiotic physical components of its environment.

Some examples help to clarify these concepts. In a forest ecosystem, a specific community may exist on the forest floor, whereas another community functions in the canopy of leaves high above. Similarly, within a lake ecosystem, the plants and animals that flourish in the bottom sediments form one community, whereas those near the surface form another (Figure 19.3). A community is identified in several ways—by its physical appearance, the species present and the abundance of each, the complex patterns of their interdependence, and the trophic (feeding) structure of the community.

Within a community, two concepts are important: habitat and niche. **Habitat** is the type of environment where an organism resides or is biologically adapted to live. In terms of physical and natural factors, most species have specific habitat requirements with definite limits and a specific regimen of sustaining nutrients.

Niche (French *nicher*, "to nest") refers to the function, or occupation, of a life form within a given community. It is the way an organism obtains and sustains the physical, chemical, and biological factors it needs to survive. A niche has several facets. Among these are a habitat niche, a trophic (food) niche, and a reproductive niche. For example, the Red-winged Blackbird (*Agelaius phoeniceus*) occurs throughout the United States and most of Canada in habitats of meadow, pastureland, and marsh. This species nests in blackberry tangles and thick vegetation in freshwater marshes, sloughs, and fields. Its trophic niche is weed seeds and cultivated seed crops throughout the year, and during the nesting season it adds insects to its diet—an aspect of its reproductive niche. These birds disperse seeds of many plants during their travels.

Other habitats produce comparable niches. In a stable community, no niche is left unfilled. The *competitive exclusion principle* states that no two species can occupy the same niche (food or space) successfully in a stable community. Thus, closely related species are spatially separated. In other words, each species operates to reduce competition. This strategy in turn leads to greater diversity as species shift and adapt (Figure 19.4, p. 628).

Some species are *symbiotic*, an arrangement where two or more species exist together in an overlapping relationship. One type of symbiosis, *mutualism*, occurs when each organism benefits and is sustained over an extended period by the relation. For example, lichen (pronounced "liken") is made up of algae and fungi living together. The alga is the producer and food source for the fungus, and the fungus provides structure and physical support. Their mutualism allows the two to occupy a niche in which neither could survive alone. Lichen developed from an earlier parasitic relationship in which the fungi broke into the algal cells. Today, the two organisms have evolved into a supportive harmony and symbiotic relationship (Figure 19.5). The partnership of corals and algae discussed in Chapter 16 is another example of mutualism in a symbiotic relationship.

By contrast, another form of symbiosis is a *parasitic* relationship, which may eventually kill the host, thus destroying the parasite's own niche and habitat. An example

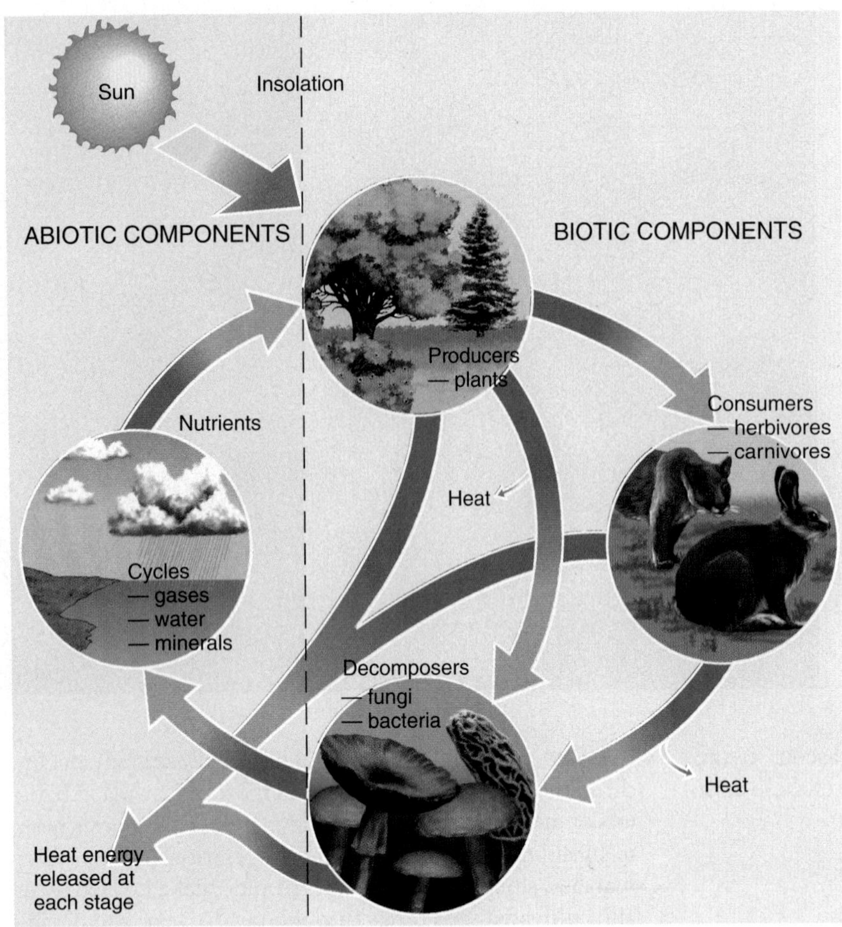

FIGURE 19.2 Biotic and abiotic components of ecosystems. (a) Solar energy is the input that drives the biotic and abiotic components. Heat energy and biomass are the outputs from the biosphere. (b) Biotic and abiotic ingredients operate together to form this temperate forest-floor ecosystem in British Columbia, with mosses beginning the process of community development. [Photo by Bobbé Christopherson.]

is parasitic mistletoe (*Phoradendron*), which lives on and may kill various kinds of trees. Some scientists are questioning whether our human society and the physical systems of Earth constitute a global-scale symbiotic relationship of mutualism (sustainable) or a parasitic one (nonsustainable).

Plants: The Essential Biotic Component

Plants are the critical biotic link between solar energy and the biosphere. *Ultimately, the fate of all members of the biosphere, including humans, rests on the success of plants and their ability to capture sunlight.*

Land plants (and animals) became common about 430 million years ago, according to fossilized remains. **Vascular plants** developed conductive tissues and true roots for internal transport of fluid and nutrients. (*Vascular* is from a Latin word for "vessel-bearing," referring to the conducting cells.)

In the present day, about 270,000 species of plants are known to exist, and most are vascular. Many more species have yet to be identified. They represent a great untapped resource base. Only about 20 species of plants provide 90% of the world's food—just three, wheat, maize (corn), and rice, comprise half of the food supply. Plants are a major source of new medicines and chemical compounds that benefit humanity. Plants also are the core of healthy, functioning ecosystems that sustain all life.

Leaves are solar-powered chemical factories, wherein photochemical reactions take place. Veins in the leaf bring in water and nutrient supplies and carry off the sugars (food) produced by photosynthesis. The veins in each leaf connect to the stems and branches of the plant and to the main circulation system.

Flows of carbon dioxide, water, light, and oxygen enter and exit the surface of each leaf (see Figure 1.4). Gases flow into and out of a leaf through small pores called **stomata** (singular: *stoma*), which usually are most numerous on the lower side of the leaf. Each stoma is surrounded by guard cells that open and close the pore, depending on the plant's changing needs.

Water that moves through a plant exits the leaves through the stomata and evaporates from leaf surfaces, thereby assisting the plant's temperature regulation. As water evaporates from the leaves, a pressure deficit is created that allows atmospheric pressure to push water up through the plant all the way from the roots, in the same manner that a drinking straw works. We can only imagine the complex operation of a 100-m (330-ft) tree!

Photosynthesis and Respiration

Powered by energy from certain wavelengths of visible light, **photosynthesis** unites carbon dioxide and hydrogen (hydrogen is derived from water in the plant). The term is

(a)

(b)

FIGURE 19.3 Different forest communities. (a) West coast forest canopy, Vancouver Island, British Columbia. Canada's largest trees grow in this region. (b) Turtles bask on a log in a subtropical swamp (low, water-logged ground) at Juniper Springs Recreation Area, Florida. [Photos by (a) Kevin Hanna; (b) Bobbé Christopherson.]

descriptive: *photo-* refers to sunlight, and *-synthesis* describes the "manufacturing" of starches and sugars through reactions within plant leaves. The process releases oxygen and produces energy-rich food for the plant.

The largest concentration of light-responsive, photosynthetic structures (known as *organelles*) in a leaf rests below the leaf's upper layers. These organelle units within cells are called *chloroplasts*, and within each resides a green, light-sensitive pigment called **chlorophyll**. Within this pigment, light stimulates photochemistry. Consequently, competition for light is a dominant factor in the formation of plant communities. This competition is expressed in the height, orientation, distribution, and structure of plants.

Only about one-quarter of the light energy arriving at the surface of a leaf is useful to the light-sensitive chlorophyll. Chlorophyll absorbs only the orange-red and violet-blue wavelengths for photochemical operations, and it reflects predominantly green hues (and some yellow). That is why trees and other vegetation look green.

Photosynthesis essentially follows this equation:

$$\underset{\text{(carbon dioxide)}}{6CO_2} + \underset{\text{(water)}}{6H_2O} + \underset{\text{(solar energy)}}{\text{Light}} \rightarrow \underset{\text{(glucose, carbohydrate)}}{C_6H_{12}O_6} + \underset{\text{(oxygen)}}{6O_2}$$

From the equation, you can see that photosynthesis removes carbon (in the form of CO_2) from Earth's atmosphere. The quantity is enormous: approximately 91 billion metric tons (100 billion tons) of carbon dioxide per year. Carbohydrates, the organic result of the photosynthetic process, are combinations of carbon, hydrogen, and oxygen. They can form simple sugars, such as *glucose* ($C_6H_{12}O_6$). Plants use glucose to build starches, which are more complex carbohydrates and the principal food stored in plants.

Plants store energy for later use. They consume this energy as needed through respiration by converting the carbohydrates to energy for their other operations. Thus, **respiration** is essentially a reverse of the photosynthetic process:

$$\underset{\text{(glucose, carbohydrate)}}{C_6H_{12}O_6} + \underset{\text{(oxygen)}}{6O_2} \rightarrow \underset{\text{(carbon dioxide)}}{6CO_2} + \underset{\text{(water)}}{6H_2O} + \underset{\text{(heat energy)}}{\text{energy}}$$

In respiration, plants oxidize carbohydrates (stored energy), releasing carbon dioxide, water, and energy as heat. The overall growth of a plant depends on a surplus of carbohydrates beyond what is lost through plant respiration. Figure 19.6 (p. 629) presents a simple schematic of this process, which produces plant growth.

The *compensation point* is the break-even point between the production and consumption of organic material. Each leaf must operate on the production side of the compensation point, or else the plant eliminates it—something each of us has no doubt experienced with a houseplant that received inadequate water or light. The difference between photosynthetic production and respiration loss is called

Net Primary Productivity The net photosynthesis for an entire plant community is its **net primary productivity**. This is the amount of stored chemical energy (biomass) that the community generates for the ecosystem. **Biomass** is the net dry weight of organic material.

Net primary productivity is measured as fixed carbon per square metre per year. ("Fixed" means chemically bound into plant tissues.) Study the map and satellite images in Figure 19.8 and you can see that on land, net primary production tends to be highest between the Tropics of Cancer and Capricorn at sea level and decreases toward higher latitudes and altitudes. Precipitation also affects productivity, as evidenced by the correlations of abundant precipitation with high productivity (adjacent to the equator) and reduced precipitation with low productivity (subtropical deserts). Even though deserts receive high amounts of solar radiation, other controlling factors limit productivity, namely water availability and soil conditions.

In the oceans, differing nutrient levels control and limit productivity. Regions with nutrient-rich upwelling

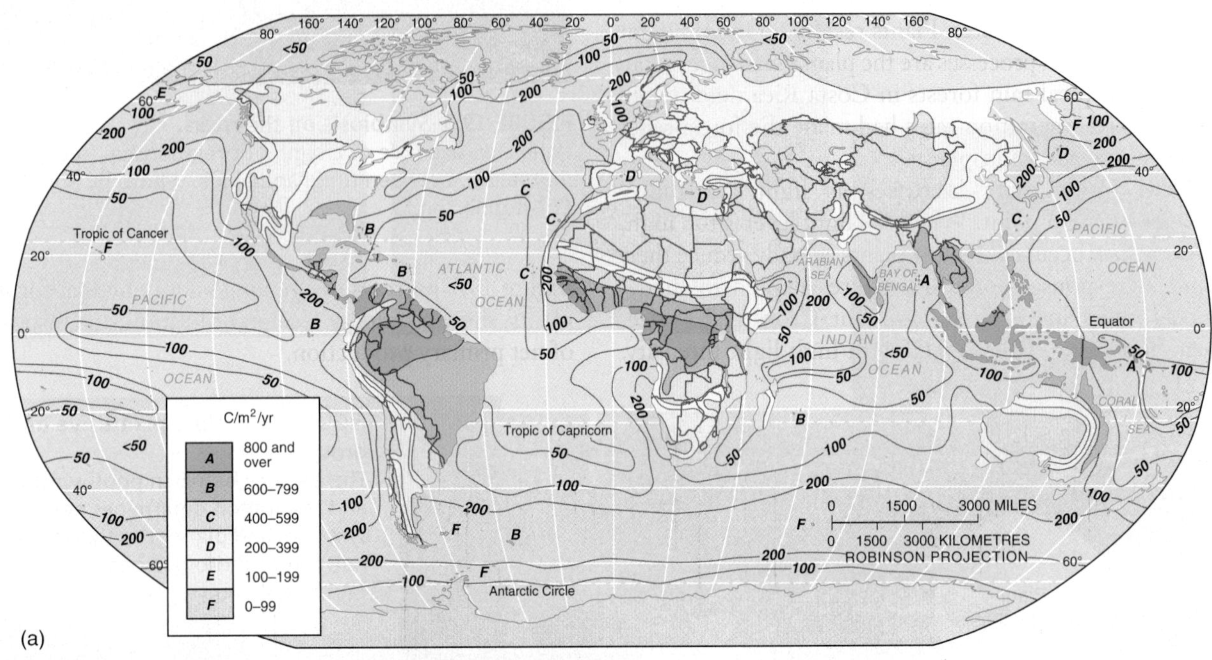

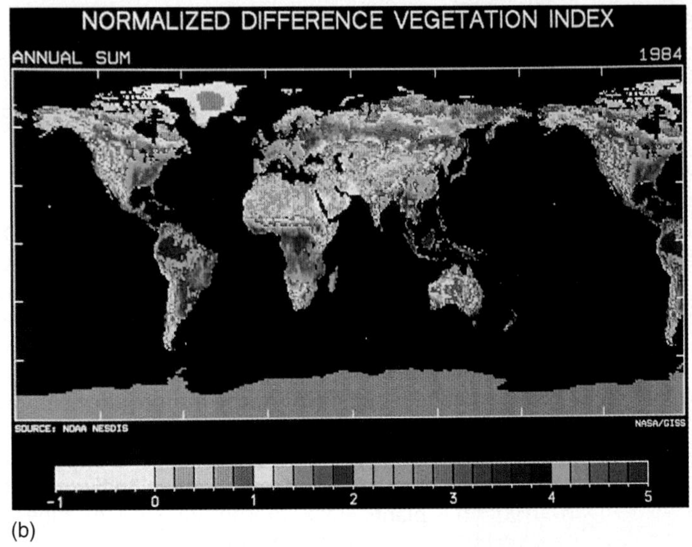

(b)

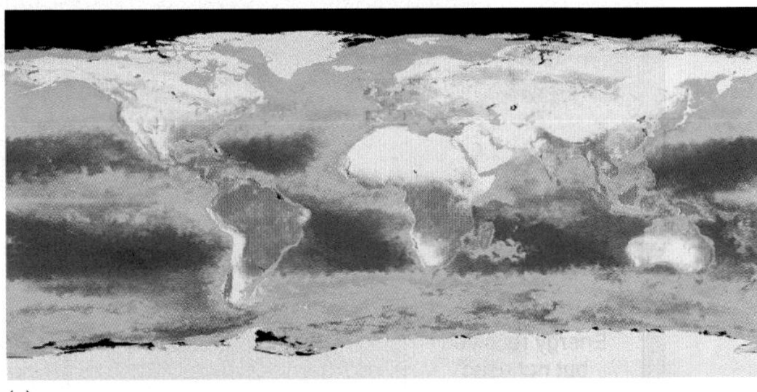

(c)

FIGURE 19.8 Net primary productivity.
(a) Worldwide net primary productivity in grams of carbon per square metre per year (approximate values). (b) Normalized difference vegetation index during 1984. False coloration indicates bare ground in browns, dense vegetation in blues. (c) *SeaWIFS* image of surface chlorophyll concentration for land and sea; intensity of green colour represents higher levels of chlorophyll. This is the first continuous record over a three-year period for the oceans. [(a) After D. E. Reichle, *Analysis of Temperate Forest Ecosystems* (Heidelberg: Springer, 1970). Adapted by permission; (b) NASA/GSFC; (c) *SeaWIFS* image by NASA/GSFC, and ORBIMAGE, Dulles, VA. Used by permission. All rights reserved.]

only when daylengtl
plant that responds i
(*Euphorbia pulcherri*
of 14-hour nights tc
Other compoı
processes. Air and sc
which chemical re
Significant temperaı
duration and the pat
peratures (Chapter
Operations of t
ability depend on pı
their seasonal distrib
quality—its mineral
and toxicity—is imp
the pattern of vege
development. All of
the limits for ecosysı
Figure 19.9 illus
temperature, precipi

currents generally are the most productive (off western coastlines). The map in Figure 19.8 shows that the tropical ocean and areas of subtropical high pressure are quite low in productivity.

In temperate and high latitudes, the rate at which carbon is fixed by vegetation varies seasonally. It increases in spring and summer as plants flourish with increasing solar input and, in some areas, with more available (nonfrozen) water, and it decreases in late fall and winter. Productivity rates in the tropics are high throughout the year, and turnover in the photosynthesis-respiration cycle is faster, exceeding by many times the rates experienced in a desert environment or in the far northern limits of the tundra. A lush hectare (2.5 acres) of sugar cane in the tropics might fix 45 metric tons (50 tons) of carbon in a year, whereas desert plants in an equivalent area might achieve only 1% of that amount.

Table 19.1 lists various ecosystems, their net primary productivity, and an estimate of net total biomass worldwide—170 billion metric tons of dry organic matter per year. Compare the various ecosystems, especially cultivated land (in *italics*) with most of the natural communities. Net productivity is generally regarded as the most important aspect of any type of community, and the distribution of productivity over Earth's surface is an important subject of biogeography.

Abiotic Ecosystem Components

Critical in each ecosystem is the flow of energy and the cycling of nutrients and water in life-supporting systems. These abiotic (nonliving) components set the stage for ecosystem operations.

Light, Temperature, Water, and Climate Solar energy powers ecosystems, so the pattern of solar energy receipt is crucial. Solar energy enters an ecosystem by way of photosynthesis, and heat energy is dissipated from the system at many points. Of the total energy intercepted at Earth's surface and available for work, only about 1.0% is actually fixed by photosynthesis as chemical energy (energy stored as carbohydrates in plants).

The duration of Sun exposure is the *photoperiod.* Along the equator, days are essentially 12 hours long year-round; however, with increasing distance from the equator, seasonal effects become pronounced, as discussed in Chapter 2. Plants have adapted their flowering and seed germination to seasonal changes in insolation. Some seeds germinate

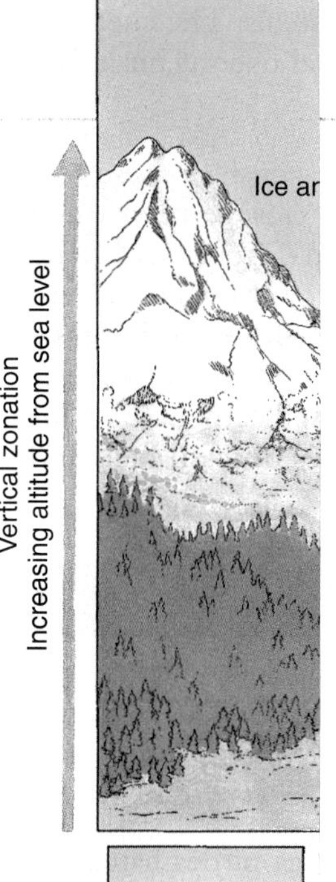

FIGURE 19.10 Vertica
(a) Progression of plan
ecosystem in the Canac
line of trees marks the
which no trees grow. [

Table 19.1 Net Primary Productivity and Plant Biomass on Earth

Ecosystem	Area (10^6km^2)[a]	Net Primary Productivity per Unit Area (g/m^2/yr)[b] Normal Range	Mean	World Net Biomass (10^9/tons/yr)[c]
Tropical rain forest	17.0	1000–3500	2200	37.4
Tropical seasonal forest	7.5	1000–2500	1600	12.0
Temperate evergreen forest	5.0	600–2500	1300	6.5
Temperate deciduous forest	7.0	600–2500	1200	8.4
Boreal forest	12.0	400–2000	800	9.6
Woodland and shrubland	8.5	250–1200	700	6.0
Savanna	15.0	200–2000	900	13.5
Temperate grassland	9.0	200–1500	600	5.4
Tundra and alpine region	8.0	10–400	140	1.1
Desert and semidesert scrub	18.0	10–250	90	1.6
Extreme desert, rock, sand, ice	24.0	0–10	3	0.07
Cultivated land	*14.0*	*100–3500*	*650*	*9.1*
Swamp and marsh	2.0	800–3500	2000	4.0
Lake and stream	2.0	100–1500	250	0.5
Total continental	**149.0**	—	**773**	**115.17**
Open ocean	332.0	2–400	125	41.5
Upwelling zones	0.4	400–1000	500	0.2
Continental shelf	26.6	200–600	360	9.6
Algal beds and reefs	0.6	500–4000	2500	1.6
Estuaries	1.4	200–3500	1500	2.1
Total marine	**361.0**	—	**152**	**55.0**
Grand total	**510.0**	—	**333**	**170.17**

Source: R. H. Whittaker, *Communities and Ecosystems* (Heidelberg: Springer, 1975), p. 224. Reprinted by permission.
[a]1 km^2 = 0.39 mi^2.
[b]1 g per m^2 = 8.92 lb per acre.
[c]1 metric ton (10^6 g) = 1.1023 tons.

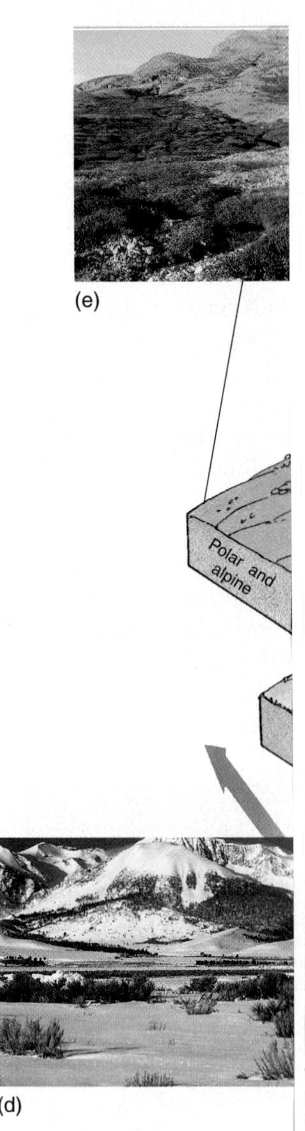

FIGURE 19.9 How tempe
(a) Climate controls (wetn
(c) Sonoran desert of Arizo
rain forest of Puerto Rico.
(i) Moist tundra of Spitsbe
Christopherson; (f) Tom Be

(a)

(b)

(c)

(d)

FIGURE 19.23 Agricultural ecosystems.
(a) The Sacramento Valley of California is one of the most intensively farmed regions of the world. Field crops including irrigated rice, an irrigation canal, and the Sacramento River are in the scene. (b) A pine tree plantation (farm) in Ontario, principally for the production of wood pulp—the forest ecosystem is reduced to efficient rows for clear-cutting when mature. Depleting of soil nutrients over time, this farming practice requires subsidies of chemical fertilizers and herbicides to eliminate competing vegetation. (c) Modern mechanized farming and a freshly mowed field of oats near Dokka, Norway. (d) Highly fragmented, fertile agricultural land along the north German plain. [Photos (a), (c), and (d) by Bobbé Christopherson; (b) courtesy of Peaceful Parks.]

years ago, deserts began developing in the southwestern United States. Mountain-building processes created higher elevations, causing rain-shadow aridity and affecting plant distribution.

Recall, too, that the movement of Earth's tectonic plates created climate changes important in the evolution and distribution of plants and animals (see Figure 11.18a–e). Europe and North America were joined in Pangaea and positioned near the equator, where vast swamps formed (the site of coal deposits today). The southern mass of Gondwana was extensively glaciated as it drifted at high latitudes in the Southern Hemisphere. This glaciation left matching glacial scars and specific distributions of plants and animals across South America, Africa, India, and

Australia. The diverse and majestic dinosaurs dispersed with the moving continents.

The key question for our future is this: As temperature patterns change, how fast can plants either adapt to new conditions or migrate through succession (location change) to remain within their shifting specific habitats? Rapid changes in vegetation patterns in northern latitudes since 1980 are indicated from satellite observations. Global warming during spring is reducing snow cover and raising temperatures, allowing spring greening to occur earlier, up to three weeks sooner in some high latitude locations. Likewise the onset of fall is delayed to a later date than previously experienced.

Nina Leopold Bradley is studying the Wisconsin setting her father Aldo Leopold made famous in his book *A Sand County Almanac* (Oxford University Press, 1949). He kept detailed records of all things dealing with nature and seasonal change on his tract of land. The new findings show that more than one-third of animal and plant species start spring activities 4 weeks earlier than they did 50 years ago.

Adaptation to conditions is key to evolution. Through mutation and natural selection, species have either adapted or failed to adapt to changing environmental conditions over millions of years. Current global change is occurring rapidly, at the rate of decades instead of millions of years. Thus, we see die-out and succession of different species along disadvantageous habitat margins. The displaced species may colonize new regions made more hospitable by climate change. Also shifting will be agricultural lands that produced wheat, corn, soybeans, and other commodities. Society will have to adapt to different crops growing in different places.

A study completed by biologist Margaret Davis on North American forests suggests that trees will have to respond quickly if temperatures increase. Changes in the climate inhabited by certain species could shift 100–400 km (60–250 mi) during the next 100 years. Some species, such as the sugar maple, may migrate northward, disappearing from the United States except for Maine, and moving into eastern Ontario and Québec. Davis prepared a map showing the possible impact of increasing temperatures on the distribution of beech and hemlock trees (Figure 19.24).

> Changes in the geographical distributions of plant and animal species in response to future greenhouse warming threaten to reduce biotic diversity. . . . The risk posed by CO_2-induced warming depends on the distances that regions of suitable climate are displaced northward [in the Northern Hemisphere] and on the rate of displacement. . . . If the change occurs too rapidly for colonization of newly available regions, population sizes may fall to critical levels, and extinction will occur.*

*M. B. Davis and C. Zabinski, "Changes in the geographical range resulting from greenhouse warming: Effects on biodiversity in forests," in R. L. Peters and T. E. Lovejoy, eds., *Global Warming and Biological Diversity* (New Haven, CT: Yale University Press, 1992), p. 297.

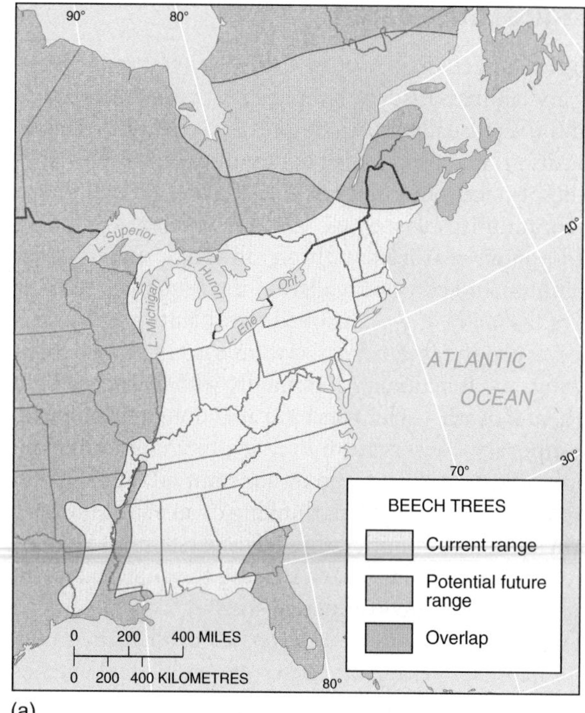

(a)

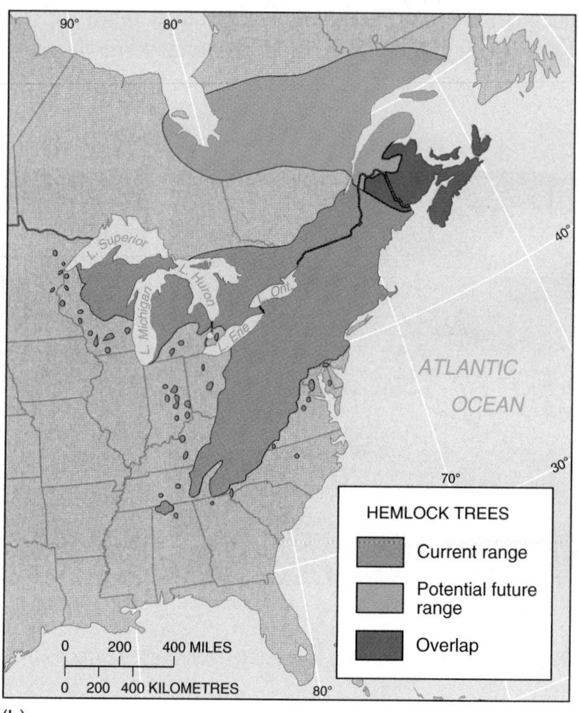

(b)

FIGURE 19.24 Present and predicted distribution of two tree species.
(a) Beech trees and (b) hemlock trees in North America. The potential future range shown for each reflects expected climate change resulting from a doubling of carbon dioxide. These maps are based on forecasts from the Goddard Fluid Dynamics Laboratory (GFDL) general circulation model. [After M. B. Davis and C. Zabinski, "Changes in the geographical range resulting from greenhouse warming: Effects on biodiversity in forests," in R. L. Peters and T. E. Lovejoy, eds., *Global Warming and Biological Diversity* (New Haven, CT: Yale University Press, 1992), p. 301.]

Ecological Succession

Ecological succession occurs when older communities of plants and animals (usually simpler) are replaced by newer communities (usually more complex)—a change of species composition. Each successive community of species modifies the physical environment in a manner suitable for a later community of species. Changes apparently move toward a more mature condition, although disturbances are common and constantly disrupt the sequence.

Traditionally, it was assumed that plants and animals formed a predictable *climax community*—a stable, self-sustaining, and functioning community with balanced birth, growth, and death—scientists have abandoned this notion. Contemporary conservation biology, biogeography, and ecology assume nature to be in constant adaptation and nonequilibrium. Rather than thinking of an ecosystem as a uniform set of communities, think of ecosystems as a patchwork mosaic of habitats—each striving to achieve an optimal range and low environmental stress.

This is the study of *patch dynamics*, or disturbed portions of habitats. Within an ecosystem, individual patches may arise only to fail later. The smaller the patch, the faster species loss occurs. Succession is the interaction among patches. Most ecosystems are in actuality made up of patches of former landscapes. Biodiversity in some respects is the result of such patch dynamics.

Given the complexity of natural ecosystems, it is obvious that real succession involves much more than a series of predictable stages ending with a specific monoclimax community. Instead, there may be several stages, or a *polyclimax* condition, with adjoining ecosystems, or patches within ecosystems, each at different stages in the same environment. Mature communities are properly thought of as being in dynamic equilibrium. Or at times, these communities may be out of phase and in nonequilibrium with the immediate physical environment because of the usual lag time in their adjustment.

Succession often requires an initiating disturbance. Examples include wind storms, severe flooding, a volcanic eruption, a devastating wildfire, or an agricultural practice such as prolonged overgrazing (Figure 19.25). When existing organisms are disturbed or removed, new communities can emerge. At such times of nonequilibrium transition, the interrelationships among species produce elements of chance, and species having an adaptive edge will succeed in the competitive struggle for light, water, nutrients, space, time, reproduction, and survival. Thus, the succession of plant and animal communities is an intricate process, both in space and time, and forced by both internal and external variables.

Land and water experience different forms of succession. We first look at terrestrial succession, which is characterized by competition for sunlight, and then at aquatic

(a)

(b)

(c)

(d)

FIGURE 19.25 Disturbances in ecosystems alter succession patterns.
(a) After flooding along Rivière des Ha!Ha!, Québec, extensive aggradation renews the sediment supply to the valley. (b) Community development proceeds in a burned forest, progressing perhaps by chance, as species with an adaptive edge, such as fireweed (*Epilobium* sp.), succeed. (c) Unwise practices cause extensive soil erosion on a hog farm in Iowa, 1999; a disrupted prairie landscape. (d) Insect infestation (spruce budworm) weakens trees that turn grey and die off. [Photos by (a) Earth Sciences Sector, Natural Resources Canada; (b) Bobbé Christopherson; (c) USDA Natural Resources Conservation Service; (d) Natural Resources Canada, Canadian Forest Service, Laurentian Forestry Centre.]

succession, characterized by progressive changes in nutrient levels.

Terrestrial Succession

An area of bare rock or a disturbed site with no vestige of a former community can be a place for **primary succession**, the beginning and development of an ecosystem. Examples include new surfaces created by mass movement of land, areas exposed by a retreating glacier, cooled lava flows and volcanic eruption landscapes, or surface mining and clear-cut logging scars, or an area of sand dunes. Illustrating primary succession are plants taking hold on new lava flows from Kīlauea volcano, Hawai'i, shown in Figure 19.26. In terrestrial ecosystems, succession begins with early species that form a **pioneer community**. You can see these plants taking hold in the photo. Primary succession often begins with lichens, mosses, and ferns growing on bare rock. These early inhabitants prepare the way for further succession to grasses, shrubs, and trees (see Figure 19.5).

More common in nature is **secondary succession**, which begins if some aspects of a previously functioning community are present. An area where the natural community has been destroyed or disturbed, but where the underlying soil remains intact, may experience secondary succession. Examples of secondary succession are most of the areas affected by the Mount St. Helens eruption and blast in 1980 (Figure 19.27). Some soils, young trees, and plants were protected under ash and snow, so community development began almost immediately after the event. About 38,450 hectares (95,000 acres) of trees were blown down and burned, however, and as the photos show, the effects of the eruption were devastating and lingering. Of course, the areas completely destroyed near the Mount St. Helens volcano or those buried beneath the massive landslide north of the mountain became candidates for primary succession.

As succession progresses, soil develops and a different set of plants and animals with different niche requirements may adapt. Further niche expansion follows as the community matures. Succession, which is really the developmental process forming new communities, is a dynamic set of interactions with sometimes unpredictable outcomes, steered by sometimes random, unpredictable events that trigger a threshold leap to a new set of relations—the basis of *dynamic ecology*.

Succession Through the Ice Age Glaciation is a large-scale disturbance that well illustrates how succession operates. As Earth cycled through glacial and interglacial ages (Chapter 17), the ecological succession in all ecosystems was affected repeatedly. Imagine the milder midlatitude climate at the beginning of an interglacial warming, with lush herb and shrub vegetation slowly giving way to pioneer trees of birch, aspen, and pine. Winds and animals dispersed seeds, and changing communities readily spread in response to changing conditions. During the warm interglacial, trees increased shade and the organic content of soil increased. Deciduous trees such as oak, elm, and ash spread freely on well-drained soils; willow, cottonwood, and alder grew on poorly drained land.

FIGURE 19.26 Primary succession.
Ferns take hold as primary succession on new lava flows that came from the Kīlauea volcano, Hawai'i. [Photo by Bobbé Christopherson.]

As climates cooled with the approach of the next glacial, soils became more acidic, so podzolization (cool, moist, forested) processes dominated (see Chapter 18), helped by the acidity of spruce and fir trees. Ecosystems slowly returned to the vegetation community that existed at the beginning of the interglacial. The increased cold produced open regions of disturbed ecosystems. Freezing and the advance of ice disrupted highly acidic soils.

The Holocene (the past 10,000 years) is apparently atypical, because of the development of human societies and agriculture. Civilization is creating an artificial and accelerated succession, similar in some ways to the closing centuries of an interglacial. The challenge for biogeographers is to understand such long-term developmental change principles, at the accelerated pace that change is occurring in the industrial and post-industrial era.

Wildfire and Fire Ecology Fire and its effects are one of Earth's significant ecosystem and economic processes. In Canada, during 2003, more than 1.6 million hectares burned in wildfires—8218 fires started by lightning and by human activity. This total was well below the ten-year average, but occurred in heavily populated areas of the country resulting in loss of life and property.

Over the past 50 years, the role of fire in ecosystems has been the subject of much scientific research and experimentation. Today, fire is recognized as a natural component of most ecosystems and not the enemy of nature that was once thought. In fact, in many forests, undergrowth and surface litter is purposely burned in controlled "cool fires" to remove fuel that could enable a catastrophic and destructive "hot fire." Forestry experts have learned that, when fire-prevention strategies are too rigidly followed, they can lead to the abundant undergrowth accumulation

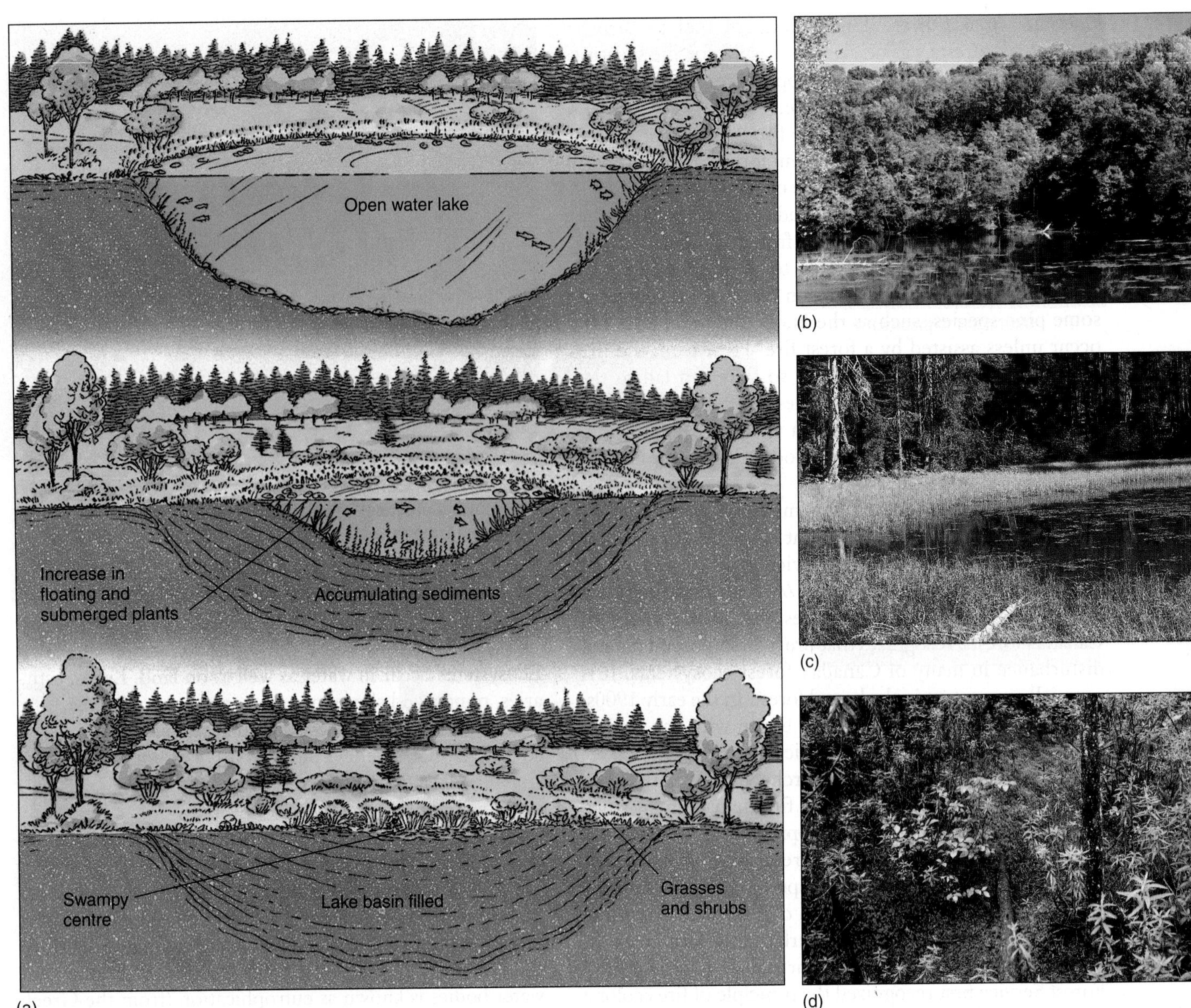

FIGURE 19.29 Lake–bog–meadow succession.
(a) What begins as a lake gradually fills with organic and inorganic sediments, which successively shrink the area of the pond. A bog forms, then a marshy area, and finally a meadow completes the successional stages. (b) Spring Mill Lake, Indiana. (c) Aquatic succession in a mountain lake. (d) The Richmond bog was ocean just 8000 years ago. Fraser River sediment created the mudflats and set the stage for the evolution of this sphagnum bog with acidic soils that "quakes" when you walk on it. Plants in the bog include moss, shore pine, hemlock, blueberry, salal shrubs, and Labrador tea, among others. [Photos by Bobbé Christopherson.]

fertilizer, or other nutrient inputs occur. Even large bodies of water may have eutrophic areas along the shore. As society dumps sewage, agricultural runoff, and pollution in waterways, the nutrient load is enhanced beyond the cleansing ability of natural biological processes. The result is *cultural eutrophication*, which hastens succession in aquatic systems. As with all ecosystems, we must be aware of the signals that unwanted change is occurring so that mitigating action can be taken. (Refer to the map of the dead zone in the Gulf of Mexico in News Report 19.2.)

The Freshwater Web site (**http://www.ec.gc.ca/water/e_main.html**) outlines the nature of water, water policy and legislation, water management, and water and culture, and provides links to useful resources about water in Canada, including links to aquatic ecosystems. Focus Study 19.1 examines the Great Lakes of North America and their geographically and biologically diverse aquatic ecosystems. These lakes are interrelated with the surrounding terrestrial ecosystems. This is the largest lake system on Earth and is jointly managed by Canada and the United States.

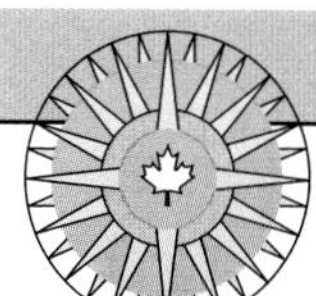

Focus Study 19.1

The Great Lakes

The basins of the Great Lakes are gifts of the last ice age to North America (see Figure 17.30). The glaciers advanced and retreated over this region, excavating the basins for five large lakes. This international waterway of lakes and connecting rivers has played an important role in the history of Canada and the United States. Today, about 10% of the U.S. population and 25% of Canada's population live in the Great Lakes drainage basin (Figure 1). Major agricultural regions surround the lakes, as do many centres of industrial activity. Tourism, sport fishing, and maritime commerce are also important.

Society asks much of the Great Lakes: to dilute wastes from cities and industry, to dissipate thermal pollution from power plants, to provide municipal drinking water and irrigation water, and to sustain unique and varied ecosystems—open lake, coastal shore, coastal marsh, lakeplain (former lake bed), inland wetlands, and inland terrestrial (upland areas of forest, prairie, and barrens). Here is a brief profile of this important hydrological and ecological resource. (See Environment Canada's Our Great Lakes Web site at **http://www.on.ec.gc.ca/water/greatlakes/**; management policy for the Great Lakes is found on the International Joint Commission Web site (**http://www.ijc.org/en/home/main_accueil.htm**).

Geography and Physical Characteristics

The Great Lakes—Superior, Michigan, Huron, Erie, and Ontario—contain 18% of the total volume of all freshwater lakes in the world, some 23,000 km^3 (5500 mi^3) of water. Their combined surface area covers 244,000 km^2 (94,000 mi^2). The entire drainage basin embraces 528,000 km^2 (204,000 mi^2), or an area about the size of Manitoba.

As we tour the lakes, it is useful to follow along in Figure 1 and to look at their profile in Figure 2a. Lake Superior is the highest in elevation, highest in latitude, deepest, and largest in the system. It drains through St. Mary's River into Lake Huron. Lake Michigan, the only lake of the five that lies entirely within the United States, is at the same level as Lake Huron because it is joined by the wide connection through the Straits of Mackinac. (This is why, in Figure 2, we combine these two lakes on one hydrograph.)

The St. Clair River, Lake St. Clair, and the Detroit River carry water on to Lake Erie, the shallowest lake in the system. Compared to an average water retention time of 191 years in Lake Superior, Lake Erie has the shortest retention time of 2.6 years. The Niagara River, plunging dramatically over Niagara Falls, transports water into Lake Ontario. Lake Ontario is drained by the St. Lawrence River, which carries the entire discharge of the Great Lakes system to the Gulf of St. Lawrence and eventually into the North Atlantic Ocean. The entire basin extends over 10° of latitude (41° N to 51° N) and 18° of longitude (75° W to 93° W).

Because of the large size of the overall Great Lakes system, its associated climate, soils, and topography vary widely. Dominating the north are colder microthermal climates, exposed portions of the Canadian Shield bedrock, and vast stands of conifers and acidic soils. To the south, warmer mesothermal climates and fertile glacially deposited soils provide a vast agricultural base. Farms and urbanization replaced previous stands of mixed forest. Virtually none of the original land cover is undisturbed.

Prevailing winds from the west and seasonal change mix air masses from different source regions, producing variable weather. The presence of the Great Lakes Basin strongly influences passing air masses and weather systems producing lake-effect snowfall to the east (see Figure 8.5). Precipitation over the drainage basin feeds the lake storage as part of the renewable hydrologic cycle. Figure 2 illustrates Great Lakes water levels from 1918 to 2003. Water levels were above average during 1996 and 1997. During 1998 through 2002, water levels lowered to below average levels, reflecting near-drought conditions across the region. However, through 2003 and 2004, trends have changed and lake levels are moving nearer the 1985 datum.

Short-term lake levels vary from winter to summer; they are higher in summer after snowmelt and the arrival of maximum summer precipitation. Over the long term, highest lake levels occur after a series of years of heavier precipitation and during times of cooler temperatures, which reduce evaporation. Wind also affects lake levels. A wind setup (wind-driven water) occurs along the downwind shoreline, as water is pushed higher onshore.

The Great Lakes Ecosystem

The Great Lakes ecosystem should be thought of as young and a fruitful laboratory for ecological studies. These lakes are not simply large bodies of water with a uniform mixture. A stratification occurs in them related to density and temperature differences. In the summer, the surface and shallow waters are warmed and become less dense so that the lakes develop a sharp stratification. The warm surface water and light penetration in the upper layers support most biotic production and adequate dissolved oxygen. This layering affects water quality because it can prevent mixing of pollution and other effluents with cooler bottom water during the summer months.

As the fall season matures, surface water cools and sinks, displacing deeper water and creating a turnover of the lake mass. By midwinter, the temperature from the surface to the bottom is uniformly around 4°C (39°F, the point at which water is densest); temperatures at the surface are near freezing.

The lakes support a food chain of producers and consumers, as does any aquatic ecosystem. Native fish populations have been greatly affected by human activities: overfishing, introduced non-native species, pollution

(continued)

carnivore (p. 640)
omnivore (p. 640)
detritivore (p. 640)
decomposer (p. 640)

15. What role is played in an ecosystem by producers and consumers?
16. Describe the relationship among producers, consumers, decomposers, and detritus feeders in an ecosystem. What is the trophic nature of an ecosystem? What is the place of humans in a trophic system?
17. What are biomass and population pyramids? Describe how these models help explain the nature of food chains and communities of plants and animals.
18. Follow the flow of energy and biomass through the Silver Springs, Florida, ecosystem. Describe the pathways in Figures 19.14 and 19.19a.

Relate how biological evolution led to the biodiversity of life on Earth.

Biodiversity (a combination of *bio*logical and *diversity*) includes the number of different species and quantity of each species, the genetic diversity in species (number of genetic characteristics), as well as ecosystem and habitat diversity. The greater the biodiversity within an ecosystem, the more stable and resilient it is, and the more productive it will be. Modern agriculture often creates a nondiverse monoculture that is particularly vulnerable to failure.

Evolution states that single-cell organisms adapted, modified, and passed along inherited changes to multicellular organisms. The genetic makeup of successive generations was shaped by environmental factors, physiological functions, and behaviours that created a greater rate of survival and reproduction that were passed along through natural selection.

biodiversity (p. 644)
evolution (p. 644)

19. Referring back to Figure 1 in Focus Study 1.1, define the scientific method.
20. Construct a simple model to show the progressive stages that lead to the development of a theory, such as the theory of evolution.

Define succession and _outline_ the stages of general ecological succession in both terrestrial and aquatic ecosystems.

Ecological succession describes the process whereby older communities of plants and animals are replaced by newer communities that are usually more complex. Past glacial and interglacial climatic episodes have created a long-term succession. An area of bare rock and soil with no trace of a former community can be a site for **primary succession**. The initial community that occupies an area of early succession is a **pioneer community**. **Secondary succession** begins in an area that has a vestige of a previously functioning community in place. Rather than progressing smoothly to a definable stable point, ecosystems tend to operate in a dynamic condition, with succeeding communities overlapping in time and space. Wildfire is one external factor that disrupts a successional community. Aquatic ecosystems also experience community succession, as exemplified by the eutrophication of a lake ecosystem.

The science of **fire ecology** has emerged in an effort to understand the natural role of fire in ecosystem maintenance and succession.

ecological succession (p. 650)
primary succession (p. 651)
pioneer community (p. 651)
secondary succession (p. 651)
fire ecology (p. 653)

21. What is meant by ecosystem stability?
22. How does ecological succession proceed? What are the relationships between existing communities and new, invading communities?
23. Discuss the concept of fire ecology in the context of the British Columbia fires of 1988.
24. Summarize the process of succession in a body of water. What is meant by cultural eutrophication?

Critical Thinking

A. This chapter states, "Some scientists are questioning whether our human society and the physical systems of Earth constitute a global-scale symbiotic relationship of mutualism (sustainable) or a parasitic one (nonsustainable)." Referring to the definition of these terms, what is your response to the statement? How do you equate our planetary economic system with the need to sustain life-supporting natural systems? Mutualism? Parasitism?

B. Over the next several days as you travel between home and campus, a job, or other areas, observe the landscape. What types of ecosystem disturbances do you see? Imagine that several hectares in the same area escaped any disruptions for a century or more. Describe what some of these ecosystems and communities might be like.

Career Link 19.1

Danika van Proosdij, Assistant Professor, Saint Mary's University, Halifax

Born in Montreal to European immigrants (her mother is Latvian, her father Dutch), Danika van Proosdij spent her early years in Toronto and learned to love the outdoors while working summers at a Girl Guide camp. As a lifeguard, canoe instructor, and field-trip guide, she became fascinated with the physical landscape sculpted by glaciers and the movement of water. "A dynamic geography teacher in Grade 11 really stimulated my interest in physical geography," Danika recalls, "and helped me understand how the features I would see on my trips in central and northern Ontario were formed. In fact, the experience and knowledge I gained in that class through my term project helped me get my first job as an undergraduate student at the University of Guelph—research assistant in geography."

FIGURE 1 Danika van Proosdij, Assistant Professor, Saint Mary's University. Danika is seen here on a section of the Bluff Wilderness Trail in Nova Scotia, testing new GPS equipment to plot the trail. [Photo by Judy Bell.]

Danika attained an honours B.Sc. in biology with a physical geography minor. For her thesis, she researched the impact of nearshore processes on colonization patterns of zebra mussels. She entered Guelph's M.Sc. program in the fall of 1995, then transferred to the Ph.D. program in the winter of 1996. While studying sedimentation in a Bay of Fundy tidal salt marsh, Danika accepted a tenure-track appointment as senior lecturer in geography at Saint Mary's University in Halifax in September 1999. This put her Ph.D. on hold until 2001, when she successfully defended her thesis and was promoted to assistant professor in the Department of Geography at Saint Mary's. She serves as an elected member of the Saint Mary's University Senate.

Danika balances a multitude of activities, including teaching, supervision, research and contract work, administration, professional service, and community service. Her undergraduate teaching load covers introductory physical geography, biogeography, GIS concepts and applications, and coastal geomorphology. She also teaches a course on research techniques in the Master of Applied Science program, counsels students, supervises thesis research projects (both undergraduate and graduate), and supervises research assistants and co-op students. Danika coordinates the Maritime Provinces Spatial Analysis Research Centre and is an active member of SMARTS (Salt Marsh and Restricted Tidal Systems), a working group of the Bay of Fundy Ecosystem Partnership (BoFEP).

Danika cautions that "academic life is a juggling act—you have to learn where to draw the line to enable you to have a private life as well." She says, "Geography has really opened my eyes to the world around me. I like being able to know how the environment around me was formed or operates as I am hiking, camping, canoeing, kayaking, or simply gardening."

Much of Danika's research focuses on the Bay of Fundy—salt marsh sedimentation and evolution and ecosystem health. She regularly collaborates with NSERC (Natural Resources and Engineering Research Council), provincial departments of transportation and agriculture, Environment Canada, and BoFEP. She presents papers at regional, national, and international academic conferences and assisted on a research project on mangrove ecology in Campeche, Mexico. For three years, she was involved in a CIDA project helping Cuban universities develop a master's program in integrated coastal zone management. This involved training Cuban faculty in Canada and teaching classes in Cuba.

Danika is enthusiastic about geography as a career choice. "Now that I work in the field, teaching students, conducting research, and volunteering in the community," she tells us, "I realize what a well-rounded discipline geography is and how geographers can contribute in the fields of environmental protection, planning, and emergency measures, for example. I find that my background in both biology and physical geography enables me to have a greater appreciation for the interaction between biotic and abiotic environments and to be quite comfortable working with my ecology, environmental, and geoscience counterparts."

We asked Danika what she most enjoys about her work. "Diversity in experiences," she replies, "from teaching to international travel, from working with the community to being outdoors, and discovering and learning new technologies such as GIS and GPS." In the field, she says, it's "experiencing the awesome power of the coastal environment, especially the Bay of Fundy and the resilience of the ecosystems within it."

One aspect of her job that particularly excites Danika is "seeing students get turned on by science." She sees the development of "highly qualified personnel" as being an important part of her work—training the young people "who are the future," she states. Considering her own path, she advises students to "seize the day, and take advantage of available opportunities and seek out those that might not be as readily apparent." And "learn at least one other language," she says, drawing from her experience.

For the future, Danika sees herself continuing to teach, "yet still having a balanced research program both in Canada and internationally. There will always be a need for teachers, and the use of geomatics will continue to increase both within geography and [in] other disciplines such as biology, marketing, and environmental science." She adds that she would like "to ensure that a part of my research remains of an applied nature so that I can assist in problem solving and mitigating human impacts in the coastal environment."

patterns of environmental factors (temperatures and changing frost periods; precipitation timing and amounts; air, water, and soil chemistry; and a redistribution of nutrients). We know from history that the effect of climate change on ecosystems will be significant. Two Harvard researchers assessed the impact of these alterations on ecosystems:

> Based on more than a decade of research, it is obvious that the CO_2-rich atmosphere of our future will have direct and dramatic effects on the composition and operation of ecosystems. According to the best scientific evidence, we see no reason to be sanguine [optimistic] about the response of these habitats to our changing environment.*

What will the quotations about Earth's environment be like 130 years from now, about the same time interval since G. P. Marsh made his assessment? Humans now have become the most powerful biotic agent on Earth, influencing all ecosystems on a planetary scale.

In this chapter: We explore Earth's major terrestrial ecosystems, conveniently grouped into 10 biomes. Each biome is an idealized assemblage because much alteration of the natural environment has occurred. The discussion covers biome appearance, structure, and location; the present conditions of related plants, animals, and environment; and biodiversity. Table 20.1 brings together most of the information about Earth's physical systems that is presented through the pages of this text. Through biomes we synthesize the physical geography of place and region.

Biogeographic Realms

Figure 20.1 shows Earth's biogeographic realms. The upper map illustrates the botanical (plant) realms worldwide. The lower map shows the zoological (animal) realms. Each realm contains many distinct ecosystems that distinguish it from other realms.

A **biogeographic realm** is a geographic region where a group of plant and animal species evolved. As you can see, these realms correspond generally to continents. The main topographic barrier that separates these realms is the ocean. Every species attempts to migrate worldwide according to its niche requirements, reproductive success, and competition but is constrained by climatic and topographic barriers. The collective effort of all species to seek optimal habitats and to maximize each personal niche requirement results in the generalized realms shown on the maps. Recognition that such distinct regions of flora (plants) and fauna (animals) exist was an early beginning for *biogeography* as a discipline.

The Australian realm is unique, giving rise to 450 species of *Eucalyptus* among its plants and 125 species of marsupials (animals such as kangaroos, that carry their young in pouches, where gestation is completed). Australia's uniqueness is the result of its early isolation from the other continents (Figure 20.2). During critical evolutionary times, Australia drifted away from Pangaea (see Chapter 11) and never again was reconnected by a land bridge, even when sea level lowered during repeated glacial ages. New Zealand's isolation from Australia also undoubtedly explains why no native marsupials exist in New Zealand.

*F. A. Bazzaz and E. D. Fajer, "Plant life in a CO_2-rich world," *Scientific American* 256, no. 1 (January 1992): 74.

Transition Zones

Alfred Wallace (1823–1913), the first scholar of *zoogeography*, used the stark contrast in animal species among islands in present-day Indonesia to delimit a boundary between the Oriental and Australian realms (Figure 20.1b). He thought that deep water in the straits had completely prevented species crossover. However, he later recognized that a boundary line actually is a wide transition zone, where one region grades into the other. Boundaries between natural systems are "zones of shared traits." Thus, despite distinctions among individual realms and our discussion of biomes, it is best to think of their borders as transition zones of mixed identity and composition, rather than as rigidly defined boundaries.

A boundary transition zone between adjoining ecosystem regions is an **ecotone**. Because ecotones are defined by different physical factors, they vary in width—think of a transition zone instead of a line. Climatic ecotones usually are more gradual than physical ecotones where differences in soil or topography sometimes form abrupt boundaries. An ecotone between prairies and northern forests may occupy many kilometres of land. The ecotone is an area of tension as similar species of plants and animals compete for the resource base.

Scientists have identified these boundary and edge areas as generating biodiversity (a species richness) as adaptation and natural selection favour the population with reproductive success. Organisms may compete, yet they may act to facilitate other organisms in a positive interaction in whatever strategies affect rates of ecosystem productivity, such as pollinating insects. A process of *coevolution* is possible where interacting populations in the tension zone can lead to genetic changes in each population

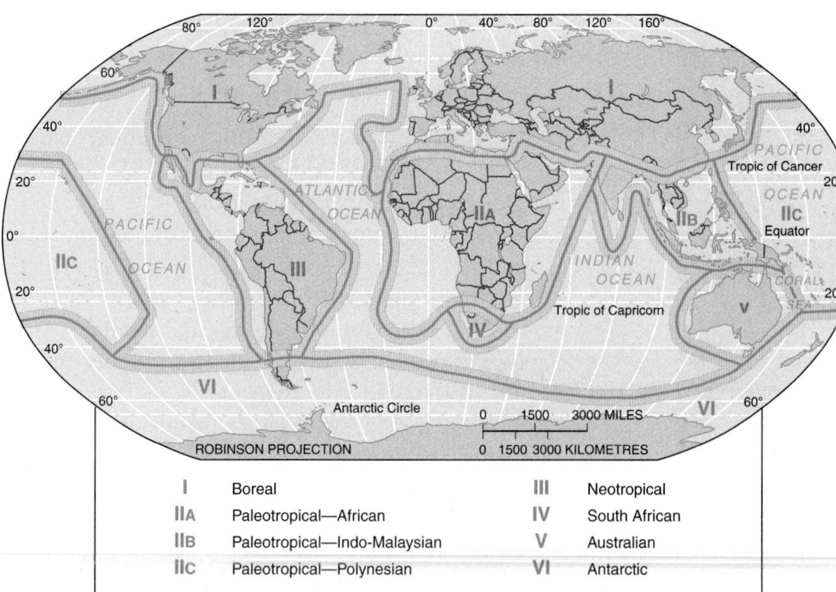

(a) Botanical geographic realms

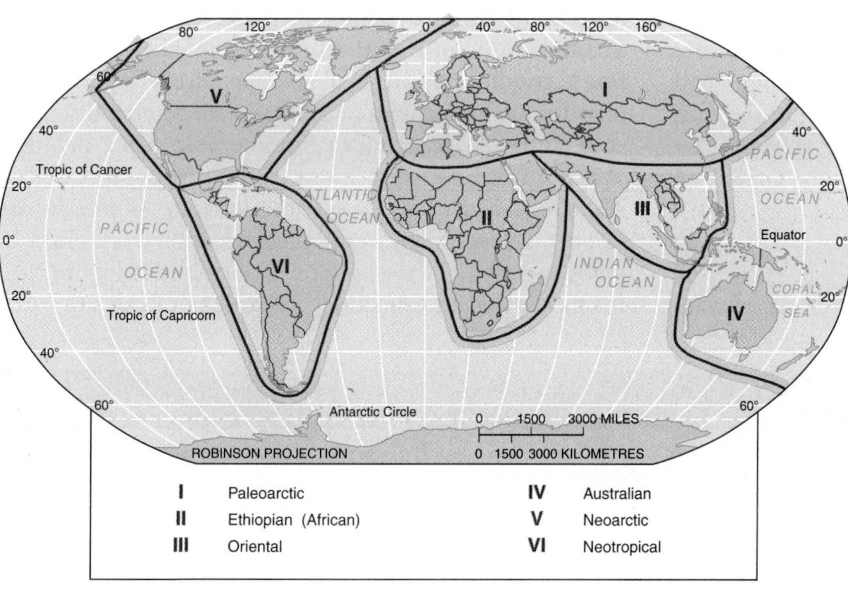

(b) Zoological geographic realms

FIGURE 20.1 Biogeographic realms. (a) Botanical geographic realms (after R. D. Good, 1947). (b) Zoological geographic realms (after L. F. deBeaufort, 1951). [Adapted from E. P. Odum, *Fundamentals of Ecology*, 3rd ed., reprinted with permission of Brooks/Cole, an imprint of the Wadsworth Group, a div. of Thomson Learning.]

(microevolution). Edges and ecotones are dynamic areas in the evolution of ecosystems and communities.

Terrestrial Ecosystems

A **terrestrial ecosystem** is a self-sustaining association of land-based plants and animals and their abiotic environment, characterized by specific plant formation classes. Plants are the most visible part of the biotic landscape, and they are key members of Earth's terrestrial ecosystems. In their growth, form, and distribution, plants reflect Earth's physical systems: its energy patterns; atmospheric composition; temperature and winds; air masses; water quantity, quality, and seasonal timing; soils; regional climates; geomorphic processes; and ecosystem dynamics. As discussed in the previous chapter, aquatic ecosystems are likewise important and result from the interaction of physical systems (see News Report 20.1).

A brief review of the ways that living organisms relate to the environment and to each other is helpful at this point. Interacting populations of plants and animals in an area form a *community*. An *ecosystem* involves the interplay between a community of plants and animals and their abiotic physical environment. Each plant and animal occupies an area in which it is biologically suited to live—its *habitat*—and within that habitat it performs a basic operational function—its *niche* (see Chapter 19).

A **biome** is a large, stable terrestrial ecosystem characterized by specific plant and animal communities. Each biome usually is named for its *dominant vegetation*, because that is the single most easily identified feature. We can generalize Earth's wide-ranging plant species into six broad

FIGURE 20.2 The unique Australian realm.
The flora and fauna of Australia form a special assemblage of communities. [Photo by Mark Newman/Photo Researchers, Inc.]

biomes: *forest*, *savanna*, *grassland*, *shrubland*, *desert*, and *tundra*. Because plant distributions respond to environmental conditions and reflect variations in climate and soil, the world climate map in Figure 10.5 is a helpful reference for this chapter. (The biome concept can also be applied to aquatic ecosystems: polar seas, temperate seas, tropical seas, seafloor, shoreline, and coral reef.)

More specific characteristics are used for the structural classification of plants themselves. *Life-form designations* are based on the outward physical properties of individual plants or the general form and structure of a vegetation cover. These physical life forms include:

- *Trees* (large woody main trunk, perennial; usually exceeds 3 m, or 10 ft, in height)
- *Lianas* (woody climbers and vines)
- *Shrubs* (smaller woody plants; stems branching at the ground)
- *Herbs* (small plants without woody stems; includes grasses and other nonwoody vascular plants)
- *Bryophytes* (nonflowering, spore-producing plants; includes mosses and liverworts)
- *Epiphytes* (plants growing above the ground on other plants, using them for support)
- *Thallophytes* (lack true leaves, stems, or roots; includes bacteria, fungi, algae, lichens)

These plant assemblages in their general biomes are divided into more-specific vegetation units called **formation classes**, which refer to the structure and appearance of dominant plants in a terrestrial ecosystem. Examples are equatorial rain forest, northern needleleaf forest, Mediterranean shrubland, and arctic tundra. Each formation class includes numerous plant communities, and each community includes innumerable plant habitats. Within those habitats, Earth's diversity is expressed in 270,000 plant species. Despite this intricate complexity, we can generalize Earth's numerous formation classes into 10 global terrestrial biome regions, as portrayed in Figure 20.3, for the world and Canada, and detailed in Table 20.1.

News Report 20.1

Aquatic Ecosystems and Marine Protected Areas

Oceans, estuaries, and freshwater bodies (streams and lakes) are home to aquatic ecosystems. Poor understanding of aquatic ecosystems has led to the demise of species such as herring in the Georges Bank of the Atlantic Ocean and an overall decline in fisheries worldwide. The conservation and protection of marine life and their habitats is the goal of marine protected areas (MPA). A marine protected area is an area of the sea within Canada's territory that is designated for conservation and protection of one or more of the following: (a) commercial and non-commercial fishery resources, including marine mammals and their habitats; (b) endangered or threatened marine species, and their habitats; (c) unique habitats; (d) marine areas of high biodiversity or biological productivity; and (e) any other marine resource or habitat as is necessary to fulfill the mandate of the Minister of the Department of Fisheries and Oceans Canada.

As of 2004, two MPAs have been designated. The first, designated in March 2003, is the Endeavour Hydrothermal Vents, which lies in 2250 m of water, 250 km southwest of Vancouver Island. The vents are part of the active spreading zone where the tectonic plates diverge and new ocean floor is created. The cold seawater percolates down through the crust, is heated and enriched in particles, and then emerges as superheated fluid. The features produced by the vents are called black smokers and the enrichment of the seawater in the vicinity of the chimneys supports abundant organisms (see Figure 11.13b). This MPA was designated to protect the vents and the unique ecosystems associated with them.

The second MPA, designated in May 2004, is the Gully, a part of the Eastern Scotian Shelf in the Atlantic Ocean located about 200 km east of Nova Scotia, near Sable Island. The Gully is a canyon on the edge of the Continental Shelf where bathymetry quickly drops by over 2.5 km. The 65-km long and 15-km wide canyon formed when sea levels were much lower and is one of the most prominent features of the undersea area of eastern Canada. The Gully was designated a marine protected area to safeguard and conserve the biological diversity of the region. For more information see the MPA Web site (**http://www.dfo-mpo.gc.ca/canwaters-eauxcan/oceans/mpa-zpm/index_e.asp**).

Table 20.1 Major Terrestrial Biomes and Their Characteristics

Biome and Ecosystems (map symbol)	Vegetation Characteristics	Soil Orders—CSSC and Soil Taxonomy	Climate Type	Annual Precipitation Range	Temperature Patterns	Water Balance
Equatorial and Tropical Rain Forest (ETR) Evergreen broadleaf forest Selva	Leaf canopy thick and continuous; broadleaf evergreen trees, vines (lianas), epiphytes, tree ferns, palms	Oxisols Ultisols (on well-drained uplands)	Tropical	180–400 cm (>6 cm/mo)	Always warm (21–30°C; avg. 25°C)	Surpluses all year
Tropical Seasonal Forest and Scrub (TrSF) Tropical monsoon forest Tropical deciduous forest Scrub woodland and thorn forest	Transitional between rain forest and grasslands; broadleaf, some deciduous trees; open parkland to dense undergrowth; acacias and other thorn trees in open growth	Oxisols Ultisols Vertisols (in India) Some Alfisols	Tropical monsoon savanna	130–200 cm (<40 rainy days during 4 driest months)	Variable, always warm (18°C)	Seasonal surpluses and deficits
Tropical Savanna (TrS) Tropical grassland Thorn tree scrub Thorn woodland	Transitional between seasonal forests, rain forests, and semiarid tropical steppes and desert; trees with flattened crowns, clumped grasses, and bush thickets; fire association	Alfisols (dry: Ultalfs) Ultisols Oxisols	Tropical savanna	9–150 cm, seasonal	No cold-weather limitations	Tends toward deficits, therefore fire- and drought-susceptible
Midlatitude Broadleaf and Mixed Forest (MBME) Temperate broadleaf Midlatitude deciduous Temperate needleleaf	Mixed broadleaf and needleleaf trees; deciduous broadleaf, losing leaves in winter; southern and eastern evergreen pines demonstrate fire association	Podzols, red and yellow Ultisols Some Alfisols	Humid subtropical warm summer Humid continental warm summer	75–150 cm	Temperate with cold season	Seasonal pattern with summer maximum PRECIP and POTET (PET); no irrigation needed
Needleleaf Forest and Montane Forest (NF/MF) Taiga Boreal forest Other montane forests and highlands	Needleleaf conifers, mostly evergreen pine, spruce, fir; Russian larch, a deciduous needleleaf	Gleysols Podzols Spodosols Histosols Inceptisols Alfisols (Boralfs: cold)	Subarctic Humid continental cool summer	30–100 cm	Short summer, cold winter	Low POTET (PET), moderate PRECIP, moist soils, some waterlogged and frozen in winter; no deficits
Temperate Rain Forest (TeR) West-coast forest Coast redwoods (U.S.)	Narrow margin of lush evergreen and deciduous trees on windward slopes; redwoods, tallest trees on Earth	Podzols Spodosols Inceptisols (mountainous environs)	Marine west coast	150–500 cm	Mild summer and mild winter for latitude	Large surpluses and runoff
Mediterranean Shrubland (MSh) Sclerophyllous shrubs Australian eucalyptus forest	Short shrubs, drought adapted, tending to grassy woodlands and chaparral	Luvisols Alfisols (Xeralfs) Mollisols (Xerolls)	Mediterranean dry summer	25–65 cm	Hot, dry summers, cool winters	Summer deficits, winter surpluses
Midlatitude Grasslands (MGr) Temperate grassland Sclerophyllous shrub	Tallgrass prairies and shortgrass steppes, highly modified by human activity; major areas of commercial grain farming; plains, pampas, and veld	Chernozemic Mollisols Aridisols	Humid subtropical Humid continental hot summer	25–75 cm	Temperate continental regimes	Soil moisture utilization and recharge balanced; irrigation and dry farming in drier areas
Warm Desert and Semidesert (DBW) Subtropical desert and scrubland	Bare ground graduating into xerophytic plants including succulents, cacti, and dry shrubs	Aridisols Entisols (sand dunes)	Desert Arid	<2 cm	Average annual temperature, around 18°C, highest temperatures on Earth	Chronic deficits, irregular precipitation events, PRECIP $<\frac{1}{2}$POTET (PET)
Cold Desert and Semidesert (DBC) Midlatitude desert, scrubland, and steppe	Cold desert vegetation includes short grass and dry shrubs	Aridisols Entisols	Steppe Semiarid	2–25 cm	Average annual temperature around 18°C	PRECIP$>\frac{1}{2}$POTET (PET)
Arctic and Alpine Tundra (AAT)	Treeless; dwarf shrubs, stunted sedges, mosses, lichens, and short grasses; alpine, grass meadows	Organic Cryosols Gelisols Histosols Entisols (permafrost)	Tundra Subarctic very cold	15–180 cm	Warmest months >10°C, only 2 or 3 months above freezing	Not applicable most of the year, poor drainage in summer
Ice			Ice sheet ice cap			

Now let us go on a tour of Earth's biomes, keeping in mind that they synthesize all we have learned about the atmosphere, hydrosphere, lithosphere, and biosphere in the pages of this text. Here we bring it all together.

Earth's Major Terrestrial Biomes

Few natural communities of plants and animals remain; most biomes have been greatly altered by human intervention. Thus, the "natural vegetation" identified on many biome maps reflects *ideal potential* mature vegetation, given the environmental characteristics in a region. Even though human practices have greatly altered these ideal forms, it is valuable to study the natural (undisturbed) biomes to better understand the environment and to assess the extent of human-caused alteration.

Knowing the ideal in a region guides us to a closer approximation of natural vegetation in the plants we introduce. In Canada and the United States, we humans are perpetuating a type of *transition community*, somewhere between grasslands and a forest—an artificial successional stage, produced by large-scale interruption and disturbance. We plant trees and lawns and then must invest energy, water, and capital to sustain such artificial modifications. Or we graze animals and plant crops that perpetuate this disturbed transitional state.

When these activities cease, natural succession recovers, and we see the land slowly return to its various vegetation-cover potentials. Some irreversible damage might occur when plants, animals, and organisms are knowingly or accidentally brought into an ecosystem or biome in which they are not native. These exotic species pose an increasing concern to scientists and society—a subject of News Report 20.2.

The global distribution of Earth's major terrestrial biomes, based on vegetation formation classes, is portrayed in Figure 20.3. Table 20.1 describes each biome on the map and summarizes other pertinent information gathered from throughout *Geosystems*.

Now is a good time to refer to "The Living Earth" composite image that appears in the Map Reference Library on the *Student Animation* CD-ROM that accompanies this text. A computer artist using hundreds of thousands of satellite images produced this cloudless view of Earth in natural colour typical of a local summer day. Compare the map in Figure 20.3 with this remarkable composite image and see what correlation you can make. Then compare the biomes with population distribution as indicated by the nighttime lighting display that you activate with the slider on the CD.

News Report 20.2

Alien Invaders of Exotic Species

The above title sounds like that of a cult science fiction movie; instead, it refers to a real problem in the integrity of many ecosystems, both aquatic and terrestrial. Animal and plant species brought or somehow getting into biomes outside their native home is an important subject in biogeography and invasion biology. Niche takeovers by non-native species can prove damaging to otherwise healthy ecosystems. These intruders are known as *exotic species*, or *alien* or *non-native species*.

Environment Canada's Biodiversity Convention Office hosts the Invasive Alien Species Web site at **http://www.cbin.ec.gc.ca/primers/ias.cfm?lang=e**. The site lists some of the most recent invasive species in Canada including purple loosestrife, the zebra mussel (Figure 1c), and the brown spruce long-horned beetle. Alien species total 27% of all vascular plants, 181 insects that feed on woody plants, 24 birds, 26 mammals, 2 reptiles, 4 amphibians, and 55 freshwater fish in Canada. Several invasive species that have established in Canada are included on the World Conservation Union's list of 100 worst invasive alien species including Dutch elm disease, purple loosestrife, leafy spurge, Japanese knotweed, green crab, spiny water flea, gypsy moth, carp, rainbow trout, starling, domestic (feral) cat, and rats.

The Institute for Biological Invasions at the University of Tennessee at **http://invasions.bio.utk.edu/bio_invasions/index.html** is dedicated to these invasive plants, animals, and other organisms. Some states post warning signs at their borders (Figure 1a) and others offer Web sites, such as the Minnesota Department of Natural Resources (**http://www.dnr.state.mn.us/ecological_services/invasives.html**).

The African "killer bees" are frequently in the headlines, as are brown tree snakes in Guam, zebra mussels in the Great Lakes, and Eurasian cheatgrass in the Utah desert, to name but a few examples. Brought from Africa to the central coast of Brazil in 1957 to increase honey production, killer bees now have interbred with native bees and range to southern California, Arizona, New Mexico, Texas, and Puerto Rico. More than 1000 people have died from their attacks, although the dangers are in their mass response to disturbances and that some people are allergic to even one bee sting. This is a classic case of geographical diffusion of an exotic species.

Probably 90% of exotic species fail when they try to move into established niches in a community. The 10% that succeed, some 4500 species documented in a 1993 U.S. Office of Technology Assessment report, prove damaging to as much as one-fifth of ecosystems they invade. Figures 1b and c show two such alien invaders: purple loosestrife (*Lythrum salicaria*) and zebra mussels (*Dreissena polymorpha*).

Purple loosestrife was introduced from Europe in the 1800s as a desired ornamental and had some medicinal applications. The plant's seeds also arrived in ships that used soil for bal-

(a)

(b)

(c)

(d)

FIGURE 1 Exotic species.
(a) A sign in Wallowa County, Washington state, pleas for awareness and help in this agricultural country, listing noxious (non-native, often problematic) weeds at the county line. (b) Invasive purple loosestrife near Lake Michigan and the Indiana Dunes National Lakeshore, Indiana (foreground and left centre). (c) Zebra mussels cover all hard surfaces in the Great Lakes. (d) Gorse (yellow flowering shrub), intended for barriers between pastures, is loose across the landscape in West Point, Falkland Islands. [Photos (a), (b), and (d) by Bobbé Christopherson; (c) David M. Dennis/Maxximages.com.]

last. A hardy perennial, it got loose and invaded wetlands across the eastern portions of Canada and the United States, through the upper Midwest and as far west as Vancouver Island, British Columbia, replacing plants on which native wildlife depend (Figure 1b). The plant is known to infect drier landscapes as well and poses a potential threat to agriculture.

Gorse was introduced into the timber-poor Falkland Islands as a barrier plant, like a substitute fence. Its thorny stickers and dense growth were meant to keep grazing sheep and a few cattle under control. The plant got loose and spread beyond this intended use (Figure 1d).

In learning about biomes, we find out about native plant, animal, and organism locations and the unique place each species occupies. We must avoid knowingly or perhaps unconsciously adding to this escalating problem by bringing exotic species into non-native sites.

Equatorial and Tropical Rain Forest

Earth is girdled with a lush biome—the **equatorial and tropical rain forest**. In a climate of consistent year-round daylength (12 hours), high insolation, average annual temperatures around 25°C (77°F), and plentiful moisture, plant and animal populations have responded with the most diverse expressions of life on the planet.

As Figure 20.3 shows, the Amazon region, also called the *selva*, is the largest tract of equatorial and tropical rain forest. In addition, rain forests cover equatorial regions of Africa, Indonesia, the margins of Madagascar and Southeast Asia, the Pacific coast of Ecuador and Colombia, and the east coast of Central America, with small discontinuous patches elsewhere. The cloud forests of western Venezuela are such tracts of rain forest at high elevation, perpetuated by high humidity and cloud cover. Undisturbed tracts of rain forest are rare.

Rain forests represent approximately one-half of Earth's remaining forests, occupying about 7% of the total land area worldwide. This biome is stable in its natural state, resulting from the long-term residence of these continental plates near equatorial latitudes and their escape from glacial activity.

Rain forests feature ecological niches that are distributed vertically rather than horizontally because of the competition for light. Biomass in a rain forest is concentrated high up in the canopy, that dense mass of overhead leaves. The canopy is filled with a rich variety of plants and animals. Lianas (vines) stretch from tree to tree, entwining them with cords that can reach 20 cm (8 in.) in diameter. Epiphytes flourish there too—plants such as orchids, bromeliads, and ferns live entirely above ground, supported physically but not nutritionally by the structures of other plants. Windless conditions on the forest floor make pollination difficult, so pollination is by insects, other animals, and self-pollination.

The rain forest canopy forms three levels—see Figure 20.4. The upper level is not continuous but features emergent tall trees whose high crowns rise above the middle canopy. This upper level appears as a broken *overstory* of tall trees breaking through a middle canopy that is nearly

FIGURE 20.4 The three levels of a rainforest canopy.
(a) Lower, middle, and high levels of the rain forest. (b) Undisturbed rain forest on the Peninsula de Osa in Costa Rica. Note a few high-level canopy trees that extend above the dense, continuous cover of the middle canopy. [Photo by Barbara Cushman Rowell/Mountain Light Photography, Inc.]

continuous (Figure 20.4b). The broad leaves block much of the light and create a darkened *understory* area and forest floor. The lower level is composed of seedlings, ferns, bamboo, and the like, leaving the litter-strewn ground level in deep shade and fairly open.

Aerial photographs of a rain forest, or views along riverbanks covered by dense vegetation, or the false Hollywood-movie imagery of the jungle, makes it difficult to imagine the shadowy environment of the actual rainforest floor, which receives only about 1% of the sunlight arriving at the canopy (Figure 20.5a). The constant moisture, rotting fruit and mouldy odours, strings of thin roots and vines dropping down from above, windless air, and echoing sounds of life in the trees together create a unique environment.

The smooth, slender trunks of rainforest trees are covered with thin bark and buttressed by large wall-like flanks that grow out from the trees to brace the trunks (Figure 20.5b). These buttresses form angular, open enclosures, a ready habitat for various animals. There are usually no branches for at least the lower two-thirds of the tree trunks.

The wood of many rainforest trees is extremely hard, heavy, and dense—in fact, some species will not even float in water. (Exceptions are balsa and a few others, which are light.) Varieties of trees include mahogany, ebony, and rosewood. Logging is difficult because individual species are widely scattered; a species may occur only once or twice per square kilometre. Selective cutting is required for species-specific logging, whereas pulpwood production takes everything. Conversion of the forest to pasture usually is done by setting destructive fires.

Rainforest soils, principally Oxisols (Soil Taxonomy), are essentially infertile, yet they support rich vegetation. The trees have adapted to these soil conditions with root systems able to capture nutrients from litter decay at the soil surface. High precipitation and temperatures work to produce deeply weathered and leached soils, characteristic of the laterization process, with a clay-like texture sometimes breaking up into a granular structure. Oxisols lack nutrients and colloidal material. With much investment in fertilizers, pesticides, and machinery, these soils can be productive.

The animal and insect life of the rain forest is diverse, ranging from small decomposers (bacteria) working the surface detritus to many animals living exclusively in the upper stories of the trees. These tree dwellers are referred to as *arboreal*, from the Latin for "tree," and include sloths, monkeys, lemurs, parrots, and snakes. Beautiful birds of many colours, tree frogs, lizards, bats, and a rich insect community that includes more than 500 species of butterflies are found in rain forests. Surface animals include pigs (bushpigs and the giant forest hog in Africa, wild boar and bearded pig in Asia, and peccary in South America), species of small antelopes (bovids), and mammalian predators (the tiger in Asia, jaguar in South America, and leopard in Africa and Asia).

The present human assault on Earth's rain forests has put this diverse fauna and the varied flora at risk. It also jeopardizes an important recycling system for atmospheric carbon dioxide and a potential source of valuable pharma-

(a)

(b)

FIGURE 20.5 The rain forest.
(a) Equatorial rain forest is thick along the Amazon River where light breaks through to the surface, producing a rich gallery of vegetation. (b) The rainforest floor in Corcovado, Costa Rica, with typical buttressed trees and lianas. [Photos by (a) Wolfgang Kaehler Photography; (b) Frank S. Balthis.]

ceuticals and many types of new foods—and so much is still unknown and undiscovered.

Deforestation of the Tropics

More than half of Earth's original rain forest is gone, cleared for pasture, timber, fuel wood, and farming. Worldwide an area nearly the size of the three Maritime provinces and the island of Newfoundland is lost each year (169,000 km^2, 65,000 mi^2) and about a third more is disrupted by selective cutting of canopy trees, a damage that occurs along the *edges* of deforested areas.

When orbiting astronauts look down on the rain forests at night, they see thousands of human-set fires. During the day, the lower atmosphere in these regions is choked with the smoke. These fires are used to clear land for agriculture, which is intended to feed the domestic population as well as to produce cash exports of beef, rubber, coffee, and other commodities. Edible fruits are not abundant in an undisturbed rain forest, but cultivated clearings produce bananas (plantains), mangos, jack fruit, guava, and starch-rich roots such as manioc and yams.

Because of the poor soil fertility, the cleared lands are quickly exhausted under intensive farming and are then generally abandoned in favour of newly burned and cleared lands, unless fertility is maintained artificially. Unfortunately, the dominant trees require from 100 to 250 years to reestablish themselves after major disturbances. Once cleared, the former forest becomes a mass of low bushes intertwined with vines and ferns, slowing the return of the forests.

Figure 20.6a to c shows satellite false-colour images of a portion of western Brazil called Rondônia, recorded in June 1975 (*Landsat 2*), August 1986 (*Landsat 5*), June 1992 (*Landsat 4*), and a true-colour image (d) in June 2001 (*Terra*, MODIS). These images give a sense of the level of rainforest destruction in progress. You can clearly see encroachment along new roads branching from highway BR364. The *edges* of every road and cleared area represent a significant portion of the species habitat disturbance, population dynamic changes, and carbon losses to the atmosphere—perhaps as much as 1.5 times more impact occurs along these edges than in the tracts of clear-cut logging. The hotter, drier, and windier edge conditions penetrate the forest up to 100 m. Figure 20.6e shows a tract of former rain forest that has just been burned to begin the clearing and roadbuilding process.

Scientists with the Goddard Space Flight Center and the Brazilian government completed a GIS analysis of these rainforest losses to guide policy decisions. In 1998, despite all the efforts to introduce sustainable forestry practices, deforestation increased 27% over 1997—some 16,800 km^2 (6500 mi^2)—and rose again to 19,836 km^2 lost in 2000, according to the Brazilian Environment Ministry in Brasilia (an area roughly equivalent to southwestern Ontario west of Waterloo). In 2004 alone losses in the Amazon slightly exceeded the equivalent area of New Jersey in the States.

Since 1972, this loss has brought total deforestation to more than 15% of the entire Amazon Basin—more than the area of the combined Atlantic Provinces, including Labrador (Figure 20.6f), or equivalent to the area of France, in 30 years! Remember, in 1970 only about 1% of the Brazilian Amazon had been deforested.

The United Nations Food and Agricultural Organization (FAO) estimates that if this destruction to rain forests continues unabated, these forests will be completely removed by about A.D. 2050! By continent, rain forest losses are estimated at more than 50% in Africa, more than 40% in Asia, and 40% in Central and South America.

To slow this continuing catastrophe of deforestation, in 1985 the FAO, the UN Development Programme, the World Bank, the World Resources Institute, and several nongovernmental organizations initiated the Tropical

(a)

(b)

FIGURE 20.19 Arctic tundra.
(a) Tundra on the Kamchatka Peninsula, Russia. The Uzon Caldera is in the centre-background mountain range. (b) Lush by tundra standards, flowers, grasses, mosses, and dwarf willow flourish in the cold climate of the Arctic. [Photos by (a) Wolfgang Kaehler Photography; (b) Bobbé Christopherson.]

FIGURE 20.20 Alpine tundra conditions.
An alpine tundra and grazing mountain goats near Mount Evans, Colorado, at 3660 m (12,000 ft) elevation. [Photo by Bobbé Christopherson.]

News Report 20.3

ANWR Faces Threats

Planning continues for oil exploration and development of the Arctic National Wildlife Refuge (ANWR) on Alaska's North Slope. The May 2001 U.S. *National Energy Policy* recommends oil exploration and development in ANWR, using the latest environmentally sensitive techniques. However, the U.S. Senate defeated the plan in 2002. Political and corporate pressure is fairly constant to exploit these expected reserves of fossil fuels, and the U.S. Congress again began another push for drilling authorization in 2005.

This pristine wilderness is above the Arctic Circle, bordering on the Beaufort Sea and adjoining the Yukon Territory (Figure 1). The refuge area sustains almost 200,000 caribou, polar and grizzly bears, musk oxen, and wolves. Some have referred to it as "America's Serengeti," given the annual migration of hundreds of thousands of large animals.

The ANWR remains the only portion of Alaska's Arctic coast that is not open to oil and gas exploration at this time—the other 90% is open. But controversy over this refuge continues, as political and corporate pressures mount to begin oil exploration. In 1995, Congress considered potential ANWR lease revenues in its Budget Resolution, implying a green light for development. A presidential veto stopped this Budget Reconciliation Act. A 1998 USGS assessment disclosed that the oil under the Arctic Refuge coastal plain is likely held in many small reservoirs. Recovering this oil would require extensive alteration of the Arctic National Wildlife Refuge landscape, a point disputed in the National Energy Policy.

Petroleum development could be devastating to arctic wildlife. The porcupine caribou herd, for example, is a population of barren ground caribou that inhabit Alaska, Yukon, and Northwest Territories (Figure 2). Most of the herd migrates to the Alaska coastal plain to calve in early June. The calving area is fairly small and 80–85% of the herd use it year after year. Because the caribou come from areas both within ANWR and from areas in Yukon and Northwest Territories, this is truly a transboundary issue. In Yukon Territory (Figure 3), the Canadian and territorial governments and First Nations people established the Ivvavik and Vuntut National Parks to protect the coastal tundra and adjacent mountains. Oil exploration is not permitted in these areas.

In addition to wildlife, oil extraction could be devastating to the fragile tundra according to a USGS study released in 2002. The cost of development would price the oil at over $30 per barrel. The estimated oil reserve in the ANWR, approximately 3.2 billion barrels (less than a 5-month supply at present U.S. demand levels), could be offset simply by a small increase in U.S. automobile efficiency. However, 2002 and 2003 marked years when mileage efficiency decreased. In 2002, federal funding toward improving automobile mileage efficiency was formally dropped and research monies for hybrid car technology stopped in favour of fuel cell research for the future. Clearly, economic ventures should be weighed against the ecosystem itself, its limitations and its uniqueness, and a total assessment of all costs to the consumer.

FIGURE 1 Arctic National Wildlife Refuge. In Alaska's Arctic National Wildlife Refuge, Mount Chamberlin, the second highest peak of the Brooks Range, overlooks tundra in the foreground. Is this region destined for petroleum exploration and development or for continued preservation as wilderness? [Photo by Scott T. Smith.]

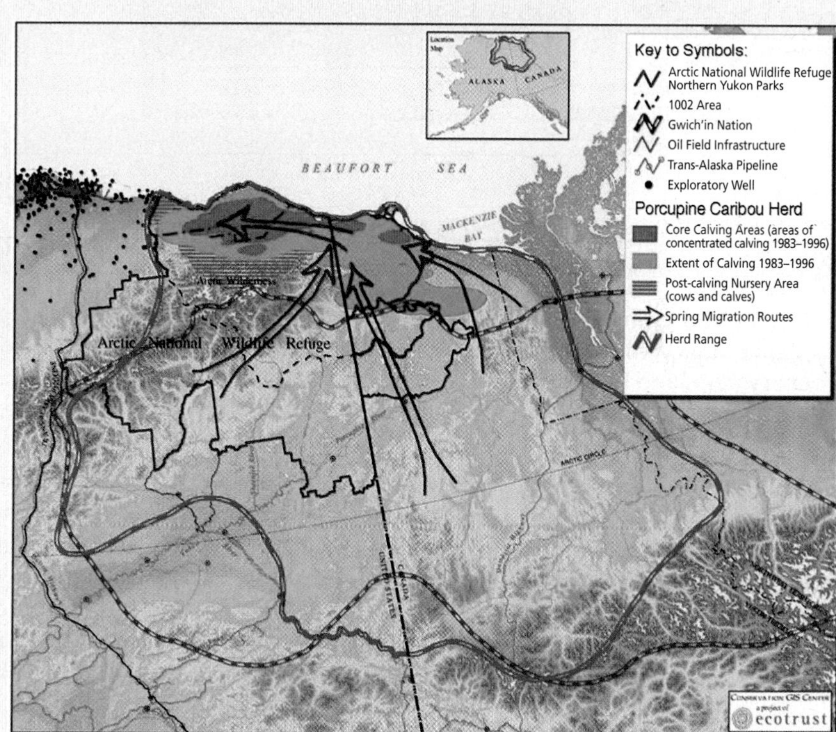

FIGURE 2 Caribou migration routes and calving grounds in the Arctic National Wildlife Refuge. [Courtesy of the Alaska Center for the Environment.]

(continued)

News Report 20.3 *(continued)*

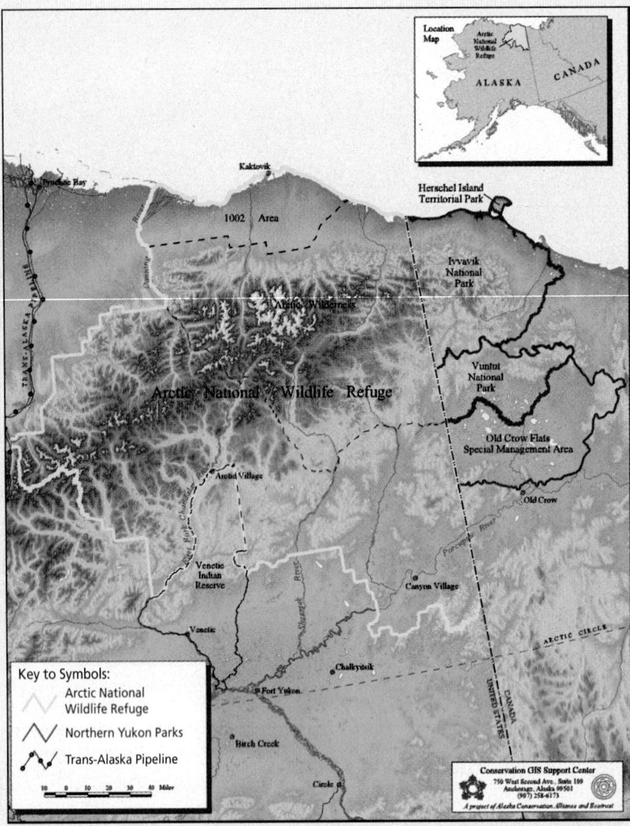

FIGURE 3 Arctic National Wildlife Refuge and Yukon parks and reserves share a boundary. This map shows the birthplace and nursery grounds of the porcupine caribou herd. [Courtesy of the Alaska Center for the Environment.]

Summary and Review—Terrestrial Biomes

Define the concept of biogeographic realms of plants and animals and *define* ecotone, terrestrial ecosystem, and biome.

Earth is the only planet in the Solar System with a biosphere. An impressive feature of the living Earth is its diversity, which biogeographers categorize into discrete spatial biomes for analysis and study. The interplay among supporting physical factors within Earth's ecosystem determines the distribution of plant and animal communities. A **biogeographic realm** of plants and animals is a geographic region in which a group of species evolved. This recognition was a start at understanding distinct regions of flora and fauna and the broader pattern of terrestrial ecosystems. A boundary transition zone adjoining ecosystems is an **ecotone**.

A **terrestrial ecosystem** is a self-sustaining association of plants and animals and their abiotic environment that is characterized by specific plant formation classes. A **biome** is a large, stable ecosystem characterized by specific plant and animal communities. Biomes carry the name of the dominant vegetation because it is the most easily identified feature: forest, savanna, grassland, shrubland, desert, tundra.

biogeographic realm (p. 666)
ecotone (p. 666)
terrestrial ecosystem (p. 667)
biome (p. 667)

1. Reread the opening quotation and analysis in this chapter. What clue does it give you to the path ahead for Earth's forests? Is our future direction controllable? Explain.
2. What is a biogeographic realm? How is the world subdivided according to plant and animal types?
3. Describe a transition zone between two ecosystems. How wide is an ecotone? Explain.
4. Define biome. What is the basis of the designation?

Define six formation classes and the life-form designations and *explain* their relationship to plant communities.

Biomes are divided into more specific vegetation units called **formation classes**. The structure and appearance of the vegetation is described: rain forest, needleleaf forest, Mediterranean shrubland, arctic tundra, and so forth. Specific life-form designations include trees, lianas, shrubs, herbs, bryophytes, epiphytes (plants growing above ground on other plants), and thallophytes (lacking true leaves, stems, or roots, including bacteria, fungi, algae, and lichens).

formation classes (p. 668)

5. Distinguish between formation classes and life-form designations as a basis for spatial classification.

Describe 10 major terrestrial biomes and locate them on a world map.

Biomes are Earth's major terrestrial ecosystems, each named for its dominant plant community. The 10 major biomes are generalized from numerous formation classes that describe vegetation. Ideally, a biome represents a mature community of natural vegetation. In reality, few undisturbed biomes exist in the world, for most have been modified by human activity. Many of Earth's plant and animal communities are experiencing an accelerated rate of change that could produce dramatic alterations within our lifetime.

For an overview of Earth's 10 major terrestrial biomes and their vegetation characteristics, soil orders, climate-type designation, annual precipitation range, temperature patterns, and water balance characteristics, please review Table 20.1.

equatorial and tropical rain forest (p. 673)
tropical seasonal forest and scrub (p. 680)
tropical savanna (p. 680)
midlatitude broadleaf and mixed forest (p. 682)
needleleaf forest (p. 682)
boreal forest (p. 682)
taiga (p. 682)
montane forest (p. 682)
temperate rain forest (p. 683)
Mediterranean shrubland (p. 685)
chaparral (p. 686)
midlatitude grasslands (p. 686)
warm desert and semidesert (p. 688)
cold desert and semidesert (p. 688)
arctic tundra (p. 689)
alpine tundra (p. 689)

6. Using the integrative chart in Table 20.1 and the world map in Figure 20.3, select any two biomes and study the correlation of vegetation characteristics, soil, moisture, and climate with their spatial distribution. Then, contrast the two using each characteristic.
7. Describe the equatorial and tropical rain forests. Why is the rainforest floor somewhat clear of plant growth? Why are logging activities for specific species so difficult there?
8. What issues surround the deforestation of the rain forest? What is the impact of these losses on the rest of the biosphere? What new threat to the rain forest has emerged?
9. What do *caatinga*, *chaco*, *brigalow*, and *dornveld* refer to? Explain.
10. Describe the role of fire or fire ecology in the tropical savanna biome and the midlatitude broadleaf and mixed forest biome.
11. Why does the northern needleleaf forest biome not exist in the Southern Hemisphere? Where is this biome located in the Northern Hemisphere, and what is its relationship to climate type?
12. In which biome do we find Earth's tallest trees? Which biome is dominated by small, stunted plants, lichens, and mosses?
13. What type of vegetation predominates in the Mediterranean dry summer climates? Describe the adaptation necessary for these plants to survive.
14. What is the significance of the 98th meridian in terms of North American grasslands? What types of inventions enabled humans to cope with the grasslands?
15. Describe some of the unique adaptations found in a desert biome.
16. What is desertification (review from Chapter 15 and this chapter)? Explain its impact.
17. What physical weathering processes are specifically related to the tundra biome? What types of plants and animals are found there?

Relate human impacts, real and potential, to several of the biomes.

The equatorial and tropical rain forest biome is undergoing rapid deforestation. Because the rain forest is Earth's most diverse biome and is important to the climate system, such losses are creating great concern among citizens, scientists, and nations. Efforts are under way worldwide to set aside and protect remaining representative sites within most of Earth's principal biomes. These biosphere reserves are coordinated by the Man and the Biosphere (MAB) Programme of UNESCO. Nearly 300 such biosphere reserves, covering some 12 million hectares (30 million acres), are now operated voluntarily in 76 countries.

18. What is the relationship between island biogeography and biosphere reserves? Describe a biosphere reserve. What are the goals?
19. Compare the map in Figure 20.3 with the composite satellite image inside the front cover of this text. What correlations can you make between the local summertime portrait of Earth's biosphere and the biomes identified on the map?

Critical Thinking

A. Given the information presented in this chapter about deforestation in the tropics, assess the present situation for yourself. What are the main issues? What natural assets are at stake? Natural resources versus sovereign state rights? How are global biodiversity and greenhouse warming related to these issues? What is the perspective of the less-developed countries that possess most of the rain forest? What is the perspective of the more-developed countries and their transnational corporations and millions of environmentally active citizens? What kind of action plan would you cast to accommodate all parties? How would you proceed?

B. Using Figure 20.3 (biomes), Figure 10.5 (climates), Figures 10.2 and 9.6 (precipitation), and Figure 8.2 (air masses), and the printed graphic scales on these four maps, consider the following hypothetical. Assume a northward climatic shift in Canada and the United States of 500 km (310 mi) (in other words move North America 500 km north). Describe your analysis of the new conditions in the Prairies of Canada. Describe your analysis of the new conditions from New York through New England and into the Canadian Maritime provinces. What economic dislocations and relocations do you envision as a result of this hypothetical climate shift?

Dr. Robert Corell, Chair of the Arctic Climate Impact Assessment Integration Team, welcomes nearly 400 scientists, managers, government and nongovernmental representatives, student researchers, and indigenous people of the Arctic, including many Canadians, to a first-ever Arctic climate symposium, held in Reykjavik, Iceland, November 2004. The ACIA released their climate impact assessment to the Arctic Council and to a global audience. [Photo by Bobbé Christopherson.]

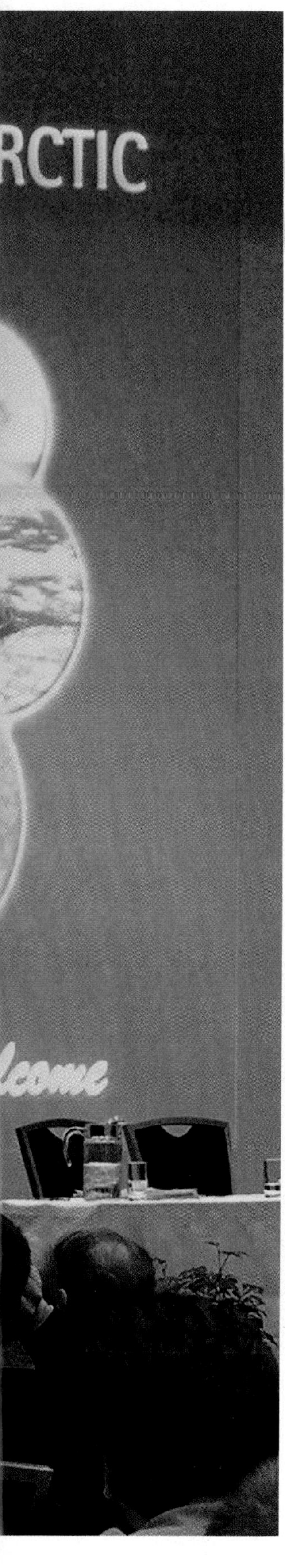

21 Earth and the Human Denominator

Key Learning Concepts

After reading the chapter, you should be able to:

- *Determine* an answer for Carl Sagan's question, "Who speaks for Earth?"
- *Describe* the growth in human population and *speculate* on possible future trends.
- *Analyze* "An Oily Bird" and *relate* your analysis to energy consumption patterns in Canada and the United States.
- *List* the subjects of recent environmental agreements, conventions, and protocols and *relate* them to physical geography and Earth systems science (geosystems).
- *List* 12 paradigms for the 21st century.
- *Appraise* your place in the biosphere and *realize* your relation to Earth systems.

> During my space flight, I came to appreciate my profound connection to the home planet and the process of life evolving in our special corner of the Universe, and I grasped that I was part of a vast and mysterious dance whose outcome will be determined largely by human values and actions.*

Earth can be observed from profound vantage points, as this astronaut experienced on the 1969 *Apollo IX* mission. Our vantage point in this book is that of physical geography. We examine Earth's many systems: its energy, atmosphere, winds, ocean currents, water, weather, climate, endogenic and exogenic systems, soils, ecosystems, and biomes. We are reminded daily of the power of Earth system operations (Figure 21.1). However, the inhabitants of the planet who have the greatest impact on these natural systems are human beings. What changes have we made?

We stand in the first decade of the 21st century. The 21st century will be an adventure for the global society, historically unparalleled in experimenting with Earth's life-

*Rusty Sweickart, "Our backs against the bomb, our eyes on the stars," *Discovery*, July 1987, p. 62.

supporting systems. You will spend the majority of your life in this century. What preparations and "future thinking" are we doing to understand all that is to occur?

In his 1980 book and public television series, *Cosmos*, astronomer Carl Sagan asked:

> What account would we give of our stewardship of the planet Earth? We have heard the rationales offered by the nuclear superpowers. We know who speaks for the nations. But who speaks for the human species? Who speaks for Earth?*

Indeed, who does speak for Earth? We might answer: Perhaps we physical geographers, and other scientists who have studied Earth and know the operations of the global ecosystem, should speak for Earth. However, some might say that questions of technology, environmental politics, and future thinking belong outside of science, and that our job is merely to learn how Earth's processes work and to leave the spokesperson's role to others. Biologist–ecologist Marston Bates addressed this line of thought in 1960:

> Then we came to humans and their place in this system of life. We could have left humans out, playing the ecological game of "let's pretend humans don't exist." But this seems as unfair as the corresponding game of the economists, "let's pretend nature doesn't exist." The economy of nature and the ecology of humans are inseparable and attempts to separate them are more than misleading, they are dangerous. Human destiny is tied to nature's destiny and the arrogance of the engineering mind does not change this. Humans may be a very peculiar animal, but they are still a part of the system of nature.†

A fact of life is that Earth's more-developed countries (MDCs), through their economic dominance, speak for the billions who live in less-developed countries (LDCs). The gross state product (GSP) of California's 35.5 million people was $1.3 trillion in 2002, which was greater by more than $100 billion than the gross domestic product (GDP) of China and its 1.3 billion people. The scale of disparity on our home planet is difficult to comprehend.

The fate of traditional modes of life may rest in some distant financial capital. But, economics aside, the reality is that the remote lands of Siberia are linked by Earth systems to the Pampas of Argentina to the Great Plains in North America and to those harvesting grain by hand in the remote Pamirs of Tajikistan (Figure 21.2).

FIGURE 21.1 The Wreckhouse area of Newfoundland. Valleys cut through the Long Range Mountains overlook the Codroy Lowlands, just north of Port-aux-Basques. These valleys funnel strong winds that are known to overturn transport trucks and derail trains on occasion. These winds are known as the "wreckhouse effect" and remind us that we live within the natural processes of Earth's systems. [Photo by Mary-Louise Byrne.]

FIGURE 21.2 Lands distant from the global centres of power. These lands were depopulated under Stalin when they were part of the former USSR. Only in the last decade or so have people returned to this traditional rural landscape in the Pamirs of Tajikistan, beginning life again, so distant from the more-developed countries. [Photo by Stephen F. Cunha.]

*C. Sagan, *Cosmos* (New York: Random House, 1980), p. 329.

†M. Bates, *The Forest and the Sea* (New York: Random House, 1960), p. 247.

To understand these linkages among Earth's myriad systems is our quest in *Geosystems* (Figure 21.3). We explored the atmosphere, hydrosphere, lithosphere, and biosphere, synthesizing operating systems into the web of life. We now see global linkages among physical and living systems and how actions in one place can affect change elsewhere. In this sense Earth can be compared to a spaceship. In the same way the members of a crew aboard the Space Shuttle are inextricably linked to each other's lives and survival, we too are each connected through the operation of planetary systems. Admittedly, the pace of popular culture makes these connections difficult to perceive.

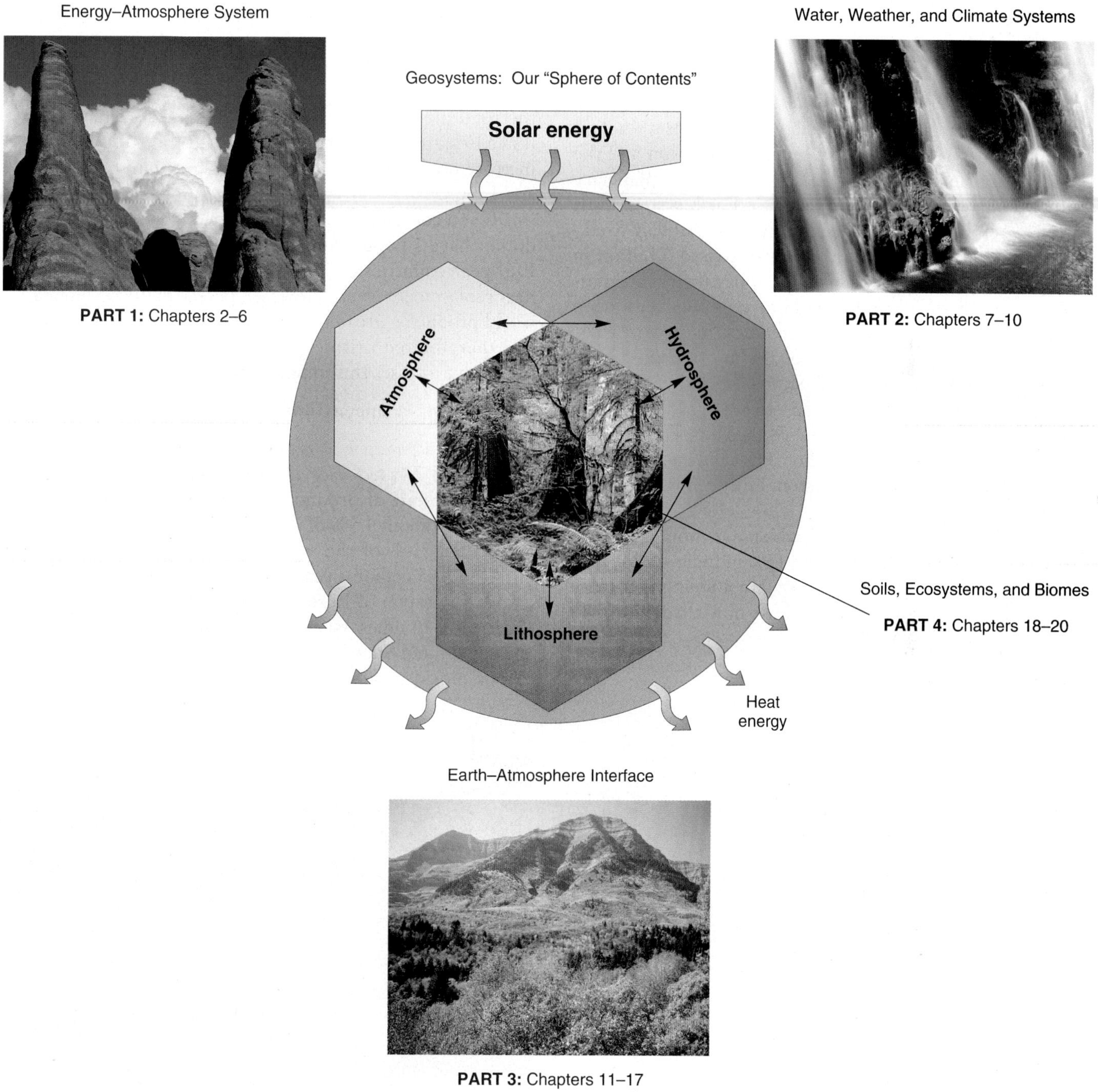

FIGURE 21.3 The spheres within *Geosystems*.
Through this text we covered the atmosphere, hydrosphere, lithosphere, and the synthesizing biosphere—the culmination of life-sustaining interactions. The systems approach shows us the flow of energy and matter and the sequence of events through time, within each sphere and among the spheres through their complex linkages. Ultimately, *Geosystems* describes the support systems of life. [Atmosphere and hydrosphere photos by Robert W. Christopherson; lithosphere and biosphere photos by Bobbé Christopherson.]

Growing international environmental awareness in the public sector is gradually prodding governments into action. People, when informed, generally favour environmental protection and public health progress over economic interests. A survey by American polling firm Louis Harris and Associates confirmed these opinion trends. Majorities in 22 nations are willing to "endorse environmental protection at the risk of slowing down economic growth." The public seems to know they are saving money as consumers if things are done right with the environment.

The Human Count and the Future

Because human influence is pervasive, we consider the totality of our impact the *human denominator*. Just as the denominator in a fraction tells how many parts a whole is divided into, so the growing human population and the increasing demand for resources and rising planetary impact suggest how much the whole Earth system must adjust. Yet, Earth's resource base remains relatively fixed.

The human population of Earth passed 6 billion in August 1999; more people are alive today than at any previous point in the planet's long history, unevenly arranged in 192 countries and numerous colonies. In the year leading up to this milestone, 83,000,000 more people were added. Population growth has slowed since then to about 70 million more people per year—this is 192,000 a day, or a new U.S. population every 4.2 years. At the end of 2004, world population was at 6.4 billion. Over the span of human history these billion-mark milestones are occurring at closer intervals (Figure 21.4).

Thirty-eight percent of Earth's population live in just two countries (21% in China and 17% in India—2.4 billion people combined). Moreover, we are a young planetary population, with some 30% of those now alive under the age of 15 (2004 data from Population Reference Bureau and U.S. Bureau of Census *POPClock Projection:* **http://www.census.gov/population/www/popclockus.html**).

Virtually all new population growth is in the less-developed countries, which now possess 81%, or about 5.1 billion, of the total population (Figure 21.5); the MDCs have the other 19%, or 1.3 billion. Table 21.1 illustrates this natural increase principle and the differences found in the MDCs and LDCs.

If you consider only the population count, the MDCs do not have a population growth problem. In fact, some European countries are actually declining in growth or are near replacement levels. However, people in the developed world produce a greater impact on the planet per person and therefore constitute a population impact crisis. An equation expresses this impact concept:

$$\text{Planetary impact } (I) = P \cdot A \cdot T$$

where P is *population*; A is *affluence*, or consumption per person; and T is *technology*, or the level of environmental impact per unit of production. Canada and the United States, with about 4.5% of the world's population, produce more than 50% of the world's gross domestic product (almost $10.5 trillion a year) and use more than double the energy per capita of Europeans, more than 7 times Latin Americans, 10 times Asians, and 20 times Africans. Canada and the United States produce 20 metric tons (22 tons) of carbon dioxide emissions per person per year.

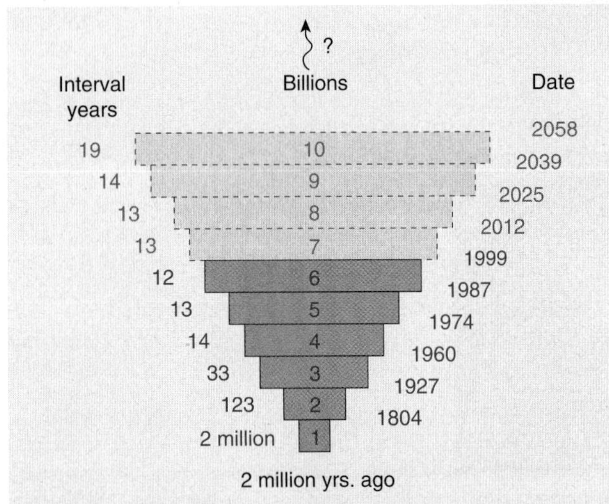

FIGURE 21.4 Human population growth.
The number of years required for the human population to add 1 billion to the count grows shorter and shorter. The 21st century should mark a slowing of this history of growth if policy actions are taken. Note the population forecasts for the next half-century.

FIGURE 21.5 Dhaka, Bangladesh.
The Bangladesh capital typifies the plight of the less-developed world as millions converge on cities to find work and more modern lifestyles. [Photo by Bruce Bander/Photo Researchers, Inc.]

Table 21.1 Planetary Population Increase Rates

	Birth Rate (per 1000)	Death Rate (per 1000)	Natural Increase (%)	Population Growth 2004–2050 (%)
World—2004	**21**	**9**	**1.3**	45%
More developed	**11**	**10**	**0.1**	4%
United States	14	8	0.6	43%
Japan	9	8	0.1	–21%
United Kingdom	12	10	0.1	10%
Less developed	**24**	**8**	**1.5**	55%
LDC exclu. China	**27**	**9**	**1.8**	69%
Mexico	25	5	2.1	41%
Nigeria	42	13	2.9	124%
India	25	8	1.7	50%

Source: World Population Data Sheet 2004. Population Reference Bureau, Washington, DC, **http://www.prb.org**.

Therefore, consideration by people in the MDCs of the state of Earth systems, natural resources, and sustainability of current practices is critical. Earth systems science is here to provide a high level of planetary monitoring and analysis to assist this process. The MDCs not only should affect change in their own planetary impact but could provide direction for the LDCs, which have a right to move along the road of progress and improve their living conditions. Let us examine this idea of global impact.

An Oily Bird

At first glance, the chain of events that exposes wildlife to oil contamination seems to stem from a technological problem. An oil tanker splits open at sea and releases its petroleum cargo, which is moved by ocean currents toward shore, where it coats coastal waters, beaches, and animals. In response, concerned citizens mobilize and try to save as much of the spoiled environment as possible (Figure 21.6). But the real problem goes far beyond the physical facts of the spill.

FIGURE 21.6 An oily bird.
A Western Grebe contaminated with oil from the *Exxon Valdez* tanker accident in Prince William Sound, Alaska. This oily bird is the result of a long chain of events and mistakes. [Photo by Geoffrey Orth/SIPA Press.]

In Prince William Sound off the southern coast of Alaska in clear weather and calm seas, the *Exxon Valdez*, a single-hulled supertanker operated by Exxon Corporation, struck a reef. The tanker spilled 42 million litres (11 million gallons) of oil. It took only 12 hours for the *Exxon Valdez* to empty its contents, yet a complete cleanup is impossible, and costs and private claims exceeded $15 billion. Scientists are still finding damage and residual oil spill.

Eventually, more than 2400 km (about 1500 mi) of sensitive coastline was ruined for years to come, affecting three national parks and eight other protected areas. For perspective, had this spill occurred farther south, every beach and bay along the Pacific Coast from southern Oregon to the Mexican border would have been blackened (Figure 21.7).

The death toll of animals was massive: At least 5000 sea otters died, or about 30% of resident otters; about 300,000 birds and uncounted fish, shellfish, plants, and aquatic microorganisms also perished. Sublethal effects, namely mutations, now are appearing in fish. The Pacific herring is still in significant decline, as are the harbour seals; other species are in recovery, such as the Bald Eagle and Common Murre. More than a decade and a half later, oil remains in mudflat and marsh soils and still can be scooped from beneath rocks along shorelines.

The immediate problem of cleaning oil off a bird symbolizes a national and international concern with far-reaching spatial significance. And while we search for answers, oil slicks continue their contamination. In just 1 year following the *Exxon Valdez* disaster, nearly 76 million litres (20 million gallons) of oil were spilled in 10,000 accidents worldwide, as evidenced on the startling map in Figure 21.7a. This is an average of 27 accidents a day, ranging from a few disastrous spills to numerous small ones.

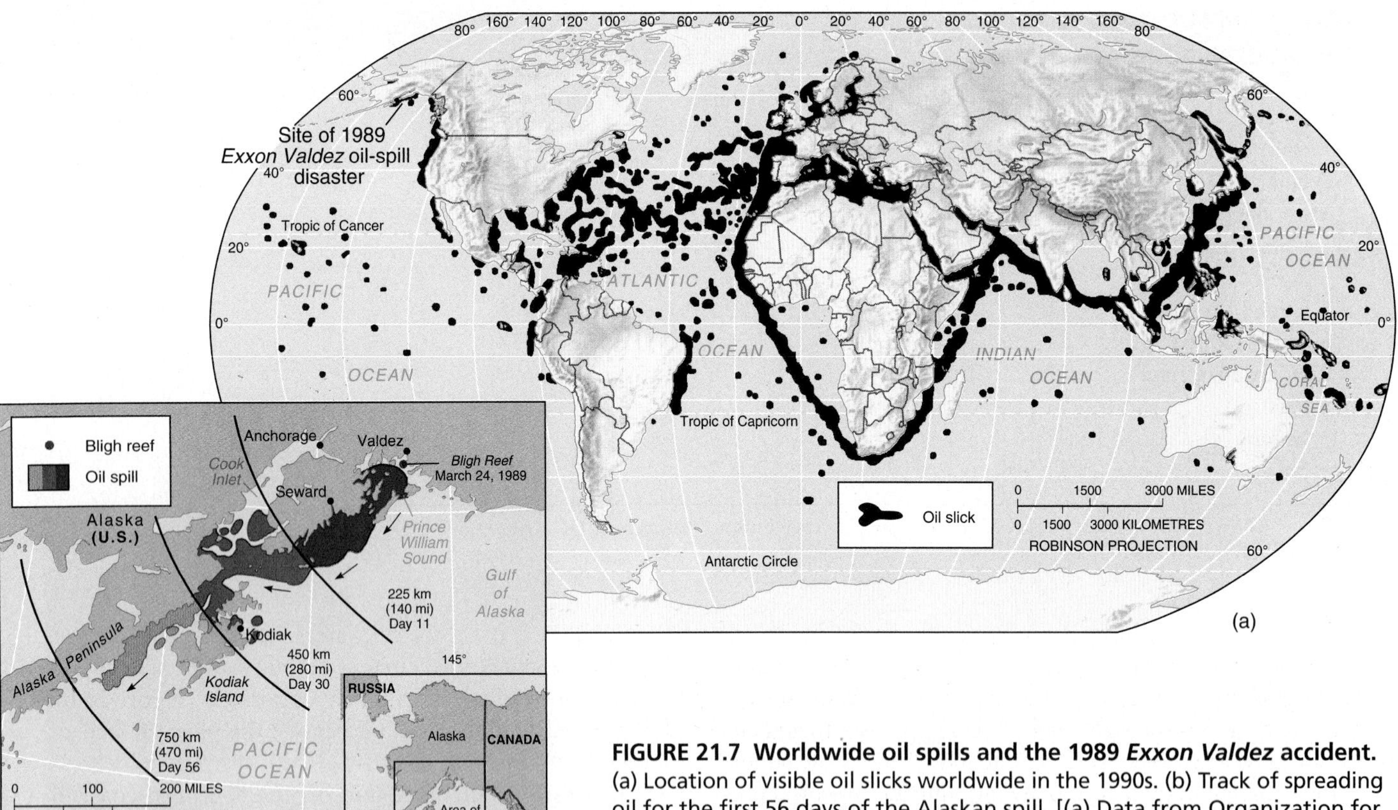

FIGURE 21.7 Worldwide oil spills and the 1989 *Exxon Valdez* accident. (a) Location of visible oil slicks worldwide in the 1990s. (b) Track of spreading oil for the first 56 days of the Alaskan spill. [(a) Data from Organization for Economic Cooperation and Development.]

There were 50 spills equal to the *Exxon Valdez* or larger since 1970. In addition to oceanic oil spills, people improperly dispose of crankcase oil from their automobiles in a volume that annually exceeds these tanker spills!

The immediate effect of global oil spills on wildlife is contamination and death. But the issues involved are much bigger than dead birds. Let's ask some fundamental questions about the *Exxon Valdez* accident:

- Why was the oil tanker there in the first place?
- Why are only a few of the 28 tankers that traverse the Prince William Sound of the safer double-hulled design?
- Why is petroleum imported into the continental United States from Alaska in such enormous quantities? Is the demand for petroleum products based on real need and the operation of efficient systems?
- The U.S. demand for oil is higher per capita than the demand of any other country. Efficiencies in the U.S. transportation sector again fell in the 2002 fleet of cars and trucks, with SUVs (light trucks) leading in sales. Why?

A combination of economic growth, waste, low prices, and a lack of alternatives has spurred the demand for petroleum. In addition, our land-use policies continue to foster a diffuse sprawl of our population, thereby adding stress to transportation systems. All of these factors increased U.S. demand for oil to more than 8 billion barrels a year alone.

Yet, hypocrisy is apparent in our outrage over energy politics and oil-spill accidents. We continue to consume gasoline at record levels in inefficient vehicles, thus creating the demand for oil imports. The task of physical geography is to analyze all the spatial aspects of these events in the environment and the ironies that are symbolized by an oily bird.

The Need for International Cooperation

The idea for a global meeting on the environment was put forward at the 1972 U.N. Conference on the Human Environment held in Stockholm. The United Nations Environment Program (UNEP) grew out of this meeting and many international agreements have developed as a result. From a Canadian perspective, two are particularly important. First, the Vienna Convention (1985) and the Montréal Protocol (1987) are United Nations treaties designed to reduce ozone-destroying gases and to protect stratospheric ozone. Most countries have ratified the Montréal Protocol, legally binding them to adhere to the principles set out in the document.

Second, the U.N. General Assembly in 1987 achieved a landmark in global planning by agreeing to hold the Earth Summit. *Our Common Future*, a book written at the time, set the tone for the 1992 Earth Summit:

> The Earth is one but the world is not. We all depend on one biosphere for sustaining our lives. Yet each community, each country, strives for survival and

prosperity with little regard for its impact on others. Some consume the Earth's resources at a rate that would leave little for future generations. Others, many more in number, consume far too little and live with the prospect of hunger, squalor, disease, and early death.*

The setting in Rio de Janeiro for the 1992 Earth Summit was ironic, for many of the very problems discussed at the conference were evident on the city's streets, with their abundant air pollution, water pollution, toxics, noise, wealth and poverty, and daily struggle for health and education.

Five agreements were written at the Earth Summit: the Climate Change Framework, Biological Diversity Treaty, the Management, Conservation, and Sustainable Development of All Types of Forests, the Earth Charter (a nonbinding statement of 27 environmental and economic principles), and Agenda 21 for Sustainable Development. A product of the Earth Summit was the United Nations Framework Convention on Climate Convention (FCCC) that led to a series of Convention of the Parties (COP) meetings. The Kyoto Protocol, agreed to in 1997 to reduce global carbon emissions was finalized in Marrakech, Morocco, in 2001 at *COP-7* (Figure 21.8). Canada ratified the Kyoto Protocol December 17, 2002, promising an emissions reduction of 3.3%. Environment Canada is responsible for recording, monitoring, and verifying the reduction of greenhouse gas emissions. Subsequent COP meetings were held in New Delhi, The Hague, Milan, and *COP-10* in Buenos Aires in December 2004. Following Russian ratification, the Kyoto Protocol and Rulebook became international law in March 2005, without United States or Australian participation.

Asking whether the Earth Summit "succeeded" or "failed" is the wrong question. The occurrence of this largest-

FIGURE 21.8 The Marrakech, Morocco, Climate Summit, November 2001.
The Marrakech Climate Summit (*COP-7*) voted to accept the terms of the Kyoto Protocol. A consensus was reached on the reduction of global carbon dioxide emissions and the Kyoto Rulebook. [Photo courtesy of IISD/ENB-Leila Mead.]

ever official gathering is a remarkable accomplishment. From the Earth Summit emerged a new organization—the U.N. Commission on Sustainable Development—to oversee the promises made in the five agreements. This momentum led to Earth Summit 2002 (**http://www.earthsummit2002.org/**) in Johannesburg, South Africa, with an agenda including climate change, freshwater, gender issues, global public goods, HIV/AIDS, sustainable finance, and the five Rio Conventions agreements.

Members of society must work to move the solutions for environmental and developmental problems off the bench and into play. We need international cooperation to consider our symbiotic relations with each other and with Earth's resilient, yet fragile, life-support systems (News Report 21.1).

*World Commission on Environment and Development, *Our Common Future* (Oxford, UK: Oxford University Press, 1987), p. 27.

News Report 21.1

Gaia Hypothesis Triggers Debate

Some view Earth as one vast, self-regulating organism. The concept is one of global symbiosis, or mutualism. This controversial concept is called the *Gaia hypothesis* (Gaia was the Earth Mother goddess in ancient mythology). It was proposed in 1979 by James Lovelock, a British astronomer and inventor, and elaborated by American biologist Lynn Margulis.

Gaia is the ultimate synergistic relationship, in which the whole greatly exceeds the sum of the individual interacting components. The hypothesis contends that life processes control and shape Earth's inorganic physical and chemical processes, with the ecosphere so interactive that a very small mass can affect a very large mass. Thus, Lovelock and Margulis think that the material environment and the evolution of species are tightly joined; as species evolve through natural selection, they (including us) in turn affect their environment. The present oxygen-rich composition of the atmosphere is given as proof of this co-evolution of living and nonliving systems.

From the perspective of physical geography, the Gaia hypothesis permits a view of all Earth and the spatial interrelations among systems. In fact, such a perspective is necessary for analyzing specific environmental issues. Many variables interact synergistically, producing both wanted and unwanted results.

One disturbing aspect of this unity is that any biotic threat to the operation of an ecosystem tends to move toward extinction itself. This trend preserves the system overall. Earth-systems

(continued)

News Report 21.1 ***(continued)***

operation and feedback naturally tend to eliminate offensive members. The degree to which humans represent a planetary threat, then, becomes a topic of great concern, for Earth (Gaia) will prevail, regardless of the outcome of the human experiment.

The maladies of Gaia do not last long in terms of her life span. Anything that makes the world uncomfortable to live in tends to induce the evolution of those species that can achieve a new and more comfortable environment. It follows that, if the world is made unfit by what we do, there is the probability of a change in regime to one that will be better for life but not necessarily better for us.*

The debate is vigorous regarding the true applicability of this hypothesis to nature, or whether it is true science at all. Regardless, it remains philosophically intriguing in its portrayal of the relationship between humans and Earth.

*J. Lovelock, *The Ages of Gaia—A Biography of Our Living Earth* (New York: Norton, 1988), p. 178.

A critical corollary to these international efforts is the linkage of academic disciplines. A positive step in that direction is the Earth systems science (geosystems) approach that synthesizes content from across the disciplines to create a holistic perspective. Exciting progress toward an integrated understanding of Earth's physical and biological systems is in progress. Such a multidisciplinary effort began in 2000 at a Ministerial Meeting of the Arctic Council, when the Arctic Climate Impact Assessment (ACIA) was launched. The ACIA final report, *Climate Change in the Arctic*, was released in November 2004 (see chapter-opening photo). The effort involved 300 scientists, eight countries, and six circumpolar indigenous peoples' organizations. For a look at this international triumph of cooperative science, see High Latitude Connection 21.1 (see **http://www.acia.uaf.edu/**).

More than a decade ago, *Time* magazine gave Earth an interesting honour and is today a time capsule of activist suggestions (Figure 21.9, p. 704). As if a victim of short-lived fame, we wonder where Earth awareness fits into the global scheme of things today. Is there a follow-up in pop culture to making the cover of *Time*?

Twelve Paradigms for the 21st Century

As we conclude, a brief list of the dominant themes and patterns of concern for the 21st century seems appropriate. Hopefully these *paradigms* will provide a useful framework for brainstorming and discussion of the central issues that will affect us in the new century. The paradigms for thought:

1. Population increases in the less-developed countries
2. Planetary impact per person (on the biosphere and resources; $I = P{\cdot}A{\cdot}T$)
3. Feeding the world's population
4. Global and national disparities of wealth and resource allocation
5. Status of women and children (health, welfare, rights)
6. Global climate change (temperatures, sea level, weather and climate patterns, disease, and diversity)
7. Energy supplies and energy demands; renewables and demand management
8. Loss of biodiversity (habitats, genetic wealth, and species richness)
9. Pollution of air, surface water (quality and quantity), groundwater, oceans, and land
10. The persistence of wilderness (biosphere reserves and biodiversity hot spots)
11. Globalization versus cultural diversity
12. Conflict resolution

Who Speaks for Earth?

Geographic awareness and education is an increasingly positive force on Earth. The Canadian Council for Geographic

High Latitude Connection 21.1

Report from Reykjavik—Arctic Climate Impact Assessment

Temperature, precipitation, ocean salinity, spatial distribution of pack ice, and flora and fauna are changing in the northern high latitudes. Some of the most rapid and severe climate change on Earth is occurring now in the Arctic Region. These dynamic conditions will accelerate over this century, resulting in major physical, ecological, social, and economic impacts, as scientists working on the Intergovernmental Panel on Climate Change (IPCC) *Third Assessment Report* (2001) initially described.

The Arctic Council decided to act in a first-ever regional scale scientific investigation. The Arctic Council, a ministerial intergovernmental forum (Canada, Denmark/Greenland, Faroe Islands, Finland, Iceland, Norway, Russia, Sweden, and the United States;

(a)

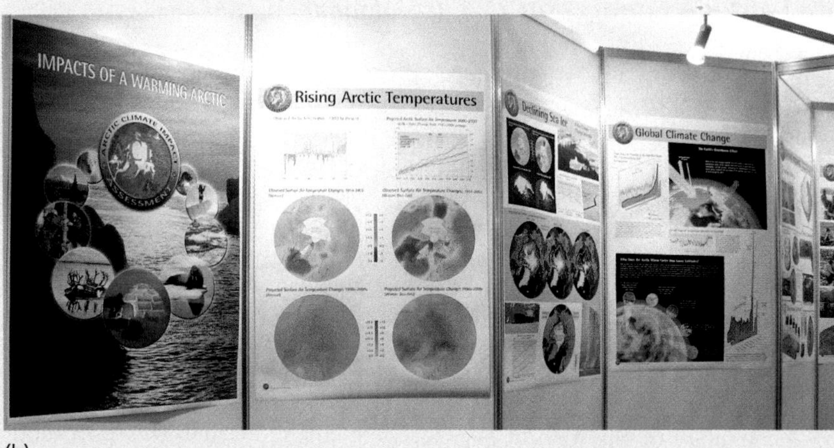

(b)

FIGURE 1 ACIA process and scientific symposium.
(a) The logo of the Arctic Climate Impact Assessment. (b) Scientific papers, panels, and poster sessions delivered the findings of the ACIA process to the attendees at the Reykjavik symposium. [Photos by Bobbé Christopherson.]

at http://www.arctic-council.org/), is joined by six indigenous peoples' organizations. Official observers include Germany, France, The Netherlands, Poland, United Kingdom, several nongovernmental organizations, and several international scientific bodies.

The Arctic Council initiated the Arctic Climate Impact Assessment (ACIA, http://www.acia.uaf.edu/, Figure 1a) in 2000 and charged its working groups to complete the research—Arctic Monitoring and Assessment Program (AMAP, http://www.amap.no/), the Conservation of Flora and Fauna (CAFF, http://www.caff.is), along with the International Arctic Science Committee (IASC, http://www.iasc.no/), comprising national scientific organizations, including 18 national academies of science. The Arctic Council Ministers declared that the goal of ACIA is to "evaluate and synthesize knowledge on climate variability and change and increased ultraviolet radiation, and support policy-making processes and the work of the IPCC, and address environmental, human health, social, cultural, and economic impacts and consequences, including policy recommendations."

Following four years of research and field investigations by more than 300 scientists divided into 18 working groups, and an intensive review process, the ACIA report was forwarded to the Arctic Council and to the international science community and governments at a first-ever ACIA Symposium held in Reykjavik, Iceland, in November 2004 (see photo that opens this chapter and Figure 1b). The ACIA Synthesis report is *Impacts of a Warming Arctic—Arctic Climate Impact Assessment* (Cambridge: Cambridge University Press, 2004; ISBN: 0-521-61778-2). The full 1200-page science report was distributed in January 2005.

The meeting began with the announcement by the Deputy Head of the Russian Roshydromet (Hydrometeorological Bureau) that Russia has ratified the Kyoto Protocol to limit emissions of greenhouse gases—an action, taken along with 130 countries, that makes the Protocol international law, without the participation of the United States and Australia.

ACIA science reinforces earlier discussion in this text on global climate change. Using the conservative "B2" computer model scenario of carbon dioxide and other greenhouse gases as a base line, and drawing information from five general circulation models (GCMs) from the IPCC in all, this state-of-the-art science work portrays worsening conditions in the circumpolar Arctic environment.

The ACIA report concludes that the region is warming more rapidly than previously thought, at nearly twice the rate of the rest of the globe. Dr. Robert Corell, Chair of the ACIA Integration Team stated, "The impacts of global warming are affecting people now in the Arctic. The impacts of climate change on the region and the globe are projected to increase substantially in the years to come." Evelyn Hurwich, President of the Circumpolar Conservation Union, said, "Climate change is a weapon of mass destruction staring us in the face, threatening all of creation. The science is in and the evidence before us. There is now a moral duty to act on it."

A particular strength of the ACIA effort is the integration of traditional knowledge and experience from the region's indigenous people. Chief Gary Harrison of the Arctic Athabaskan Council summarized, "Everything is under threat, our homes are threatened by storms and melting permafrost, our livelihoods are threatened by changes to plants and animals we harvest. Even our lives are threatened, as traditional travel routes become dangerous."

ACIA findings affirm the 2001 IPCC *Third Assessment Report*, that greenhouse gases produced by the human combustion of fossil fuels are the root cause of the warming. These climate changes are exceeding that attributable to natural cycles and oscillations of climate. By 2100 temperatures in the region are forecast to increase by 4–7 C° (7–13 F°), a large amount of temperature change (compare with IPCC forecasts in Chapter 10). Consider the past 50 years in Alaska, Western Canada, and Eastern Russia where the average winter temperature increased 3–4 C° (5–7 F°).

Increased temperatures will accelerate the ongoing loss of Arctic Ocean

(continued)

High Latitude Connection 21.1 *(continued)*

sea ice, melt a significant portion of the Greenland Ice Sheet, and continue the freshening of the northern oceans. In turn, these events will contribute to global sea-level rise and further affect the global climate engine, intensifying warming effects. Imagine a near complete ice-free Arctic Ocean. If this opens the Arctic to freighter and tanker traffic and resource exploitation such as oil and gas mining, then a whole new suite of environmental impacts looms ahead.

A summary of the *Key Findings* presented at the ACIA Symposium and detailed in the Synthesis report and final science report follows:

1. Arctic climate is now warming rapidly and much larger changes are projected.
2. Arctic warming and its consequences have worldwide implications.
3. Arctic vegetation zones are very likely to shift, causing wide-ranging impacts.
4. Animal species' diversity, ranges, and distribution will change.
5. Many coastal communities and facilities face increasing exposure to storms.
6. Reduced sea ice is very likely to increase marine transport and access to resources.
7. Thawing ground will disrupt transportation, buildings, and other infrastructure.
8. Indigenous communities are facing major economic and cultural impacts.
9. Elevated ultraviolet radiation levels will affect people, plants, and animals.
10. Multiple influences interact to cause impacts to people and ecosystems.

As Sheila Watt-Cloutier of the Inuit Circumpolar Conference concluded, "The Arctic is the early warning system for the rest of the world. We must all take what action we can to slow the pace of climate change." The ACIA process that is in motion is an important component in the preparation for the International Polar Year of science and research in the high latitudes of both polar regions, to be conducted from March 1, 2007 to March 1, 2009 (see **http://www.ipy.org/**).

FIGURE 21.9 Earth made the cover of *Time*.
More than a decade ago, global concerns about environmental impacts prompted *Time* magazine to deviate from its 60-year tradition of naming a prominent citizen as its person of the year, instead naming Earth the "Planet of the Year." The magazine devoted 33 pages to Earth's physical and human geography. Importantly, *Time* also offered positive policy strategies for consideration—an interesting time capsule for comparison with real events over the years. [*Time*, January 2, 1989 issue, copyright © 1989 The Time Inc. Magazine Company. Reprinted by permission.]

Education was established in 1993 to serve as the education program of the Royal Canadian Geographical Society. Geographic educators from elementary, secondary, college, or university levels from across the country comprise the Council. Each year, the Council sponsors *The Great Canadian Geography Challenge*, a national competition for students from Grades 4 to 10. There are two levels of competition at provincial and national levels: Level 1, for Grades 4 to 6; Level 2, for Grades 7 to 10. (See the results of the latest competition at **http://geochallenge.ca/geochallenge/en/default.asp?catID=10**). The National Geography World Championship (formerly the International Geography Olympiad) is now an annual event (Figure 21.10). People are learning more about Earth–human relationships.

Yet, ideological and ethical differences still remain within society. This dichotomy was addressed by biologist Edward O. Wilson:

> The evidence of swift environmental change calls for an ethic uncoupled from other systems of belief. Those committed by religion to believe that life was put on Earth in one divine stroke will recognize that we are destroying the Creation; and those who perceive biodiversity to be the product of blind evolution will agree. . . . Defenders of both premises seem destined to gravitate toward the same position on conservation. . . . For what, in the final analysis, is morality but the command of conscience seasoned by a rational examination of consequences? . . . An enduring environmental ethic will aim to preserve not only the health and freedom of our species, but access to the world in which the human spirit was born.*

*E. O. Wilson, *The Diversity of Life* (Cambridge, MA: Harvard University Press, 1992), p. 351.

FIGURE 21.10 National Geographic World Championship.
Students from across the globe met in Vancouver, British Columbia, August 2001, for the fifth National Geographic World Championship (name changed from International Geography Olympiad), sponsored by the National Geographic Society, with Canadian Alex Trebek of *Jeopardy!* fame as moderator. Here Alex congratulates the Canadian team on their second-place finish—the United States placed first, the Hungarian team third in the final standings. The 7th National Geographic World Championship will be held in 2005. The championship is an indicator of growing international geographic awareness. [Photo by O. Louis Mazzatenta, 2001 National Geographic Society.]

United Nations Secretary-General Kofi Annan, recipient of the 2001 Nobel Peace Prize, spoke to the Association of American Geographers annual meeting (Figure 21.11) on March 1, 2001, and offered us this thought:

> The idea of interdependence is old hat to geographers, but for most people it is a new garment they are only now trying on for size. Getting it to fit—and getting it imprinted on the mental maps that guide our voices and our choices—is one of the crucial projects of human geography for the 21st century. I look forward to working with you in that all-important journey.

The late Carl Sagan asked, "Who speaks for Earth?" He answered with this perspective:

> We have begun to contemplate our origins: starstuff pondering the stars; organized assemblages of ten billion billion billion atoms considering the evolution of atoms; tracing the long journey by which, here at least, consciousness arose. Our loyalties are to the species and the planet. We speak for Earth. Our obligation to survive is owed not just to ourselves but also to that Cosmos, ancient and vast, from which we spring.*

FIGURE 21.11 Secretary-General Kofi Annan addresses the AAG.
U.N. Secretary-General and Nobel Prize winner speaks to more than 3000 geographers at the Association of American Geographers Annual Meeting in New York City, March 1, 2001. [Photo courtesy of the Association of American Geographers, by Kevin J. McCormick.]

May we all perceive our spatial importance within Earth's ecosystems and do our part to maintain a life-supporting and sustaining Earth for ourselves and countless generations in the future.

*C. Sagan, *Cosmos* (New York: Random House, 1980), p. 345.

Critical Thinking and Learning

A. What part do you think technology, politics, and thinking about the future should play in science courses?

B. Assess population growth issues: the count, the impact per person, and future projection. What strategies do you see as important?

C. According to the discussion in the chapter, what worldwide factors led to the *Exxon Valdez* accident? Describe the complexity of that event from a global perspective. In your analysis, examine both supply-side (corporations and utilities) and demand-side (consumers) issues, as well as environmental and strategic factors. And, what about the oily bird?

D. What is meant by the Gaia hypothesis? Describe several concepts from this text that might pertain to this hypothesis.

E. Relate the content of the various chapters in this text to the integrative Earth systems science concept. Which chapters help you to better understand Earth–human relations and human impacts?

F. After examining the list of 12 paradigm issues for the 21st century, suggest items that need to be added to the list, omitted from the list, or expanded in coverage. Rearrange and organize the list as needed to match your concerns.

G. This chapter states that we already know many of the solutions to the problems we face. Why do you think these solutions are not being implemented at a faster pace?

H. Who speaks for Earth?

Appendix A
Maps in This Text and Topographic Maps

Maps Used in This Text

Geosystems uses several map projections: Goode's homolosine, Robinson, and Miller cylindrical, among others. Each was chosen to best present specific types of data. **Goode's homolosine projection** is an interrupted world map designed in 1923 by Dr. J. Paul Goode of the University of Chicago. Rand McNally *Goode's Atlas* first used it in 1925. Goode's homolosine equal-area projection (Figure 1) is a combination of two oval projections (*homolo*graphic and *sin*usoidal projections).

Two equal-area projections are cut and pasted together to improve the rendering of landmass shapes. A *sinusoidal projection* is used between 40° N and 40° S latitudes. Its central meridian is a straight line; all other meridians are drawn as sinusoidal curves (based on sine-wave curves) and parallels are evenly spaced. A *Mollweide projection*, also called a *homolographic projection*, is used from 40° N to the North Pole and from 40° S to the South Pole. Its central meridian is a straight line; all other meridians are drawn as elliptical arcs, and parallels are unequally spaced—farther apart at the equator, closer together poleward. This technique of combining two projections preserves areal size relationships, making the projection excellent for mapping spatial distributions when interruptions of oceans or continents do not pose a problem.

We use Goode's homolosine projection throughout this book. Examples include the world climate map and smaller climate type maps in Chapter 10, topographic regions and continental shields maps (Figures 12.3 and 12.4), world karst map (Figure 13.15), world sand regions and loess deposits (Figures 15.12 and 15.15), and the terrestrial biomes map in Chapter 20 (Figure 20.3).

Another projection we use is the **Robinson projection**, designed by the late Arthur Robinson in 1963 (Figure 2). This projection is neither equal area nor true shape, but is a compromise between the two. The North and South Poles appear as lines slightly more than half the length of the equator; thus higher latitudes are exaggerated less than on other oval and cylindrical projections. Some of the Robinson maps employed include the latitudinal geographic zones map in Chapter 1 (Figure 1.14), daily net radiation map (Figure 2.11), the world temperature range map in Chapter 5 (Figure 5.16), the maps of lithospheric plates of crust and volcanoes and earthquakes in Chapter 11 (Figures 11.19 and 11.22), and the global oil spills map in Chapter 21 (Figure 21.7).

Another compromise map, the **Miller cylindrical projection**, is used in this text (Figure 3). Examples of this projection include the world time zone map (Figure 1.18), global temperature maps in Chapter 5 (Figures 5.13 and 5.15), two global pressure maps in Chapter 6 (Figure 6.11),

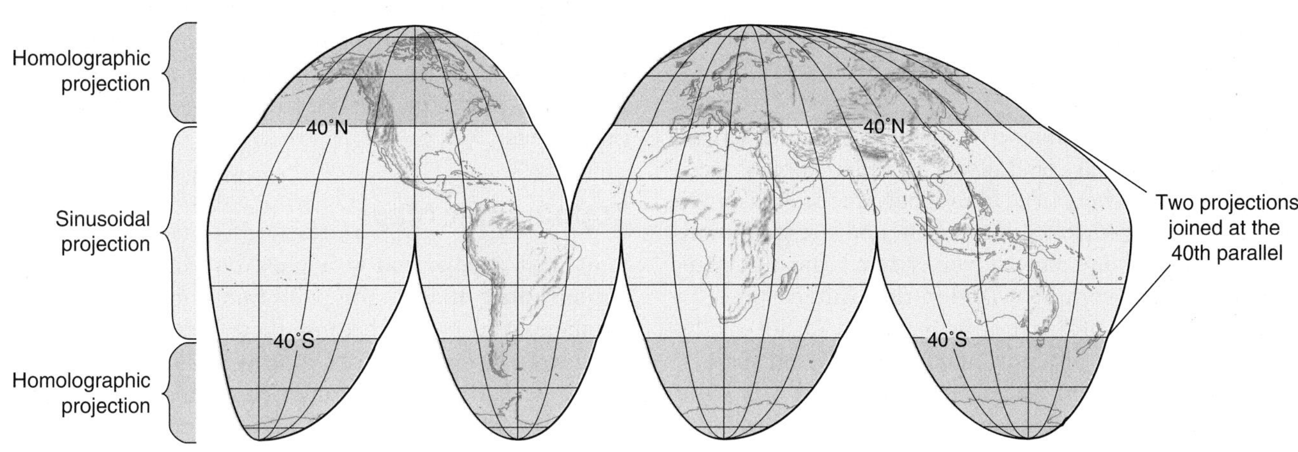

FIGURE 1 Goode's homolosine projection.
An equal-area map. [Copyright by the University of Chicago. Used by permission of the University of Chicago Press.]

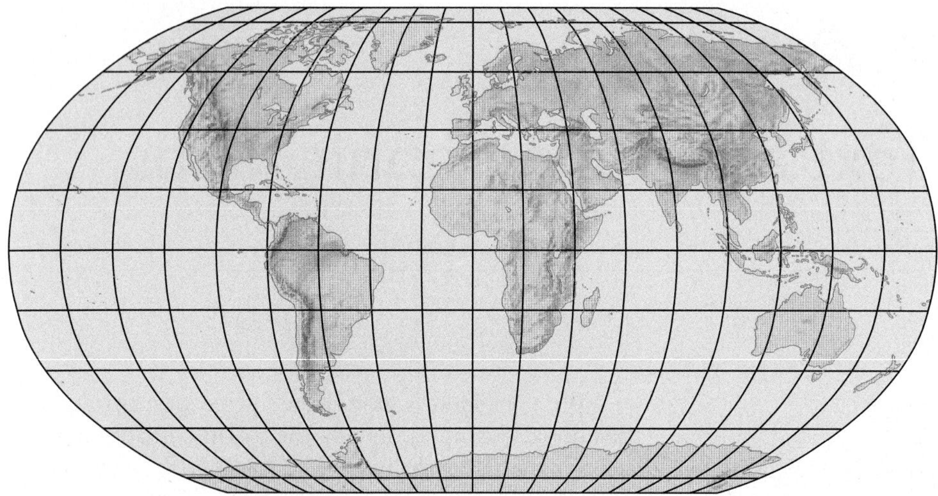

FIGURE 2 Robinson projection. A compromise between equal area and true shape. [Developed by Arthur H. Robinson, 1963.]

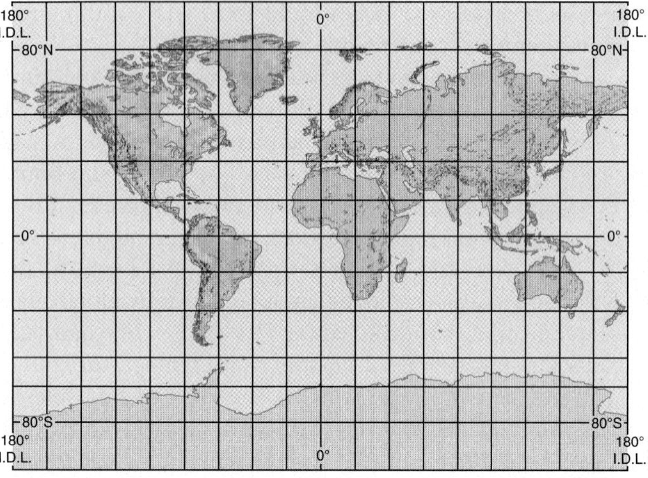

FIGURE 3 Miller cylindrical projection. A compromise map projection between equal area and true shape. [Developed by Osborn M. Miller, American Geographical Society, 1942.]

and the degradation map in Chapter 18 (Figure 18.9). This projection is neither true shape nor true area but is a compromise that avoids the severe scale distortion of the Mercator. The Miller projection frequently appears in world atlases. The American Geographical Society presented Osborn Miller's map projection in 1942.

Mapping, Quadrangles, and Topographic Maps

The westward expansion across the vast North American continent demanded a land survey for the creation of accurate maps. Maps were needed to subdivide the land and to guide travel, exploration, settlement, and transportation. In 1785, the Public Lands Survey System began surveying and mapping government land in the United States. In 1836, the Clerk of Surveys in the Land Office of the Department of the Interior directed public-land surveys. The Bureau of Land Management replaced this Land Office in 1946. The actual preparation and recording of survey information fell to the U.S. Geological Survey (USGS), also a branch of the Department of the Interior (see **http://usgs.gov/**).

In Canada, Natural Resources Canada conducts the national mapping program. Canadian mapping includes base maps, thematic maps, aeronautical charts, federal topographic maps, and the *National Atlas of Canada*, now in its sixth edition (see **http://atlas.gc.ca/site/index.html**).

The NRC and USGS depict survey information on quadrangle maps, so called because they are rectangular maps with four corner angles. The angles are junctures of parallels of latitude and meridians of longitude rather than political boundaries. These quadrangle maps utilize the Albers equal-area projection, from the conic class of map projections.

Topographic Maps

The most popular and widely used quadrangle maps are **topographic maps**. You will find topographic maps throughout *Geosystems* because they portray landscapes so effectively. As examples, see Figures 13.16 and 13.17, karst landscapes and sinkholes near Orleans, Indiana, and Winter Park, Florida; Figure 14.8, river drainage patterns; Figure 14.21, river meander scars; Figure 15.19, an alluvial fan in Montana; Figure 17.3, glaciers in Alaska; and Figure 17.19, drumlins in Peterborough, Ontario.

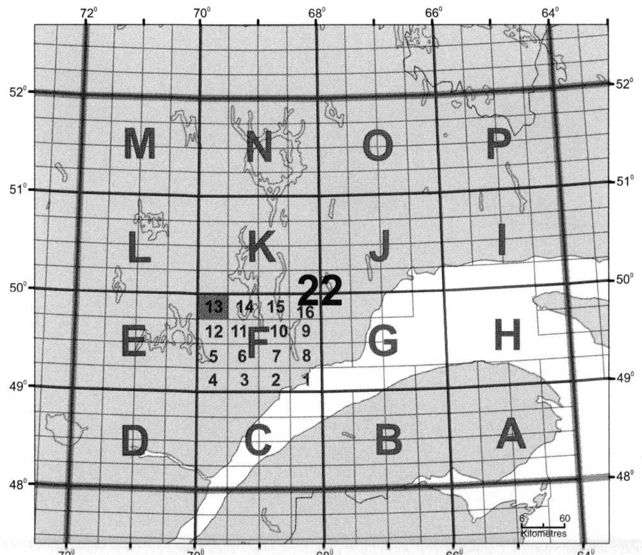

FIGURE 4 National Topographic System map index. The index displays the NTS system in which the 1:250,000 map is 22F. Further subdivisions of the system are portrayed in this block (22F 13 is a 1:50,000 map).

The National Topographic System (NTS) provides general-purpose topographic map coverage of Canada. The maps depict both the physical and human features of the landscape, including ground relief (landforms and terrain), drainage (lakes and rivers), forest cover, administrative areas, populated areas, transportation routes and facilities (including roads and railways), and other human-made features in detail. Natural Resources Canada produces maps that conform to the NTS and are available in two standard scales: 1:50,000 and 1:250,000. The area covered by a single 1:250,000 map is determined by its latitude and longitude and identified by a combination of letters A through P. These maps are then divided into 16 segments and numbered consecutively to form the blocks that make up the 1:50,000 map sheets.

The 1:50,000-scale topographic map is the most commonly used map series because it is an ideal scale for recreational activities (Figure 5). In this scale, a sheet covers an area approximately 40 km by 28 km. Hills, valleys, lakes, rivers, streams, rapids, portages, trails and wooded areas; major, secondary, and side roads; and all human-made features such as buildings, power lines, dams, and cut lines are accurately represented on these maps. Maps at this scale are used by all levels of government and industry for flood control, forest-fire control, real-estate planning, development of natural resources, environmental issues, highway planning, and depiction of crop areas.

The 1:250,000-scale topographic map series is the next most common scale. Maps of this scale are commonly used for field reconnaissance. This scale is popular not only as an overview of a large area, but also as a road map for use when travelling. A standard 1:250,000-scale map shows an area approximately the size of Prince Edward Island.

The Centre for Topographic Information Web site (**http://maps.nrcan.gc.ca/index_e.php**) presents an online seminar called MAPS 101 that provides a list of commonly asked questions and explanations for topographic terms, and offers a legend of the many symbols used on Canadian topographic maps.

FIGURE 5 An example of a topographic map from Ontario.
Creemore, Ontario, scanned from the Collingwood map sheet, 41 A8 in the 1:50,000 map series from the National Togographic System. Note the steep slope to the south and west of the Mad River and the flat land to the north and east.

(a)

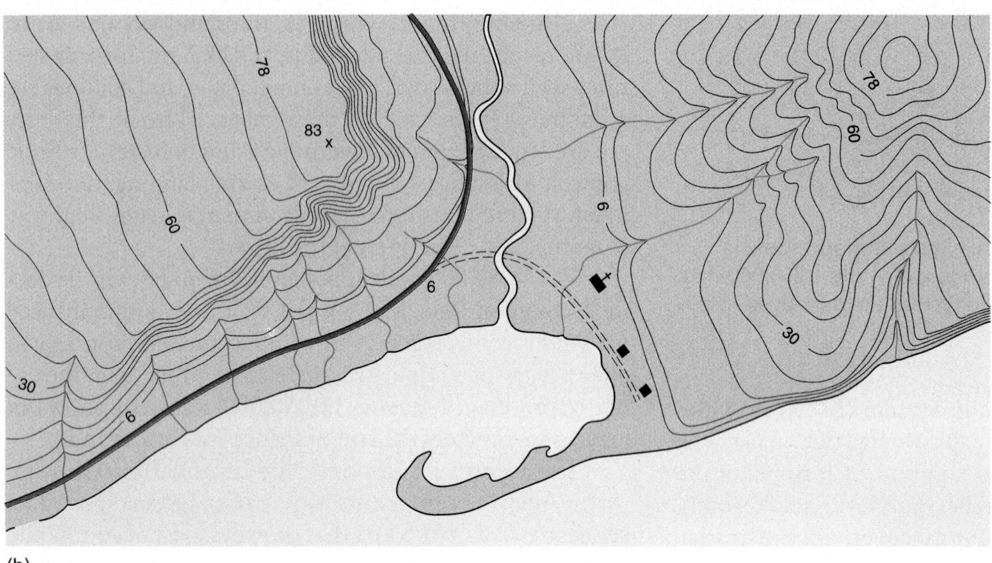

(b)

FIGURE 6 Topographic map of a hypothetical landscape.
(a) Perspective view of a hypothetical landscape. (b) Depiction of that landscape on a topographic map. The contour interval on the map is 6 m (19.7 ft). [After the U.S. Geological Survey.]

A **planimetric map** shows the horizontal position (latitude/longitude) of boundaries, land-use aspects, bodies of water, and economic and cultural features. A highway map is a common example of a planimetric map.

A topographic map adds a vertical component to show topography (configuration of the land surface), including slope and relief (the vertical difference in local landscape elevation). These fine details are shown through the use of elevation contour lines (Figure 6). A *contour line* connects all points at the same elevation. Elevations are shown above or below a vertical datum, or reference level, which is usually mean sea level. The contour interval is the vertical distance in elevation between two adjacent contour lines (6 m [19.7 ft] in Figure 6b).

The topographic map in Figure 6b shows a hypothetical landscape, demonstrating how contour lines and intervals depict slope and relief, which are the three-dimensional aspects of terrain. The pattern of lines and the spacing between them indicates slope. The steeper a slope or cliff, the closer together the contour lines appear—in the figure, note the narrowly spaced contours that represent the cliffs to the left of the highway. A wider spacing of these contour lines portrays a more gradual slope, as you can see from the widely spaced lines on the beach and to the right of the river valley.

The margins of a topographic map contain a wealth of information about its concept and content. In the margins of topographic maps, you find the name, position in the latitude–longitude and other coordinate systems, title, legend, magnetic declination (alignment of magnetic north) and compass information, datum plane, symbols used for roads and trails, the dates and history of the survey of that particular quad, and more.

Topographic maps may be purchased in the U.S. directly from the USGS. In Canada, topographic maps may be purchased through various map dealers recommended by the Centre for Topographic Information, NRC (**http://maps.nrcan.gc.ca/index_e.php**). To find a list of authorized dealers, go to the Canada Map Office (**http://maps.nrcan.gc.ca/distribution_e.php**).

Control data and monuments	
Vertical control	
Third order or better, with tablet	BM×16.3
Third order or better, recoverable mark	×120.0
Bench mark at found section corner	BM 18.6
Spot elevation	× 5.3

Contours	
Topographic	
Intermediate	
Index	
Supplementary	
Depression	
Cut; fill	
Bathymetric	
Intermediate	
Index	
Primary	
Index primary	
Supplementary	

Boundaries	
National	
State or territorial	
County or equivalent	
Civil township or equivalent	
Incorporated city or equivalent	
Park, reservation, or monument	

Surface features	
Levee	Levee
Sand or mud area, dunes, or shifting sand	Sand
Intricate surface area	Strip mine
Gravel beach or glacial moraine	Gravel
Tailings pond	Tailings pond

Mines and caves	
Quarry or open pit mine	
Gravel, sand, clay, or borrow pit	
Mine dump	Mine dump
Tailings	Tailings

Vegetation	
Woods	
Scrub	
Orchard	
Vineyard	
Mangrove	Mangrove

Glaciers and permanent snowfields	
Contours and limits	
Form lines	

Marine shoreline	
Topographic maps	
Approximate mean high water	
Indefinite or unsurveyed	
Topographic-bathymetric maps	
Mean high water	
Apparent (edge of vegetation)	

Coastal features	
Foreshore flat	Mud
Rock or coral reef	Reef
Rock bare or awash	
Group of rocks bare or awash	
Exposed wreck	
Depth curve; sounding	3
Breakwater, pier, jetty, or wharf	
Seawall	

Rivers, lakes, and canals	
Intermittent stream	
Intermittent river	
Disappearing stream	
Perennial stream	
Perennial river	
Small falls; small rapids	
Large falls; large rapids	
Masonry dam	
Dam with lock	
Dam carrying road	
Perennial lake; intermittent lake or pond	
Dry lake	Dry lake
Narrow wash	
Wide wash	Wide wash
Canal, flume, or aquaduct with lock	
Well or spring; spring or seep	

Submerged areas and bogs	
Marsh or swamp	
Submerged marsh or swamp	
Wooded marsh or swamp	
Submerged wooded marsh or swamp	
Rice field	Rice
Land subject to inundation	Max pool 431

Buildings and related features	
Building	
School; church	
Built-up area	
Racetrack	
Airport	
Landing strip	
Well (other than water); windmill	
Tanks	
Covered reservoir	
Gaging station	
Landmark object (feature as labeled)	
Campground; picnic area	
Cemetery: small; large	Cem

Roads and related features

Roads on Provisional edition maps are not classified as primary, secondary, or light duty. They are all symbolized as light duty roads.

Primary highway	
Secondary highway	
Light duty road	
Unimproved road	
Trail	
Dual highway	
Dual highway with median strip	

Railroads and related features	
Standard gauge single track; station	
Standard gauge multiple track	
Abandoned	

Transmission lines and pipelines	
Power transmission line; pole; tower	
Telephone line	Telephone
Aboveground oil or gas pipeline	
Underground oil or gas pipeline	Pipeline

FIGURE 7 Standardized topographic map symbols used on USGS maps.
English units still prevail, although a few USGS maps are in metric. [From USGS, Topographic Maps, 1969.]

Appendix B

The 12 Soil Orders of the U.S. Soil Taxonomy

The U.S. soil classification system, *Soil Taxonomy—A Basic System of Soil Classification for Making and Interpreting Soil Surveys*, was published in 1975 and revised in a new second edition in 1999. Soil scientists refer to it as **Soil Taxonomy**. Over the years, various revisions and clarifications in the system were published in *Keys to the Soil Taxonomy*, now in its ninth edition (2003, **http://soils.usda.gov/technical/classification/tax_keys/**), which includes all the revisions to the 1975 Soil Taxonomy. Major revisions include the addition of two new soil orders: Andisols (volcanic soils) in 1990 and Gelisols (cold and frozen soils) in 1998. Much of the information in this appendix is derived from these two keystone publications.

The classification system divides soils into six categories, creating a hierarchical sorting system (Table 1). The smallest, most-detailed category is the soil series, which ideally includes only one polypedon but may include adjoining polypedons. In sequence from smallest category to the largest, the Soil Taxonomy recognizes *soil series*, *soil families*, *soil subgroups*, *soil great groups*, *soil suborders*, and *soil orders*.

Diagnostic Soil Horizons

To identify a specific soil series within the Soil Taxonomy, the U.S. Natural Resources Conservation Service describes diagnostic horizons in a pedon. A *diagnostic horizon* reflects a distinctive physical property (colour, texture, structure, consistence, porosity, moisture) or a dominant soil process (discussed with the soil types).

In the solum (A, E, and B horizons), two diagnostic horizons may be identified: the epipedon and the subsurface. The presence or absence of either of these diagnostic horizons usually distinguishes a soil for classification.

- The **epipedon** (literally, "over the soil") is the diagnostic horizon at the surface where most of the rock structure has been destroyed. It may extend downward through the A horizon, even including all or part of an illuviated B horizon. It is visibly darkened by organic matter and sometimes is leached of minerals. Excluded from the epipedon are alluvial deposits, eolian deposits, and cultivated areas, because soil-forming processes have lacked the time to erase these relatively short-lived characteristics.
- The **diagnostic subsurface horizon** originates below the surface at varying depths. It may include part of the A or B horizon or both. Many diagnostic subsurface horizons have been identified.

The 12 Soil Orders of the Soil Taxonomy

At the heart of the Soil Taxonomy are 12 general soil orders, listed in Table 2. Their worldwide distribution is shown in Figure 1. Please consult this table and the map as you read the discussion of the Canadian System of Soil Classification (CSSC) where similar soil orders correlate. Because the Soil Taxonomy evaluates each soil order on its own characteristics, there is no priority to the classification. However, you will find a progression in the table and map legend, for the 12 orders are arranged loosely by latitude, beginning with Oxisols along the equator as in Chapters 10 (climates) and 20 (terrestrial biomes).

Table 1 U.S. Soil Taxonomy

Soil Category	Number of Soils Included
Orders	12
Suborders	47
Great groups	230
Subgroups	1,200
Families	6,000
Series	15,000

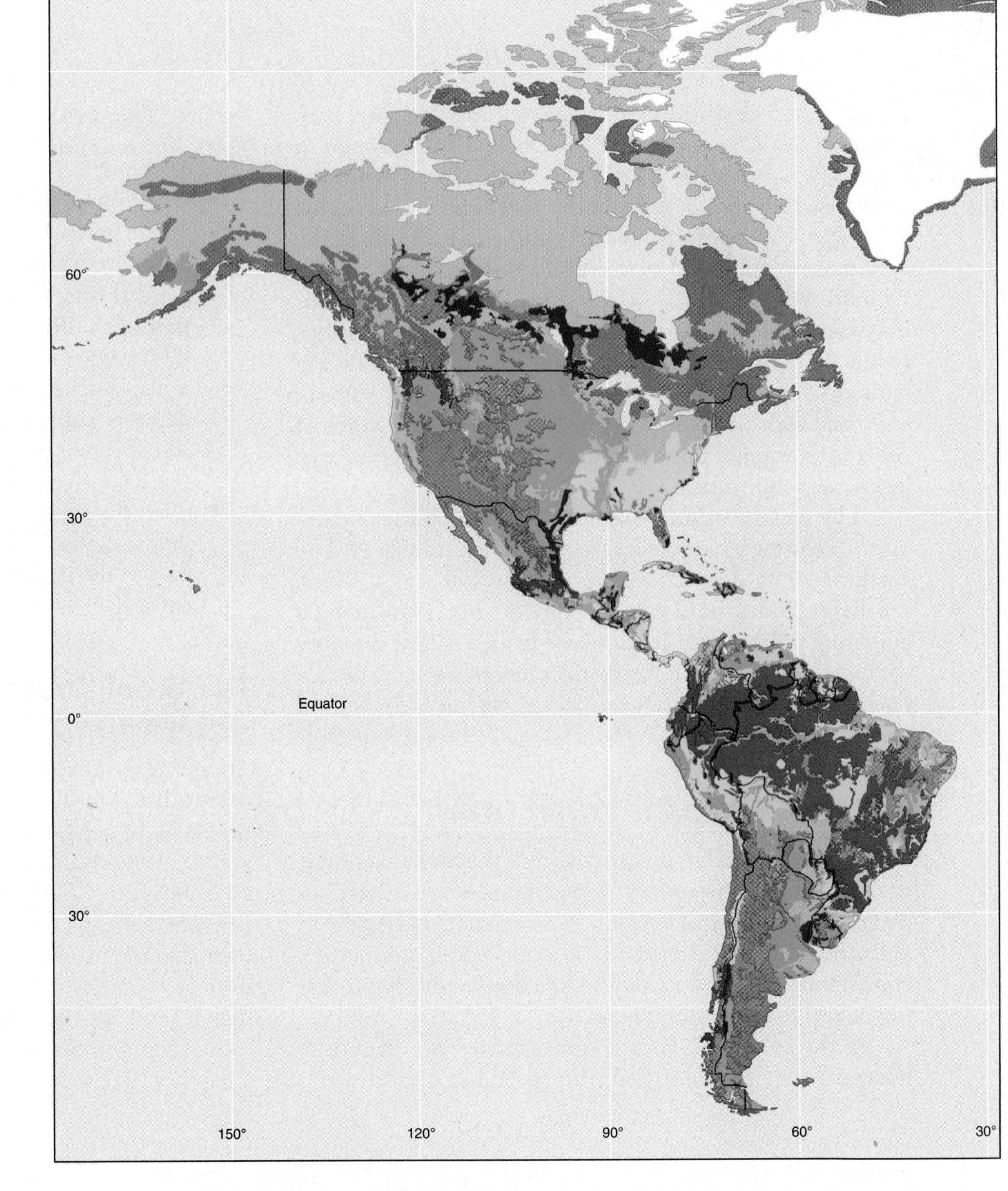

FIGURE 1 Soil Taxonomy. Worldwide distribution of the Soil Taxonomy's 12 soil orders. [Adapted from maps prepared by World Soil Resources Staff, Natural Resources Conservation Service, USDA, 1999.]

- Oxisols
- Aridisols
- Mollisols
- Alfisols
- Ultisols
- Spodosols
- Entisols
- Inceptisols
- Vertisols
- Histosols
- Andisols
- Gelisols
- Rock land
- Shifting sands
- Ice fields

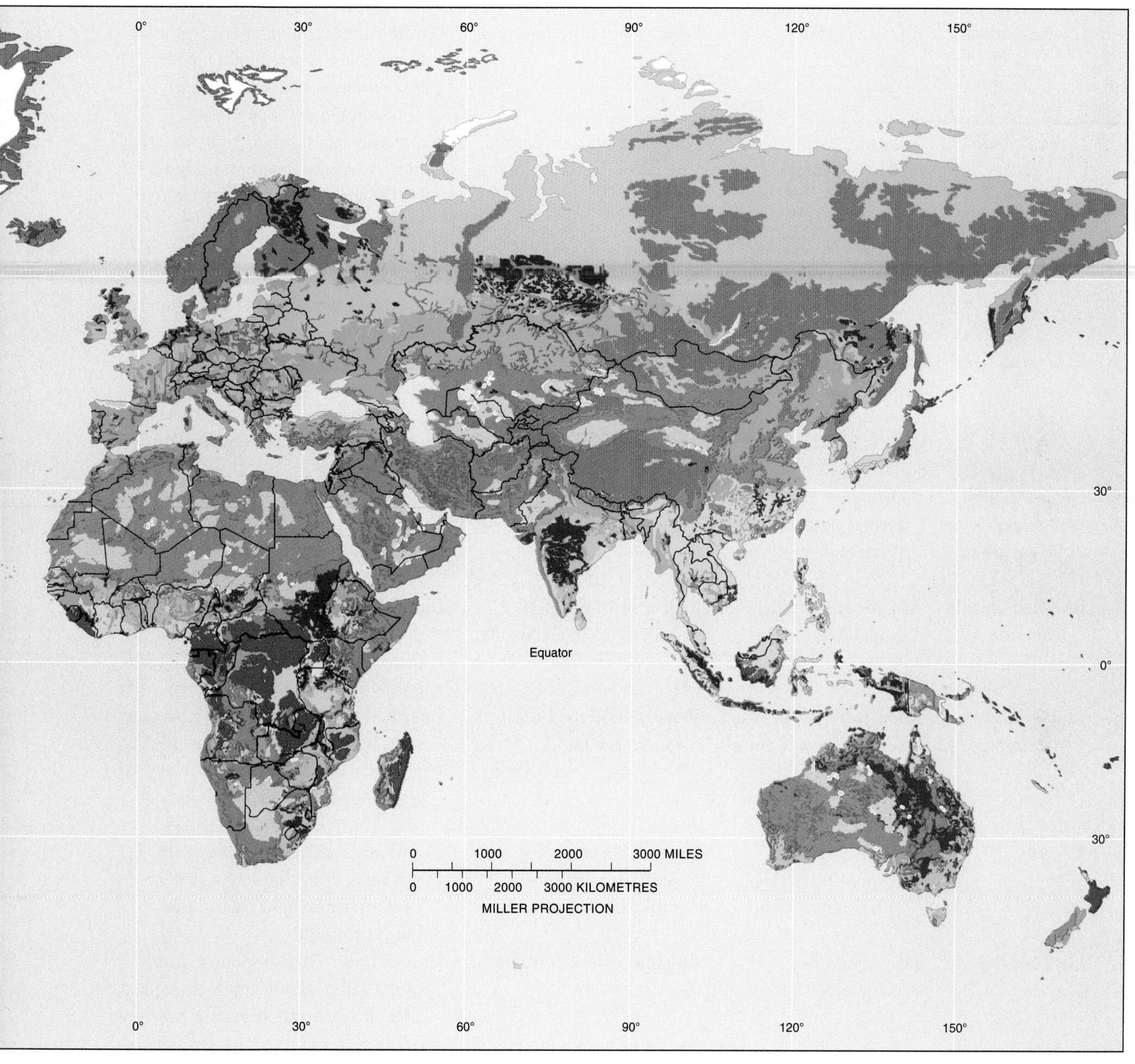
0°
30°
60°
90°
120°
150°
30°
Equator
0°
30°
0 1000 2000 3000 MILES
0 1000 2000 3000 KILOMETRES
MILLER PROJECTION

Table 2 Soil Taxonomy Soil Orders

Order	Derivation of Term	Marbut, 1938* (Canadian System†)	General Location and Climate	Description
Oxisols	Fr. *oxide*, "oxide" Gr. *oxide*, "acid or sharp"	Latosols lateritic soils	Tropical soils, hot, humid areas	Maximum weathering of Fe and Al and eluviation, continuous plinthite layer
Aridisols	L. *aridos*, "dry"	Reddish desert, grey desert, sierozems	Desert soils, hot, dry areas	Limited alteration of parent material, low climate activity, light colour, low humus content, subsurface illuviation of carbonates
Mollisols	L. *mollis*, "soft"	Chestnut, chernozem (Chernozemic)	Grassland soils; subhumid, semiarid lands	Noticeably dark with organic material, humus rich, base saturation high, friable surface with well-structured horizons
Alfisols	Invented syllable	Grey-brown podzolic, degraded chernozem (Luvisol)	Moderately weathered forest soils, humid temperate forests	B horizon high in clays, moderate to high degree of base saturation, illuviated clay accum., no pronounced colour change with depth
Ultisols	L. *ultimus*, "last"	Red-yellow podzolic, reddish yellow lateritic	Highly weathered forest soils, subtropical forests	Similar to Alfisols, B horizon high in clays, generally low amount of base saturation, strong weathering in subsurface horizons, redder than Alfisols
Spodosols	Gr. *spodos* or L. *spodus*, "wood ash"	Podzols, brown podzolic (Podzol)	Northern conifer forest soils, cool humid forests	Illuvial B horizon of Fe/Al clays, humus accum.; without structure, partially cemented; highly leached, strongly acid; coarse texture of low bases
Entisols	Invented syllable from *recent*	Azonal soils, tundra (some Regosols)	Recent soils, profile undeveloped, all climates	Limited development; inherited properties from parent material; pale colour, low humus, few specific properties; hard and massive when dry
Inceptisols	L. *inceptum*, "beginning"	Ando, subarctic brown forest lithosols, some humic gleys (Brunisol, Cryosol with permafrost, Gleysol wet)	Weakly developed soils, humid regions	Intermediate development; embryonic soils, but few diagnostic features; further weathering possible in altered or changed subsurface horizons
Vertisols	L. *verto*, "to turn"	Grumusols (1949) tropical black clays (Vertisolic)	Expandable clay soils; subtropics, tropics; sufficient dry period	Forms large cracks on drying, self-mixing action, contains >30% in swelling clays, light colour, low humus content
Histosols	Gr. *histos*, "tissue"	Peat, muck, bog (Organic)	Organic soils, wet places	Peat or bog, >20% organic matter, much with clay >40 cm thick, surface, organic layers, no diagnostic horizons
Andisols	L. *ando*, "volcanic ash"	—	Areas affected by frequent volcanic activity (formerly within Inceptisols and Entisols)	Volcanic parent materials, particularly ash and volcanic glass; weathering and mineral transformation important; high CEC and organic content, generally fertile
Gelisols	L. *gelatio*, "freezing"	Formerly Inceptisols and Entisols (Cryosols, some Brunisols)	High latitudes in Northern Hemisphere, southern limits near tree line	Permafrost within 100 cm of the soil surface; evidence of cryoturbation (frost churning) and/or an active layer; patterned-ground

*C. F. Marbut, USDA soil scientist, developed the first American system of soil classification in the 1930s, first published in the USDA *Yearbook of Agriculture* in 1938.

†For comparison, these are soil orders from the Canadian System of Soil Classification (CSSC), last revised in 1998.

Appendix C
The Köppen Climate Classification System

The Köppen climate classification system was designed by Wladimir Köppen (1846–1940), a German climatologist and botanist, and is widely used for its ease of comprehension. The basis of any empirical classification system is the choice of criteria used to draw lines on a map to designate different climates. Köppen-Geiger climate classification uses average monthly temperatures, average monthly precipitation, and total annual precipitation to devise its spatial categories and boundaries. But we must remember that boundaries really are transition zones of gradual change. The trends and overall patterns of boundary lines are more important than their precise placement, especially with the small scales generally used on world maps.

Take a few minutes to examine the Köppen system, the criteria, and the considerations for each of the principal climate categories. The modified Köppen-Geiger system has its drawbacks, however. It does not consider winds, temperature extremes, precipitation intensity, quantity of sunshine, cloud cover, or net radiation. Yet the system is important because its correlations with the actual world are reasonable and the input data are standardized and readily available.

Köppen's Climatic Designations

Figure 2 on page A.14 shows the distribution of each of Köppen's six climate classifications on the land. This generalized map shows the spatial pattern of climate. The Köppen system uses capital letters (A, B, C, D, E, H) to designate climatic categories from the equator to the poles. The guidelines for each of these categories are in the margins of Figure 1.

Five of the climate classifications are based on thermal criteria:

- A Tropical (equatorial regions)
- C Mesothermal (Mediterranean, humid subtropical, marine west coast regions)
- D Microthermal (humid continental, subarctic regions)
- E Polar (polar regions)
- H Highland (compared to lowlands at the same latitude, highlands have lower temperatures—recall the normal lapse rate—and more efficient precipitation due to lower moisture demand)

Only one climate classification is based on moisture as well:

- B Dry (deserts and semiarid steppes)

Within each climate classification additional lowercase letters are used to signify temperature and moisture conditions. For example, in a tropical rain forest *Af* climate, the *A* tells us that the average coolest month is above 18°C (64.4°F, average for the month), and the *f* indicates that the weather is constantly wet, with the driest month receiving at least 6 cm (2.4 in.) of precipitation. (The designation *f* is from the German *feucht*, for moist.) As you can see on the climate map, the tropical rain forest *Af* climate dominates along the equator and equatorial rain forest.

In a *Dfa* climate, the *D* means that the average warmest month is above 10°C (50°F), with at least one month falling below 0°C (32°F); the *f* says that at least 3 cm (1.2 in.) of precipitation falls during every month; and the *a* indicates a warmest summer month averaging above 22°C (71.6°F). Thus, a *Dfa* climate is a humid-continental, hot-summer climate in the microthermal category.

What's in a Boundary?

Originally, Köppen proposed that the isotherm boundary between mesothermal C and microthermal D climates be a coldest month of –3°C (26.6°F) or lower. That might be an accurate criterion for Europe, but for conditions in North America, the 0°C isotherm is considered more appropriate. The difference between the 0°C and isotherms for January covers an area about the width of the state of Ohio. Remember, these isotherm lines are really transition zones and do not mean abrupt change from one temperature to another.

A line denoting at least one month below freezing extends from New York City roughly along the Ohio River, trending westward until it meets the dry climates in the southeastern corner of Colorado. The line marking –3°C as the coldest month extends farther north along Lake Erie and the southern tip of Lake Michigan. In addition, from year to year, the position of the 0°C isotherm for January can shift back and forth several hundred kilometres as weather conditions vary. The map in Figure 1 uses the 0°C isotherm for the C–D climate boundary.

FIGURE 1 World climates and their guidelines according to the Köppen classification system.

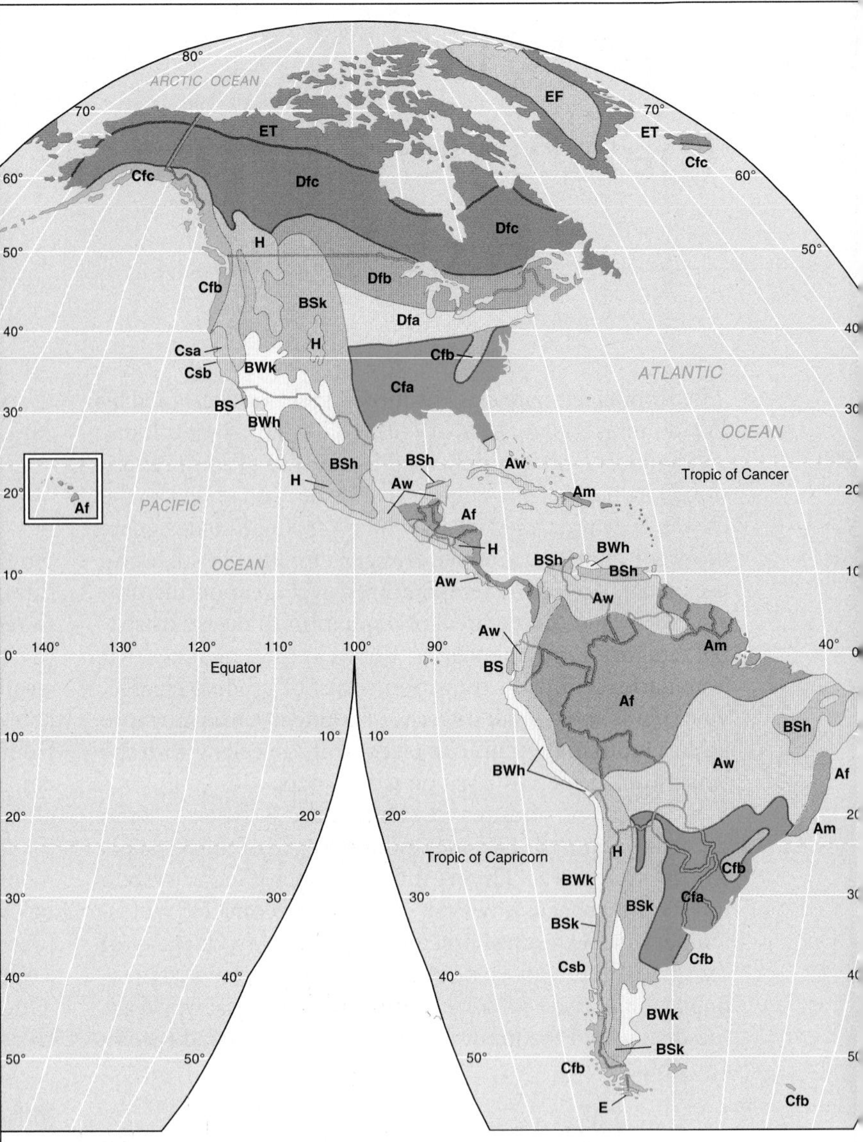

Köppen Guidelines

Tropical Climates — A

Consistently warm with all months averaging above 18°C (64.4°F); annual water supply exceeds water demand.

Af — Tropical rain forest:
f = All months receive precipitation in excess of 6 cm (2.4 in.).

Am — Tropical monsoon:
m = A marked short dry season with 1 or more months receiving less than 6 cm (2.4 in.) precipitation; an otherwise excessively wet rainy season. ITCZ 6–12 months dominant.

Aw — Tropical savanna:
w = Summer wet season, winter dry season; ITCZ dominant 6 months or less, winter water-balance deficits.

Mesothermal Climates — C

Warmest month above 10°C (50°F); coldest month above 0°C (32°F) but below 18°C (64.4°F); seasonal climates.

Cfa, Cwa — Humid subtropical:
a = Hot summer; warmest month above 22°C (71.6°F).
f = Year-round precipitation.
w = Winter drought, summer wettest month 10 times more precipitation than driest winter month.

Cfb, Cfc — Marine west coast, mild-to-cool summer:
f = Receives year-round precipitation.
b = Warmest month below 22°C (71.6°F) with 4 months above 10°C.
c = 1–3 months above 10°C.

Csa, Csb — Mediterranean summer dry:
s = Pronounced summer drought with 70% of precipitation in winter.
a = Hot summer with warmest month above 22°C (71.6°F).
b = Mild summer; warmest month below 22°C.

Microthermal Climates — D

Warmest month above 10°C (50°F); coldest month below 0°C (32°F); cool temperate-to-cold conditions; snow climates. In Southern Hemisphere, occurs only in highland climates.

Dfa, Dwa — Humid continental:
a = Hot summer; warmest month above 22°C (71.6°F).
f = Year-round precipitation.
w = Winter drought.

Dfb, Dwb — Humid continental:
b = Mild summer; warmest month below 22°C (71.6°F).
f = Year-round precipitation.
w = Winter drought.

Dfc, Dwc, Dwd — Subarctic:
Cool summers, cold winters.
f = Year-round precipitation.
w = Winter drought.
c = 1–4 months above 10°C.
d = Coldest month below –38°C (–36.4°F), in Siberia only.

Dry Arid and Semiarid Climates — B

Potential evapotranspiration* (natural moisture demand) exceeds precipitation (natural moisture supply) in all B climates. Subdivisions based on precipitation timing and amount and mean annual temperature.

Earth's arid climates:
BWh — Hot low-latitude desert
BWk — Cold midlatitude desert
BW = Precipitation less than 1/2 natural moisture demand.
h = Mean annual temperature >18°C (64.4°F).
k = Mean annual temperature <18°C.

Earth's semiarid climates:
BSh — Hot low-latitude steppe
BSk — Cold midlatitude steppe
BS = Precipitation more than 1/2 natural moisture demand but not equal to it.
h = Mean annual temperature >18°C.
k = Mean annual temperature <18°C.

Polar Climates — E

Warmest month below 10°C (50°F); always cold; ice climates.

ET — Tundra:
Warmest month 0–10°C (32–50°F); precipitation exceeds small potential evapotranspiration demand*; snow cover 8–10 months.

EF — Ice cap:
Warmest month below 0°C (32°F); precipitation exceeds a very small potential evapotranspiration demand; the polar regions.

EM — Polar marine:
All months above –7°C (20°F), warmest month above 0°C; annual temperature range <17 C° (30 F°).

*Potential evapotranspiration = the amount of water that would evaporate or transpire if it were available — the natural moisture demand in an environment; see Chapter 7.

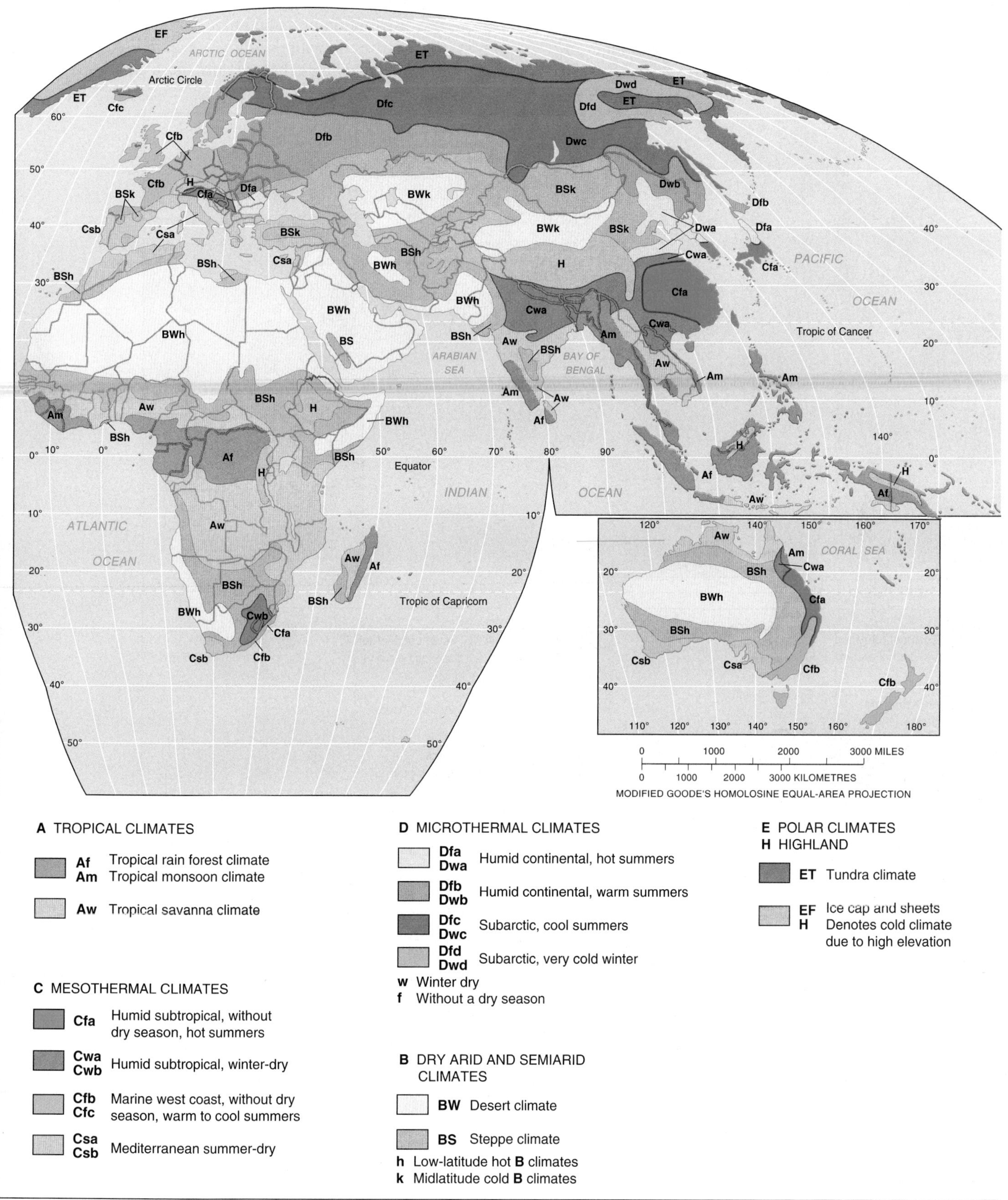
ARCTIC OCEAN
Arctic Circle
EF
ET
Cfc
Dfc
Dwd
Dfd
Dwc
Dfb
Cfb
H
Cfa
Dfa
BSk
Csb
Csa
BWk
Dwb
Dwa
Cwa
PACIFIC
OCEAN
BSh
BWh
BS
Cfa
Cwa
Tropic of Cancer
ARABIAN SEA
BAY OF BENGAL
Aw
Am
Af
Equator
INDIAN
OCEAN
ATLANTIC
OCEAN
Tropic of Capricorn
Cwb
CORAL SEA
MODIFIED GOODE'S HOMOLOSINE EQUAL-AREA PROJECTION
0 1000 2000 3000 MILES
0 1000 2000 3000 KILOMETRES
A TROPICAL CLIMATES
Af Tropical rain forest climate
Am Tropical monsoon climate
Aw Tropical savanna climate
C MESOTHERMAL CLIMATES
Cfa Humid subtropical, without dry season, hot summers
Cwa Cwb Humid subtropical, winter-dry
Cfb Cfc Marine west coast, without dry season, warm to cool summers
Csa Csb Mediterranean summer-dry
D MICROTHERMAL CLIMATES
Dfa Dwa Humid continental, hot summers
Dfb Dwb Humid continental, warm summers
Dfc Dwc Subarctic, cool summers
Dfd Dwd Subarctic, very cold winter
w Winter dry
f Without a dry season
B DRY ARID AND SEMIARID CLIMATES
BW Desert climate
BS Steppe climate
h Low-latitude hot B climates
k Midlatitude cold B climates
E POLAR CLIMATES
H HIGHLAND
ET Tundra climate
EF Ice cap and sheets
H Denotes cold climate due to high elevation

Köppen Guidelines

The Köppen guidelines and map portrayal are in Figure 1. First, check the guidelines for a climate type, then the colour legend for the subdivisions of the type, and then check out the distribution of that climate on the map. You may want to compare this with the climate map in Figure 2 that presents causal elements that produce these climates.

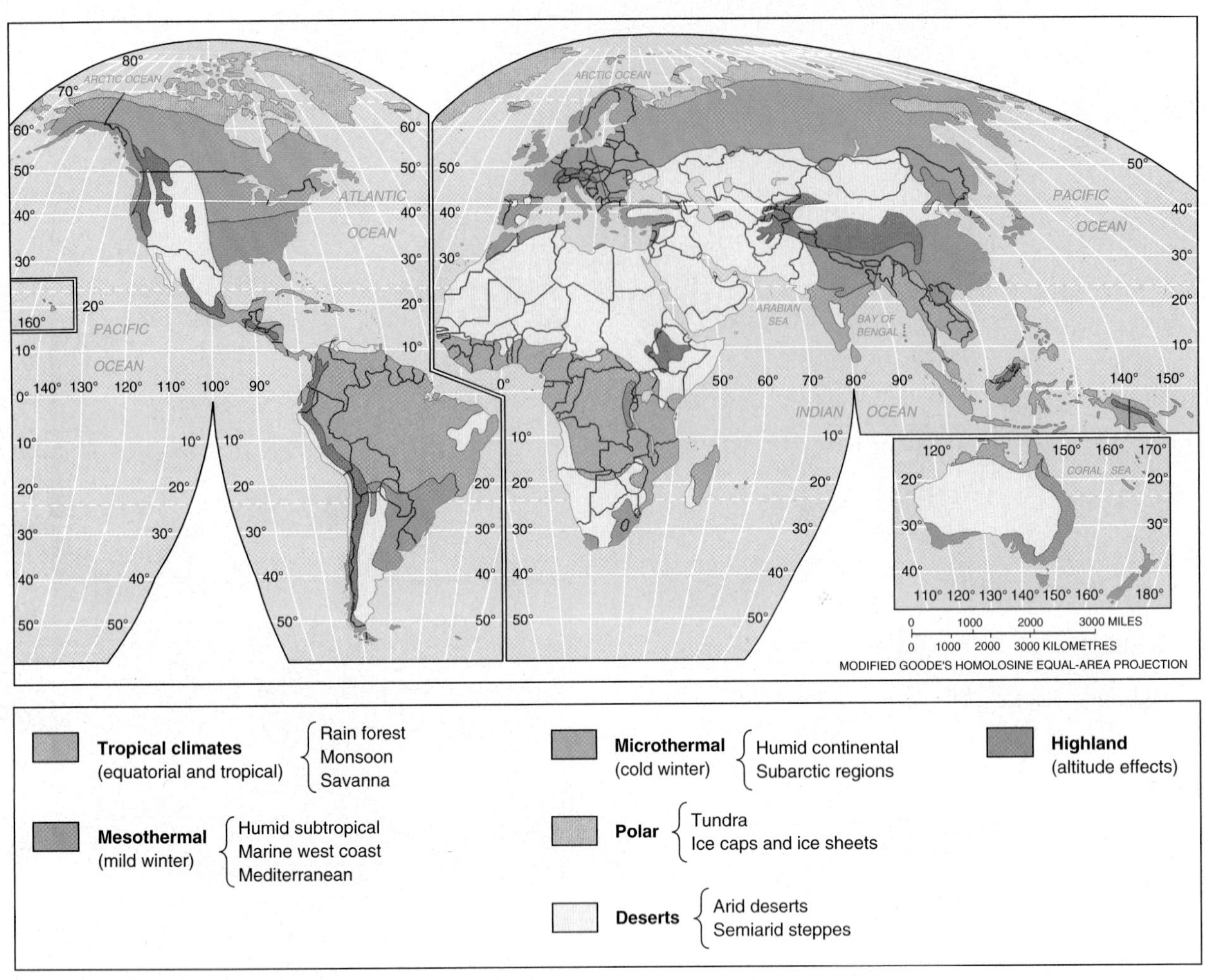

FIGURE 2 Climate regions generalized.
Six general climate categories.

Appendix D

Common Conversions

Metric to English

Metric Measure	Multiply by	English Equivalent
Length		
Centimetres (cm)	0.3937	Inches (in.)
Metres (m)	3.2808	Feet (ft)
Metres (m)	1.0936	Yards (yd)
Kilometres (km)	0.6214	Miles (mi)
Nautical miles	1.15	Statute miles
Area		
Square centimetres (cm^2)	0.155	Square inches ($in.^2$)
Square metres (m^2)	10.7639	Square feet (ft^2)
Square metres (m^2)	1.1960	Square yards (yd^2)
Square kilometres (km^2)	0.3831	Square miles (mi^2)
Hectares (ha) 10,000 (m^2)	2.4710	Acres (a)
Volume		
Cubic centimetres (cm^3)	0.06	Cubic inches ($in.^3$)
Cubic metres (m^3)	35.30	Cubic feet (ft^3)
Cubic metres (m^3)	1.3079	Cubic yards (yd^3)
Cubic kilometres (km^3)	0.24	Cubic miles (mi^3)
Litres (l)	1.0567	Quarts (qt), U.S.
Litres (l)	0.88	Quarts (qt), Imperial
Litres (l)	0.26	Gallons (gal), U.S.
Litres (l)	0.22	Gallons (gal), Imperial
Mass		
Grams (g)	0.03527	Ounces (oz)
Kilograms (kg)	2.2046	Pounds (lb)
Metric tons (tonne) (t)	1.10	Short tons (tn), U.S.
Velocity		
Metres/second (mps)	2.24	Miles/hour (mph)
Kilometres/hour (kmph)	0.62	Miles/hour (mph)
Knots (kn) (nautical mph)	1.15	Miles/hour (mph)
Temperature		
Degrees Celsius (°C)	1.80 (then add 32)	Degrees Fahrenheit (°F)
Celsius degrees (C°)	1.80	Fahrenheit degrees (F°)
Additional water measurement		
Gallons (Imperial)	1.201	Gallons (U.S.)
Gallons (gal)	0.000003	Acre-feet

1 cubic foot per second per day = 86,400 cubic feet = 1.98 acre-feet

Additional energy and power measurements

1 watt (W) = joule/s	1 W/m^2 = 2.064 cal/cm^3 day^{-1}
1 joule = 0.239 calories	1 W/m^2 = 61.91 cal/cm^2 $month^{-1}$
1 calorie = 4.186 joules	1 W/m^2 = 753.4 cal/cm^2 $year^{-1}$
1 W/m^2 = 0.001433 cal/min	100 W/m^2 = 75 $kcal/cm^2$ $year^{-1}$
697.8 W/m^2 = 1 cal/cm^2 min^{-1}	Solar constant: 1372 W/m^2 2 cal/cm2 min^{-1}

English to Metric

English Measure	Multiply by	Metric Equivalent
Length		
Inches (in.)	2.54	Centimetres (cm)
Feet (ft)	0.3048	Metres (m)
Yards (yd)	0.9144	Metres (m)
Miles (mi)	1.6094	Kilometres (km)
Statute miles	0.8684	Nautical miles
Area		
Square inches (in.^{2})	6.45	Square centimetres (cm^2)
Square feet (ft^2)	0.0929	Square metres (m^2)
Square yards (yd^2)	0.8361	Square metres (m^2)
Square miles (mi^2)	2.5900	Square kilometres (km^2)
Acres (a)	0.4047	Hectares (ha)
Volume		
Cubic inches (in.^{3})	16.39	Cubic centimetres (cm^3)
Cubic feet (ft^3)	0.028	Cubic metres (m^3)
Cubic yards (yd^3)	0.765	Cubic metres (m^3)
Cubic miles (mi^3)	4.17	Cubic kilometres (km^3)
Quarts (qt), U.S.	0.9463	Litres (l)
Quarts (qt), Imperial	1.14	Litres (l)
Gallons (gal), U.S.	3.8	Litres (l)
Gallons (gal), Imperial	4.55	Litres (l)
Mass		
Ounces (oz)	28.3495	Grams (g)
Pounds (lb)	0.4536	Kilograms (kg)
Short ton (tn), U.S.	0.91	Metric tons (tonne) (t)
Velocity		
Miles/hour (mph)	0.448	Metres/second (mps)
Miles/hour (mph)	1.6094	Kilometres/hour (kmph)
Miles/hour (mph)	0.8684	Knots (kn) (nautical mph)
Temperature		
Degrees Fahrenheit (°F)	0.556 (after subtracting 32)	Degrees Celsius (°C)
Fahrenheit degrees (F°)	0.556	Celsius degrees (C°)
Additional water measurements		
Gallons (U.S.)	0.833	Gallons (Imperial)
Acre-feet	325,872	Gallons (gal)

Additional Notation

Multiples	Prefixes	
$1{,}000{,}000{,}000 = 10^9$	giga	G
$1{,}000{,}000 = 10^6$	mega	M
$1{,}000 = 10^3$	kilo	k
$100 = 10^2$	hecto	h
$10 = 10^1$	deka	da
$1 = 10^0$		
$0.1 = 10^{-1}$	deci	d
$0.01 = 10^{-2}$	centi	c
$0.001 = 10^{-3}$	milli	m
$0.000001 = 10^{-6}$	micro	μ

Glossary

The chapter in which each term appears **boldfaced** is in parentheses and is followed by a specific definition relevant to the term's usage in the chapter.

Aa (12) Basaltic lava with a rough, jagged, and clinkery, basaltic lava with sharp edges. This texture is because the lava lost trapped gases, flowing slowly, developing a thick skin that cracks into the jagged surface.
Abiotic (1) Nonliving; Earth's nonliving systems of energy and materials.
Ablation (17) Loss of glacial ice through melting, sublimation, wind removal by deflation, or the calving of blocks of ice (see deflation).
Abrasion (14, 15, 17) Mechanical wearing and erosion of bedrock accomplished by the rolling and grinding of particles and rocks carried in a stream, removed by wind in a "sandblasting" action, or imbedded in glacial ice.
Absorption (4) Assimilation and conversion of radiation from one form to another in a medium. In the process, the temperature of the absorbing surface is raised, thereby affecting the rate and wavelength of radiation from that surface.
Active layer (17) A zone of seasonally frozen ground that exists between the subsurface permafrost layer and the ground surface. The active layer is subject to consistent daily and seasonal freeze-thaw cycles (see permafrost, periglacial).
Actual evapotranspiration (9) ACTET; the actual amount of evaporation and transpiration that occurs; derived in the water balance by subtracting the deficit (DEFIC) from potential evapotranspiration in the surface.
Adiabatic (7) Pertaining to the cooling of an ascending parcel of air through expansion or the warming of a descending parcel of air through compression, without any exchange of heat between the parcel and the surrounding environment.
Advection (4) Horizontal movement of air or water from one place to another (compare with convection).
Advection fog (7) Active condensation formed when warm, moist air moves laterally over cooler water or land surfaces, causing the lower layers of the air to be chilled to the dew-point temperature.
Aggradation (14) The general building of land surface because of deposition of material; opposite of degradation. When the sediment load of a stream exceeds the stream's capacity to carry it, the stream channel becomes filled through this process.
Air mass (8) A distinctive, homogeneous body of air that has taken on the moisture and temperature characteristics of its source region.
Air pressure (3) Pressure produced by the motion, size, and number of gas molecules in the air and exerted on surfaces in contact with the air. Normal sea-level pressure, as measured by the height of a column of mercury (Hg), is expressed as 1013.2 millibars, or 760 mm of Hg. Kilopascal equivalents are reported placing normal at 101.32 kPa; 10 mb = 1 kPa. Air pressure can be measured with mercury or aneroid barometers (see listing for both).
Albedo (4) The reflective quality of a surface, expressed as the percentage of reflected insolation to incoming insolation; a function of surface colour, angle of incidence, and surface texture.
Aleutian low (6) See subpolar low-pressure cell.
Alfisols (18) A soil order in the Soil Taxonomy. Moderately weathered forest soils that are moist versions of Mollisols, with productivity dependent on specific patterns of moisture and temperature; rich in organics. Most wide-ranging of the soil orders.
Alluvial fan (15) Fan-shaped fluvial landform at the mouth of a canyon; generally occurs in arid landscapes where streams are intermittent.
Alluvial terraces (14) Level areas that appear as topographic steps above a stream, created by the stream as it scours with renewed downcutting into its floodplain; composed of unconsolidated alluvium (see alluvium).
Alluvium (14) General descriptive term for clay, silt, sand, gravel, or other unconsolidated rock, and mineral fragments transported by running water and deposited as sorted or semisorted sediment on a floodplain, delta, or stream bed.
Alpine glacier (17) A glacier confined in a mountain valley or walled basin, consisting of three subtypes: valley glacier (within a valley), piedmont glacier (coalesced at the base of a mountain, spreading freely over nearby lowlands), and outlet glacier (flowing outward from a continental glacier).
Alpine tundra (20) Tundra conditions at high elevation (see Arctic tundra).
Altitude (2) The angular distance between the horizon (a horizontal plane) and the Sun (or any point in the sky).
Altocumulus (7) Middle-level, puffy clouds that occur in several forms: patchy rows, wave patterns, a "mackerel sky," or lens-shaped "lenticular" clouds.
Andisols (18) A soil order in the Soil Taxonomy; derived from volcanic parent materials in areas of volcanic activity. A new order, created in 1990, of soils previously considered under Inceptisols and Entisols.
Anemometer (6) A device that measures wind velocity.
Aneroid barometer (6) A device that measures air pressure using a partially evacuated, sealed cell (see air pressure).
Angle of repose (13) The steepness of a slope that results when loose particles come to rest; an angle of balance between driving and resisting forces, ranging between 33° and 37° from a horizontal plane.
Antarctic high (6) A consistent high-pressure region centered over Antarctica; source region for an intense polar air mass that is dry and associated with the lowest temperatures on Earth.
Anthropogenic atmosphere (3) Earth's future atmosphere, so named because humans appear to be the principal causative agent.
Anticline (12) Upfolded rock strata, in which layers slope downward from the axis of the fold, or central ridge (compare syncline).
Anticyclone (6) A dynamically or thermally caused area of high atmospheric pressure with descending and diverging airflows that rotate clockwise in the Northern Hemisphere and counterclockwise in the Southern Hemisphere (compare cyclone).
Aphelion (2) The point of Earth's greatest distance from the Sun in its elliptical orbit; reached on July 4 at a distance of 152,083,000 km (94.5 million mi); variable over a 100,000-year cycle (compare perihelion).
Aquiclude (9) A body of rock that does not conduct groundwater in usable amounts; an impermeable rock layer, related to an aquitard that slows but does not block water flow (compare aquifer).
Aquifer (9) A body of rock that conducts groundwater in usable amounts; a permeable layer of rock (compare aquiclude).
Aquifer recharge area (9) The surface area where water enters an aquifer to recharge the water-bearing strata in a groundwater system.
Arctic and alpine tundra (20) A biome in the northernmost portions of North America and northern Europe and Russia, featuring low ground-level herbaceous plants as well as some woody plants.
Arête (17) A sharp ridge that divides two cirque basins. Derived from "knife edge" in French, these form sawtooth and serrated ridges in glaciated mountains.
Aridisols (18) A soil order in the Soil Taxonomy; largest soil order. Typical of dry climates; low in organic matter and dominated by calcification and salinization.
Artesian water (9) Pressurized groundwater that rises in a well or a rock structure above the local water table; may flow out onto the ground without pumping (see potentiometric surface).
Asthenosphere (11) Region of the upper mantle just below the lithosphere; the least rigid portion of Earth's interior and known as the plastic layer, flowing very slowly under extreme heat and pressure.
Atmosphere (1) The thin veil of gases surrounding Earth, which forms a protective boundary between outer space and the biosphere; generally considered to extend out about 480 km (300 mi) from Earth's surface.

Aurora (2) A spectacular glowing light display in the ionosphere, stimulated by the interaction of the solar wind with oxygen and nitrogen gases and atoms at high latitudes, called aurora borealis in the Northern Hemisphere and aurora australis in the Southern Hemisphere.
Autumnal (September) equinox (2) The time around September 22–23 when the Sun's declination crosses the equatorial parallel (0° latitude) and all places on Earth experience days and nights of equal length. The Sun rises at the South Pole and sets at the North Pole (compare vernal equinox).
Available water (9) The portion of capillary water that is accessible to plant roots; usable water held in soil moisture storage (see capillary water).
Axial parallelism (2) Earth's axis remains aligned the same throughout the year (it "remains parallel to itself"); thus, the axis extended from the North Pole points into space always near Polaris, the North Star.
Axial tilt (2) Earth's axis tilts 23.5° from a perpendicular to the plane of the ecliptic (plane of Earth's orbit around the Sun).
Axis (2) An imaginary line, extending through Earth from the geographic North Pole to the geographic South Pole, around which Earth rotates.
Azores high (6) A subtropical high-pressure cell that forms in the Northern Hemisphere in the eastern Atlantic (see Bermuda high); associated with warm, clear water and large quantities of sargassum, or gulf weed, characteristic of the Sargasso Sea.
Backswamp (14) A low-lying, swampy area of a floodplain; adjacent to a river, with the river's natural levee on one side and higher topography on the other (see floodplain, yazoo tributary).
Bajada (15) A continuous apron of coalesced alluvial fans, formed along the base of mountains in arid climates; presents a gently rolling surface from fan to fan (see alluvial fan).
Barrier beach (16) Narrow, long, depositional feature, generally composed of sand, that forms offshore roughly parallel to the coast; may appear as barrier islands and long chains of barrier beaches (see barrier island).
Barrier island (16) Generally, a broadened barrier beach (see barrier beach).
Barrier spit (16) A depositional landform that develops when transported sand or gravel in a barrier beach or island is deposited in long ridges that are attached at one end to the mainland and partially cross the mouth of a bay.
Basalt (11) A common extrusive igneous rock, fine-grained, comprising the bulk of the ocean-floor crust, lava flows, and volcanic forms; gabbro is its intrusive form.
Base level (14) A hypothetical level below which a stream cannot erode its valley, and thus the lowest operative level for denudation processes; in an absolute sense, it is represented by sea level, extending under the landscape.
Basin and Range Province (15) A region of dry climates, few permanent streams, and interior drainage patterns in the western United States; a faulted landscape composed of a sequence of horsts and grabens.
Batholith (11) The largest plutonic form exposed at the surface; an irregular intrusive mass; it invades crustal rocks, cooling slowly so that large crystals develop (see pluton).
Bay barrier (16) An extensive barrier spit of sand or gravel that encloses a bay, cutting it off completely from the ocean and forming a lagoon; produced by littoral drift and wave action; sometimes referred to as a baymouth bar (see barrier spit, lagoon).
Beach (16) The portion of the coastline where an accumulation of sediment is in motion.
Beach drift (16) Material, such as sand, gravel, and shells, that is moved by the longshore current in the effective direction of the waves.
Beaufort wind scale (6) A descriptive scale for the visual estimation of wind speeds; originally conceived in 1806 by Admiral Beaufort of the British Navy.
Bed load (14) Coarse materials that are dragged along the bed of a stream by traction or by the rolling and bouncing motion of saltation; involves particles too large to remain in suspension (see traction, saltation).
Bedrock (13) The rock of Earth's crust that is below the soil and is basically unweathered; such solid crust sometimes is exposed as an outcrop.
Bergschrund (17) These form when a crevasse or wide crack opens along the headwall of a glacier; most visible in summer when covering snow is gone.
Bermuda high (6) A subtropical high-pressure cell that forms in the western North Atlantic (see Azores high).
Biodiversity (19) A principle of ecology and biogeography: the more diverse the species population in an ecosystem (both in number of species, quantity of members in each species, and genetic content), the more risk is spread over the entire community, which results in greater overall stability, greater productivity, and increased use of nutrients, as compared to a monoculture of little or no diversity.
Biogeochemical cycle (19) One of several circuits of flowing elements and materials (carbon, oxygen, nitrogen, phosphorus, water) that combine Earth's biotic (living) and abiotic (nonliving) systems; the cycling of materials is continuous and renewed through the biosphere and the life processes.
Biogeographic realm (20) One of eight regions of the biosphere, each representative of evolutionary core areas of related flora (plants) and fauna (animals); a broad geographical classification scheme.
Biogeography (19) The study of the distribution of plants and animals and related ecosystems; the geographical relationships with their environments over time.
Biomass (19) The total mass of living organisms on Earth or per unit area of a landscape; also, the weight of the living organisms in an ecosystem.
Biome (20) A large terrestrial ecosystem characterized by specific plant communities and formations; usually named after the predominant vegetation in the region (see terrestrial ecosystem).
Biosphere (1) That area where the atmosphere, lithosphere, and hydrosphere function together to form the context within which life exists; an intricate web that connects all organisms with their physical environment.
Biotic (1) Living; referring to Earth's living system of organisms.
Blowout depression (15) Eolian (wind) erosion in which deflation forms a basin in areas of loose sediment. Diameter may range up to hundreds of metres (see deflation).
Bolson (15) The slope and basin area between the crests of two adjacent ridges in a dry region.
Boreal forest (20) See needleleaf forest.
Brackish (16) Descriptive of seawater with a salinity of less than 35‰; for example, the Baltic Sea (contrast to brine).
Braided stream (14) A stream that becomes a maze of interconnected channels laced with excess sediment. Braiding often occurs with a reduction of discharge that reduces a stream's transporting ability or with an increase in sediment load.
Breaker (16) The point where a wave's height exceeds its vertical stability and the wave breaks as it approaches the shore.
Brine (16) Seawater with a salinity of more than 35‰; for example, the Persian Gulf (contrast to brackish).
Brunisolic (18) A CSSC soil order with sufficiently developed horizons to distinguish from Regosolic order. Soils under forest cover with brownish horizons, although various colours are possible. Also, can be with mixed forest, shrubs, and grass.
Calcification (18) The illuviated (deposited) accumulation of calcium carbonate or magnesium carbonate in the B and C soil horizons.
Caldera (12) An interior sunken portion of a composite volcano's crater; usually steep-sided and circular, sometimes containing a lake; also can be found in conjunction with shield volcanoes.
Canadian System of Soil Classification (CSSC) (18) A soil classification system based on observable soil properties actually seen in the field; published in 1987 by the Canada Soil Survey Committee. Adapted to Canada's environment, the CSSC consists of 10 soil orders.
Capillary water (9) Soil moisture, most of which is accessible to plant roots; held in the soil by the water's surface tension and cohesive forces between water and soil (see also available water, field capacity, hygroscopic water, and wilting point).
Carbonation (13) A chemical weathering process in which weak carbonic acid (water and carbon dioxide) reacts with many minerals that contain calcium, magnesium, potassium, and sodium (especially limestone), transforming them into carbonates.
Carbon monoxide (3) An odourless, colourless, tasteless combination of carbon and oxygen produced by the incomplete combustion of fossil fuels or other carbon-containing substances; toxicity to humans is due to its affinity for hemoglobin, displacing oxygen in the bloodstream; CO.

Carnivore (19) A secondary consumer that principally eats meat for sustenance. The top carnivore in a food chain is considered a tertiary consumer (compare herbivore).

Cartography (1) The making of maps and charts; a specialized science and art that blends aspects of geography, engineering, mathematics, graphics, computer science, and artistic specialties.

Cation-exchange capacity (CEC) (18) The ability of soil colloids to exchange cations between their surfaces and the soil solution; a measured potential that indicates soil fertility (see soil colloid, soil fertility).

Chaparral (20) Dominant shrub formations of Mediterranean dry-summer climates; characterized by sclerophyllous scrub and short, stunted, tough forests; derived from the Spanish *chapparo*; specific to California (see Mediterranean shrubland).

Chemical weathering (13) Decomposition and decay of the constituent minerals in rock through chemical alteration of those minerals. Water is essential, with rates keyed to temperature and precipitation values. Chemical reactions are active at microsites even in dry climates. Processes include hydrolysis, oxidation, carbonation, and solution.

Chernozemic (18) A CSSC soil order with well to imperfectly drained soils of the steppe–grassland–forest transition in Southern Alberta; Saskatchewan; Manitoba; Okanagan Valley, BC; Palouse Prairie, BC. Accumulation of organic matter in surface horizon.

Chinook wind (8) North American term for a warm, dry, downslope airflow; characteristic of the rain-shadow region on the leeward side of mountains; known as föhn, or foehn, winds in Europe (see rain shadow).

Chlorofluorocarbons (CFC) (3) A manufactured molecule (polymer) made of chlorine, fluorine, and carbon; inert and possessing remarkable heat properties; also known as one of the halogens. After slow transport to the stratospheric ozone layer, CFCs react with ultraviolet radiation, freeing chlorine atoms that act as a catalyst to produce reactions that destroy ozone; manufacture banned by international treaties.

Chlorophyll (19) A light-sensitive pigment that resides within chloroplasts (organelles) in leaf cells of plants; the basis of photosynthesis.

Cinder cone (12) A volcanic landform of pyroclastics and scoria, usually small and cone-shaped and generally not more than 450 m (1500 ft) in height, with a truncated top.

Circle of illumination (2) The division between light and dark on Earth; a day–night great circle.

Circum-Pacific belt (12) A tectonically and volcanically active region encircling the Pacific Ocean; also known as the "ring of fire."

Cirque (17) A scooped-out, amphitheatre-shaped basin at the head of an alpine glacier valley; an erosional landform.

Cirrus (7) Wispy, filamentous ice-crystal clouds that occur above 6000 m (20,000 ft); appear in a variety of forms, from feathery hairlike fibres to veils of fused sheets.

Classification (10) The process of ordering or grouping data or phenomena in related classes; results in a regular distribution of information; a taxonomy.

Climate (10) The consistent, long-term behaviour of weather over time, including its variability; in contrast to weather, which is the condition of the atmosphere at any given place and time.

Climatic regions (10) An area of homogenous climate that features characteristic regional weather and air mass patterns.

Climatology (10) The scientific study of climate and climatic patterns and the consistent behaviour of weather, including its variability and extremes, over time in one place or region; includes the effects of climate change on human society and culture.

Climograph (10) A graph that plots daily, monthly, or annual temperature and precipitation values for a selected station; may also include additional weather information.

Closed system (1) A system that is shut off from the surrounding environment so that it is entirely self-contained in terms of energy and materials; Earth is a closed material system (compare open system).

Cloud (7) An aggregate of tiny moisture droplets and ice crystals; classified by altitude of occurrence and shape.

Cloud-albedo forcing (4) An increase in albedo (the reflectivity of a surface) caused by clouds due to their reflection of incoming insolation.

Cloud-condensation nuclei (7) Microscopic particles necessary as matter on which water vapour condenses to form moisture droplets; can be sea salts, dust, soot, or ash.

Cloud-greenhouse forcing (4) An increase in greenhouse warming caused by clouds because they can act like insulation, trapping longwave (infrared) radiation.

Col (17) Formed by two headward-eroding cirques that reduce an arête (ridge crest) to form a high pass or saddlelike narrow depression.

Cold desert and semidesert (20) A type of desert biome found at higher latitudes than warm deserts. Interior location and rain-shadow locations produce these cold deserts in North America.

Cold front (8) The leading edge of an advancing cold air mass; identified on a weather map as a line marked with triangular spikes pointing in the direction of frontal movement (compare warm front).

Community (19, 20) A convenient biotic subdivision within an ecosystem; formed by interacting populations of animals and plants in an area.

Composite volcano (12) A volcano formed by a sequence of explosive volcanic eruptions; steep-sided, conical in shape; sometimes referred to as a stratovolcano, although composite is the preferred term (compare shield volcano).

Conduction (4) The slow molecule-to-molecule transfer of heat through a medium, from warmer to cooler portions.

Cone of depression (9) The depressed shape of the water table around a well after active pumping. The water table adjacent to the well is drawn down by the water removal.

Confined aquifer (9) An aquifer that is bounded above and below by impermeable layers of rock or sediment (see artesian water, unconfined aquifer).

Constant isobaric surface (6) An elevated surface in the atmosphere on which all points have the same pressure, usually 500 mb. Along this constant-pressure surface, isobars mark the paths of upper-air winds.

Consumer (19) Organism in an ecosystem that depends on producers (organisms that use carbon dioxide as their sole source of carbon) for its source of nutrients; also called a heterotroph (compare producer).

Consumptive use (9) A use that removes water from a water budget at one point and makes it unavailable further downstream (compare withdrawal).

Continental divide (14) A ridge or elevated area that separates drainage on a continental scale; specifically, that ridge in North America that separates drainage to the Pacific on the west side from drainage to the Atlantic and Gulf on the east side and to Hudson Bay and the Arctic Ocean in the north.

Continental drift (11) A proposal by Alfred Wegener in 1912 stating that Earth's landmasses have migrated over the past 225 million years from a supercontinent he called Pangaea to the present configuration; the widely accepted plate tectonics theory today (see plate tectonics).

Continental effect (5) A quality of regions that lack the temperature-moderating effects of the sea and that exhibit a greater range of minimum and maximum temperatures, both daily and annually (see marine, land–water heating differences).

Continental glacier (17) A continuous mass of unconfined ice, covering at least 50,000km^2 (19,500 mi^2); most extensive at present as ice sheets covering Greenland and Antarctica (compare alpine glacier).

Continental landmasses (12) The broadest category of landform, including those masses of crust that reside above or near sea level and the adjoining undersea continental shelves along the coastline; sometimes synonymous with continental platforms.

Continental shield (12) Generally, old, low-elevation heartland regions of continental crust; various cratons (granitic cores) and ancient mountains exposed at the surface.

Contour lines (Appendix A) Isolines on a topographic map that connect all points at the same elevation relative to a reference elevation called the vertical datum.

Convection (4) Transfer of heat from one place to another through the physical movement of air; involves a strong vertical motion (compare to advection).

Convectional lifting (8) Air passing over warm surfaces gains buoyancy and lifts, initiating adiabatic processes.

Convergent lifting (8) Airflows in conflict force lifting and displacement of air upward, initiating adiabatic processes.

Coordinated Universal Time (UTC) (1) The official reference time in all countries, formerly known as Greenwich Mean Time; now measured by six primary standard atomic clocks, the time calculations are collected in Paris at the International Bureau of Weights and Measures (BIPM); the legal reference for time in all countries and broadcast worldwide.
Coral (16) A simple, cylindrical marine animal with a saclike body that secretes calcium carbonate to form a hard external skeleton and, cumulatively, landforms called reefs; lives symbiotically with nutrient-producing algae; presently in a worldwide state of decline due to bleaching (loss of algae).
Core (11) The deepest inner portion of Earth, representing one-third of its entire mass; differentiated into two zones—a solid-iron inner core surrounded by a dense, molten, fluid metallic-iron outer core.
Coriolis force (6) The apparent deflection of moving objects (wind, ocean currents, missiles) from traveling in a straight path, in proportion to the speed of Earth's rotation at different latitudes. Deflection is to the right in the Northern Hemisphere and to the left in the Southern Hemisphere; maximum at the poles and zero along the equator.
Crater (12) A circular surface depression formed by volcanism; built by accumulation, collapse, or explosion; usually located at a volcanic vent or pipe; can be at the summit or on the flank of a volcano.
Crevasse (17) A vertical crack that develops in a glacier as a result of friction between valley walls, or tension forces of extension on convex slopes, or compression forces on concave slopes.
Crust (11) Earth's outer shell of crystalline surface rock, ranging from 5 to 60 km (3 to 38 mi) in thickness from oceanic crust to mountain ranges. Average density of continental crust is 2.7g/cm^3, whereas oceanic crust is 3.0g/cm^3.
Cryosphere (1, 7, 10, 17, 20) The frozen portion of Earth's waters, including ice sheets, ice caps and fields, glaciers, ice shelves, sea ice, and subsurface ground ice and frozen ground (permafrost).
Crysolic (18) A CSSC soil order that dominates the northern third of Canada, with permafrost closer to the surface and composed of mineral and organic soil deposits. Generally found north of the treeline, or in fine-textured soils in subarctic forest, or in some organic soils in boreal forests.
Cumulonimbus (7) A towering, precipitation-producing cumulus cloud that is vertically developed across altitudes associated with other clouds; frequently associated with lightning and thunder and thus sometimes called a thunderhead.
Cumulus (7) Bright and puffy cumuliform clouds up to 2000 m (6500 ft) in altitude.
Cyclogenesis (8) An atmospheric process that describes the birth of a midlatitude wave cyclone, usually along the polar front. Also refers to strengthening and development of a midlatitude cyclone along the eastern slope of the Rockies, other north–south mountain barriers, and along the North American and Asian east coasts (see midlatitude cyclone, polar front).
Cyclone (6) A dynamically or thermally caused area of low atmospheric pressure with converging and ascending airflows. Rotates counterclockwise in the Northern Hemisphere and clockwise in the Southern Hemisphere (compare anticyclone; see midlatitude cyclone, tropical cyclone).
Daylength (2) Duration of exposure to insolation, varying during the year depending on latitude; an important aspect of seasonality.
Daylight saving time (1) Time is set ahead 1 hour in the spring and set back 1 hour in the fall in the Northern Hemisphere. In the United States and Canada, time is set ahead on the first Sunday in April and set back on the last Sunday in October—except in Hawai'i, Arizona, portions of Indiana, and Saskatchewan, which exempt themselves.
Debris avalanche (13) A mass of falling and tumbling rock, debris, and soil; can be dangerous because of the tremendous velocities achieved by the onrushing materials.
Declination (2) The latitude that receives direct overhead (perpendicular) insolation on a particular day; the subsolar point migrates annually through 47° of latitude between the Tropics of Cancer (23.5° N) and Capricorn (23.5° S).
Decomposer (19) Bacteria and fungi that digest organic debris outside their bodies and absorb and release nutrients in an ecosystem (see detritivores).
Derechos (8) Strong linear winds in excess of 26 m/sec (58 mph), associated with thunderstorms and bands of showers crossing a region.
Deficit (9) DEFIC; in a water balance, the amount of unmet (unsatisfied) potential evapotranspiration; a natural water shortage (refer to POTET, or PE).
Deflation (15) A process of wind erosion that removes and lifts individual particles, literally blowing away unconsolidated, dry, or noncohesive sediments (see blowout depression).
Delta (14) A depositional plain formed where a river enters a lake or an ocean; named after the triangular shape of the Greek letter delta, Δ.
Denudation (13) A general term that refers to all processes that cause degradation of the landscape: weathering, mass movement, erosion, and transport.
Deposition (14) The process whereby weathered, wasted, and transported sediments are laid down by air, water, and ice.
Desalination (9) In a water resources context, the removal of organics, debris, and salinity from seawater through distillation or reverse osmosis to produce potable water.
Desert biome (20) Arid landscapes of uniquely adapted dry-climate plants and animals.
Desertification (15) The expansion of deserts worldwide, related principally to poor agricultural practices (overgrazing and inappropriate agricultural practices), improper soil-moisture management, erosion and salinization, deforestation, and the ongoing climatic change; an unwanted semipermanent invasion into neighbouring biomes.
Desert pavement (15) On arid landscapes, a surface formed when wind deflation and sheetflow remove smaller particles, leaving residual pebbles and gravels to concentrate at the surface; resembles a cobblestone street (see deflation, sheetflow).
Detritivores (19) Detritus feeders and decomposers that consume, digest, and destroy organic wastes and debris. *Detritus feeders*—worms, mites, termites, centipedes, snails, crabs, even vultures, among others—consume detritus and excrete nutrients and simple inorganic compounds that fuel an ecosystem. Compare with decomposers (see decomposers).
Dew-point temperature (7) The temperature at which a given mass of air becomes saturated, holding all the water it can hold. Any further cooling or addition of water vapour results in active condensation.
Diagnostic subsurface horizon (18) A soil horizon that originates below the epipedon at varying depths; may be part of the A and B horizons; important in soil description as part of the Soil Taxonomy.
Differential weathering (13) The effect of different resistances in rock, coupled with variations in the intensity of physical and chemical weathering.
Diffuse radiation (4) The downward component of scattered incoming insolation from clouds and the atmosphere.
Discharge (14) The measured volume of flow in a river that passes by a given cross section of a stream in a given unit of time; expressed in cubic metres per second or cubic feet per second.
Dissolved load (14) Materials carried in chemical solution in a stream, derived from minerals such as limestone, dolomite, or from soluble salts.
Downwelling current (6) An area of the sea where a convergence or accumulation of water thrusts excess water downward; occurs, for example, at the western end of the equatorial current or along the margins of Antarctica (compare upwelling currents).
Drainage basin (14) The basic spatial geomorphic unit of a river system; distinguished from a neighbouring basin by ridges and highlands that form divides, marking the limits of the catchment area of the drainage basin or its watershed.
Drainage density (14) A measure of the overall operational efficiency of a drainage basin, determined by the ratio of combined channel lengths to the unit area.
Drainage pattern (14) A distinctive geometric arrangement of streams in a region, determined by slope, differing rock resistance to weathering and erosion, climatic and hydrologic variability, and structural controls of the landscape.
Drawdown (9) See cone of depression.
Drumlin (17) A depositional landform related to glaciation that is composed of till (unstratified, unsorted) and is streamlined in the direction of continental ice movement—blunt end upstream and tapered end downstream with a rounded summit.

Dry adiabatic rate (DAR) (7) The rate at which an unsaturated parcel of air cools (if ascending) or heats (if descending); a rate of 10 C° per 1000 m (5.5 F° per 1000 ft) (see adiabatic; compare moist adiabatic rate).
Dune (15) A depositional feature of sand grains deposited in transient mounds, ridges, and hills; extensive areas of sand dunes are called sand seas.
Dust dome (4) A dome of airborne pollution associated with every major city; may be blown by winds into elongated plumes downwind from the city.
Dynamic equilibrium (1) Increasing or decreasing operations in a system demonstrate a trend over time, a change in average conditions.
Dynamic equilibrium model (13) The balancing act between tectonic uplift and erosion, between the resistance of crust materials and the work of denudation processes. Landscapes evidence ongoing adaptation to rock structure, climate, local relief, and elevation.
Earthquake (12) A sharp release of energy that sends waves traveling through Earth's crust at the moment of rupture along a fault or in association with volcanic activity. The moment magnitude scale (formerly the Richter scale) estimates Earthquake magnitude; intensity is described by the Mercalli scale.
Earth systems science (1) An emerging science of Earth as a complete, systematic entity. An interacting set of physical, chemical, and biological systems that produce the processes of a whole Earth system. A study of planetary change resulting from system operations; includes a desire for a more quantitative understanding among components, rather than qualitative description.
Ebb tide (16) Falling or lowering tide during the daily tidal cycle (compare flood tide).
Ecological succession (19) The process whereby different and usually more complex assemblages of plants and animals replace older and usually simpler communities; communities are in a constant state of change as each species adapts to conditions. Ecosystems do not exhibit a stable point or successional climax condition as previously thought (refer to primary succession, secondary succession).
Ecology (19) The science that studies the relations between organisms and their environment and among various ecosystems.
Ecosphere (1) Another name for the biosphere.
Ecosystem (19, 20) A self-regulating association of living plants, animals, and their nonliving physical and chemical environments.
Ecotone (20) A boundary transition zone between adjoining ecosystems that may vary in width and represent areas of tension as similar species of plants and animals compete for the resources (see ecosystem).
Effusive eruption (12) A volcanic eruption characterized by low-viscosity basaltic magma and low-gas content, which readily escapes. Lava pours forth onto the surface with relatively small explosions and few pyroclastics; tends to form shield volcanoes (see shield volcano, lava, pyroclastics; compare explosive eruption).
Elastic-rebound theory (12) A concept describing the faulting process in Earth's crust, in which the two sides of a fault appear locked despite the motion of adjoining pieces of crust, but with accumulating strain they rupture suddenly, snapping to new positions relative to each other, generating an earthquake.
Electromagnetic spectrum (2) All the radiant energy produced by the Sun placed in an ordered range, divided according to wavelengths.
Eluviation (18) The removal of finer particles and minerals from the upper horizons of soil; an erosional process within a soil body (compare illuviation).
Empirical classification (10) A climate classification based on weather statistics or other data; used to determine general climate categories (compare genetic classification).
Endogenic system (11) The system internal to Earth, driven by radioactive heat derived from sources within the planet. In response, the surface fractures, mountain building occurs, and earthquakes and volcanoes are activated (compare exogenic system).
Entisols (18) A soil order in the Soil Taxonomy. Specifically lacks vertical development of horizons; usually young or undeveloped. Found in active slopes, alluvial-filled floodplains, poorly drained tundra.
Environmental lapse rate (3) The actual lapse rate in the lower atmosphere at any particular time under local weather conditions; may deviate above or below the normal lapse rate of 6.4 C° per 1000 m (3.5 F° per 1000 ft). (Compare normal lapse rate.)
Eolian (15) Caused by wind; refers to the erosion, transportation, and deposition of materials; spelled aeolian in some countries.
Epipedon (18) The diagnostic soil horizon that forms at the surface; not to be confused with the A horizon; may include all or part of the illuviated B horizon.
Equal area (1) A trait of a map projection; indicates the equivalence of all areas on the surface of the map, although shape is distorted (see map projections).
Equatorial and tropical rain forest (20) A lush biome of tall broadleaf evergreen trees and diverse plants and animals, roughly between 23.5° N and 23.5° S. The dense canopy of leaves is usually arranged in three levels.
Equatorial low-pressure trough (6) A thermally caused low-pressure area that almost girdles Earth, with air converging and ascending all along its extent; also called the intertropical convergence zone (ITCZ).
Erg desert (15) A sandy desert, or area where sand is so extensive that it constitutes a sand sea.
Erosion (14) Denudation by wind, water, or ice, which dislodges, dissolves, or removes surface material.
Esker (17) A sinuously curving, narrow deposit of coarse gravel that forms along a meltwater stream channel, developing in a tunnel beneath a glacier.
Estuary (14) The point at which the mouth of a river enters the sea, where freshwater and seawater are mixed; a place where tides ebb and flow.
Eustasy (7) Refers to worldwide changes in sea level that are not related to movements of land but rather to a rise and fall in the volume of water in the oceans.
Evaporation (9) The movement of free water molecules away from a wet surface into air that is less than saturated; the phase change of water to water vapour.
Evaporation fog (7) A fog formed when cold air flows over the warm surface of a lake, ocean, or other body of water; forms as the water molecules evaporate from the water surface into the cold, overlying air; also known as steam fog or sea smoke.
Evaporation pan (9) A weather instrument consisting of a standardized pan from which evaporation occurs, with water automatically replaced and measured; an evaporimeter.
Evapotranspiration (9) The merging of evaporation and transpiration water loss into one term (see potential and actual evapotranspiration).
Evolution (19) A theory that single-cell organisms adapted, modified, and passed along inherited changes to multicellular organisms. The genetic makeup of successive generations is shaped by environmental factors, physiological functions, and behaviours that created a greater rate of survival and reproduction and were passed along through natural selection.
Exfoliation dome (13) A dome-shaped feature of weathering, produced by the response of granite to the overburden removal process, which relieves pressure from the rock. Layers of rock slough ("sluff") off in slabs or shells in a sheeting process.
Exogenic system (11) Earth's external surface system, powered by insolation, which energizes air, water, and ice and sets them in motion, under the influence of gravity. Includes all processes of landmass denudation (compare endogenic system).
Exosphere (3) An extremely rarefied outer atmospheric halo beyond the thermopause at an altitude of 480 km (300 mi); probably composed of hydrogen and helium atoms, with some oxygen atoms and nitrogen molecules present near the thermopause.
Exotic stream (14) A river that rises in a humid region and flows through an arid region, with discharge decreasing toward the mouth; for example, the Nile River and the Colorado River.
Explosive eruption (12) A violent and unpredictable volcanic eruption, the result of magma that is thicker (more viscous), stickier, and higher in gas and silica content than that of an effusive eruption; tends to form blockages within a volcano; produces composite volcanic landforms (see composite volcano; compare effusive eruption).
Faulting (12) The process whereby displacement and fracturing occur between two portions of Earth's crust; usually associated with earthquake activity.

Feedback loop (1) Created when a portion of system output is returned as an information input, causing changes that guide further system operation (see negative feedback, positive feedback).

Field capacity (9) Water held in the soil by hydrogen bonding against the pull of gravity, remaining after water drains from the larger pore spaces; the available water for plants (see available water, capillary water).

Fire ecology (19) The study of fire as a natural agent and dynamic factor in community succession.

Firn (17) Snow of a granular texture that is transitional in the slow transformation from snow to glacial ice; snow that has persisted through a summer season in the zone of accumulation.

Firn line (17) The snow line that is visible on the surface of a glacier, where winter snows survive the summer ablation season; analogous to a snow line on land (see ablation).

Fjord (17) A drowned glaciated valley, or glacial trough, along a seacoast.

Flash flood (15) A sudden and short-lived torrent of water that exceeds the capacity of a stream channel; associated with desert and semiarid washes.

Flood (14) A high water level that overflows the natural riverbank along any portion of a stream.

Floodplain (14) A flat, low-lying area along a stream channel, created by and subject to recurrent flooding; alluvial deposits generally mask underlying rock.

Flood tide (16) Rising tide during the daily tidal cycle (compare ebb tide).

Fluvial (14) Stream-related processes; from the Latin *fluvius* for "river" or "running water."

Fog (7) A cloud, generally stratiform, in contact with the ground, with visibility usually reduced to less than 1 km (3300 ft).

Folding (12) The bending and deformation of beds of rock strata subjected to compressional forces.

Food chain (19) The circuit along which energy flows from producers (plants), which manufacture their own food, to consumers (animals); a one-directional flow of chemical energy, ending with decomposers.

Food web (19) A complex network of interconnected food chains (see food chain).

Formation class (20) That portion of a biome that concerns the plant communities only, categorized by size, shape, and structure of the dominant vegetation.

Friction force (6) The effect of drag by the wind as it moves across a surface; may be operative through 500 m (1600 ft) of altitude. Surface friction slows the wind and therefore reduces the effectiveness of the Coriolis force.

Frost action (13) A powerful mechanical force produced as water expands up to 9% of its volume as it freezes. Water freezing in a cavity in a rock can break the rock if it exceeds the rock's tensional strength.

Funnel cloud (8) The visible swirl extending from the bottom side of a cloud, which may or may not develop into a tornado. A tornado is a funnel cloud that has extended all the way to the ground (see tornado).

Fusion (2) The process of forcibly joining positively charged hydrogen and helium nuclei under extreme temperature and pressure; occurs naturally in thermonuclear reactions within stars, such as our Sun.

Gelifluction (13, 17) Refers to soil flow in periglacial environments, a progressive, lateral movement; a type of solifluction formed under periglacial conditions of permafrost and frozen ground (see solifluction).

Gelisols (18) A new soil order in the Soil Taxonomy, added in 1998, describing cold and frozen soils at high latitudes or high elevations; characteristic tundra vegetation (see Canadian System of Soil Classification for similar types).

General circulation model (GCM) (10) Complex, computer-based climate model that produces generalizations of reality and forecasts of future weather and climate conditions. Complex GCMs (three-dimensional models) are in use in the United States and in other countries.

Genetic classification (10) A climate classification that uses causative factors to determine climatic regions; for example, an analysis of the effect of interacting air masses (compare empirical classification).

Geodesy (1) The science that determines Earth's shape and size through surveys, mathematical means, and remote sensing (see geoid).

Geographic information system (GIS) (1) A computer-based data processing tool or methodology used for gathering, manipulating, and analyzing geographic information to produce a holistic, interactive analysis.

Geography (1) The science that studies the interdependence and interaction among geographic areas, natural systems, processes, society, and cultural activities over space—a spatial science. The five themes of geographic education are location, place, movement, regions, and human–Earth relationships.

Geoid (1) A word that describes Earth's shape; literally, "the shape of Earth is Earth-shaped." A theoretical surface at sea level that extends through the continents; deviates from a perfect sphere.

Geologic cycle (11) A general term characterizing the vast cycling that proceeds in the lithosphere. It encompasses the hydrologic cycle, tectonic cycle, and rock cycle.

Geologic time scale (11) A depiction of eras, periods, and epochs that span Earth's history; shows both the sequence of rock strata and their absolute dates, as determined by methods such as radioactive isotopic dating.

Geomagnetic reversal (11) A polarity change in Earth's magnetic field. With uneven regularity, the magnetic field fades to zero, then returns to full strength but with the magnetic poles reversed. Reversals have been recorded 9 times during the past 4 million years.

Geomorphic threshold (13) The threshold up to which landforms change before lurching to a new set of relationships, with rapid realignments of landscape materials and slopes.

Geomorphology (13) The science that analyzes and describes the origin, evolution, form, classification, and spatial distribution of landforms.

Geostrophic wind (6) A wind moving between areas of different pressure along a path that is parallel to the isobars. It is a product of the pressure gradient force and the Coriolis force (see isobar, pressure gradient force, Coriolis force).

Geothermal energy (11, 12) The energy in steam and hot water heated by subsurface magma near groundwater. Geothermal energy literally refers to heat from Earth's interior, whereas *geothermal power* relates to specific applied strategies of geothermal electric or geothermal direct applications. This energy is used in Iceland, New Zealand, Italy, and northern California, among other locations.

Glacial drift (17) The general term for all glacial deposits, both unsorted (till) and sorted (stratified drift).

Glacial ice (17) A hardened form of ice, very dense in comparison to normal snow or firn.

Glacier (17) A large mass of perennial ice resting on land or floating shelflike in the sea adjacent to the land; formed from the accumulation and recrystallization of snow, which then flows slowly under the pressure of its own weight and the pull of gravity.

Glacier surge (17) The rapid, lurching, unexpected forward movement of a glacier.

Glacio-eustatic (7) Changes in sea level in response to changes in the amount of water stored on Earth as ice; the more water that is bound up in glaciers and ice sheets, the lower the sea level (compare eustasy).

Gleysation (18) A process of humus and clay accumulation in cold, wet climates with poor drainage.

Gleysolic (18) A CSSC soil order defined on the basis of colour and mottling that results from chronic reducing conditions inherent in poorly drained mineral soils under wet conditions. High water table and long periods of water saturation.

Global positioning system (GPS) (1) Latitude, longitude, and elevation are accurately calibrated using this handheld instrument that calibrates radio signals from satellites.

Goode's homolosine projection (Appendix A) An equal-area projection formed by splicing together a sinusoidal and a homolographic projection.

Graben (12) Pairs or groups of faults that produce downward-faulted blocks; characteristic of the basins of the interior western United States (compare horst; see Basin and Range Province).

Graded stream (14) An idealized condition in which a stream's load and the landscape mutually adjust. This forms a dynamic equilibrium among erosion, transported load, deposition, and the stream's capacity.

Gradient (14) The drop in elevation from a stream's headwaters to its mouth, ideally forming a concave slope.

Granite (11) A coarse-grained (slow-cooling) intrusive igneous rock of 25% quartz and more than 50% potassium and sodium feldspars; characteristic of the continental crust.

Gravitational water (9) That portion of surplus water that percolates downward from the capillary zone, pulled by gravity to the groundwater zone.
Gravity (2) The mutual force exerted by the masses of objects that are attracted one to another and produced in an amount proportional to each object's mass.
Great circle (1) Any circle drawn on a globe with its centre coinciding with the centre of the globe. An infinite number of great circles can be drawn, but only one parallel is a great circle—the equator (compare small circle).
Greenhouse effect (4) The process whereby radiatively active gases (carbon dioxide, water vapour, methane, and CFCs) absorb insolation and emit the energy at longer wavelengths, which are retained longer, delaying the loss of infrared to space. Thus, the lower troposphere is warmed through the radiation and re-radiation of infrared wavelengths. The approximate similarity between this process and that of a greenhouse explains the name.
Greenwich Mean Time (GMT) (1) Former world standard time, now reported as Coordinated Universal Time (UTC) (see Coordinated Universal Time).
Ground ice (17) Subsurface water that is frozen in regions of permafrost. The moisture content of areas with ground ice may vary from nearly absent in regions of drier permafrost to almost 100% in saturated soils (compare permafrost).
Groundwater (9) Water beneath the surface that is beyond the soil-root zone; a major source of potable water.
Groundwater mining (9) Pumping an aquifer beyond its capacity to flow and recharge; an overuse of the groundwater resource.
Gulf Stream (5) A strong, northward-moving, warm current off the east coast of North America, which carries its water far into the North Atlantic.
Habitat (19, 20) A physical location to which an organism is biologically suited. Most species have specific habitat parameters and limits (compare to niche).
Hail (8) A type of precipitation formed when a raindrop is repeatedly circulated above and below the freezing level in a cloud, with each cycle freezing more moisture onto the hailstone until it becomes too heavy to stay aloft.
Hair hygrometer (7) An instrument for measuring relative humidity; based on the principle that human hair will change as much as 4% in length between 0% and 100% relative humidity.
Heat (3) The flow of kinetic energy from one body to another because of a temperature difference between them.
Herbivore (19) The primary consumer in a food web, which eats plant material formed by a producer (plant) that has photosynthesized organic molecules (compare carnivore).
Heterosphere (3) A zone of the atmosphere above the mesopause, 80 km (50 mi) in altitude; composed of rarefied layers of oxygen atoms and nitrogen molecules; includes the ionosphere.
Histosols (18) A soil order in the Soil Taxonomy. Formed from thick accumulations of organic matter, such as beds of former lakes, bogs, and layers of peat.
Homosphere (3) A zone of the atmosphere from Earth's surface up to 80 km (50 mi), composed of an even mixture of gases, including nitrogen, oxygen, argon, carbon dioxide, and trace gases.
Horn (17) A pyramidal, sharp-pointed peak that results when several cirque glaciers gouge an individual mountain summit from all sides.
Horst (12) Upward-faulted blocks produced by pairs or groups of faults; characteristic of the mountain ranges of the interior of the western United States (see graben and Basin and Range Province).
Hot spot (11) An individual point of upwelling material originating in the asthenosphere, or deeper in the mantle; tends to remain fixed relative to migrating plates; some 100 are identified worldwide, exemplified by Yellowstone National Park, Hawai'i, and Iceland.
Human–Earth relationships (1) One of the oldest themes of geography (the human-land tradition); includes the spatial analysis of settlement patterns, resource utilization and exploitation, hazard perception and planning, and the impact of environmental modification and artificial landscape creation.
Humidity (7) Water vapour content of the air. The capacity of the air to hold water vapour is mostly a function of the temperature of the air and the water vapour.
Humus (18) A mixture of organic debris in the soil worked by consumers and decomposers in the humification process; characteristically formed from plant and animal litter deposited at the surface.
Hurricane (8) A tropical cyclone that is fully organized and intensified in inward-spiraling rainbands; ranges from 160 to 960 km (100 to 600 mi) in diameter, with wind speeds in excess of 119 kmph (65 knots, or 74 mph); a name used specifically in the Atlantic and eastern Pacific (compare typhoon).
Hydration (13) A chemical weathering process involving water that is added to a mineral, which initiates swelling and stress within the rock, mechanically forcing grains apart as the constituents expand (contrast to hydrolysis).
Hydraulic action (14) The erosive work accomplished by the turbulence of water; causes a squeezing and releasing action in joints in bedrock; capable of prying and lifting rocks.
Hydrograph (14) A graph of stream discharge (in cms or cfs) over a period of time (minutes, hours, days, years) at a specific place on a stream. The relationship between stream discharge and precipitation input is illustrated on the graph.
Hydrologic cycle (9) A simplified model of the flow of water, ice, and water vapour from place to place. Water flows through the atmosphere, across the land, where it is also stored as ice, and within groundwater. Solar energy empowers the cycle.
Hydrology (14) The science of water, its global circulation, distribution, and properties, specifically water at and below Earth's surface.
Hydrolysis (13) A chemical weathering process in which minerals chemically combine with water; a decomposition process that causes silicate minerals in rocks to break down and become altered (contrast with hydration).
Hydrosphere (1) An abiotic open system that includes all of Earth's water.
Hygroscopic water (9) That portion of soil moisture that is so tightly bound to each soil particle that it is unavailable to plant roots; the water, along with some bound capillary water, that is left in the soil after the wilting point is reached (see wilting point).
Ice age (17) A cold episode, with accompanying alpine and continental ice accumulations, that has repeated roughly every 200 to 300 million years since the late Precambrian era (1.25 billion years ago); includes the most recent episode during the Pleistocene Ice Age, which began 1.65 million years ago.
Iceberg (17) Floating ice created by ice calving (a large piece breaking off) and floating adrift; a hazard to shipping because about nine-tenths of the ice is submerged and can be irregular in form.
Ice cap (17) A large, dome-shaped glacier, less extensive than an ice sheet ($<50{,}000 km^2$, $<19{,}300 mi^2$), although it buries mountain peaks and the local landscape.
Ice-crystal fog (7) A type of fog that develops at very low temperatures in a continental arctic air mass. Visibility is seriously limited when the air becomes full of ice crystals that have formed by sublimation.
Ice field (17) The least extensive form of a glacier, with mountain ridges and peaks visible above the ice; less than an ice cap or ice sheet.
Icelandic low (6) See subpolar low-pressure cell.
Ice sheet (17) An enormous continuous continental glacier. The bulk of glacial ice on Earth covers Antarctica and Greenland in two ice sheets.
Ice shelf (17) A very thick sheet of ice with a gently undulating to level surface that extends over the sea and floats on water. It is attached to the land along a coastal grounding line and also may be attached where ice flows around islands. On the seaward side, it is bounded by a steep cliff called the ice front that can be 2 to 50 m or more above sea level.
Ice storm (8) A major hazard in which supercooled precipitation freezes on contact with surfaces. The severity of the event is determined by the thickness of ice accumulation associated with a storm, the storm's duration, and the extent of area affected. Typically, an ice storm will last for 45 to 65 hours and will deposit, at most, 30 to 40 mm of ice.
Ice wedge (17) Formed when water enters a thermal contraction crack in permafrost and freezes. Repeated seasonal freezing and melting of the water progressively expands the wedge.

Igneous rock (11) One of the basic rock types; it has solidified and crystallized from a hot molten state (either magma or lava). (Compare metamorphic rock, sedimentary rock.)
Illuviation (18) The downward movement and deposition of finer particles and minerals from the upper horizon of the soil; a depositional process. Deposition usually is in the B horizon, where accumulations of clays, aluminum, carbonates, iron, and some humus occur (compare eluviation; see calcification).
Inceptisols (18) A soil order in the Soil Taxonomy. Weakly developed soils that are inherently infertile; usually young soils that are weakly developed, although they are more developed than Entisols.
Industrial smog (3) Air pollution associated with coal-burning industries; it may contain sulphur oxides, particulates, carbon dioxide, and exotics.
Infiltration (9) Water access to subsurface regions of soil moisture storage through penetration of the soil surface.
Insolation (2) Solar radiation that is incoming to Earth systems.
Interception (9) Delays the fall of precipitation toward Earth's surface; caused by vegetation or other ground cover.
Internal drainage (14) In regions where rivers do not flow into the ocean, the outflow is through evaporation or subsurface gravitational flow. Portions of Africa, Asia, Australia, and the western United States have such drainage.
International Date Line (1) The 180° meridian, an important corollary to the prime meridian on the opposite side of the planet; established by the treaty of 1884 to mark the place where each day officially begins.
Intertropical convergence zone (ITCZ) (6) See equatorial low-pressure trough.
Ionosphere (3) A layer in the atmosphere above 80 km (50 mi) where gamma, X-ray, and some ultraviolet radiation is absorbed and converted into infrared and where the solar wind stimulates the auroras.
Isobar (6) An isoline connecting all points of equal atmospheric pressure.
Isostasy (11) A state of equilibrium in Earth's crust formed by the interplay between portions of the lithosphere and the asthenosphere and the principle of buoyancy. The crust depresses under weight and recovers with its removal, for example, the melting of glacial ice. The uplift is known as isostatic rebound.
Isotherm (5) An isoline connecting all points of equal temperature.
Jet stream (6) The most prominent movement in upper-level westerly wind flows; irregular, concentrated, sinuous bands of geostrophic wind, traveling at 300 kmph (190 mph). (See polar jet stream, subtropical jet stream.)
Joint (13) A fracture or separation in rock that occurs without displacement of the sides; increases the surface area of rock exposed to weathering processes.
Kame (17) A depositional feature of glaciation; a small hill of poorly sorted sand and gravel that accumulates in crevasses or in ice-caused indentations in the surface.
Karst topography (13) Distinctive topography formed in a region of chemically weathered limestone with poorly developed surface drainage and solution features that appear pitted and bumpy; originally named after the Krš Plateau in Slovenia.
Katabatic winds (6) Air drainage from elevated regions, flowing as gravity winds. Layers of air at the surface cool, become denser, and flow downslope; known worldwide by many local names.
Kettle (17) Forms when an isolated block of ice persists in a ground moraine, an outwash plain, or valley floor after a glacier retreats; as the block finally melts, it leaves behind a steep-sided hole that frequently fills with water.
Kinetic energy (3) The energy of motion in a body; derived from the vibration of the body's own movement and stated as temperature.
Köppen-Geiger climate classification (10, Appendix B) An empirical classification system that uses average monthly temperatures, average monthly precipitation, and total annual precipitation to establish regional climate designations.
Lagoon (16) An area of coastal seawater that is virtually cut off from the ocean by a bay barrier or barrier beach; also, the water surrounded and enclosed by an atoll.
Landfall (8) The location along a coast where a storm moves onshore.
Land–sea breeze (6) Wind along coastlines and adjoining interior areas created by different heating characteristics of land and water surfaces—onshore (landward) breeze in the afternoon and offshore (seaward) breeze at night.
Landslide (13) A sudden rapid downslope movement of a cohesive mass of regolith and/or bedrock in a variety of mass-movement forms under the influence of gravity; a form of mass movement.
Land–water heating difference (5) Differences in the degree and way that land and water heat, as a result of contrasts in transmission, evaporation, mixing, and specific heat capacities. Land surfaces heat and cool faster than water and have continentality, whereas water provides a marine influence.
Latent heat (7) Heat energy is stored in one of three states—ice, water, or water vapour. The energy is absorbed or released in each phase change from one state to another. Heat energy is absorbed as the latent heat of melting, vaporization, or evaporation. Heat energy is released as the latent heat of condensation and freezing (or fusion).
Latent heat of condensation (7) The heat energy released to the environment in a phase change from water vapour to liquid; under normal sea-level pressure, 540 calories are released from each gram of water vapour that changes phase to water at boiling; and 585 calories are released from each gram of water vapour that condenses at 20°C (68°F).
Latent heat of sublimation (7) The heat energy absorbed or released in the phase change from ice to water vapour or water vapour to ice—no liquid phase. The change from water vapour to ice is also called deposition.
Latent heat of vaporization (7) The heat energy absorbed from the environment in a phase change from liquid to water vapour at the boiling point; under normal sea-level pressure, 540 calories must be added to each gram of boiling water to achieve a phase change to water vapour.
Lateral moraine (17) Debris transported by a glacier that accumulates along the sides of the glacier and is deposited along these margins.
Laterization (18) A pedogenic process operating in well-drained soils that occur in warm and humid regions; typical of Oxisols. Plentiful precipitation leaches soluble minerals and soil constituents. Resulting soils usually are reddish or yellowish.
Latitude (1) The angular distance measured north or south of the equator from a point at the centre of Earth. A line connecting all points of the same latitudinal angle is called a parallel (compare longitude).
Lava (11, 12) Magma that issues from volcanic activity onto the surface; the extrusive rock that results when magma solidifies (see magma).
Life zone (19) A zonation by altitude of plants and animals that form distinctive communities. Each life zone possesses its own temperature and precipitation relations.
Lightning (8) Flashes of light caused by tens of millions of volts of electrical charge heating the air to temperatures of 15,000° to 30,000°C.
Limestone (11) The most common chemical sedimentary rock (nonclastic); it is lithified calcium carbonate; very susceptible to chemical weathering by acids in the environment, including carbonic acid in rainfall.
Limiting factor (19) The physical or chemical factor that most inhibits biotic processes, either through lack or excess.
Lithification (11) The compaction, cementation, and hardening of sediments into sedimentary rock.
Lithosphere (1) Earth's crust and that portion of the upper-most mantle directly below the crust, extending down to about 70 km (45 mi). Some sources use this term to refer to the entire Earth.
Littoral drift (16) Transport of sand, gravel, sediment, and debris along the shore; a more comprehensive term, considers *beach drift* and *longshore drift* combined.
Littoral zone (16) A specific coastal environment; that region between the high-water line during a storm and a depth at which storm waves are unable to move sea-floor sediments.
Loam (18) A soil that is a mixture of sand, silt, and clay in almost equal proportions, with no one texture dominant; an ideal agricultural soil.
Location (1) A basic theme of geography dealing with the absolute and relative position of people, places, and things on Earth's surface.
Loess (15) Large quantities of fine-grained clays and silts left as glacial outwash deposits; subsequently blown by the wind great distances and redeposited as a generally unstratified, homogeneous blanket of material covering existing landscapes; in China, loess originated from desert lands.
Longitude (1) The angular distance measured east or west of a prime meridian from a point at the centre of Earth. A line connecting all points of the same longitude is called a meridian.

Longshore current (16) A current that forms parallel to a beach as waves arrive at an angle to the shore; generated in the surf zone by wave action, transporting large amounts of sand and sediment (see littoral current, beach drift).

Luvisolic (18) A CSSC soil order with eluviation-illuviation processes produce a light-coloured **Ae** horizon and a diagnostic **Bt** horizon. Soils of mixed deciduous–coniferous forests. Major occurrence is the St. Lawrence lowland. Luvisols do not have a solonetzic **B** horizon.

Lysimeter (9) A weather instrument for measuring potential and actual evapotranspiration; isolates a portion of a field so that the moisture moving through the plot is measured.

Magma (11) Molten rock from beneath Earth's surface; fluid, gaseous, under tremendous pressure, and either intruded into existing country rock or extruded onto the surface as lava (see lava).

Magnetosphere (2) Earth's magnetic force field, which is generated by dynamo-like motions within the planet's outer core; deflects the solar wind flow toward the upper atmosphere above each pole.

Mangrove swamp (16) A wetland ecosystem between 30° N or S and the equator; tends to form a distinctive community of mangrove plants (compare salt marsh).

Mantle (11) An area within the planet representing about 80% of Earth's total volume, with densities increasing with depth and averaging 4.5g/cm^3; occurs between the core and the crust; is rich in iron and magnesium oxides and silicates.

Map (1, Appendix A) A generalized view of an area, usually some portion of Earth's surface, as seen from above at a greatly reduced size (see scale and map projection).

Map projection (1, Appendix A) The reduction of a spherical globe onto a flat surface in some orderly and systematic realignment of the latitude and longitude grid.

Marine effect (5) A quality of regions that are dominated by the moderating effect of the ocean and that exhibit a smaller range of minimum and maximum temperature than continental stations (see continentality, land–water heating differences).

Mass movement (13) All unit movements of materials propelled by gravity; can range from dry to wet, slow to fast, small to large, and free-falling to gradual or intermittent.

Mass wasting (13) Gravitational movement of nonunified material downslope; a specific form of mass movement.

Meandering stream (14) The sinuous, curving pattern common to graded streams, with the energetic outer portion of each curve subjected to the greatest erosive action and the lower-energy inner portion receiving sediment deposits (see graded stream).

Mean sea level (MSL) (16) The average of tidal levels recorded hourly at a given site over a long period, which must be at least a full lunar tidal cycle.

Medial moraine (17) Debris transported by a glacier that accumulates down the middle of the glacier, resulting from two glaciers merging their lateral moraines; forms a depositional feature following glacial retreat.

Mediterranean shrubland (20) A major biome dominated by Mediterranean dry-summer climates and characterized by sclerophyllous scrub and short, stunted, tough forests (see chapparal).

Mercator projection (1) A true-shape projection, with meridians appearing as equally spaced straight lines and parallels appearing as straight lines that are spaced closer together near the equator. The poles are infinitely stretched, with the 84th north parallel and 84th south parallel fixed at the same length as that of the equator. It presents false notions of the size (area) of midlatitude and poleward landmasses but presents true compass direction (see rhumb line).

Mercury barometer (6) A device that measures air pressure using a column of mercury in a tube, one end of which is sealed, and the other end inserted in an open vessel of mercury (see air pressure).

Meridian (1) See longitude; a line designating an angle of longitude.

Mesocyclone (8) A large, rotating atmospheric circulation, initiated within a parent cumulonimbus cloud at midtroposphere elevation; generally produces heavy rain, large hail, blustery winds, and lightning; may lead to tornado activity.

Mesosphere (3) The upper region of the homosphere from 50 to 80 km (30 to 50 mi) above the ground; designated by temperature criteria; atmosphere extremely rarified.

Metamorphic rock (11) One of three basic rock types, it is existing igneous and sedimentary rock that has undergone profound physical and chemical changes under increased pressure and temperature. Constituent mineral structures may exhibit foliated or nonfoliated textures (compare igneous rock and sedimentary rock).

Meteorology (8) The scientific study of the atmosphere, including its physical characteristics and motions; related chemical, physical, and geological processes; the complex linkages of atmospheric systems; and weather forecasting.

Microclimatology (4) The study of local climates at or near Earth's surface, or that height above the Earth's surface where the effects of the surface are no longer of effect.

Midlatitude broadleaf and mixed forest (20) A biome in moist continental climates in areas of warm-to-hot summers and cool-to-cold winters; relatively lush stands of broadleaf forests trend northward into needleleaf evergreen stands.

Midlatitude cyclone (8) An organized area of low pressure, with converging and ascending airflow producing an interaction of air masses; migrates along storm tracks. Such lows or depressions form the dominant weather pattern in the middle and higher latitudes of both hemispheres.

Midlatitude grassland (20) The major biome most modified by human activity; so named because of the predominance of grasslike plants, although deciduous broadleafs appear along streams and other limited sites; location of the world's breadbaskets of grain and livestock production.

Mid-ocean ridge (11) A submarine mountain range that extends more than 65,000 km (40,000 mi) worldwide and averages more than 1000 km (600 mi) in width; centred along sea-floor spreading centres (see sea-floor spreading).

Milky Way Galaxy (2) A flattened, disk-shaped mass in space estimated to contain up to 400 billion stars; includes our Solar System.

Miller cylindrical projection (Appendix A) A compromise map projection that avoids the severe distortion of the Mercator projection (see map projection).

Mineral (11) An element or combination of elements that forms an inorganic natural compound; described by a specific formula and crystal structure.

Model (1) A simplified version of a system, representing an idealized part of the real world.

Mohorovičić discontinuity, or Moho (11) The boundary between the crust and the rest of the lithospheric upper mantle; named for the Yugoslavian seismologist Mohorovičić; a zone of sharp material and density contrasts; also known as the Moho.

Moist adiabatic rate (MAR) (7) The rate at which a saturated parcel of air cools in ascent; a rate of 6 C° per 1000 m (3.3 F° per 1000 ft). This rate may vary, with moisture content and temperature, from 4 C° to 10 C° per 1000 m (2 F° to 6 F° per 1000 ft) (see adiabatic; compare dry adiabatic rate).

Moisture droplet (7) A tiny water particle that constitutes the initial composition of clouds. Each droplet measures approximately 0.002 cm (0.0008 in.) in diameter and is invisible to the unaided eye.

Mollisols (18) A soil order in the Soil Taxonomy. These have a mollic epipedon and a humus-rich organic content high in alkalinity. Some of the world's most significant agricultural soils are Mollisols.

Moment magnitude scale (12) An earthquake magnitude scale. Considers the amount of fault slippage, the size of the area that ruptured, and the nature of the materials that faulted in estimating the magnitude of an earthquake—an assessment of the seismic moment. Replaces the Richter scale (amplitude magnitude); especially valuable in assessing larger-magnitude events.

Monsoon (6) An annual cycle of dryness and wetness, with seasonally shifting winds produced by changing atmospheric pressure systems; affects India, Southeast Asia, Indonesia, northern Australia, and portions of Africa. From the Arabic word *mausim*, meaning "season."

Montane forest (20) Needleleaf forest associated with mountain elevations (see needleleaf forest).

Moraine (17) Marginal glacial deposits (lateral, medial, terminal, ground) of unsorted and unstratified material.

Mountain–valley breeze (6) A light wind produced as cooler mountain air flows downslope at night and as warmer valley air flows upslope during the day.

Movement (1) A major theme in geography involving migration, communication, and the interaction of people and processes across space.

Mudflow (13) Fluid downslope flows of material containing more water than earthflows.

Natural levee (14) A long, low ridge that forms on both sides of a stream in a developed floodplain; they are depositional products (coarse gravels and sand) of river flooding.

Neap tide (16) Unusually low tidal range produced during the first and third quarters of the Moon, with an offsetting pull from the Sun (compare spring tide).

Needleleaf forest (20) Forests of pine, spruce, fir, and larch, stretching from the east coast of Canada westward to Alaska and continuing from Siberia westward across the entire extent of Russia to the European Plain; called the *taiga* (a Russian word) or the *boreal forest*; principally in the microthermal climates. Includes montane forests that may be at lower latitudes at higher elevation.

Negative feedback (1) Feedback that tends to slow or dampen response in a system; promotes self-regulation in a system; far more common than positive feedback in living systems (see feedback loop, compare to positive feedback).

Net primary productivity (19) The net photosynthesis (photosynthesis minus respiration) for a given community; considers all growth and all reduction factors that affect the amount of useful chemical energy (biomass) fixed in an ecosystem.

Net radiation (NET R) (4) The net all-wave radiation available at Earth's surface; the final outcome of the radiation balance process between incoming shortwave insolation and outgoing longwave energy.

Niche (19, 20) The basic function, or occupation, of a life form within a given community; the way an organism obtains its food, air, and water.

Nickpoint (knickpoint) (14) The point at which the longitudinal profile of a stream is abruptly broken by a change in gradient; for example, a waterfall, rapids, or cascade.

Nimbostratus (7) Rain-producing, dark, grayish, stratiform clouds characterized by gentle drizzle.

Nitrogen dioxide (3) A noxious (harmful) reddish-brown gas produced in combustion engines; can be damaging to human respiratory tracts and to plants; participates in photochemical reactions and acid deposition.

Noctilucent cloud (3) A rare, shining band of ice crystals that may glow at high latitudes long after sunset; formed within the mesosphere, where cosmic and meteoric dust act as nuclei for the formation of ice crystals.

Normal fault (12) A type of geologic fault in rocks. Tension produces strain that breaks a rock, with one side moving vertically relative to the other side along an inclined fault plane (compare reverse fault).

Normal lapse rate (3) The average rate of temperature decrease with increasing altitude in the lower atmosphere; an average value of 6.4 C° per km, or 1000 m (3.5 F° per 1000 ft). (Compare environmental lapse rate.)

Occluded front (8) In a cyclonic circulation, the overrunning of a surface warm front by a cold front and the subsequent lifting of the warm air wedge off the ground; initial precipitation is moderate to heavy.

Ocean basin (12) The physical container (a depression in the lithosphere) holding an ocean.

Omnivore (19) A consumer that feeds on both producers (plants) and consumers (meat)—a role occupied by humans, among other animals (compare consumer, producer).

Open system (1) A system with inputs and outputs crossing back and forth between the system and the surrounding environment. Earth is an open system in terms of energy (compare closed system).

Organic (18) A CSSC soil order with peat, bog, and muck soils, largely composed of organic material. Most water-saturated for prolonged periods. Are widespread in association with poorly to very poorly drained depressions, although Folisols are found under upland forest environments. Exceed 17% organic carbon and 30% organic matter overall.

Orogenesis (12) The process of mountain building that occurs when large-scale compression leads to deformation and uplift of the crust; literally, the birth of mountains.

Orographic lifting (8) The uplift of a migrating air mass as it is forced to move upward over a mountain range—a topographic barrier. The lifted air cools adiabatically as it moves upslope; clouds may form and produce increased precipitation.

Outgassing (7) The release of trapped gases from rocks, forced out through cracks, fissures, and volcanoes from within Earth; the terrestrial source of Earth's water.

Outwash plain (17) Glacial stream deposits of stratified drift of meltwater-fed, braided, and overloaded streams; occurs beyond a glacier's morainal deposits.

Overland flow (9) Surplus water that flows across the land surface toward stream channels. Together with precipitation and subsurface flows, it constitutes the total runoff from an area.

Oxbow lake (14) A lake that was formerly part of the channel of a meandering stream; isolated when a stream eroded its outer bank forming a cutoff through the neck of the looping meander (see meandering stream). In Australia, known as a billabong (Aboriginal for "dead river").

Oxidation (13) A chemical weathering process in which oxygen dissolved in water oxidizes (combines with) certain metallic elements to form oxides; most familiar is the "rusting" of iron in a rock or soil (Ultisols, Oxisols), which produces a reddish-brown stain of iron oxide.

Oxisols (18) A soil order in the Soil Taxonomy. Tropical soils that are old, deeply developed, and lacking in horizons wherever well drained; heavily weathered, low in cation-exchange capacity, and low in fertility.

Ozone layer (3) See ozonosphere.

Ozonosphere (3) A layer of ozone occupying the full extent of the stratosphere (20 to 50 km, or 12 to 30 mi) above the surface; the region of the atmosphere where ultraviolet wavelengths of insolation are extensively absorbed and converted into heat.

Pacific high (6) A high-pressure cell that dominates the Pacific in July, retreating southward in the Northern Hemisphere in January; also known as the Hawaiian high.

Pahoehoe (12) Basaltic lava that is more fluid than aa. Pahoehoe forms a thin crust that forms folds and appears "ropy," like coiled, twisted rope.

Paleoclimatology (10, 17) The science that studies the climates, and the causes of variations in climate, of past ages, throughout historic and geologic time.

Paleolake (17) An ancient lake, such as Lake Bonneville or Lake Lahonton, associated with former wet periods when the lake basins were filled to higher levels than today.

Palsa (17) A rounded or elliptical mound of peat that contains thin perennial ice lenses rather than an ice core, as in a pingo. Palsas can be 2 to 30 m wide by 1 to 10 m high and usually are covered by soil or vegetation over a cracked surface.

PAN (3) See peroxyacetyl nitrate.

Pangaea (11) The supercontinent formed by the collision of all continental masses approximately 225 million years ago; named in the continental drift theory by Wegener in 1912 (see plate tectonics).

Parallel (1) See latitude; a line, parallel to the equator, that designates an angle of latitude.

Parent material (13) The unconsolidated material, from both organic and mineral sources, that is the basis of soil development.

Particulate matter (PM) (3) Dust, dirt, soot, salt, sulphate aerosols, fugitive natural particles, or other material particles suspended in air.

Paternoster lake (17) One of a series of small, circular, stair-stepped lakes formed in individual rock basins aligned down the course of a glaciated valley; named because they look like a string of rosary (religious) beads.

Patterned ground (17) Areas in the periglacial environment where freezing and thawing of the ground create polygonal forms of arranged rocks at the surface; can be circles, polygons, stripes, nets, and steps.

Pedogenic regime (18) A specific soil-forming process keyed to a specific climatic regime: laterization, calcification, salinization, and podzolization, among others; not the basis for soil classification in the Soil Taxonomy.

Pedon (18) A soil profile extending from the surface to the lowest extent of plant roots or to the depth where regolith or bedrock is encountered; imagined as a hexagonal column; the basic soil sampling unit.

Percolation (9) The process by which water permeates the soil or porous rock into the subsurface environment.

Periglacial (17) Cold-climate processes, landforms, and topographic features along the margins of glaciers, past and present; periglacial char-

acteristics exist on more than 20% of Earth's land surface; includes permafrost, frost action, and ground ice.
Perihelion (2) That point of Earth's closest approach to the Sun in its elliptical orbit; occurs on January 3 at 147,255,000 km (91,500,000 mi); variable over a 100,000-year cycle (compare aphelion).
Permafrost (17) Forms when soil or rock temperatures remain below 0°C (32°F) for at least 2 years in areas considered periglacial; criterion is based on temperature and not on whether water is present (compare frozen ground; see periglacial).
Permeability (9) The ability of water to flow through soil or rock; a function of the texture and structure of the medium.
Peroxyacetyl nitrate (PAN) (3) A pollutant formed from photochemical reactions involving nitric oxide (NO) and volatile organic compounds (VOCs). PAN produces no known human health effect, but it is particularly damaging to plants.
Phase change (7) The change in phase, or state, among ice, water, and water vapour; involves the absorption or release of latent heat (see latent heat).
Photochemical smog (3) Air pollution produced by the interaction of ultraviolet light, nitrogen dioxide, and hydrocarbons; produces ozone and PAN through a series of complex photochemical reactions. Automobiles are the major source of the contributive gases.
Photogrammetry (1) The science of obtaining accurate measurements from aerial photos and remote sensing; used to create and to improve surface maps.
Photosynthesis (19) The process by which plants produce their own food from carbon dioxide and water, powered by solar energy. The joining of carbon dioxide and hydrogen in plants, under the influence of certain wavelengths of visible light; releases oxygen and produces energy-rich organic material, sugars, and starches (compare respiration).
Physical geography (1) The science concerned with the spatial aspects and interactions of the physical elements and processes that make up the environment: energy, air, water, weather, climate, landforms, soils, animals, plants, microorganisms, and Earth.
Physical weathering (13) The breaking and disintegrating of rock without any chemical alteration; sometimes referred to as mechanical or fragmentation weathering.
Pingo (17) Large areas of frozen ground (soil-covered ice) that develop a heaved-up, circular, ice-cored mound, rising above a periglacial landscape as water freezes into ice and expands; sometimes results from pressure developed by freezing artesian water that is injected into permafrost; occasionally exceeds 60 m in height (200 ft).
Pioneer community (19) The initial plant community in an area; usually found on new surfaces or those that have been stripped of life, as in beginning primary succession; including lichens, mosses, and ferns growing on bare rock.
Place (1) A major theme in geography, focused on the tangible and intangible characteristics that make each location unique; no two places on Earth are alike.
Plane of the ecliptic (2) A plane (flat surface) intersecting all the points of Earth's orbit.
Planetesimal hypothesis (2) Proposes a process by which early protoplanets formed from the condensing masses of a nebular cloud of dust, gas, and icy comets; a formation process now being observed in other parts of the galaxy.
Planimetric map (Appendix A) A basic map showing the horizontal position of boundaries, land-use activities, and political, economic, and social outlines.
Plateau basalt (12) An accumulation of horizontal flows formed when lava spreads out from elongated fissures onto the surface in extensive sheets; associated with effusive eruptions; also known as flood basalts (see basalt).
Plate tectonics (11) The conceptual model and theory that encompasses continental drift, sea-floor spreading, and related aspects of crustal movement; accepted as the foundation of crustal tectonic processes (see continental drift).
Playa (15) An area of salt crust left behind by evaporation on a desert floor usually in the middle of a desert or semiarid bolson or valley; intermittently wet and dry.
Pluton (11) A mass of intrusive igneous rock that has cooled slowly in the crust; forms in any size or shape. The largest partially exposed pluton is a batholith (see batholith).
Podzolic (18) A CSSC soil order of the coniferous forests and sometimes heath, leaching of overlying horizons occurs in moist, cool to cold climates.
Podzolization (18) A pedogenic process in cool, moist climates; forms a highly leached soil with strong surface acidity because of humus from acid-rich trees.
Point bar (14) In a stream the inner portion of a meander, where sediment fill is redeposited.
Polar easterlies (6) Variable weak, cold, and dry winds moving away from the polar region; an anticyclonic circulation.
Polar front (6) A significant zone of contrast between cold and warm air masses; roughly situated between 50° and 60° N and S latitude.
Polar high-pressure cells (6) A weak, anticyclonic, thermally produced pressure system positioned roughly over each pole; the region of the lowest temperatures on Earth (see Antarctic high).
Polypedon (18) The identifiable soil in an area, with distinctive characteristics differentiating it from surrounding polypedons that form the basic mapping unit; composed of many pedons (see pedon).
Porosity (9) The total volume of available pore space in soil; a result of the texture and structure of the soil.
Positive feedback (1) Feedback that amplifies or encourages responses in a system (compare to negative feedback, feedback loop).
Potential evapotranspiration (9) POTET, or PE; the amount of moisture that would evaporate and transpire if adequate moisture were available; it is the amount lost under optimum moisture conditions, the moisture demand.
Potentiometric surface (9) A pressure level in a confined aquifer, defined by the level to which water rises in wells; caused by the fact that the water in a confined aquifer is under the pressure of its own weight; also known as a piezometric surface. This surface can extend above the surface of the land, causing water to rise above the water table in wells in confined aquifers (see artesian water).
Precipitation (9) Rain, snow, sleet, and hail—the moisture supply; called PRECIP, or P, in the water balance.
Pressure gradient force (6) Causes air to move from an area of higher barometric pressure to an area of lower barometric pressure due to the pressure difference.
Primary succession (19) Succession that occurs among plant species in an area of new surfaces created by mass movement of land, areas exposed by a retreating glacier, cooled lava flows and volcanic eruption landscapes, or surface mining and clear-cut logging scars, or an area of sand dunes, with no trace of a former community.
Prime meridian (1) An arbitrary meridian designated as 0° longitude, the point from which longitudes are measured east or west, at Greenwich, England, selected by international agreement in an 1884 treaty.
Process (1) A set of actions and changes that occur in some special order; analysis of processes is central to modern geographic synthesis.
Producer (19) Organism (plant) in an ecosystem that uses carbon dioxide as its sole source of carbon, which it chemically fixes through photosynthesis to provide its own nourishment; also called an autotroph (compare consumer).
Pyroclastic (12) An explosively ejected rock fragment launched by a volcanic eruption; sometimes described by the more general term tephra.
Radiation fog (7) Formed by radiative cooling of a land surface, especially on clear nights in areas of moist ground; occurs when the air layer directly above the surface is chilled to the dew-point temperature, thereby producing saturated conditions.
Rain gauge (9) A weather instrument; a standardized device that captures and measures rainfall.
Rain shadow (8) The area on the leeward slope of a mountain range, where precipitation receipt is greatly reduced compared to the windward slope on the other side (see orographic lifting).
Reflection (4) The portion of arriving insolation that is returned directly to space without being absorbed and converted into heat and without performing any work (see albedo).
Refraction (4) The bending effect on electromagnetic waves that occurs when insolation enters the atmosphere or another medium; the same

process by which a crystal, or prism, disperses the component colours of the light passing through it.
Region (1) A geographic theme that focuses on areas that display unity and internal homogeneity of traits; includes the study of how a region forms, evolves, and interrelates with other regions.
Regolith (13) Partially weathered rock overlying bedrock, whether residual or transported.
Regosolic (18) A CSSC soil order with weakly developed limited soils, the result of any number of factors: young materials; fresh alluvial deposits; material instability; mass-wasted slopes; or dry, cold climatic conditions.
Relative humidity (7) The ratio of water vapour actually in the air (content) compared to the maximum water vapour the air could hold (capacity) at that temperature; expressed as a percentage (compare vapour pressure, specific humidity).
Relief (12) Elevation differences in a local landscape; an expression of local height difference of landforms.
Remote sensing (1) Information acquired from a distance, without physical contact with the subject; for example, photography, orbital imagery, or radar.
Respiration (19) The process by which plants use food to derive energy for their operations; essentially, the reverse of the photosynthetic process; releases carbon dioxide, water, and heat energy into the environment (compare photosynthesis).
Reverse fault (12) Compressional forces produce strain that breaks a rock so that one side moves upward relative to the other side; also called a thrust fault (compare normal fault).
Revolution (2) The annual orbital movement of Earth about the Sun; determines the length of the year and the seasons.
Rhumb line (1) A line of constant compass direction, or constant bearing, which crosses all meridians at the same angle; a portion of a great circle.
Richter scale (12) An open-ended, logarithmic scale that estimates earthquake magnitude; designed by Charles Richter in 1935; now replaced by the moment magnitude scale (see moment magnitude scale).
Rime fog (7) A fog that consists of supercooled water droplets that turn into rime frost on contact with freezing objects.
Ring of fire (12) See circum-Pacific belt.
Robinson projection (Appendix A) A compromise (neither equal area nor true shape) oval projection developed in 1963 by Arthur Robinson.
Roche moutonnée (17) A glacial erosion feature; an asymmetrical hill of exposed bedrock; displays a gently sloping upstream side that has been smoothed and polished by a glacier and an abrupt, steep downstream side.
Rock (11) An assemblage of minerals bound together, or sometimes a mass of a single mineral.
Rock cycle (11) A model representing the interrelationships among the three rock-forming processes: igneous, sedimentary, and metamorphic; shows how each can be transformed into another rock type.
Rockfall (13) Free-falling movement of debris from a cliff or steep slope, generally falling straight or bounding downslope.
Rossby wave (6) An undulating horizontal motion in the upper-air westerly circulation at middle and high latitudes.
Rotation (2) The turning of Earth on its axis, averaging about 24 hours in duration; determines day–night relation; counterclockwise when viewed from above the North Pole and from above the equator, west to east or eastward.
Salinity (16) The concentration of natural elements and compounds dissolved in solution, as solutes; measured by weight in parts per thousand (‰) in seawater.
Salinization (18) A pedogenic process that results from high potential evapotranspiration rates in deserts and semiarid regions. Soil water is drawn to surface horizons, and dissolved salts are deposited as the water evaporates.
Saltation (14, 15) The transport of sand grains (usually larger than 0.2 mm, or 0.008 in.) by stream or wind, bouncing the grains along the ground in asymmetrical paths.
Salt marsh (16) A wetland ecosystem characteristic of latitudes poleward of the 30th parallel (compare to mangrove swamp).
Sand sea (15) An extensive area of sand and dunes; characteristic of Earth's erg deserts (contrast to reg deserts).
Saturated (7) Air that is holding all the water vapour that it can hold at a given temperature, known as the dew-point temperature.
Scale (1) The ratio of the distance on a map to that in the real world; expressed as a representative fraction, graphic scale, or written scale.
Scarification (13) Human-induced mass movements of Earth materials, such as large-scale open-pit mining and strip mining.
Scattering (4) Deflection and redirection of insolation by atmospheric gases, dust, ice, and water vapour; the shorter the wavelength, the greater the scattering, thus skies in the lower atmosphere are blue.
Scientific method (1) An approach that uses applied common sense in an organized and objective manner; based on observation, generalization, formulation, and testing of a hypothesis, and ultimately the development of a theory.
Sea-floor spreading (11) As proposed by Hess and Dietz, the mechanism driving the movement of the continents; associated with upwelling flows of magma along the worldwide system of mid-ocean ridges (see mid-ocean ridge).
Secondary succession (19) Succession that occurs among plant species in an area where vestiges of a previously functioning community are present; an area where the natural community has been destroyed or disturbed, but where the underlying soil remains intact.
Sediment (13) Fine-grained mineral matter that is transported and deposited by air, water, or ice.
Sedimentary rock (11) One of three basic rock types; formed from the compaction, cementation, and hardening of sediments derived from other rocks (compare igneous rock, metamorphic rock).
Seismic wave (11) The shock wave sent through the planet by an earthquake or underground nuclear test. Transmission varies according to temperature and the density of various layers within the planet; provides indirect diagnostic evidence of Earth's internal structure.
Seismograph (12) A device that measures seismic waves of energy transmitted throughout Earth's interior or along the crust.
Sensible heat (3) Heat that can be measured with a thermometer; a measure of the concentration of kinetic energy from molecular motion.
Sheet flow (14) Surface water that moves downslope in a thin film as overland flow, not concentrated in channels larger than rills.
Sheeting (13) A form of weathering associated with fracturing or fragmentation of rock by pressure release; often related to exfoliation processes (see exfoliation dome).
Shield volcano (12) A symmetrical mountain landform built from effusive eruptions (low-viscosity magma); gently sloped, gradually rising from the surrounding landscape to a summit crater; typical of the Hawaiian Islands (compare to effusive eruption; composite volcano).
Sinkhole (13) Nearly circular depression created by the weathering of karst landscapes with subterranean drainage; also known as a doline in traditional studies; may collapse through the roof of an underground space (see karst topography).
Sleet (8) Freezing rain, ice glaze, or ice pellets.
Sling psychrometer (7) A weather instrument that measures relative humidity using two thermometers—a dry bulb and a wet bulb—mounted side-by-side.
Slipface (15) On a sand dune, formed as dune height increases above 30 cm (12 in.) on the leeward side at an angle at which loose material is stable—its angle of repose (30 to 34°).
Slope (13) A curved, inclined surface that bounds a landform.
Small circle (1) A circle on a globe's surface that does not share Earth's centre; for example, all parallels of latitude other than the equator (compare to great circle).
Snow line (17) A temporary line marking the elevation where winter snowfall persists throughout the summer; seasonally, the lowest elevation covered by snow during the summer.
Soil (18) A dynamic natural body made up of fine materials covering Earth's surface in which plants grow, composed of both mineral and organic matter.
Soil colloid (18) A tiny clay and organic particle in soil; provides chemically active sites for mineral ion adsorption (see cation-exchange capacity).
Soil creep (13) A persistent mass movement of surface soil where individual soil particles are lifted and disturbed by the expansion of soil moisture as it freezes or by grazing livestock or digging animals.

Soil fertility (18) The ability of soil to support plant productivity when it contains organic substances and clay minerals that absorb water and certain elemental ions needed by plants through adsorption (see cation-exchange capacity, CEC).
Soil horizon (18) The various layers exposed in a pedon; roughly parallel to the surface and identified as O, A, Ae, B, C, and R (bedrock).
Soil-moisture recharge (9) Water entering available soil storage spaces.
Soil-moisture storage (9) STRGE, the retention of moisture within soil; it is a savings account that can accept deposits (soil-moisture recharge) or experiences withdrawals (soil-moisture utilization) as conditions change.
Soil-moisture utilization (9) The extraction of soil moisture by plants for their needs; efficiency of withdrawal decreases as the soil storage is reduced.
Soil science (18) Interdisciplinary science of soils. Pedology concerns the origin, classification, distribution, and description of soil. Edaphology focuses on soil as a medium for sustaining higher plants.
Soil Taxonomy (18) A soil classification system based on observable soil properties actually seen in the field; published in 1975 by the U.S. Soil Conservation Service and revised in 1990 and 1998 by the Natural Resources Conservation Service to include 12 soil orders.
Soil-water budget (9) An accounting system for soil moisture using inputs of precipitation and outputs of evapotranspiration and gravitational water.
Solar constant (2) The amount of insolation intercepted by Earth on a surface perpendicular to the Sun's rays when Earth is at its average distance from the Sun; a value of 1370W/m^2, or 1.968 calories/cm^2 per minute; averaged over the entire globe at the thermopause.
Solar wind (2) Clouds of ionized (charged) gases emitted by the Sun and traveling in all directions from the Sun's surface. Effects on Earth include auroras, disturbance of radio signals, and possible influences on weather.
Solifluction (13, 17) Gentle downslope movement of a saturated surface material (soil and regolith) in various climatic regimes where temperatures are above freezing (compare gelifluction).
Solonetzic (18) A CSSC soil order where solonetz denotes saline or alkaline soils. Well to imperfectly drained mineral soils developed under grasses in semiarid to subhumid climates. Limited areas of central and north-central Alberta.
Solum (18) A true soil profile in the pedon; ideally, a combination of O, A, E, and B horizons (see pedon).
Spatial (1) The nature or character of physical space, as in an area; occupying or operating within a space. Geography is a spatial science; spatial analysis its essential approach.
Spatial analysis (1) The examination of spatial interactions, patterns, and variations over area and/or space; a key integrative approach of geography.
Specific heat (5) The increase of temperature in a material when energy is absorbed; water has a higher specific heat (can store more heat) than a comparable volume of soil or rock.
Specific humidity (7) The mass of water vapour (in grams) per unit mass of air (in kilograms) at any specified temperature. The maximum mass of water vapour that a kilogram of air can hold at any specified temperature is termed its maximum specific humidity (compare vapour pressure, relative humidity).
Speed of light (2) Specifically, 299,792 kilometres per second (186,282 miles per second), or more than 9.4 trillion kilometres per year (5.9 trillion miles per year)—a distance known as a light-year; at light speed Earth is 8 minutes and 20 seconds from the Sun.
Spheroidal weathering (13) A chemical weathering process in which the sharp edges and corners of boulders and rocks are weathered in thin plates that create a rounded, spheroidal form.
Spodosols (18) A soil order in the Soil Taxonomy classification that occurs in northern coniferous forests; best developed in cold, moist, forested climates; lacks humus and clay in the A horizons, with high acidity associated with podzolization processes.
Spring tide (16) The highest tidal range, which occurs when the Moon and the Sun are in conjunction (at new Moon) or in opposition (at full Moon) stages (compare neap tide).
Squall line (8) A zone slightly ahead of a fast-advancing cold front, where wind patterns are rapidly changing and blustery and precipitation is strong.
Stability (7) The condition of a parcel, whether it remains where it is or changes its initial position. The parcel is stable if it resists displacement upward, unstable if it continues to rise.
Stationary front (8) A frontal area of contact between contrasting air masses that shows little horizontal movement; winds in opposite direction on either side of the front flow parallel along the front.
Steady-state equilibrium (1) The condition that occurs in a system when rates of input and output are equal and the amounts of energy and stored matter are nearly constant around a stable average.
Stomata (19) A small opening on the undersides of leaves through which water and gasses pass.
Storm surge (8) A large quantity of seawater pushed inland by the strong winds associated with a tropical cyclone.
Storm tracks (8) Seasonally shifting paths followed by migrating low-pressure systems.
Stratified drift (17) Sediments deposited by glacial meltwater that appear sorted; a specific form of glacial drift (compare till).
Stratigraphy (11) A science that analyzes the sequence, spacing, geophysical and geochemical properties, and spatial distribution of rock strata.
Stratocumulus (7) A lumpy, grayish, low-level cloud, patchy with sky visible, sometimes present at the end of the day.
Stratosphere (3) That portion of the homosphere that ranges from 20 to 50 km (12.5 to 30 mi) above Earth's surface, with temperatures ranging from −57°C (−70°F) at the tropopause to 0°C (32°F) at the stratopause. The functional ozonosphere is within the stratosphere.
Stratus (7) A stratiform (flat, horizontal) cloud generally below 2000 m (6500 ft).
Strike-slip fault (12) Horizontal movement along a faultline, that is, movement in the same direction as the fault; also known as a transcurrent fault. Such movement is described as right lateral or left lateral, depending on the relative motion observed across the fault (see transform fault).
Subduction zone (11) An area where two plates of crust collide and the denser oceanic crust dives beneath the less dense continental plate, forming deep oceanic trenches and seismically active regions.
Sublimation (7) A process in which ice evaporates directly to water vapour or water vapour freezes to ice (deposition).
Subpolar low-pressure cell (6) A region of low pressure centred approximately at 60° latitude in the North Atlantic near Iceland and in the North Pacific near the Aleutians, as well as in the Southern Hemisphere. Airflow is cyclonic; it weakens in summer and strengthens in winter (refer to cyclone).
Subsolar point (2) The only point receiving perpendicular insolation at a given moment—the Sun directly overhead (see declination).
Subtropical high-pressure cell (6) One of several dynamic high-pressure areas covering roughly the region from 20° to 35° N and S latitudes; responsible for the hot, dry areas of Earth's arid and semiarid deserts (refer to anticyclone).
Sulphate aerosols (3) Sulphur compounds in the atmosphere, principally sulphuric acid; principal sources relate to fossil fuel combustion; scatters and reflects insolation.
Sulphur dioxide (3) A colourless gas detected by its pungent odour; produced by the combustion of fossil fuels, especially coal, that contain sulphur as an impurity; can react in the atmosphere to form sulphuric acid, a component of acid deposition.
Summer (June) solstice (2) The time when the Sun's declination is at the Tropic of Cancer, at 23.5° N latitude, June 20–21 each year (compare to winter [December] solstice).
Sunrise (2) That moment when the disk of the Sun first appears above the horizon.
Sunset (2) That moment when the disk of the Sun totally disappears.
Sunspot (2) Magnetic disturbances on the surface of the Sun, occurring in an average 11-year cycle; related flares, prominences, and outbreaks produce surges in solar wind.
Surface creep (15) A form of eolian transport that involves particles too large for saltation; a process whereby individual grains are impacted by moving grains and slide and roll.
Surplus (9) (SURPL) The amount of moisture that exceeds potential evapotranspiration; moisture oversupply when soil moisture storage is at field capacity; extra or surplus water.

Suspended load (14) Fine particles held in suspension in a stream. The finest particles are not deposited until the stream velocity nears zero.
Swell (16) Regular patterns of smooth, rounded waves in open water; can range from small ripples to very large waves.
Syncline (12) A trough in folded strata, with beds that slope toward the axis of the downfold (compare anticline).
System (1) Any ordered, interrelated set of materials or items existing, separate from the environment, or within a boundary; energy transformations and energy and matter storage and retrieval occur within a system.
Taiga (20) See needleleaf forest.
Talik (17) An unfrozen portion of the ground that may occur above, below, or within a body of discontinuous permafrost or beneath a body of water in the continuous region, such as a deep lake; may extend to bedrock and noncryotic soil under large deep lakes.
Talus slope (13) Formed by angular rock fragments that cascade down a slope along the base of a mountain; poorly sorted, cone-shaped deposits.
Tarn (17) A small mountain lake, especially one that collects in a cirque basin behind risers of rock material or in an ice-gouged depression.
Temperate rain forest (20) A major biome of lush forests at middle and high latitudes; occurs along narrow margins of the Pacific Northwest in North America, among other locations; includes the tallest trees in the world.
Temperature (5) A measure of sensible heat energy present in the atmosphere and other media; indicates the average kinetic energy of individual molecules within a substance.
Temperature inversion (3) A reversal of the normal decrease of temperature with increasing altitude; can occur anywhere from ground level up to several thousand meters; functions to block atmospheric convection and thereby trap pollutants.
Terminal moraine (17) Eroded debris that is dropped at a glacier's farthest extent.
Terrane (12) A migrating piece of Earth's crust, dragged about by processes of mantle convection and plate tectonics. Displaced terranes are distinct in their history, composition, and structure from the continents that accept them.
Terrestrial ecosystem (20) A self-regulating association characterized by specific plant formations; usually named for the predominant vegetation and known as a biome when large and stable (see biome).
Thermal equator (5) The isoline on an isothermal map that connects all points of highest mean temperature.
Thermohaline circulation (6) Deep ocean currents produced by differences in temperature and salinity with depth; Earth's deep currents.
Thermokarst (17) Topography of hummocky, irregular relief marked by cave-ins, bogs, small depressions, and pits formed as ground ice melts; an erosion process caused by ground ice melting; not related to solution processes and chemical weathering associated with limestone (karst).
Thermopause (2, 3) A zone approximately 480 km (300 mi) in altitude that serves conceptually as the top of the atmosphere; an altitude used for the determination of the solar constant.
Thermosphere (3) A region of the heterosphere extending from 80 to 480 km (50 to 300 mi) in altitude; contains the functional ionosphere layer.
Threshold (1) A moment in which a system can no longer maintain its character, so it lurches to a new operational level, which may not be compatible with previous conditions.
Thrust fault (12) A reverse fault where the fault plane forms a low angle relative to the horizontal; an overlying block moves over an underlying block.
Thunder (8) The violent expansion of suddenly heated air, created by lightning discharges, sending out shock waves as an audible sonic bang.
Tide (16) A pattern of daily oscillations in sea level produced by astronomical relations among the Sun, the Moon, and Earth; experienced in varying degrees around the world (see neap and spring tides).
Till (17) Direct ice deposits that appear unstratified and unsorted; a specific form of glacial drift (compare stratified drift).
Till plain (17) A large, relatively flat plain composed of unsorted glacial deposits behind a terminal or end moraine. Low-rolling relief and unclear drainage patterns are characteristic.
Tombolo (16) A landform created when coastal sand deposits connect the shoreline with an offshore island outcrop or sea stack.
Topographic map (Appendix A) A map that portrays physical relief through the use of elevation contour lines that connect all points at the same elevation above or below a vertical datum, such as mean sea level.
Topography (12) The undulations and configurations, including its relief, that give Earth's surface its texture, portrayed on topographic maps.
Tornado (8) An intense, destructive cyclonic rotation, developed in response to extremely low pressure; generally associated with mesocyclone formation.
Total runoff (9) Surplus water that flows across a surface toward stream channels; formed by sheet flow, combined with precipitation and subsurface flows into those channels.
Traction (14) A type of sediment transport that drags coarser materials along the bed of a stream (see bed load).
Trade wind (6) Wind from the northeast and southeast that converges in the equatorial low-pressure trough, forming the intertropical convergence zone.
Transform fault (11) A type of geologic fault in rocks. An elongated zone along which faulting occurs between mid-ocean ridges; produces a relative horizontal motion with no new crust formed or consumed; strike-slip motion is either left or right lateral (see strike-slip fault).
Transmission (4) The passage of shortwave and longwave energy through space, the atmosphere, or water.
Transparency (5) The quality of a medium (air, water) that allows light to easily pass through it.
Transpiration (9) The movement of water vapour out through the pores in leaves; the water is drawn by the plant roots from soil-moisture storage.
Transport (14) The actual movement of weathered and eroded materials by air, water, and ice.
Tropical cyclone (8) A cyclonic circulation originating in the tropics, with winds between 30 and 64 knots (39 to 73 mph); characterized by closed isobars, circular organization, and heavy rains (see hurricane and typhoon).
Tropical savanna (20) A major biome containing large expanses of grassland interrupted by trees and shrubs; a transitional area between the humid rain forests and tropical seasonal forests and the drier, semiarid tropical steppes and deserts.
Tropical seasonal forest and scrub (20) A variable biome on the margins of the rain forests, occupying regions of lesser and more erratic rainfall; the site of transitional communities between the rain forests and tropical grasslands.
Tropic of Cancer (2) The northernmost point of the Sun's declination during the year, 23.5° N latitude.
Tropic of Capricorn (2) The southernmost point of the Sun's declination during the year, 23.5° S latitude.
Tropopause (3) The top zone of the troposphere defined by temperature; wherever –57°C (–70°F) occurs.
Troposphere (3) The home of the biosphere; the lowest layer of the homosphere, containing approximately 90% of the total mass of the atmosphere; extends up to the tropopause; occurring at an altitude of 18 km (11 mi) at the equator, 13 km (8 mi) in the middle latitudes, and at lower altitudes near the poles.
True shape (1) A map property showing the correct configuration of coastlines, a useful trait of conformality for navigational and aeronautical maps, although areal relationships are distorted (see map projection; compare equal area).
Tsunami (16) A seismic sea wave, traveling at high speeds across the ocean, formed by sudden motion in the sea floor, such as a sea-floor earthquake, submarine landslide, or eruption of an undersea volcano.
Typhoon (8) A tropical cyclone in excess of 65 knots (74 mph) that occurs in the western Pacific; same as a hurricane except for location.
Ultisols (18) A soil order in the Soil Taxonomy. Features highly weathered forest soils, principally in the humid subtropical climatic classification. Increased weathering and exposure can degenerate an Alfisol into the reddish colour and texture of these more humid to tropical Ultisols. Fertility is quickly exhausted when Ultisols are cultivated.
Unconfined aquifer (9) An aquifer that is not bounded by impermeable strata. It is simply the zone of saturation in water-bearing rock strata with

no impermeable overburden, and recharge is generally accomplished by water percolating down from above.

Undercut bank (14) In streams, a steep bank formed along the outer portion of a meandering stream; produced by lateral erosive action of a stream; sometimes called a cutbank (compare to point bar).

Uniformitarianism (11) An assumption that physical processes active in the environment today are operating at the same pace and intensity that has characterized them throughout geologic time; proposed by Hutton and Lyell (compare to catastrophism).

Upslope fog (7) Forms when moist air is forced to higher elevations along a hill or mountain and is thus cooled (compare valley fog).

Upwelling current (6) An area of the sea where cool, deep waters, which are generally nutrient rich, rise to replace the vacating water, as occurs along the west coasts of North and South America (compare to downwelling current).

Urban heat island (4) An urban microclimate that is warmer on the average than areas in the surrounding countryside because of the interaction of solar radiation and various surface characteristics.

Valley fog (7) The settling of cooler, more dense air in low-lying areas; produces saturated conditions and fog.

Vapour pressure (7) That portion of total air pressure that results from water vapour molecules, expressed in millibars (mb). At a given dew-point temperature, the maximum capacity of the air is termed its saturation vapour pressure.

Vascular plant (19) A plant having internal fluid and material flows through its tissues; almost 250,000 species exist on Earth.

Ventifact (15) A piece of rock etched and smoothed by eolian erosion—abrasion by windblown particles.

Vernal (March) equinox (2) The time around March 20–21 each year when the Sun's declination crosses the equatorial parallel and all places on Earth experience days and nights of equal length. The Sun rises at the North Pole and sets at the South Pole (compare to autumnal equinox).

Vertisolic (18) A CSSC soil order that occurs in heavy-textured material that is high in clay content (≥ 60% clay), especially smectite, a shrinking and swelling clay. These soils have little development of horizons, and are marked by slickensides and severe disruption.

Vertisols (18) A soil order in the Soil Taxonomy. Features expandable clay soils; composed of more than 30% swelling clays. Occurs in regions that experience highly variable soil moisture balances through the seasons.

Volatile organic compounds (3) Compounds, including hydrocarbons, produced by the combustion of gasoline, from surface coatings and from electric utility combustion; participates in the production of PAN through reactions with nitric oxides.

Volcano (12) A mountainous landform at the end of a magma conduit, which rises from below the crust and vents to the surface. Magma rises and collects in a magma chamber deep below, erupting effusively or explosively and forming composite, shield, or cinder-cone volcanoes.

Warm desert and semidesert (20) A desert biome caused by the presence of subtropical high-pressure cells; dry air and low precipitation.

Warm front (8) The leading edge of an advancing warm air mass, which is unable to push cooler, passive air out of the way; tends to push the cooler, underlying air into a wedge shape; identified on a weather map as a line with semicircles pointing in the direction of frontal movement (compare to cold front).

Wash (15) An intermittently dry streambed that fills with torrents of water after rare precipitation events in arid lands.

Watershed (14) The catchment area of a drainage basin; delimited by divides (see drainage basin).

Waterspout (8) An elongated, funnel-shaped circulation formed when a tornado exists over water.

Water table (9) The upper surface of groundwater; that contact point between the zone of saturation and aeration in an unconfined aquifer (see zone of aeration, zone of saturation).

Wave (16) An undulation of ocean water produced by the conversion of solar energy to wind energy and then to wave energy; energy produced in a generating region or a stormy area of the sea.

Wave-cut platform (16) Or shore platform, is a flat or gently sloping tablelike bedrock surface that develops in the tidal zone, where wave action cuts a bench that extends from the cliff base out into the sea.

Wave cyclone (8) See midlatitude cyclone.

Wavelength (2) A measurement of a wave; the distance between the crests of successive waves. The number of waves passing a fixed point in 1 second is called the frequency of the wavelength.

Wave refraction (16) A bending process that concentrates wave energy on headlands and disperses it in coves and bays; the long-term result is coastal straightening.

Weather (8) The short-term condition of the atmosphere, as compared to climate, which reflects long-term atmospheric conditions and extremes. Temperature, air pressure, relative humidity, wind speed and direction, daylength, and Sun angle are important measurable elements that contribute to the weather.

Weathering (13) The processes by which surface and subsurface rocks disintegrate, or dissolve, or are broken down. Rocks at or near Earth's surface are exposed to physical and chemical weathering processes.

West Antarctic ice sheet (10) A vast grounded ice mass held back by the Ross, Ronne, and Filcher ice shelves in Antarctica, drained by several active ice streams, such as the active Pine Island Glacier.

Westerlies (6) The predominant surface and aloft windflow pattern from the subtropics to high latitudes in both hemispheres.

Western intensification (6) The piling up of ocean water along the western margin of each ocean basin, to a height of about 15 cm (6 in.); produced by the trade winds that drive the oceans westward in a concentrated channel.

Wetland (16) A narrow, vegetated strip occupying many coastal areas and estuaries worldwide; highly productive ecosystems with an ability to trap organic matter, nutrients, and sediment.

Wilting point (9) That point in the soil-moisture balance when only hygroscopic water and some bound capillary water remains. Plants wilt and eventually die after prolonged stress from a lack of available water.

Wind (6) The horizontal movement of air relative to Earth's surface; produced essentially by air pressure differences from place to place; its direction is influenced by the Coriolis force and surface friction.

Wind vane (6) A weather instrument used to determine wind direction; winds are named for the direction from which they originate.

Winter (December) solstice (2) That time when the Sun's declination is at the Tropic of Capricorn, at 23.5° S latitude, December 21–22 each year. The day is 24 hours long south of the Antarctic Circle. The night is 24 hours long north of the Arctic Circle (compare to Summer [June] solstice).

Withdrawal (9) Sometimes called *offstream use*, the removal of water from the natural supply, after which it is used for various purposes and then is returned to the water supply.

Wrangellia terrane (12) One of many terranes that became cemented together to form present-day North America and the Wrangell Mountains, arriving from approximately 10,000 km (6200 mi) away; a former volcanic island arc and associated marine sediments.

Yardang (15) A streamlined rock structure formed by deflation and abrasion; appears elongated and aligned with the most effective wind direction.

Yazoo tributary (14) A small tributary stream draining alongside a floodplain; blocked from joining the main river by its natural levees and elevated stream channel (see backswamp).

Zone of aeration (9) A zone above the water table that has air in its pore spaces and may or may not have water.

Zone of saturation (9) A groundwater zone below the water table in which all pore spaces are filled with water.

Index